STATICS
and
DYNAMICS

STATICS
and
DYNAMICS

By **LAWRENCE E. GOODMAN**

Professor of Mechanics

Department of Aeronautics and Engineering Mechanics

University of Minnesota

and **WILLIAM H. WARNER**

Associate Professor

Department of Aeronautics and Engineering Mechanics

University of Minnesota

Wadsworth Publishing Company, Inc.

Belmont, California

Harold M. DeGroff, consulting editor

STATICS AND DYNAMICS

by Lawrence E. Goodman and William H. Warner

L.C. Cat. Card No.:   64-12224

Printed in the United States of America

STATICS

PREFACE

For some years we have presented a first course in mechanics for engineering students who have previously studied calculus. *Statics* and its companion volume, *Dynamics*, are intended to supplement this course by providing material to which students may refer for details of proofs of theorems, for ancillary illustrative material, and for exercises. By this means the lecturer will be freed, it is hoped, from the need to present every proof and pertinent illustration in the course of his lectures. He will be better able to emphasize important, difficult, or especially interesting aspects of the subject.

We believe that a first course in mechanics should provide engineering students with the professional background needed to deal with mechanical analyses that are not limited to two spatial dimensions. The approach we have adopted, therefore, is "vectorial," so that the three-dimensional theory may be presented with reasonable completeness and rigor. At the same time, care has been taken to smooth the transition from vector symbolism to the representation of vectors in specific coordinate systems. The engineer, when coming to grips with specific problems, usually finds that there is some symmetry present which makes a special coordinate system advantageous.

A glance at the Table of Contents will tell the reader that the order and coverage of topics is that of a standard syllabus in professional engineering training, except, perhaps, for the complete discussion of the principles of statics prior to the consideration of applications. (Chapter I, dealing with vector algebra, may be omitted by those who have studied that subject in earlier training.) We usually devote about one-third of an academic year to the material of *Statics*, two-thirds to that of *Dynamics*. On the other hand, virtual work is treated in dynamics rather than in statics. We believe that a knowledge of kinematics is essential for an understanding of the virtual work principle. In presenting the applications of the principles of statics we have tried to bear in mind that for the student of technology the study of statics is normally a forerunner to a course in "strength of materials" or deformable-body mechanics, as well as to dynamics. The rather full discussion of statical determinacy and indeterminacy in Chapter III is intended to provide background for such a course. So is the presentation of distributed force applications—hydrostatics, aerostatics, loaded cables, and the computation of resultant bending moments and shear forces—in Chapter IV. In the fifth chapter we have ventured to present, in necessarily abbreviated form, some of the leading ideas of modern research into the friction of rubbing solids.

The text is reasonably self-contained. There is, we feel, a sufficiently wide choice of applications to permit the individual lecturer to select those he considers most interesting and important. This choice is bound to vary from lecturer to lecturer and even from year to year. Instructors who devote more than thirty lecture hours to statics should have no difficulty finding material for a longer course. Sections and paragraphs of the text set in smaller type are considered to be not essential to the main development. The solved Examples, also in smaller type, are an integral part of the text material and, we trust, illuminate the theory. A conventional numbering system has been used for easy cross-reference; for example, Eq. 2.4-5 is the fifth equation in Section four of Chapter II. The exercises, for which no special originality can be claimed, have in many cases been set as examination questions at the University of Minnesota. They are graduated in difficulty somewhat, the first in each set being the simplest; most, we feel, are of moderate difficulty.

Again we are happy to acknowledge the assistance of many who have helped us, both in the preparation of manuscript and in the development of our ideas: the staff members of Wadsworth Publishing Company, who have dealt patiently with what must at times have seemed a rather exacting pair of authors; the instructors who have taught recitation sections using our notes; Mrs. Helen Woodward, who has typed the various versions of the manuscript; Professor B. J. Lazan, head of the Department of Aeronautics and Engineering Mechanics at the University of Minnesota, and our colleagues who regularly teach the courses in mechanics; Professor Harold De Groff of Purdue University, for his comments on the final manuscript; the delegates of the Clarendon Press, Oxford, for permission to quote the material of Table I, Chapter V; the Cambridge University Press for permission to include among the exercises a number of problems set in examinations at the University of Cambridge; and all of the students of engineering at the University of Minnesota whom we have taught.

L.E.G.

W.H.W.

CONTENTS

Contents

Contents

HISTORICAL INTRODUCTION

La Dynamique est la science des forces accélératrices ou retardatrices et des mouvements variés qu'elles doivent produire. Cette science est due entièrement aux modernes, et Galilée est celui qui en a jeté les premiers fondements.... Les découvertes des satellites de Jupiter, des phases de Venus, des taches du Soleil, etc., ne demandaient que des télescopes et de l'assiduité; mais il fallait un génie extraordinaire pour démêler les lois de la nature dans des phénomènes que l'on avait toujours eus sous les yeux, mais dont l'explication avait néanmoins toujours échappé aux recherches des philosophes.... La Mécanique devint une science nouvelle entre les mains de Newton, et ses *Principes mathématiques,* qui parurent, pour la première fois, en 1687, furent l'époque de cette révolution. *J. L. Lagrange*

The aim of theoretical mechanics is to provide quantitative predictions of the motions of material objects. The practical applications of such predictive power are obvious, and a mastery of the subject has been a longstanding objective of men. In succeeding chapters matters are treated from a logical approach which ignores the false starts and obscurities so common in the history of science. The history of mechanics is, however, of considerable cultural and intellectual interest of itself; its influence may be detected even in modern treatments of the subject. For this reason it seems worthwhile to sketch that history briefly.

Although ancient civilizations must have had a grasp of practical mechanics for the erection of their impressive structural monuments, it is to the Greeks that we owe the first recorded systematic efforts to provide a theoretical basis for the subject. Among them, the great name is that of Archimedes (287?–212 B.C.). He appears to have been trained in Alexandria, that center of hellenistic culture where Euclid (c. 330–c. 260 B.C.) had been master. In his works *On the Equilibrium of Planes* and *On Floating Bodies*, Archimedes begins, in the manner of Euclid, by setting out a number of postulates considered as self-evident. With these as foundation he derives a variety of propositions on the equilibrium of levers and on centers of mass, as well as the celebrated theorem in hydrostatics that bears his name. The inspiration for these propositions cannot be known to us with certainty, but, judging from the evidence available, it would seem that the scaffolding for the finished logical structure was provided by experiment. For example, Archimedes is reported to have cut out and weighed a segment of a parabola while investigating the formula for its area. The proofs themselves have been criticized—after two thousand years—on the grounds that they embody rather subtle unstated assumptions. Their cogency, however, is undeniable. Later, the idea of the moment of a force was generalized by Hero of Alexandria (c. 150), and other simple machines were analyzed.

No understanding of dynamics comparable to Archimedes' grasp of statics was achieved for almost sixteen hundred years. We can only conjecture why this long hiatus should have occurred. It has been attributed to the fact that the Roman economy was a slave economy, which provided little incentive for the development of technology. Many of the Roman wars were simply large-scale slave raids. The feudal economy that followed was based on the labor of the serf, whose condition was scarcely better. Partly, too, progress was retarded by the fact that, among Greek thinkers, it was the great logician Aristotle (384–322 B.C.), rather than Archimedes, whose work was accepted by the schoolmen of the early middle ages. In natural science Aristotle's primary interest lay in biology; he was led to identify motion with growth and change generally. Every body had a "natural" place in the universe. Motion toward this position was "natural" and would persist; other motion was "unnatural" or "violent" and would decay. These ideas did not promote the development of mechanics. Also, the completely geometrical approach of the Greeks was a handicap in the treatment of kinematical questions.

It must not be thought, however, that the period prior to the Renaissance was void of activity in science. Modern historical scholarship has brought to light the names of many who preceded Galileo. Robert Grosseteste, Chancellor of the University of Oxford and Bishop of Lincoln in 1235, questioned the mechanics of Aristotle. He inspired John Duns Scotus (c. 1266–1308), Roger Bacon (1214?– 1294), and William of Occam (c. 1270–1349). In the period 1325– 1350, a group associated with Merton College, Oxford, led by Thomas Bradwardine, William Heytesbury, Richard Swineshead, and John Dumbleton, worked out the kinematics of rectilinear motion. In France, Jean Buridan, who was in 1325 rector of the University of Paris, advanced the idea that a body in motion possessed a certain *impetus*, a quantity very like present-day momentum. His pupil, Nicole Oresme (?–1382), devised a semi-graphical analysis of the kinematics of rectilinear motion in which, essentially, velocity was plotted against time and the area of the diagram used to determine distance traversed. In Spain, Dominic Soto (1494–1560) worked out the laws of freely falling bodies. Finally Simon Stevin (1548–1620), a Netherlands engineer, brilliantly matched the statical achievements of Archimedes. Starting from an analysis of the inclined plane which was based on the impossibility of perpetual motion, he proved the vectorial addition of forces. In hydrostatics he was first to conceive the notion of the principle of solidification, which permitted him to find the pressure exerted by a fluid on its container by considering that any portion of the fluid may be regarded as a frozen solid, without disturbing equilibrium or the pressures in the remainder of the fluid.

At first slowly, and then more rapidly, progress developed. The year 1543 saw the publication of Copernicus' *On the Revolution of the Heavenly Spheres* (and also of Vesalius' book *On the Fabric of the Human Body*, which freed medicine from dependence upon Galen). Galileo Galilei (1564–1642), whose writings and whose discoveries with the telescope did much to secure acceptance for the Copernican theory, may be regarded as the first of the "moderns" in mechanics. It was he who introduced that combination of experiment and analysis that is the hallmark of the best scientific work. He established the elementary theory of projectile motion and can be credited with a rudimentary grasp of the idea of inertia. His writings exerted wide influence. They read well, even today, and we may recall the visit that the young Milton paid him in his old age and to which Milton refers in several places in his poetry. After the time of Galileo it was no longer completely respectable to draw conclusions about natural phenomena solely from authority. Huyghens (1629–1695) perfected and completed Galileo's mechanical discoveries and developed the analysis of the motion of the pendulum.

The year of the death of Galileo saw the birth of Isaac Newton (1642–1727), whose great achievements in mechanics may be judged by the quotation from Lagrange that begins this Introduction: "Mechanics became a new science in the hands of Newton, and his *Principia*, which appeared in 1687, broke the way for this revolution." Indeed, it is no exaggeration to say that the *Principia* and Locke's *Essay on the Human Understanding* (1690) marked the opening of that movement which its followers termed the Age of Reason. Newton introduced the concepts of force and mass and stated the laws of motion in the form in which we use them today. Furthermore, he developed the mathematical calculus by means of which the planetary laws so painfully extracted by the dedicated labor of Kepler from the observations of Tycho Brahe could be seen to follow directly from the laws of motion. The principle of universal gravitation is also his, though here credit must be shared with Robert Hooke (1635–1703) and others. The material of the present text is that upon which he set the mark of his genius, and it may properly be denominated *newtonian mechanics*.

The treatment of statical problems by the principle of virtual work was at this time systematized by John Bernoulli (1667–1748). In 1717 he enunciated the first comprehensive statement of this principle (sometimes termed the principle of virtual velocities or virtual displacements). The basic idea can be traced to hellenistic mechanics; it was known to Stevin in a primitive form. Galileo recognized that only the component of the velocity in the direction of the force is effective. Bernoulli also took as basic the product of the force and the virtual velocity component in the direction of the force, but he appreciated that the sum of all such products must vanish for any possible small displacement, if the force system is in statical balance.

The eighteenth and early nineteenth centuries saw the rapid extension of newtonian mechanics. The era was not one of uniform progress, however. There was, for example, an extended controversy between those who felt that the proper measure of a force was the change in kinetic energy produced by it and those who preferred the change in momentum. Leibniz, who had independently developed the calculus, played a role in this dispute, which we now recognize as arising from alternative ways of integrating the second law of motion. The leaders in the main stream of the consolidation of newtonian mechanics during this period were Leonhard Euler (1707–1783) and Jean le Rond d'Alembert (1717?–1783).

Euler's is certainly one of the greatest names in mathematical physics. A prolific writer, he undertook a series of fundamental texts covering not only the mechanics of particles but hydrodynamics and the mechanics of deformable solids as well. He was one of the first to make full use of calculus in solving Newton's differential equations of motion—Newton, in the *Principia*, employed geometrical methods, which he felt would be more understandable to his readers. Euler's treatises served to train most European workers in applied mechanics well into the nineteenth century. In the mechanics of rigid bodies, we owe to Euler, among other things, the angular co-ordinates used to describe spatial position; the fundamental kinematical theorem, which asserts that any motion of a rigid body can be decomposed into a translation followed by a rotation; the extension of Newton's equations of motion from the single-particle system to the rigid body (an extension which required an appreciation of the inertia tensor); and the solution of those extended equations to describe free precessional motion. The calculus of variations was in large part created by him as a result of the stimulation presented by the early development of variational principles in mechanics. Many of the fundamental ideas in the development of mechanics that are now associated with other names find their earliest lucid expression and rigorous proof in his work.

D'Alembert was also the author of a text celebrated in the history of mechanics. His *Treatise on Dynamics*, first published in 1743, amended in 1758, contains many illustrations of the method he devised for analyzing the motion of systems of rigid bodies subject to constraints. He also is to be credited with the first introduction of the idea of a vector *field*, and with showing that conservation of mechanical energy was a consequence of Newton's laws of motion. Like Newton, d'Alembert took an active part in the political and intellectual life of his day. For a long time he was joint editor of Diderot's *Encyclopedia*, that remarkable expression of the humanistic philosophy which did so much to discredit well-established institutions such as human slavery, colonialism, religious intolerance, and war, and which emphasized the importance of industry, the value of technical knowledge, and the dignity of labor.

The contribution of d'Alembert was subsumed into an approach to the equations of motion due to J. L. Lagrange (1736–1813). The *Analytical Mechanics* of Lagrange was published in 1788, one hundred years after Newton's *Principia*. Lagrange's inspiration was to use the scalar quantities work and energy rather than the vector quantities force and acceleration to determine the motion of mechanical systems. Combining d'Alembert's principle with the principle of virtual work, he derived a form of the equations of motion that is today the starting point for most advanced treatments of mechanics. The lagrangian approach does not, indeed, give us the solution of any particular problem that could not equally well be treated by direct reference to Newton's laws of motion (from which it is derived), but it does make it possible to draw conclusions about the behavior of large classes of systems. An analysis for one system will hold for any other whose energy depends upon the position coordinates in the same way. When the concept of energy was enlarged to include electric and magnetic effects, the motion of electromechanical systems became a natural subject for treatment by Lagrange's method.

During the nineteenth century, in the hands of Maxwell, Joule, Clausius, Carnot, Gibbs, and W. Thomson, thermodynamics developed along lines suggested by the progress in mechanics. Continuum mechanics—stress analysis, fluid dynamics, and the theory of sound—became well-developed disciplines in their own right, underlying much of today's engineering. Among the leaders in these fields were Navier, Cauchy, Kirchhoff, and de St. Venant; Helmholtz, Stokes, Joukowsky, and Rayleigh. Meanwhile, two whose names are familiar to students of elementary mechanics were Gaspard Coriolis (1792–1843), who completed the kinematic analysis of particle acceleration referred to moving axes, and J. B. L. Foucault (1819–1868), who devised the gyroscope and pendulum that bear his name. Foucault succeeded, where Galileo had failed, in devising a laboratory demonstration of the rotation of the earth. It should perhaps be noted that Coriolis and Foucault were men of diverse attainments: the former was director of studies at the prestigious École Polytechnique; the latter was a science reporter for the Paris press. The mathematical theory in which the Coriolis component of acceleration explains the behavior of Foucault's pendulum followed, rather than preceded, the experiments. In 1846 newtonian mechanics achieved what was, in some respects, its crowning success with the discovery of the planet Neptune in precisely the position that U. J. J. LeVerrier and J. C. Adams, after analysis of small anellipticities of the orbit of Uranus, predicted it should occupy.

All of the foregoing work was based upon the three laws of motion due to Newton and upon the principle of virtual work. Is there a single principle from which Newton's laws, and, consequently, all other mechanical effects, may be derived? As we have seen, Lagrange took a long step toward achieving this goal, which occupies an important place in the history of mechanics. As early as 1740, Pierre Louis Moreau de Maupertuis (1698–1759) asserted that the line integral of the quantity $m\mathbf{v} \cdot d\mathbf{s}$, which he termed the *action* of the particle, is always a minimum. In the integrand, m denotes the mass of the particle, $\mathbf{v}$ its velocity, and $d\mathbf{s}$ an element of arc-length along the path of the particle. Maupertuis had the misfortune to fall out with Voltaire, then a fellow member of the Prussian Academy of Arts and Science, and to be hilariously caricatured in *The Diatribe of Dr. Akakia*. Euler, who retained a high opinion of his colleague, while remaining in the good graces of Voltaire, showed, in 1744, that the orbit of a particle moving under the influence of a central force would indeed be one in which the action would have a stationary value. Lagrange, in the *Analytical Mechanics*, presented a more general proof, in which he showed that the action would be a minimum for a particle in a conservative force field, subject to time-independent constraints, and would have a stationary value in other cases. The proof of the *principle of least action* used today is due to K. G. J. Jacobi (1804–1851) and was published posthumously in his *Lectures on Dynamics* (1866). Newton's equations of motion can be derived from the principle of least action; the converse is also true. By starting with an extremal principle of this type, it is possible to dispense with the concept of force as a fundamental one.

The principle of least action differs from the newtonian approach to particle motion by dealing with an integrated effect taken over a length of path rather than with the relation between force and acceleration at any instant. Methods of this sort are known as variational methods. They occupy a distinguished position in mechanical analysis and have an extensive history of their own. The most important such principle is *Hamilton's Principle*, due to W. R. Hamilton (1805–1865), which asserts that, for a particle moving in a conservative force field, among the various possible neighboring paths the particle may take between any two points the time average of the difference between the kinetic and potential energies has a stationary value over the actual path traversed. (The principle requires modification if the force field is not conservative or if velocity-dependent constraints are present.) Both Newton's and Lagrange's forms of the equations of motion may be derived from Hamilton's principle. It is this formulation of the laws of classical mechanics that has proved most fruitful for the purposes of quantum mechanics.

With technological and scientific progress, increasingly accurate measurements become possible and increasingly broad scientific theories are demanded. In recent decades, minute departures from the predictions of newtonian mechanics have made men realize that, on a macroscopic scale, newtonian mechanics is inappropriate for bodies moving with speeds approaching the speed of light just as, on a microscopic scale, it is inappropriate for describing motions in the nucleus. On the other hand, the variational formulation of the principles of mechanics, being invariant with respect to coordinate transformations, could be modified by Einstein, Poincaré, and Lorentz into modern relativistic mechanics. This development in no way diminishes the lustre of conventional or, as it is called, *classical* mechanics—which, in fact, has played a leading role in the development of the modern einsteinian and quantum mechanics and which forms the basis of present-day technology.

Suggestions for Further Reading

Clagett, M., *Science of Mechanics in the Middle Ages* (University of Wisconsin Press, 1959).

Dugas, R., *A History of Mechanics* (New York: Central Book Co., 1955).

McKenzie, A. E. E., *The Major Achievements of Science*, Vol. I (Cambridge University Press, 1960).

CHAPTER I

Vector Algebra and Allied

Geometrical Concepts

1.1 Introduction

Mechanics is concerned with the motion of material systems of all kinds. The subject is conventionally divided into statics and dynamics, of which the former deals with those structures and machine elements that are at rest—or, more precisely, whose parts all have zero acceleration—and the latter with accelerating objects. From a broad point of view, statics is only a special case of dynamics, a case in which all accelerations have the particular value zero. In engineering and technology, however, the importance of this special case is so great that it demands a separate treatment. Most of the structures designed by the engineer are intended to remain in equilibrium; even moving elements of machinery, if accelerations are not large, will be found to be designed on a statical basis. Continuum mechanics of deformable solids, stress analysis of structures and machinery, hydrostatics, and soil mechanics all take an understanding of statics as the starting point of engineering design and analysis. Statics is, in fact, the basis of much day-to-day engineering design,

I

and the well-trained engineer must be able to use the principles of statics, in all their various forms, with the same effortless skill displayed by any good craftsman in the handling of his tools.

1.2 Vector and Scalar Quantities

It is desirable to begin by establishing an efficient notation for the description of the quantities encountered in mechanics (and in other branches of science as well). Many of these quantities involve the idea of direction as well as magnitude. For example, the position of a point P relative to a point O may be specified by means of the directed line segment drawn from O to P. If O' and P' are any other two points such that the direction and the distance from O' to P' is the same as the direction and the distance from O to P, we say that the position of P' relative to O' is the same as the position of P relative to O. Another way of putting these statements is to say that a particle moving from O to P has experienced a *displacement* or change of position given by the directed line segment $\overline{OP}$. Such a directed line segment is conveniently represented by an arrow drawn from O to P—that is, with its initial point at O and its terminus at P. From our

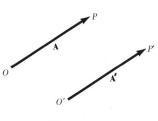

Fig. 1.2-1

present point of view the displacement $\overline{O'P'}$ would be represented by an arrow drawn from O' to P'. This arrow has the same direction and the same length as the arrow $\overline{OP}$, which corresponds with the fact that the displacement from O to P is the same as the displacement from O' to P' or that the position of point P relative to O is the same as the position of point P' relative to O'. Quantities like displacement, which can be represented by a directed line segment drawn to uniform scale and which combine physically according to the rules or elementary operations of the next section, are known as *vector quantities*. The arrow that represents the quantity is called its *vector*. The length of the arrow is called the *magnitude* of the vector. Note that from our present point of view a vector has magnitude and direction but is not localized in space; e.g., the vector which represents $\overline{OP}$ is regarded as the same as the one that represents $\overline{O'P'}$. When we wish to emphasize this aspect of the vector quantity we speak of it as a *free* vector quantity; later on, in the consideration of moment and force vectors, the concepts of bound and sliding vectors will be introduced.·

Vectors are of such common occurrence that it is convenient to have a special symbol for them. It is common practice, in print, to use boldface type for vectors.* For example, we denote the directed line segment $\overline{OP}$ by the special symbol **A** and the directed line segment $\overline{O'P'}$ by the symbol **A'**. It must be remembered that such a symbol represents more than an ordinary number; it stands for a quantity whose complete specification involves direction as well as magnitude. We may, however, still borrow the equality sign from algebra and write

$$\mathbf{A} = \mathbf{A'} \qquad\qquad \text{1.2-1}$$

provided we interpret this expression as meaning "the vector **A** has the same magnitude and the same direction as the vector **A'**." An advantage accruing from the use of boldface type (or the overbar) is that ordinary type can then serve to denote the magnitude of the vector. The magnitude of the vector **A** is written simply as A. In Fig. 1.2-1, A represents the distance from O to P. It follows from Eq. 1.2-1 that

$$A = A'. \qquad\qquad \text{1.2-2}$$

Notice, however, that this is only one of the conclusions that may be drawn from Eq. 1.2-1. Furthermore, the symbols A and A' denote ordinary numbers whereas Eq. 1.2-1 is a *vector equation*. A variation in notation sometimes encountered is the use of the symbol $|\mathbf{A}|$ in place of A to emphasize the fact that it is the magnitude of a vector that is being represented, and not some other numerical quantity.

While many of the important quantities encountered in mechanics have directional properties, there are others that require only a single number for their complete specification. These are called *scalar quantities*. We may say, for example, that a box has a volume of twelve cubic feet. The word "volume" indicates the kind of quantity we have in mind, the words "cubic feet" denote the *unit*, and the word "twelve" denotes the *measure*, that is, the number of units contained in this example of the quantity under discussion. When we deal with a scalar quantity, attention tends to center on the

---

* In manuscript or typescript, the use of an overbar on the symbol for the vector is one way of indicating a vector quantity.

measure, since this is the number that appears in mathematical equations. The ordinary real number provides the typical example of a scalar quantity, just as displacement typifies the vector quantity. Ordinary weight type is used for the measure numbers of scalar quantities.

Not all quantities of physical interest are represented by scalars or vectors; the student may well inquire about quantities dependent on two or more directions. These general *tensor* quantities are also important in mechanics; scalars and vectors are special cases of them. In the elementary courses in dynamics and deformable-body mechanics, the student will become acquainted with a few such tensor quantities: the inertia tensor, the stress tensor, and the strain or strain-rate tensor, for example. Other physical quantities, such as finite rotations of bodies, do not fit into the scalar-vector-tensor pattern at all and are described by mathematical entities behaving differently from those we treat here.

1.3 Elementary Operations

If the introduction of special vector symbols is to be justified, we must be able to manipulate these symbols in meaningful ways, just as the symbols representing ordinary numbers are handled in

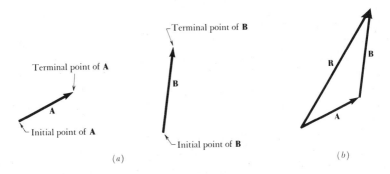

Fig. 1.3-1

conventional algebra. To accomplish this, certain operations are defined. The first is called *vector addition*. To form what is known as the sum of two vectors, such as **A** and **B** shown in Fig. 1.3-1a, we must first shift the vectors, without changing their magnitudes or directions, until the initial point of **B** coincides with the terminal point of **A**, as shown in Fig. 1.3-1b. Then the sum of **A** and **B** is defined as the vector represented by the directed line segment from the initial point of **A** to the terminal point of **B**. This vector is

denoted **R** in Fig. 1.3-1b.   One could equally well form **R** by making
the initial points of **A** and **B** coincide and completing the parallelogram, as shown in Fig. 1.3-2, to locate the terminal point of **R**.   The
method of construction shown in Fig. 1.3-1b is known as the triangle
law of addition, while that shown in Fig. 1.3-2 is known as the parallelogram law.   The two procedures are, of course,
completely equivalent, since the directed line segment $\overline{PQ}$ in Fig. 1.3-2 is (vectorially) equal to the
vector **B**.   It is customary to denote the operation
of vector addition by borrowing the $+$ sign from
algebra and to write

$$\mathbf{A} + \mathbf{B} = \mathbf{R}. \qquad\qquad \text{1.3-1}$$

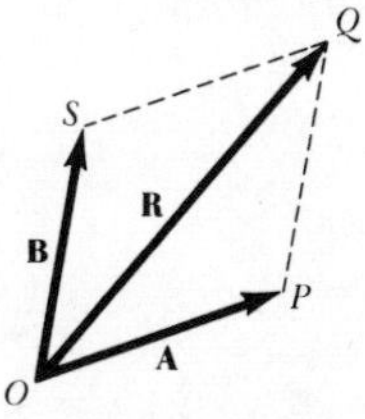

The vector **R** is known as the *sum* or the *resultant*
of **A** and **B**.   The vectors **A** and **B** are called
components of **R**.

Fig. 1.3-2

We can form the sum of more than two vectors by adding the
first two, then adding their resultant to the third, and so on.   It is
simpler to omit the intermediate steps and to form the vector polygon,
as shown in Fig. 1.3-3.   (Note that point S is not necessarily in the
plane of points OPQ.)   The sum of the vectors **A**, **B**, and **C** is the
vector **R** and we write

$$\mathbf{A} + \mathbf{B} + \mathbf{C} = \mathbf{R}. \qquad\qquad \text{1.3-2}$$

It may happen, of course, that the point S in Fig. 1.3-3 coincides
with the point O.   In that case we say that the
resultant is a *null vector*.   This null vector is represented by the symbol **o** or, where no confusion
between vectors and scalars is likely to result,
simply by the ordinary symbol for zero, o.   The
null vector may be regarded as a vector of zero
magnitude and arbitrary direction.

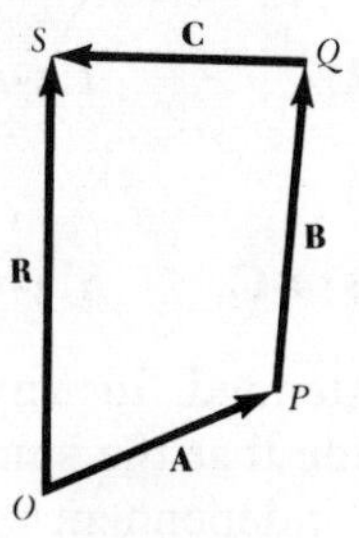

Next we define the negative of a vector as
another vector having the same magnitude as the
original one, but reversed in direction.   We borrow
the minus sign from algebra to indicate this and
denote the negative of **A** by $-\mathbf{A}$.   Then the sub-
traction of **A** from **B** consists in the addition of $-\mathbf{A}$ to **B**.   This is
pictured in Fig. 1.3-4.

Fig. 1.3-3

The borrowing of symbols such as $+$, $-$, $=$ from the algebra
of ordinary real numbers (scalars) requires justification.   The algebra

of ordinary real numbers is based on certain fundamental laws of which two apply to the operations of addition and subtraction. The first of these, the commutative addition law, asserts that, for any two real numbers a and b, $a+b=b+a$. It follows from the definition of

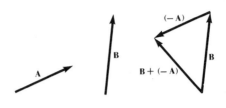

Fig. 1.3-4

vector addition that we may make a like statement for any two vectors, **A** and **B**. In Fig. 1.3-2 the vector $\overline{SQ}$ is the same as **A** and $\overline{PQ}$ is the same as **B**, so that we reach the same point Q whether we add **B** to **A**, as in triangle OPQ, or **A** to **B**, as in triangle OSQ. The second addition law of algebra, the associative addition law, asserts that, for any three real numbers a, b, c, the equation $a+(b+c)=(a+b)+c$ holds. This rule also holds for vector addition. To prove it we note that $(\mathbf{B}+\mathbf{C})$ in Fig. 1.3-5 is represented by $\overline{PS}$, so that

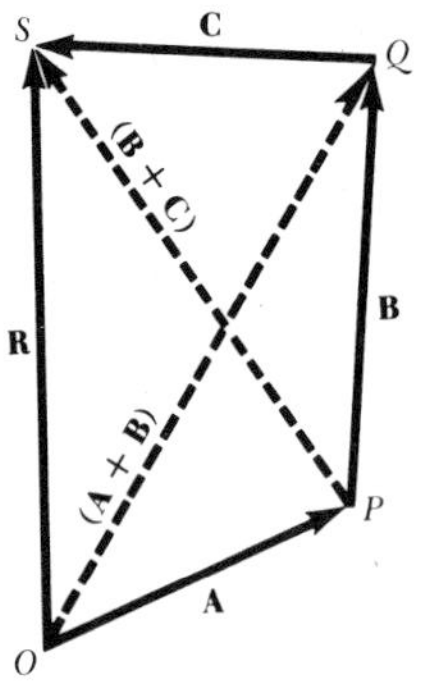

$$\mathbf{A}+(\mathbf{B}+\mathbf{C}) = \mathbf{R}. \qquad \textbf{1.3-3}$$

Similarly $(\mathbf{A}+\mathbf{B})$ is represented by $\overline{OQ}$ so that

$$(\mathbf{A}+\mathbf{B})+\mathbf{C} = \mathbf{R}. \qquad \textbf{1.3-4}$$

It follows at once that

$$\mathbf{A}+(\mathbf{B}+\mathbf{C}) = (\mathbf{A}+\mathbf{B})+\mathbf{C}. \qquad \textbf{1.3-5}$$

Fig. 1.3-5

The argument is readily extended to any number of terms. We conclude that the sum of any number of vectors is independent of the grouping of the terms.

If we add to the vector **A** another vector **A** we have, according to the rule for vector addition, a resultant vector which has the same direction as **A** and whose magnitude is twice as great as that of **A**. It is only natural to want to describe this fact symbolically by writing $\mathbf{A}+\mathbf{A}=2\mathbf{A}$. But the symbol 2 denotes a typical scalar quantity, and so we are led to define the product of a vector, **A**, and a positive scalar quantity, m, as a vector having the same direction as **A** but with magnitude m times as great. If m is negative, m**A** is again a vector whose magnitude is that of **A** multiplied by the absolute value of m but whose direction, in accordance with the definition of the negative of a vector, is reversed. That is, for negative values of m we would write $m\mathbf{A} = -(-m\mathbf{A})$. This operation is known as multiplication by a scalar.

We must verify the fact that the operation of multiplication by a scalar conforms to the fundamental laws of the algebra of real numbers. The so-called "commutative" multiplication law $m\mathbf{A} = \mathbf{A}m$ is satisfied if we define post-multiplication ($\mathbf{A}m$) of a vector by a scalar just as we have defined pre-multiplication. The "associative" law $n(m\mathbf{A}) = m(n\mathbf{A})$ follows at once from the definition of multiplication by a scalar and the ordinary laws of arithmetic, as does the "distributive" law in the form $(m + n)\mathbf{A} = m\mathbf{A} + n\mathbf{A}$. It remains to prove that

$$m(\mathbf{A} + \mathbf{B}) = m\mathbf{A} + m\mathbf{B}. \qquad \textbf{1.3-6}$$

To show this, let $\overline{OP}$ in Fig. 1.3-6 represent **A** and $\overline{PQ}$ represent **B**. The directed line segment $\overline{OR}$ may be taken to represent m**A** while $(\mathbf{A} + \mathbf{B})$ will be represented by $\overline{OQ}$. If OQ is extended to a point S chosen so that RS is parallel to PQ it follows from the geometrical similarity of triangles OPQ and ORS that

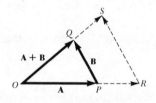

$$\frac{RS}{PQ} = \frac{OR}{OP}. \qquad \textbf{1.3-7}$$

Fig. 1.3-6

But $(OR/OP) = m$, so that the directed line segment $\overline{RS}$ is both parallel to **B** and m times as large. Therefore $\overline{RS}$ represents the vector m**B**. Similarly

$$\frac{OS}{OQ} = \frac{OR}{OP}, \qquad \textbf{1.3-8}$$

so that $\overline{OS}$ represents the vector $m(\mathbf{A} + \mathbf{B})$. Equation 1.3-6 now follows directly from the triangle law of vector addition applied to the large triangle ORS of Fig. 1.3-6.

Now that the operations of vectorial addition, subtraction, and multiplication by a scalar have been shown to conform to all the fundamental rules of algebra, we may bring all the resources of that powerful mathematical tool to bear upon vector equations in which these operations are involved. It must be remembered, however, that only those operations that have been defined may legitimately be employed, and that not every conceivable arrangement of symbols is meaningful. For example, an expression such as $\mathbf{A} - 3\mathbf{B} = 27$ is nonsense because the quantity on the left-hand side of the equality sign is a vector, while that on the right-hand side is a scalar. The two cannot possibly be "equal" in any sense. In mechanics, as in every field of intellectual activity, once a man falls into the habit of writing symbols without troubling himself to formulate the ideas which they represent, his ability to carry out a rational analysis is lost.

Example **1.3-1**

Two vectors, **A** and **B**, *are related to a third vector,* **C**, *through the equations*

$$6\mathbf{A} + \mathbf{B} = 0,$$

$$-4\mathbf{A} + 2\mathbf{B} = -8\mathbf{C}.$$

Solve for **A** *and* **B**.

Solution: We treat the equations just as in the algebra of ordinary real numbers. Multiply the first equation by 2, the second by -1, and add to get

$$16\mathbf{A} = 8\mathbf{C} \quad \text{or} \quad \mathbf{A} = \frac{1}{2}\mathbf{C}.$$

Substitute this result in the first of the given equations to find

$$6\left(\frac{1}{2}\mathbf{C}\right) + \mathbf{B} = 0 \quad \text{or} \quad \mathbf{B} = -3\mathbf{C}.$$

We conclude that the vector **A** is parallel to **C** and that its magnitude is half as great as the magnitude of **C**. The vector **B** is also parallel to **C** and its magnitude is three times as great as that of **C**. The minus sign before the numeral 3 must be interpreted as meaning that the sense or direction of **B** is opposite to that of **C**. The positive sign, which is understood to appear before the symbol $\frac{1}{2}$, means that the arrowhead on the **A** vector points in the same direction as the arrow associated with the vector **C**.

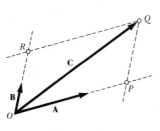

Fig. 1.3-7

Example **1.3-2**

Show that any vector, **C**, *which lies in the plane of the vectors* **A** *and* **B** *can be expressed in the form* $m\mathbf{A} + n\mathbf{B}$.

Solution: The vectors **A** and **B** are shown in Fig. 1.3-7, together with the third vector, **C**. All three have been translated so as to have the same origin O.   From point Q, the terminus of **C**, we construct parallels to **A** and **B**; these intersect the lines of **A** and **B** at points P and R, respectively, as shown.   Now $\overline{OP}$ is a vector that is a suitable multiple of **A**, say m**A**, and $\overline{OR}$ is a vector that is a multiple of **B**, say n**B**.   It follows from the parallelogram law that $\mathbf{C} = m\mathbf{A} + n\mathbf{B}$.   The argument assumes that **A** and **B** are not parallel and, of course, neither of them may be a null vector.   The figure is drawn for the case in which m, n exceed unity; the student should sketch the case in which, say, $0 < m < 1$ and the case $m < 0$.

Example 1.3-3

The vector from an origin O to a point P is **s** *and the vector from P to another point Q is* **t**.   *What is the vector* **r** *from O to the midpoint of PQ?*

Solution: The vectors **s** and **t** are shown in Fig. 1.3-8, as is the wanted vector **r** from the origin to the midpoint, R, of PQ.   The vector $\overline{PR}$ has

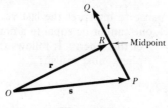

Fig. 1.3-8

the same direction as **t** and half of **t**'s magnitude.   From the triangle OPR we have

$$\mathbf{r} = \mathbf{s} + \frac{1}{2}\mathbf{t}.$$

Note that if R, instead of being the midpoint, is *any* point on the line PQ, $\overline{PR}$ will be represented by a vector m**t**, where m is some number.   The vector equation $\mathbf{r} = \mathbf{s} + m\mathbf{t}$ is, therefore, the equation of the line through P in the direction of the vector **t**.   By giving m an appropriate value we can locate any point, R, on that line and to every value of m there corresponds one point on the line.

Example 1.3-4

Show that the line from a vertex of a parallelogram to the center of an opposite side intersects a diagonal of the parallelogram in such a way as to divide it into two parts, one of which is twice as long as the other.

Solution: In Fig. 1.3-9a the vertices of the parallelogram are shown, labeled $OPQR$.   The parallelogram is determined by the two non-parallel vectors **A** and **B**, which represent adjacent sides $\overline{OP}$ and $\overline{OR}$, respectively. Of the other two sides, $\overline{PQ}$ is **B** and $\overline{QR}$ is $-$**A**. It follows that the diagonal $\overline{PR}$ is **B**$+(-$**A**$)$ or simply **B**$-$**A**. The vector from O to the midpoint of PQ is **A**$+\frac{1}{2}$**B**. Let us call the intersection of these last two vectors S. We want to show that the distance from P to S is one-third of the distance from P to R. To do this we note that, since S is a point on the line PR, the vector $\overline{PS}$ will be some multiple of **B**$-$**A**, say $m($**B**$-$**A**$)$. And since S is also a point on the line of the vector **A**$+\frac{1}{2}$**B** it follows that $\overline{OS}$ is represented by the vector $n($**A**$+\frac{1}{2}$**B**$)$. Our task now is to find the value of m. From the triangle OPS shown in Fig. 1.3-9b we have

$$\mathbf{A}+m(\mathbf{B}-\mathbf{A}) = n\left(\mathbf{A}+\frac{\text{I}}{2}\,\mathbf{B}\right),$$

or

$$\mathbf{A}(\text{I}-m-n) = \mathbf{B}\left(\frac{\text{I}}{2}\,n-m\right). \qquad \textbf{1.3-9}$$

At this point we must pause to interpret the last vector equation. Since **A** and **B** are not parallel, one cannot be equal to a non-zero scalar multiple of the other. It follows that both scalar multipliers must vanish:

$$\text{I}-m-n = \text{o},$$

$$\frac{\text{I}}{2}\,n-m = \text{o}.$$

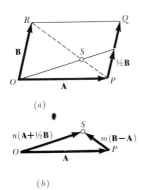

(a)

(b)

Fig. 1.3-9

As a consequence, we have at once $m=\frac{1}{3}$ and $n=\frac{2}{3}$. The fact that $m=\frac{1}{3}$ means that the vector $\overline{PS}$ is one-third as long as the vector $\overline{PR}$, which implies that S divides the line PR into two parts, one of which is one-third of PR and the other of which is two-thirds of PR in length. That is what we set out to prove. Notice that the vector equation 1.3-9 yields two ordinary scalar equations in this case. We also learn from it that $n=\frac{2}{3}$, which shows that the distance OS is two-thirds of the distance from O to the center of the side PQ. It must not be thought that vector algebra is intended to supply proofs of theorems in plane geometry, but the exercise in formulation and interpretation is useful.

Example **1.3-5**

The resultant of three forces is a null vector. Show that the magnitude of each force is proportional to the sine of the angle between the other two.

Solution: The concept of force and its representation by a vector will be discussed in Chapter II; here force is assumed to be a vector quantity. Then if the three forces be denoted **A, B, C** we have

$$\mathbf{A+B+C} = 0.$$

Notice that the forces must lie in the plane of the triangle shown in Fig. 1.3-10.   The triangle itself, of course, corresponds to the vector equation just written.   Now the magnitude of **A** is A, so that the distance PQ is A, and similarly the distance QR is B and the distance RP is C. From the law of sines of trigonometry,

$$\frac{A}{\sin \alpha} = \frac{B}{\sin \beta} = \frac{C}{\sin \gamma},$$

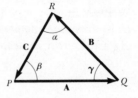

which is the result wanted.   This result, one of the oldest theorems in mechanics, is known as Lamy's Theorem after its discoverer Fr.

Fig. 1.3-10

Bernard Lamy (1645–1715).   Although it may be utilized in the analysis of simple equilibrium problems involving three forces, the procedure is not recommended.   We shall learn more effective and less restricted ways of handling such analyses.

1.4 Unit Vectors; Rectangular Cartesian Components

We have seen that the multiplication of a vector, **A**, by a scalar $m > 0$ results in a vector whose magnitude is mA and whose direction is the same as that of **A**.   Division of a vector by a scalar may be regarded as multiplication by the reciprocal of the scalar, i.e.,

$$\frac{\mathbf{A}}{m} = \left(\frac{1}{m}\right)\mathbf{A}. \qquad\qquad 1.4\text{-}1$$

In particular, if the number m is the same as the magnitude of **A**, the vector resulting from the division will have a magnitude of unity. Its direction, of course, will be the same as that of **A**.   Such *unit vectors* play an important role in vector algebra.   When we come to analyze particular machines and structures, there is usually some symmetry present which makes a particular set of axes convenient. Rectangular cartesian axes $Oxyz$, pictured in Fig. 1.4-1a, constitute the commonest such set.   It is customary to denote the unit vector in the x-direction by the symbol **i**, the unit vector in the y-direction by the symbol **j**, and the unit vector in the z-direction by the symbol **k**.   The unit vectors **i, j, k** then form what is known as an *orthogonal triad*.   Now suppose that we have a vector **A** whose projection on the x-axis is A_x, on the y-axis is A_y, and on the z-axis is A_z.   This vector is shown in Fig. 1.4-1b.   In Fig. 1.4-1c it is shown shifted so that its origin is at the origin of the cartesian coordinates.   We see that the vector **A** may be expressed as the sum of three vectors given by the directed line segments $\overline{OP}, \overline{PQ}, \overline{QR}$. But the vector $\overline{OP}$ is conveniently written $A_x\mathbf{i}$ because the distance OP is A_x and the direction of $\overline{OP}$ is the same as that of the unit vector **i**. Similarly, $\overline{PQ}$ is represented by $A_y\mathbf{j}$ and $\overline{QR}$ by $A_z\mathbf{k}$. Summing up:

$$\mathbf{A} = A_x\mathbf{i} + A_y\mathbf{j} + A_z\mathbf{k}. \qquad \textbf{1.4-2}$$

Written in this way the vector is said to be expressed as the sum of its *cartesian components* $A_x\mathbf{i}$, $A_y\mathbf{j}$, and $A_z\mathbf{k}$. The numbers A_x, A_y, A_z are known as *scalar* cartesian components of **A**. They may be

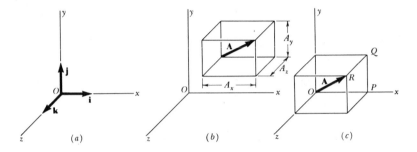

Fig. 1.4-1

positive or negative, depending on whether **A** points toward the positive or negative end of the x-, y-, or z-axis. Often, where no confusion will result, A_x, A_y, and A_z are called simply cartesian components of **A**. It would be pedantic always to insist on preserving the distinction between $A_x\mathbf{i}$, the cartesian component in the x-direction, and A_x, the scalar cartesian component associated with the x-direction.

Once a vector has been expressed as the sum of its cartesian components it is a simple matter to compute the magnitude of the vector and the angles it makes with the coordinate axes. We see from Fig. 1.4-1c that the distance RP is $(A_y^2 + A_z^2)^{1/2}$ and that OPR is a right triangle. It follows that

$$A = (A_x^2 + A_y^2 + A_z^2)^{1/2}. \qquad \textbf{1.4-3}$$

The cosine of the angle between OR and the positive x-axis is OP/OR; i.e., it is A_x/A. If we denote the direction cosines of the line OR by the symbols l, m, n we have

$$l = \frac{A_x}{A}, \qquad m = \frac{A_y}{A}, \qquad n = \frac{A_z}{A}. \qquad \textbf{1.4-4}$$

It follows from the substitution of Eqs. 1.4-4 in Eq. 1.4-3 that $l^2 + m^2 + n^2 = 1$. The separation of a vector into its cartesian components is so common a first step in mechanical analysis that it seems worthwhile to direct attention specifically to the implication of Eqs. 1.4-4. The scalar component of any vector in the direction of any axis is the product of the magnitude of the vector and the cosine of the angle between the vector and the axis.

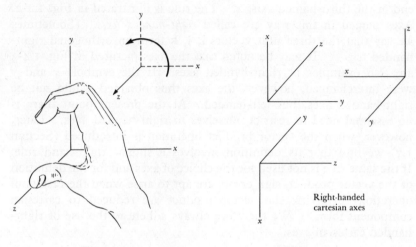

Fig. 1.4-2   **Fig. 1.4-3**

We see from Eq. 1.4-2 that a vector requires three ordinary real numbers for its complete specification. This implies that, in general, a vector equation will be equivalent to three ordinary scalar equations. For example, the equation

$$\mathbf{A} + 3\mathbf{B} = 2\mathbf{j}$$

implies

$$(A_x\mathbf{i} + A_y\mathbf{j} + A_z\mathbf{k}) + 3(B_x\mathbf{i} + B_y\mathbf{j} + B_z\mathbf{k}) = 2\mathbf{j},$$

$$\mathbf{i}(A_x + 3B_x) + \mathbf{j}(A_y + 3B_y - 2) + \mathbf{k}(A_z + 3B_z) = 0$$

and this can be satisfied only if *all* the parenthetical terms vanish: i.e.,

$$A_x = -3B_x, \qquad A_y = 2 - 3B_y, \qquad A_z = -3B_z.$$

Of course if the vectors lie in one plane, say the xy-plane, the z-components of all the vectors in the equation will be zero and one of the three equations will simply say that $0 = 0$. In Example 1.3-4 we have seen that a planar vector equation yields two scalar equations.

Before leaving the subject of unit vectors and their relation to the use of cartesian axes, an important convention used in labeling the x-, y-, z-axes should be mentioned. These axes are named in accordance with what is known as the *right-hand rule*. This rule may be stated in a variety of ways. Probably the simplest is that when the fingertips of the right hand are made to pass from the positive end of the first-named axis, x, to the positive end of the second-named axis, y, the thumb of the right hand points toward the positive end of the third-named axis, z. The rule is illustrated in Fig. 1.4-2. Axes named in this way are called *right-handed axes*. (Sometimes we say that the three unit vectors $\mathbf{i}$, $\mathbf{j}$, $\mathbf{k}$ form an orthogonal right-handed triad.) It may be noted that the axes pictured in Fig. 1.4-3 are also examples of right-handed axes. If the symbols x and y were interchanged, however, the axes thus obtained would not be right-handed axes, but left-handed. At the present point there is no essential need to restrict ourselves to right-handed axes. Later, however, when the vector product operation is introduced (Section 1.7) we find that its definition involves a similar right-hand rule. If the same rule is not used for the choice of axes and for the definition of the vector product, sign errors are apt to arise when the results of operations involving the vector product are reduced to cartesian component form.★ We therefore always adhere to the use of right-handed cartesian axes.

Example 1.4-1

What is the resultant $\mathbf{R}$ *of the vectors*

$$\mathbf{F}_1 = 2\mathbf{i}+\mathbf{j}-2\mathbf{k}, \qquad \mathbf{F}_2 = 4\mathbf{i}+7\mathbf{j}-4\mathbf{k}, \qquad \mathbf{F}_3 = -8\mathbf{i}-9\mathbf{j}+12\mathbf{k}\,?$$

Solution: These vectors have been expressed in terms of their cartesian components. Since $a\mathbf{i}+b\mathbf{i} = (a+b)\mathbf{i}$, and similarly for the $\mathbf{j}$ and $\mathbf{k}$ components, we need only add the scalar components algebraically:

$$\mathbf{F}_1+\mathbf{F}_2+\mathbf{F}_3 = (2\mathbf{i}+\mathbf{j}-2\mathbf{k})+(4\mathbf{i}+7\mathbf{j}-4\mathbf{k})+(-8\mathbf{i}-9\mathbf{j}+12\mathbf{k}),$$

$$\mathbf{F}_1+\mathbf{F}_2+\mathbf{F}_3 = (2+4-8)\mathbf{i}+(1+7-9)\mathbf{j}+(-2-4+12)\mathbf{k} = -2\mathbf{i}-\mathbf{j}+6\mathbf{k},$$

$$\mathbf{R} = -2\mathbf{i}-\mathbf{j}+6\mathbf{k}.$$

This is the sum or resultant vector. Its magnitude is

$$R = [(-2)^2+(-1)^2+(6)^2]^{\frac{1}{2}} = 6.403.$$

★ More important theoretically, some characteristics of the vector product are not preserved under such right- to left-handed "reflections"; this has interesting consequences in, among other areas, the theory of turbulent fluid flow.

The direction cosines of the resultant are

$$l = \frac{-2}{6.403} = -0.312, \quad m = \frac{-1}{6.403} = -0.156, \quad n = \frac{6}{6.403} = 0.937$$

so that the resultant vector, **R**, makes an angle of 108.2° with the positive x-axis, an angle of 99° with the positive y-axis, and an angle of 20.4° with the positive z-axis. It may be seen from this example that the efficient way to add and subtract vectors is first to separate them into their rectangular cartesian components.*

Example 1.4-2

What is the unit vector in the direction of $\mathbf{A} = 6\mathbf{i} - 10\mathbf{j} + 15\mathbf{k}$?
Solution: The magnitude of **A** is

$$A = (36 + 100 + 225)^{\frac{1}{2}} = 19.$$

The unit vector having the direction of **A** is $(1/A)\mathbf{A}$. If we use the symbol $\mathbf{e}_A$ to denote this unit vector,

$$\mathbf{e}_A = \frac{1}{19}(6\mathbf{i} - 10\mathbf{j} + 15\mathbf{k}) = \frac{6}{19}\mathbf{i} - \frac{10}{19}\mathbf{j} + \frac{15}{19}\mathbf{k}.$$

The student should notice that any vector may be written in the form $\mathbf{A} = A\mathbf{e}_A$. When the vector **A** of this example is so expressed it is written

$$\mathbf{A} = 19\left(\frac{6}{19}\mathbf{i} - \frac{10}{19}\mathbf{j} + \frac{15}{19}\mathbf{k}\right).$$

The numbers $6/19$, $-10/19$, $15/19$ are the direction cosines of the vector **A**.

Example 1.4-3

The origin of the vector **V** *is at the point whose coordinates are* $(1, 2, 3)$ *and its terminus is at the point* $(9, -7, 15)$. *Express this vector as the sum of its cartesian components.*
Solution: The vector is pictured in Fig. 1.4-4. In proceeding from point A, the origin of the vector, to point B, its terminus, we proceed from a point whose x-coordinate is 1 to a point whose x-coordinate is 9—that is, 8 units in the positive x-direction. Similarly we proceed 9 units in the negative y-direction and 12 units in the positive z-direction. It follows that $V_x = 8$, $V_y = -9$, $V_z = 12$, and

$$\mathbf{V} = 8\mathbf{i} - 9\mathbf{j} + 12\mathbf{k}.$$

---

* Or any other set of orthogonal components, such as those in the polar coordinate systems of the next section.

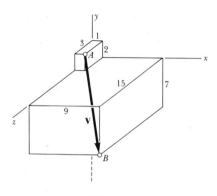

Fig. 1.4-4

Example **1.4-4**

Two vectors, **A** *and* **B**, *intersect at* O.   *Find the equation of the bisector of the angle between* **A** *and* **B**.

Solution: Construct the unit vectors e_A and e_B in the directions of **A** and **B**, respectively, as shown in Fig. 1.4-5:

$$e_A = \left(\frac{1}{A}\right)A, \qquad e_B = \left(\frac{1}{B}\right)B.$$

Now complete the parallelogram whose sides are e_A and e_B. The vertex of the parallelogram opposite O (point M in Fig. 1.4-5) lies on the bisector of the angle between **A** and **B** because all sides of the parallelogram are of the same unit length. Hence $e_A + e_B$ is a vector whose terminus lies on the bisector. The vector, **r**, to any point on the bisector may therefore be written

$$\mathbf{r} = m\left[\left(\frac{1}{A}\right)A + \left(\frac{1}{B}\right)B\right] \qquad \mathbf{1.4\text{-}5}$$

where m is simply a scalar multiplier. By assigning numerical values to

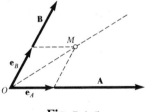

Fig. 1.4-5

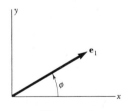

Fig. 1.4-6

m we may have **r** be the vector to any point on the angle bisector, so that Eq. 1.4-5 is described as the equation of the bisector.

Example 1.4-5

Find the cartesian components of a unit vector in the xy-plane making an angle ϕ with the x-axis (Fig. 1.4-6).

Solution: The x-component of the vector, which we may call e_1, is the magnitude of the vector, 1, multiplied by the cosine of the angle between e_1 and the x-axis; the y-component will be 1 multiplied by the cosine of $(\pi/2) - \phi$. We have then

$$e_1 = (\cos \phi)\mathbf{i} + (\sin \phi)\mathbf{j}.$$

It is easy to verify that this is indeed a vector of unit magnitude.

1.5 Plane and Cylindrical Polar Coordinates

Although rectangular cartesian coordinates form the most commonly encountered coordinate system, a wide variety of special coordinate systems appears in the literature of mechanics. Cylindrical polar coordinates find application when the question under

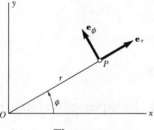

Fig. 1.5-1

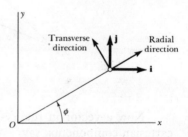

Fig. 1.5-2

analysis is symmetrical about some axis. We begin with the case of vectors lying in the xy-plane. Associated with every point P there is a value of the radial distance r measured from the origin or pole, O, and an angle ϕ measured counterclockwise from the positive end of the x-axis, as shown in Fig. 1.5-1. Introduce unit vectors e_r directed radially outward from P and e_ϕ at right angles to e_r in the direction of increasing ϕ. Clearly any vector passing through P may be described by means of components in these *radial* and *transverse directions*. As is evident in Fig. 1.5-2, the unit vector in the x-direction will have a component in the radial direction equal to the product of its magnitude, 1, and the cosine of the angle ϕ between the x-axis and the radial direction, together with a component in the transverse direction equal to the magnitude, 1, multiplied by the cosine of the angle $\phi + (\pi/2)$ between the x-axis and the transverse direction. In symbols, since $\cos\,[\phi + (\pi/2)] = -\sin\,\phi$,

$$\mathbf{i} = \mathbf{e}_r \cos\,\phi - \mathbf{e}_\phi \sin\,\phi. \qquad \textbf{1.5-1a}$$

Similarly,

$$\mathbf{j} = \mathbf{e}_r \sin\,\phi + \mathbf{e}_\phi \cos\,\phi. \qquad \textbf{1.5-1b}$$

We may solve these equations to find the cartesian components of $\mathbf{e}_r$ and $\mathbf{e}_\phi$:

$$\mathbf{e}_r = \quad \mathbf{i} \cos\,\phi + \mathbf{j} \sin\,\phi,$$

$$\mathbf{e}_\phi = -\mathbf{i} \sin\,\phi + \mathbf{j} \cos\,\phi. \qquad \textbf{1.5-2}$$

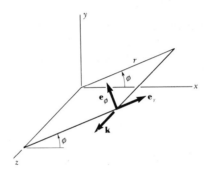

Fig. 1.5-3

Now a vector in the xy-plane may be expressed in terms of its cartesian components, say

$$\mathbf{A} = A_x\mathbf{i} + A_y\mathbf{j};$$

or, alternatively, in terms of its plane polar components,

$$\mathbf{A} = A_r\mathbf{e}_r + A_\phi\mathbf{e}_\phi.$$

Since the vector $\mathbf{A}$ is independent of the coordinate system we use to describe it,

$$A_x\mathbf{i} + A_y\mathbf{j} = A_r\mathbf{e}_r + A_\phi\mathbf{e}_\phi.$$

In view of Eq. 1.5-1 this implies

$$A_x(\mathbf{e}_r \cos\,\phi - \mathbf{e}_\phi \sin\,\phi) + A_y(\mathbf{e}_r \sin\,\phi + \mathbf{e}_\phi \cos\,\phi) = A_r\mathbf{e}_r + A_\phi\mathbf{e}_\phi,$$

$$\mathbf{e}_r(A_x \cos\,\phi + A_y \sin\,\phi - A_r) + \mathbf{e}_\phi(-A_x \sin\,\phi + A_y \cos\,\phi - A_\phi) = 0.$$

This relation can be satisfied only if each of the quantities in parentheses vanishes. We may infer that the relations between the plane polar components of a vector and its plane cartesian components are

$$A_r = A_x \cos \phi + A_y \sin \phi,$$

$$A_\phi = -A_x \sin \phi + A_y \cos \phi. \qquad \textbf{1.5-3}$$

These ideas are easily extended to three dimensions by introducing a z-axis through the pole O, at right angles to the $r\phi$-plane. This is the same as the z-axis of the cartesian frame. The unit vectors $\mathbf{e}_r$, $\mathbf{e}_\phi$, $\mathbf{k}$, taken in that order, form a right-handed orthogonal triad, as shown in Fig. 1.5-3. The coordinates (r, ϕ, z) are known as *cylindrical polar coordinates*. The z-direction is, in this context, sometimes called the axial direction.

Example **1.5-1**

Express the magnitude of a vector in terms of its cylindrical polar components.

Solution: We have

$$A = (A_x^2 + A_y^2 + A_z^2)^{1/2}.$$

If we solve Eqs. 1.5-3 for A_x and A_y in terms of A_r and A_ϕ we have

$$A_x = A_r \cos \phi - A_\phi \sin \phi,$$

$$A_y = A_r \sin \phi + A_\phi \cos \phi.$$

On substituting these in the expression for A we find that

$$A = (A_r^2 + A_\phi^2 + A_z^2)^{1/2}.$$

This result reflects the fact that cylindrical polar coordinates form an *orthogonal coordinate system*, just as the rectangular cartesian coordinates do.

1.6 The Scalar Product; Orthogonal Projection and Scalar Components

In the last two sections the scalar components of a vector relative to some particular orthogonal coordinate systems were found. In this section, we discuss the problem of finding the (orthogonal) scalar component of a vector in any direction of space. Further, we introduce a most important operation on two vectors—an operation that both generalizes the scalar component concept and permits us to speak about some relations between vectors independently of the choice of a particular coordinate system.

We take as fundamental the theorem which states that, given any point in space and any line not passing through the point, one and only one perpendicular may be drawn from the point to the line. The point of intersection of the given line and the perpendicular is called the *orthogonal projection* of the original point on the line. In order to treat all cases, if the given line passes through the given point, the point itself is taken as its projection.

Project two points orthogonally on the given line. The two points in space determine a line segment; the two projection points also determine a segment on the line of projection. The latter segment is the orthogonal projection of the first. If we now assign directions to the lines involved, we may unambiguously assign an algebraic sign to the lengths of the projections and add the projections of many line segments to determine a resultant projection. We may also define the angle between two directed lines.

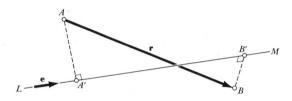

Fig. 1.6-1

Suppose the fixed line LM in space is our line of projection, and we pick a direction on it by assigning a unit vector **e** along it (Fig. 1.6-1). Consider the line segment joining any two points A and B in space, and give it direction by taking it as a vector **r** from, say, A to B. Project A and B on LM, obtaining points A' and B'; the segment $A'B'$ is the projection of $\overline{AB}$ or of **r**. If the points A', B' taken in order define a segment having the sense of **e**, then we attach a positive sign to the length of $A'B'$; if $A'B'$ is opposed to **e**, we count the length as negative. The signed scalar quantity $A'B'$ is the *orthogonal scalar component* of **r** on the directed line LM. Clearly, if we change the assigned direction on LM, i.e., take $-$**e** or M to L as the direction, we change the sign of the scalar projection of **r**; and, if we change the order of A and B, i.e., use $-$**r** or B to A, we change the sign of the projection on LM.

The next fundamental result is that the sum of the (signed) projections on a fixed line is the projection of the resultant, or sum, of the vectors projected—"the sum of the components is the component of the sum." Consider three points A, B, C and a fixed line LM with direction $\mathbf{e}$ given on it (Fig. 1.6-2). Let the directed line segment $\overline{AC}$ be the vector $\mathbf{R}$; the segment $\overline{CB}$, the vector $\mathbf{p}$;

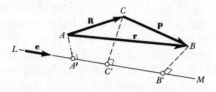

Fig. 1.6-2

and the segment $\overline{AB}$, the vector $\mathbf{r}$ again. Clearly $\mathbf{r} = \mathbf{R} + \mathbf{p}$, by the triangle law definition of vector addition. Let A', B', and C' be the projections of A, B, and C on LM. Our assertion is that the sum of the signed distances $A'C'$ and $C'B'$ equals the signed distance $A'B'$. In Fig. 1.6-2, all three projections are shown as positive; it is clear that the theorem is true in all cases, however, from the very definition of projection. The projection $A'B'$ of $\mathbf{r}$ is, by definition, determined by the projections A' and B' of the points A and B. Wherever the projection C' on LM of point C may be, one starts at the projection of A and ends at the projection of B; symbolically, $A'C' + C'B' = A'B'$, in which ordinary algebraic addition of real numbers is used.

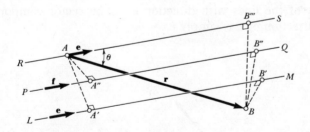

Fig. 1.6-3

From this theorem, it follows that the projection on a fixed line of the vector sum of any finite number of vectors $\mathbf{r}_1$, $\mathbf{r}_2$, $\mathbf{r}_3$, ... $\mathbf{r}_N$, taken in order with one vector starting where the previous one stops, is the algebraic sum of the projections of the separate vectors.

The third fundamental theorem about projections that we need enables us to remove the restriction to projections on a fixed line and hence to define the angle between two lines in space. This theorem states that the projections of a given vector on two parallel lines oriented in the same way are equal. Suppose that we consider the configuration of Fig. 1.6-1 again, but draw another line PQ parallel to LM, assign a unit vector $\mathbf{f}$ on PQ to orient PQ, and project AB on PQ orthogonally obtaining $A''B''$ (Fig. 1.6-3). If $\mathbf{f} = \mathbf{e}$, the theorem asserts that $A''B'' = A'B'$. (Of course, if PQ is oriented oppositely to LM, i.e., $\mathbf{f} = -\mathbf{e}$, then the signed projection $A''B'' = -A'B'$.) We have already used the idea of this theorem implicitly in defining equality of vectors along different lines and in moving vectors together to define their sum by the triangle or parallelogram law—the idea that a vector may be translated parallel to itself without changing its magnitude or direction or scalar component in any direction.

In particular, draw the line RS through A parallel to LM, and orient RS in the same way as LM (Fig. 1.6-3). A is then its own projection on RS; let B''' be the projection of B, so that $A'B' = A''B'' = AB'''$. The two intersecting lines AB and RS determine a plane; in this plane, we may measure the angle θ between AB and RS. We take θ between $0°$ and $180°$, measured between the positive senses of AB and RS, or of $\mathbf{r}$ and $\mathbf{e}$. The orthogonal scalar component of AB in the direction of RS is then the product of the magnitude of AB and the cosine of θ: $AB''' = r \cos \theta$. This is the same as the scalar component of $\mathbf{r}$ on any similarly oriented line parallel to RS, and the angle θ is, by definition, the angle between $\mathbf{r}$ (or $\overline{AB}$) and any of the lines with direction $\mathbf{e}$. The vector component of $\mathbf{r}$ in the direction of $\mathbf{e}$ is simply $r \cos \theta \mathbf{e}$.

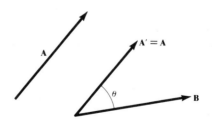

Fig. 1.6-4

These results are independent of the choice of a coordinate system relative to which the points and lines are given coordinate values or direction cosines. It is convenient—more, it is both necessary for a coherent theoretical treatment and useful for computational purposes—to denote the operation of "projection of a vector" in a special way. Indeed, we generalize the projection operation to an operation on any two vectors **A** and **B** (Fig. 1.6-4). Move one, say **A**, parallel to itself, until it coincides with the equal vector **A′** emanating from the initial point of **B**. The two lines along which **A′** and **B** lie determine a plane in which the included angle θ between the directions of **A** = **A′** and **B** may be measured. We define the symbol **A**·**B** by

$$\mathbf{A}\cdot\mathbf{B} = AB \cos \theta, \qquad \textbf{1.6-1}$$

where A and B are, as usual, the magnitudes of **A** and **B**. The operation indicated by **A**·**B** is known as the *scalar product*, or the "dot" product, of the vectors **A** and **B**. It is a "scalar" because the result of the operation is an ordinary real number; it is a "product" because the operation has some of the algebraic properties of ordinary multiplication.

Let us investigate some of the properties of the scalar product. First, we see that the orthogonal projection or scalar component operation can be represented symbolically by the scalar product. If **B** is a unit vector, its magnitude is unity; then **A**·**B** = $A \cos \theta$, the scalar component of **A** in the direction of **B**. For the configuration of Fig. 1.6-1 or 1.6-3 the scalar component of **r** in the direction LM (or PQ or RS) is **r**·**e**. Second, the scalar product of a vector with itself is the square of the magnitude of the vector:

$$\mathbf{A}\cdot\mathbf{A} = A^2. \qquad \textbf{1.6-2}$$

This is true since the "included" angle between a vector and itself is zero. Third, the scalar product provides a test for orthogonality or perpendicularity. When $\theta = 90°$, $\cos \theta$ is zero; thus the scalar product of two non-vanishing vectors is zero if, and only if, the vectors are orthogonal (**A**·**B** = 0, **A** ≠ 0, **B** ≠ 0). In particular, these results are useful in expressing the relations among the members of the orthogonal unit triad **i**, **j**, **k** along the positive axes of a rectangular cartesian system:

$$\mathbf{i}\cdot\mathbf{i} = \mathbf{j}\cdot\mathbf{j} = \mathbf{k}\cdot\mathbf{k} = 1;$$

$$\mathbf{i}\cdot\mathbf{j} = \mathbf{j}\cdot\mathbf{k} = \mathbf{k}\cdot\mathbf{i} = \mathbf{j}\cdot\mathbf{i} = \mathbf{k}\cdot\mathbf{j} = \mathbf{i}\cdot\mathbf{k} = 0. \qquad \textbf{1.6-3}$$

Let us turn now to the mathematical properties that lead us to call $\mathbf{A} \cdot \mathbf{B}$ a "product." First of all, the scalar product is *commutative*, as is ordinary multiplication; this follows from the definition, Eq. 1.6-1:

$$\mathbf{A} \cdot \mathbf{B} = AB \cos \theta = \mathbf{B} \cdot \mathbf{A}. \qquad \textbf{1.6-4}$$

Also, multiplication by a scalar is *associative* over the scalar product:

$$k(\mathbf{A} \cdot \mathbf{B}) = (k\mathbf{A}) \cdot \mathbf{B} = \mathbf{A} \cdot (k\mathbf{B}). \qquad \textbf{1.6-5}$$

Finally, the scalar product is *distributive over vector addition*:

$$\mathbf{A} \cdot (\mathbf{B} + \mathbf{C}) = \mathbf{A} \cdot \mathbf{B} + \mathbf{A} \cdot \mathbf{C}, \qquad \textbf{1.6-6a}$$

$$(\mathbf{B} + \mathbf{C}) \cdot \mathbf{A} = \mathbf{B} \cdot \mathbf{A} + \mathbf{C} \cdot \mathbf{A}. \qquad \textbf{1.6-6b}$$

We shall prove the theorem embodied in Eq. 1.6-6b; Eq. 1.6-6a then follows from the law of commutativity (Eq. 1.6-4).

Equation 1.6-6b follows from the projection theorems and Eq. 1.6-5. Consider any three vectors $\mathbf{A}$, $\mathbf{B}$, and $\mathbf{C}$; bring $\mathbf{B}$ and $\mathbf{C}$ together in order to add them by the triangle law, and draw the line

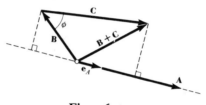

Fig. 1.6-5

through the initial point of $\mathbf{B}$ with the direction of $\mathbf{A}$, i.e., assign the direction $\mathbf{e}_A = \mathbf{A}/|\mathbf{A}|$ to it (Fig. 1.6-5). Since the projection of a sum on a fixed line equals the sum of the projections,

$$(\mathbf{B} + \mathbf{C}) \cdot \mathbf{e}_A = \mathbf{B} \cdot \mathbf{e}_A + \mathbf{C} \cdot \mathbf{e}_A.$$

Now multiply by the magnitude of $\mathbf{A}$; by Eq. 1.6-5,

$$A(\mathbf{B} + \mathbf{C}) \cdot \mathbf{e}_A = (\mathbf{B} + \mathbf{C}) \cdot (A\mathbf{e}_A) = (\mathbf{B} + \mathbf{C}) \cdot \mathbf{A},$$

and $A(\mathbf{B} \cdot \mathbf{e}_A + \mathbf{C} \cdot \mathbf{e}_A) = \mathbf{B} \cdot \mathbf{A} + \mathbf{C} \cdot \mathbf{A}$, thus proving Eq. 1.6-6b.

Although, for the reasons given in the last two paragraphs, it is legitimate and suggestive to give the name of scalar *product* to the operation $\mathbf{A} \cdot \mathbf{B}$ on the two vectors $\mathbf{A}$ and $\mathbf{B}$, the reader should be aware that this newly defined operation does not have all the properties of the product of ordinary real numbers. For example, the product, abc, of three scalars a, b, and c is a perfectly definite number whereas the group of symbols $(\mathbf{A} \cdot \mathbf{B}) \cdot \mathbf{C}$ is meaningless. Further, the law of cancellation does not hold. As we have already noted, whereas $ab = 0$ implies either $a = 0$ or $b = 0$, the equation $\mathbf{A} \cdot \mathbf{B} = 0$ allows a third possibility: $\mathbf{A}$ and $\mathbf{B}$ are perpendicular, i.e., make a right angle with one another. Equivalently, whereas the scalar equation $ab = cb$ implies that $a = c$ if $b \neq 0$, the vector equation $\mathbf{A} \cdot \mathbf{B} = \mathbf{C} \cdot \mathbf{B}$, with $\mathbf{B} \neq 0$, implies that either $\mathbf{A} = \mathbf{C}$ or $\mathbf{A} - \mathbf{C}$ is orthogonal to $\mathbf{B}$.

In the development of the theory of mechanics, symbolic operation with the scalar product is often an efficient way of obtaining results generally true without regard to the choice of a particular coordinate frame. In solving particular problems, however, a particular set of coordinates is usually introduced, and we must have a way of reducing the scalar product to a computational form suitable for use. For rectangular cartesian coordinates, this is easily found from the distributive law 1.6-6 and the unit triad relations 1.6-3. Suppose two vectors $\mathbf{A}$ and $\mathbf{B}$ have the representations $\mathbf{A} = A_x \mathbf{i} + A_y \mathbf{j} + A_z \mathbf{k}$, $\mathbf{B} = B_x \mathbf{i} + B_y \mathbf{j} + B_z \mathbf{k}$ in some fixed (x, y, z) system. Then

$$
\begin{aligned}
\mathbf{A} \cdot \mathbf{B} &= \mathbf{A} \cdot (B_x \mathbf{i} + B_y \mathbf{j} + B_z \mathbf{k}) \\
&= \mathbf{A} \cdot (B_x \mathbf{i}) + \mathbf{A} \cdot (B_y \mathbf{j}) + \mathbf{A} \cdot (B_z \mathbf{k}) \\
&= A_x B_x (\mathbf{i} \cdot \mathbf{i}) + A_y B_x (\mathbf{j} \cdot \mathbf{i}) + A_z B_x (\mathbf{k} \cdot \mathbf{i}) \\
&\quad + A_x B_y (\mathbf{i} \cdot \mathbf{j}) + A_y B_y (\mathbf{j} \cdot \mathbf{j}) + A_z B_y (\mathbf{k} \cdot \mathbf{j}) \\
&\quad + A_x B_z (\mathbf{i} \cdot \mathbf{k}) + A_y B_z (\mathbf{j} \cdot \mathbf{k}) + A_z B_z (\mathbf{k} \cdot \mathbf{k})
\end{aligned}
$$

or

$$
\mathbf{A} \cdot \mathbf{B} = A_x B_x + A_y B_y + A_z B_z. \qquad \text{1.6-7}
$$

Finally, we may note that the scalar component and orthogonal projection concept is not the only useful one expressed by the scalar product. We shall see others in the examples of this section and in later sections. In dynamics, the important concept of the power of a force is expressed by the scalar product; if $\mathbf{A}$ is the force on a particle and $\mathbf{B}$ is the instantaneous velocity of the particle, $\mathbf{A} \cdot \mathbf{B}$ is the power, or time-rate of doing work, of the force.

Example **1.6-1**

What is the angle between the vectors $\mathbf{A} = 2\mathbf{i} - 5\mathbf{j} + 6\mathbf{k}$ *and* $\mathbf{B} = 4\mathbf{i} - 2\mathbf{j} - 3\mathbf{k}$ *?*
Solution: Since $\mathbf{A} \cdot \mathbf{B} = AB \cos \theta$, we have

$$
\cos \theta = \frac{(\mathbf{A} \cdot \mathbf{B})}{AB}.
$$

Here, $\mathbf{A} \cdot \mathbf{B} = A_x B_x + A_y B_y + A_z B_z = 8 + 10 - 18 = 0$; therefore, $\cos \theta = 0$, $\theta = 90°$, and $\mathbf{A}$ and $\mathbf{B}$ are perpendicular.

Example 1.6-2

Find the vector or vectors $\mathbf{A} = A_y \mathbf{j} + 4\mathbf{k}$ *making an angle of* 60° *with* $\mathbf{B} = \mathbf{i} + \mathbf{j} + \mathbf{k}$.

Solution: Since $\mathbf{A} \cdot \mathbf{B} = AB \cos \theta = AB \cos 60° = \frac{1}{2} AB$, we have

$$\mathbf{A} \cdot \mathbf{B} = A_y + 4 = \left(\frac{1}{2}\right)\left(\sqrt{16 + A_y^2}\right)\left(\sqrt{3}\right).$$

Upon squaring, we obtain a quadratic equation for the determination of A_y; note that only roots greater than -4 are valid. We find

$$A_y^2 + 8A_y + 16 = 12 + \frac{3}{4} A_y^2,$$

$$A_y^2 + 32A_y + 16 = 0,$$

$$A_y = -16 \pm 4\sqrt{15}.$$

The only root that leads to a solution is $A_y = -16 + 4\sqrt{15}$, and the only vector is

$$\mathbf{A} = -0.508\mathbf{j} + 4\mathbf{k}.$$

Example 1.6-3

Derive the law of cosines of trigonometry.

Solution: Refer to Fig. 1.6-5, where a triangle with sides $B = |\mathbf{B}|$, $C = |\mathbf{C}|$, and $D = |\mathbf{D}| = |\mathbf{B} + \mathbf{C}|$ is shown. Let ϕ be the angle included by the sides of length B and C. We wish to prove $D^2 = B^2 + C^2 - 2BC \cos \phi$. We have

$$D^2 = (\mathbf{B} + \mathbf{C}) \cdot (\mathbf{B} + \mathbf{C}) = B^2 + 2\mathbf{B} \cdot \mathbf{C} + C^2.$$

Now $\mathbf{B} \cdot \mathbf{C} = BC \cos \theta$, where θ is the angle included between $\mathbf{B}$ and $\mathbf{C}$. The angle ϕ is the supplement of θ, i.e., $\phi = \pi - \theta$; therefore

$$\mathbf{B} \cdot \mathbf{C} = BC \cos (\pi - \phi) = -BC \cos \phi.$$

Thus

$$D^2 = B^2 + C^2 - 2BC \cos \phi.$$

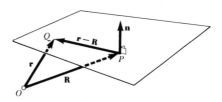

Fig. 1.6-6

Example 1.6-4

A plane in space is determined by one point in the plane and the normal to the plane. Find the equation of the plane.

Solution: Let **R** be the position vector to the given point, P, in the plane from some fixed origin, O; let **n** be a unit vector normal to the plane; and let **r** be the position vector from O to a general point, Q, in the plane (Fig. 1.6-6). Since **n** is normal to the plane, any vector in the plane is orthogonal to **n**. Thus **r** − **R**, the position of Q relative to P, is perpendicular to **n**, and the equation of the plane is

$$(\mathbf{r} - \mathbf{R}) \cdot \mathbf{n} = 0.$$

1.7 The Vector Product; Moment of a Vector about a Point

A second operation on two vectors, this time producing a vector instead of a scalar and having some attributes of ordinary multiplication, is of fundamental importance for the expression of many

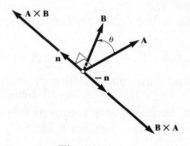

Fig. 1.7-1

physical concepts.   Among these may be mentioned the moment of a force, moment of momentum, the force induced by a magnetic field on a moving charge, and the velocity of a point in a rotating rigid body.   The *vector product*, or "cross" product, of two vectors is defined, independently of any particular coordinate system, by the relation:

$$\mathbf{A} \times \mathbf{B} = AB \sin \theta \mathbf{n}. \qquad\qquad \textbf{1.7-1}$$

Here A and B are the magnitudes of **A** and **B** and θ is the angle included between **A** and **B**, as defined in the previous section.   The vector **n** is a unit vector orthogonal to the plane determined by **A** and **B** when they are made to come together by parallel translation. The direction of **n** is determined by the right-hand rule for rotation (Fig. 1.7-1); i.e., if the fingers of one's right hand are made to curl from the direction of **A** to the direction of **B**, the right thumb points in the direction of **n** (see Section 1.4).

Let us investigate the properties of the vector product as we did those of the scalar product. First, the vanishing of the vector product is a test for parallelism of two non-zero vectors. If $\mathbf{A} \times \mathbf{B} = \mathbf{0}$, with $\mathbf{A} \neq \mathbf{0}$, $\mathbf{B} \neq \mathbf{0}$, then sin θ must vanish and $\theta = 0°$ or $180°$. Thus **A** and **B** have the same or opposite directions and hence are parallel. This means that the cancellation law of scalar multiplication cannot be extended to the cross product: if $\mathbf{A} \times \mathbf{B} = \mathbf{A} \times \mathbf{C}$, we cannot conclude that $\mathbf{B} = \mathbf{C}$, since the equation is also satisfied if $\mathbf{B} - \mathbf{C}$ is parallel to **A**. The vector product of a vector with itself vanishes.

The vector product operation is not commutative, either; in fact, by the very definition, the inversion of the two "factors" changes the sign of the product:

$$\mathbf{B} \times \mathbf{A} = BA \sin \theta(-\mathbf{n}) = -\mathbf{A} \times \mathbf{B}. \qquad \textbf{1.7-2}$$

The vectors $\mathbf{A} \times \mathbf{B}$ and $\mathbf{B} \times \mathbf{A}$ thus have the same magnitudes but opposite directions (Fig. 1.7-1).

Multiplication of the vector product by a scalar is "associative," i.e.,

$$k(\mathbf{A} \times \mathbf{B}) = (k\mathbf{A}) \times \mathbf{B} = \mathbf{A} \times (k\mathbf{B}). \qquad \textbf{1.7-3}$$

The student should have no difficulty proving this last result for himself.

Meaning can be given to a vector triple product, $\mathbf{A} \times (\mathbf{B} \times \mathbf{C})$; however, the associative law does not hold:

$$\mathbf{A} \times (\mathbf{B} \times \mathbf{C}) \neq (\mathbf{A} \times \mathbf{B}) \times \mathbf{C}.$$

Since $\mathbf{B} \times \mathbf{C}$ is perpendicular to the plane of **B** and **C**, $\mathbf{A} \times (\mathbf{B} \times \mathbf{C})$ must lie in the plane of **B** and **C**. Similarly, $(\mathbf{A} \times \mathbf{B}) \times \mathbf{C}$ must lie in the plane of **A** and **B**. These two planes will not in general be the same, and the two vectors, therefore, will not be equal.

The vector product is distributive over vector addition:

$$\mathbf{A} \times (\mathbf{B} + \mathbf{C}) = \mathbf{A} \times \mathbf{B} + \mathbf{A} \times \mathbf{C},$$

$$(\mathbf{B} + \mathbf{C}) \times \mathbf{A} = \mathbf{B} \times \mathbf{A} + \mathbf{C} \times \mathbf{A}. \qquad \textbf{1.7-4}$$

This will be proved in the next section in Example 1.8-1. One cautionary note is in order: because of the non-commutative nature of the cross product, the order of the symbols must be the same on each side of a vector equation such as 1.7-4.

It may be seen that very few of the attributes of ordinary multiplication are carried over to the vector product. Yet the facts that the distributive law holds as well as that the ordinary product of the two magnitudes appears in the definition are sufficient to justify the use of the word "product" for this operation.

One important concept defined directly in terms of the vector product is that of the *moment of a vector about a point*. Let a vector

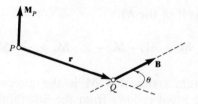

Fig. 1.7-2

B emanate from point Q in space, and let P be any other point in space (Fig. 1.7-2). Let **r** be the position of Q with respect to P. Then the moment vector $\mathbf{M}_P$ of **B** with respect to, or about, P is defined to be

$$\mathbf{M}_P = \mathbf{r} \times \mathbf{B}. \qquad \textbf{1.7-5}$$

In statics, the moment with which we shall be most concerned is the moment of a force vector.

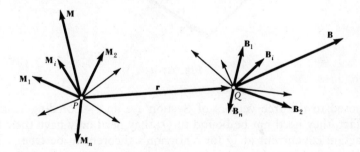

Fig. 1.7-3

There are two basic theorems about moments of vectors that we need. The first is the vector form of *Varignon's theorem*: The sum of the moments of any (finite) number of vectors emanating from one point, Q, about any other point, P, is the moment about point P of the resultant vector. Consider any set of vectors $\mathbf{B}_1, \mathbf{B}_2, \ldots \mathbf{B}_n$ (or simply $\mathbf{B}_i$, $i = 1, 2, \ldots n$) emanating from Q and any other point P

such that $\mathbf{r}$ is the position of Q relative to P (Fig. 1.7-3). Let $\mathbf{M}_1, \ldots \mathbf{M}_n$ be the moments about P of $\mathbf{B}_1, \ldots \mathbf{B}_n$: $\mathbf{M}_i = \mathbf{r} \times \mathbf{B}_i$, $i = 1, 2, \ldots n$. Let $\mathbf{B}$ be the resultant of the $\mathbf{B}_i$:

$$\mathbf{B} = \mathbf{B}_1 + \mathbf{B}_2 + \ldots \mathbf{B}_n = \sum_{i=1}^{n} \mathbf{B}_i,$$

and $\mathbf{M}$ the resultant of the $\mathbf{M}_i$:

$$\mathbf{M} = \mathbf{M}_1 + \mathbf{M}_2 + \ldots \mathbf{M}_n = \sum_{i=1}^{n} \mathbf{M}_i.$$

Varignon's theorem states that $\mathbf{M}$ is the moment of $\mathbf{B}$ about P: $\mathbf{M} = \mathbf{r} \times \mathbf{B}$. The proof follows from the distributive property of the vector product, which we shall prove in Section 1.8:

$$\mathbf{r} \times \mathbf{B} = \mathbf{r} \times \left(\sum_{i=1}^{n} \mathbf{B}_i \right) = \sum_{i=1}^{n} (\mathbf{r} \times \mathbf{B}_i) = \sum_{i=1}^{n} \mathbf{M}_i = \mathbf{M}. \qquad \textbf{1.7-6}$$

For Varignon's theorem as stated, we must have all vectors emanating from Q; that is, the vectors are *bound*, or tied, to the point Q—as

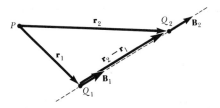

Fig. 1.7-4

opposed to the free vectors of Section 1.2 and succeeding sections. In fact, they need not be bound to Q; they need only have their lines of action concurrent at Q for Varignon's theorem to be true. That is, they need only be *sliding* vectors with concurrent lines of action. The sliding vector is one not free to move anywhere in space for the purposes of the computation to be made, but one which may be "slid" along its line of action (the line through a point on the vector in the direction of the vector itself) without affecting the result of whatever operation is to be performed on it.

In particular, the moment of a vector about a point P is independent of the choice of the point Q from which the vector emanates, provided only that Q be some point on the line of action of the vector.

This is the second fundamental theorem concerning moments. Consider two vectors $\mathbf{B}_1 = \mathbf{B}_2 = \mathbf{B}$ equal in magnitude and direction and having the same line of action, one emanating from Q_1 and the other from Q_2 (Fig. 1.7-4). Let $\mathbf{r}_1$ and $\mathbf{r}_2$ be the positions of Q_1 and Q_2 relative to P. Then the moment of $\mathbf{B}_2$ about P is $\mathbf{r}_2 \times \mathbf{B}_2 = \mathbf{r}_2 \times \mathbf{B}$ and the moment of $\mathbf{B}_1$ is $\mathbf{r}_1 \times \mathbf{B}_1 = \mathbf{r}_1 \times \mathbf{B}$. We have

$$\mathbf{r}_2 \times \mathbf{B}_2 = [\mathbf{r}_1 + (\mathbf{r}_2 - \mathbf{r}_1)] \times \mathbf{B} = \mathbf{r}_1 \times \mathbf{B} + (\mathbf{r}_2 - \mathbf{r}_1) \times \mathbf{B}.$$

But $\mathbf{r}_2 - \mathbf{r}_1$ is the position of Q_2 relative to Q_1 and hence lies along the line $Q_1 Q_2$, i.e., is parallel to $\mathbf{B}$. Therefore, $(\mathbf{r}_2 - \mathbf{r}_1) \times \mathbf{B} = 0$, and

$$\mathbf{r}_2 \times \mathbf{B}_2 = \mathbf{r}_1 \times \mathbf{B}_1.$$

As in the case of the scalar product, we must find a scheme for computing the vector product in a particular coordinate system. This may be done quite simply for right-handed orthogonal systems with the aid of the fundamental definition of the vector product and the distributive law. We introduce, in particular, a right-handed rectangular cartesian system (x, y, z) with unit triad $\mathbf{i}$, $\mathbf{j}$, $\mathbf{k}$, as in Section 1.4.* Since the system is right-handed, the unit triad has the following cross-products:

$$\mathbf{i} \times \mathbf{i} = \mathbf{j} \times \mathbf{j} = \mathbf{k} \times \mathbf{k} = 0,$$
$$\mathbf{i} \times \mathbf{j} = -\mathbf{j} \times \mathbf{i} = \mathbf{k},$$
$$\mathbf{j} \times \mathbf{k} = -\mathbf{k} \times \mathbf{j} = \mathbf{i}, \qquad \text{1.7-7}$$
$$\mathbf{k} \times \mathbf{i} = -\mathbf{i} \times \mathbf{k} = \mathbf{j}.$$

The derivation of these follows immediately from the definition of $\mathbf{A} \times \mathbf{B}$. If two vectors $\mathbf{A}$ and $\mathbf{B}$ have the cartesian representations $A_x\mathbf{i} + A_y\mathbf{j} + A_z\mathbf{k}$ and $B_x\mathbf{i} + B_y\mathbf{j} + B_z\mathbf{k}$, then the distributive law and Eqs. 1.7-7 lead to

---

* The fact that we must restrict ourselves to right-handed coordinate systems to preserve the vectorial character of the cross-product is sometimes reflected in the use of the term "pseudo-vector" for moment vectors and cross-product vectors in general. "True" vectors are those which preserve magnitude and direction under transformations of coordinates that include reflections and rotations; the "pseudo-vector" behaves as a vector only under so-called proper rotations that do not change the orientation of the axes. We cannot pursue this topic here, for it is not of concern in elementary rigid-body statics and dynamics. It is of some importance in the formulation of the mechanical theory of the general motions of deformable bodies.

$$\mathbf{A} \times \mathbf{B} = \mathbf{A} \times (B_x \mathbf{i}) + \mathbf{A} \times (B_y \mathbf{j}) + \mathbf{A} \times (B_z \mathbf{k})$$
$$= A_x B_x (\mathbf{i} \times \mathbf{i}) + A_y B_x (\mathbf{j} \times \mathbf{i}) + A_z B_x (\mathbf{k} \times \mathbf{i})$$
$$+ A_x B_y (\mathbf{i} \times \mathbf{j}) + A_y B_y (\mathbf{j} \times \mathbf{j}) + A_z B_y (\mathbf{k} \times \mathbf{j})$$
$$+ A_x B_z (\mathbf{i} \times \mathbf{k}) + A_y B_z (\mathbf{j} \times \mathbf{k}) + A_z B_z (\mathbf{k} \times \mathbf{k}),$$

or

$$\mathbf{A} \times \mathbf{B} = (A_y B_z - A_z B_y) \mathbf{i} + (A_z B_x - A_x B_z) \mathbf{j} + (A_x B_y - A_y B_x) \mathbf{k}. \quad \textbf{1.7-8}$$

If $\mathbf{A} \times \mathbf{B} = \mathbf{C} = C_x \mathbf{i} + C_y \mathbf{j} + C_z \mathbf{k}$, we see that the scalar equivalents to the vector equation $\mathbf{A} \times \mathbf{B} = \mathbf{C}$ are the three equations

$$C_x = A_y B_z - A_z B_y,$$
$$C_y = A_z B_x - A_x B_z, \quad \textbf{1.7-9}$$
$$C_z = A_x B_y - A_y B_x.$$

A convenient way of remembering the sign conventions for the components of the cross product is given by introducing a symbolic determinant. Another way of writing 1.7-9 is by means of two-by-two determinants:

$$C_x = \begin{vmatrix} A_y & A_z \\ B_y & B_z \end{vmatrix},$$

$$C_y = \begin{vmatrix} A_z & A_x \\ B_z & B_x \end{vmatrix} = - \begin{vmatrix} A_x & A_z \\ B_x & B_z \end{vmatrix},$$

$$C_z = \begin{vmatrix} A_x & A_y \\ B_x & B_y \end{vmatrix}.$$

Then $\mathbf{C} = C_x \mathbf{i} + C_y \mathbf{j} + C_z \mathbf{k}$ may be written

$$\mathbf{C} = \mathbf{i} \begin{vmatrix} A_y & A_z \\ B_y & B_z \end{vmatrix} + (-1)\mathbf{j} \begin{vmatrix} A_x & A_z \\ B_x & B_z \end{vmatrix} + \mathbf{k} \begin{vmatrix} A_x & A_y \\ B_x & B_y \end{vmatrix},$$

or

$$\mathbf{C} = \mathbf{A} \times \mathbf{B} = \begin{vmatrix} \mathbf{i} & \mathbf{j} & \mathbf{k} \\ A_x & A_y & A_z \\ B_x & B_y & B_z \end{vmatrix}. \quad \textbf{1.7-10}$$

The evaluation of the symbolic determinant Eq. 1.7-10 by minors of the first row leads to the extended form (Eq. 1.7-8) of the vector product in cartesian coordinates.

Example 1.7-1

What are the two unit vectors perpendicular to $\mathbf{A} = 3\mathbf{i} - 4\mathbf{j} + 12\mathbf{k}$ *and* $\mathbf{B} = 5\mathbf{i} + 12\mathbf{j}$?

Solution: $\mathbf{A} \times \mathbf{B}$ is orthogonal to both $\mathbf{A}$ and $\mathbf{B}$; thus the unit vectors $\mathbf{n}_1$, $\mathbf{n}_2$ perpendicular to $\mathbf{A}$ and $\mathbf{B}$ are given by

$$\mathbf{n}_1 = -\mathbf{n}_2 = \frac{\mathbf{A} \times \mathbf{B}}{|\mathbf{A} \times \mathbf{B}|}.$$

Now

$$\mathbf{A} \times \mathbf{B} = \begin{vmatrix} \mathbf{i} & \mathbf{j} & \mathbf{k} \\ 3 & -4 & 12 \\ 5 & 12 & 0 \end{vmatrix} = -144\mathbf{i} + 60\mathbf{j} + 56\mathbf{k},$$

$$|\mathbf{A} \times \mathbf{B}| = [(-144)^2 + (60)^2 + (56)^2]^{1/2} = 4\sqrt{1717}.$$

Therefore,

$$\mathbf{n}_1 = -\mathbf{n}_2 = \frac{\sqrt{1717}}{1717}(-36\mathbf{i} + 15\mathbf{j} + 14\mathbf{k})$$

$$\cong -0.869\mathbf{i} + 0.362\mathbf{j} + 0.338\mathbf{k}.$$

The reader may check that $\mathbf{n}_1 \cdot \mathbf{A} = \mathbf{n}_1 \cdot \mathbf{B} = 0$.

Example 1.7-2

Find the area of a parallelogram of sides A and B and included angle θ (*Fig.* 1.7-5a).

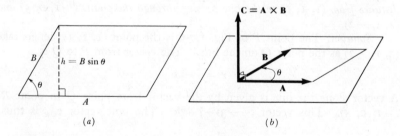

(a)   *(b)*

Fig. 1.7-5

Solution: The area is, of course, $Ah = AB \sin \theta$. If we introduce vectors $\mathbf{A}$, $\mathbf{B}$ along the sides of the parallelogram (Fig. 1.7-5b) so that θ is the angle included between their positive directions, the area is given by

$$AB \sin \theta = |\mathbf{A} \times \mathbf{B}|.$$

Thus the magnitude of the cross product of two vectors can be given geometrical interpretation as the area of the parallelogram based on the two vectors as sides. Indeed, the concept of a vectorial representation of area can be developed. This concept is of use in fluid mechanics and other parts of physics where the transport, or flow, of some quantity through a surface is important.

Example **1.7-3**

Given a point and a line, find the perpendicular distance from the point to the line.

Solution: Let P be the given point, Q any point on the given line at position $\mathbf{r}$ from P, and $\mathbf{e}$ a unit vector along the given line (Fig. 1.7-6).

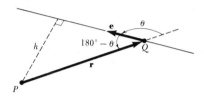

Fig. 1.7-6

Then $|\mathbf{r} \times \mathbf{e}| = r \sin \theta = r \sin (\pi - \theta) = h$, the desired distance. Note that, if $\mathbf{e}$ were reversed in direction, θ would be replaced by $\pi - \theta$ directly in the definition of the vector product.

Example **1.7-4**

Use the result of the previous example to compute the perpendicular distance from $(1, 1, 1)$ *to the line passing through the points* $(-1, 0, 5)$ *and* $(2, 1, -2)$.

Solution: The point P of Fig. 1.7-6 is the point $(1, 1, 1)$; let us take $(2, 1, -2)$ as the point Q on the line. The vector from P to Q is

$$\mathbf{r} = \mathbf{i} - 3\mathbf{k}.$$

A vector along the line is given by the vector from point Q to point R: $(-1, 0, 5)$. This vector is $-3\mathbf{i} - \mathbf{j} + 7\mathbf{k}$. The unit vector $\mathbf{e}_{QR}$ is thus

$$\mathbf{e}_{QR} = \frac{1}{\sqrt{59}} (-3\mathbf{i} - \mathbf{j} + 7\mathbf{k}).$$

Now

$$\mathbf{r} \times \mathbf{e}_{QR} = \frac{1}{\sqrt{59}} \begin{vmatrix} \mathbf{i} & \mathbf{j} & \mathbf{k} \\ 1 & 0 & -3 \\ -3 & -1 & 7 \end{vmatrix} = \frac{1}{\sqrt{59}} (-3\mathbf{i} + 2\mathbf{j} - \mathbf{k}),$$

and the perpendicular distance is

$$|\mathbf{r} \times \mathbf{e}_{QR}| = \sqrt{\frac{14}{59}} \cong 0.487.$$

Example 1.7-5

A force of magnitude 10 lb has line of action passing through $(1, -1, 1)$
and $(4, -5, 13)$ *inches. Find the moment of the force about the point*
$(0, +1, -1)$.

$$\text{Solution: } \mathbf{F} = 10\mathbf{e}_F; \mathbf{e}_F = \frac{(4-1)\mathbf{i}+(-5+1)\mathbf{j}+(13-1)\mathbf{k}}{[3^2+(-4)^2+12^2]^{\frac{1}{2}}}.$$

The force vector is, therefore,

$$\mathbf{F} = \frac{10}{13}(3\mathbf{i}-4\mathbf{j}+12\mathbf{k}) \quad \text{lb.}$$

The vector for the moment arm is

$$\mathbf{r} = (1-0)\mathbf{i}+(-1-1)\mathbf{j}+(1+1)\mathbf{k}$$
$$= \mathbf{i}-2\mathbf{j}+2\mathbf{k} \quad \text{in.}$$

Hence

$$\mathbf{M} = \mathbf{r}\times\mathbf{F} = \frac{10}{13}\begin{vmatrix} \mathbf{i} & \mathbf{j} & \mathbf{k} \\ 1 & -2 & 2 \\ 3 & -4 & 12 \end{vmatrix} = \frac{10}{13}(-16\mathbf{i}-6\mathbf{j}+2\mathbf{k})$$

$$= -\frac{160}{13}\mathbf{i}-\frac{60}{13}\mathbf{j}+\frac{20}{13}\mathbf{k} \quad \text{lb-in.}$$

The reader should sketch the vectors $\mathbf{r}$, $\mathbf{F}$, and $\mathbf{M}$ to an appropriate scale.

1.8 The Scalar Triple Product; the Moment of a Vector about a Line

Two important extensions of the concept of the product of
vectors are needed to complete the discussion of the algebra of
vectors in three dimensions. One extension is the *scalar*, or *mixed*,
triple product $(\mathbf{A}\times\mathbf{B})\cdot\mathbf{C}$ of three vectors; the other is the *vector triple
product* $(\mathbf{A}\times\mathbf{B})\times\mathbf{C}$, treated in the next section. In mechanics, the
definition of a scalar "turning moment" or torque about an axis due
to a force on a body leads to the expression of that torque as a scalar
component of an appropriate moment vector. In terms of the force,
the torque may be written in a form given by a scalar triple product.
We shall return to this formulation of the moment about an axis
after discussing the properties of the scalar triple product for any
type of vector.

As the adjective "scalar" implies, $(\mathbf{A}\times\mathbf{B})\cdot\mathbf{C}$ is an ordinary real
number. If θ is the angle between $\mathbf{A}$ and $\mathbf{B}$, so that $\mathbf{A}\times\mathbf{B} = AB\sin\theta\mathbf{n}$,
and ϕ is the angle between $\mathbf{n}$ and $\mathbf{C}$, then

$$(\mathbf{A}\times\mathbf{B})\cdot\mathbf{C} = ABC\sin\theta\cos\phi. \qquad \textbf{1.8-1}$$

Since $0 \leqq \phi \leqq \pi$, we see that the scalar triple product may be positive, negative, or zero. Assuming that none of the vectors is the zero vector and that **A** is not parallel to **B**($\theta \neq 0$, π), we see that the sign of $(\mathbf{A} \times \mathbf{B}) \cdot \mathbf{C}$ is determined by the relative orientation of **A**, **B**, and **C** (Fig. 1.8-1). In Fig. 1.8-1a, **A**, **B**, and **C** are oriented in a right-handed way, with $0 \leqq \phi < \pi/2$, and $(\mathbf{A} \times \mathbf{B}) \cdot \mathbf{C}$ is positive; in Fig. 1.8-1b, $\pi/2 < \phi \leqq \pi$, the three vectors have a left-handed orientation, and $(\mathbf{A} \times \mathbf{B}) \cdot \mathbf{C}$ is negative. When the scalar triple product vanishes with $\phi = \pi/2$, the three vectors are coplanar.

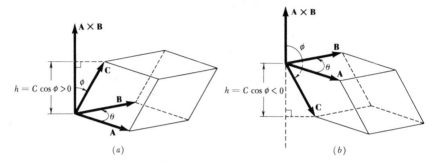

Fig. 1.8-1

A simple geometrical interpretation may be given to the scalar triple product. The magnitude $AB \sin \theta$ of $\mathbf{A} \times \mathbf{B}$ is the area of the parallelogram with sides along **A** and **B** (see Example 1.7-2). The quantity $C \cos \phi$ is the signed altitude of the parallelepiped based on **A** and **B**, with **C** along the slant side. Therefore, $(\mathbf{A} \times \mathbf{B}) \cdot \mathbf{C}$ is the signed volume of the parallelepiped. The two parallelepipeds of Figs. 1.8-1a and 1.8-1b have positive and negative volumes, respectively, according to this sign convention.[*]

The interpretation of the scalar triple product as a volume leads to the statement of the fundamental property of the scalar triple product. Since the volume does not depend on which face of the parallelepiped is taken as base and on whether the area of the base is pre- or post-multiplied by the altitude, we deduce that the value of $(\mathbf{A} \times \mathbf{B}) \cdot \mathbf{C}$ depends only on the relative, or cyclic, order of the three vectors and not on their absolute order or on the placing of the vector and scalar

---

[*] If one wishes to keep volume as a positive quantity, then one must either take the volume as $|(\mathbf{A} \times \mathbf{B}) \cdot \mathbf{C}|$ or else choose a right-handed order (**B**, **A**, **C** in Fig. 1.8-1b) from the three.

product operations. That is, the value will be the same if the "dot" and "cross" are interchanged; and the value will be the same if the cyclic order *ABCAB* is preserved:

$$(\mathbf{A} \times \mathbf{B}) \cdot \mathbf{C} = \mathbf{A} \cdot (\mathbf{B} \times \mathbf{C}) = (\mathbf{B} \times \mathbf{C}) \cdot \mathbf{A} = \mathbf{B} \cdot (\mathbf{C} \times \mathbf{A})$$
$$= (\mathbf{C} \times \mathbf{A}) \cdot \mathbf{B} = \mathbf{C} \cdot (\mathbf{A} \times \mathbf{B}). \quad \textbf{1.8-2}$$

In Fig. 1.8-1, the volume of either parallelepiped is equally well given by the area of the front face based on **A** and **C** multiplied by the altitude given by the projection of **B** on the normal to the front face. To preserve the algebraic sign of the result, we see that we must have $(\mathbf{C} \times \mathbf{A}) \cdot \mathbf{B}$ and not $(\mathbf{A} \times \mathbf{C}) \cdot \mathbf{B}$ for the volume. This gives the equality of the first and fifth terms in Eq. 1.8-2. An alternative proof of the relations given in Eqs. 1.8-2 which makes no appeal to geometric intuition is given in Example 1.8-5. In summary, the foregoing considerations show that the scalar triple product may have either sign, that it vanishes if the three vectors are coplanar, that the dot and cross may be interchanged:

$$(\mathbf{B} \times \mathbf{C}) \cdot \mathbf{A} = \mathbf{B} \cdot (\mathbf{C} \times \mathbf{A}), \quad \textbf{1.8-3a}$$

and that the sign depends on the cyclic order of the vectors:

$$(\mathbf{A} \times \mathbf{B}) \cdot \mathbf{C} = (\mathbf{B} \times \mathbf{C}) \cdot \mathbf{A} \quad \textbf{1.8-3b}$$

but

$$(\mathbf{A} \times \mathbf{B}) \cdot \mathbf{C} = -(\mathbf{B} \times \mathbf{A}) \cdot \mathbf{C}. \quad \textbf{1.8-3c}$$

The last result follows from the non-commutative nature of the vector product.

Using the properties of the scalar triple product, we are now in a position to prove the distributive law for the vector product operation (Eq. 1.7-4). The proofs of Varignon's theorem and other results of the last section will then be complete.

Example **1.8-1**

Prove the distributive law for the vector product

$$\mathbf{A} \times (\mathbf{B} + \mathbf{C}) = \mathbf{A} \times \mathbf{B} + \mathbf{A} \times \mathbf{C}.$$

Solution: Let $\mathbf{V} = \mathbf{A} \times (\mathbf{B} + \mathbf{C}) - \mathbf{A} \times \mathbf{B} - \mathbf{A} \times \mathbf{C}$; if we can show **V** to be the zero vector, then the distributive law will follow at once. To compute the magnitude of **V**, we take the dot product of each side of the defining equation with **V**:

$$\mathbf{V} \cdot \mathbf{V} = V^2 = \mathbf{V} \cdot [\mathbf{A} \times (\mathbf{B} + \mathbf{C})] - \mathbf{V} \cdot (\mathbf{A} \times \mathbf{B}) - \mathbf{V} \cdot (\mathbf{A} \times \mathbf{C}).$$

This step is legitimate because the distributive law holds for the scalar product operation (Eq. 1.6-6). In view of Eq. 1.8-3a, the dot and cross operations in each scalar triple product may be interchanged:

$$V^2 = (\mathbf{V} \times \mathbf{A}) \cdot (\mathbf{B} + \mathbf{C}) - (\mathbf{V} \times \mathbf{A}) \cdot \mathbf{B} - (\mathbf{V} \times \mathbf{A}) \cdot \mathbf{C}.$$

Making use of the distributive law for the scalar product once again, we may "factor out" $\mathbf{V} \times \mathbf{A}$ and find

$$V^2 = (\mathbf{V} \times \mathbf{A}) \cdot [(\mathbf{B} + \mathbf{C}) - \mathbf{B} - \mathbf{C}] = 0.$$

Therefore, $\mathbf{V} = \mathbf{0}$, since it has zero magnitude, and Eq. 1.7-4 follows directly.

The computation of the scalar triple product when the vectors are given in cartesian components is straightforward. The symbolic determinant representation of Eq. 1.7-10 for the cross product may be used:

$$\mathbf{D} = (\mathbf{A} \times \mathbf{B}) = \begin{vmatrix} \mathbf{i} & \mathbf{j} & \mathbf{k} \\ A_x & A_y & A_z \\ B_x & B_y & B_z \end{vmatrix}.$$

Now $(\mathbf{A} \times \mathbf{B}) \cdot \mathbf{C} = \mathbf{D} \cdot \mathbf{C}$ is given by

$$(\mathbf{A} \times \mathbf{B}) \cdot \mathbf{C} = \begin{vmatrix} \mathbf{i} & \mathbf{j} & \mathbf{k} \\ A_x & A_y & A_z \\ B_x & B_y & B_z \end{vmatrix} \cdot (C_x \mathbf{i} + C_y \mathbf{j} + C_z \mathbf{k}),$$

or

$$(\mathbf{A} \times \mathbf{B}) \cdot \mathbf{C} = \begin{vmatrix} C_x & C_y & C_z \\ A_x & A_y & A_z \\ B_x & B_y & B_z \end{vmatrix}. \qquad \textbf{1.8-4a}$$

The order properties (Eq. 1.8-2) that we have found for the scalar product are reflected in the row-interchange properties of the determinant, as the student may verify. In particular, the result that $(\mathbf{A} \times \mathbf{B}) \cdot \mathbf{C} = (\mathbf{B} \times \mathbf{C}) \cdot \mathbf{A}$ leads to an alternate form of 1.8-4a that is easier to remember, since the elements of the determinant are in the same order, row by row, as are the vector symbols in the triple product:

$$(\mathbf{A} \times \mathbf{B}) \cdot \mathbf{C} = \begin{vmatrix} A_x & A_y & A_z \\ B_x & B_y & B_z \\ C_x & C_y & C_z \end{vmatrix}. \qquad \textbf{1.8-4b}$$

Let us now consider the concept of the moment of a vector about a line, which was mentioned earlier. We give a rough definition first, make it more precise, then show the relation between the concepts of vector moment about a point and scalar moment about a line. Suppose we are given a line JK (the *moment axis*) in space and a vector $\mathbf{A}$ emanating from a point R. Drop the perpendicular from R on JK, obtaining point S; the line SR of length h is called the *moment arm* (Fig. 1.8-2). The scalar moment of $\mathbf{A}$ about the line

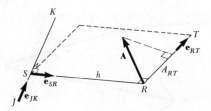

Fig. 1.8-2

JK is defined to be the product of the length h of the moment arm and the component A_{RT} of $\mathbf{A}$ in a direction RT perpendicular to both JK and SR, i.e., perpendicular to both moment axis and moment arm:

$$M_{JK} = \pm h A_{RT}. \qquad \text{1.8-5}$$

The algebraic sign is determined, if A_{RT} is considered positive, by introducing a right-hand rule for rotations about the moment axis and hence a sign convention for moments.

Let us make this elementary definition of the moment about a line as "moment arm times perpendicular component of the vector" more precise. Choose a direction on JK by assigning a unit vector $\mathbf{e}_{JK}$ (Fig. 1.8-2); direct SR by $\mathbf{e}_{SR}$; and direct the mutual perpendicular RT to JK and SR by $\mathbf{e}_{RT} = \mathbf{e}_{JK} \times \mathbf{e}_{SR}$. The three unit vectors $\mathbf{e}_{JK}$, $\mathbf{e}_{SR}$, $\mathbf{e}_{RT}$ form a right-handed orthogonal triad by construction. Define A_{RT} as the scalar component of $\mathbf{A}$ in the direction of $\mathbf{e}_{RT}$: $A_{RT} = \mathbf{A} \cdot \mathbf{e}_{RT}$; then, letting A_{RT} be positive or negative, the choice of the plus sign in 1.8-5 will define a signed moment M_{JK} by a right-hand rule on the directions of JK, SR, and RT. Furthermore, if the vector moment $\mathbf{M}_S$ of A about point S is projected on the line JK, we can show that M_{JK} is equal to that projection. That is, M_{JK} is the scalar component of $\mathbf{M}_S$ in the direction JK:

$$M_{JK} = h A_{RT} = \mathbf{M}_S \cdot \mathbf{e}_{JK} = (h\mathbf{e}_{SR} \times \mathbf{A}) \cdot \mathbf{e}_{JK}. \qquad \text{1.8-6}$$

This last is easy to prove, using Eq. 1.8-2; for

$$(h\mathbf{e}_{SR} \times \mathbf{A}) \cdot \mathbf{e}_{JK} = (\mathbf{e}_{JK} \times h\mathbf{e}_{SR}) \cdot \mathbf{A} = h\mathbf{e}_{RT} \cdot \mathbf{A} = h A_{RT}.$$

We are now prepared to generalize. We know, from the previous section, that the moment of $\mathbf{A}$ about a point, S, is independent of the location of **A** along its line of action.   That is, RS need not be the perpendicular from a point on the line of action PQ of **A** (Fig. 1.8-3)

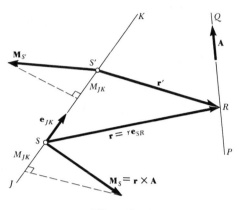

Fig. 1.8-3

to the line JK, but may be any line segment from S to PQ.   It must, however, be directed properly: let $\mathbf{r} = r\mathbf{e}_{SR}$ be the vector *from* point S on the moment axis *to* any point R on the line of action of the vector. Then

$$M_{JK} = (\mathbf{r} \times \mathbf{A}) \cdot \mathbf{e} \qquad \text{1.8-7}$$

where we set $\mathbf{e} = \mathbf{e}_{JK}$.   We see, in fact, that S may be any point on JK, just as R is any point on PQ.   For, choosing any other point S' on JK, we see that $\mathbf{r}' - \mathbf{r}$ is parallel to $\mathbf{e}$, so that

$$\mathbf{M}_{S'} \cdot \mathbf{e} = (\mathbf{r}' \times \mathbf{A}) \cdot \mathbf{e} = (\mathbf{r} \times \mathbf{A}) \cdot \mathbf{e} + [(\mathbf{r}' - \mathbf{r}) \times \mathbf{A}] \cdot \mathbf{e}$$

$$= M_{JK} + [\mathbf{e} \times (\mathbf{r}' - \mathbf{r})] \cdot \mathbf{A} = M_{JK}. \qquad \text{1.8-8}$$

This is a fundamental result: the moment of a sliding vector about an axis is the scalar component in the direction of the axis of the vector moment about any point on the axis.   In particular, the (x, y, z) components of the moment of a vector about the origin are the moments of that vector about the coordinate axes.

The scalar form of Varignon's theorem follows immediately; that is, the moment about an axis of the resultant of a number of concurrent vectors is the sum of the moments of the separate vectors about that axis.   This follows from the vectorial form of the theorem (Section 1.7) and the fact that the moment about the axis is simply the projection on the axis of the moment about any point on the axis.   Thus, take the vector equation expressing the vector theorem, $\mathbf{r} \times (\sum \mathbf{A}_i) = \sum (\mathbf{r} \times \mathbf{A}_i)$, and take the scalar product of each side with the appropriate unit vector $\mathbf{e}$.

Example 1.8-2

Find the scalar triple product $\mathbf{A} \cdot (\mathbf{C} \times \mathbf{L})$ *if*

$$\mathbf{A} = 3\mathbf{i} - 2\mathbf{j} + 5\mathbf{k}, \qquad \mathbf{C} = \mathbf{i} + \mathbf{j} + 2\mathbf{k}, \qquad \mathbf{L} = -\mathbf{i} - \mathbf{j}.$$

Solution: (a) We can compute the cross-product, and then the dot-product:

$$\mathbf{C} \times \mathbf{L} = \begin{vmatrix} \mathbf{i} & \mathbf{j} & \mathbf{k} \\ 1 & 1 & 2 \\ -1 & -1 & 0 \end{vmatrix} = 2\mathbf{i} - 2\mathbf{j},$$

$$\mathbf{A} \cdot (\mathbf{C} \times \mathbf{L}) = (3)(2) + (-2)(-2) + (5)(0) = 10.$$

(b) We can compute the triple product directly:

$$\mathbf{A} \cdot (\mathbf{C} \times \mathbf{L}) = \begin{vmatrix} A_x & A_y & A_z \\ C_x & C_y & C_z \\ L_x & L_y & L_z \end{vmatrix} = \begin{vmatrix} 3 & -2 & 5 \\ 1 & 1 & 2 \\ -1 & -1 & 0 \end{vmatrix}.$$

By any of the standard evaluation methods, the answer is, of course, 10.

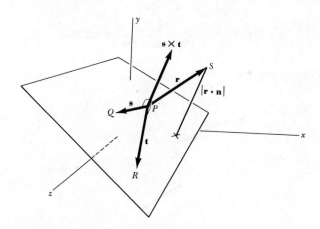

Fig. 1.8-4

Example 1.8-3

A plane passes through three points, P: (1, 1, 1); Q: (−1, 2, 3); and R: (4, 5, 13). What is the perpendicular distance from the point S: (3, 1, −5) to the plane (Fig. 1.8-4)?

Solution: The perpendicular distance from a point S to a plane PQR is the magnitude of the component of a vector from a point in the plane to S in a direction normal to the plane. With three points given in the plane, two vectors lying in the plane are known. Their cross-product will give a vector normal to the plane. Symbolically, let the directed segment $\overline{PS}$ be $\mathbf{r}$, the segment $\overline{PQ}$ be $\mathbf{s}$, and the segment $\overline{PR}$ be $\mathbf{t}$. Then $\mathbf{s} \times \mathbf{t}$ is normal to the plane, with $\mathbf{n} = (\mathbf{s} \times \mathbf{t})/|\mathbf{s} \times \mathbf{t}|$ being a unit normal vector. Then the desired distance is

$$|\mathbf{r} \cdot \mathbf{n}| = \frac{|\mathbf{r} \cdot (\mathbf{s} \times \mathbf{t})|}{|\mathbf{s} \times \mathbf{t}|}.$$

In this example, we have

$$\mathbf{r} = 2\mathbf{i} - 6\mathbf{k}, \quad \mathbf{s} = -2\mathbf{i} + \mathbf{j} + 2\mathbf{k}, \quad \mathbf{t} = 3\mathbf{i} + 4\mathbf{j} + 12\mathbf{k};$$

hence

$$\mathbf{s} \times \mathbf{t} = \begin{vmatrix} \mathbf{i} & \mathbf{j} & \mathbf{k} \\ -2 & 1 & 2 \\ 3 & 4 & 12 \end{vmatrix} = 4\mathbf{i} + 30\mathbf{j} - 11\mathbf{k},$$

$$\mathbf{r} \cdot (\mathbf{s} \times \mathbf{t}) = \begin{vmatrix} 2 & 0 & -6 \\ -2 & 1 & 2 \\ 3 & 4 & 12 \end{vmatrix} = 74,$$

$$|\mathbf{r} \cdot \mathbf{n}| = \frac{74}{\sqrt{16 + 900 + 121}} = 2.298.$$

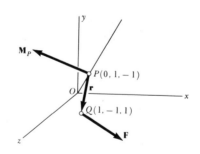

Fig. 1.8-5

Example **1.8-4**

A force vector $\mathbf{F} = (10/13)(3\mathbf{i} - 4\mathbf{j} - 12\mathbf{k})$ *lb has line of action passing through* Q: $(1, -1, 1)$ *in.* (*Fig.* 1.8-5). *Find its moment about the line joining the origin to* P: $(0, 1, -1)$; *check the answer by an alternative computation.*

Solution: This is the configuration of Example 1.7-5, wherein we found $\mathbf{r} \times \mathbf{F} = \mathbf{M}_P = -(160/13)\mathbf{i} - (60/13)\mathbf{j} + (20/13)\mathbf{k}$ lb-in. The unit vector $\mathbf{e}$ in the direction OP is $\mathbf{j} - \mathbf{k}$ divided by its magnitude, i.e., $\mathbf{e} = (\sqrt{2}/2)(\mathbf{j} - \mathbf{k})$. Therefore, the moment of $\mathbf{F}$ about OP is

$$M_{OP} = (\mathbf{r} \times \mathbf{F}) \cdot \mathbf{e} = \mathbf{M}_P \cdot \mathbf{e} = -\frac{40}{13}\sqrt{2} \quad \text{lb-in.}$$

Note that, by our sign convention based on the right-hand rule, M_{PO} is the negative of this, i.e., a positive $(40/13)\sqrt{2}$ lb-in.

An alternate computation would be to find the moment of $\mathbf{F}$ about some other point on OP, then project that vector on OP; that is, we also have

$$M_{OP} = \mathbf{M}_O \cdot \mathbf{e} = (\mathbf{r}_{OQ} \times \mathbf{F}) \cdot \mathbf{e}$$

$$= \begin{vmatrix} 0 & \dfrac{\sqrt{2}}{2} & -\dfrac{\sqrt{2}}{2} \\ 1 & -1 & 1 \\ \dfrac{30}{13} & -\dfrac{40}{13} & \dfrac{120}{13} \end{vmatrix} = \frac{5}{13}\sqrt{2} \begin{vmatrix} 0 & 1 & -1 \\ 1 & -1 & 1 \\ 3 & -4 & 12 \end{vmatrix}$$

$$= \frac{5}{13}\sqrt{2} \begin{vmatrix} 0 & 1 & -1 \\ 1 & 0 & 0 \\ 3 & -4 & 12 \end{vmatrix} = \frac{-5}{13}\sqrt{2} \begin{vmatrix} 1 & -1 \\ -4 & 12 \end{vmatrix}$$

$$= -\frac{40}{13}\sqrt{2} \quad \text{lb-in.}$$

Example 1.8-5

Derive relations 1.8-2 without appeal to the geometry of the parallelepipeds of Fig. 1.8-1.

Solution: It is sufficient to show that $(\mathbf{A} \times \mathbf{B}) \cdot \mathbf{C} = (\mathbf{B} \times \mathbf{C}) \cdot \mathbf{A}$; the cyclic ordering property may then be carried one step more to show that these are equal to $(\mathbf{C} \times \mathbf{A}) \cdot \mathbf{B}$, and the commutative property of the scalar product then gives the other three terms of Eq. 1.8-2.

The proof of the formal abstract property is very similar to the arguments given for the triple product representation of the moment about a line, and the reader may wish to compare what follows with that discussion, especially the part dealing with the construction of a right-handed unit triad.

Let $\mathbf{A} = A\mathbf{e}_A$ and $\mathbf{B} = B\mathbf{e}_B$, $\mathbf{e}_A \times \mathbf{e}_B \neq \mathbf{0}$, in the usual way, with $\mathbf{A} \times \mathbf{B} = AB \sin\theta\mathbf{n} = AB\mathbf{e}_A \times \mathbf{e}_B$ defining the unit vector $\mathbf{n}$. Let ϕ be the angle between $\mathbf{C}$ and $\mathbf{n}$, so that $\mathbf{C} \cdot \mathbf{n} = C \cos\phi$. By definition, $(\mathbf{A} \times \mathbf{B}) \cdot \mathbf{C} = ABC \sin\theta \cos\phi$ (Eq. 1.8-1). Write $\mathbf{C} = C \cos\phi\mathbf{n} + \mathbf{D}$; $\mathbf{D}$ must be orthogonal to $\mathbf{n}$ and hence can be expressed as a linear combination of $\mathbf{e}_A$ and $\mathbf{e}_B$. Therefore,

$$\mathbf{C} = C \cos\phi\mathbf{n} + C_A\mathbf{e}_A + C_B\mathbf{e}_B.$$

Note that these are generally oblique components of **C**, not orthogonal components. Now

$$\mathbf{B} \times \mathbf{C} = BC \cos \phi \mathbf{e}_B \times \mathbf{n} + C_A \mathbf{e}_B \times \mathbf{e}_A,$$

$$(\mathbf{B} \times \mathbf{C}) \cdot \mathbf{A} = ABC \cos \phi (\mathbf{e}_B \times \mathbf{n}) \cdot \mathbf{e}_A + C_A (\mathbf{e}_B \times \mathbf{e}_A) \cdot \mathbf{e}_A.$$

We have reduced the problem to an argument on the unit vectors $\mathbf{e}_A$, $\mathbf{e}_B$, and $\mathbf{n}$. The last term is zero, since the scalar triple product is zero whenever two of the vectors appearing in it are the same. Thus

$$(\mathbf{B} \times \mathbf{C}) \cdot \mathbf{A} = ABC \cos \phi (\mathbf{e}_B \times \mathbf{n}) \cdot \mathbf{e}_A.$$

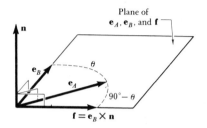

Fig. 1.8-6

Let us consider $(\mathbf{e}_B \times \mathbf{n}) \cdot \mathbf{e}_A$. The cross-product $\mathbf{e}_B \times \mathbf{n} = \mathbf{f}$ is in the plane of $\mathbf{e}_A$ and $\mathbf{e}_B$ and, moreover, is a unit vector. The first statement follows from the orthogonality of $\mathbf{n}$ and $\mathbf{e}_A$, $\mathbf{e}_B$; the second, from the definition of the vector product and the orthogonality of $\mathbf{n}$ and $\mathbf{e}_B$. The three unit vectors $(\mathbf{e}_B, \mathbf{n}, \mathbf{f})$, in that order, form a right-handed orthogonal triad by construction.

Now express $\mathbf{e}_A$ in terms of $\mathbf{e}_B$ and $\mathbf{f}$: since θ is the angle between **A** and **B**, we have (Fig. 1.8-6)

$$\mathbf{e}_A = \cos \theta \mathbf{e}_B \pm \sin \theta \mathbf{f}$$

where we must resolve the ambiguity of sign. It is here that the right-handed nature of the constructed unit vectors is essential. We now have

$$(\mathbf{B} \times \mathbf{C}) \cdot \mathbf{A} = ABC \cos \phi \mathbf{f} \cdot \mathbf{e}_A = \pm ABC \cos \phi \sin \theta,$$

and we must show that the positive sign is the proper choice. But we know

$$\mathbf{e}_A \times \mathbf{e}_B = \sin \theta \mathbf{n} = \pm \sin \theta \mathbf{f} \times \mathbf{e}_B;$$

since the unit vectors $(\mathbf{e}_B, \mathbf{n}, \mathbf{f})$ are a right-handed triad, $\mathbf{f} \times \mathbf{e}_B = \mathbf{n}$ and we must choose the positive sign:

$$(\mathbf{B} \times \mathbf{C}) \cdot \mathbf{A} = ABC \cos \phi \sin \theta = (\mathbf{A} \times \mathbf{B}) \cdot \mathbf{C}.$$

1.9 The Vector Triple Product

The vector triple product, $(\mathbf{A} \times \mathbf{B}) \times \mathbf{C}$, of three vectors, **A**, **B**, and **C**, is a fourth vector, **D**. In this expression, both the position of the parentheses and the order of the terms must be maintained unaltered for an unambiguous prescription of the result.* As we have seen in Section 1.7, the vector product does not obey the associative law, so that $(\mathbf{A} \times \mathbf{B}) \times \mathbf{C}$ is not equal to $\mathbf{A} \times (\mathbf{B} \times \mathbf{C})$.

If we write

$$\mathbf{D} = (\mathbf{A} \times \mathbf{B}) \times \mathbf{C}, \qquad \text{1.9-1}$$

we observe that $\mathbf{D}$ lies in the plane of $\mathbf{A}$ and $\mathbf{B}$. This follows from the fact that $(\mathbf{A} \times \mathbf{B})$ is perpendicular to that plane. The cross-product with $\mathbf{C}$ provides another ninety-degree rotation, putting the final vector $\mathbf{D}$ back in the plane of $\mathbf{A}$ and $\mathbf{B}$. We know, therefore, that $\mathbf{D}$ may be expressed as the sum of vectors proportional to $\mathbf{A}$ and $\mathbf{B}$

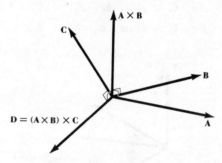

Fig. 1.9-1

(Example 1.3-2): $\mathbf{D} = \alpha \mathbf{A} + \beta \mathbf{B}$. To determine α and β, we follow the pattern of Example 1.8-5 and express $\mathbf{C}$ in terms of oblique components in the directions of $\mathbf{A}$, $\mathbf{B}$, and $\mathbf{A} \times \mathbf{B}$.

Let $\mathbf{A} = A\mathbf{e}_A$, $\mathbf{B} = B\mathbf{e}_B$, $\mathbf{e}_A \times \mathbf{e}_B = \sin \theta \mathbf{n} \neq \mathbf{0}$ in the usual way, and write

$$\mathbf{C} = a\mathbf{e}_A + b\mathbf{e}_B + c\mathbf{n}. \qquad \text{1.9-2}$$

Then

$$\mathbf{D} = (\mathbf{A} \times \mathbf{B}) \times \mathbf{C} = AB \sin \theta \mathbf{n} \times \mathbf{C}$$
$$= AB \sin \theta (a\mathbf{n} \times \mathbf{e}_A + b\mathbf{n} \times \mathbf{e}_B).$$

Let $\mathbf{f}$ be the unit vector $\mathbf{e}_B \times \mathbf{n}$, as in Example 1.8-5, so that $(\mathbf{e}_B, \mathbf{n}, \mathbf{f})$ form a right-handed triad; then, as shown in that example, $\mathbf{e}_A = \cos \theta \mathbf{e}_B + \sin \theta \mathbf{f}$ (Fig. 1.9-2).

---

* In the scalar triple product $(\mathbf{A} \times \mathbf{B}) \cdot \mathbf{C}$, the parentheses may be dropped, since there is only one way to give a meaningful interpretation to $\mathbf{A} \times \mathbf{B} \cdot \mathbf{C}$. It is not good practice, however, for one new to the concept to eliminate the parentheses.

Therefore,

$$\mathbf{D} = AB \sin \theta[a \cos \theta(-\mathbf{f}) + a \sin \theta \mathbf{e}_B - b\mathbf{f}]$$
$$= ABa \sin^2 \theta \mathbf{e}_B - AB(a \cos \theta + b) \sin \theta \mathbf{f}.$$

But we want $\mathbf{D}$ in oblique $\mathbf{e}_A$ and $\mathbf{e}_B$ components; therefore, we must replace $\mathbf{f}$. We have $\sin \theta \mathbf{f} = \mathbf{e}_A - \cos \theta \mathbf{e}_B$, so that

$$\mathbf{D} = -AB(a \cos \theta + b)\mathbf{e}_A + AB(a + b \cos \theta)\mathbf{e}_B$$
$$= -B(a \cos \theta + b)\mathbf{A} + A(a + b \cos \theta)\mathbf{B}. \qquad \textbf{1.9-3}$$

What are the coefficients of $\mathbf{A}$ and $\mathbf{B}$ in Eq. 1.9-3? From Eq. 1.9-2, we find

$$\mathbf{A} \cdot \mathbf{C} = A\mathbf{e}_A \cdot \mathbf{C} = A(a + b\mathbf{e}_B \cdot \mathbf{e}_A) = A(a + b \cos \theta),$$
$$\mathbf{B} \cdot \mathbf{C} = B\mathbf{e}_B \cdot \mathbf{C} = B(a\mathbf{e}_B \cdot \mathbf{e}_A + b) = B(a \cos \theta + b).$$

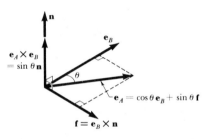

Fig. 1.9-2

Finally, therefore, we obtain the fundamental reduction formula for the vector triple product:

$$(\mathbf{A} \times \mathbf{B}) \times \mathbf{C} = (\mathbf{A} \cdot \mathbf{C})\mathbf{B} - (\mathbf{B} \cdot \mathbf{C})\mathbf{A}. \qquad \textbf{1.9-4}$$

Similarly, the vector triple product obtained by the alternative placing of the parentheses may be written

$$\mathbf{A} \times (\mathbf{B} \times \mathbf{C}) = (\mathbf{A} \cdot \mathbf{C})\mathbf{B} - (\mathbf{A} \cdot \mathbf{B})\mathbf{C}. \qquad \textbf{1.9-5}$$

The non-associative nature of the vector product is apparent here, since the right-hand sides of 1.9-4 and 1.9-5 are different.

The vector triple product and the reduction formula for it are of great use in dynamical theory; in statics proper, we use it only for some considerations of higher-order moments in the next chapter. In the solution of vector equations, the vector triple product expansion is useful, as the first example of Section 1.10 shows.

Example 1.9-1

Given two non-parallel vectors **A** and **B**, construct three mutually orthogonal vectors **D**, **E**, and **F** in terms of **A** and **B**.

Solution: Choose **D** equal to any one of the three vectors, say **A**, and **E** equal to **A** × **B**; then **D** and **E** are orthogonal. Furthermore, **D** × **E** = **F** must be orthogonal to both **D** and **E** (Fig. 1.9-3):

$$F = D \times E = A \times (A \times B) = (A \cdot B)A - (A \cdot A)B$$
$$= (A \cdot B)A - A^2B.$$

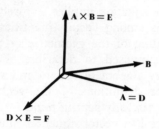

Fig. 1.9-3

Example 1.9-2

Find the vector triple product (**B** × **C**) × **A** of

$$A = 2i - 3j, \qquad B = k - i, \qquad C = i + j + k.$$

Solution:

(a) $B \times C = k \times C - i \times C = j - i - k + j = 2j - i - k;$

$(B \times C) \times A = (2j - i - k) \times (2i - 3j) = -4k + 3k - 2j - 3i = -3i - 2j - k.$

(b) $(B \times C) \times A = (B \cdot A)C - (C \cdot A)B = -2C + B$

$$= -2i - 2j - 2k + k - i = -3i - 2j - k.$$

Example 1.9-3

Find the vector **D** = (**A** × **B**) × **C** + (**B** × **C**) × **A** + (**C** × **A**) × **B** in terms of **A**, **B**, **C**.

Solution: Note that **D** is the sum of all possible triple products (with the parentheses in the same place) formed from **A**, **B**, and **C** in cyclic order. By the reduction formula 1.9-4,

$$(A \times B) \times C = (A \cdot C)B - (B \cdot C)A,$$
$$(B \times C) \times A = (B \cdot A)C - (C \cdot A)B,$$
$$(C \times A) \times B = (C \cdot B)A - (A \cdot B)C.$$

Summing these and using the commutative nature of the scalar product, we see that $\mathbf{D} = \mathbf{o}$; i.e., for any three vectors $\mathbf{A}$, $\mathbf{B}$, and $\mathbf{C}$,

$$(\mathbf{A} \times \mathbf{B}) \times \mathbf{C} + (\mathbf{B} \times \mathbf{C}) \times \mathbf{A} + (\mathbf{C} \times \mathbf{A}) \times \mathbf{B} = \mathbf{o}.$$

1.10 Vector Equations

The operations defined in preceding sections are intended for use in the solution of equations arising in mechanical analysis and in the development of the theory of mechanics. Such use, to be effective, requires a clear understanding of what the operations mean and of what a vector equation implies. Purely formal manipulation of algebraic relations among vector quantities is not enough for a complete understanding of the geometric or physical model which the quantities are supposed to describe. Furthermore, analogies between the ordinary algebra of scalars and vector algebra may be over-extended if the definitions of the vector operation symbols $+$, $-$, $\cdot$, $\times$ are not carefully kept in mind.

To be meaningful, a vector equation must express an equality between two vectors, not between a vector and a scalar. Expressions such as $7\mathbf{A} - 5\mathbf{B} = 12$ are meaningless. The fact that an ordinary zero symbol is often used for the null vector, as in $7\mathbf{A} - 5\mathbf{B} = \mathbf{o}$, should not lead one to put other scalars in its place. More subtle forms of this error are sometimes encountered: $7\mathbf{A} - 5\mathbf{B} = (\mathbf{A} \times \mathbf{B}) \cdot \mathbf{C}$ is also meaningless. Care in the formulation of equations is an essential first step. Only operations that have been defined should be employed. There is, for example, no operation on vectors corresponding to the division of one number by another, and expressions such as $\mathbf{B}/\mathbf{A}$, $\mathbf{C}^{-1}$, $6\mathbf{i}/(\mathbf{k} + 2\mathbf{j})$ are also meaningless. The reason why it would be fruitless to attempt to define such an operation is, as we have noted, that the ordinary cancellation law of the algebra of scalars does not hold for either the scalar or the vector product of two vectors. That is, neither of the two equations $\mathbf{A} \cdot \mathbf{B} = \mathbf{A} \cdot \mathbf{C}$ and $\mathbf{A} \times \mathbf{B} = \mathbf{A} \times \mathbf{C}$ ensures that $\mathbf{B} = \mathbf{C}$ even when $\mathbf{A} \neq \mathbf{o}$. We shall investigate the complete solution of $\mathbf{A} \times \mathbf{B} = \mathbf{A} \times \mathbf{C}$ in one of the examples of this section.

When a set of vector equations is linear in the vector symbols, with scalar coefficients, they may be solved by the process of successive elimination of unknowns—just as is done in the solution of simultaneous linear equations in scalar unknowns. The technique was demonstrated in Example 1.3-1. Alternatively, a particular coordinate system may be introduced and the set of scalar equations equivalent to the vector equations may be written. In three-dimensional space, there will be three such scalar equations for each vector equation because there can be three linearly independent vectors in the space—for example, $\mathbf{i}$, $\mathbf{j}$, and $\mathbf{k} = \mathbf{i} \times \mathbf{j}$. Conversely, since there cannot be more than three linearly independent vectors in three dimensions, so that all vectors can be expressed linearly in terms of three such independent ones, there cannot be more than three independent scalar equations corresponding to any set of linear vector algebraic equations. Thus, problems of the *consistency* of sets of four or more vector equations are more complex than the corresponding consistency problems for sets of scalar equations. True understanding of the vector addition, subtraction, and scalar multiplication operations, coupled with the knowledge that the component of a vector in any direction is fixed once its components in three independent directions are given, is essential for the establishment of the independence and consistency of the equations written in any given situation.

When a vector equation embodies any of the product operations on vectors, the geometric relations inherent in the definitions of the scalar and vector products are of use in interpreting and simplifying the equation. Conditions of orthogonality and parallelism can be expressed simply in terms of these operations; orthogonality, for instance, has been useful already in obtaining the vector equation of a plane (Example 1.6-4). The interpretation of the magnitude of the cross-product as an area and of the scalar triple product as a volume is also a useful device.

In the remainder of this text, emphasis is placed on the physical concepts underlying the analysis of mechanical systems in equilibrium. Vector symbolism provides a natural mathematical language to use in expressing these physical concepts. Care taken in its use will help in understanding the physical interrelationships to be described, just as care taken in formulating the physical principles aids in the development of the appropriate equations.

Example **I.IO-I**

Solve the vector equation $\mathbf{A} \times \mathbf{x} = \mathbf{B}$ *for the unknown vector* $\mathbf{x}$ *in terms of the known vectors* $\mathbf{A}$ *and* $\mathbf{B}$.

Solution: The vectors $\mathbf{A}$ and $\mathbf{B}$, though "known" or "given," cannot be assigned in a completely arbitrary fashion. The vector $\mathbf{B}$ must be perpendicular to $\mathbf{A}$; if it is not, the equation is self-contradictory and meaningless. Similarly, any solution vector $\mathbf{x}$ and the vector $\mathbf{B}$ must be perpendicular. These conclusions follow from the definition of the cross product. They suggest that we look for a particular solution, $\mathbf{x}$, which is also perpendicular to $\mathbf{A}$, i.e., which satisfies $\mathbf{x} \cdot \mathbf{A} = 0$.

If we take the cross product of each side of the given equation with $\mathbf{A}$, we have

$$(\mathbf{A} \times \mathbf{x}) \times \mathbf{A} = \mathbf{B} \times \mathbf{A}.$$

Making use of the fundamental identity Eq. 1.9-4 for the vector triple product, we may write

$$(\mathbf{A} \cdot \mathbf{A})\mathbf{x} - (\mathbf{x} \cdot \mathbf{A})\mathbf{A} = \mathbf{B} \times \mathbf{A};$$

since $\mathbf{x} \cdot \mathbf{A}$ is to vanish,

$$\mathbf{x} = \frac{\mathbf{B} \times \mathbf{A}}{A^2}.$$

This is certainly a particular solution that satisfies the requirement that $\mathbf{x} \cdot \mathbf{A} = 0$ since it makes $\mathbf{x}$ perpendicular to both $\mathbf{B}$ and $\mathbf{A}$. If we substitute it back into the original equation, the solution is easily checked. Is it, however, the complete solution? Any vector parallel to $\mathbf{A}$—a vector $m\mathbf{A}$, where m is any scalar—may be added to any solution $\mathbf{x}$, since the cross product of $\mathbf{A}$ with such a vector will be the null vector. The complete solution then is

$$\mathbf{x} = \frac{\mathbf{B} \times \mathbf{A}}{A^2} + m\mathbf{A},$$

where m is an arbitrary number.

Example **1.10-2**

If $\mathbf{A} \times \mathbf{B} = \mathbf{A} \times \mathbf{C}$, *what are the possible values of* $\mathbf{B}$?

Solution: The equation can readily be reduced to the one discussed in the last example. It is as simple, however, to note that $\mathbf{B} = \mathbf{C}$ is certainly a particular solution and that we may add to this any vector whose vector product with $\mathbf{A}$ is zero: in symbols,

$$\mathbf{B} = \mathbf{C} + m\mathbf{A},$$

where m is again an arbitrary number.

In solving $\mathbf{A} \times \mathbf{B} = \mathbf{C} \times \mathbf{A}$, note that the non-commutative nature of the cross product must be taken into account, the solution now being

$$\mathbf{B} = -\mathbf{C} + m\mathbf{A}.$$

Example **1.10-3**

Given the vector $\mathbf{a}$ *and the scalar* m, *solve the equation* $(\mathbf{a} \times \mathbf{x}) + \mathbf{x} + m\mathbf{a} = 0$ *for the vector* $\mathbf{x}$.

Solution: We shall obtain $\mathbf{x}$ by arguing directly from the meanings of the symbols and also by formal algebraic operations. If $\mathbf{a} \times \mathbf{x}$ is not zero, then it must be perpendicular to both $\mathbf{a}$ and $\mathbf{x}$ and hence to the vector $\mathbf{x} + m\mathbf{a}$ in the plane of $\mathbf{a}$ and $\mathbf{x}$. The sum of $(\mathbf{a} \times \mathbf{x})$ and $(\mathbf{x} + m\mathbf{a})$ could not then be zero. Therefore, $\mathbf{a} \times \mathbf{x} = 0$ and $\mathbf{x} = -m\mathbf{a}$.

Formal algebraic solutions can be found in many ways. The simplest is the one corresponding to the argument just given. Take the scalar product of each side of the equation with the vector $\mathbf{a} \times \mathbf{x}$, obtaining

$$(\mathbf{a} \times \mathbf{x}) \cdot (\mathbf{a} \times \mathbf{x}) + (\mathbf{a} \times \mathbf{x}) \cdot \mathbf{x} + (\mathbf{a} \times \mathbf{x}) \cdot m\mathbf{a} = 0.$$

Since a scalar triple product vanishes if two terms are identical, $(\mathbf{a} \times \mathbf{x}) \cdot \mathbf{x} = 0$ and $(\mathbf{a} \times \mathbf{x}) \cdot m\mathbf{a} = m[(\mathbf{a} \times \mathbf{x}) \cdot \mathbf{a}] = 0$. Therefore,

$$(\mathbf{a} \times \mathbf{x}) \cdot (\mathbf{a} \times \mathbf{x}) = |(\mathbf{a} \times \mathbf{x})|^2 = 0,$$

$\mathbf{a} \times \mathbf{x} = 0$, and $\mathbf{x} = -m\mathbf{a}$ as before. Note that this solution is unique.

Exercises

1.2-1: If you have encountered any of the following quantities in your previous experience you should be able to identify them as scalars, vectors, or as neither scalar nor vector: (1) volume, (2) force, (3) displacement (in the sense of change of position), (4) mass, (5) acceleration, (6) stress, (7) temperature, (8) magnetic field intensity.

1.3-1: Solve the vector equations $13\mathbf{A} - 5\mathbf{B} = 49\mathbf{C}$ and $-4\mathbf{A} + \mathbf{B} = -14\mathbf{C}$ to find $\mathbf{A}$ and $\mathbf{B}$ in terms of $\mathbf{C}$.
Ans.: $\mathbf{A} = 3\mathbf{C}$, $\mathbf{B} = -2\mathbf{C}$.

1.3-2: Solve the three vector equations $5\mathbf{A} - \mathbf{B} + 3\mathbf{C} - 3\mathbf{D} = 0$, $10\mathbf{A} + 8\mathbf{B} + 4\mathbf{D} = 0$, $35\mathbf{A} + 14\mathbf{B} - 6\mathbf{C} = 0$ to find $\mathbf{A}$, $\mathbf{B}$, and $\mathbf{C}$ in terms of $\mathbf{D}$. Are the vectors $\mathbf{A}$ and $\mathbf{B}$ necessarily parallel?
Ans.: $\mathbf{A} = (2/5)\mathbf{D}$, $\mathbf{B} = -\mathbf{D}$, $\mathbf{C} = 0$.

1.3-3: Show that if $p\mathbf{A} + q\mathbf{B} + r\mathbf{C} = 0$, where p, q, r are any three non-zero numbers, the vectors $\mathbf{A}$, $\mathbf{B}$, $\mathbf{C}$ must all lie in the same plane.

1.3-4: Show that $|\mathbf{A}| + |\mathbf{B}| \geq |\mathbf{A} + \mathbf{B}|$. Under what circumstances does the equality sign hold?

1.3-5: Show that $||\mathbf{A}| - |\mathbf{B}|| \leq |\mathbf{A} - \mathbf{B}|$. Under what circumstances does the equality sign hold?

1.3-6: The points $PQRSTU$ are the vertices of a regular hexagon. Denote the vector $\overline{PQ}$ by $\mathbf{A}$, the vector $\overline{QR}$ by $\mathbf{B}$, and the vector $\overline{RS}$ by $\mathbf{C}$. Express $\mathbf{C}$ in terms of $\mathbf{A}$ and $\mathbf{B}$.
Ans.: $\mathbf{C} = \mathbf{B} - \mathbf{A}$.

1.3-7: Three vectors, $\mathbf{A}$, $\mathbf{B}$, and $\mathbf{C} = 4\mathbf{A} - 3\mathbf{B}$, have the same origin. Show that their termini lie on a straight line.

1.3-8: Show that if $p\mathbf{A} + q\mathbf{B} + r\mathbf{C} = 0$, where p, q, r are any three numbers such that $p + q + r = 0$ and $\mathbf{A}$, $\mathbf{B}$, $\mathbf{C}$ are vectors with a common origin, the termini of $\mathbf{A}$, $\mathbf{B}$, $\mathbf{C}$ will lie on a straight line. Show that the previous exercise is a special case of this one.

1.3-9: Prove that the diagonals of a parallelogram bisect each other.

1.3-10: The vector $\mathbf{A}$ is six inches long and is directed toward the northeast. The vector $\mathbf{B}$ is three inches long and is directed toward the west.
(a) Express the vector $\mathbf{C}$ which is twelve inches long and is directed to the south in the form $\mathbf{C} = m\mathbf{A} + n\mathbf{B}$.

(b) Do the same for the vector **D** which is one inch long and is directed toward the north.

Ans.: C $= -2\sqrt{2}\mathbf{A} - 4\mathbf{B}$ in., **D** $= \dfrac{1}{3}\mathbf{B} + \dfrac{\sqrt{2}}{6}\mathbf{A}$ in.

1.3-11: What vector must be added to the vectors **A** and **B** in order to produce a null resultant? **A** is five inches long and is directed toward the southwest; **B** is eight inches long and is directed toward the north.
Ans.: Magnitude: 5.69 in.; direction: 51.6° south of east.

1.3-12: Prove that the line segment joining the midpoints of two sides of a triangle is parallel to the third side and half as long.

1.3-13: Show that the resultant of the medians of a triangle is a null vector.

1.3-14: A parallelepiped is determined by three vectors **A**, **B**, **C** having a common origin. Express the body diagonal of the parallelepiped in terms of **A**, **B**, and **C**.
Ans.: A + B + C.

1.3-15: (Desargues' theorem) Two triangles *ABC* and *DEF* are so positioned in space that the lines *AD*, *BE*, *CF* intersect at *O*. Then the lines *AB* and *DE* intersect, as do the lines *AC* and *DF* and the lines *BC* and *EF*. Show that these points of intersection are collinear.

1.4-1: What is the resultant of the forces $\mathbf{F}_1 = 6\mathbf{i} + 8\mathbf{j}$ lb, $\mathbf{F}_2 = \mathbf{i} - 2\mathbf{j} + 2\mathbf{k}$ lb, $\mathbf{F}_3 = 4\mathbf{i} + 4\mathbf{j} - 7\mathbf{k}$ lb? What is its magnitude and what angle does it make with the *y*-axis? Sketch this vector.
Ans.: R $= 11\mathbf{i} + 10\mathbf{j} - 5\mathbf{k}$ lb, $|\mathbf{R}| = 15.7$ lb, $\beta = 50.4°$.

1.4-2: What vector must be added to the vectors $\mathbf{F}_1 = 24\mathbf{i} - 45\mathbf{j} + 68\mathbf{k}$ and $\mathbf{F}_2 = 21\mathbf{i} - 40\mathbf{j} - 72\mathbf{k}$ in order to produce a null resultant vector? What is the magnitude of this so-called *equilibrating* vector and what are its direction cosines?
Ans.: $-45\mathbf{i} + 85\mathbf{j} + 4\mathbf{k}$; 96.3; -0.467, 0.883, 0.042.

1.4-3: What is the unit vector in the direction of the vector $\mathbf{A} = 6\mathbf{i} - 10\mathbf{j} + 15\mathbf{k}$?
Ans.: $\mathbf{e}_A = \dfrac{1}{19}(6\mathbf{i} - 10\mathbf{j} + 15\mathbf{k})$.

1.4-4: What is the unit vector in the direction opposite to that of the vector $\mathbf{A} = 8\mathbf{i} + 9\mathbf{j} - 12\mathbf{k}$?
Ans.: $\dfrac{-1}{17}(8\mathbf{i} + 9\mathbf{j} - 12\mathbf{k})$.

1.4-5: What is the vector equation of the straight line through the termini of the vectors $\mathbf{A} = 13\mathbf{i} + 14\mathbf{j} + 34\mathbf{k}$ and $\mathbf{B} = 24\mathbf{i} - 45\mathbf{j} + 68\mathbf{k}$? **A** and **B** emanate from the origin of coordinates.
Ans.: $(13 + 11m)\mathbf{i} + (14 - 59m)\mathbf{j} + 34(1 + m)\mathbf{k}$.

1.4-6: Show that the bisector of an angle of a triangle intersects the opposite side dividing it into two segments, the ratio of whose lengths is the same as the ratio of the lengths of the other two sides.

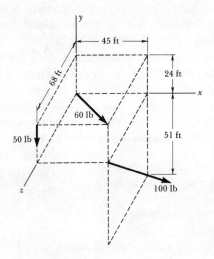

Exer. 1.4-7

1.4-7: Find the resultant of the three vectors shown. What is its magnitude? What are the direction cosines of its line of action?

Ans.: 31.8i − 93.1j − 32k lb; 103.5 lb; 0.307, − 0.900, − 0.309.

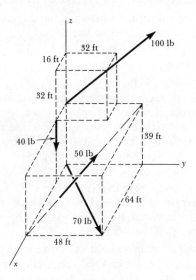

Exer. 1.4-8

1.4-8: Find the resultant of the four vectors shown.   What is its magnitude ? What are the direction cosines of its line of action ?
Ans.: $53.4\mathbf{i} + 135.6\mathbf{j} + 48.6\mathbf{k}$ lb; 153.6 lb; 0.348, 0.883, 0.316.

1.4-9: A vector of magnitude 10 is directed along the line from the point P: $(13, -5, 0)$ to the point Q: $(0, 9, 34)$.   What are the cartesian components of this vector ?
Ans.: $-3.33\mathbf{i} + 3.59\mathbf{j} + 8.72\mathbf{k}$.

1.4-10: What is the equation of the line in the plane formed by the origin O and the points P and Q of the previous exercise bisecting the angle POQ ?
Ans.: $\mathbf{r} = m(0.933\mathbf{i} - 0.103\mathbf{j} + 0.967\mathbf{k})$.

1.4-11: Consider the planar vector $\mathbf{A} = 3\mathbf{i} + 4\mathbf{j}$.   What will the cartesian components of this vector be if the x-, y-axes are rotated counterclockwise through an angle of 120 degrees ?
Ans.: $A_{x'} = 1.96$, $A_{y'} = -4.60$.

1.4-12: Show that the three angle bisectors of a triangle intersect at a common point.

1.4-13: Find the cartesian components of a unit vector making equal angles with the axes and directed from the origin into the first octant. What is the angle between the vector and any one of the axes ?
Ans.: $\mathbf{e} = \dfrac{1}{\sqrt{3}} (\mathbf{i} + \mathbf{j} + \mathbf{k})$; $54.7°$.

1.4-14: Taking an x-axis directed toward the east and a y-axis directed northward, solve Exercise 1.3-11 by expressing all vectors in cartesian form.

1.4-15: Show that the sum of the squares of the diagonals of a parallelogram is equal to the sum of the squares of the sides.

1.5-1: If $\mathbf{e}_r = 0.6\mathbf{i} + 0.8\mathbf{j}$, express the vector $\mathbf{A} = 4\mathbf{i} + 3\mathbf{j} - 12\mathbf{k}$ in terms of its cylindrical polar components.
Ans.: $\mathbf{A} = 4.8\mathbf{e}_r - 1.4\mathbf{e}_\phi - 12\mathbf{k}$.

1.5-2: Suppose a set of rectangular cartesian coordinates (x, y, z) and a set of cylindrical polar coordinates (r, ϕ, z) are given, the z-direction of both being the same.   The angle between the x-direction and the r-direction is $30°$.   A vector $\mathbf{A} = 10\mathbf{e}_r + 7.5\mathbf{k}$ is given.   Find the magnitude of $\mathbf{A}$ and its direction cosines with respect to the (x, y, z) axes.
Ans.: $|\mathbf{A}| = 12.5$; $(\cos \alpha, \cos \beta, \cos \gamma) = (0.693, 0.4, 0.6)$.

1.5-3: If a set of cylindrical polar coordinates (r, ϕ, z) is based on the vector $\mathbf{A} = 3\mathbf{i} + 4\mathbf{j} + 12\mathbf{k}$, i.e., if $\mathbf{A} = A_r\mathbf{e}_r + 12\mathbf{k}$, what are the polar components in that set of the vector $\mathbf{B} = -4\mathbf{i} + 3\mathbf{j} - 12\mathbf{k}$?
Ans.: $B_r = 0$, $B_\phi = 5$, $B_z = -12$.

1.5-4: If, in the same set of cylindrical polar coordinates, three vectors $\mathbf{A} = 10\mathbf{e}_r - 5\mathbf{k}$, $\mathbf{B} = 3\mathbf{e}_r + 2\mathbf{e}_\phi + 7\mathbf{k}$, $\mathbf{C} = -2\mathbf{e}_r + 2\mathbf{e}_\phi - 2\mathbf{k}$ are given, what is the magnitude of $\mathbf{A} + \mathbf{B} + \mathbf{C}$?
Ans.: 11.7.

1.5-5: At any point in the vicinity of a long, magnetized, straight rod the magnetic field exerts a radial force on a charged particle, the magnitude of the attraction varying inversely as the square of the distance of the particle from the rod and being unity when that distance is unity. Write an expression for the force exerted on the particle by the field as a function of the coordinates of the point at which the charged particle is located. Do this first using cylindrical, then cartesian coordinates.

Ans.: $\mathbf{F} = -\dfrac{1}{r^2}\,\mathbf{e}_r = -\dfrac{x\mathbf{i}+y\mathbf{j}}{[x^2+y^2]^{3/2}}.$

1.5-6: The velocity of a point in a rigid body rotating about a fixed z-axis is proportional to the distance of the point from the axis of rotation and is directed at right angles to that axis and to the shortest line joining the point to the axis. Denote the constant of proportionality by the symbol ω and express the velocity vector of any point in the body in cylindrical polar components.

Ans.: $\mathbf{v} = \omega r \mathbf{e}_\phi = \omega(-y\mathbf{i}+x\mathbf{j}).$

1.6-1: Find the scalar component of the vector $\mathbf{A}=3\mathbf{i}-4\mathbf{j}+12\mathbf{k}$ in the direction of:
(a) the line through the origin making equal angles with the coordinate axes;
(b) the line from $(-2, 1, -6)$ to $(-5, 5, -18)$;
(c) the line from $(1, 1, 1)$ to $(-1, 2, -3)$.

Ans.: (c) $-58\sqrt{21}/21.$

1.6-2: Find the angle between $\mathbf{A}=6\mathbf{i}-2\mathbf{j}+5\mathbf{k}$ and $\mathbf{B}=2\mathbf{i}+\mathbf{k}$.

Ans.: arccos $(17\sqrt{13}/65).$

1.6-3: Determine the value or values of x that make $\mathbf{A}=x\mathbf{i}-2\mathbf{j}+4\mathbf{k}$ orthogonal to $\mathbf{B}=3\mathbf{i}+2\mathbf{j}-2\mathbf{k}$.

1.6-4: Are there any vectors in the yz-plane perpendicular to the line making equal angles with the coordinate axes? If so, find the unit vector or vectors that are.

Ans.: $\pm\dfrac{\sqrt{2}}{2}\,(\mathbf{j}-\mathbf{k}).$

1.6-5: The position vector $\mathbf{r}$ to any point in a plane passing through $\mathbf{r}_0$ and having unit normal vector $\mathbf{n}$ satisfies the relation $(\mathbf{r}-\mathbf{r}_0)\cdot\mathbf{n}=0$. Suppose three points with coordinates $(1, 1, 1)$, $(2, -1, 5)$, and $(-1, -1, 0)$ are given. Find a unit normal vector $\mathbf{n}$ perpendicular to the plane through the three points.

Ans.: $\mathbf{n} = \pm(0.735\mathbf{i}-0.515\mathbf{j}-0.441\mathbf{k}).$

1.6-6: If $\mathbf{A}=3\mathbf{i}+4\mathbf{j}+12\mathbf{k}$, $\mathbf{B}=-4\mathbf{i}+3\mathbf{j}$, use the scalar products $\mathbf{C}\cdot\mathbf{A}$ and $\mathbf{C}\cdot\mathbf{B}$ to show that all vectors $\mathbf{C}=C_x\mathbf{i}+C_y\mathbf{j}+C_z\mathbf{k}$ perpendicular to both $\mathbf{A}$ and $\mathbf{B}$ can be written in the form

$$\mathbf{C} = \pm\frac{|\mathbf{C}|}{65}\,(-36\mathbf{i}-48\mathbf{j}+25\mathbf{k}).$$

1.6-7: What is the angle between the line making equal angles with the positive (xyz) coordinate directions and the line in the xz-plane making equal angles with the negative coordinate directions ?
Ans.: arccos $(-\sqrt{6}/3) \cong 144.7°$.

1.6-8: A cone with vertex at the origin has semi-vertical angle $45°$ and axis along the x-axis. Find the position vector $\mathbf{r}$ from the origin to any point in the conical surface.
Ans.: $\mathbf{r} = \sqrt{y^2 + z^2}\,\mathbf{i} + y\mathbf{j} + z\mathbf{k}$.

1.6-9: Two vectors $\mathbf{A} = 6\mathbf{e}_r - 7\mathbf{k}$ and $\mathbf{B} = 5\mathbf{e}_r - 2\mathbf{e}_\phi + 4\mathbf{k}$ are given in the same set of cylindrical polar coordinates. What is the angle between them ?
Ans.: $88.1°$.

1.6-10: For each pair of vectors $\mathbf{A}$ and $\mathbf{B}$ that follow, find (i) the scalar component of $\mathbf{B}$ in the direction of $\mathbf{A}$ and (ii) the angle θ between $\mathbf{A}$ and $\mathbf{B}$.
(a) $\mathbf{A} = \mathbf{i} - \mathbf{j} - \mathbf{k}$, $\mathbf{B} = 5\mathbf{i} + 6\mathbf{j}$;
(b) $\mathbf{A} = \mathbf{i} - \mathbf{j} - 2\mathbf{k}$, $\mathbf{B} = \mathbf{i} - 3\mathbf{j} + 2\mathbf{k}$;
(c) $\mathbf{A} = 3\mathbf{i} - 4\mathbf{j} + 12\mathbf{k}$, $\mathbf{B} = -4\mathbf{i} - 9\mathbf{j} - \mathbf{k}$;
(d) $\mathbf{A} = -\mathbf{i} - \mathbf{j} + 2\mathbf{k}$, $\mathbf{B} = -3\mathbf{i} - 9\mathbf{j} + 2\mathbf{k}$.
Ans.: (a) $\theta = 94.25°$; (c) $\theta = 84.65°$.

1.7-1: Find the vector product $\mathbf{A} \times \mathbf{B}$ of:
(a) $\mathbf{A} = 3\mathbf{i} - 2\mathbf{j} + 5\mathbf{k}$, $\mathbf{B} = \mathbf{i} - \mathbf{j} - \mathbf{k}$;
(b) $\mathbf{A} = \mathbf{i} - \mathbf{j} + \mathbf{k}$, $\mathbf{B} = -6\mathbf{i} + 6\mathbf{j} - 6\mathbf{k}$;
(c) $\mathbf{A} = \mathbf{i} - \mathbf{j} - \mathbf{k}$, $\mathbf{B} = 3\mathbf{i} - 2\mathbf{j} + 5\mathbf{k}$;
(d) $\mathbf{A} = \mathbf{i} + 2\mathbf{j} + \mathbf{k}$, $\mathbf{B}$ the vector from $(1, 1, 1)$ to $(3, 0, 0)$.
Sketch the vectors $\mathbf{A}$, $\mathbf{B}$, and $\mathbf{A} \times \mathbf{B}$.
Ans.: (a) $7\mathbf{i} + 8\mathbf{j} - \mathbf{k}$; (d) $-\mathbf{i} + 3\mathbf{j} - 5\mathbf{k}$.

1.7-2: Find the moment of the force $\mathbf{F} = 3\mathbf{i} - 2\mathbf{j} + 6\mathbf{k}$ newtons acting at $\mathbf{r} = 2\mathbf{i} - 2\mathbf{j}$ meters about the point $\mathbf{R} = 7\mathbf{k}$ meters.
Ans.: $-26\mathbf{i} - 33\mathbf{j} + 2\mathbf{k}$ newton-meters.

1.7-3: Given two non-parallel vectors $\mathbf{A}$ and $\mathbf{B}$, construct an orthogonal triad $\mathbf{e}_1$, $\mathbf{e}_2$, $\mathbf{e}_3$ of unit vectors.
Ans.: $\mathbf{e}_1 = \mathbf{A}/A$, $\mathbf{e}_2 = \mathbf{A} \times \mathbf{B}/|\mathbf{A} \times \mathbf{B}|$, $\mathbf{e}_3 = \mathbf{e}_1 \times \mathbf{e}_2$ is one such set.

1.7-4: Solve Exercise 1.6-5 using the cross product.

1.7-5: Suppose that, in addition to the force $\mathbf{F}$ of Exercise 1.7-2, we have a second force $-\mathbf{F}$ acting at $3\mathbf{i} + 3\mathbf{k}$ meters. Find the sum of the moment vectors of $\mathbf{F}$ and $-\mathbf{F}$ about $\mathbf{R} = 7\mathbf{k}$. What is the sum of the moment vectors of $\mathbf{F}$ and $-\mathbf{F}$ about the origin ? Generalize to any vectors $(\mathbf{A}, -\mathbf{A})$ acting at points $\mathbf{r}_1$, $\mathbf{r}_2$.
Ans.: $-18\mathbf{i} - 3\mathbf{j} + 8\mathbf{k}$ newton-meters for $(\mathbf{F}, -\mathbf{F})$ about any point of space.

1.7-6: Derive the result of Exercise 1.6-6 using the vector product.

1.7-7: Derive the result of Exercise 1.6-7 using the vector product.

1.7-8: Derive the result of Exercise 1.6-9 using the vector product.

1.7-9: For each pair of vectors $\mathbf{A}$ and $\mathbf{B}$ of Exercise 1.6-10, find the vector product $\mathbf{B} \times \mathbf{A}$ and the sine of the angle between $\mathbf{A}$ and $\mathbf{B}$.

1.7-10: Suppose that two lines in space are given, one passing through the origin and making equal angles with the axes and the other passing through the points (o, o, 1) and (3, 2, o). Find the length of the common perpendicular to these two lines.

Ans.: $\sqrt{26}/26$.

1.8-1: Find the moment of the force **F** of Exercise 1.7-2 about a line through **R** = 7**k** meters making equal angles with the axes.

Ans.: $-19\sqrt{3}$ newton-meters.

1.8-2: A parallelepiped has face $ABCD$ in the xz-plane, with the 10 in. edge AB along the z-axis and the 8 in. edge AD at 60° to AB in the first quadrant of the xz-plane (draw a picture). The opposite face, $A'B'C'D'$, is so situated that corner A', 6 in. away from A, lies on the line through the origin A and the point $3\mathbf{i}+12\mathbf{j}+4\mathbf{k}$ in. Find the volume of the parallelepiped.

Ans.: 383.7 in³.

1.8-3: A line with direction $\mathbf{e}_1$ passes through point $\mathbf{r}_1$; a line with direction $\mathbf{e}_2$ passes through point $\mathbf{r}_2$. What is the length of the common perpendicular to the two lines?

Ans.: $|(\mathbf{r}_2-\mathbf{r}_1)\cdot(\mathbf{e}_1\times\mathbf{e}_2)|/|\mathbf{e}_1\times\mathbf{e}_2|$.

1.8-4: Check the answer to Exercise 1.7-10 using the result of Exercise 1.8-3.

1.8-5: In each of the following parts, a vector **B** and a point **r** on its line of action are given. An axis through the origin is specified in direction by the vector **A** in each case. Find the moment of **B** about that axis.
(a) $\mathbf{A} = 3\mathbf{i}-2\mathbf{j}+5\mathbf{k}$, $\mathbf{B} = \mathbf{i}-\mathbf{j}-\mathbf{k}$, $\mathbf{r} = \mathbf{i}+\mathbf{j}+\mathbf{k}$;
(b) $\mathbf{A} = \mathbf{i}-\mathbf{j}+\mathbf{k}$, $\mathbf{B} = -6\mathbf{i}+6\mathbf{j}-6\mathbf{k}$, $\mathbf{r} = -2\mathbf{j}+3\mathbf{k}$;
(c) $\mathbf{A} = \mathbf{i}-\mathbf{j}-\mathbf{k}$, $\mathbf{B} = 3\mathbf{i}-2\mathbf{j}+5\mathbf{k}$, $\mathbf{r} = -2\mathbf{i}+4\mathbf{j}+4\mathbf{k}$;
(d) $\mathbf{A} = \mathbf{i}+2\mathbf{j}+\mathbf{k}$, $\mathbf{B} = -2\mathbf{i}-4\mathbf{j}-2\mathbf{k}$, $\mathbf{r} = \mathbf{i}+\mathbf{j}+\mathbf{k}$.

Ans.: (a) $-7\sqrt{38}/19$; (b) o; (c) $14\sqrt{3}/3$; (d) o.

1.9-1: Find the vector product $\mathbf{B}\times(\mathbf{C}\times\mathbf{A})$ of $\mathbf{A}=\mathbf{i}+\mathbf{j}$, $\mathbf{B}=7\mathbf{i}-2\mathbf{k}$, $\mathbf{C}=6\mathbf{i}-\mathbf{j}-2\mathbf{k}$ both by carrying out the indicated products and by using the fundamental identity for the reduction of such products.

Ans.: $-4\mathbf{i}-53\mathbf{j}-14\mathbf{k}$.

1.9-2: Show that the component of $\mathbf{A}\times(\mathbf{A}\times\mathbf{B})$ in the direction of **B** is never positive and hence that $(\mathbf{A}\cdot\mathbf{B})^2 \leq A^2B^2$. (Hint: use both the reduction identity for the vector triple product and the cross-dot interchange identity for the scalar triple product.)

1.9-3: Show that, if $\mathbf{A}\neq\mathbf{o}$, $\mathbf{B}\neq\mathbf{o}$, the vanishing of $\mathbf{A}\times[\mathbf{B}\times(\mathbf{A}\times\mathbf{B})]$ implies that either **A** is parallel to **B** or **A** is perpendicular to **B**.

1.9-4: Given the three vectors $\mathbf{A}=2\mathbf{i}-5\mathbf{j}+6\mathbf{k}$, $\mathbf{B}=\mathbf{i}-\mathbf{j}-\mathbf{k}$, $\mathbf{C}=\mathbf{i}+\mathbf{j}+4\mathbf{k}$, compute all possible different vector triple products that can be formed from these. Do not include both products if two differ by only a factor of -1.

1.10-1: Prove that, if $\mathbf{A}$ and $\mathbf{B}$ are any two vectors and $\mathbf{e}$ is a unit vector at right angles to the plane of $\mathbf{A}$ and $\mathbf{B}$, then the expression $(\mathbf{A} \times \mathbf{B}) \times \mathbf{C} = [(\mathbf{A} \times \mathbf{B}) \cdot \mathbf{e}][\mathbf{e} \times \mathbf{C}]$ is true for any vector $\mathbf{C}$ whatsoever; i.e., the expression is an identity, whatever $\mathbf{C}$ may be.

1.10-2: Given any two vectors, $\mathbf{A}$ and $\mathbf{B}$, show that $|\mathbf{A} \times \mathbf{B}|^2 = A^2 B^2 - (\mathbf{A} \cdot \mathbf{B})^2$. Derive the result of Exercise 1.9-2 from this. What is the trigonometrical interpretation of this identity when $\mathbf{A}$ and $\mathbf{B}$ are unit vectors which include an angle θ?

1.10-3: What is the general solution of the equation $\mathbf{a} \cdot \mathbf{x} = \mathbf{a} \cdot \mathbf{b}$?
Ans.: $\mathbf{x} = \mathbf{b} + \mathbf{a} \times \mathbf{c}$, where $\mathbf{c}$ is an arbitrary vector.

1.10-4: Find a vector $\mathbf{x}$ that satisfies the equations $\mathbf{a} \times \mathbf{x} = \mathbf{b}$ and $\mathbf{a} \cdot \mathbf{x} = b$, where $\mathbf{a} \cdot \mathbf{b} = 0$.

Ans.: $\mathbf{x} = \dfrac{1}{a^2}(b\mathbf{a} + \mathbf{b} \times \mathbf{a})$.

1.10-5: Solve the simultaneous equations
$$\mathbf{x} + \mathbf{y} + \mathbf{z} = \mathbf{a},$$
$$\mathbf{x} - \mathbf{y} + \mathbf{z} = \mathbf{b},$$
$$\mathbf{x} + \mathbf{y} - \mathbf{z} = \mathbf{c},$$
for the unknown vectors $\mathbf{x}$, $\mathbf{y}$, $\mathbf{z}$, given the constant vectors $\mathbf{a}$, $\mathbf{b}$, and $\mathbf{c}$.

1.10-6: (a) Solve the simultaneous equations
$$\mathbf{w} + \mathbf{x} + \mathbf{y} + \mathbf{z} = \mathbf{a},$$
$$\mathbf{w} + \mathbf{x} - \mathbf{y} + \mathbf{z} = \mathbf{b},$$
$$\mathbf{w} + \mathbf{x} + \mathbf{y} - \mathbf{z} = \mathbf{c},$$
$$\mathbf{w} - \mathbf{x} + \mathbf{y} + \mathbf{z} = \mathbf{d},$$
for the unknown vectors $\mathbf{w}$, $\mathbf{x}$, $\mathbf{y}$, $\mathbf{z}$, given the constant vectors $\mathbf{a}$, $\mathbf{b}$, $\mathbf{c}$, and $\mathbf{d}$.
Ans.: $\mathbf{x} = (\mathbf{a} - \mathbf{d})/2$, $\mathbf{w} = (-\mathbf{a} + \mathbf{b} + \mathbf{c} + \mathbf{d})/2$.

(b) Suppose $2\mathbf{a} - 3\mathbf{b} + \mathbf{c} - \mathbf{d} = 0$ is the relation expressing the linear dependence of $\mathbf{a}$, $\mathbf{b}$, $\mathbf{c}$, and $\mathbf{d}$. What are $\mathbf{w}$, $\mathbf{x}$, $\mathbf{y}$, and $\mathbf{z}$ in terms of $\mathbf{a}$, $\mathbf{b}$, and $\mathbf{c}$? What is the relation among $\mathbf{w}$, $\mathbf{x}$, $\mathbf{y}$, $\mathbf{z}$ expressing the linear dependence of these four vectors?
Ans.: $\mathbf{w} - \mathbf{x} - 5\mathbf{y} + 3\mathbf{z} = 0$.

1.10-7: Given four vectors $\mathbf{a}$, $\mathbf{b}$, $\mathbf{c}$, and $\mathbf{d}$, solve the equation $\mathbf{x} \times \mathbf{a} + (\mathbf{x} \cdot \mathbf{b})\mathbf{c} = \mathbf{d}$ for the unknown vector $\mathbf{x}$. It may be assumed that $\mathbf{a} \cdot \mathbf{b}$ and $\mathbf{a} \cdot \mathbf{c}$ are not equal to zero.

Ans.: $\mathbf{x} = \dfrac{1}{(\mathbf{a} \cdot \mathbf{b})} \left[\dfrac{(\mathbf{d} \cdot \mathbf{a})}{(\mathbf{c} \cdot \mathbf{a})}(\mathbf{c} \times \mathbf{b} + \mathbf{a}) - \mathbf{d} \times \mathbf{b} \right]$.

CHAPTER II

Principles of Statics

2.1 Newton's Laws of Motion; Equilibrium of a Particle

Mechanics is based upon Newton's laws of motion which, in modern language, take the form:

(1) A particle acted on by forces whose resultant always vanishes will move with constant velocity.

(2) A particle acted on by forces whose resultant is not zero will move in such a way that the time rate of change of its momentum will at any instant be proportional to the resultant force.

(3) If one particle, *A*, exerts a force on a second particle, *B*, then *B* exerts a collinear force of equal magnitude and opposite direction on *A*.

The study of the motion of material systems has been developed by systematic generalization and extension of these laws. Here we shall say only enough to indicate the general pattern of this development; detailed proofs are left to dynamical studies.*

---

* See L. E. Goodman and W. H. Warner, *Dynamics* (Belmont, Calif: Wadsworth Publishing Company, Inc., 1963), Chapters I and II.

First, we note that the laws relate to the motion of "particles." The particle plays the same role in mechanics that the point plays in geometry. An actual object may be treated as a particle if, insofar as its motion is concerned, it can be regarded with sufficient accuracy as a moving point. The laws of motion, therefore, presuppose a space in which the particle moves. To that space certain properties— homogeneity, isotropy, and continuity—must be attributed so that changes in position may be measured. The familiar Euclidean three-dimensional space of elementary geometry has the properties wanted and is the one used in newtonian mechanics. Time is introduced as a scalar variable taking on the values of the real-number continuum. Regarding position vectors as functions of this scalar variable, we can define the rate of change of the position vector, called the *velocity* vector. This definition requires the development of a vector calculus, with velocity as the derivative of position. *Acceleration* is also a vector quantity, the time derivative of velocity. The interrelationships between the position, velocity, and acceleration vectors is that subject of study known as *kinematics*. Finally, a time scale is introduced by our comparing the motions we study to a standard observable motion, say the rotation of the earth.

Further attributes are given to particles by introducing the concepts of "force," related to a measure of the mutual influence of particles on one another's motion, and "mass," a scalar property of each particle which does not change with time or location. Mass may be defined by considering a hypothetical experiment in which two particles are supposed to move free from all influences except their mutual interaction. Since force is a measure of this interaction, the third law assures us that the two particles will move under the action of forces of equal magnitude. The accelerations of the two particles will, however, usually have different magnitudes; one particle will, in general, be more sluggish or inert than the other. To account for this property of inertia, a measure of it called *mass* is assigned to each particle, the more sluggish particle being said to have the larger mass. To be precise, the ratio of the masses of the two particles is taken as the reciprocal of the ratio of the magnitudes of their accelerations at any instant. Once a standard body or mass is selected, all other masses are determined by comparison with it, by means of the experiment described or by means of one shown to be equivalent. The *momentum* vector of a particle then is taken as the product of the scalar mass and the vector velocity, and the second law states that the derivative of this is the proper measure of the change of motion of the particle due to other particles.

This derivative of the momentum is the product of mass and acceleration.

Force is defined through the second law as the derivative of the momentum vector. The second law requires only a proportionality, but by proper choice of units of measurement—so-called *dynamically consistent units*—the constant of proportionality may be taken as unity. Since the derivative of a vector is a vector, force is a vector quantity. Apparently we are then introducing an unnecessary name for a previously defined vector, the product of mass and acceleration. However, force has a definite utility as a separate concept. As a name for the "mechanical interaction" (i.e., effect on motion) it is subject to the third law. The third law is of great use in statics. It makes possible the simplification of the analysis of complex systems by permitting the examination of parts of the system without introducing completely new and unknown "interactions" (i.e., forces) at each step. Through it, we may extend newtonian mechanics from particles to objects of finite size. The vectorial character of force as defined by the second law enables us to combine, by vectorial addition, the forces arising from a number of sources; and, finally, we have learned to recognize a variety of interactions and write appropriate mathematical expressions for them as force vectors to use in the equations of motion. In the next few sections, we shall discuss some of the important types of forces and their representations.

We now come to the fundamental concept underlying statics: that of equilibrium. The first law of motion states that, when the resultant interaction effect on a particle vanishes—when the vector sum of the forces on it is the zero vector—the particle moves with constant velocity. First of all, this law asserts the existence of at least one preferred coordinate frame relative to which the constant velocity is measured. Such a frame of reference is called *inertial*, *newtonian*, or *galilean*. In practice, of course, we cannot apply the test of removing an object from all influence. What we do is use a convenient frame of reference and check the predictions of the laws of motion against experiment. Accurate agreement between prediction and measurement in a very wide range of physical and engineering situations is the basis for the enormous power and scope of the methods of newtonian mechanics. For most engineering problems axes fixed in the earth, regarded as stationary, form a satisfactory inertial frame. More complex problems, such as the motion of a gyrocompass, require that we not ignore the rotation of the earth and, indeed, problems of celestial mechanics require an astronomical frame of reference fixed with respect to the so-called "fixed" stars.

The existence of other inertial frames, granted the existence of one such frame, is not a matter of immediate concern. The important assumption is that one exists, relative to which a particle free of mechanical influence moves at constant velocity. Since velocity is a vector, this means the particle moves at constant speed, or magnitude of velocity, in a straight line—a fixed direction. The particle is said to be in *equilibrium*. There are two apparent aspects to such an equilibrium motion: the vanishing of the resultant force and hence of the acceleration, and the steady motion of the particle. Which is the proper basis for generalization of the concept of equilibrium to more complex systems? It can be shown that, if a particle is moving with constant velocity relative to an inertial frame of reference, then there is another inertial frame relative to which the particle has zero velocity; i.e., it is at *rest*. It is this concept of equilibrium that is taken as fundamental for generalization to systems of particles. A system is in equilibrium if no part of the system has any acceleration and if the system is at rest in some inertial frame of reference.

Statics, then, is the study of material systems in equilibrium. If we regard our material system as a particle, we conclude directly from the laws of motion that it is in equilibrium if and only if the resultant force on the particle vanishes. We must see how this principle is to be generalized as we consider more and more complex models of systems. In the remainder of this chapter, we shall be concerned with two things. First, how do we describe particular forces and work with them mathematically? Second, how do we describe systems and develop the principles of equilibrium for them?

2.2 Force and Moment Vectors; the Couple

Force, as defined by the second law of motion, is a vector quantity. The separate effects on a particle's motion due to any number of other particles are represented by force vectors $\mathbf{F}_1, \mathbf{F}_2, \ldots \mathbf{F}_n$ acting on the particle; the vector nature of force then implies that these may be replaced by a single vector $\mathbf{F}$, the *resultant force*, given by the sum of the separate force vectors:

$$\mathbf{F} = \mathbf{F}_1 + \mathbf{F}_2 + \ldots \mathbf{F}_n = \sum_{i=1}^{n} \mathbf{F}_i. \qquad \text{2.2-1}$$

In statics, we are concerned with the case in which $\mathbf{F} = \mathbf{0}$.

The force vectors are *bound vectors* in the sense in which they are used at present; they have a definite point of application. To say that another force is completely equivalent to a given force means

more than the simple statement that the vectors representing the
forces have the same magnitude and direction, i.e. are equal vectors
in the sense of Chapter I. They must also be given the same point
of application in general. That is, though force is a vector quantity,
not all of its properties are represented by its vector alone. This
"bound vector" concept of force will be relaxed later when we
consider distributed mass systems, moments, and the definition of
mechanical equivalence, or equipollence, of force sets.

In the course of scientific progress large classes of interactions between particles and between finite bodies have come to be
recognized and have found mathematical expression as force vectors.
Among those commonly encountered in mechanics and engineering,
contact forces, gravitational forces, electromagnetic forces, and
viscous drag forces deserve special mention. Whenever two objects
are in contact, forces of the first type mentioned arise. Such forces
may be considered as distributed over an area or idealized as concentrated forces. In technology, cases of common occurrence are
those of two massive objects connected by a light cable or by a light
spring; the forces representing the action of the cable or spring are
usually idealized as concentrated contact loads. Gravitational forces,
including the weight force on an object near the earth, are introduced
as a consequence of Newton's law of universal gravitation. Coulomb's
law for the force on electrically charged particles takes the same inverse
square form as the gravitational force. Viscous drag forces, dependent on the velocity of a body relative to a fluid, and frictional forces
at a rough contact are also common representations of interaction
effects. As we proceed through the developments of the next few
sections, we shall see how we represent the force vectors of some of
the more important of these.

A unit of magnitude is required for the force vector. In statics,
we need only be sure that all forces are measured in the same units,
the unit itself being unimportant since we shall set the resultant force
equal to zero. In dynamics a set of dynamically consistent units is
needed for force, mass, length, and time (and hence acceleration)
if we are to write $\mathbf{F} = m\mathbf{a}$. A complete discussion of the various metric
and English, "scientific" and "engineering," absolute and gravita-
tional systems of units would be out of place in material concerned
only with statics.* In technology, as in everyday speech, it is customary in English-speaking countries to use the pound-force as the unit

---

* See *Dynamics*, Section 2.3.

of force and to refer to it simply as the *pound*. This is the force necessary to give a standard of mass (the so-called engineering unit of mass or "slug") an acceleration of one foot per second per second. Alternatively, the unit of mass may be taken as the pound-mass avoirdupois and the unit of force as that force necessary to give one pound-mass avoirdupois an acceleration of one foot per second per second. This unit of force, called the *poundal*, is not much used in engineering. One pound-force is the same as 32.174 poundals. Multiples of the pound-force are the kilopound, or "kip," and the ton. In metric units, the unit of force, known as the *newton*, is that force necessary to give a mass of one kilogram an acceleration of one meter per second per second. One pound is the same as 4.44 newtons. Where a smaller unit of force is wanted, the *dyne*, which is 10^{-5} newtons, is employed. Continental European and South American engineers usually employ the kilogram-force as a unit; one kilogram-force is the same as 9.811 newtons. Whatever unit is chosen, it should be associated with the magnitude of the force vector or with its scalar components and not with the unit direction vector.

The necessary and sufficient condition for particle equilibrium is the vanishing of the resultant force **F** on the particle. From this, a secondary condition follows: if a particle is in equilibrium, the resultant moment of the forces on the particle must vanish. In Chapter I, we defined the moment of any vector with respect to an arbitrarily chosen base point. We also proved Varignon's theorem, that the resultant of the moment vectors of the separate forces is the moment of the resultant of the forces. It is a trivial consequence of the force equilibrium condition, then, to say that the moment must also be zero if the particle is in equilibrium. The vanishing of the moment about one point is not, however, a sufficient condition for particle equilibrium. That is, if we know that the resultant moment M_P of the forces on a particle about a point P vanishes, we cannot conclude that the force vanishes and hence that the particle is in equilibrium. For a particle, the establishment of equilibrium conditions in terms of moments is not an important task; for extended systems, we shall want to develop moment conditions necessary for equilibrium as well as the ordinary force equilibrium equations that are necessary. Now we point out only that we shall need moments of force vectors; that we shall need the interpretation of scalar components of moments as moments about axes; that moment vectors have units: pound-feet, kilogram-force-meters, newton-meters, pound-inches, etc.; and that moment vectors should be considered in general as bound vectors, with point of application at the base point for moments.

Varignon's theorem treats of the moments of vectors with concurrent lines of action. The forces on extended systems of bodies will not have concurrent lines of action in general. We need a means of extending the resultant moment concept to such forces. The formalism by which this may be done is based on consideration of a special force system, called a *couple*. A couple is a pair of force vectors equal in magnitude, opposite in direction, and on parallel lines of action. That is, if two forces $\mathbf{F}_1$ and $\mathbf{F}_2$ act on a body so that the vectors representing the forces are negatives of one another $(\mathbf{F}_2 = -\mathbf{F}_1 = -\mathbf{F})$ but the lines of action of the forces are not the same (and hence are parallel, since the line of action of a force has, by

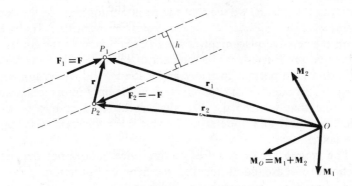

Fig. 2.2-1

definition, the same direction as the force), then we call the pair of force vectors $(\mathbf{F}_1, \mathbf{F}_2) = (\mathbf{F}, -\mathbf{F})$ a couple. The plane containing the parallel lines of action is called the *plane of the couple*.

Let us consider the formal force-and-moment resultant properties of a couple, even though we are not yet prepared to discuss the physical significance of these. Let $(\mathbf{F}_1, \mathbf{F}_2) = (\mathbf{F}, -\mathbf{F})$ be a couple, with P_1 and P_2 the points of application of $\mathbf{F}_1$ and $\mathbf{F}_2$, respectively (Fig. 2.2-1). Choose any point O of space and let $\mathbf{r}_1$ be the position of P_1 relative to O, $\mathbf{r}_2$ the position of P_2 relative to O, and $\mathbf{r} = \mathbf{r}_1 - \mathbf{r}_2$ the position of P_1 relative to P_2. The vector sum of the two forces is zero:

$$\mathbf{F}_1 + \mathbf{F}_2 = \mathbf{F} + (-\mathbf{F}) = \mathbf{0}. \qquad \text{2.2-2}$$

It can be shown (see *Dynamics*, Section 4.3) that, if a body is subject only to a couple, its mass center will have no acceleration. The body will, however, rotate about its mass center: to see this, think of the couple as consisting of two oppositely directed forces applied at the ends of a bar and directed at right angles to the bar. A measure of the rotational effect of the forces is given by their resultant moment. Let us take moments about an arbitrary point O for the couple shown in Fig. 2.2-1. The moment $\mathbf{M}_1$ about O of $\mathbf{F}_1$ is given by $\mathbf{r}_1 \times \mathbf{F}_1 = \mathbf{r}_1 \times \mathbf{F}$; the moment $\mathbf{M}_2$ about O of $\mathbf{F}_2$ is given by $\mathbf{r}_2 \times \mathbf{F}_2 = \mathbf{r}_2 \times (-\mathbf{F})$. The formal moment resultant, $\mathbf{M}_O$, of the two moments is their vector sum:

$$\mathbf{M}_O = \mathbf{M}_1 + \mathbf{M}_2 = \mathbf{r}_1 \times \mathbf{F} + \mathbf{r}_2 \times (-\mathbf{F}) = (\mathbf{r}_1 - \mathbf{r}_2) \times \mathbf{F},$$

or

$$\mathbf{M}_O = \mathbf{r} \times \mathbf{F}. \qquad \text{2.2-3}$$

Examining this result, we see that the resultant moment of the couple is *independent of the choice of the base point for moments*. It depends only on the relative placement of the lines of action of the forces and the force vector $\mathbf{F}$ itself. The moment of a couple is its only characteristic that is important in many applications, and the vector representing the moment of the couple is often the only information about the couple that is needed. We shall speak of a couple vector $\mathbf{C}$ applied to a body and understand by this that a moment $\mathbf{C}$ is applied to the body.

The couple vector is a *free* vector, since it does not depend on the choice of base point for the moment computation. For this reason, a couple is often called a "pure moment" or "pure torque." Since the moment computation is independent of where along its line of action the force vector is placed, we may use *any* relative position vector $\mathbf{r}$ from the line of action of $\mathbf{F}_2$ to the line of $\mathbf{F}_1 = \mathbf{F}$ to find $\mathbf{C} = \mathbf{r} \times \mathbf{F}$. In particular, the magnitude of the couple vector is Fh, where F is the magnitude of either force constituting the couple and h is the perpendicular distance between the lines of action of the forces. The direction of $\mathbf{C}$ must be determined by the usual right-hand rule; one must be careful only to take $\mathbf{r}$ *from* $\mathbf{F}_2$ *to* $\mathbf{F}_1$, once one has chosen which of the two force vectors is to be $\mathbf{F}_1 = \mathbf{F}$. The direction of $\mathbf{C}$ is, of course, perpendicular to the plane of the couple.

It is well to reiterate that $\mathbf{C}$ is a moment vector and must not be added to force vectors in equations. Indeed, a couple has zero force resultant. If a couple is acting, however, it must be added into all vectorial moment equations, whatever base point has been chosen.

Given a couple vector $\mathbf{C}$, all representations of it in terms of forces in any plane perpendicular to the direction of $\mathbf{C}$ are considered "equivalent." That is, take forces of half the magnitude of our original $\mathbf{F}_1$ and $\mathbf{F}_2$ but on lines of action a distance $2h$ apart; this couple will also have moment $\mathbf{C}$.   Take a pair of forces whose vectors are the same as those of $\mathbf{F}_1$ and $\mathbf{F}_2$, but in a plane parallel to the original plane of the couple; this couple will also have moment $\mathbf{C}$. This does not mean that these force systems are equivalent in all their physical effects on the motion of general systems, but only that their force and moment sums are the same.   We shall examine later in just what sense such a mathematical equivalence has significance as a physical equivalence.

Example 2.2-1

A particle in equilibrium is subjected to four forces, $\mathbf{F}_i$, $i=1$, 2, 3, 4. Three of the forces are $\mathbf{F}_1 = 2\mathbf{i} - 5\mathbf{j} + 6\mathbf{k}$ lb, $\mathbf{F}_2 = \mathbf{i} + 3\mathbf{j} - 7\mathbf{k}$ lb, $\mathbf{F}_3 = 2\mathbf{i} - 2\mathbf{j} - 3\mathbf{k}$ lb.   What is $\mathbf{F}_4$?

Solution: The resultant of all forces must vanish since the particle is in equilibrium:

$$\sum_{i=1}^{4} \mathbf{F}_i = \mathbf{F}_1 + \mathbf{F}_2 + \mathbf{F}_3 + \mathbf{F}_4 = \mathbf{0}.$$

Therefore, $\mathbf{F}_4$ is the negative of the resultant of the other three:

$$\begin{aligned}
\mathbf{F}_4 &= -(\mathbf{F}_1 + \mathbf{F}_2 + \mathbf{F}_3) \\
&= -(5\mathbf{i} - 4\mathbf{j} - 4\mathbf{k}) \\
&= -5\mathbf{i} + 4\mathbf{j} + 4\mathbf{k} \quad \text{lb.}
\end{aligned}$$

Example 2.2-2

A couple consists of forces $\mathbf{F}_1 = 2\mathbf{i} - 3\mathbf{j}$ newtons, acting at $-5\mathbf{j} + 2\mathbf{k}$ meters, and $\mathbf{F}_2 = -2\mathbf{i} + 3\mathbf{j}$ newtons, acting at $\mathbf{i} - 2\mathbf{j}$ meters.   What is the couple vector $\mathbf{C}$?

Solution: Let $\mathbf{F}_1 = \mathbf{F}$; then $\mathbf{C} = \mathbf{r} \times \mathbf{F}$, where $\mathbf{r}$ is a vector from $\mathbf{F}_2$ to $\mathbf{F}_1$.   Therefore,

$$\mathbf{r} = (-5\mathbf{j} + 2\mathbf{k}) - (\mathbf{i} - 2\mathbf{j}) = -\mathbf{i} - 3\mathbf{j} + 2\mathbf{k},$$

$$\mathbf{C} = \mathbf{r} \times \mathbf{F} = \begin{vmatrix} \mathbf{i} & \mathbf{j} & \mathbf{k} \\ -1 & -3 & 2 \\ 2 & -3 & 0 \end{vmatrix} = 6\mathbf{i} + 4\mathbf{j} + 9\mathbf{k} \quad \text{newton-meters.}$$

Example 2.2-3

Can the couple of the previous example be replaced by an equivalent couple $(-\mathbf{P}, \mathbf{P})$ acting at points $(1, 1, 1)$ and $(3, -2, -1)$ meters respectively?

Solution: Let $\mathbf{R}$ be the vector from $(1, 1, 1)$ to $(3, -2, -1)$: $\mathbf{R} = 2\mathbf{i} - 3\mathbf{j} - 2\mathbf{k}$.   The question asked is: can $\mathbf{P}$ be found such that $\mathbf{R} \times \mathbf{P} = \mathbf{C} = 6\mathbf{i} + 4\mathbf{j} + 9\mathbf{k}$?   The answer is no; for $\mathbf{C}$ would have to be perpendicular to $\mathbf{R}$, and the given $\mathbf{C}$ and $\mathbf{R}$ are not:

$$\mathbf{C} \cdot \mathbf{R} = 12 - 12 - 18 = -18 \neq 0.$$

Example **2.2-4**

Find the resultant of the three forces shown in Fig. 2.2-2 *as well as the total moment of these forces about the point O.*

Solution: We first express the various forces in cartesian form:

$$\mathbf{F}_1 = 10(\cos 45°\mathbf{i} + \cos 65°\mathbf{j} + \cos 55.5°\mathbf{k}) = 7.07\mathbf{i} + 4.23\mathbf{j} + 5.66\mathbf{k} \quad \text{lb};$$

$$\mathbf{F}_2 = 15\left[-\left(\frac{15}{19}\right)\mathbf{i} + \left(\frac{6}{19}\right)\mathbf{j} - \left(\frac{10}{19}\right)\mathbf{k}\right] = -11.84\mathbf{i} + 4.74\mathbf{j} - 7.89\mathbf{k} \quad \text{lb};$$

$$\mathbf{F}_3 = 20\left(\frac{15}{17}\mathbf{j} - \frac{8}{17}\mathbf{k}\right) = 17.65\mathbf{j} - 9.41\mathbf{k} \quad \text{lb}.$$

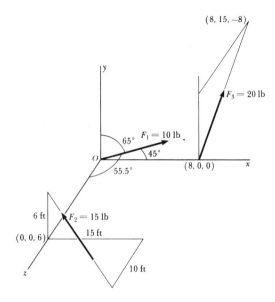

Fig. 2.2-2

We find the resultant simply by adding components:

$$\mathbf{F} = \mathbf{F}_1 + \mathbf{F}_2 + \mathbf{F}_3 = -4.77\mathbf{i} + 26.62\mathbf{j} - 11.64\mathbf{k} \quad \text{lb}.$$

The magnitude of the resultant is

$$[(-4.77)^2 + (26.62)^2 + (-11.64)^2]^{1/2} = 29.44 \quad \text{lb}.$$

The angles that the resultant force makes with the positive directions of the *x, y, z* axes are

$$\theta_x = \arccos\left(\frac{-4.77}{29.44}\right) = \arccos(-0.162) = 99.3°,$$

$$\theta_y = \arccos\left(\frac{26.62}{29.44}\right) = \arccos(0.904) = 25.3°,$$

$$\theta_z = \arccos\left(\frac{-11.64}{29.44}\right) = \arccos\left(-0.395\right) = 113.3°.$$

Since the cartesian form determines the magnitude and direction angles of a vector, we shall not in future compute these quantities unless they are of particular interest.

We turn now to the moment computation. It is clear that $\mathbf{F}_1$ has zero moment about O, since it passes through O. The force $\mathbf{F}_2$ passes through a point whose coordinates are (0, 6, 6) ft and the force $\mathbf{F}_3$ passes through the point whose coordinates are (8, 0, 0) ft. Therefore

$$\mathbf{M}_O = (6\mathbf{j} + 6\mathbf{k}) \times \mathbf{F}_2 + 8\mathbf{i} \times \mathbf{F}_3$$

$$= \begin{vmatrix} \mathbf{i} & \mathbf{j} & \mathbf{k} \\ 0 & 6 & 6 \\ -11.84 & 4.74 & -7.89 \end{vmatrix} + \begin{vmatrix} \mathbf{i} & \mathbf{j} & \mathbf{k} \\ 8 & 0 & 0 \\ 0 & 17.65 & -9.41 \end{vmatrix}$$

$$\cong (-76\mathbf{i} - 71\mathbf{j} + 71\mathbf{k}) + (75\mathbf{j} + 141\mathbf{k}) = -76\mathbf{i} + 4\mathbf{j} + 212\mathbf{k} \quad \text{lb-ft.}$$

This means that the forces can be regarded as producing a torque of magnitude 225 lb-ft about an axis through O whose direction cosines are $-0.34, 0.02, 0.94.$

Example 2.2-5

Given a force, say $\mathbf{F} = 21\mathbf{i} + 40\mathbf{j} + 72\mathbf{k}$ *lb, and a direction, say the direction of the unit vector* $\mathbf{e} = 0.800\mathbf{i} + 0.424\mathbf{j} + 0.424\mathbf{k}$, *show how to express* $\mathbf{F}$ *as the sum of two components,* $\mathbf{F}_1$ *parallel to* $\mathbf{e}$, *and* $\mathbf{F}_2$ *perpendicular to* $\mathbf{e}$.

Solution: We first find the scalar component of $\mathbf{F}$ in the given direction. This is $\mathbf{F} \cdot \mathbf{e} = 64.3$ lb. Then $\mathbf{F}_1 = (\mathbf{F} \cdot \mathbf{e})\mathbf{e} = 51.4\mathbf{i} + 27.3\mathbf{j} + 27.3\mathbf{k}$ lb. The other component, $\mathbf{F}_2$, is most easily found when we observe that $\mathbf{F}_1 + \mathbf{F}_2 = \mathbf{F}$ so that

$$\mathbf{F}_2 = \mathbf{F} - \mathbf{F}_1 = \mathbf{F} - (\mathbf{F} \cdot \mathbf{e})\mathbf{e} = -30.4\mathbf{i} + 12.7\mathbf{j} + 44.7\mathbf{k} \quad \text{lb.}$$

We can check the fact that $\mathbf{F}_2$ is at right angles to $\mathbf{F}_1$ by observing that $\mathbf{F}_1 \cdot \mathbf{F}_2 = 0$.

Example 2.2-6

A pair of vertical forces comprising a couple act at points A and B of the wrench shown in Fig. 2.2-3a. Replace these by a pair of horizontal forces at points C and D. The replacement forces are to produce the same moment about any axis as would be produced by the original set.

Solution: The forces at A and B comprise a couple whose magnitude is $(10)(14) = 140$ lb-in. and whose direction is at right angles to the (vertical) plane containing the forces of the couple. If we choose (x, y, z) axes as shown, this plane is the xy-plane and the moment vector is $-140\mathbf{k}$, as shown. The replacement forces at C and D must form a couple with the same moment vector. Since these forces are to be horizontal, the distance

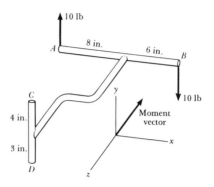

Fig. 2.2-3a

between them will be 7 in. and the forces must therefore be of magnitude 20 lb. They must produce a clockwise moment as viewed from the positive end of the z-axis. The necessary forces are shown in Fig. 2.2-3b.

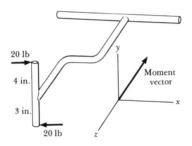

Fig. 2.2-3b

The sets of forces shown in Figs. 2.2-3a and b each have zero resultant force vector and the same moment vector. It follows that the moment produced by the first set of forces about any point will be the same as the moment produced by the second set of forces about any point.

Example 2.2-7

A cube of metal in a turret lathe is being drilled simultaneously along lines at right angles to two adjacent faces and along a body diagonal, as shown in Fig. 2.2-4. Assuming that each drill exerts a torque of 50 lb-in., what is the magnitude of the resultant torque about the center of the cube and what is the direction of the axis about which this torque acts?

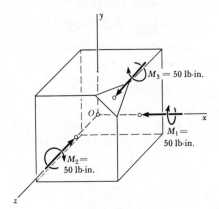

Fig. 2.2-4

Solution: The couples acting about the x and z axes are

$$\mathbf{M}_1 = -50\mathbf{i}, \qquad \mathbf{M}_2 = -50\mathbf{k} \quad \text{lb-in.}$$

The couple exerted by the twist drill acting along the body diagonal is

$$\mathbf{M}_3 = \left(\frac{-50}{\sqrt{3}}\right)(\mathbf{i}+\mathbf{j}+\mathbf{k}) \quad \text{lb-in.}$$

Adding these we have

$$\mathbf{M}_O = \left(\frac{-50}{\sqrt{3}}\right)[(1+\sqrt{3})(\mathbf{i}+\mathbf{k})+\mathbf{j}]$$

$$= -115(0.684\mathbf{i}+0.251\mathbf{j}+0.684\mathbf{k}) \quad \text{lb-in.}$$

The resultant moment vector has been put into the standard form in which the quantity in parentheses is a vector of unit magnitude. We conclude that the magnitude of the resultant torque is 115 lb-in. and that it acts about an axis whose direction cosines are 0.684, 0.251, 0.684. This axis is pictured in Fig. 2.2-5 as the directed line segment $\overline{OA}$. The minus sign in the expression for $\mathbf{M}_O$ tells us that $\mathbf{M}_O$ will be clockwise as viewed from A looking toward O, as it is pictured in the figure. This follows from the right-hand rule which is used to give the sense of a moment vector; when the thumb of the right hand points along the directed line segment $\overline{OA}$ in its positive direction, from O to A, the fingers of the right hand curl round the axis in a counterclockwise direction, as viewed from A. We conclude that a positive sign on the magnitude of $\mathbf{M}_O$ would be associated with a counterclockwise moment as viewed from A. A negative sign must therefore mean a clockwise moment as viewed from A. In the present case, of course, the sense of the moment vector is fairly obvious from inspection of Fig. 2.2-4. Notice that if we were to write

$$\mathbf{M}_O = 115(-0.684\mathbf{i} - 0.251\mathbf{j} - 0.684\mathbf{k})$$

we should come to exactly the same conclusion. The axis would then be the extension of the one shown in Fig. 2.2-5 into the region on the other side of the origin, which is the same as saying it would be the directed line segment $\overline{AO}$ rather than $\overline{OA}$.

In the statement of the example we are asked for the resultant torque about the *center* of the cube. Since we dealt only with pure couples, why do we need to mention any particular point? The answer lies in the fact

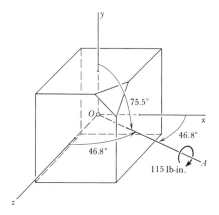

Fig. 2.2-5

that in reality any practical drill will exert an axial force as well as a torque. In Fig. 2.2-4 these forces would be directed along the x-, z-, and body-diagonal axes toward the origin O at the center of the cube. Since, for the purpose of this example, we have not wished to include these forces, the statement has been worded in such a way that their presence would not affect the answer.

2.3 The Mechanical System and the Free-Body Diagram

At this point we introduce the concept of a *mechanical system*, an idea that is of fundamental importance in all mechanical analysis. A mechanical system is an identified set of material objects. It may be a steel beam, the gas enclosed in the cylinder of an internal combustion engine, or the armature of an electric motor—mechanics admits the most diverse material systems imaginable. Once the system has been selected, however, there are two classes of objects in the universe: those that are part of the system and those that are not. The objects that are not part of the system exert forces on the system wherever they come in contact with it (and even, in the case of electromagnetic and gravitational effects, where there is no actual contact). These forces exerted on the system by something outside the system are known as *external forces*. Forces exerted on one part of the system by another part of the system are known as *internal forces*. The distinction is fundamental because, as we shall see, it is the external forces that are critical in the study of mechanical systems in equilibrium.

The foregoing definition of a system is the same as that which is employed in thermodynamics.* There, however, the "identified set of material objects" is usually a fluid. The boundary of the prescribed material often changes shape. This boundary, or some other boundary chosen to contain the material system, is said to enclose a *control volume*; a distinction is sometimes made between so-called *closed systems*, in which no material enters or leaves the control volume, and so-called *open systems*, for which such a mass change is possible. In statics we deal for the most part with solids. These fall naturally into the class of closed systems.

The first step in mechanical analysis, then, is the isolation of a system. This should be self-evident, perhaps, but lack of clear identification of the system is a common source of confusion and error. To aid in this identification a second step is made, which involves drawing a picture of the system and of all the external forces exerted on it. This picture is known as a *free-body diagram*. It is important that the student actually draw the free-body diagram and not merely imagine it. Teaching experience shows the folly of elaborate calculations based on a false concept of the physical system under investigation. In the free-body diagram the external forces are represented by a combination of arrow for direction and symbol for magnitude—either a literal symbol such as T or F, or a positive number. If coordinate axes are to be used, as they generally are when we come to grips with particular problems, the positive directions of these axes must appear upon the figure. Then, in writing the scalar equations of equilibrium (or of motion in general), a force component is entered as a positive quantity if its arrow in the free-body diagram points in the positive direction. If the arrow points

---

* See, e.g., J. H. Keenan, *Thermodynamics* (New York: John Wiley & Sons, Inc., 1949), p. 1, or N. A. Hall and W. E. Ibele, *Engineering Thermodynamics* (Englewood Cliffs, N.J.: Prentice-Hall, Inc., 1960), p. 4ff.

in the negative direction, the force component is entered as a negative quantity. Clearly, in the case of an unknown force which is itself the object of investigation, we must begin by assuming a direction for the arrow associated with the unknown force. Should the direction assumed be incorrect, the equations of equilibrium will subsequently indicate this because their solution will give a negative numerical value to the symbol representing the magnitude of the unknown force.

The mathematical model by means of which we choose to describe the behavior of a particular piece of engineering equipment may be as simple or as elaborate as is felt necessary for the purposes at hand. The particle model discussed in the first section of this chapter is useful as the representation of a pendulum bob or a piston or even the earth itself in some problems. In most examples dealt with in this text, however, we shall want to treat beams and shafts, airplanes, framed structures, and other products of engineering design which cannot be regarded as single particles. More will be said about models of extended systems later in this section, and in Section 2.5 we shall consider in detail the rigid-body model and the equilibrium conditions for it.

$$(a) \qquad\qquad\qquad (b)$$

Fig. 2.3-1

Let us consider some of the standard representations of interactions between systems by force vectors. The first force we consider is the gravitational force on an isolated particle. Suppose a particle P has mass m and is subjected to the gravitational attraction of another particle Q of mass M (Fig. 2.3-1a). Newton's *law of universal gravitation* asserts that the force on P due to Q has magnitude proportional to the product of the masses of the two particles and inversely proportional to the square of the distance between them. The direction of the force on P is from P toward Q. The constant of proportionality is the *universal gravitational constant* G, the same for any two bodies; the numerical value of G depends on the units of measurement used for mass, force, and distance. Let $\mathbf{r}$ be the position of P relative to Q; then $\mathbf{e}_r = \mathbf{r}/r$ is the unit vector from Q to P. The force function is then

$$\mathbf{F} = -\frac{GmM}{r^2}\mathbf{e}_r = -\frac{GmM}{r^3}\mathbf{r}. \qquad\qquad \textbf{2.3-1}$$

The force on Q due to P is, by the third law of motion or by the gravitational force law itself, the negative of $\mathbf{F}$. On a free-body diagram of P as our isolated system, the force $\mathbf{F}$ is shown as in Fig. 2.3-1b: an arrow from P to Q giving the direction of the force and a letter F representing the magnitude of the force. Since the form of the magnitude function, GmM/r^2, is known, we can also insert that as shown.

By assumption, every particle of matter in the universe exerts a gravitational attraction on every other. In most engineering problems, all gravitational attractions are neglected except that of the earth. In most problems, also, the anomalies of gravitation due to the non-uniformity of mass distribution in the earth, its non-spherical shape, and its rotation may be neglected. That is, we may treat the attraction of the earth on bodies exterior to it as though the earth were a particle of mass equal to the mass of the earth placed at the center of the earth. A particle of mass m in free fall near the surface of the earth has an acceleration $g = 32.2$ ft/sec^2 (a number accurate enough for most engineering purposes) and is subject to a force of magnitude GmM/R^2, where M is the mass of the earth and R is its mean radius. The second law of motion, $\mathbf{F} = m\mathbf{a}$, applied to the particle leads to $GmM/R^2 = mg$, or $g = GM/R^2$. The force $GmM/R^2 = mg$ is the *weight* force on the particle at the earth's surface. For a particle near the earth's surface, the gravitational force may be considered as a weight force of constant magnitude $W = mg$ directed toward the earth's center. Suppose the particle is at altitude h above the surface, or a distance $r = R + h$ from the center; its weight at that altitude has magnitude w given by

$$w = \frac{GmM}{r^2} = \frac{GmM}{(R+h)^2} = \frac{GmM}{R^2\left(1+\dfrac{h}{R}\right)^2} = \frac{mg}{\left(1+\dfrac{h}{R}\right)^2}. \qquad \textbf{2.3-2}$$

For small h/R ratios, i.e., small distances from the earth's surface, we can expand the denominator in a Taylor's series:

$$w = W\left(1+\frac{h}{R}\right)^{-2} \cong W\left[1 - 2\left(\frac{h}{R}\right) + 3\left(\frac{h}{R}\right)^2 - \cdots\right]. \qquad \textbf{2.3-3}$$

For $h/R \ll 1$, $w \cong W$, the weight at the surface. On a free-body diagram, the weight force is shown as an arrow pointing vertically downward and the constant magnitude is denoted by the symbol W (Fig. 2.3-2).

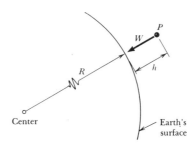

Fig. 2.3-2

In connection with gravitational forces, we may comment on the use of the words "light" and "heavy" in mechanics problems. The use of the word "light," even in dynamics problems, almost always means that the mass of the body may be neglected and the body may be considered as in equilibrium with no weight force acting on it. Physically, this usually means that the other loads or forces acting on the body are of so much greater magnitude than the weight force that the latter may be neglected in the analysis. "Heavy" does not have such a usual meaning; it always means that the weight force on that body must be considered if the body is part of the system. Sometimes it may mean that other weights may be neglected by comparison with it.

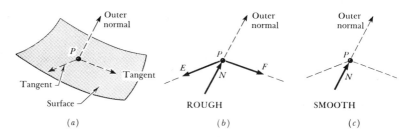

Fig. 2.3-3

Next we consider contact forces. Suppose a particle P, which can be fixed or moving, is in contact with a given surface, which can also be fixed or moving (Fig. 2.3-3a). When we isolate the particle, how is the effect of the surface on the particle represented as a contact force? Such a condition on the position of a point—in this case, that the position coordinates of the point must satisfy the equation of the surface—is known as a *constraint condition*, and the force exerted by the surface is a *constraint force* or *constraint reaction*. Here the constraint is *one-sided*; that is, the material that exerts the force on the particle lies on one side of the surface, and the constraint can be broken by lifting the particle. The surface may, in general, exert a force of arbitrary magnitude in an arbitrary direction in space, subject to a condition to be discussed shortly. The force is ordinarily represented in *normal* and *tangential* components. An *outer normal* direction away from the surface into space is supposed known, and a component of magnitude N (the *normal force*) acting on the particle (Figs. 2.3-3b, c) is drawn in that direction, as shown by the arrow. Once that direction is assumed, the one-sided nature of the constraint is established by the inequality $N \geqq 0$. That is, it is assumed that an inward force toward the surface cannot be exerted on the particle by the material surface. The other components of the force are given by the *tangential forces* of magnitudes E and F (Fig. 2.3-3b), which are drawn in orthogonal directions in the tangent plane to the surface at P. Such tangential forces are also called *frictional forces*; since the vectors **E** and **F** are orthogonal, the total friction force has magnitude $[E^2 + F^2]^{1/2}$. If non-zero frictional forces can be exerted on the particle, the surface is called *rough*; a *smooth* surface exerts only a normal force (Fig. 2.3-3c). In our first statical analyses, we shall assume smooth contacts for the most part. The laws of friction will be studied in Chapter V.

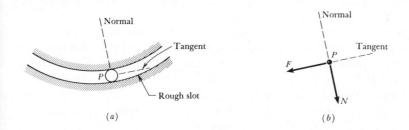

(a) (b)

Fig. 2.3-4

A *two-sided constraint* is exemplified by a particle constrained to move between two surfaces—a pin moving in a slot, for example. The representation of the contact force from both surfaces by a single vector of unknown magnitude and direction can be given by the division into normal and frictional components, with the normal force now unrestricted by the $N \geqq 0$ condition. But what does $N < 0$

mean? What is the "negative magnitude" of a vector? As mentioned earlier, if the solution of a problem gives $N < 0$, it simply means that the wrong direction for the vector **N** has been assumed originally.

Two-dimensional counterparts of the general surface contact problem are given by particles constrained to move in a given plane in contact with a curve or in a groove. Forces perpendicular to the plane are neglected and only forces in the plane are shown. Figure 2.3-4a shows a pin in a rough plane slot; Fig. 2.3-4b is a free-body diagram of the pin showing the normal and frictional reactions on it.

The force exerted by a cord or cable on a particle is a "one-sided" type of constraint force, because our basic assumption about "cords" is that they can transmit only a tensile force in a direction tangent to the cord. That is, the cable must be either taut or slack;

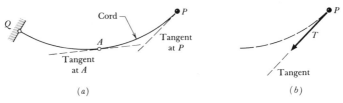

(a)

(b)

Fig. 2.3-5

when it is slack it transmits zero force, and when it is taut it transmits a tensile force. Consider our particle P at one end of a cord (Fig. 2.3-5a), the other end of which is at Q. When we isolate P (Fig. 2.3-5b), the effect of the cord is represented by a force of magnitude T and direction tangent to the cord and pointing from P toward the cord. If $T > 0$, the cord is taut; if $T = 0$, the cord is slack; and T can never be less than zero.

The fact that the cord does not exert a reactive force normal to itself is expressed by the statement that the cord is assumed to be *perfectly flexible* and has no *stiffness in shear*—that is, it does not transmit shear forces. We usually make two further idealizing assumptions about cords. We may assume the cord to be *inextensible*; i.e., neglect any stretching of the cord and assume its length to be constant. We may also assume the cord to be *light*; i.e., neglect its mass so that it is always in equilibrium. If a cable in equilibrium has a shape like that in Fig. 2.3-5a, some other force, such as the weight of the cable, must be acting on the cable. The light, inextensible cord is straight when it is taut and the force exerted by it is directed from P to the other end Q of the cord (Figs. 2.3-6a, b).

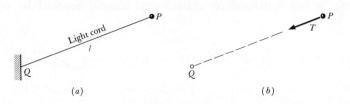

Fig. 2.3-6

A stiff rod, AB, with the particle P attached to end B while end A is attached to a foundation in some way (Fig. 2.3-7a) is a "two-sided" constraint in the sense that the force component tangent to the rod may be in either direction: tensile, as in Fig. 2.3-6b, or compressive, as N is shown to be in the free-body diagram (Fig. 2.3-7b) of the particle. A force normal to the rod—the shearing force Q of Fig. 2.3-7b—is also generally exerted. The assumptions of perfect flexibility, inextensibility, and lightness made for the cord have counterparts here. Usually in elementary work inextensibility

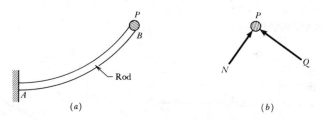

Fig. 2.3-7

and *no* flexibility in shear are assumed to hold; these are expressed by saying that AB is *rigid*, i.e., that any two points in the bar are always the same distance apart. If we assume also that the rigid bar is *light*, again neglecting its mass, we can replace N and Q by a single force having line of action AB (Figs. 2.3-8a, b); the reason for this will be given in the next section, where such "two-force" members will be discussed.

The elastic spring is the next fundamental element we wish to discuss. An elastic body is, roughly, one that deforms under load in such a way that it recovers its initial shape at once when the loads are removed. The only such body we shall consider here is the *ideal linear spring.* The ideal spring is considered to be massless and hence always in equilibrium. When no force is applied to the spring, it has a natural or undeformed length, denoted by l_0 (Fig.

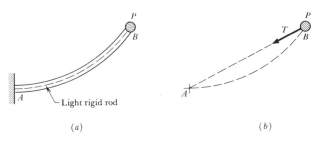

Fig. 2.3-8

2.3-9a). Suppose one end is fixed to a foundation point and a force is applied at the other end; the line of action of the force is the line joining the ends of the spring (Fig. 2.3-9). Under the action of **F**, the spring changes length to a final length l. The extension, or deformation, of the spring is $e = l - l_0$, positive when **F** is tensile

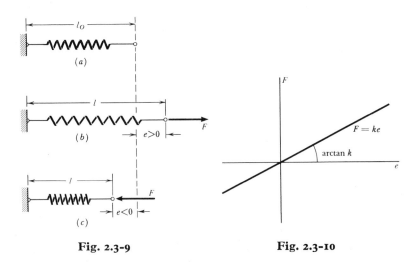

Fig. 2.3-9   **Fig. 2.3-10**

(Fig. 2.3-9b) and negative when **F** is compressive (Fig. 2.3-9c). Thus, if we draw the force always as a tensile force as in Fig. 2.3-9b, then a negative magnitude F will correspond to a compressive force and a negative extension e.

If F is plotted against e (Fig. 2.3-10), we shall assume that the graph is a straight line (linear elasticity) with slope k. The number k is known as the *spring constant*, with dimensions force/length; k and the unstretched length l_0 are the properties of the ideal linear spring which, together with the geometry of the spring, are needed to specify the spring force. The adjective "linear" in "ideal linear spring" refers, by the way, to the fact that the spring is considered to lie along a straight line and transmit a force along that line, not to the fact that the force-deformation graph is linear. Later we shall consider the ideal *torsional* spring which transmits a pure torque, and "linear" is to be contrasted with "torsional."

An analytical expression can be written for the spring force on a particle as a function of the relative position of the ends of the spring. If the particle P is attached to one end of the spring while the other end is at Q (Fig. 2.3-11a), with $\mathbf{r}$ the position of P relative to Q, then

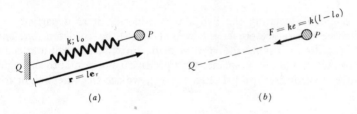

(a)   (b)

Fig. 2.3-11

the force on P due to the spring is represented on the free-body diagram (Fig. 2.3-11b) by an arrow pointing toward Q and a magnitude $F = ke$ (supposing the spring to be in tension). The vector $\mathbf{F}$ has the opposite direction to $\mathbf{r}$ and has magnitude equal to the product of the spring constant k and the extension $e = l - l_0$, where l is the magnitude of $\mathbf{r} = l\mathbf{e}_r$. Therefore, the force on the particle is

$$\mathbf{F} = -k(l - l_0)\mathbf{e}_r = -k(\mathbf{r} - \mathbf{r}_0) \qquad \textbf{2.3-4}$$

where $\mathbf{r}_0 = l_0\mathbf{e}_r$. It is easy to see that the compressive case $(e < 0)$ is also properly represented by this. Since the force *on the particle* always "points back" to a position where the spring is unstretched, the spring force is sometimes called a *restoring force*.

Before considering the isolation of systems containing more than a single particle, let us work a few examples utilizing the force functions considered so far.

Example 2.3-1

A small ball weighing 5 lb rests on a smooth incline of slope angle 20°; *it is held in position by a light inextensible cord which is fastened at its other end at a point such that the taut cord makes an angle of* 30° *with the vertical (Fig. 2.3-12). Draw the free-body diagram of the particle; introduce a coordinate system and write the force vectors in components.*

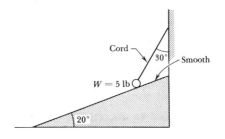

Fig. 2.3-12

Solution: Isolating the ball and considering it as a particle, we see that three forces act on it: the weight force, the cord tension, and the slope reaction. Taking the vertical plane through the ball and the other end of the cord as the *xy*-plane, with positive *x* horizontal to the right and positive *y* vertically upward (Fig. 2.3-13), we see that the weight force is

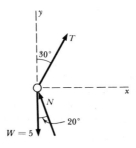

Fig. 2.3-13

known in magnitude and direction, while the cord tension and the normal reaction of the smooth incline are known only in direction. The three forces, with all pertinent information, are shown in the complete free-body diagram 2.3-13. The analytical expressions for the forces are

$$\mathbf{W} = -5\mathbf{j}, \quad \mathbf{T} = T(\sin 30°\mathbf{i} + \cos 30°\mathbf{j}), \quad \mathbf{N} = N(-\sin 20°\mathbf{i} + \cos 20°\mathbf{j}).$$

Since the unit of *W* is the pound, *T* and *N* should be given in that unit also.

Example 2.3-2

Three identical springs of constant k and unstretched length a are attached to a particle of weight W. The other ends of the springs are attached to a horizontal ceiling at the vertices of an equilateral triangle of side b (Fig. 2.3-14). The particle is found to be in equilibrium at a distance h below the ceiling. What is the free-body diagram of the particle? What is the force in each spring?

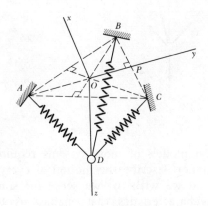

Fig. 2.3-14

Solution: Four forces act on the isolated particle: three spring forces and the weight force. Because of the symmetry of *both* geometrical *and* spring-force characteristic conditions, we may assume that all (tensile) spring forces have the same magnitude and that the particle will be on the vertical line through the centroid of the equilateral triangle. The free-body diagram is given in Fig. 2.3-15, where axes have been chosen as in Fig. 2.3-14: positive z vertically downward, positive y along an altitude of the triangle, and positive x parallel to a side so that (x, y, z) form a right-handed system. There remains only to compute the magnitude F of each spring force. The locations of the points A, B, and C relative to the axes are given in Fig. 2.3-15, from the properties of an equilateral triangle. The lengths of all three springs are given by

$$\left[h^2 + \left(\frac{b\sqrt{3}}{3}\right)^2\right]^{\frac{1}{2}} = \left[h^2 + \left(\frac{b\sqrt{3}}{6}\right)^2 + \left(\frac{b}{2}\right)^2\right]^{\frac{1}{2}} = \left[h^2 + \frac{b^2}{3}\right]^{\frac{1}{2}}.$$

Therefore,

$$F = k\left\{\left[h^2 + \frac{b^2}{3}\right]^{\frac{1}{2}} - a\right\}.$$

The relation between the distance h and the weight W of the particle can now be found from the equilibrium equation in the vertical direction.

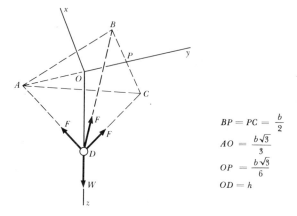

$$BP = PC = \frac{b}{2}$$

$$AO = \frac{b\sqrt{3}}{3}$$

$$OP = \frac{b\sqrt{3}}{6}$$

$$OD = h$$

Fig. 2.3-15

Mathematical models of most systems require more than one particle. We cannot describe the motion of every point in a complex body, nor do we wish to; we settle for some description of average motion characteristics that enables us to say something meaningful about the system. Moreover, we may not be able to write down appropriate expressions for the force interactions in all cases. It is for such systems that the multiparticle and continuous models are made, and where the third law of motion becomes important for developing the governing principles and equations.

    Let us start with a system that we model as two particles: the earth and the moon, perhaps. Each particle has its own free-body diagram as a separate isolated system; we take, as a first free-body

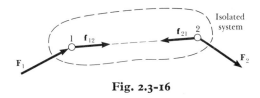

Fig. 2.3-16

diagram of the two-particle system, the two diagrams together. Let the internal force on the first particle due to the second particle be denoted by $\mathbf{f}_{12}$ and the force on the second due to the first, by $\mathbf{f}_{21}$. Let the resultant external force on the first particle (due to all other bodies except the second) be $\mathbf{F}_1$, and the corresponding force on the second particle be $\mathbf{F}_2$ (Fig. 2.3-16). The third law of motion tells us that $\mathbf{f}_{12} = -\mathbf{f}_{21}$ and that the forces are collinear. Because of the third law, we shall find that we can express the principles of motion and equilibrium in terms of the external forces only. This means that, on a free-body diagram, we need only show the external forces; for the two-particle system of Fig. 2.3-16, a second free-body diagram of this type would therefore show only $\mathbf{F}_1$ and $\mathbf{F}_2$.

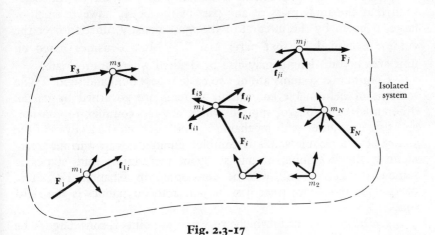

Fig. 2.3-17

The general discrete multiparticle system has a free-body diagram, including internal forces, of the schematic type of Fig. 2.3-17; if internal forces need not be considered, then they need not be shown on the diagram. The system here consists of N particles. We speak of the typical element as the i-th particle where i has the numerical range (i.e., may take on any of the values) 1, 2, 3,... N. The i-th particle has mass m_i and position $\mathbf{r}_i$. The resultant external force on the i-th particle is $\mathbf{F}_i$. If another particle, say number j, with mass m_j is located at $\mathbf{r}_j$, then the relative position of the i-th with respect to the j-th is $\mathbf{r}_i - \mathbf{r}_j$, which we denote by $\mathbf{r}_{ij}$. The internal force on the i-th due to the j-th is $\mathbf{f}_{ij}$; by the third law, $\mathbf{f}_{ji} = -\mathbf{f}_{ij}$. The resultant internal force $\mathbf{f}_i$ on the i-th particle is the sum of the $\mathbf{f}_{ij}$ over all other particles j, $j \neq i$:

$$\mathbf{f}_i = \sum_{\substack{j=1 \\ j \neq i}}^{N} \mathbf{f}_{ij}, \quad i = 1, 2,... N. \qquad \text{2.3-5}$$

No force functions other than those similar to the types we have described already need be introduced for such a multiparticle system.

The important steps are (1) the isolation of a system with a clear statement, through the use of the free-body diagram, of just what is included in the system, and (2) a clear identification of the external, and sometimes the internal, forces acting on the system.

Most often, the many-particle model we make is that of a *continuous system*, or continuum. We ignore the atomic or molecular constitution of matter and say that we may consider the mass of a body to be given by a density function ρ of position in the body such that the total mass of any part of the body, however small or large, is given by the integral of the mass density function over the volume occupied by that part: $\int_V \rho \, dV$. Mass densities based on unit area or unit length may also be defined where appropriate.

Continuous systems are of two basic types: fluid and solid. The motions of deformable continuous systems are governed by partial differential equations of motion which are too complex to consider at a first encounter with mechanics. Indeed, even the analysis of the statics of deformable solids is complex enough not to warrant treatment at the beginning of our study of mechanics; fluid statics is somewhat simpler and will be considered in Chapter IV. The continuous model we treat first in statics and dynamics is the rigid solid.

A *rigid body* is one in which every pair of points is considered to be at a constant distance apart at all times. Such a model is an excellent first approximation to the behavior of real solids for the analysis of many engineering problems. Some of the reasons for its mathematical usefulness and simplicity in theoretical work will be brought out later both in statics and in dynamics. It must not be forgotten, however, that its utility as a concept is based on its practicality as well as on theory. Our interest in the rigid body is a natural result of the fact that, for many well-designed engineering products, deformations are small and do not affect the mechanical analysis. The student should appreciate, however, that model systems consisting of rigid parts will not serve for all purposes. The rigid model would not enable us to determine internal stresses in most cases and would be completely inappropriate for the purposes, say, of fluid mechanics. The principles of statics apply to any of the mathematical models; it is only for the rigid body, however, that we may base our analysis in many cases on the principles of statics alone without the need for supplementary physical hypotheses.

Besides the forces due to the connections we have discussed already, which may equally well connect points on two extended bodies, there are a number of others that may be mentioned. Some

of the commoner ones are shown in Fig. 2.3.18. The symbolic
representation of the connection is shown in the left-hand column.
The free-body diagram of the attached member, in the vicinity of
the connection, is shown in the second column. It should be noted

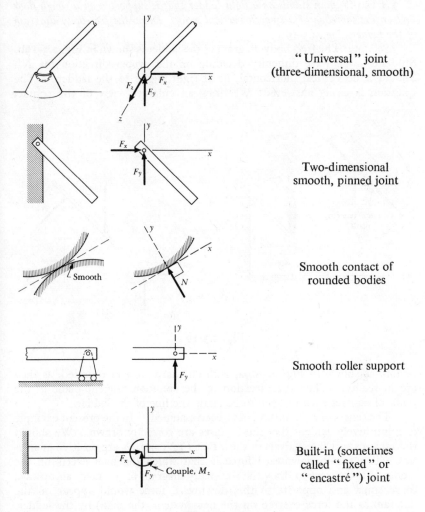

"Universal" joint
(three-dimensional, smooth)

Two-dimensional
smooth, pinned joint

Smooth contact of
rounded bodies

Smooth roller support

Built-in (sometimes
called "fixed" or
"encastré") joint

Fig. 2.3-18

that at the built-in joint the forces shown are due to a distribution
over the end face of the horizontal member; these forces give rise
to a moment about the z-axis as well as to forces in the x- and y-
directions. Also, if the connections given are rough instead of

smooth, couples as well as the forces shown should be considered as applied to the members.

Example 2.3-3

A 150-lb man stands on a light ladder that is supported on a rough floor and on the top edge of a smooth vertical wall. Draw the free-body diagram of the ladder (Fig. 2.3-19).

Solution: The free-body diagram of the ladder is shown in Fig. 2.3-19b. Students often have difficulty deciding on the proper direction for N_2. Should it be vertical, horizontal, or at right angles to the ladder? The question is easily answered: We draw an enlarged view of the contact

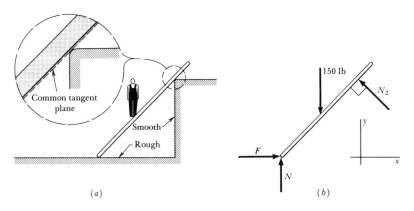

Fig. 2.3-19

region, as shown in Fig. 2.3-19a, with all sharp corners rounded, as they are in reality. Then the direction of the common tangent plane at the point of contact is easily seen to be along the line of the ladder.

The senses of F, N and N_2 have been assumed. In the present example it is intuitively evident that these senses are correctly drawn. We should therefore expect the analysis to show that F, N, and N_2 are positive quantities. The 150-lb downward force is that which the man exerts on the ladder. If we were to draw the free-body diagram of the man, an upward force equal and opposite to this downward force would appear on the diagram as the force exerted on the new system (the man) by the ladder. There would also appear on the free-body diagram of the man a downward force of 150 lb exerted on him by the gravitational attraction of the earth.

Example 2.3-4

Suppose that the smooth wall of the previous example is high enough so that the ladder cannot reach its upper edge and must, instead, rest against the side of the wall (Fig. 2.3-20a). Draw the free-body diagram of the ladder.

Solution: The free-body diagram for the ladder is shown in Fig. 2.3-20b. Note that the force N_2 exerted by the wall on the ladder is now

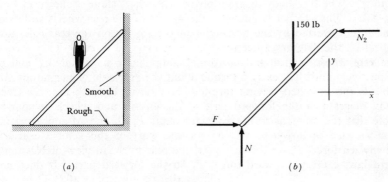

Fig. 2.3-20

horizontal. The student should sketch a magnified view of the neighborhood of the contact to assure himself that the tangent plane at the point of contact is now vertical. Of course the numerical values of F, N, and N_2 will be different in this case than in that of Fig. 2.3-19.

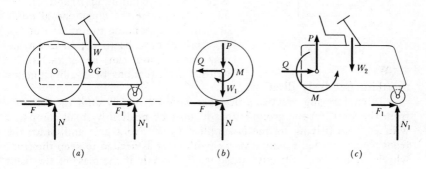

Fig. 2.3-21

Example 2.3-5

Draw the free-body diagram (a) of a light farm tractor, (b) of its rear wheels and axle, and (c) of its chassis and front wheels.

Solution: The free-body diagram of the tractor is shown in Fig. 2.3-21a. The downward force W is the weight of the entire tractor. This force is actually the resultant of a distributed force, acting on every particle of the system.   As we shall see, and as is probably well known to the student through his study of elementary physics, this distributed force may be replaced by a concentrated one acting through the mass center.   The point G must therefore be the mass center of the entire tractor.   Since the ground is rough, we have, in general, both a normal and a frictional force exerted at the ground contact.   The free-body diagram of the rear wheel alone is shown in Fig. 2.3-21b.   The symbol W_1 denotes the weight of the rear wheels and axle. The forces exerted by the remainder of the tractor on the rear axle now appear on the diagram, since these are now external forces.   They have a resultant whose vertical and horizontal components are denoted P and Q respectively and they exert a torque about the rear axle of magnitude M. This is the so-called driving torque.   Finally, in Fig. 2.3-21c, the free-body diagram of the forward part of the chassis and wheels is shown. Note that the moment and force components P, Q, and M appear again, *now reversed in direction.*   If the forward part of the vehicle exerts a downward force, P, on the rear part, the rear must, in view of Newton's third law, exert an upward force, P, on the forward part.   It does not matter that the directions of P, Q, and M are unknown.   What is essential is that the assumptions made in drawing the free-body diagrams must not embody any implicit violation of the third law.   The attentive student will have noticed that Figs. 2.3-21a, b, and c are not independent.   In fact, Fig. 2.3-21a may be regarded as the result of combining (b) and (c).   It follows that, once the equations of equilibrium corresponding to any two of (a), (b), and (c) have been written down, no new information can be extracted by writing the equations of equilibrium for the third free-body diagram.

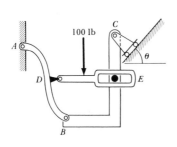

Fig. 2.3-22

In engineering practice a designer would probably omit the force F_1 from the start, on the grounds that it must be negligibly small compared with F.   No driving torque is supplied to the front axle and, since the front wheels are light, only a very small torque is needed to keep the front wheels in motion.   Strictly speaking, $F_1 = 0$ only if the mass of the front wheels is negligible.

Example 2.3-6

   Draw the free-body diagrams for members AB, BC, and DE of the plane framework shown in Fig. 2.3-22.   Neglect the weights of the members and all friction.

   Solution: The free-body diagrams are shown in Fig. 2.3-23.   The only point that requires comment is associated with the direction of the force exerted on bar *BC* at *C*.   This force must be directed upward and

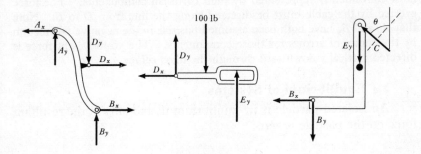

Fig. 2.3-23

to the left rather than downward to the right.   If, on analysis, it should
appear that the force C is negative, the rollers would, in reality, lift off
the base.   A support such as that at C is an example of a one-sided constraint.   At A, on the other hand, the forces of constraint may turn out
to be either positive or negative without affecting the applicability of the
analysis.

Example **2.3-7**

The tailgate of a truck is a uniform rectangle $ABCD$ weighing 50 lb.
It is hinged at A and B and supported at an angle θ to the horizontal by a
cable connected to the tailgate at D and to the truck at a point E vertically
above B.   Draw the free-body diagram of the tailgate.

Solution: The free-body diagram is shown in Fig. 2.3-24.   The hinges
at A and B can each supply a force with any direction: these forces are

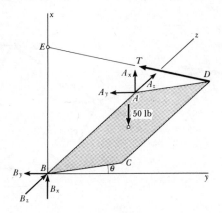

Fig. 2.3-24

most conveniently represented by their cartesian components. The force exerted by the cable must be directed along the line from D to E. Note that A_y and B_y have both been assumed positive in the negative y-direction by the choice of arrows for those components. The 50-lb weight force is directed vertically downward through the mass center.

2.4 Equilibrium of Systems

An isolated particle is in equilibrium if, and only if, the resultant force on the particle is zero:

$$F = \sum_{i=1}^{n} F_i = 0. \qquad\qquad 2.4\text{-}1$$

The vector equation of equilibrium 2.4-1 is equivalent to three scalar *equations of equilibrium.* We may, therefore, solve Eq. 2.4-1 for, at most, three independent scalar unknowns.

The equilibrium condition for a particle is a necessary and sufficient condition: if the particle is in equilibrium, the resultant force necessarily vanishes; and it is sufficient that the resultant force vanish in order that the particle be in equilibrium. This follows from the first law of motion and the meaning of the term equilibrium. As a consequence, if the particle is in equilibrium, the moment of the resultant force about any point, and hence about any axis, in space is zero. The fact that the resultant, F, has no moment about some particular point, however, does not ensure that $F = 0$; the point might be on the line of action of F.

Now consider an isolated multiparticle system like that of Fig. 2.3-17, repeated here as Fig. 2.4-1. A necessary condition for the

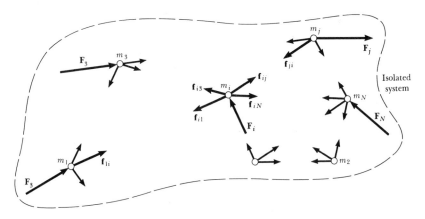

Fig. 2.4-1

equilibrium of such a system is the vanishing of the resultant external force, i.e., of the formal vector sum of the external forces on each particle. We assume that the system is in equilibrium. We recall that this means for a system that there is an inertial frame of reference with respect to which every particle is at rest. Since each particle is individually in equilibrium, Eq. 2.4-1 holds for each one. For the i-th particle, the resultant force is the sum of the resultant external force, $\mathbf{F}_i$, and the resultant internal force, $\mathbf{f}_i$; the latter, in turn, is the sum of the internal forces, $\mathbf{f}_{ij}$, on the i-th particle (as given by Eq. 2.3-5):

$$\mathbf{f}_i = \sum_{\substack{j=1 \\ j \neq i}}^{N} \mathbf{f}_{ij}.$$

The restriction that $j \neq i$ may be removed by defining the symbol $\mathbf{f}_{ii}$ to be the zero vector $\mathbf{o}$. Then the equilibrium equations for the separate particles may be written

$$\mathbf{F}_i + \sum_{j=1}^{N} \mathbf{f}_{ij} = \mathbf{o}, \quad i = 1, 2, 3, \ldots N. \qquad \text{2.4-2}$$

These N vector equations are equivalent to $3N$ scalar equations. We may now eliminate the internal forces by adding the N equations vectorially:

$$\sum_{i=1}^{N} \mathbf{F}_i + \sum_{i=1}^{N} \sum_{j=1}^{N} \mathbf{f}_{ij} = \mathbf{o}. \qquad \text{2.4-3}$$

The first term is the resultant, $\mathbf{F}$, of the external forces only. The second term is the resultant internal force, and we assert that this vanishes. For, in the terms where i and j are the same, $\mathbf{f}_{ii} = \mathbf{o}$ by definition; and where $i \neq j$, the terms vanish in pairs. Consider $\mathbf{f}_{ij}$, the force exerted on particle i by particle j; it may be paired off in the double summation with the force $\mathbf{f}_{ji}$ exerted on particle j by particle i. In view of Newton's third law, these are negatives of one another and therefore the sum of them is zero. Therefore, all the non-zero terms in the double sum may be rearranged so that the sum of each pair vanishes. We have shown the desired result:

If a system of particles is in equilibrium, the resultant external force is zero:

$$\mathbf{F} = \mathbf{o}. \qquad \text{2.4-4}$$

The same principle may be extended to continuous systems immediately, providing we assume that the internal forces in a continuous system obey the third law of motion and are of such magnitude as to keep accelerations finite. While $\mathbf{F} = \mathbf{0}$ for any system which is in equilibrium, the fact that $\mathbf{F} = \mathbf{0}$ does not assure that the system will, in fact, be in equilibrium. If we imagine a system consisting of two particles connected by a spring, and if we stretch the spring, release the particles, and suppose that all effects other than the spring may be ignored, the external force on the system particles-and-spring is zero. The individual particles are certainly not in equilibrium. For a system consisting of either particle alone, there is an external force exerted by the spring.

Another necessary condition for the equilibrium of a multiparticle or a continuous mechanical system is the vanishing of the resultant moment of the external forces about any point whatever. To prove this, we suppose the system of Fig. 2.4-1 is in equilibrium with the i-th particle at rest at position $\mathbf{r}_i$ relative to an arbitrary point O fixed in the inertial frame. Since each particle is in equilibrium, the resultant moment about O of the forces on the particle is zero; the N moment equations are

$$\mathbf{r}_i \times \mathbf{F}_i + \mathbf{r}_i \times \left(\sum_{j=1}^{N} \mathbf{f}_{ij} \right) = \mathbf{0}, \quad i = 1, 2, 3, \ldots N. \qquad 2.4\text{-}5$$

Add the N equations, as was done with the force equations 2.4-2; then we have

$$\sum_{i=1}^{N} \mathbf{r}_i \times \mathbf{F}_i + \sum_{i=1}^{N} \left\{ \mathbf{r}_i \times \left(\sum_{j=1}^{N} \mathbf{f}_{ij} \right) \right\} = \mathbf{0}. \qquad 2.4\text{-}6$$

The first sum is the sum of the moment vectors of the external forces; we define this to be the *resultant external moment* about O, $\mathbf{M}_O$. The second sum is the resultant internal moment, and this vanishes as does the resultant internal force. Rearrange the summation:

$$\sum_{i=1}^{N} \left\{ \mathbf{r}_i \times \left(\sum_{j=1}^{N} \mathbf{f}_{ij} \right) \right\} = \sum_{i=1}^{N} \sum_{j=1}^{N} (\mathbf{r}_i \times \mathbf{f}_{ij}).$$

Each term with $i = j$ is zero since $\mathbf{f}_{ii} = \mathbf{0}$. To each term with $i \neq j$, add the corresponding term with i and j interchanged:

$$\mathbf{r}_i \times \mathbf{f}_{ij} + \mathbf{r}_j \times \mathbf{f}_{ji}.$$

Since $\mathbf{f}_{ji} = -\mathbf{f}_{ij}$, we have

$$\mathbf{r}_i \times \mathbf{f}_{ij} + \mathbf{r}_j \times \mathbf{f}_{ji} = \mathbf{r}_i \times \mathbf{f}_{ij} + \mathbf{r}_j \times (-\mathbf{f}_{ij}) = (\mathbf{r}_i - \mathbf{r}_j) \times \mathbf{f}_{ij}.$$

But $\mathbf{r}_i - \mathbf{r}_j = \mathbf{r}_{ij}$, the position vector of m_i relative to m_j, and this is parallel to $\mathbf{f}_{ij}$. Therefore, the non-zero terms in the internal moment sum also vanish by pairs.   The extension of the result to continuous systems again follows from the hypotheses on internal forces, and we have the result:

If a system is in equilibrium, the resultant moment of the external forces only about any point fixed in an inertial frame must be zero:

$$\mathbf{M}_O = \mathbf{0}. \qquad\qquad\qquad 2.4\text{-}7$$

The equations of equilibrium 2.4-4 and 2.4-7 in vector or equivalent scalar form are the equations with which we shall work. There are no other independent equations involving external forces only that can be written, although we shall look at some other equations equivalent to these.   The force equation and the moment equation with respect to one point are the only independent ones; adding another moment equation with respect to a second point may be useful but will give no information not contained in or implied by $\mathbf{F} = \mathbf{0}$ and $\mathbf{M}_O = \mathbf{0}$.   Higher-order moments $[\mathbf{r} \times (\mathbf{r} \times \mathbf{F})]$ do not help in three-dimensional space, since any vector can be expressed in components in three independent directions only, say the directions of $\mathbf{r}$, $\mathbf{F}$, and $\mathbf{M} = \mathbf{r} \times \mathbf{F}$.

We shall consider two examples of the application of the equilibrium equations before turning to a more detailed study of the equilibrium of a rigid body.   These examples introduce the useful concepts of the *two-force* and *three-force* members.

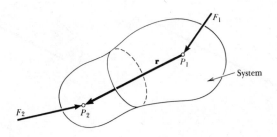

Fig. 2.4-2

Example 2.4-1

Show that if a system is in equilibrium with but two external forces acting on it, the forces must be equal in magnitude, be opposite in direction, and have the same line of action which passes through their points of application.

Solution: Suppose the system is isolated and its free-body diagram drawn with but two external forces acting on it, $\mathbf{F}_1$ at P_1 and $\mathbf{F}_2$ at P_2 (Fig. 2.4-2).   Since the system is given in equilibrium, Eq. 2.4-4 holds:

$F_1 + F_2 = 0$, or $F_1 = -F_2 = F$. The magnitudes F_1 and F_2 are equal; the directions are opposed. The two forces must, therefore, constitute at most a couple (Fig. 2.4-3). The resultant external moment about any

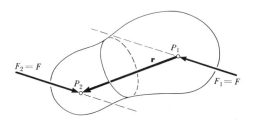

Fig. 2.4-3

point must vanish also (Eq. 2.4-7). Take P_1 as the base point for moments and r as the vector from P_1 to P_2; then F_1 has no moment about P_1, and the moment equilibrium equation is

$$M_{P_1} = r \times F_2 = 0.$$

By hypothesis, $F_2 \neq 0$; therefore either $r = 0$ or r and F_2 are parallel. If the latter is true, the line of action of F_2, and hence of F_1, is the same as the line of r, i.e., the line P_1P_2 (Fig. 2.4-4a). If $r = 0$, P_1 and P_2 coincide, the two forces are applied at the same point, and, since they are negatives of one another, they necessarily have the same line of action (Fig. 2.4-4b).

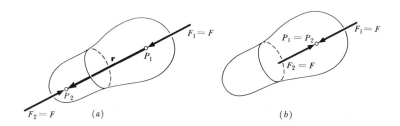

Fig. 2.4-4

    Bodies subject to just two external forces are known as *two-force members*. If a two-force member is in equilibrium, we know what the line of action of the forces on it must be and need not solve for the direction. In splitting up complex systems, when we remove a two-force member, we need only represent the equivalent mechanical action by appropriate force vectors in the known direction with (usually) unknown magnitudes. We have already encountered some simple two-force members in the last section: the ideal spring, the light cord, and the light rigid rod loaded at its

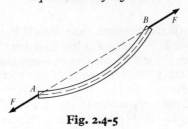

Fig. 2.4-5

ends.   For instance, the light rod of Fig. 2.3-8 will have a free-body diagram as in Fig. 2.4-5.

Example 2.4-2

If a system is in equilibrium under three external forces, show that the force vectors must be coplanar and concurrent or coplanar and parallel.

Solution: Let Fig. 2.4-6 be the free-body diagram of the isolated system

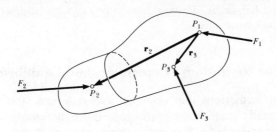

Fig. 2.4-6

in equilibrium. Take moments about P_1, with $\mathbf{r}_2$ and $\mathbf{r}_3$ the position vectors of P_2 and P_3:

$$\mathbf{r}_2 \times \mathbf{F}_2 + \mathbf{r}_3 \times \mathbf{F}_3 = \mathbf{0}.$$

Since $\mathbf{r}_2 \times \mathbf{F}_2 = -\mathbf{r}_3 \times \mathbf{F}_3$, the line normal to the plane of $\mathbf{r}_2$ and $\mathbf{F}_2$ is the same as the line normal to the plane of $\mathbf{r}_3$ and $\mathbf{F}_3$.   Both these planes pass

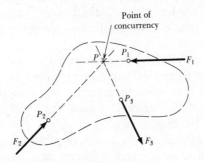

Fig. 2.4-7

through P_1 and so are in fact the same plane: $\mathbf{F}_2$ and $\mathbf{F}_3$ lie in the same plane. Since $\mathbf{F}_1 + \mathbf{F}_2 + \mathbf{F}_3 = \mathbf{0}$, $\mathbf{F}_1 = -(\mathbf{F}_2 + \mathbf{F}_3)$ has direction that is parallel to the plane of the other two. Since $\mathbf{F}_1$ has line of action through P_1, it must lie in the plane of the other two. The three force vectors are coplanar, in the plane of points P_1, P_2, and P_3. Let us look at that plane (Fig. 2.4-7), which is a section of the body shown in Fig. 2.4-6. Either $\mathbf{F}_1$ and $\mathbf{F}_2$ are parallel or they are not. If they are not, since they are in the same plane their lines of action must intersect at some point P. Using P as a base point for moments, then, only $\mathbf{F}_3$ could have a moment. Since this must vanish for equilibrium, the line of action of $\mathbf{F}_3$ must also pass through P and the three forces have lines of action that intersect at P, i.e., they are concurrent. If $\mathbf{F}_1$ is parallel to $\mathbf{F}_2$, then $\mathbf{F}_3$ is also parallel to these since $\mathbf{F}_3 = -(\mathbf{F}_1 + \mathbf{F}_2)$. The three parallel lines of action could be said to be concurrent, also, if we admit a point at infinity as the point of concurrency.

Bodies subjected to three external forces are called *three-force members*; the knowledge that the forces must be concurrent and coplanar for equilibrium is often helpful in drawing free-body diagrams and writing appropriate moment equations.

2.5 The Rigid Body: Constraints and Equilibrium

The deformations that occur in well-designed structures under load are usually small in comparison with the dimensions of the body when it is not loaded. For many engineering purposes, as we have remarked, we take a rigid body as the appropriate model of the system or of part of the system. The ideal rigid body is characterized by internal constraints on its motion, which keep every pair of points at a constant distance apart throughout the motion. As we shall see, this assumption has important consequences in the mathematical theory of mechanics. But the simplifications in the mathematics that arise from the hypothesis of rigidity are not the primary justification for introducing the concept of the rigid body. The fact that the engineering applications of rigid-body motion analysis have proved to be useful and most satisfactory for many purposes provides that justification.

The basic simplification that the rigid body introduces into dynamical theory is one of sufficiency. That is, the equations of motion—and, for our immediate purposes, of equilibrium in particular—in terms of the external forces alone are sufficient for the determination of the motion of a rigid body. The analysis of motion and equilibrium of deformable bodies requires additional hypotheses about the nature of the internal forces, i.e., requires assumptions about the material properties of the body. The rigidity hypothesis allows us to ignore the nature of the material of which the rigid body is formed.

We shall not prove that the six independent scalar equations of equilibrium in terms of external forces and couples are sufficient to ensure rigid-body equilibrium. That is a task for dynamics,[*] following a discussion of the kinematics of a rigid body and the development of the full equations of motion. The general argument of the proof may be described briefly, however. It consists in showing that by the assignation of values to six independent scalar position coordinates a rigid body can be completely restrained from moving.

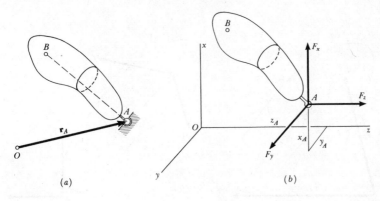

Fig. 2.5-1

Six equations would be needed to determine these position coordinates if they were unknown; the equilibrium equations are special forms of the general equations of motion sufficient for the task.

How can we fix the position of a rigid body? First of all, we can fix the position $\mathbf{r}_A$ of some point A in the body. This is equivalent to fixing the values of three scalar quantities, say the cartesian components (x_A, y_A, z_A) of the position of A. By doing this, we have prevented translational motion of the body as a whole; the only motion still permitted for the body is a rotational motion about A as a "pivot point." That is, the rigidity of the body requires that any other point, B, in the body must move on a spherical surface about A, the radius of the sphere on which B moves being the distance AB. The smooth ball-and-socket joint (Fig. 2.5-1a) of the last section

---

[*] See *Dynamics*, Section 6.8.

will constrain point A in the desired fashion. On a free-body diagram of the body, the connection at A is represented as shown in Fig. 2.5-1b in terms of the cartesian components (F_x, F_y, F_z) of the constraint force $\mathbf{F}$.

Let us now continue further to fix the location of the body. Let us also prescribe the position $\mathbf{r}_B$ of a second point B. We cannot, however, prescribe the three components of $\mathbf{r}_B$ independently, for B must be a constant distance from A if the body is rigid. Only two new independent scalar quantities have been fixed. Equivalently, what we have done is to fix the direction from A to B, i.e., fixed the direction of the axis AB in space. A way of doing this is to introduce a *smooth sleeve bearing* at B with the axis of the bearing

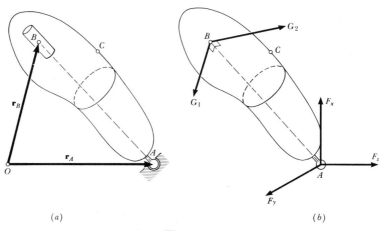

(a)   (b)

Fig. 2.5-2

along AB. The bearing provides a reaction force $\mathbf{G}$ normal to the line AB, with two independent components G_1, G_2, when the body is isolated (Fig. 2.5-2).

With these two constraints, the only way the body can move is by rotation about the axis AB. Now fix the body entirely by requiring a plane ABC in the body to be fixed in space. Fixing the position $\mathbf{r}_C$ of C does not require three additional independent scalars, but only one, to be prescribed; for the coordinates of C are subject to the internal constraints that the distances from A and B to C must be constant. By placing a smooth roller at C between parallel planes, such a constraint is obtained; when the body is isolated, the constraint is represented by a force $\mathbf{H}$ normal to the planes (Fig. 2.5-3).

Once three such points are fixed by the assignation of values to six independent generalized position coordinates, the position of any other point in the body is fixed by the rigidity condition and the geometry of the body.   There are, of course, other means of providing the necessary geometrical constraints than by the three particular ones mentioned above; in the examples and exercises, others will be used.   The important point is that six independent kinematical quantities determine general rigid-body motion, and that there are exactly six independent equations of motion in terms of external forces and couples.   It is on this basis that we may argue that the equilibrium equations in terms of external loads are both necessary and sufficient for rigid-body equilibrium.

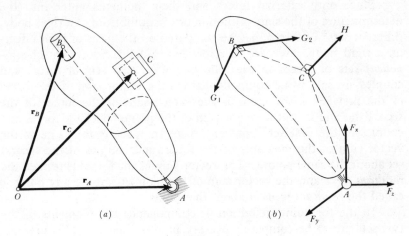

Fig. 2.5-3

One consequence of the fact that only formal vector sums of external forces and their moments are needed for the determination of rigid-body motion and equilibrium is the so-called *principle of transmissibility* of force.   As we have seen in Chapter I, any vector may be considered as a "free" vector for purposes of vector addition if that is the only principle of combination of vectors we wish to use; and any vector may be considered as a "sliding" vector if we also wish to preserve the moment of the vector about a point.   That is, the vector may be considered to act at any point along its line of action and it will still have the same moment about any point of space. Since only the sums of force vectors and of their moments are of concern in the equations governing rigid bodies, any external force *acting on a rigid body* may be considered to be a "sliding" vector.

The mechanical effects of the force on the rigid body are independent of the point of application of the force on its line of action. This transmissibility of force in its motional effects is limited to its effect on a single rigid body, and does not hold for non-rigid systems, or indeed for the submembers of a complex rigid system such as a truss. "Transmissibility" of external forces may, of course, be used for computing the moments needed in the over-all equations that necessarily govern any system in equilibrium. But we must not forget that the forces have effects on bodies that are not rigid other than those given by their vectorial resultant and moment.

2.6 Equipollent Sets of Forces; Reduction of Sets of Forces

Since only external forces and their moments enter into the determination of the state of motion or of equilibrium of a rigid body, different sets* of forces may be compared on the basis of their effects on a rigid body. We are therefore led to define equivalent or *equipollent* sets of forces in the following way: two sets of forces and couples are said to be equipollent if (1) the vector sum of the forces of the first set is the same as the vector sum of the forces of the second set and if (2) the vector sum of the moments of the forces and couples of the first set about any point in space is the same as the vector sum of the moments of the forces and couples of the second set about the same point. The vector sum of the forces is termed the *resultant force* and the vector sum of the moments about any point is called the *resultant moment* about that point.

In the foregoing definition of equipollence the moments of the two sets are to be compared at every point of space. This presents obvious difficulties. The need for comparison at every point may be removed by a fundamental theorem which relates the resultant force and the resultant moment about any particular point to the resultant moment about any other particular point. Let the forces of the set be denoted $\mathbf{F}_i$, with $i = 1, 2, \ldots m$, and the couples, $\mathbf{C}_j$, with $j = 1, 2, \ldots n$. Suppose that $P_1, P_2, \ldots P_m$ are points on the lines of action of $\mathbf{F}_1, \mathbf{F}_2, \ldots \mathbf{F}_m$, respectively, and that the directed line segments from some point O to points $P_1, P_2, \ldots P_m$ are called $\mathbf{r}_1, \mathbf{r}_2, \ldots$

---

* What we are calling a "force set," meaning a particular collection of forces and couples applied to a mechanical system, is sometimes called a "force system." We have selected the present terminology so that there will be no confusion between the mechanical *system* under discussion and any particular *set* of forces exerted on that system.

$\mathbf{r}_m$, respectively. Then for this force and couple set the resultant moment about O is

$$\mathbf{M}_O = \sum_{j=1}^{n} \mathbf{C}_j + \sum_{i=1}^{m} \mathbf{r}_i \times \mathbf{F}_i. \qquad \textbf{2.6-1}$$

Now let P be some other point, with the relative position of P and O given by the directed line segment $\overline{PO}$ or by the vector $\mathbf{r}_{PO}$ (see Fig. 2.6-1). Then the directed line segment from P to P_1 is the

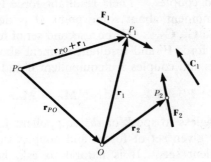

Fig. 2.6-1

vector sum of the directed line segment from P to O and the directed line segment from O to P_1. The moment of the force and couple set about P is given by the expression

$$\mathbf{M}_P = \sum_{j=1}^{n} \mathbf{C}_j + \sum_{i=1}^{m} (\mathbf{r}_{PO} + \mathbf{r}_i) \times \mathbf{F}_i. \qquad \textbf{2.6-2}$$

In this equation $\mathbf{r}_{PO}$, being the same in every term, may be factored out of the summation. Then

$$\mathbf{M}_P = \sum_{j=1}^{n} \mathbf{C}_j + \mathbf{r}_{PO} \times \left(\sum_{i=1}^{m} \mathbf{F}_i \right) + \sum_{i=1}^{m} \mathbf{r}_i \times \mathbf{F}_i. \qquad \textbf{2.6-3}$$

In view of Eq. 2.6-1, the first and third terms on the right-hand side of Eq. 2.6-3 are equal to $\mathbf{M}_O$. If we denote the resultant force by $\mathbf{F}$, i.e., take

$$\mathbf{F} = \sum_{i=1}^{m} \mathbf{F}_i, \qquad \textbf{2.6-4}$$

we have

$$\mathbf{M}_P = \mathbf{M}_O + \mathbf{r}_{PO} \times \mathbf{F}. \qquad \textbf{2.6-5}$$

This is a basic result that is used in dynamical theory as well as in statics. Once the resultant force, $\mathbf{F}$, of a force set and the resultant moment, $\mathbf{M}_O$, are known for any point O, the moment about any other point, P, is determined. We can now appreciate why there are no more than six independent scalar force and moment equations of equilibrium for a given system; if the resultant force and the resultant moment about any one point vanish, the moment about every point must vanish. We are also in a position to rephrase the definition of equipollent force sets. Let $\mathbf{F}_1, \mathbf{F}_2, \ldots \mathbf{F}_m$ and $\mathbf{C}_1, \mathbf{C}_2, \ldots \mathbf{C}_n$ be a set of forces and couples. Their resultant force is denoted $\mathbf{F}$ and their resultant moment about some point O is denoted $\mathbf{M}_O$. Let $\mathbf{F}_1', \mathbf{F}_2', \ldots \mathbf{F}_k'$ and $\mathbf{C}_1', \mathbf{C}_2', \ldots \mathbf{C}_l'$ be a second set of forces and couples having resultant force $\mathbf{F}'$ and resultant moment about O, $\mathbf{M}_O'$. The two sets of forces and couples are equipollent if and only if

$$\mathbf{F}' = \mathbf{F} \quad \text{and} \quad \mathbf{M}_O' = \mathbf{M}_O. \qquad \text{2.6-6}$$

It is meaningless to speak of *the* equipollent force set. Corresponding to any given set of forces and couples there will be many possible equipollent sets. It is natural to ask, however, whether there is a simplest possible force set which can be regarded as typifying all sets equipollent to it. Given a set of forces $\mathbf{F}_1, \mathbf{F}_2, \ldots \mathbf{F}_m$ and couples $\mathbf{C}_1, \mathbf{C}_2, \ldots \mathbf{C}_n$ having a resultant force $\mathbf{F}$ and moment $\mathbf{M}_O$ we can find an equipollent set consisting of a single force $\mathbf{F}'$ and a single couple $\mathbf{C}'$. Furthermore, we may choose any point as the point of application of the force $\mathbf{F}'$. Say that we select the point P whose position relative to O is given by the vector $\mathbf{r}$. Then if we choose

$$\mathbf{F}' = \mathbf{F} = \mathbf{F}_1 + \mathbf{F}_2 + \ldots \mathbf{F}_m$$

and

$$\mathbf{C}' = \mathbf{M}_O - \mathbf{r} \times \mathbf{F}, \qquad \text{2.6-7}$$

both of Eqs. 2.6-6 will be satisfied. The single force $\mathbf{F}'$ applied at the point with position vector $\mathbf{r}$ together with the single couple $\mathbf{C}'$ will be equipollent to the force and couple set $\mathbf{F}_1, \mathbf{F}_2, \ldots \mathbf{F}_m$ and $\mathbf{C}_1, \mathbf{C}_2, \ldots \mathbf{C}_n$. The force and couple set $\mathbf{F}', \mathbf{C}'$ is called a *resultant force set* and the process of replacing any set of forces by an equipollent resultant force set is described as *reduction* of the force set.

Needless to say, corresponding to any force set having resultant force $\mathbf{F}$ and moment $\mathbf{M}_O$ there will be any number of equipollent resultant force sets, one for each choice of $\mathbf{r}$ which locates the line of action of $\mathbf{F}$. Is it possible to choose $\mathbf{r}$ so that the couple $\mathbf{C}'$ is zero?

In view of the second of Eqs. 2.6-7, this condition requires that $\mathbf{r}$ be chosen so as to satisfy the vector equation

$$\mathbf{r} \times \mathbf{F} = \mathbf{M}_O. \qquad\qquad \text{2.6-8}$$

This vector equation has been discussed previously (see Example 1.10-1). If it is to be a meaningful equation the vector $\mathbf{M}_O$ must be at right angles to the vector $\mathbf{F}$. But both $\mathbf{F}$ and $\mathbf{M}_O$ are given properties of the original force system. It follows that it is possible to choose $\mathbf{r}$ so that $\mathbf{C}'$ vanishes only if $\mathbf{F}$ and $\mathbf{M}_O$ happen to be orthogonal. It is, however, always possible to choose $\mathbf{r}$ (i.e., to locate the point of application of $\mathbf{F}$) so that the vector $\mathbf{C}'$ is parallel to the vector $\mathbf{F}'$. To see how this is done, write $\mathbf{C}' = l\mathbf{F}$ in Eqs. 2.6-7 and rearrange the terms. Then

$$\mathbf{r} \times \mathbf{F} = (\mathbf{M}_O - l\mathbf{F}). \qquad\qquad \text{2.6-9}$$

This equation contains two unknowns, l and $\mathbf{r}$. If we take the scalar product of each side with $\mathbf{F}$, the left-hand side will vanish because $(\mathbf{r} \times \mathbf{F}) \cdot \mathbf{F} = 0$: the scalar triple product represents the volume of a parallelepiped whose edges are the three vectors, and it therefore vanishes whenever two of those vectors are identical. We have, then,

$$0 = \mathbf{M}_O \cdot \mathbf{F} - lF^2, \qquad \text{and} \qquad l = \frac{\mathbf{M}_O \cdot \mathbf{F}}{F^2}. \qquad \text{2.6-10}$$

This determines the scalar unknown l which has the dimensions of a length. If we take the vector product of each side of Eq. 2.6-9 with $\mathbf{F}$ we have

$$(\mathbf{r} \times \mathbf{F}) \times \mathbf{F} = \mathbf{M}_O \times \mathbf{F} - l\mathbf{F} \times \mathbf{F}.$$

The last term is zero. The left-hand side may be expanded by means of Eq. 1.9-4:

$$(\mathbf{r} \cdot \mathbf{F})\mathbf{F} - F^2\mathbf{r} = \mathbf{M}_O \times \mathbf{F}.$$

This equation is satisfied by taking (note the interchange of $\mathbf{F}$ and $\mathbf{M}_O$ in the cross-product)

$$\mathbf{r} = \frac{\mathbf{F} \times \mathbf{M}_O}{F^2} \qquad\qquad \text{2.6-11}$$

which makes $\mathbf{r}$ perpendicular to $\mathbf{F}$ so that $\mathbf{r} \cdot \mathbf{F} = 0$. Equations 2.6-10 and 11 determine l and $\mathbf{r}$. The student will have noted that the solution of Eq. 2.6-9 for $\mathbf{r}$ parallels Example 1.10-1. It was there shown, and is obvious here, that we may add to $\mathbf{r}$, as determined by Eq. 2.6-11, any vector parallel to $\mathbf{F}$ without changing the value of

$\mathbf{r} \times \mathbf{F}$. Physically this simply means that, having found a particular point on the line of action of the resultant, we can shift the force along its line of action without affecting its equipollent nature. The particular resultant force set in which $\mathbf{C}'$ and $\mathbf{F}'$ are parallel vectors is known technically as a *wrench*. It may be visualized as a thrust combined with a twist about the line of action of the thrust. The discovery that every set of forces and couples is equipollent to a wrench is due to Poinsot.*

The exceptional case mentioned in the previous paragraph, in which the given $\mathbf{M}_O$ and $\mathbf{F}$ are orthogonal, is actually of considerable practical importance. It occurs whenever the given set consists of (a) forces all of which lie in the same plane, or (b) forces that are parallel. In the former case we may think of the plane in which all the forces lie as the xy-plane and take the point O as the origin of coordinates in this plane. Then the resultant force set consists of a single force $\mathbf{F}'$ acting at a point whose coordinates are $(x, y, 0)$. Equations 2.6-6 then require that

$$\mathbf{F}' = \sum_{i=1}^{m} \mathbf{F}_i = F_x \mathbf{i} + F_y \mathbf{j}$$

and

$$\mathbf{M}'_O = (x\mathbf{i} + y\mathbf{j}) \times (F_x \mathbf{i} + F_y \mathbf{j}) = M_O \mathbf{k}.$$

Note that the forces, lying in the xy-plane, can produce a moment of magnitude M_O only about the z-axis. The coordinates of the point of application are given by any values of x and y which satisfy this last requirement, that is, which satisfy the equation

$$xF_y - yF_x = M_O. \qquad \text{2.6-12}$$

The latter case, (b), is of interest in connection with the idea of a center of mass, to be developed in the next section. Suppose that the given set of forces consists of two parallel forces $F_1 \mathbf{e}$, $F_2 \mathbf{e}$ applied at points P_1, P_2 whose positions relative to O are given by the vectors $\mathbf{r}_1$, $\mathbf{r}_2$, as shown in Fig. 2.6-2. These two forces may be replaced by a single force acting at a point on the line joining P_1 and P_2. In order to satisfy the first of Eqs. 2.6-6 we must take this force to be $(F_1 + F_2)\mathbf{e}$, and in order to satisfy the second of Eqs. 2.6-6 we must locate the force at a point whose position vector $\mathbf{r}$ satisfies the relation

$$\mathbf{r} \times (F_1 + F_2)\mathbf{e} = \mathbf{r}_1 \times F_1 \mathbf{e} + \mathbf{r}_2 \times F_2 \mathbf{e}.$$

---

* L. Poinsot, *Éléments de statique*, 1806. The term "couple" appears also to have originated with Poinsot.

Take $\mathbf{r} = \mathbf{r}_1 + x(\mathbf{r}_2 - \mathbf{r}_1)$; this locates the point of application of the single equivalent force at a point on the line* joining P_1 and P_2, the precise position to be determined by the unknown x.   Inserting this trial value of $\mathbf{r}$ in the preceding expression we find

$$(F_1 + F_2)\mathbf{r}_1 \times \mathbf{e} + x(F_1 + F_2)(\mathbf{r}_2 - \mathbf{r}_1) \times \mathbf{e} = F_1 \mathbf{r}_1 \times \mathbf{e} + F_2 \mathbf{r}_2 \times \mathbf{e},$$

or

$$[F_2 - x(F_1 + F_2)](\mathbf{r}_1 - \mathbf{r}_2) \times \mathbf{e} = \mathbf{0}.$$

This is satisfied whatever $\mathbf{e}$ and $\mathbf{r}_1 - \mathbf{r}_2$ may be if we choose

$$x = \frac{F_2}{F_1 + F_2}.$$ 2.6-13

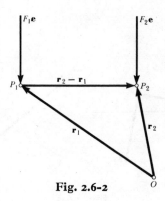

Fig. 2.6-2

This elementary result has interesting consequences.   We see that the location of the equipollent force is between the points P_1 and P_2 if F_1 and F_2 have the same sign, i.e., if the forces $F_1 \mathbf{e}$, $F_2 \mathbf{e}$ are in the same direction.   Otherwise the point of application lies outside the line segment $P_1 P_2$.   Of course the case $F_1 = -F_2$ makes the given force set a couple; we tacitly exclude this case from the discussion.   It is important to note that the location of the resultant force given by Eq. 2.6-13 is unchanged if we increase the magnitudes of both the given forces by any common multiple; that is, x depends only on the ratio F_1/F_2.   The location is also unchanged if the

---

* Indeed, the equation for $\mathbf{r}$ is the vector equation of the line through P_1 and P_2; see Example 1.3-3, and compare the equation here with the equation $\mathbf{r} = \mathbf{s} + m\mathbf{t}$ occurring in that example.

directions of the given forces are altered, provided they remain parallel. This follows from the fact that **e** does not enter Eq. 2.6-13. If now we consider the reduction of three or more parallel forces applied at points P_1, P_2, P_3, ..., we see that this may be accomplished by taking the resultant force for any two of them, then combining it with the third force, and so on. Ultimately we arrive at a single equipollent force whose magnitude is the sum of the magnitudes of the given parallel forces (with due regard for sign), whose direction is parallel to the given forces, and whose point of application is determined. The point of application determined in this way depends only on the relative magnitudes of the forces and on the location of the points P_1, P_2, etc. It is sometimes termed the *center* of the set of parallel forces.

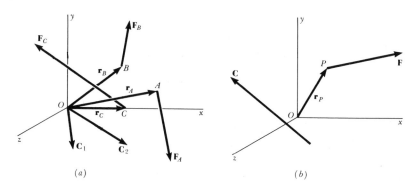

(a)   (b)

Fig. 2.6-3

Example 2.6-1

A body is subjected to forces $F_A = 9i - 2j + 6k$ *lb acting at* $r_A = 5i - 2k$ *in.,* $F_B = 3j - 2k$ *lb at* $r_B = i + j - 2k$ *in., and* $F_C = -6i + 4j - k$ *lb at* $r_C = 4i$ *in. Couples* $C_1 = 4i - 2j + 5k$ *lb-in and* $C_2 = 3i - j + 2k$ *lb-in are also applied. Replace the force set by an equipollent one consisting of a couple* **C** *and a force* **F** *acting at* $r_P = i + j + k$ *in.*

Solution: Figure 2.6-3a shows the original force set. The resultant force **F** is given by

$$F = F_A + F_B + F_C = 3i + 5j + 3k \quad lb;$$

we place **F** on a line of action through P (Fig. 2.6-3b). We must now compute **C**. Let us do this by computing the resultant moment of the two sets about P. For the resultant force set of Fig. 2.6-3b, we have

$$M_P = C + 0 \times F = C.$$

For the original set, we have

$$\mathbf{M}_P = \mathbf{C}_1 + \mathbf{C}_2 + (\mathbf{r}_A - \mathbf{r}_P) \times \mathbf{F}_A + (\mathbf{r}_B - \mathbf{r}_P) \times \mathbf{F}_B + (\mathbf{r}_C - \mathbf{r}_P) \times \mathbf{F}_C$$

$$= (7\mathbf{i} - 3\mathbf{j} + 7\mathbf{k}) + (4\mathbf{i} - \mathbf{j} - 3\mathbf{k}) \times \mathbf{F}_A + (-3\mathbf{k}) \times \mathbf{F}_B + (3\mathbf{i} - \mathbf{j} - \mathbf{k}) \times \mathbf{F}_C$$

$$= (7\mathbf{i} - 3\mathbf{j} + 7\mathbf{k}) + \begin{vmatrix} \mathbf{i} & \mathbf{j} & \mathbf{k} \\ 4 & -1 & -3 \\ 9 & -2 & 6 \end{vmatrix} + \begin{vmatrix} \mathbf{i} & \mathbf{j} & \mathbf{k} \\ 0 & 0 & -3 \\ 0 & 3 & -2 \end{vmatrix} + \begin{vmatrix} \mathbf{i} & \mathbf{j} & \mathbf{k} \\ 3 & -1 & -1 \\ -6 & 4 & -1 \end{vmatrix}$$

$$= (7\mathbf{i} - 3\mathbf{j} + 7\mathbf{k}) + (-12\mathbf{i} - 51\mathbf{j} + \mathbf{k}) + (9\mathbf{i}) + (5\mathbf{i} + 9\mathbf{j} + 6\mathbf{k})$$

$$= 9\mathbf{i} - 45\mathbf{j} + 14\mathbf{k} \quad \text{lb-in.}$$

Setting the two expressions for $\mathbf{M}_P$ equal, we see that

$$\mathbf{C} = 9\mathbf{i} - 45\mathbf{j} + 14\mathbf{k} \quad \text{lb-in.}$$

Example 2.6-2

Replace the resultant force set of the last example by another with **F** *through the origin O.*

Solution: The force, **F**, of the two sets is of course the same: $\mathbf{F} = 3\mathbf{i} + 5\mathbf{j} + 3\mathbf{k}$ lb. It remains to compute the couple $\mathbf{C}'$ that must be adjoined if **F** passes through O. We may compute $\mathbf{C}'$ by setting it equal to $\mathbf{M}_O = \mathbf{C}_1 + \mathbf{C}_2 + \mathbf{r}_A \times \mathbf{F}_A + \mathbf{r}_B \times \mathbf{F}_B + \mathbf{r}_C \times \mathbf{F}_C$ of the original set; or we may compute $\mathbf{C}'$ from the corresponding computation for the resultant set, **F** at $\mathbf{r}_P$ and **C**, of the last example. For our new set, we have $\mathbf{M}_O = \mathbf{C}'$, of course; for the old set, we have (by Eq. 2.6-5)

$$\mathbf{M}_O = \mathbf{M}_P - \mathbf{r}_{PO} \times \mathbf{F}$$

$$= \mathbf{C} + \mathbf{r}_P \times \mathbf{F}$$

$$= 9\mathbf{i} - 45\mathbf{j} + 14\mathbf{k} + \begin{vmatrix} \mathbf{i} & \mathbf{j} & \mathbf{k} \\ 1 & 1 & 1 \\ 3 & 5 & 3 \end{vmatrix}$$

$$= 7\mathbf{i} - 45\mathbf{j} + 16\mathbf{k} \quad \text{lb-in.}$$

Therefore, $\mathbf{C}'$ should be chosen to be

$$\mathbf{C}' = 7\mathbf{i} - 45\mathbf{j} + 16\mathbf{k} \quad \text{lb-in.}$$

Example 2.6-3

Replace the set of forces and the couple shown by an equipollent set consisting of a single force and a couple about a parallel axis. Where does the line of action of the single force intersect the plane ABCD of the figure?

Solution: Choose cartesian axes as shown. Then for the given force set (note that the couple vector is *not* added to the force vectors)

$$\mathbf{F} = -20\mathbf{j} + 30\left(\frac{12}{15}\mathbf{k} + \frac{9}{15}\mathbf{i}\right)$$

$$= 18\mathbf{i} - 20\mathbf{j} + 24\mathbf{k} \quad \text{lb,}$$

and

$$\mathbf{M}_B = 12\mathbf{k} \times (-20\mathbf{j}) + 156\left(\frac{-5}{13}\mathbf{j} + \frac{12}{13}\mathbf{k}\right)$$

$$= 240\mathbf{i} - 60\mathbf{j} + 144\mathbf{k} \quad \text{lb-ft.}$$

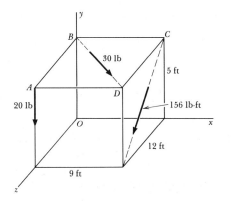

Fig. 2.6-4

The equipollent wrench will consist of the force $\mathbf{F}$ and the couple $\mathbf{C} = l\mathbf{F}$. According to Eq. 2.6-10, l is given by the expression

$$l = \frac{\mathbf{F} \cdot \mathbf{M}_B}{F^2} = \frac{(18)(240) + (-20)(-60) + (24)(144)}{(18)^2 + (-20)^2 + (24)^2} = 6.90 \quad \text{ft,}$$

so that

$$\mathbf{C} = 6.90(18\mathbf{i} - 20\mathbf{j} + 24\mathbf{k}) = 124\mathbf{i} - 138\mathbf{j} + 166\mathbf{k} \quad \text{lb-ft.}$$

To locate a point on the line of action of $\mathbf{F}$ we may use Eq. 2.6-11:

$$\mathbf{r} = \frac{\mathbf{F} \times \mathbf{M}_B}{F^2} = \frac{1}{1300} \begin{vmatrix} \mathbf{i} & \mathbf{j} & \mathbf{k} \\ 18 & -20 & 24 \\ 240 & -60 & 144 \end{vmatrix} = \frac{24}{1300} \begin{vmatrix} \mathbf{i} & \mathbf{j} & \mathbf{k} \\ 9 & -10 & 12 \\ 20 & -5 & 12 \end{vmatrix}$$

$$= \frac{24}{1300}(-60\mathbf{i} + 132\mathbf{j} + 155\mathbf{k}) = -1.11\mathbf{i} + 2.44\mathbf{j} + 2.86\mathbf{k} \quad \text{ft.}$$

Note that this **r** is measured from point B since moments were taken about B. Clearly this point of application does not lie in the plane $ABCD$, which is the plane $y = 5$ ft from O and hence $y = 0$ from B. But we can slide the force **F** along its line of action. That is, we can take for **r** the vector

$$\mathbf{r} = \frac{\mathbf{F} \times \mathbf{M}_B}{F^2} + c\mathbf{F}$$

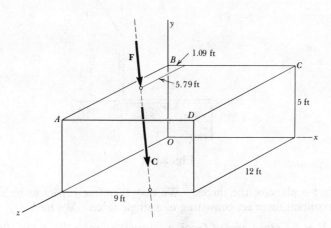

Fig. 2.6-5

where c is arbitrary. Let us give c such a value that the y-coordinate of **r** is 0 ft. Then, since

$$\mathbf{r} = -1.11\mathbf{i} + 2.44\mathbf{j} + 2.86\mathbf{k} + c(18\mathbf{i} - 20\mathbf{j} + 24\mathbf{k})$$
$$= (18c - 1.11)\mathbf{i} + (2.44 - 20c)\mathbf{j} + (2.86 + 24c)\mathbf{k},$$

we have

$$2.44 - 20c = 0, \qquad c = 0.122 \quad \text{ft/lb.}$$

With this value of c, $\mathbf{r} = 1.09\mathbf{i} + 5.79\mathbf{k}$ ft, measured from B. The resultant force set is a single force $\mathbf{F} = 18\mathbf{i} - 20\mathbf{j} + 24\mathbf{k}$ lb applied at a point $x = 1.09$ ft, $z = 5.79$ ft in the plane $ABCD$ together with a couple $\mathbf{C} = 124\mathbf{i} - 138\mathbf{j} + 166\mathbf{k}$ lb-ft. The force and couple vectors are parallel. This wrench is pictured in Fig. 2.6-5.

Example 2.6-4

The forces and couple shown in Fig. 2.6-6 act on a 10 in. by 20 in. angle. Find an equipollent single force and indicate where it should be applied along the x-axis.

Solution: The couple in the given force set has been indicated in the figure by a curved arrow. This is a conventional representation. It may be visualized as being produced, say, by an upward force slightly less than 8 in. from B and a downward force of equal magnitude slightly more than 8 in. from B. In any case, if we take x-, y-axes as shown, the axis of the couple will be along the (negative) z-axis and therefore at right

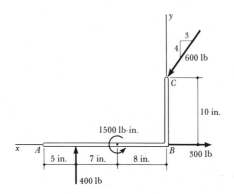

Fig. 2.6-6

angles to the plane of the forces. We may therefore expect to be able to find a resultant force set consisting of a single force. We have

$$F = (-480j + 360i) + (400j) + (-300i) = 100(0.6i - 0.8j) \quad \text{lb},$$

$$M_B = -(360)(10) + (400)(15) - 1500 = 900 \quad \text{lb-in}.$$

Of course $M_B = M_B k$; it is unnecessary to indicate the vectorial nature of the moment explicitly here since the forces can produce moment only

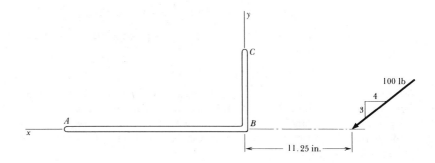

Fig. 2.6-7

about the z-axis. The positive direction of that axis must be into the paper (away from the reader) if (x, y, z) are to be right-handed. Therefore the positive sense of moment is clockwise. Now the force F is to be applied at a point on the x-axis so located as to produce a clockwise moment of

900 lb-in about *B*.   Let the location of this force be the point (x, o); then

$$-80x = 900 \qquad \text{or} \qquad x = -11.25 \quad \text{in.}$$

The equipollent force set is pictured in Fig. 2.6-7.

Example 2.6-5

Replace the three parallel forces shown in Fig. 2.6-8 by a single force, and indicate where it should be applied in order to be equipollent to them.

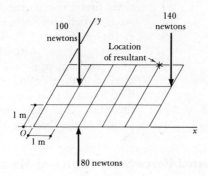

Fig. 2.6-8

Solution: Choosing axes as shown (z is positive upwards) we have

$$\mathbf{F} = (-100 + 80 - 140)\mathbf{k} = -160\mathbf{k} \quad \text{newtons,}$$

$$\mathbf{M}_O = (-200\mathbf{i} + 100\mathbf{j}) + (-160\mathbf{j}) + (-280\mathbf{i} + 700\mathbf{j})$$

$$= -480\mathbf{i} + 640\mathbf{j} \quad \text{newton-meters.}$$

If the equipollent force $\mathbf{F}$ is located at $\mathbf{r} = x\mathbf{i} + y\mathbf{j}$ we must have

$$(x\mathbf{i} + y\mathbf{j}) \times (-160\mathbf{k}) = -480\mathbf{i} + 640\mathbf{j},$$

$$160(x\mathbf{j} - y\mathbf{i}) = -480\mathbf{i} + 640\mathbf{j}$$

so that $y = 3$ meters and $x = 4$ meters.   The location of the resultant, a downward force of magnitude 160 newtons, is shown in Fig. 2.6-8.

Example 2.6-6

Three equal forces $\mathbf{P}$ *act at points A, B, C.   Show that they are equipollent to a single force* $3\mathbf{P}$ *acting at the point of intersection of the medians of the triangle formed by A, B, and C.*

Solution: Since the forces are parallel we know they are equipollent to a single force. That force must be the sum of the individual forces, i.e., 3**P**. To find its point of application, first combine the forces at *A* and *B*. From Eq. 2.6-13 (or simply by taking moments about *A* or *B*) we see that the two forces at *A* and *B* may be replaced by a single force 2**P** located at the midpoint of *AB*. This force is now combined with the one at *C*. But the resultant force must lie on the line joining *C* to the midpoint of *AB*, i.e., on the median to the side *AB* of the triangle *ABC*. Similarly, if we first combine the forces at *B* and *C*, we find that their resultant force must act at the midpoint of the line *BC* and, when this is combined with the force at *A*, the final resultant must act at a point on the median to the side *BC* of the triangle *ABC*. The location of the equipollent force must therefore be at the common point of intersection of the three medians.

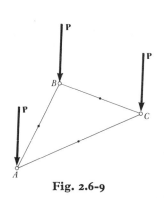

Fig. 2.6-9

2.7 Distributed Force Sets; Center of Mass and of Gravity

The forces considered thus far have all been idealized as concentrated forces with particular points of application and lines of action. This concept follows naturally from the equations of particle motion and equilibrium. However, when we come to consider the force exerted by a magnet on a large block of steel, or the effect of its own dead weight on the deformation of a beam, the representation of force at a point contact is no longer our intuitive interpretation of the physical situation. Instead we naturally suppose that the forces are distributed over a volume or an area or a length of the body in question and we speak of a *force density* (force per unit volume, or per unit area, or per unit length as the case may be). The resultant concentrated force and the resultant moment are then found by summing the individual elements of volume, area, or length, each multiplied by the force density at the location of the element. The summation entails the integration of a vector quantity.

Probably the commonest distributed force encountered in engineering is that exerted on a body as a result of the gravitational attraction of the earth. It is convenient in connection with this force (and also for the purposes of dynamics) to define the mass center of a mechanical system. We begin with a system consisting of n discrete particles of masses $m_1, m_2, \ldots m_n$ located at points $P_1, P_2, \ldots P_n$ whose position vectors, measured from some fixed point O, are $\mathbf{r}_1, \mathbf{r}_2, \ldots \mathbf{r}_n$. The mass center of this system is defined as the point P^* whose location is specified by the vector $\mathbf{r}^*$, where

$$\mathbf{r}^* = \frac{m_1\mathbf{r}_1 + m_2\mathbf{r}_2 + \ldots m_n\mathbf{r}_n}{m_1 + m_2 + \ldots m_n}; \qquad \text{2.7-1a}$$

or, in a somewhat more succinct notation,

$$\mathbf{r}^* = \frac{1}{m} \sum_{i=1}^{n} m_i\mathbf{r}_i, \qquad \text{2.7-1b}$$

where

$$m = \sum_{i=1}^{n} m_i = m_1 + m_2 + \ldots m_n \qquad \text{2.7-2}$$

denotes the total mass of the system. The definition is readily extended to a solid having a continuous distribution of mass. We have only to replace the summations in Eqs. 2.7-1 by integrations over the volume of the solid. Suppose that the density (mass per unit volume) of the body is denoted by the symbol ρ. Of course ρ is, in general, a function of spatial position; i.e., if cartesian coordinates are used, ρ is a function of x, y, z. We indicate this by writing $\rho = \rho(\mathbf{r}) = \rho(x, y, z)$. Then, if the element of volume is denoted dV, the mass of that element is $\rho\, dV$ and the total mass is

$$m = \int \rho\, dV. \qquad \text{2.7-3}$$

If cartesian coordinates are used, $dV = dx\, dy\, dz$ and Eq. 2.7-3 becomes the triple integral

$$m = \int \int \int \rho(x, y, z)\, dx\, dy\, dz. \qquad \text{2.7-4}$$

The position vector from O to the location of a typical volume element dV is $\mathbf{r}$ so that Eq. 2.7-1 becomes, for the continuous body,

$$\mathbf{r}^* = \frac{1}{m} \int \rho\mathbf{r}\, dV, \qquad \text{2.7-5}$$

where the integration is again extended over the entire solid. The definite integral of a vector quantity is another vector and may be defined by the condition that the component of the integral vector in any fixed direction in space is the integral of the component in that direction of the vector to be integrated. Here, if fixed cartesian coordinates are used, $\mathbf{r} = x\mathbf{i} + y\mathbf{j} + z\mathbf{k}$ and

$$\mathbf{r}^* = \frac{1}{m} \int \int \int (x\mathbf{i} + y\mathbf{j} + z\mathbf{k})\rho \, dx \, dy \, dz. \qquad \textbf{2.7-6}$$

Since $\mathbf{i}$, $\mathbf{j}$, $\mathbf{k}$ are constant both in magnitude and in direction,

$$\mathbf{r}^* = \left(\frac{1}{m} \int \int \int x\rho \, dx \, dy \, dz\right)\mathbf{i} + \left(\frac{1}{m} \int \int \int y\rho \, dx \, dy \, dz\right)\mathbf{j}$$
$$+ \left(\frac{1}{m} \int \int \int z\rho \, dx \, dy \, dz\right)\mathbf{k}. \qquad \textbf{2.7-7}$$

The mass center, as defined by Eq. 2.7-1 or Eq. 2.7-5, is in most mechanical problems taken to be the same as the *center of gravity* of a system. The center of gravity of a system is that point where the resultant gravitational force on the system due to a second system—usually the earth—can be considered to act. We wish to consider the circumstances under which we can identify the mass center and the center of gravity.

Let us consider, in fact, a set of forces of more general type than the gravitational forces acting on our system. We shall treat once more the mechanical system consisting of n particles, with masses m_i located at points P_i with position vectors $\mathbf{r}_i$ relative to the fixed point O. (Continuous systems may be treated by replacing the sums by appropriate integrals.) Let the i-th particle be subject to a force $\mathbf{F}_i$ with line of action through O; i.e., $\mathbf{F}_i$ and $\mathbf{r}_i$ are parallel for each i, $i = 1, 2, \ldots n$. Such a force is called a *central force*, and the point O is called the pole or *center of force*. Since $\mathbf{F}_i$ and $\mathbf{r}_i$ are parallel, we must have

$$\mathbf{F}_i = k_i \mathbf{r}_i \qquad \textbf{2.7-8}$$

where the k_i are scalar proportionality factors. Of particular interest are force functions in which the k_i are of the same functional form $k(m, r)$ for all particles and depend at most on the mass of the particle, its distance from O, and some characteristic "strength" factor for the center of force. In particular, if $k = -\mu m/r^3$, $\mu > 0$, then the magnitude of $\mathbf{F} = k\mathbf{r}$ is $\mu m/r^2$ and the force law is of the "inverse-square" type, with O as a center of attraction of strength μ. If a particle of mass M is placed at O with $\mu = GM$, then the force function is the newtonian gravitational force.

The resultant of the set of forces 2.7-8 is $\mathbf{F} = \sum k_i \mathbf{r}_i$; it must, of course, have line of action passing through the point O, since each force has zero moment about O. If we now ask for a second point $\mathbf{r}^{**}$ on the line of action of $\mathbf{F}$ such that $\mathbf{F}$ has the same form as each of the separate $\mathbf{F}_i$, we are led by analogy with the definition 2.7-1 for the mass center to

$$\mathbf{F} = k^{**}\mathbf{r}^{**} = \sum k_i \mathbf{r}_i, \qquad \textbf{2.7-9}$$

with one possible definition of k^{**} being

$$k^{**} = \sum k_i. \qquad \textbf{2.7-10}$$

Even assuming $\sum k_i \neq 0$, this definition for k^{**} is of utility only if we can interpret k^{**} in terms of simple physical quantities. For the mass center, we can interpret $\sum m_i$ as the total mass m of the system and think of an equivalent particle of mass m placed at $\mathbf{r}^*$. For the inverse-square law, we have $k_i = -\mu m_i/r_i^3$; then we would want k^{**} to be of the form $-\mu m/(r^{**})^3$ and not of the form 2.7-10. Under these conditions, $\mathbf{r}^{**}$, the center of gravity of the particle system relative to the attractive center O, is defined (from 2.7-9) by

$$\frac{\mathbf{r}^{**}}{(r^{**})^3} = \frac{1}{m} \sum_{i=1}^{n} \frac{m_i \mathbf{r}_i}{r_i^3}. \qquad \textbf{2.7-11}$$

The center of gravity does not appear, in general, to be even approximately the same as the center of mass. When does the $\mathbf{r}^{**}$ of 2.7-9 agree with the $\mathbf{r}^*$ of 2.7-1?

First of all, we can identify $\mathbf{r}^{**}$ with $\mathbf{r}^*$ (although $\mathbf{r}^{**}$ will not be given by Eq. 2.7-11 in this case) if all the particles are on the same line through O; certainly $\mathbf{F}$ and all the $\mathbf{F}_i$ pass through the mass center then. Second, if each k_i is strictly proportional to the mass m_i of the i-th particle, then 2.7-9 (with 2.7-10 for k^{**}) reduces to the mass center definition. Third, if we think of the points $P_1, P_2, \ldots P_n$ as fixed and the center of force O as remote from any of the P_i, the forces of the set may be made as nearly parallel as desired. The "center" $\mathbf{r}^{**}$ of a set of parallel forces was discussed in Section 2.6, and its location was shown to depend on the relative magnitude of the forces. If the magnitude of each is taken proportionate to the mass of the corresponding particle and if the distance dependence of the magnitude can be considered as constant because of the remoteness of the force center, then $\mathbf{r}^{**} \cong \mathbf{r}^*$. That is, if the particle-to-particle distances are all small compared to the mean distance to O, all the distances r_i can be replaced by a constant $r \cong r^{**}$. Under these conditions, Eq. 2.7-11, for example, reduces to

$$\mathbf{r}^{**} \cong \frac{1}{m} \sum m\, \mathbf{r} = \mathbf{r}^*.$$

The gravitational attraction of the earth provides a force proportional to the mass of each particle attracted and, if all the interparticle distances or the dimensions of the volume occupied by a solid body are small compared to the radius of the earth, these forces may be regarded as parallel forces of the type just considered. It follows that for the purposes of technology the mass center may be regarded as the true center of gravity. We replace the effect of the earth's attraction by a concentrated force acting at the mass center in the direction opposite to the local vertical. The magnitude of this force, proportional to the mass of the body, is termed the *weight* of the body.

The foregoing observations are the basis for the usual practical method of measuring mass by means of an equal-arm balance. What is compared is actually the ratio of two weights, but since each is proportional to the corresponding mass, the mass of one of the bodies is found in terms of the mass of the other or "standard" body. Mass measured in this way, with the aid of a gravitational field, is sometimes termed *gravitational mass* in contradistinction to *inertial mass*, which would be determined by an experiment such as that described in Section 2.1. In point of fact, however, the most refined experiments have failed to detect any measurable difference between the two. In relativistic mechanics the identity of inertial and gravitational mass is a fundamental postulate; in newtonian mechanics it is simply a consequence of Newton's law of gravitation.

In technology the terms "center of mass" and "center of gravity" are used interchangeably. As has been pointed out, however, correspondence is based upon an approximation. The mass center of a body is a definite point in the body; it remains the same point in the body regardless of the body's position in space or its orientation. The center of gravity is also a definite point in the body; its location, however, depends, in general, upon the relative positions of the body and the attracting mass. Only in the case of a body with symmetry, like a sphere, does the position of the center of gravity remain unchanged when the focus of attraction is moved, and in this case the center of gravity coincides with the mass center exactly. Because its position depends upon the location of the focus of attraction, the center of gravity, when distinct from the mass center, is not a very useful concept; we generally prefer to replace the gravitational force, in cases where the distinction must be made, by a concentrated force at the mass center and a couple. The distinction is rarely of importance in engineering, but it is of some interest in celestial mechanics. Since the earth is not exactly a sphere, there is no one point in it through which the attraction of the sun (and moon) always acts. This attraction therefore exerts a variable torque about the earth's mass center which is responsible for a gradual change in the direction of the earth's axis of rotation. The effect is known in astronomy as the precession of the equinoxes.

We may also see from Eq. 2.7-1 that any part of the system may be replaced by a single particle of mass equal to the total mass of that part, located at the mass center of the part, without affecting the location of the mass center of the system as a whole.   Suppose we replace the particles $P_1, P_2, \ldots P_k$ by a single particle of mass $m' = m_1 + m_2 + \ldots m_k$ located at P', the vector $\overline{OP'}$ being given by the expression

$$\mathbf{r}' = \frac{1}{m'} \sum_{i=1}^{k} m_i \mathbf{r}_i.$$

Then the mass center will be at the position

$$\mathbf{r}^* = \frac{1}{m} \left(m' \mathbf{r}' + \sum_{i=k+1}^{n} m_i \mathbf{r}_i \right) = \frac{1}{m} \sum_{i=1}^{n} m_i \mathbf{r}_i,$$

and this is the same as the mass center of the original system, given by Eq. 2.7-1.   This result is of practical utility in the location of mass centers of irregular bodies.

If the origin of coordinates is taken at the mass center, we see from Eq. 2.7-7 that

$$\iiint x\rho \, dx \, dy \, dz = 0$$

and also that

$$\iiint y\rho \, dx \, dy \, dz = 0, \qquad \iiint z\rho \, dx \, dy \, dz = 0.$$

The integrals are sometimes termed the first moments of the mass with respect to the yz-, xz-, and xy-planes, respectively.   The first moment of the mass with respect to any plane through the mass-center is zero.   For other choice of origin, the coordinates of $\mathbf{r}^*$, which we may call x^*, y^*, z^*, are given by the expressions

$$x^* = \frac{\iiint x\rho \, dx \, dy \, dz}{\iiint \rho \, dx \, dy \, dz}, \quad y^* = \frac{\iiint y\rho \, dx \, dy \, dz}{\iiint \rho \, dx \, dy \, dz},$$

$$z^* = \frac{\iiint z\rho \, dx \, dy \, dz}{\iiint \rho \, dx \, dy \, dz}. \qquad \textbf{2.7-12}$$

If the density is uniform, ρ can be taken outside the integral sign. It then disappears from these expressions.   Under these circumstances the mass center is simply a geometric property of the volume and is sometimes then called the *centroid* of the body.   In the determination of the mass center it is not usually necessary to carry out all three integrations.   Many of the objects of concern in technology have a uniform thickness, like a disk or a sheet (lamina) or a shell. In this case the volume density, ρ, may be replaced by a surface density (mass per unit area) and one of the integrations at least eliminated. If there is any plane of symmetry the centroid must be in that plane, and if there is any axis of symmetry the centroid must lie on that axis. Whenever the object can be regarded as built up of component parts each of which has a known mass center, the mass center of the assembly may be found by replacing each part by a single particle of mass equal to the total mass of the component and located at the mass center of the component. In many practical cases involving shapes which are not geometrically simple, it is ultimately necessary, however, to perform one or more of the integrations 2.7-12 approximately, either by graphical or numerical means.

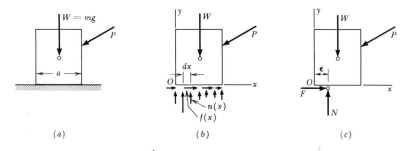

(*a*)   (*b*)   (*c*)

Fig. 2.7-1

Another form of distributed force commonly encountered in mechanics is that exerted at an interface, where solids come in contact either with other solids or with fluids. Consider, for example, a brick on a table. Suppose it to be subject to its own weight $W = mg$ and to an oblique force P, as shown in Fig. 2.7-1a. The distributed weight force may, as we have seen, be replaced by a concentrated force W (or mg) equal to the total weight of the brick and acting at the mass center of the brick. The reaction of the table on the brick may be regarded as distributed over the base. At a typical element of length, dx, as shown in Fig. 2.7-1b, there will be a force per unit length which may conveniently be separated into a normal component, $n(x)$, and a tangential or "frictional" component, $f(x)$. The resultant upward force exerted on the brick by the table is given by the expression

$$N = \int_0^a n(x)\, dx$$

and the total tangential force is given by

$$F = \int_0^a f(x)\, dx.$$

These forces are shown in Fig. 2.7-1c. They are the equipollent concentrated forces for the distributed force system shown in (b). Note that the point of application of the equipollent force has been taken at the point $x = \epsilon$. Taking moments about O, we see that for equipollence

$$\epsilon = \frac{1}{N} \int_0^a xn(x)\, dx = \frac{\int_0^a xn(x)\, dx}{\int_0^a n(x)\, dx}.$$

So long as we treat the brick as a rigid body we cannot hope to learn the actual distribution of the distributed force on the base of the brick. We therefore draw the free-body diagram as shown in Fig. 2.7-1c and use the equations of equilibrium to determine F, N, and ϵ. If the force P is increased gradually from zero it may eventually become large enough to cause the block to tip. When $P = 0$, clearly $F = 0$, $N = W$, and $\epsilon = a/2$. As P increases, ϵ decreases; and, just before the block begins to rotate about O, the reaction of the table is concentrated at the corner O. At this instant $\epsilon = 0$. Variations of the free-body diagram shown in Fig. 2.7-1c are, of course, quite allowable. For example, F and N may be replaced by a single force at an unknown angle to the axes. If the interface is a fluid-solid interface, the pressure on the solid will at all points be normal to the surface, at least so long as the fluid is in equilibrium. In this case there is no tangential component such as $f(x)$.

The bodies on either side of the interface across which distributed forces are exerted need not be physically distinct. Consider

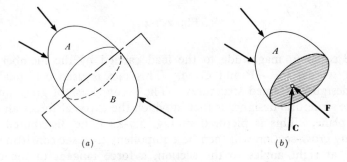

(a)   (b)

Fig. 2.7-2

a body of arbitrary shape loaded by arbitrary forces and suppose that a section is passed dividing the body into two parts, A and B, as shown in Fig. 2.7-2. The forces exerted by B on A are distributed over this section. They are equivalent to a concentrated force **F** and couple **C**, as shown in Fig. 2.7-2. If the original set of forces in Fig. 2.7-2a is a null set, the whole body is in equilibrium and therefore part A, whose free-body diagram is shown in Fig. 2.7-2b, is in

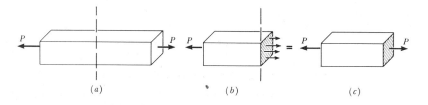

(a)   (b)   (c)

Fig. 2.7-3

equilibrium. Knowing the original set of external forces, we may therefore expect to be able to determine the "internal" forces **F** and **C** from the equations of equilibrium. Two cases deserve special mention. If the body in question is a two-force member (Section 2.4) the situation is as pictured in Fig. 2.7-3. The distributed force acting on any cross-section must be equipollent to a concentrated

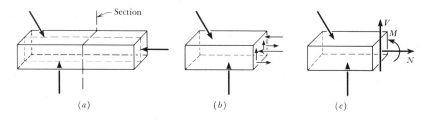

(a)   (b)   (c)

Fig. 2-7-4

force equal in magnitude to the load carried by the member. In other words, $\mathbf{F} = -\mathbf{P}$ and $\mathbf{C} = 0$. This fact is used continually in the design of framed structures. The second case of great interest to the structural designer is that in which the external forces all lie in one plane. This is pictured in Fig. 2.7-4. The distributed force on any cross-section will then be equipollent to a set consisting of a force at right angles to the section, a force tangent to the cross-section, and a couple whose vector is at right angles to the original set of external forces. We may denote these vectors as **N**, **V**, and **M**, respectively. In the case $\mathbf{N}=\mathbf{V}=\mathbf{o}$ for all cross-sections, the structural element is said to be a beam in pure flexure or bending. If **N** alone vanishes at all cross-sections, it is said to be a beam in flexure without tension, or simply a beam.

In engineering stress analysis, interest centers in the way in which the force distribution varies over any given cross-section. This is manifestly not revealed by a knowledge of the over-all force and moment resultants. Any given resultant may be produced by a wide variety of distributions. The determination of the way in which the traction at any point varies with the orientation of the cross-section and the location of the point requires additional physical hypotheses about the nature and behavior of the solid. By supplementing the equations of equilibrium with other equations based on the load-deformation properties of the material and on the fact that these deformations, however small, must be such as will preserve geometric continuity, this point-to-point variation can be determined. That is in fact the primary task of continuum mechanics. The interested student should refer to a text in deformable-body mechanics where this matter is treated in detail.* In Chapter IV, however, we shall consider some cases of equilibrium under distributed load where separate equations for the deformations need not be considered.

A listing of mass centers of a variety of bodies of uniform mass distribution appears in the table following the Appendix.

Example 2.7-1

Locate the mass center of (a) a triangular plate, (b) a tetrahedron, and (c) a cone, all of uniform density.

Solution: (a) The mass center of a straight wire or rod of uniform mass per unit length lies at the midpoint of the rod. If we think of the triangular plate ABC as built up of line elements parallel to one of the sides (say the side BC), the mass center of each element will be at its midpoint. It follows that the mass center of the triangular plate lies on the median from A, the line from A to the midpoint of the opposite side BC, as shown in Fig. 2.7-5. If we decompose the plate into line elements parallel to the

---

* See S. H. Crandall and N. C. Dahl, eds., *An Introduction to the Mechanics of Solids* (New York: McGraw-Hill Book Company, Inc., 1959). For a more advanced treatment, the reader may refer to S. Timoshenko and J. N. Goodier, *Theory of Elasticity*, 2nd ed. (New York: McGraw-Hill Book Company, Inc., 1951) or I. S. Sokolnikoff, *Mathematical Theory of Elasticity*, 2nd ed. (New York: McGraw-Hill Book Company, Inc., 1956).

side *AB* we find that the mass center lies on the median from *C*. In fact, the mass center of the triangular plate must lie at the intersection of the medians. (In Example 2.6-6 we found the same conclusion for three

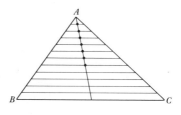

Fig. 2.7-5

equal mass particles at points *A*, *B*, *C*.) This intersection lies two-thirds of the way along the median from the vertex to the middle of the opposite side.

(b) Divide the tetrahedron into lamina parallel to one of the faces—say *ABC* in Fig. 2.7-6. The mass center of each triangular face lies at the intersection of the medians. It follows that the mass center of the tetrahedron as a whole lies along the line connecting the vertex *D* to the intersection of the medians of the opposite face. But it must then lie at the

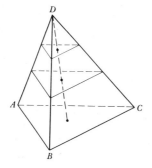

Fig. 2.7-6

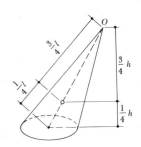

Fig. 2.7-7

intersection of the lines from each of the four vertices to the intersections of the medians of the opposite faces. The mass center of the solid tetrahedron therefore coincides with the mass center of four equal particles at points *A*, *B*, *C*, *D*. It lies three-quarters of the way from any vertex to the intersection of the medians of the opposite face.

(c) Suppose that instead of a cone, we have a pyramid with a polygonal base. This polygon may be split up into triangles, each of which, together with the vertex *O*, determines a tetrahedron. The mass center of the pyramid therefore lies along the line connecting O to the centroid of the base, three-quarters of that distance from O, as shown in Fig. 2.7-7. Since a curved base may be approximated to any desired degree of approximation by a polygon, we conclude that the same result holds for a cone as for the pyramid, a result, that can also be derived, of course, by direct computation.

Example 2.7-2

Find (a) the mass center of a uniform rod bent to a circular arc of radius R subtending a central angle $2\theta_0$, and (b) the mass center of a uniform plate in the shape of a sector of a circle of radius R and central angle $2\theta_0$.

Solution: (a) Take origin at the center of the circular arc, with y as axis of symmetry. Then $x^* = 0$. Using polar coordinates, as shown in Fig. 2.7-8, a typical element of the rod will have length $R\,d\theta$ and mass

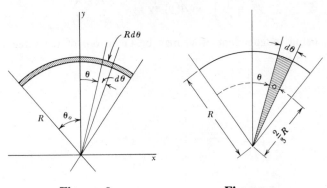

Fig. 2.7-8   **Fig. 2.7-9**

$\mu R\,d\theta$, where μ denotes the mass of the rod per unit length. The total mass of the rod is $2\mu R\theta_0$; consequently

$$y^* = \frac{1}{2\mu R\theta_0} \int_{-\theta_0}^{\theta_0} (R\cos\theta)(\mu R\,d\theta) = \frac{R\sin\theta_0}{\theta_0}.$$

The term $(R\cos\theta)$ in the integrand represents the y-coordinate of the mass center of the typical element. For a semicircular rod, $\theta_0 = \pi/2$ and $y^* = 2R/\pi$.

(b) Divide the sector into elementary "triangles" of which a typical one is shown in Fig. 2.7-9. The mass center of each element will, according to Example 2.7-1a, lie at a distance $2R/3$ from O. We see that the entire sector is equivalent to a circular arc of radius $2R/3$. From part (a) of this example, the y^*-coordinate of such an arc is

$$y^* = \left(\frac{2R}{3}\right) \frac{\sin\theta_0}{\theta_0}.$$

For a semicircular plate, $\theta_0 = \pi/2$ and $y^* = 4R/3\pi$.

Example 2.7-3

A body of uniform density has the property that the area of any cross-section at right angles to some axis, y, has an area $A(y)$. If the solid is bounded by the planes $y = a, b$, show that

$$y^* = \frac{\int_a^b yA(y)\, dy}{\int_a^b A(y)\, dy}.$$

Solution: Take as typical element of the solid the part intercepted by two parallel planes distant dy, as shown in Fig. 2.7-10. The mass of a typical element is $\rho A\, dy$. Thus

$$m = \int_a^b \rho A(y)\, dy$$

and

$$y^* = \frac{1}{m} \int_a^b \rho y A(y)\, dy = \frac{\int_a^b yA(y)\, dy}{\int_a^b A(y)\, dy}$$

since ρ, being independent of y, may be taken out of the integral sign.

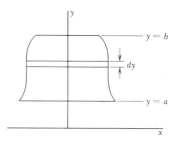

Fig. 2.7-10

If the solid is a solid of revolution with y as its axis of symmetry, $A(y) = \pi x^2$. Then if the bounding curve is $x = f(y)$, the formula above gives y^* immediately from the shape of the bounding curve. For a hemisphere of radius R with base on the plane $y = 0$ we have $a = 0$, $b = R$, $f(y) = (R^2 - y^2)^{1/2}$ and $A(y) = \pi(R^2 - y^2)$:

$$y^* = \frac{\pi \int_0^R y(R^2 - y^2)\, dy}{\pi \int_0^R (R^2 - y^2)\, dy} = \frac{\frac{1}{4}R^4}{\frac{2}{3}R^3} = \frac{3}{8} R.$$

Example 2.7-4

Show that, if a uniform solid of revolution is generated by revolving an area about an axis in its plane, the volume of the solid is equal to the generating area multiplied by the length of the path of its centroid.

Solution: Take the y-axis as the axis of revolution and a typical area element in the cross-section $dx \, dy = dA$, as shown in Fig. 2.7-11. As the area is rotated about the y-axis this element sweeps out a total volume $(2\pi x) \, dA$ so that the volume of the solid is

$$V = 2\pi \int x \, dA,$$

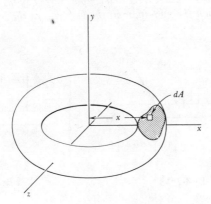

Fig. 2.7-11

the integration being extended over the area of the cross-section in the xy-plane. The x-coordinate of the centroid of this area is given by the expression

$$x^* = \frac{\rho \int x \, dA}{\rho \int dA} = \frac{V}{2\pi A}.$$

We have at once $(2\pi x^*)A = V$, which is the desired result. This theorem is one of two due originally to Pappus of Alexandria (A.D. 300) and discovered independently by Guldinus in the seventeenth century. The other of Pappus' theorems appears in the list of exercises.

If we know the volume of a solid of revolution and the area of its cross-section, this theorem may be used to find the location of the centroid of half the cross-section. For example, an ellipsoid of volume

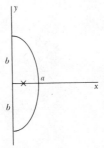

Fig. 2.7-12

$4\pi a^2 b/3$ is generated by revolving a half ellipse about its major diameter, $2b$. The area of the semi-ellipse, shown in Fig. 2.7-12, is $(\pi ab)/2$. It follows that the centroid of the half ellipse is at

$$x^* = \frac{V}{2\pi A} = \frac{(4\pi a^2 b)/3}{(2\pi)(\pi ab)/2} = \frac{4a}{3\pi}.$$

It is interesting to note that this result, being independent of b, must agree with the result for a half-circle given in Example 2.7-2b.

Example 2.7-5

A beam is supported on rollers at one end and on a smooth pin joint at the other. It carries a distributed load and a concentrated load, as shown (Fig. 2.7-13). Find the resultant force and couple exerted by the material to the right of a section through the mid-span on the material to the left of the section.

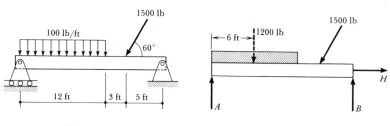

| Fig. 2.7-13 | Fig. 2.7-14 |

Solution: We note that the free-body diagram of the beam as a whole is as shown in Fig. 2.7-14. The left-hand reaction, A, is vertical because of the smooth rollers. The reactions A, B, and H are easily computed from the equilibrium equations; for this purpose the distributed load may

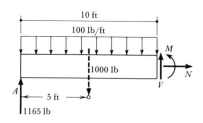

Fig. 2.7-15

be replaced by a concentrated force of 1200 lb (shown dotted in Fig. 2.7-14) at a point 6 ft from the left-hand end of the bearing. Then, taking moments about A, we have

$$20B - 7200 - (1300)(15) = 0, \qquad B = 1335 \text{ lb.}$$

Taking moments about B, we have

$$-20A + (1200)(14) + (1300)(5) = 0, \qquad A = 1165 \text{ lb.}$$

As a check we see that $A + B = 2500$ lb, the total downward load. Summing forces in the horizontal direction we have

$$H - 750 = 0, \qquad H = 750 \text{ lb.}$$

Next we proceed to the free-body diagram of that part of the beam to the left of a section through the midspan. This is shown in Fig. 2.7-15. The distributed forces exerted by the material to the right of the section have been replaced by their resultant, a force with components N and V and a couple M. It is these that we are asked to find. Again we replace the distributed 1000 lb/ft load by an equipollent concentrated force, this time of 1000 lb magnitude and located 5 ft from A. Now, summing forces vertically and horizontally, we have for equilibrium:

$$1165 - 1000 + V = 0, \qquad V = -165 \quad \text{lb}; \qquad N = 0.$$

Taking moments about point A, we find:

$$M + 10V - (1000)(5) = 0;$$

$$M + (10)(-165) - (1000)(5) = 0;$$

$$M = 6650 \text{ lb-ft.}$$

These are the wanted quantities.

Exercises

2.2-1: The resultant force on a particle at position O has zero moment about axes PQ, QR, and RP, where P, Q, R are three points not on the same straight line. If none of the three axes passes through O, can we correctly conclude that the particle is necessarily in equilibrium?
Ans.: No.

2.2-2: The four force vectors shown are drawn to a scale of 1 in. $\sim$ 5 lb. What is the resultant moment of the system about the origin? About the point $(2, 3, -1)$ in.?
Ans.: 100k lb-in.

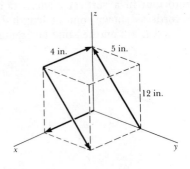

Exer. 2.2-2

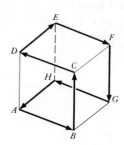

Exer. 2.2-3

2.2-3: Eight forces proportional in magnitude to the sides of a cube are given in direction as shown. What is the force sum? The moment sum about A? Can the force system be replaced by two forces along BC and GF? If it can be done, what are they?

2.2-4: A force $\mathbf{F} = 3\mathbf{i} - 4\mathbf{j} + 12\mathbf{k}$ newtons acts at point $\mathbf{r} = \mathbf{i} + \mathbf{j} - 3\mathbf{k}$ meters. A second force $(-\frac{1}{2}\mathbf{F})$ acts at $(-\frac{1}{2}\mathbf{r})$; a third force $(-\frac{1}{2}\mathbf{F})$ acts at $\mathbf{i} - \frac{1}{2}\mathbf{r}$. Find the moment vector of the resultant couple.
Ans.: C $= -25.5\mathbf{j} - 8.5\mathbf{k}$ newton-meters.

2.2-5: A particle is in equilibrium in a plane under three forces:

$$\mathbf{F}_1 = -10\mathbf{j} \text{ lb,}$$
$$\mathbf{F}_2 = U(\cos 120°\mathbf{i} + \sin 120°\mathbf{j}) \text{ lb,}$$
and
$$\mathbf{F}_3 = T(\cos \theta\mathbf{i} + \sin \theta\mathbf{j}) \text{ lb.}$$

The angle θ lies in the range $0 \leq \theta \leq \pi/2$.
(a) Solve for the magnitudes T and U as functions of θ.
(b) For what θ will T be a minimum? What will be the values of T and U for this value of θ?
Ans.: (a) $T = (10 \sec \theta)/(\tan \theta + \sqrt{3})$ lb, $U = 20/(\tan \theta + \sqrt{3})$ lb; (b) $\theta = 30°$.

2.2-6: A particle in equilibrium is subjected to four forces:

$$\mathbf{F}_1 = -10\mathbf{k} \text{ lb,}$$
$$\mathbf{F}_2 = U[(4/13)\mathbf{i} - (12/13)\mathbf{j} + (3/13)\mathbf{k}] \text{ lb,}$$
$$\mathbf{F}_3 = V[-(4/13)\mathbf{i} - (12/13)\mathbf{j} + (3/13)\mathbf{k}] \text{ lb,}$$
$$\mathbf{F}_4 = W(\cos \theta\mathbf{i} + \sin \theta\mathbf{j}) \text{ lb,}$$

where $0 \leq \theta \leq \pi$.
(a) Solve for U, V, and W as functions of θ.
(b) If U, V, W are all to be positive—say, that they are cord tensions—what is the allowable range of θ?
Ans.: (a) $U = 65(1 - 3 \cot \theta)/3$ lb; (b) $71.6° < \theta < 108.4°$.

2.3-1: A particle of mass m is in equilibrium in a vertical plane. It is suspended from two light inextensible cords as shown, one of length L, the other $3L$; the points of suspension A and B are on the same horizontal level at a distance $3L$ apart.

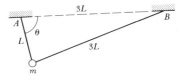

Exer. 2.3-1

(a) Draw a free-body diagram of the particle. Of the particle and the two cords together.

(b) Find the cord tensions for equilibrium.

Ans.: $T_A = 0.958\ mg$, $T_B = 0.169\ mg$.

2.3-2: Suppose, in the previous exercise, the cord to support B is replaced by a light ideal spring of natural length $2L$. What must the spring constant k be if the configuration of Exercise 2.3-1 is still an equilibrium configuration? Draw the free-body diagram of the particle, cord, and spring.

Ans.: $k = 0.169\ \dfrac{mg}{L}$.

2.3-3: An object of weight W at point O is suspended by three cables. The cable OC is horizontal. The other two, OA and OB, are attached to a wall which is at right angles to the horizontal cable, the points of attachment being 27 ft horizontally and 36 ft vertically distant from the point of suspension, as shown in the figure, and 28 and 108 ft from the vertical plane through the point of suspension and the horizontal cable. Find the tensions in the cables.

Ans.: $T_{OA} = 1.169W$, $T_{OB} = 0.669W$, $T_{OC} = 0.75W$.

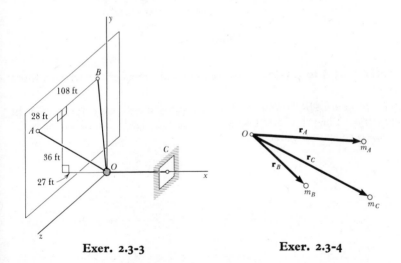

Exer. 2.3-3   **Exer. 2.3-4**

2.3-4: Three particles of masses m_A, m_B, m_C are located at $\mathbf{r}_A$, $\mathbf{r}_B$, $\mathbf{r}_C$; the only forces acting on each are due to their mutual gravitational attractions.

(a) Take all three masses as the system. Draw a free-body diagram showing external forces only; draw one showing external and internal forces.

(b) Do part (a) for a system consisting of A and C only; of B only.

2.3-5: The three particles of the previous problem are connected by light rigid rods and supported in a vertical plane by a cord and springs. A 10-lb load is applied to A. Draw free-body diagrams showing external forces only for systems consisting of (a) the three particles and rods; (b) particles A and C and their connecting rod; (c) particle B only.

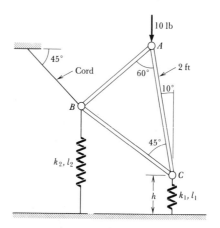

Exer. 2.3-5

Exercises 2.3-6 to 2.3-17: Draw free-body diagrams of the systems listed below.

2.3-6: System $ABCDEFG$. This is a pin-jointed plane truss of light rigid bars. The pin connection at A to the foundation is smooth, as is the two-sided roller and guide at D.

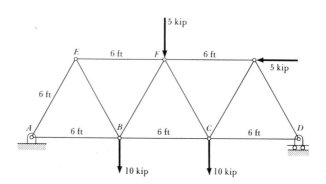

Exer. 2.3-6

2.3-7: The light rigid bar *BF* in the truss of Exercise 2.3-6.

2.3-8: The rigid triangle *BEF* (including the pins at the ends) of the truss of Exercise 2.3-6.

2.3-9: System *ABCDEFGHI*. This is a smoothly connected rigid space truss of light rigid bars, with the congruent triangular elements *ABC*, *DEF*, and *GHI* vertical. The truss is supported by a smooth ball-and-socket joint at *A*, light vertical cables at *C* and *I*, and a light horizontal rigid rod at *H*.

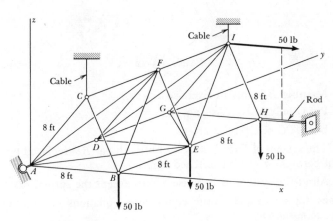

Exer. 2.3-9

2.3-10: The uniform rigid disk, of radius 2 ft and weight 10 lb. Suppose the contact with the horizontal plane to be (a) smooth, (b) rough.

2.3-11: The rigid top of weight *W*. Suppose the pivot at *O* to be (a) smooth, (b) rough.

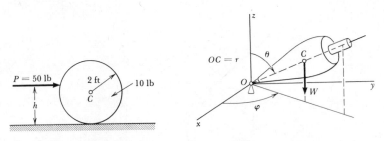

Exer. 2.3-10   **Exer. 2.3-11**

2.3-12: The A-frame shown. It consists of smoothly pinned, light rigid members *ABC*, *CDE*, and *BD*. The foundation pin at *A* and the roller at *E* are smooth. Load *P* is applied on the pin at *C*.

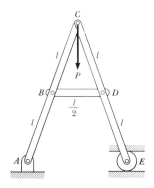

Exer. 2.3-12

2.3-13: Member BD only in Exercise 2.3-12.

2.3-14: Pin C only in Exercise 2.3-12.

2.3-15: Bar ABC of Exercise 2.3-12.

2.3-16: The system of Exercise 2.3-12 but with bar BD replaced by a light spring of constant k and unstretched length l.

2.3-17: All of the system of Exercise 2.3-16 except the spring.

Exercises 2.4-1 to 2.4-6: Write equilibrium equations for the following systems; *do not attempt to solve.*

2.4-1: The system of Exercise 2.3-6.

2.4-2: The system of Exercise 2.3-9.

2.4-3: The system of Exercise 2.3-10b.

2.4-4: The system of Exercise 2.3-12.

2.4-5: The system of Exercise 2.3-14.

2.4-6: The system of Exercise 2.3-15.

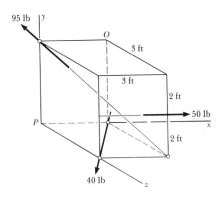

Exer. 2.6-1

2.6-1: Replace the force set shown by an equipollent resultant set consisting of a single force applied at O and a couple.

Ans.: $F = -27.2i + 65.2j - 20.6k$ lb; $C = -113i + 3.37j - 209k$ lb-ft.

2.6-2: Replace the force set of Exercise 2.6-1 by an equipollent set consisting of a single force applied at P and a couple.

Ans.: F is the same as the previous exercise; $C = -196i + 65.1j + 95.5k$ lb-ft.

2.6-3: Replace the force set of Exercise 2.6-1 by a wrench (force and couple about parallel axis). Where should the line of action of the force intersect the vertical plane through O and P?

Ans.: F is the same as in the previous two exercises; $C = 1.40 F$ lb-ft, with F applied at $-1.27i + 7.66j$ ft from P.

2.6-4: Which two of the following force sets are equipollent?

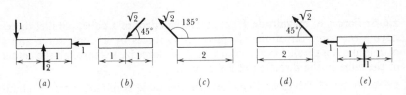

Exer. 2.6-4

2.6-5: Which of the following force and couple sets is not equipollent to any of the others?

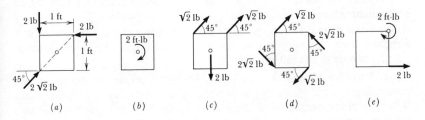

Exer. 2.6-5

2.6-6: Replace the set of four parallel forces shown by a single equipollent force, and indicate the point at which it should be applied. Each square is of 1 ft edge.

Ans.: $-170k$ lb at $(3/17, 9/17)$ ft.

2.6-7: What must be the ratio of the dimensions a and b of the rectangular parallelepiped shown if the force set is to be equivalent to a single force applied at P?

Ans.: $a/b = 5/8$.

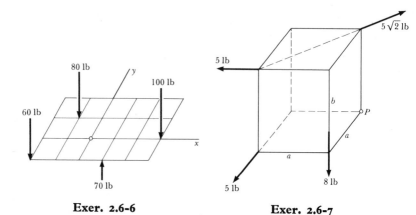

Exer. 2.6-6   **Exer. 2.6-7**

2.6-8: Forces of magnitude P act along the edges of a cube, parallel forces having the same direction. Replace these forces by a single force and a couple about a parallel axis. Show that this force passes through the center of the cube in the direction of a diagonal.

2.6-9: A set of forces and couples has the same resultant moment about each of three non-collinear points. What conclusions may be drawn about the nature of the force set? If the moment in question is zero, are the resultant force and couple both zero?
Ans.: F = 0; yes.

2.6-10: Forces of magnitude P act along two of the non-intersecting edges of a regular tetrahedron of edge length $2a$. Replace these forces by an equipollent wrench.
Ans.: Force of magnitude $P\sqrt{2}$ acting at the center of the tetrahedron in a direction from the midpoint of one side to the center of the tetrahedron; parallel couple of magnitude Pa.

2.7-1: Particles of mass 30 kg, 50 kg, 80 kg are located at points having coordinates (1, 2), (5, 8), (7, 0) meters, respectively, in a vertical plane. What are the coordinates of their mass center? If the particles lie in a horizontal plane, where is the mass center? If the particles are located near the surface of the earth, where is the center of gravity in each case?
Ans.: $x^* = 5.25$ m, $y^* = 2.875$ m in each case.

2.7-2: A set of n masses $m_1, m_2, \ldots m_n$ at points $P_1, P_2, \ldots P_n$ has mass center $\mathbf{r}^*$. Some of the masses, say $1, 2, \ldots s$, are shifted to new positions $P_1', P_2', \ldots P_s'$ where the vector $\overline{P_1P_1'}$ is denoted by $\Delta\mathbf{r}_1$, the vector $\overline{P_2P_2'}$ by $\Delta\mathbf{r}_2$, etc. The mass center shifts from P^* to a point whose directed distance from P^* is given by the vector $\Delta\mathbf{r}^*$. Show that

$$\Delta\mathbf{r}^* = \frac{1}{m}\sum_{i=1}^{s} m_i\,\Delta\mathbf{r}_i, \quad \text{where } m = \sum_{i=1}^{n} m_i.$$

2.7-3: Three particles of masses m_1, m_2, m_3 are distances a, a, $a/2$ apart in a vertical plane near the earth's surface, as shown. Where is the center of gravity located relative to m_2?

2.7-4: The inner and outer radii of a uniform hemispherical shell are R_1 and R_0, respectively. What is the distance from the geometrical center of the shell to the mass center?

Ans.: $3(R_0+R_1)(R_0^2+R_1^2)/8(R_0^2+R_0R_1+R_1^2)$.

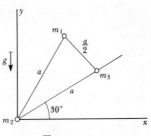

Exer. 2.7-3

2.7-5: Show that if an arc of a plane curve is revolved about an axis that the arc does not intersect, the area of the resulting surface is equal to the length of the arc multiplied by the length of the path of the centroid of the arc. (This is the other theorem of Pappus to which reference was made in Example 2.7-4.)

2.7-6: A plate is cut from a piece of sheet metal in the form of a parabola, being bounded by the curves $y=h[1-(x^2/a^2)]$ and $y=0$. Find the mass center.
Ans.: $y^* = 2h/5$.

2.7-7: Find the mass center of a paraboloidal solid bounded by the plane $y=0$ and the surface formed by rotating the curve $y=h[1-(x^2/a^2)]$, $y \geqq 0$, about the y-axis.
Ans.: $y^* = h/3$.

2.7-8: A container of mass m is filled with fluid of mass m'. Owing to a small hole in its bottom, fluid leaks out of the container. Show that the mass center of the system (fluid and container) is at a minimum height above the base of the container when the depth of fluid remaining in the container is the same as that height.

2.7-9: A child builds a staircase using blocks of length L, the overhang of each block being p. The staircase tumbles when a vertical line through the mass center of all but the bottom block falls outside the bottom block. Show that this occurs as soon as the total number of blocks used exceeds the number given by the expression L/p.

2.7-10: Show that if the child of the previous exercise has an unlimited number of blocks at his disposal he can, by shrewdly varying the amount of the overhang of each block, get the staircase to extend as far out from its base as he wishes.

2.7-11: Locate the mass center of the earth-fill dam whose cross-section is shown. The core has a density of 120 lb/ft³ while the outer fill has a density of 90 lb/ft³.

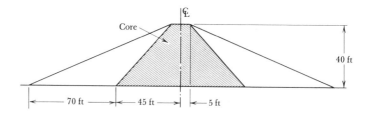

Exer. 2.7-11

2.7-12: Locate the mass center of the rotor whose cross-section is shown. The copper coils have a net density of 400 lb/ft³ while the steel frame has a density of 485 lb/ft³.

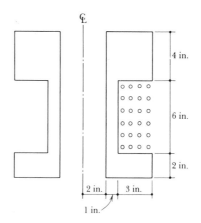

Exer. 2.7-12

2.7-13: Locate the mass center of the angle iron shown. Ignore the rounding of the corners.

Ans.: From corner of angle $x^* = 0.7$ in., $y^* = 2.2$ in.

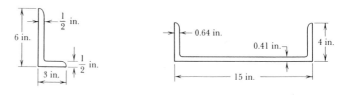

Exer. 2.7-13   **Exer. 2.7-14**

2.7-14: Locate the mass center of the channel section shown.
Ans.: 1.0 in. from base.

2.7-15: The gas in a spherical container is at an absolute pressure of five atmospheres. If the radius of the container is 10 ft, what is the magnitude of the single force equipollent to the net atmospheric and gas pressure acting on half the container?
Ans.: $2.66 (10)^6$ lb.

2.7-16: The simply-supported beam shown is subjected to a load distribution, as shown, of $p = p_0 \sin (\pi x/l)$ units of force per unit length. Replace the distribution by a single concentrated load; where does the load act?

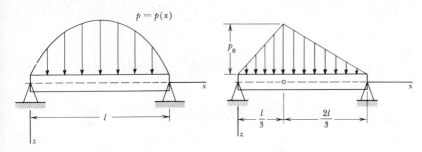

Exer. 2.7-16   Exer. 2.7-17

2.7-17: Solve Exercise 2.7-16 for the triangular load shown.

2.7-18: A circular rod of radius a is twisted by end loads τ lbs/in.^{2} in magnitude, directed perpendicularly to the radius line from the axis of the rod. Given that τ increases linearly with the radial distance r, replace the distributed force system by an equipollent resultant system.

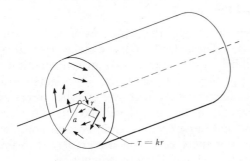

Exer. 2.7-18

CHAPTER III

Analysis of Statically
Determinate States of
Equilibrium

3.1 Statically Determinate and Statically Indeterminate Equilibrium

In the previous chapter the principles of mechanical equilibrium were developed. These lead to the conclusion that a mechanical system in equilibrium must satisfy certain mathematical relationships known as the equations of equilibrium. It is noteworthy that these equations are concerned only with the external forces acting on the system; they express the fact that these forces must have zero resultant in any direction and must produce zero moment about any axis. In the present chapter these equations are employed to investigate the equilibrium loads and equilibrium configurations of a number of systems commonly encountered in engineering practice. For the most part, discussion is restricted to loads applied at points (rather than to distributed loads, which are dealt with more fully in Chapter

IV) and to mechanical systems consisting of elements that deform so little under load that they may be regarded as rigid.

The first step in the analysis of the statical equilibrium of a mechanical system consists in isolating the system and drawing a free-body diagram that displays all the external forces and couples acting on the system—both those forces and couples whose magnitude and direction are known and those whose determination is the object of the analysis. The proper choice of a system, the decision as to what forces have to be considered in a meaningful analysis, and the representation of these forces as vectors is not always an easy matter. Good physical judgment is required at this point since we are really selecting an appropriate mathematical model of an engineering structure. Appropriate "model-making" is a skill developed by practice. Its possession is the hallmark of the well-trained engineer. Some of the more common representations of force systems were discussed in Chapter II and others are developed in the examples of this chapter.

Once a mechanical system has been isolated and the forces and couples acting on it have been identified, we may, supposing the system to be in equilibrium, write down the six independent scalar equations of equilibrium. Of course some of the equations may be what is technically known as *trivial*; that is, they may be of the form $0 = 0$. If, for example, the set of external forces and couples consists of forces all lying in one plane (say the xy-plane) they can have no moment about the x- and y-axes and no components in the z-direction. The equations that express these facts will then be trivial. We need not even bother to write them down. In this example, then, there could be no more than three non-trivial equations of equilibrium. The unknowns in the equations of equilibrium will be either forces of constraint which are not known initially and whose determination is the object of the analysis or else geometrical quantities, such as lengths or angles, which define the configuration of the system. These unknowns are constants so that the equations of equilibrium take the form of simultaneous algebraic (or trigonometric) equations. In dynamics, on the other hand, the governing equations of motion are differential equations. If the unknowns are concentrated forces or couples, the equations of equilibrium will be linear. When the equations of equilibrium can be solved so as to determine all the external forces and couples exerted by the constraints in order to hold the system in equilibrium, the system is said to be *statically determinate*. When they do not provide all the information needed for this purpose, the system is said to be *statically indeterminate* or *hyperstatic*.

Before we proceed to investigate the implications of statical determinacy and indeterminacy, the qualifying phrase "supposing the system to be in equilibrium" appearing at the outset of the preceding paragraph deserves brief reconsideration. To see what is implied by this reservation, consider a very simple illustration. A uniform bar 2 ft long, weighing 10 lb, is free to rotate about a smooth hinge or pin at one end, as shown in Fig. 3.1-1a. At the other end the bar

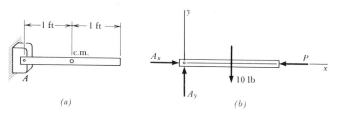

Fig. 3.1-1

carries an unknown horizontal force, P. Suppose we ask to know the magnitude of P required to maintain the bar in equilibrium in a horizontal position. The free-body diagram of the bar is shown in Fig. 3.1-1b. The sum of the moments of the external forces about the z-axis at A is -10 ft-lb and no possible values of P, A_x, and A_y

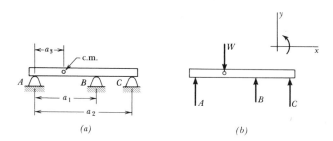

Fig. 3.1-2

will make the resultant moment vanish. The equations of equilibrium, therefore, will have no solution; i.e., there are no values of P, A_x, A_y which satisfy all of them. The physical interpretation of this situation is obvious; the horizontal position of the bar is not a possible equilibrium position under the applied loads and constraints. The system must move under the action of the forces applied, and the equations of dynamics must be employed. While it often may be easy to see by inspection of the free-body diagram whether a given configuration is or is not a possible equilibrium configuration, complex situations do arise in which only a careful analysis will reveal the existence or lack of existence of complete solutions of the equations of equilibrium.

The distinction between statically determinate and statically indeterminate states of equilibrium is a fundamental one in engineering. It too may be illustrated by means of a simple example. Consider a horizontal beam resting on three smooth supports at the same elevation, as shown in Fig. 3.1-2a. Its free-body diagram is shown in Fig. 3.1-2b. Since there are no horizontal forces, there are only two non-trivial equations of equilibrium:

$$\sum F_y = A + B + C - W = 0,$$

$$\sum M_A = Ba_1 + Ca_2 - Wa_3 = 0. \qquad \textbf{3.1-1}$$

The three unknown reactions, A, B, and C, cannot be found from the two equations of equilibrium. Nor will it help matters to attempt to find a third equation by taking a new set of axes or a new origin for the moment equation. If, for example, we take moments about an axis through B, we find

$$\sum M_B = -Aa_1 + C(a_2 - a_1) + W(a_1 - a_3) = 0. \qquad \textbf{3.1-2}$$

But this is the same thing as the first of Eqs. 3.1-1 multiplied by $-a_1$ and added to the second of Eqs. 3.1-1. It therefore provides no information not already inherent in Eqs. 3.1-1. Equations 3.1-1 and 3.1-2 are said to be *linearly dependent*. We cannot hope, therefore, to find all of the unknown reactions from the equations of equilibrium alone. Statical indeterminacy is the price we pay in this instance for idealizing our system and considering it to be rigid. In order to determine a solution, the equations of equilibrium must be supplemented by further information drawn from the mechanics of deformable bodies. If we can determine by computation or experiment that removal of the support at B would cause the beam to sag by a distance of 0.1 inch at B and that an upward force of 1 lb at B would produce an upward motion of 0.01 inches at B, we can, assuming displacement to be proportional to load, conclude that the actual reaction at the central support must be $B = 10$ lb. This additional information, together with the equations of equilibrium, readily determines the three reactions.

Another example of a statically indeterminate structure is a light bar connected by smooth pins to a large rigid body, as pictured in Fig. 3.1-3a. The three non-trivial equations of equilibrium ($\sum F_x = 0$, $\sum F_y = 0$, $\sum M_z = 0$) will not determine the four unknown components of the reactions at A and B. All they will tell us is that these end forces must be equal in magnitude and directed in opposite senses along the line joining the pins, i.e., that the bar is a two-force member. Since there are more unknowns than equations of equilibrium, we conclude that the bar is statically indeterminate. This example may serve to illustrate one of the important properties of a statically indeterminate structure: it may be in a state of self-strain even when no external load is applied. Suppose that the pins are at a distance l apart and that the holes in the bars are drilled at a distance

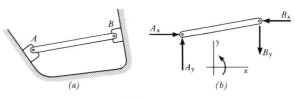

Fig. 3.1-3

$l - \epsilon$ apart. Then the bar will be in an initial state of tension whose magnitude can only be found by a consideration of the elastic properties of the bar. Similarly, a temperature change in the bar will produce a large stress due to the suppression by the attached body of the small change in length that would otherwise occur in free thermal expansion or contraction. In a statically determinate structure, on the other hand, small changes in the dimensions have only a minor influence on the loads carried by the members.

The engineer designing a structure or machine must frequently decide at the outset whether to employ a statically determinate or a statically indeterminate design. The former choice is to be preferred, for example, in the design of precision instruments whose readings are not supposed to reflect the ambient temperature, or for long bridges over three or more piers when the piers may be subject to slight settlement. On the other hand, a designer may deliberately select a statically indeterminate design in order to take advantage of the additional rigidity inherent in the extra constraint. The products of a technological civilization represent the designer's response to the sometimes conflicting requirements of function, economy, and reliability. It is always instructive to observe the ways in which these requirements have been answered.

For a system consisting of a single rigid body, such as the bar of the two previous paragraphs, statical determinacy or indeterminacy is relatively easy to recognize. When systems consist of many bodies connected together, even when the over-all structure is itself rigid, the determinacy of the problem is not as readily apparent. The

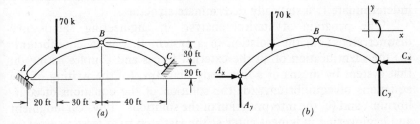

Fig. 3.1-4

equations for the entire structure may appear to lead to indeterminacy; but if we split the system into its parts and examine the equilibrium of all the separate parts, it may transpire that all the unknown external forces can be found. A simple illustration of this situation is provided by the so-called three-hinged arch pictured in Fig. 3.1-4a. We wish to find the reactions due to the presence of a 70,000 lb load located as shown. (Note the abbreviation: 70,000 lb = 70 kilopounds, written 70 k here; sometimes "kip" is used.) The free-body diagram of the arch, shown in Fig. 3.1-4b, contains four unknowns, just as did the free-body diagram of Fig. 3.1-3b. And, indeed, the equilibrium equations for the structure are

$$\sum F_x = A_x - C_x = 0,$$

$$\sum F_y = A_y + C_y - 70 = 0,$$

$$\sum M_B = 50A_x - 50A_y - 30C_x$$
$$+ 40C_y + 2100 = 0.$$

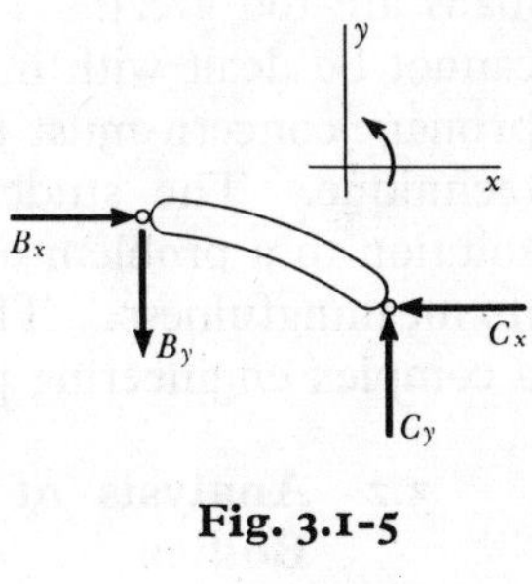

3.1-3

Fig. 3.1-5

If we now consider the segment BC alone, its free-body diagram (Fig. 3.1-5) introduces two new unknowns (the components of the force at B exerted by AB on BC) and three equations of equilibrium:

$$\sum F_x = B_x - C_x = 0,$$

$$\sum F_y = C_y - B_y = 0,$$

$$\sum M_B = 40C_y - 30C_x = 0.$$

3.1-4

These six equations suffice to determine the six unknowns. We find

$$A_x = 16 \text{ k}, \qquad B_x = 16 \text{ k}, \qquad C_x = 16 \text{ k},$$

$$A_y = 58 \text{ k}, \qquad B_y = 12 \text{ k}, \qquad C_y = 12 \text{ k}. \qquad 3.1\text{-}5$$

The presence of the third hinge at B changes the arch from a statically indeterminate to a statically determinate structure.

The program of statical analysis in engineering entails five distinct steps: (a) the isolation of a system that is in equilibrium; (b) the identification of all the external forces and couples acting on that system by means of a free-body diagram; (c) the writing of the equations of equilibrium; (d) the solution of the equations of equilibrium; and (e) the interpretation of the solution. Physical judgment and engineering judgment enter at the last step to at least as great an extent as at the first two. At the lowest level of judgment one must always ask whether the numerical solution obtained is a reasonable one. A reaction of 100,000 lb, when all the other forces involved are of about 100 lb magnitude, should probably be viewed with suspicion. Directions of vectors must be examined: a supposed cable tension should not turn out to be a compression, for example. More complex judgments arise when the results of the analysis are applied to considerations of design. A bar may buckle under the compressive load it must carry, or a cable may snap if the tension in it is too great. Deformation of the structural elements may not be negligible if the loads are too great. The more complex questions of this character cannot be dealt with in a first course to any appreciable extent; our primary concern must be the development of analytical method and technique. The student should be conscious, however, that his solution to a problem of mechanical analysis must be scrutinized for its meaningfulness. The solution itself is often only the first step in a complex engineering process.

3.2   Analysis of the Equilibrium of Systems of Rigid Bodies

In Section 3.1 the general program of statical analysis was described and a distinction was made between those cases in which the equations of equilibrium are sufficient by themselves to determine all the unknown forces of constraint and those cases in which they are not. In this section we consider efficient methods for the formulation and solution of the equations for statically determinate systems.

After a system has been isolated and the external forces acting on it have been identified, how shall the axes be chosen? Certainly it is never incorrect to write $\sum \mathbf{F} = \mathbf{0}$ and $\sum \mathbf{M}_O = \mathbf{0}$, where O is the origin of coordinates. There may, however, be better choices than the origin of coordinates as the base point for the moment equation. It may even be better to write a number of moment equations for different points rather than work with the force equation directly. By choosing our points or axes for the moment equation judiciously, the number of unknown quantities that appear in each equation can be held to a minimum. Often, axes can be chosen so that only one unknown appears in each equation. Considering the frailty of humans and the ease with which algebraic mistakes can be made in solving simultaneous equations, this is the proper choice of axes where possible. The labor of solving the equations of equilibrium is therefore greatly reduced if we pause, before writing any equations at all, to identify axes that are parallel or perpendicular to a number of unknown force components, or axes which such force components intersect.

The formalism of vector algebra is quite helpful in three-dimensional problems. It relieves much of the geometrical computation of skew moment arms and oblique components that would otherwise be necessary. In two-dimensional problems, where the forces all lie in a plane, vector notation is only a minor convenience and we can usually dispense with it. The most important function of vector notation is not that of a problem-solving aid. In any particular problem there is likely to be some special geometrical aspect that makes the use of a particular coordinate system advantageous. The vectorial notation is of value primarily because it is the natural language of statics and dynamics—and of electrodynamics and fluid mechanics as well—in which the principles of these subjects find their most succinct form of expression.

It is important to realize, as was pointed out in Section 3.1, that there are not more than six independent scalar equilibrium equations for a given mechanical system (three for a strictly planar model). Once one has the appropriate number of independent equations for a given system, no amount of additional equation writing for that system will lead to information not already contained in (if difficult at times to extract from) the original set. If, however, the system consists of n bodies interconnected in some way, we may profitably write the equations of equilibrium for any $n-1$ subdivisions of the original system in addition to the equilibrium equations for the system as a whole. In this procedure the third law of motion plays a fundamental role. When the original system is split up, new unknown forces must be introduced to represent the mechanical interaction between the parts of the system. We need not, however, introduce a complete set of new unknowns for each subsystem; the third law requires us to use, except for a reversal of direction, the same force for each pair of subsystems at their mutual point of contact. Therefore, when we increase the number of equilibrium equations we do not increase the number of new unknowns to the same extent.

Complex systems may be classified according to the amount of restraint placed on them. As we have seen, a rigid body can be completely constrained against motion in space if three of its points are fixed by means of six independent constraints against rotation and translation. Similarly, a body whose motion is restricted to a plane can be completely constrained if two points are fixed. More complex systems can also be constrained if each of the parts is constrained, directly or through connections to the other points. If a system is underconstrained, i.e., still has one or more possible modes of motion, it is called a *mechanism*; if it is completely constrained against motion, it is called a *frame*. Since mechanisms are open to the possibility of motion under the applied forces, equilibrium problems for mechanisms usually involve position or angle coordinate unknowns as well as force unknowns. Only certain configurations of the mechanism can be equilibrium configurations. These configurations will, in general, be different for different sets of applied loads. Frames, on the other hand, are fixed in space, or in a plane, by the constraint conditions. The equilibrium configuration is therefore known in advance and the only unknowns appearing in the analysis are the forces carried by the different parts of the frame. It is important to examine constraint conditions carefully, not only in order to represent the forces of constraint properly, but also in order to decide whether complete constraint is present or not.

We now turn to specific examples illustrating these points.

Example 3.2-1

   The 100 lb boom supports a 500 lb load at its end and is in turn supported in a vertical plane by a smooth pin connection and a light inextensible cable (Fig. 3.2-1a). The boom may be treated as a uniform bar. Dimensions are shown. Find the cable tension and the pin reaction.

   Solution: In Figs. 3.2-1b, c, and d, three different free-body diagrams are shown. In the first, we have split the system into two parts, the boom and the load (treated as a particle) separately. In the second and third, the load is part of the system; and in the third, the cable is part of the system also. The pin reaction is represented by its horizontal and vertical components (P_x, P_y), assumed positive in the directions shown. The cable tension is of unknown magnitude T in a known direction. The weight force of the boom is placed at its midpoint, since we treat the boom as uniform.

In Fig. 3.2-1b, the third law of motion has been used to write Q as the magnitude of the two forces, one on the boom and the opposite one on the load, exerted by the supporting cord on each member. In truth, one should also show the cord, with opposing forces of magnitude Q on it. It is clear, however, that $Q = 500$ lb for equilibrium of the load, and we

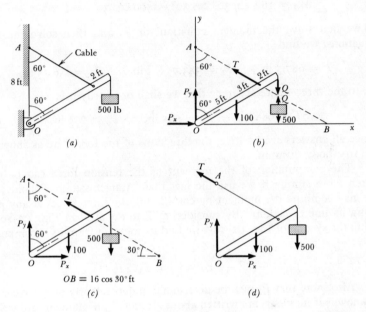

Fig. 3.2-1

would ordinarily go immediately to one of the last two diagrams or replace Q on the first diagram by 500 lb, without the formal intermediate step of solving for it.

We may now write the equilibrium equations for the system of Fig. 3.2-1c. The force equations of equilibrium are

$$\sum F_x = P_x - T \cos 30° = 0,$$

$$\sum F_y = P_y + T \sin 30° - 600 = 0. \qquad \textbf{3.2-1}$$

The moment equation should be taken about the pin, since that eliminates the unknowns (P_x, P_y) from consideration. The moment is about the z-axis at O, but, since this is a plane problem, we suppress designation of the axis and speak simply of the "moment about O." The moment of $\mathbf{T}$ is computed by the $M_z = xT_y - yT_x$ formulation. The tension force $\mathbf{T}$ is split into components $T_x = -T \cos 30°$, $T_y = T \sin 30°$, with $x = 8 \cos 30°$, $y = 8 \sin 30°$ being the coordinates of its point of application:

$$\sum M_O = (8 \cos 30°)(T \sin 30°) - (8 \sin 30°)(-T \cos 30°)$$
$$-(5 \cos 30°)(100) - (10 \cos 30°)(500) = 0,$$

or

$$\sum M_O = 16 T \sin 30° \cos 30° - 5500 \cos 30° = 0. \qquad \textbf{3.2-2}$$

If we first solve the moment equation for T, and then solve the force equations, we find

$$T = 687.5 \text{ lb}, \qquad P_x = 343.75\sqrt{3} \text{ lb}, \qquad P_y = 256.25 \text{ lb},$$

or, to the three-figure accuracy that we shall ordinarily use,

$$T = 688 \text{ lb}, \qquad P_x = 595 \text{ lb}, \qquad P_y = 256 \text{ lb}. \qquad \textbf{3.2-3}$$

Since all answers are positive, the directions of the forces are as shown on the free-body diagram.

The computation of the moment of the tension force can be done much more simply if we use the fact that "transmissibility" holds; i.e., we may compute the moment by considering the force to act at any point along its line of action. By considering **T** to act at A in Fig. 3.2-1c—or using the system of Fig. 3.2-1d—we find its moment from its x-component only:

$$-(8)(-T \cos 30°) = 4\sqrt{3}T.$$

Also, note that P_x may be determined independently of the other two unknowns if moments are written about A; and P_y, if moments are written about B (Fig. 3.2-1c):

$$\sum M_A = 8P_x - (5 \cos 30°)(100) - (10 \cos 30°)(500) = 0,$$

$$\sum M_B = -(16 \cos 30°)P_y + (11 \cos 30°)(100) + (6 \cos 30°)(500) = 0. \quad \textbf{3.2-4}$$

The only problem here is in the determination of the location of point B where the lines of action of T and P_x intersect. The three equations of equilibrium $\sum M_O = 0$, $\sum M_A = 0$, $\sum M_B = 0$ (Eqs. 3.2-2 and 3.2-4) are completely equivalent to the original set (Eqs. 3.2-1 and 3.2-2) $\sum F_x = 0$, $\sum F_y = 0$, $\sum M_O = 0$. If the three moment equations are used, the force equations should be automatically satisfied, and hence may be used as a check on the accuracy of the computations.

Example 3.2-2

Consider the boom and load of the last example again, but now supported by two cables as shown in Fig. 3.2-2a; instead of a pin at O, the support is a ball-and-socket joint. Write governing equilibrium equations and solve.

Solution: The boom and load are still in the vertical *xy*-plane.   The
support reaction now has a *z*-component, P_z.   The two cable tensions are
denoted by T_1 and T_2.   The free-body diagram is given in Fig. 3.2-2b.
Note that there are five scalar unknowns: P_x, P_y, P_z, T_1, and T_2.   There
are also five non-trivial independent equilibrium equations.   Since all
forces, known and unknown, have lines of action intersecting the boom,
the moment about the line *OE* must automatically vanish.   Thus some
linear combination of any six equilibrium equations must reduce to the
trivial $0=0$ form; only five are independent.

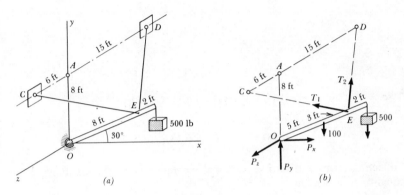

(a)   (b)

Fig. 3.2-2

Here vectorial methods are of aid in the computation.   We may write
the two weight forces as $-100\mathbf{j}$, $-500\mathbf{j}$ and the reaction force at O as
$\mathbf{P}=P_x\mathbf{i}+P_y\mathbf{j}+P_z\mathbf{k}$ immediately.   The vectorial form of the tension forces
requires the computation of the unit vectors from E to C and D:

$$\mathbf{r}_{EC} = \mathbf{r}_C-\mathbf{r}_E = (8\mathbf{j}+6\mathbf{k})-(4\sqrt{3}\mathbf{i}+4\mathbf{j}) = -4\sqrt{3}\mathbf{i}+4\mathbf{j}+6\mathbf{k} \text{ ft;}$$

$$\mathbf{r}_{ED} = \mathbf{r}_D-\mathbf{r}_E = (8\mathbf{j}-15\mathbf{k})-(4\sqrt{3}\mathbf{i}+4\mathbf{j}) = -4\sqrt{3}\mathbf{i}+4\mathbf{j}-15\mathbf{k} \text{ ft;}$$

$$\mathbf{e}_{EC} = \mathbf{r}_{EC}/|\mathbf{r}_{EC}| = -\frac{2\sqrt{3}}{5}\mathbf{i}+\frac{2}{5}\mathbf{j}+\frac{3}{5}\mathbf{k};$$

$$\mathbf{e}_{ED} = \mathbf{r}_{ED}/|\mathbf{r}_{ED}| = -\frac{4\sqrt{3}}{17}\mathbf{i}+\frac{4}{17}\mathbf{j}-\frac{15}{17}\mathbf{k}.$$

Therefore, we may write

$$\mathbf{T}_1 = T_1\left(-\frac{2\sqrt{3}}{5}\mathbf{i}+\frac{2}{5}\mathbf{j}+\frac{3}{5}\mathbf{k}\right), \qquad \mathbf{T}_2 = T_2\left(-\frac{4\sqrt{3}}{17}\mathbf{i}+\frac{4}{17}\mathbf{j}-\frac{15}{17}\mathbf{k}\right).$$

We now proceed to the writing of the equations of equilibrium.   Writing
the moment equation about O is an obvious first step, since the unknown $\mathbf{P}$
is eliminated from consideration.   Whether one proceeds directly to the

scalar equations by writing the moments about the x-, y-, and z-axes in turn or by writing the vector equation first is a matter of taste; we choose the latter procedure.   We have

$$\sum \mathbf{M}_O = \mathbf{0} = 5\left(\frac{\sqrt{3}}{2}\mathbf{i}+\frac{1}{2}\mathbf{j}\right)\times(-100\mathbf{j})+10\left(\frac{\sqrt{3}}{2}\mathbf{i}+\frac{1}{2}\mathbf{j}\right)\times(-500\mathbf{j})$$

$$+\mathbf{r}_E\times\mathbf{T}_1+\mathbf{r}_E\times\mathbf{T}_2$$

$$= -2750\sqrt{3}\mathbf{k}+\frac{4T_1}{5}\begin{vmatrix}\mathbf{i} & \mathbf{j} & \mathbf{k}\\ \sqrt{3} & 1 & 0\\ -2\sqrt{3} & 2 & 3\end{vmatrix}$$

$$+\frac{4T_2}{17}\begin{vmatrix}\mathbf{i} & \mathbf{j} & \mathbf{k}\\ \sqrt{3} & 1 & 0\\ -4\sqrt{3} & 4 & -15\end{vmatrix}$$

$$= -2750\sqrt{3}\mathbf{k}+\frac{4T_1}{5}(3\mathbf{i}-3\sqrt{3}\mathbf{j}+4\sqrt{3}\mathbf{k})$$

$$+\frac{4T_2}{17}(-15\mathbf{i}+15\sqrt{3}\mathbf{j}+8\sqrt{3}\mathbf{k}).$$

Collecting terms and setting each scalar component of the resultant vector equal to zero, we have

$$\sum M_x^O = \frac{12}{5}T_1-\frac{60}{17}T_2 = 0,$$

$$\sum M_y^O = -\frac{12}{5}\sqrt{3}T_1+\frac{60}{17}\sqrt{3}T_2 = 0, \qquad \textbf{3.2-5}$$

$$\sum M_z^O = \frac{16}{5}\sqrt{3}T_1+\frac{32}{17}\sqrt{3}T_2-2750\sqrt{3} = 0.$$

From the first, we find $T_1=(25/17)T_2$; from the third, then,

$$T_2 = (17)(2750)/(112) = 417 \text{ lb}, \qquad T_1 = (25)(2750)/(112) = 614 \text{ lb}.$$

Notice that the $\sum M_y$ equation is automatically satisfied when the $\sum M_x$ equation is, and conversely.   The two are not independent.   This is a reflection of the fact that the moment about axis OE must vanish, and that the axis OE lies in the xy-plane through O.

Now that the tensions have been determined, we can write the force equations to determine $\mathbf{P}$.   In this case, these equations are relatively straightforward:

$$\sum \mathbf{F} = \mathbf{P}+\mathbf{T}_1+\mathbf{T}_2-600\mathbf{j} = \mathbf{0},$$

or

$$\sum F_x = P_x - \frac{2}{5}\sqrt{3}T_1 - \frac{4}{17}\sqrt{3}\,T_2 = 0,$$

$$\sum F_y = P_y + \frac{2}{5}\,T_1 + \frac{4}{17}\,T_2 - 600 = 0, \qquad \text{3.2-6}$$

$$\sum F_z = P_z + \frac{3}{5}\,T_1 - \frac{15}{17}\,T_2 = 0.$$

However, note that P_x can be determined easily independently of the others by writing an additional moment equation—an equation about the z-axis through A, i.e., the axis DAC. Since $\mathbf{T}_1$, $\mathbf{T}_2$, and $P_y\mathbf{j}$ have lines of action that intersect the axis DAC, they have no moment about it; since $P_z\mathbf{k}$ is parallel to the axis, it has zero moment about the axis. Only the known weight forces and $P_x\mathbf{i}$ have moment:

$$\sum M_z^A = \sum \mathbf{M}_A \cdot \mathbf{k} = 8P_x - (5\cos 30°)(100) - (10\cos 30°)(500) = 0. \quad \text{3.2-7}$$

This is, of course, the same equation as the first of Eqs. 3.2-4 in the last example, and P_x has the same value, 595 lb. If Eq. 3.2-7 is taken as a basic equilibrium equation, then the first of 3.2-6 can no longer be so considered but may be used as a check. Similarly, since axis AE extended intersects both x- and y-axes, none of the forces except $P_z\mathbf{k}$ can have moment about it; therefore, $P_z = 0$. [This result may also be found from the last of Eqs. 3.2-6, once we know that $T_1 = (25/17)T_2$.]

Finally, P_y may be determined from the second of Eqs. 3.2-6:

$$P_y = 600 - \frac{2}{5}\,T_1 - \frac{4}{17}\,T_2 = 600 - \frac{14}{17}\,T_2 = 600 - 344 = 256 \text{ lb},$$

the same as the P_y of Example 3.2-1.

To summarize, we see that our preliminary analysis showed the problem to be statically determinate, with five unknowns and five independent equations. The five independent equations can be chosen in a number of ways. In particular, the four moment equations $\sum M_x^O = \sum M_z^O = \sum M_z^A = \sum M_{AE} = 0$ and the force equation $\sum F_y = 0$ form one such set; $\sum M_x^O = \sum M_z^O = 0$ and $\sum F_x = \sum F_y = \sum F_z = 0$ form another.

Example 3.2-3

A rigid plane frame (Fig. 3.2-3a) is constructed of two light rigid bars, AC and BC, pinned smoothly together at C and to the foundation at A and B. The frame is subjected to the 50 lb load at C as shown. Discuss the equilibrium of the frame.

Solution: A free-body diagram of the frame is shown in Fig. 3.2-3b, together with the coordinate system to be used. Before analyzing the equilibrium state, let us assure ourselves that this is a rigid frame. Each bar has at most three degrees of freedom in the plane, so the system could have six. Fixing A and B by pins fixes four of the six coordinates needed; fixing point C then indeed fixes the angles between the bars and the x-axis.

There are four unknowns, A_x, A_y, B_x, and B_y, as shown—or, equivalently, the magnitudes $A = [A_x^2 + A_y^2]^{1/2}$, $B = [B_x^2 + B_y^2]^{1/2}$ and the directions $\theta_A = \arctan (A_y/A_x)$, $\theta_B = \arctan (B_y/B_x)$ from the x-axis to the lines of the forces—and but three independent equations:

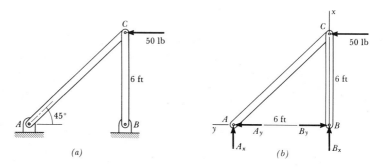

Fig. 3.2-3

$$\sum F_x = A_x + B_x = 0,$$
$$\sum F_y = A_y - B_y + 50 = 0,\qquad\qquad \textbf{3.2-8}$$
$$\sum M_B = (6)(50) - (6)(A_x) = 0.$$

We see that $A_x = -B_x = 50$ lb; that is, we have guessed wrong on the direction of B_x. However, *we do not change the diagram*; we leave it as it is and work with $B_x = -50$ lb. The second of Eqs. 3.2-8 provides a relation

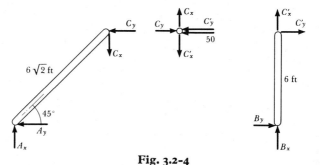

Fig. 3.2-4

between A_y and B_y, but that is all; no more information can be gained by writing any more equations. If *ABC* were a single rigid body, we would be finished. But let us split the system into its component parts and see what happens.

Now consider three subsystems: the bar AC, the bar BC, and the pin at C. (We are purposely making the analysis more complex than is necessary in order to show features that are taken for granted later on.) In Fig. 3.2-4, free-body diagrams are shown with the 50 lb load applied to the pin. Note that the reaction forces at A and B are shown in exactly the same way

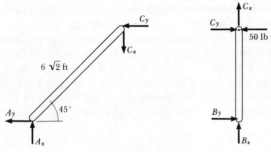

Fig. 3.2-5

here as they were in Fig. 3.2-3b. The force exerted by the pin on AC is denoted by components C_x and C_y with assumed directions as shown; the oppositely directed force is exerted on the pin by the bar. Similarly, C'_x and C'_y denote the force components for the reactions between the pin and bar BC.

The analysis may now be completed in a number of ways. The three equations for AC, coupled with $A_x = 50$ lb from our previous solution,

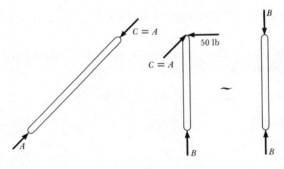

Fig. 3.2-6

determine C_x, C_y, and A_y. The two pin equations then can be used for C'_x, C'_y; and the second of Eqs. 3.2-8, for B_y. The equations for BC may then be used as checking equations.

Let us examine alternative ways of analysis, and particularly a simple method based on the "two-force member" concept. First, it should be noted that the solution for the forces at A and B would be the same wherever the 50 lb force is considered to act: on the pin or on either one of the bars.   The values of the C_x, C_y, C_x', C_y' forces will change; but not the values of A_x, A_y, B_x, and B_y.   Second, we need not separate the pin as a separate element; we can consider it as part of one of the bars.   If the pin is part of BC, then the free-body diagrams of the subsystems appear as in Fig. 3.2-5. The analysis is correspondingly simpler, with two unknowns fewer appearing.

Finally, all of this has been much too complicated from the beginning. Examining Fig. 3.2-5, we see that both bars are loaded only at their ends. Replacing the forces at each point by the resultant at that point, we see that each member is a two-force member, and that we may therefore determine the lines of action of the unknown forces, if not their magnitudes, for equilibrium (Fig. 3.2-6).   Indeed, recognizing that each bar is a two-force member, we need not split our system at all, but can put in the reactions at A and B in the proper directions to begin with (Fig. 3.2-7).   Moment

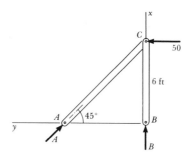

Fig. 3.2-7

equilibrium about pin C is now automatically satisfied.   Only two equations remain for the two unknowns A and B:

$$\sum F_x = B + A(\sqrt{2}/2) = 0,$$

$$\sum F_y = 50 - A(\sqrt{2}/2) = 0, \qquad\qquad \textbf{3.2-9}$$

from which we find

$$A = 50\sqrt{2}\ \text{lb}, \qquad B = -50\ \text{lb}. \qquad\qquad \textbf{3.2-10}$$

The sign of B, of course, signifies that we have chosen the wrong direction for B originally; bar BC is really in tension, while AC is in compression.

A frame such as this, consisting of two-force members, is called a *truss*; it consists of members joined at their ends and loaded only at the joints, with the weights of the bars being ignored or replaced by equipollent loads at the joints.   Analysis of trusses is the subject of the next section.

Example 3.2-4

The crank-connecting rod-piston mechanism is observed to be at rest in the position shown (Fig. 3.2-8). The uniform 5 ft crank *OA* weighs 20 lb; the 10 ft connecting rod *AB* is light; and the piston *P*, which slides in the smooth but tightly fitting vertical cylinder, weighs 10 lb. All pin connections are smooth. What must be the force of compression on the gas in the cylinder?

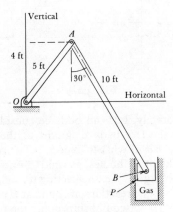

Fig. 3.2-8

Solution: This is a single-degree-of-freedom system; knowing the angle between, say, the horizontal and the crank *OA* determines the position of the whole system, but that angle is free to change since the system is not completely constrained. We are here concerned with finding the forces necessary to hold the mechanism in equilibrium in a certain position, and, although probable, it is not at all clear that a compressive force on the gas, and hence on the piston, will in fact accomplish this.

There is another aspect to this problem that deserves consideration before the exact formulation is made. We are asking here for only one of the forces, not all, needed for equilibrium, and we shall therefore attempt to set up an analysis that will determine that force as quickly as possible without finding too many of the other unknown constraint forces.

In Fig. 3.2-9, we draw a free-body diagram of the whole system. F denotes the force magnitude we wish to determine; N, the resultant normal reaction from the walls of the cylinder on the piston; and Q_x, Q_y, the components of the pin reaction at O. A set of axes is shown, as well as all dimensions of interest. Here we have four unknowns, and only the three independent equations for a plane system. Since there is no equation governing F alone immediately apparent, let us write no equations at all but proceed directly to consideration of subsystems. Here there are three: the piston P, the crank OA, and the connecting rod AB. The pins need

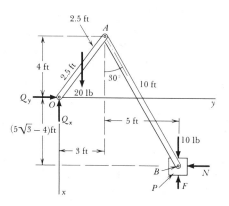

Fig. 3.2-9

not be considered separately, but can both be considered as part, say, of *AB*. Before drawing the free-body diagrams of the parts, however, we make a preliminary analysis of what to expect. The piston is to be treated as a particle; each of the other bodies, as rigid. Furthermore, *AB*—since we are considering it as "light," i.e., neglecting its weight—may be treated as a two-force member. The reactions at *A* and at *B* on *AB* must therefore be negatives of one another for equilibrium; only the piston and crank need be considered (Fig. 3.2-10a, b).

We see that, to determine *F*, only two equations need be written. The moment equation $\sum M_O = 0$ on *OA* determines *R*, the magnitude of the thrust carried by *AB*. The vertical force equation of equilibrium $\sum F_x = 0$ on *P* then determines *F*. We have, on *OA*,

$$\sum M_O = (3)(R \cos 30°) + (4)(R \sin 30°) - (1.5)(20) = 0,$$

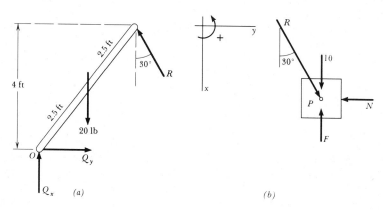

Fig. 3.2-10

$$(2 + 1.5\sqrt{3})R = 30; \qquad\qquad \textbf{3.2-11}$$

and on P:

$$\sum F_x = 10 + R \cos 30° - F = 0,$$

$$F = 10 + R \cos 30° = 10 + \frac{\sqrt{3}}{2}\left(\frac{30}{2 + 1.5\sqrt{3}}\right),$$

$$F = 15.6 \text{ lb}. \qquad\qquad \textbf{3.2-12}$$

Example 3.2-5

A bent shaft ABC is carried in smooth bearings at D and E, as shown. At C a 96 lb-in. torque is applied about the axis BC (clockwise as viewed from C

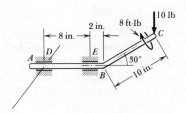

Fig. 3.2-11

to B) and a force of 10 lb acts at right angles to the plane of ABC. What torque Q must be applied to the bar at A, about the axis AB, in order to maintain equilibrium?   What forces will be exerted on the bearings?

Solution: The free-body diagram of the shaft is shown in Fig. 3.2-12. Note that vectors representing both forces and couples appear in the free-

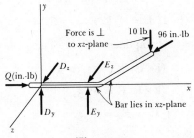

Fig. 3.2-12

body diagram.   These must not be confused and the mistake of adding couple vectors to force vectors must not be made.   (Some people denote the couple vector by a double-headed or double-shafted arrow in order to lessen the danger of making this error.) There is a real advantage in vector representation here because the couples are completely specified by their vectors and these enter the moment equations very simply. The equations of equilibrium are

$$\sum \mathbf{F} = \mathbf{D} + \mathbf{E} - 10\mathbf{j} = \mathbf{0},$$

$$\sum \mathbf{M}_D = Q\mathbf{i} + 8\mathbf{i} \times \mathbf{E} + (18.7\mathbf{i} - 5\mathbf{k}) \times (-10\mathbf{j}) + (-83\mathbf{i} + 48\mathbf{k}) = \mathbf{0}. \qquad \textbf{3.2-13}$$

We can now write $\mathbf{D} = D_y\mathbf{j} + D_z\mathbf{k}$ and $\mathbf{E} = E_y\mathbf{j} + E_z\mathbf{k}$ and separate these vector equations into scalar ones by equating the $\mathbf{i}$, $\mathbf{j}$, $\mathbf{k}$ components separately to zero. As a matter of fact the moment equation gives the wanted torque, Q, at once. The term $\mathbf{i} \times \mathbf{E}$ cannot have an $\mathbf{i}$-component. Therefore,

$$Q - 50 - 83 = 0 \quad \text{and} \quad Q = 133 \text{ lb-in.} \qquad \textbf{3.2-14}$$

Note that Q must be a clockwise torque, as viewed from A to B; this follows from the positive sign of Q in our analysis, the sense in which the $\mathbf{Q}$ vector was taken in the free-body diagram, and from the right-hand rule. Note also that if left-handed coordinate axes had mistakenly been employed, we would have got a numerically incorrect answer for Q.

Returning now to the bearing reactions, $\mathbf{E}$ is readily found from the moment equation and then $\mathbf{D}$ from the force equation. From the moment equation we have

$$\mathbf{i} \times \mathbf{E} = 17.3\mathbf{k}.$$

This makes it obvious that $\mathbf{E}$ is a vector $17.3\mathbf{j}$, but if the right-hand side of the above expression contained a $\mathbf{j}$-component as well as a $\mathbf{k}$-component the determination of $\mathbf{E}$ would be less transparent. We can, of course, always write $\mathbf{E} = E_y\mathbf{j} + E_z\mathbf{k}$ and use the scalar forms of the vector expression. But it is neater to utilize vector algebra:

$$(\mathbf{i} \times \mathbf{E}) \cdot \mathbf{j} = 17.3\mathbf{k} \cdot \mathbf{j} = 0,$$

$$(\mathbf{j} \times \mathbf{i}) \cdot \mathbf{E} = -\mathbf{k} \cdot \mathbf{E} = -E_z = 0.$$

This determines one of the components of $\mathbf{E}$. The other is found similarly:

$$(\mathbf{i} \times \mathbf{E}) \cdot \mathbf{k} = 17.3\mathbf{k} \cdot \mathbf{k},$$

$$(\mathbf{k} \times \mathbf{i}) \cdot \mathbf{E} = 17.3,$$

$$\mathbf{j} \cdot \mathbf{E} = E_y = 17.3.$$

The force $\mathbf{E}$ is, therefore,

$$\mathbf{E} = 17.3\mathbf{j} \text{ lb.} \qquad \textbf{3.2-15}$$

The force equation now yields $\mathbf{D}$:

$$\mathbf{D} = 10\mathbf{j} - \mathbf{E} = -7.3\mathbf{j} \text{ lb.} \qquad \textbf{3.2-16}$$

A final word: we are asked to find the forces exerted *on the bearings*. In the above equations the symbols **D** and **E** represent forces exerted by the bearings on the shaft. We conclude that the force exerted by the shaft on the bearing at D will be 7.3 lb in the direction of the positive y-axis (i.e., upward) and that the force exerted by the shaft on the bearing at E will be 17.3 lb in the direction of the negative y-axis (i.e., downward).

Example 3.2-6

An open-ended cylindrical tube of radius R and weight W', containing two smooth spheres of radius r and weight W, is placed on a smooth table with its axis vertical. As shown in Fig. 3.2.13a, $\frac{1}{2}R < r < R$. Show that this arrangement will tip over if r/R is less than $1 - (W'/2W)$.

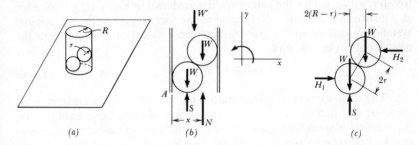

(a)   (b)   (c)

Fig. 3.2-13

Solution: We take as our system the tube and the two spheres. The free-body diagram of this system is shown in Fig. 3.2-13b. Note that this view is a cross-section containing the axis of the cylinder and the centers of the two spheres. The system is subject to the weight forces W' and W; since the mass center of the tube is on its axis, W' is shown acting along the vertical axis of the tube. The tube also comes in contact with the table that supports it. This contact is made all around the base. Its resultant is an upward force, N, acting at an unknown distance, x, from the left-hand edge, A, of the cylinder. Since the table is supposed to be smooth, there is no horizontal component. The system also comes in contact with the table at the point where the lower sphere touches the table. Here there is a normal contact force denoted S. The equations of equilibrium for the system are

$$\sum F_y = S + N - W' - 2W = 0,$$

$$\sum M_A = Nx + Sr - W'R - Wr - W(2R - r) = 0. \qquad \textbf{3.2-17}$$

These are the only non-trivial equations of equilibrium because there are no horizontal forces. Since there are three unknowns, S, N, and x, we cannot hope to find them from these two equations. We therefore pass on to a consideration of one of the possible subsystems.   Here we are faced with a choice.   Shall we isolate the upper sphere, the lower sphere, or the two of them?   In the long run it does not matter what choice we make because a systematic investigation of the subsystems will always lead to the same conclusion.   But human analysis is fallible, and it therefore pays to take the most direct path.   Our choice is guided by the following considerations.   Since the spheres are smooth, the forces acting on each will all intersect at the center of that sphere; therefore we will get only two non-trivial equations of equilibrium for each sphere.   But, with each sphere, there are two new unknown forces, the force exerted by the other sphere and the force exerted by the cylinder; therefore neither sphere, taken separately, will immediately yield a new relation between S, N, and x.   Since we must eventually consider both spheres, it will be best to do so at once.   The free-body diagram for the pair of spheres is shown in Fig. 3.2-13c.   We see at a glance that $S = 2W$.   Returning to the force equation for the original system, we find $N = W'$.   Substituting these values of S and N into the moment equation, we find

$$x = R + \frac{2W}{W'}(R - r).$$ 3.2-18

The analysis now requires interpretation.   Will the arrangement be stable or will it tip?   In order for the arrangement to be in equilibrium, the reaction N must lie somewhere inside the cross-section of the cylinder; that is, x must be greater than zero and less than $2R$.   Now the largest value of r produces the smallest value of x.   This largest value is $r = R$ (if r is any bigger the spheres won't fit in the cylinder); therefore the minimum value of x is $x = R$.   This is certainly greater than zero and less than $2R$, so there is no danger of the cylinder tipping over to the left.   On the other hand, x will be greater than $2R$ if

$$\frac{2W}{W'}(R - r) > R.$$ 3.2-19

Since both sides of this inequality are positive, we may multiply them by any positive number without altering the inequality.   Multiplying by $W'/2WR$ we have

$$1 - \frac{r}{R} > \frac{W'}{2W}.$$

Again, both sides of the inequality are positive numbers.   If we multiply them each by the same negative number, we reverse the sign of the inequality.   Multiplying by -1, we have

$$\frac{r}{R} - 1 < -\frac{W'}{2W}.$$

And now adding $+1$ to each side we see that x will be greater than $2R$ if

$$\frac{r}{R} < 1 - \frac{W'}{2W}.$$ 3.2-20

The cylinder will tip over to the right if this condition is fulfilled.   In particular, we see that if the tube is light enough it will always tip.   That is, for a given r, R, and W, we can always pick W' small enough so that $1 - \dfrac{W'}{2W}$ is as close to one in value as we wish and hence greater than r/R.

A different insight into the conditions for tipping is gained by studying the forces exerted by the spheres on the cylinder wall.   This is left to the exercises for the reader.

3.3   Analysis of Trusses

In this section and the next, methods previously developed for the analysis of statically determinate structures are applied in areas of technological importance, i.e., the determination of the loads carried by truss structures and frames.   This analysis is an essential concomitant of design: once the loads to be carried are known, the

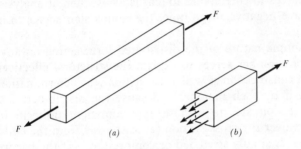

Fig. 3.3-1

member can be proportioned to bear them safely.   We begin with the simplest and most commonly encountered of all structures constructed of subunits, the *truss*.   A truss is a structure, either planar or three-dimensional, made of members each of which is a two-force body. That is, each member of the truss is attached to other members, or to the foundation, at two and only two points, and each is loaded only at those points.   Furthermore, the term is restricted to structures that may be considered to be rigid when all the members are treated as rigid bodies.   A truss is therefore a special kind of frame.   It is not a mechanism.

In practice the members or subunits of a truss, known as *bars*, are long and straight, being made up, in the case of metal trusses, of lengths of the common rolled sections—channels, angles, and wide-flange sections, with or without cover plates.   Forces (and not couples) are applied to the bars at their ends, which are called *joints*.

Since the bar is a two-force member, these forces must be equal in magnitude and opposite in direction. There are two possible situations that may arise, depending on whether the forces applied to the bar are directed toward or away from the middle of the bar. The latter case is pictured in Fig. 3.3-1a, the forces being denoted by the symbol F. If we pass a section through the bar and construct the free-body diagram of either of the two parts thus created, the action of the part removed on the part being considered consists in a stress distributed over the cross-section, as shown in Fig. 3.3-1b. This distributed force is equipollent to a concentrated force equal in magnitude and opposite in direction to the force F applied to the uncut end. We say that the bar is carrying a tensile load of magnitude F. In the other possible case the forces F are directed toward the middle of the bar and we say that the bar carries a compressive load of magnitude F. Some engineers make a practice of assuming all initially unknown forces to correspond to tensile loads; then, if analysis shows them to have negative magnitude, the minus sign serves to indicate compression.

The simple nature of the distributed force acting on any cross-section of a truss bar serves to explain the structural effectiveness of this type of construction as well as to facilitate the determination of the loads carried by each member. Because the distributed forces on any cross-section are, to a close approximation, uniform in their distribution over the cross-section (at least away from the ends of the bar), the bar is simply stretched or compressed. If the bar were not straight, or if a load were applied at a third point of the bar in a direction transverse to the axis of the bar, the bar would bend as well as stretch. The distributed forces acting on any cross-section would be equipollent to a force and a couple instead of simply to an axial force. This situation has been described in Section 2.7, and will be discussed further in Section 4.3, where the forces in beams are discussed. For the present we note that the designer of a truss is at some pains to ensure that loads shall be applied to the bars only at their ends and that these loads shall not consist of couples of any appreciable magnitude. To apply loads only at the joints, the designer arranges, where necessary, for a subsidiary system of floor beams and stringers to carry load to the joints, rather than allow this load to be applied directly to the bars. Of course the dead weight of the truss members themselves cannot be carried in this way. However, since the truss is intended to carry a load other than its own weight, the dead load of any member is usually small enough to permit it to be taken into account, where necessary, by concentrated forces equal to half the weight of the member applied at each end of the member. The joints themselves are sometimes known as *pins*, a nomenclature that survives from days when the members were solid bars of rectangular cross-section with enlarged ends (eye-bars) in which holes were drilled for steel rods.   The rods, or pins, passed through such holes in all the members meeting at a common joint.   If the pins had been smooth and the holes a loose fit, they would indeed have prevented the application of any couple to the ends of the members. The contact pressures used, however, were so high that these joints never were the smooth, freely turning joints that the theory presupposes.   Today most joints are made by riveting, welding, or bolting the adjacent members to a common gusset plate.   We can still treat the joint as a smooth pin, however, because the member is so long,

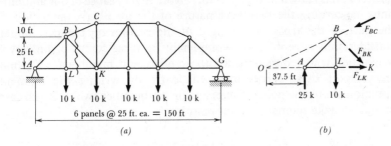

Fig. 3.3-2

compared with its lateral dimensions, that the connection is able to exert little restraint against rotation.   Loads determined on these assumptions are known as *primary stresses*.   They form the usual basis of truss design.   Where unusually short, stubby members are encountered, it is sometimes necessary to add to the primary stresses the *secondary stresses* due to rotational restraint at a joint.   This task, however, would lead us beyond the scope of the present text.

We now have a picture of a load-carrying framework consisting of a number of straight two-force members connected together at their ends by joints that may be regarded as smooth pins.   How shall we find the loads carried by the members? The basic method for finding the load carried by any particular member is to pass a curve (a surface for space trusses), called a *section*, through the truss.   The section cuts that member (and as few others as possible) and divides the truss into two separate parts.   The load carried by the member under investigation then appears as an external force in the free-body diagram of either part of the truss, and is found from the equations of equilibrium.   As a typical instance of this procedure we may consider the determination of the load carried by the diagonal bar BK of the planar bridge truss shown in Fig. 3.3-2a. (This type of truss is known as a Warren truss with a curved upper chord.) The truss carries a load of 10,000 lb = 10 k at each joint or *panel point* of the lower chord.   The end reactions are found by considering the equilibrium of the truss as a whole.   In the present case they consist of 25 k upward reactions at A and G.   The section passing through BK and separating the truss into two parts is shown in Fig. 3.3-2a by means of a wavy line.   We may take as our system either the part of the truss to the left or the part to the right of this section.   Clearly it will be simpler in this instance to isolate the part to the left, since fewer forces will then enter the analysis.   The free-body diagram of this section is shown in Fig. 3.3-2b.   Note that because of our assumptions concerning the two-force nature of the members, the action of the part of the truss to the right of the section on the part under consideration is represented completely by three forces of unknown magnitude whose directions are those of the cut members.   We find any one of these forces most efficiently by writing the moment equation about the point of intersection of the other two.   In the case of F_{BK} we take moments about point O:

$$\sum M_O = -\left(\frac{\sqrt{2}}{2} F_{BK}\right)(87.5) + (25)(37.5) - (10)(62.5) = 0,$$

$$F_{BK} = 5.05 \text{ k.} \qquad\qquad \textbf{3.3-1}$$

The diagonal member BK therefore carries a load of 5050 lb tension. It is easy to see that the load is tension and not compression: a glance at the free-body diagram shows that F_{BK} is tending to stretch the member, not to compress it.   To secure such ease of interpretation it is important that the section be drawn through members and not through the joint.   Each of the three unknown forces appearing in the free-body diagram can be obtained by means of a single equation. For example, the load carried by the lower chord member LK is found by writing the equilibrium equation of moments about point B:

$$\sum M_B = -(25)(25) + (25)(F_{LK}) = 0;$$

$$F_{LK} = 25 \text{ k tension.} \qquad\qquad \textbf{3.3-2}$$

There are two types of section that may be used in analyzing a truss: those that completely surround a single joint and those that, like the section of the previous paragraph, do not.   To find the load carried by member LK of Fig. 3.3-2a, we could start, for example, by taking a section enclosing joint A. Such a section is shown by wavy lines in Fig. 3.3-3a, and the free-body diagram of the part of the truss enclosed is shown in Fig. 3.3-3b.

The equations of equilibrium are

$$\sum F_x = F_{AL} - 0.707 F_{AB} = 0$$

and **3.3-3**

$$\sum F_y = 25 - 0.707 F_{AB} = 0,$$

whence we conclude that

$$F_{AB} = 35.3 \text{ k compression}, \qquad F_{AL} = 25 \text{ k tension} \qquad \textbf{3.3-4}$$

Next we take a section completely enclosing the joint L. It is shown by a wavy line in Fig. 3.3-3a, and the free-body diagram of the part of the truss enclosed is shown in Fig. 3.3-3c. Since we now know that

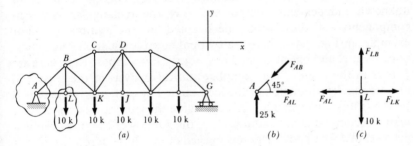

Fig. 3.3-3

$F_{AL} = 25$ k tension, the summation of forces in the x-direction tells us at once that $F_{LK} = 25$ k tension. This, of course, is the same conclusion reached previously in Eq. 3.3-2. The process of analysis in which one proceeds, joint by joint, through the truss, each time taking a section that completely encloses a joint, is sometimes known as the "method of joints." The alternative procedure, using sections such as that shown in Fig. 3.3-2 which do not completely enclose a single joint, is then called the "method of sections." This distinction seems unnecessary, since both "methods" are variations of the same basic procedure. For the beginner it may be appropriate to remark that the "method of joints" has certain drawbacks. If we want to find the load carried by a member of the truss remote from a suitable starting joint such as A in Fig. 3.3-3, we have to proceed, joint by joint, through the truss until we come to the member of interest. During this lengthy process a good deal of extraneous geometry and algebra is apt to be encountered. An error along the way perpetuates itself. Even ordinary round-off and slide rule error tends to be cumulative. For these reasons it is usually better to pass a section through the member of interest directly. On the other hand, the "method of joints" will sometimes provide a quick answer. A section surrounding joint *J*, for example, tells us at once that member *DJ* of Fig. 3.3-3 must carry a tensile load of 10,000 lb. In practice, a judicious combination of the two "methods" is most effective.

We now have a procedure for finding the loads carried by members of a truss. Will this method of analysis always serve? The question is closely related to the question of statical determinacy and is therefore of no little interest. In attempting to answer it we look first at the over-all equilibrium of a rigid planar truss. The complete truss is attached to a foundation and, when the truss as a whole is taken as an isolated system, the forces exerted by the foundation must be represented by certain unknown vectors. Let the number of unknown independent components—say the rectangular cartesian components—of these forces be denoted by the symbol *C*. For example, in Fig. 3.3-3 there are two unknown foundation force components at *A* and one at *G*, so that $C = 3$. Now suppose that there are *B* bars in the truss. The complete statical analysis of the truss will require the determination of the load carried by each bar. There will be $B + C$ unknowns in all. If we imagine the truss to be analyzed by taking sections that surround each of the *J* joints of the truss, we will get a set of *J* free-body diagrams in each of which the forces are planar and concurrent. There will therefore be $2J$ independent equations of equilibrium available. (The equilibrium equations obtained by considering the truss as a whole are simply appropriate linear combinations of the corresponding ones for the *J* joints and therefore do not furnish any further independent equations.) Now consider the number *N* where

$$N = B + C - 2J. \qquad \textbf{3.3-5}$$

If *N* is positive, there are more unknowns than equations and the truss is statically indeterminate. It may have more bars than are necessary for rigidity, in which case it is said to have one or more *redundant* members or to be *internally redundant*, or it may have too many foundation constraints, in which case it is said to be *externally redundant*. In any event, when $N > 0$, while it may be possible to find some of the foundation forces and some of the bar loads, they cannot all be determined by means of the equations of equilibrium alone.

If N is negative there are more equilibrium conditions than there are quantities at our disposal to satisfy them. The structure is then a mechanism. It may move as a whole (if $C < 3$), or parts of it may move relative to other parts, but it will not be in equilibrium, except possibly for special configurations. Finally, if N is zero the number of unknowns is exactly equal to the number of equations of equilibrium. If a planar truss is to be statically determinate—what is sometimes known as a *just-rigid* truss—it must have $N = 0$. On the other hand, the fact that $N = 0$ does not ensure that the truss is statically determinate. There exist what are known as *critical forms* in which the equations of equilibrium are inconsistent with any finite set of loads.

These matters deserve some amplification. The basic planar truss element is a triangle and the simplest possible truss is that shown in Fig. 3.3-4a. In this case $N = 0$. The structure is statically determinate; both the reactions and the bar loads can be found by

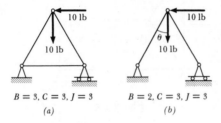

$B = 3, C = 3, J = 3$ $B = 2, C = 3, J = 3$

(a)   (b)

Fig. 3.3-4

means of the equations of equilibrium. If the horizontal bar is removed, as in Fig. 3.3-4b, $N = -1$. The structure is now a mechanism; it can only be in equilibrium for particular values of the angle θ. If the right-hand roller support of (a) is replaced by a pin, like the left-hand support, C becomes 4 and the truss is statically indeterminate. Now if we start with the original statically determinate truss of Fig. 3.3-4a and add to it another triangular element obtained by connecting some point in the plane to two points of the original triangle, the new structure has two more bars and one more joint, so that N remains zero. Any truss that can be regarded as built from an original triangular element by successive additions of two bars with a common joint will be statically determinate once its foundation reactions are known. Such trusses are called *simple trusses*. The Warren truss of Figs. 3.3-2 and 3.3-3 is an example of a truss of this kind. On the other hand, if we connect two triangular elements by means of three parallel members, as shown in Fig. 3.3-5, we get what was referred to in the last sentence of the previous paragraph as a *critical form.* Although $N = 0$ the truss is statically indeterminate. We can recognize the possibility of self-straining fairly easily in this case because the center horizontal bar could be made to carry a tensile load (say by being fabricated too short) and the upper and lower horizontal bars could carry compressive loads half as great without disturbing the equilibrium of the truss as a whole. Such a state of load could be superposed on any other set that satisfied the equations of equilibrium. If a member of a statically determinate truss such as the triangular truss of Fig. 3.3-4a is fabricated too long or too

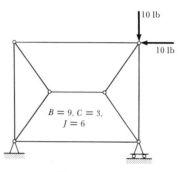

10 lb

10 lb

$B = 9, C = 3,$
$J = 6$

Fig. 3.3-5

short, the geometry of the truss changes slightly but no initial state of load is induced. For this reason, and because, as will be shown, bar loads in trusses of near-critical form are extremely high (theoretically infinite), engineers invariably avoid such forms. The simple truss built up of all-triangular elements is free of this possible design defect.

The analysis of a three-dimensional truss follows the same lines as that of the planar truss. In investigating statical determinacy, as there are now $3J$ independent equations of equilibrium, we take

$$N' = B + C - 3J. \qquad \textbf{3.3-6}$$

Again, B is the number of bars, J the number of joints, and C the number of external constraints; the critical number for the latter is six, since a rigid body can have six degrees of freedom in three-dimensional motion. If N' is less than zero, the truss is a mechanism; if N' is greater than zero, the truss is statically indeterminate. If the truss is statically determinate, $N' = 0$. Just as the triangle is the basic unit for a planar truss, so the tetrahedron or six-bar truss is the basic statically determinate spatial truss. Spatial trusses that can be regarded as built up from an original tetrahedral unit by successive additions of three non-coplanar bars with a common joint will be statically determinate.

Returning now to the planar truss, we see that in order for it to be statically determinate, the number of bars, B, joints, J, and

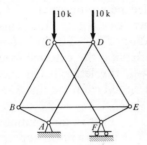

Fig. 3.3-6

foundation constraint unknowns, C, must be related by the equation $B + C = 2J$. When this condition is fulfilled, there may still be difficulty in the analysis should we encounter a situation where there is no two-member joint and in which no section separating the truss into two parts and cutting three non-parallel bars can be found. Consider, for example, the non-simple truss shown in Fig. 3.3-6. In this figure the joints are, as is conventional, indicated by small circles; where these are not present the bars overlap without being connected. Though admittedly a textbook example, this truss does present awkward features in its analysis. Since $B = 9$, $C = 3$, and $J = 6$, the condition $B + C = 2J$ is fulfilled; $N = 0$. The foundation reactions at A and R are easily found by our considering the equilibrium of the truss as a whole. But there is no joint at which only two bars are attached and no section through the truss cutting only two members. Neither the "method of sections" nor the "method of joints" can be applied directly. The simplest way to treat this situation is to remove one of the bars—say CD—and keep the truss just rigid by introducing a new bar, say BF. The situation is then as shown in Fig. 3.3-7, with the new bar shown by a broken line. The

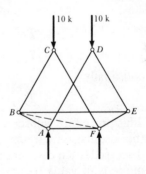

Fig. 3.3-7

truss of Fig. 3.3-7 is called a *replacement truss* for that of Fig. 3.3-6. Now the analysis is easily carried out—say, by taking sections surrounding joints C, D, E, F, and A in that order. The resulting loads may be denoted T'_{DE}, T'_{BE}, ..., including T'_{BF}, using the convention that tension is a positive load. Next, consider the replacement truss of Fig. 3.3-7 with oppositely directed unit loads, applied at the joints where a bar has been removed, in the direction of the bar, and tending to bring the two loaded points together. This loading is shown in Fig. 3.3-8. Again we easily find the corresponding bar loads T''_{DE}, T''_{BE}, ..., including T''_{BF}. Finally, consider the replacement truss simultaneously carrying the external loads shown in Fig. 3.3-7 and those of Fig. 3.3-8, the latter being increased by a factor, x. Since the equations of equilibrium are linear, the loads carried by the members will be $T'_{DE}+xT''_{DE}$, $T'_{BE}+xT''_{BE}$, ..., including $T'_{BF}+xT''_{BF}$.

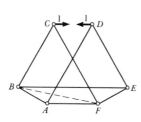

Fig. 3.3-8

That is, the solution for the combined loading is a linear superposition of the solutions for the separate loadings. If x is now given the value $-(T'_{BF}/T''_{BF})$, the member BF will carry no load. It may therefore be removed from the truss. We have evidently restored the original truss of Fig. 3.3-6 with the member CD replaced by forces of magnitude x. We conclude that the actual loads carried by the members of the truss of Fig. 3.3-6 are

$$T_{DE} = T'_{DE}-(T'_{BF}/T''_{BF})T''_{DE},$$

$$T_{BE} = T'_{BE}-(T'_{BF}/T''_{BF})T''_{BE}, \text{ etc.,} \qquad \textbf{3.3-7}$$

and finally

$$T_{CD} = -T'_{BF}/T''_{BF}.$$

This procedure will serve to complete the analysis in those cases where the ordinary methods break down. For the reasons previously discussed, such cases are not often encountered in practice. The technique is of value because it at once reveals the presence of a critical form. Such a form must be associated with a case in which the "method of sections" and the "method of joints" are inapplicable and for which the method of the present paragraph is appropriate. If T''_{BF}, the load carried by the replacement bar when the removed bar is replaced by unit forces, should be very small, the stresses given by Eq. 3.3-7 will be extremely large. When $T''_{BF}=0$, we have a critical form. When a truss of critical form is actually fabricated, using normal construction materials, it distorts under a small load until the shape is no longer quite critical. The loads carried by the members are then large but finite. For obvious reasons, critical truss forms are avoided in good engineering design.

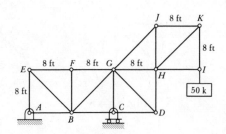

Fig. 3.3-9

Example **3.3-1**

Find the force in members DG and CD of the pin-jointed simple truss of Fig. 3.3-9, carrying a 50,000 lb load at I.

Solution: A combination of the two basic methods is useful here. Indeed, we need not solve for the reactions at A and C at all, and even if the truss were overconstrained, we could still solve for the information desired.

A cut to the right of GC divides the truss into two parts; a free-body diagram of section $DHJKI$ is given in Fig. 3.3-10. There are four unknowns, and we cannot expect to solve the problem. However, F_{CD} can be determined immediately since the lines of action of the other three unknowns pass through G. Therefore,

$$\sum M_G = -8F_{CD}-(16)(50) = 0,$$

$$F_{CD} = -100 \text{ k} = 100 \text{ k } (C). \qquad \textbf{3.3-8}$$

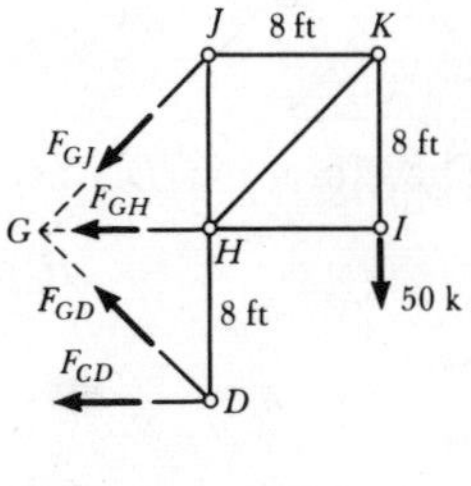

The other two equations for the section do not permit a complete determination of the other three unknowns. Vertical equilibrium does give us F_{GD} in terms of F_{GJ}:

$$F_{GD}\frac{\sqrt{2}}{2}-F_{GJ}\frac{\sqrt{2}}{2}-50 = 0,$$

$$F_{GD} = F_{GJ}+50\sqrt{2}.$$

Fig. 3.3-10

To find F_{GJ}, use the method of joints starting at I, and then proceeding to K and J. The free-body diagrams are shown in Fig. 3.3-11. For I, we have

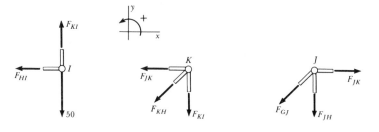

Fig. 3.3-11

$$\sum R_y = F_{KI} - 50 = 0, \qquad F_{KI} = 50\,\text{k}\ (T);$$

for K, we have

$$\sum R_y = -F_{KI} - F_{KH}\frac{\sqrt{2}}{2} = 0,$$

$$\sum R_x = -F_{JK} - F_{KH}\frac{\sqrt{2}}{2} = 0,$$

and

$$F_{JK} = -F_{KH}\frac{\sqrt{2}}{2} = F_{KI} = 50\,\text{k}\ (T);$$

for J, we find

$$\sum R_x = F_{JK} - F_{GJ}\frac{\sqrt{2}}{2} = 0,$$

$$F_{GJ} = F_{JK}\sqrt{2} = 50\sqrt{2}\,\text{k}\ (T).$$

Therefore, bar DG carries a load

$$F_{GD} = F_{GJ} + 50\sqrt{2} = 100\sqrt{2}\,\text{k}\ (T). \qquad \textbf{3.3-9}$$

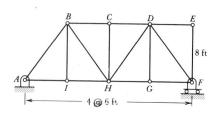

Fig. 3.3-12

Example **3.3-2**

The plane truss of Fig. 3.3-12 is subjected to two different load systems: (a) downward loads of 100 lb at joints I, C, and G; (b) downward loads of 100 lb at joints B, H, and D. What are the constraint loads at A and F? What are the loads carried by the members BI, CH, DG, and GH in the two cases?

Solution: The free-body diagrams of the whole truss for the two loadings are shown in Fig. 3.3-13. The external constraints are the same for both cases, the over-all equations of equilibrium being

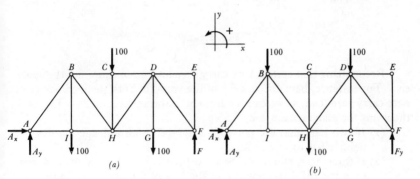

Fig. 3.3-13

$$\sum R_x = A_x = 0,$$

$$\sum M_A = 24F_y - 600 - 1200 - 1800 = 0, \qquad \textbf{3·3-10}$$

$$\sum M_F = -24A_y + 1800 + 1200 + 600 = 0,$$

with solutions

$$A_x = 0, \qquad A_y = F_y = 150 \text{ lb.} \qquad \textbf{3·3-11}$$

The forces carried by the individual struts may be different, however. Examine joints *I*, *C*, and *G* for the two cases. For vertical equilibrium, we must have bars *BI* and *DG* carrying 100 lb tensile loads and bar *CH* carrying a 100 lb compressive load in case (a); all three bars must carry zero load in case (b). Bar *GH* carries the same load in both cases. Isolate section *DEFG* and take moments about *D* (see Fig. 3.3-14); in both cases,

$$\sum M_D = 6F_y - 8F_{GH} = 0,$$

and

$$F_{GH} = \frac{3}{4} F_y = 112.5 \text{ lb } (T).$$

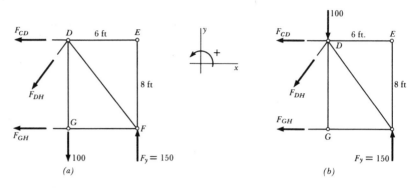

Fig. 3.3-14

Recognizing that certain bars carry zero load often simplifies the analysis. For instance, bars *DE* and *EF* of the truss for both the loadings given here carry zero load, as we can see from equilibrium of joint *E*. The basic theorems for plane trusses are:

(1) If two bars that are not collinear meet at an unloaded joint, then neither bar can carry load.

(2) If three bars, two of which are collinear, meet at an unloaded joint, then the third bar oblique to the line of the other two must carry no load.

Similar three- and four-bar, unloaded-joint theorems can be stated for space trusses.

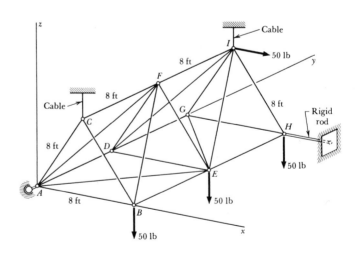

Fig. 3.3-15

It should not be thought that such zero-load bars are not needed in the truss; they generally are, to keep the structure rigid.   Removal of *BI* in the truss of Fig. 3.3-13b will turn the structure into a linkage mechanism.

Example **3.3-3**

Find the forces of constraint on the space truss of Fig. 3.3-15 *and the load carried by bar BF.*

Solution: A free-body diagram of the whole truss is given in Fig. 3.3-16. To determine the forces of constraint, we first take moments about *A*:

$$\sum \mathbf{M}_A = (4\mathbf{i}+4\sqrt{3}\mathbf{k}) \times T_1\mathbf{k}+(4\mathbf{i}+16\mathbf{j}+4\sqrt{3}\mathbf{k}) \times (50\mathbf{i}+T_2\mathbf{k})$$
$$+ 8\mathbf{i} \times (-50\mathbf{k})+(8\mathbf{i}+8\mathbf{j}) \times (-50\mathbf{k})+(8\mathbf{i}+16\mathbf{j}) \times (-H\mathbf{i}-50\mathbf{k})$$
$$= (16T_2-1200)\mathbf{i}+(1200+200\sqrt{3}-4T_1-4T_2)\mathbf{j}+(16H-800)\mathbf{k}$$
$$= 0. \qquad\qquad\qquad \textbf{3.3-12}$$

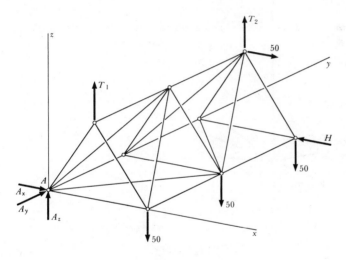

Fig. 3.3-16

Therefore,

$$\sum M_x^A = 16T_2-1200 = 0, \qquad T_2 = 75 \text{ lb};$$
$$\sum M_y^A = 1200+200\sqrt{3}-4T_1-4T_2 = 0, \quad T_1 = 225+50\sqrt{3} \cong 312 \text{ lb};$$
$$\sum M_z^A = 16H-800 = 0, \qquad H = 50 \text{ lb}. \qquad\qquad \textbf{3.3-13}$$

To determine the forces at *A*, we write the resultant force equilibrium equation:

$$\sum \mathbf{R} = (A_x\mathbf{i}+A_y\mathbf{j}+A_z\mathbf{k})+T_1\mathbf{k}+T_2\mathbf{k}-150\mathbf{k}+50\mathbf{i}-H\mathbf{i}$$
$$= (A_x+50-H)\mathbf{i}+A_y\mathbf{j}+(A_z+T_1+T_2-150)\mathbf{k} = 0. \quad \textbf{3.3-14}$$

Therefore,

$$\sum R_x = A_x + 50 - H = 0, \qquad A_x = H - 50 = 0;$$

$$\sum R_y = A_y = 0 ;$$

3.3-15

$$\sum R_z = A_z + T_1 + T_2 - 150 = 0,$$

$$A_z = 150 - (T_1 + T_2) = -150 - 50\sqrt{3} \cong -237 \text{ lb.}$$

For determining the force carried by strut BF, the "method of joints" does not suggest itself as a likely procedure. We would like to start at a joint with only three unknowns; in this case, joint H would be the only place to start. Then joint G could be considered, followed by joints

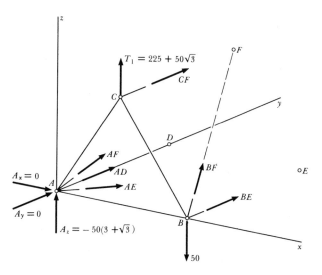

Fig. 3.3-17

I, D, E, and finally F. The "method of sections" can be used by cutting to the positive y-side of joints A, B, and C. The free-body diagram is shown in Fig. 3.3-17; there are six unknowns, not all of which intersect at the same point or intersect the same line, so that we should be able to determine BF. In fact, only one equation need be written, that for moments about the y-axis through A. Choosing A as base point eliminates three of the unknowns, AD, AE, and AF; and taking only the y-component of $\sum \mathbf{M}_A$ eliminates CF and BE, which are parallel to that axis. Since the position of F relative to B is $-4\mathbf{i} + 8\mathbf{j} + 4\sqrt{3}\mathbf{k}$ feet, the vector for the strut force is

$$(BF)\left(-\frac{\sqrt{2}}{4}\mathbf{i} + \frac{\sqrt{2}}{2}\mathbf{j} + \frac{\sqrt{6}}{4}\mathbf{k}\right).$$

3.3-16

Thus

$$\sum M_y^A = -4T_1 + (8)(50) - (8)\left(\frac{\sqrt{6}}{4}\right)(BF)$$

$$= -(900 + 200\sqrt{3}) + 400 - 2\sqrt{6}(BF) = 0,$$

and

$$BF = -\frac{500 + 200\sqrt{3}}{2\sqrt{6}} \cong 173 \text{ lb } (C). \qquad \textbf{3.3-17}$$

The student may wish to compute the rest of the bar forces on this section to gain practice in the use of three-dimensional equilibrium equations.

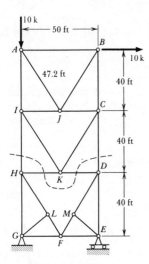

Fig. 3.3-18

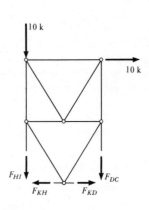

Fig. 3.3-19

Example **3.3-4**

Find the load carried by members CD and KI of the truss shown in Fig. 3.3-18.

Solution: Teaching experience shows that students have difficulty finding where to start the analysis of K-type bracing such as that shown. Yet the structure is statically determinate ($B = 23$, $C = 3$, $J = 13$) and the method of analysis is conventional. Perhaps the mental block arises from always tending to think in terms of a straight section when, in fact, no such restriction is implied by the theory. If we take the section indicated by the dotted line, and draw the free-body diagram (Fig. 3.3-19) of the material above it, we have, on taking moments about point H,

$$\sum M_H = -50F_{DC} - 400 = 0, \qquad F_{DC} = -8 \text{ k}, \qquad \textbf{3.3-18}$$

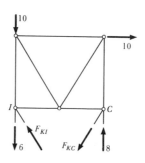

Fig. 3.3-20

so the load carried by DC is 8000 lb compression.   If moments are taken about D,

$$\sum M_D = 50F_{HI} + 500 - 800 = 0, \qquad F_{HI} = 6 \text{ k.} \qquad \textbf{3.3-19}$$

The load carried by HI is 6000 lb tension.   It is now easy to find the load carried by the diagonal KI.   A horizontal section through the middle panel yields the free-body diagram shown in Fig. 3.3-20.   Taking moments about point C, we find

$$\sum M_C = -F_{KI}\left(\frac{40}{47.2}\right)(50) + 800 - 400 = 0,$$

$$F_{KI} = 9.43 \text{ k.} \qquad \textbf{3.3-20}$$

Member KI carries a compressive load of 9430 lb.

Example **3.3-5**

Find the foundation reactions for the Wichert truss shown in Fig. 3.3-21.

Solution: The Wichert truss is a designer's attempt to obtain the advantages of a continuous structure without the disadvantages of statical indeterminacy.   It obviously does have the extra stiffness that comes from

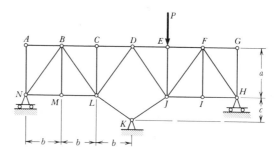

Fig. 3.3-21

having the left-hand span assist in carrying load applied to the right-hand span (and vice-versa). In this respect it is superior to two trusses, one spanning the gap from N to K and the other that from K to H. If the foundation reactions can be found, the truss will be statically determinate

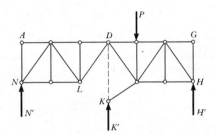

Fig. 3.3-22

and the bar loads easily found. We find that $B=24$, $C=4$, and $J=14$, so $B+C=2J$, and unless the truss is a critical form it will indeed be statically determinate.

The analysis can be performed in several ways. If we use the replacement-truss procedure described in the text immediately before Example 3.3-1, we will remove one bar, say LK, and add one, say KD, in such a way as to leave the structure just rigid and easily analyzed. When this has been done the truss has the appearance shown in Fig. 3.3-22; the new bar

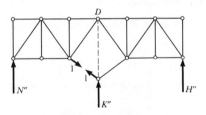

Fig. 3.3-23

is represented by a broken line. The reactions are easily found by considering two bodies, $ANLD$ and $DKHG$:

$$N' = 0, \qquad K' = \frac{2}{3} P, \qquad H' = \frac{1}{3} P. \qquad\qquad \textbf{3.3-21}$$

Also, the load in the replacement bar is

$$T'_{DK} = -\frac{2}{3} P. \qquad\qquad \textbf{3.3-22}$$

Next we remove the load P and insert unit forces at K and L in the direction of the missing bar, as shown in Fig. 3.3-23. The directions of the unit forces are always taken so as to pull the points to which they are applied together. Now if we consider the equilibrium of the left-hand half of the truss and take moments about D, we find

$$N'' = \frac{a+c}{3\sqrt{b^2+c^2}}.$$

3.3-23

Similarly, by considering the equilibrium of the right-hand side of the truss and taking moments about D, we find

$$H'' = \frac{a+c}{3\sqrt{b^2+c^2}}.$$

3.3-24

Since $N'' + H'' + K'' = 0$, we at once conclude that

$$K'' = \frac{-2(a+c)}{3\sqrt{b^2+c^2}};$$

3.3-25

and, on taking a section surrounding joint K, we find that

$$T_{DK}'' = \frac{2(a-2c)}{3\sqrt{b^2+c^2}}.$$

3.3-26

We are now in a position to test for the presence of a critical form. This will occur if and only if $T_{DK}''=0$, that is, when $a=2c$. A truss with these particular proportions will buckle. In any other case, however, the actual state of the truss is a linear combination of the single- and double-primed states. That is,

$$N = N'+xN'', \quad K = K'+xK'', \quad H = H'+xH'',$$

3.3-27

and

$$T_{DK} = T_{DK}'+xT_{DK}''.$$

But T_{DK} must be made zero because this bar is not present in the original truss, so

$$x = -\frac{T_{DK}'}{T_{DK}''} = P\frac{\sqrt{b^2+c^2}}{a-2c}.$$

3.3-28

Therefore,

$$N = 0 + \left(P\frac{\sqrt{b^2+c^2}}{a-2c}\right)\left(\frac{a+c}{3\sqrt{b^2+c^2}}\right) = \frac{1}{3}P\frac{a+c}{a-2c},$$

$$K = \frac{2}{3}P - \left(P\frac{\sqrt{b^2+c^2}}{a-2c}\right)\left(\frac{2(a+c)}{3\sqrt{b^2+c^2}}\right) = \frac{2}{3}P\left(1-\frac{a+c}{a-2c}\right),$$

3.3-29

$$H = \frac{1}{3}P + \left(P\frac{\sqrt{b^2+c^2}}{a-2c}\right)\left(\frac{a+c}{3\sqrt{b^2+c^2}}\right) = \frac{1}{3}P\left(1+\frac{a+c}{a-2c}\right).$$

These are the foundation reactions. We note, incidentally, that

$$T_{LK} = T'_{LK} + xT''_{LK} = 0 + (x)(1) = P\frac{\sqrt{b^2+c^2}}{(a-2c)}.$$

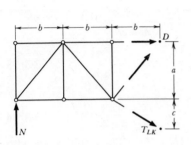

Fig. 3·3-24 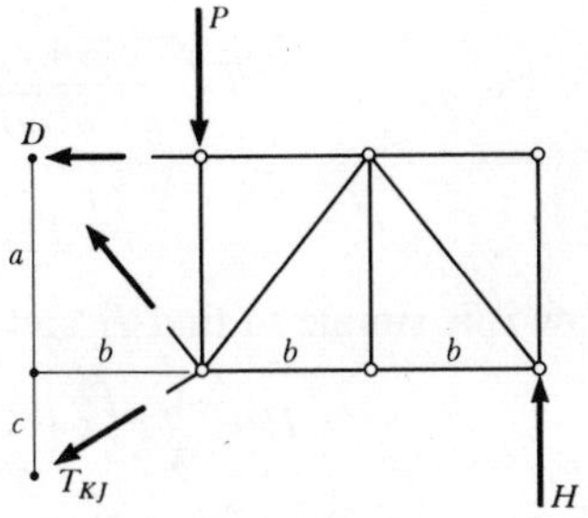   **Fig. 3·3-25**

It is instructive to look at an alternative approach. If we consider the equilibrium of the part of the truss (Fig. 3·3-24) to the left of a vertical section cutting the members *CD*, *LD*, and *LK*, we find:

$$\sum M_D = -3bN + \frac{b}{\sqrt{b^2+c^2}}T_{LK}(a+c) = 0,$$

$$N = T_{LK}\frac{a+c}{3\sqrt{b^2+c^2}}. \qquad\qquad \textbf{3·3-30}$$

Now if we consider the part of the truss (Fig. 3·3-25) to the right of a vertical section cutting members *DE*, *DJ*, and *KJ*, we find

$$\sum M_D = 3bH - Pb - \frac{b}{\sqrt{b^2+c^2}}T_{KJ}(a+c) = 0,$$

$$H = T_{KJ}\frac{a+c}{3\sqrt{b^2+c^2}} + \frac{1}{3}P. \qquad \textbf{3·3-31}$$

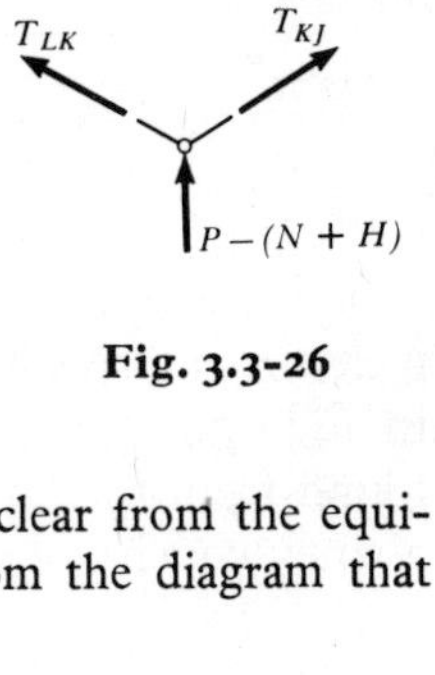

Turning now to a section surrounding the center reaction joint *K*, we have a free-body diagram as shown in Fig. 3·3-26. Note that the upward reaction at *K* has been written as $P-(N+H)$, as is clear from the equilibrium of the truss as a whole. It is clear also from the diagram that

Fig. 3·3-26

summing forces in the x-direction will show that $T_{LK} = T_{KJ}$. Summing forces in the y-direction, we have

$$P - (N + H) + T_{LK}\frac{c}{\sqrt{b^2 + c^2}} + T_{KJ}\frac{c}{\sqrt{b^2 + c^2}} = 0. \qquad \textbf{3.3-32}$$

If we substitute the expressions for H and N from Eqs. 3.3-30 and 3.3-31 into Eq. 3.3-32 and set $T_{LK} = T_{KJ}$, we find

$$P - T_{KJ}\frac{2(a + c)}{3\sqrt{b^2 + c^2}} - \frac{1}{3}P + T_{KJ}\frac{2c}{\sqrt{b^2 + c^2}} = 0,$$

$$T_{KJ} = P\frac{\sqrt{b^2 + c^2}}{a - 2c}. \qquad \textbf{3.3-33}$$

Now it is simple to find H and N:

$$H = \frac{1}{3}P\left(1 + \frac{a + c}{a - 2c}\right), \qquad N = \frac{1}{3}P\frac{a + c}{a - 2c}. \qquad \textbf{3.3-34}$$

Of course the reaction at K is simply $P - (N + H)$. The results agree with the previous analysis. They hint at the presence of a critical form when $a = 2c$. In this method, essentially, we write all the equations of equilibrium and solve them as simultaneous equations, the solution being aided in the present case by symmetry.

3.4   Analysis of Frames and Mechanisms

Unlike a truss, a general frame or mechanism may include members that are not two-force members. Such a member, even if it is a straight bar, will be subject to flexure and shear as well as to axial tension or compression. The distinction is so fundamental that

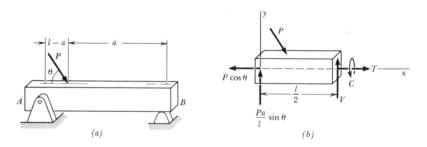

Fig. 3.4-1

it deserves a specific illustration. Consider a bar such as that chosen in Fig. 3.4-1a. The reactions at the supports A and B are readily found from the equations of equilibrium for the bar as a whole. At A they consist of a force $P\cos\theta$ directed to the left and an upward force $Pa \sin \theta/l$. If a vertical section is passed through the middle of the bar, cutting it in two, the free-body diagram of the left-hand side will be as shown in Fig. 3.4-1b. The equations of force equilibrium applied to this left-hand section of the bar are

$$\sum F_x = T + P \cos \theta - P \cos \theta = 0,$$

$$\sum F_y = -P \sin \theta + \frac{Pa}{l} \sin \theta + V = 0. \qquad \textbf{3.4-1}$$

The equation of moment equilibrium can be written (ignoring the bar thickness)

$$\sum M_A = C - P(l-a) \sin \theta + Vl/2 = 0. \qquad \textbf{3.4-2}$$

Here (T, V, C) are the resultant set corresponding to the distributed forces on the cross-section (see Section 2.7). When we solve these equations, we find that

$$T = 0, \qquad V = P \frac{l-a}{l} \sin \theta, \qquad C = \frac{P(l-a)}{2} \sin \theta. \qquad \textbf{3.4-3}$$

The lesson we learn from this illustration is that, when a three-force member is cut by a transverse section, the forces distributed over the cut face are equipollent to a force and a couple, neither of which is, in general, zero. The presence of the couple is, of course, associated with the fact that the bar flexes or bends. In the present example, the resultant force at the particular section is a transverse shear force only, and no axial component exists at the section. In a truss, on the other hand, the members are straight two-force members and only the axial component, T, is present. As a result of this distinction, the simplicity inherent in truss analysis largely disappears when we come to consider frames. There is no longer any point in passing a section through a member so as to isolate some part of the system; such a step would introduce too many new unknown quantities. Where, as is usually the case, it is necessary to consider the equilibrium of a part of the frame, the members of which the part is composed must be isolated intact.

For the foregoing reasons, the analysis of frames follows closely the methods of Section 3.2. A complex system is resolved into a number of constituent parts; the third law of motion is used to reduce the number of unknown forces acting on the parts; finally, force and moment equilibrium equations are solved to yield the desired information. There is no universal guide to the best method of choosing subsystems, though it may be remarked that the beginner usually errs by choosing subsystems that consist of too few elements and thus becomes entangled in a computation in which a large number of subsystems are involved. These are matters best learned by experience gained by working through examples such as those that follow, which deal with some of the standard elements encountered in engineering.

Example 3.4-1

The four-bar linkage mechanism (Fig. 3.4-2) consists of three identical light, rigid bars pinned smoothly together and to the foundation (which is the

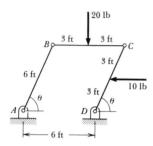

Fig. 3.4-2

"fourth bar"). For what angles θ can the linkage be in equilibrium? What are the forces acting on each member?

Solution: Figs. 3.4-3a, b, c, and d are free-body diagrams of the whole truss and of bars *AB*, *BC*, and *CD*, respectively. Note that *AB* is "light" and therefore is a two-force member, which is assumed to carry a compressive load. Note that in drawing the free-body diagram for bar *AB* we make use of the fact that *AB* is a two-force member to determine the direction of force *P*. Then, when drawing the free-body diagram of bar *BC*, we utilize the third law of motion and make the force at *B* exerted by *AB* on *BC* equal in magnitude and opposite in direction to the force at *B* exerted by *BC* on *AB*. A similar consideration governs the forces at *C* exerted on bar *CD* by bar *BC*. Later on it may turn out that C_x, say, is negative. This would reverse the direction of both forces labeled C_x; but the third law would still be satisfied. We see that in this instance we

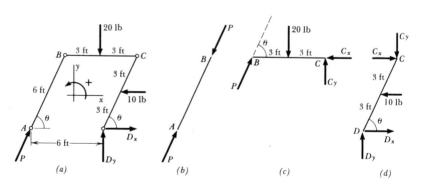

Fig. 3.4-3

shall have six unknowns (P, C_x, C_y, D_x, D_y, and θ) and six non-trivial equations of equilibrium—three from each of the free-body diagrams of Fig. 3.4-3c and d. We have already satisfied the equations of equilibrium for bar AB by our choice of the direction of the force P, and we do not get any further independent equations of equilibrium by considering the free-body diagram for the mechanism as a whole, since these equations are simply linear combinations of those for the three bars. Nevertheless, it is expeditious to begin with the equilibrium equations for the mechanism as a whole (Fig. 3.4-3a):

$$\sum M_A = 6D_y - (3 \sin \theta)(-10) + (6 \cos \theta + 3)(-20) = 0,$$

$$\sum M_D = (-6)(P \sin \theta) + (6 \cos \theta - 3)(-20) - (3 \sin \theta)(-10) = 0, \quad \textbf{3.4-4}$$

$$\sum R_x = D_x + P \cos \theta - 10 = 0.$$

The solutions of these for D_x, D_y, and P as functions of θ are

$$D_y = 10 + 20 \cos \theta - 5 \sin \theta,$$

$$P = 10 \csc \theta - 20 \cot \theta + 5, \qquad \textbf{3.4-5}$$

$$D_x = 10 - 10 \cot \theta + 20 \cot \theta \cos \theta - 5 \cos \theta.$$

As a check, note that $\sum R_y = D_y + P \sin \theta - 20 = 0$, as it should.

Turning now to the horizontal member BC (Fig. 3.4-3c), we find

$$\sum M_C = -6P \sin \theta + 60 = 0, \qquad P = 10 \csc \theta. \qquad \textbf{3.4-6}$$

Combining this with the second of Eqs. 3.4-5, we determine θ:

$$P = 10 \csc \theta = 10 \csc \theta - 20 \cot \theta + 5,$$

$$\theta = \text{arccot} (0.25) \cong 76° \text{ or } 256°. \qquad \textbf{3.4-7}$$

There are two possible equilibrium configurations. We find that D_x, D_y, and P are given by

$$\theta = 76°: D_x = 7.5 \text{ lb}, \qquad D_y = 10 \text{ lb}, \qquad P = \frac{10\sqrt{17}}{4} \cong 10.3 \text{ lb};$$

$$\theta = 256°: D_x = 7.5 \text{ lb}, \qquad D_y = 10 \text{ lb}, \qquad P = -10.3 \text{ lb}. \qquad \textbf{3.4-8}$$

The last answer means, of course, that AB must be in tension when the linkage is in its second equilibrium position.

We must now determine the components of the force at C. Completing the equilibrium equations for bar BC, we find

$$\sum M_B = 6C_y - 60 = 0, \qquad C_y = 10 \text{ lb};$$

$$\sum R_x = P \cos \theta - C_x = 0, \qquad C_x = 10 \cot \theta = 2.5 \text{ lb}. \qquad \textbf{3.4-9}$$

Since these are both positive, whichever equilibrium position has been chosen, we know that the directions assumed on the free-body diagrams are correct.   As a check on our computations, the three equations for bar *CD* may be written.

The answer desired may be given in the following way.   The linkage is in equilibrium under the given loads when $\theta = \text{arccot}\ (0.25)$, i.e., when $\theta = 76°$ or $256°$.   In both of these positions, bar *CD* is subjected to forces 7.5 lb to the right and 10 lb upward at *D*, and to forces 2.5 lb to the right and 10 lb downward at *C*—besides the applied 10 lb load.   The bar *AB* supports a 10.3 lb compressive load at each end for $\theta = 76°$, and 10.3 lb tensile loads for $\theta = 256°$.   Bar *BC* is subjected to the 20 lb central load; to a 2.5 lb load to the left and a 10 lb upward load at *C*; and to a 10.3 lb load at 76° counterclockwise from *BC* at pin *B* in both cases.

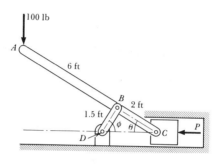

Fig. 3·4-4

Example **3·4-2**

The device shown in Fig. 3.4-4 is to be used as a hand-operated crushing machine.   Ignoring friction, how much crushing force, P, will the device exert when the angle θ is 30 degrees?

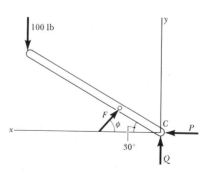

Fig. 3·4-5

Solution: The bar DB is a two-force member. Therefore the free-body diagram for AC has the form shown in Fig. 3.4-5. Note that the force component Q exerted on the bar AC by the crushing block is equal to that exerted on the crushing block by the foundation if the weight of the block is ignored. The angle ϕ is found with the aid of the sine law of trigonometry:

$$\sin \phi = \frac{2}{1.5} \sin 30° = \frac{2}{3}$$

$$\phi = 41.8°, \quad \cos \phi = \frac{\sqrt{5}}{3}.$$

We find F by taking moments about the origin and then find P from the force equilibrium equations:

$$\sum M_C = -(100)(6)\left(\frac{\sqrt{3}}{2}\right) + \left(\frac{2}{3}F\right)(\sqrt{3}) + \left(\frac{\sqrt{5}}{3}F\right)(1) = 0, \quad F = 274 \text{ lb};$$

$$\sum F_x = P - \frac{\sqrt{5}}{3}F = 0, \quad P = 204 \text{ lb}. \qquad \textbf{3.4-10}$$

In practice the dimensions and angles would probably be read from a blueprint, rather than determined by trigonometry, and the designer would want P as a function of θ.

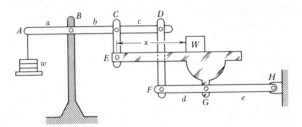

Fig. 3.4-6

Example **3.4-3**
   The platform scale of Fig. 3.4-6 is to be constructed so that the balance weight, w, is independent of the position x of the load W on the platform. (Why is this desirable?) What should be the relationship between the dimensions b, c, d, and e in order to achieve this? With this design what is the relationship between w, W, a, and b? All members are light and rigid, and the pins at B through H are smooth.
   Solution: In this mechanism, the basic element is the lever, such as AD, with fixed fulcrum point, such as B; moment equations of equilibrium are the basic ones used in the analysis. Here we are given an equilibrium

position, with bars AD and FH and the platform floor horizontal, and bars CE and DF vertical.   If all dimensions are given, the free-body diagram of the system involves four unknowns, the two components of pin reaction at B and the two at H.

Isolate as subsystems bars AD, FH, and the platform.   Since CE and DF are light and loaded only at their ends (there being no interference between DF and the platform), equilibrium requires that they be two-force members.   In Fig. 3.4-7, the free-body diagrams are shown.   For the system of Fig. 3.4-7c, we write moments about H:

$$\sum M_H = -(d+e)T_2 + eG_y = 0. \qquad \textbf{3.4-11}$$

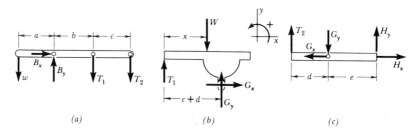

(a)   (b)   (c)

Fig. 3.4-7

For the platform (Fig. 3.4-7b), we find

$$\sum M_G = -(c+d)T_1 + [(c+d)-x]W = 0, \qquad \textbf{3.4-12}$$

$$\sum R_y = T_1 + G_y - W = 0; \qquad \textbf{3.4-13}$$

and, for AD (Fig. 3.4-7a),

$$\sum M_B = aw - bT_1 - (b+c)T_2 = 0. \qquad \textbf{3.4-14}$$

From these four equations we must determine what we wish to find; any other equations will involve other unknowns.   The horizontal force equilibrium equations serve to show that $B_x = G_x = H_x = 0$; the other two vertical force equilibrium equations determine B_y and H_y, once the other forces are known.   In the four equations, we have four unknowns: T_1, T_2, G_y, and w, if W, x, and all bar dimensions are given.   What we wish to do is to find dimensions such that x disappears from the problem.   Eliminate G_y from Eqs. 3.4-11 and 13:

$$eW - eT_1 - (d+e)T_2 = 0;$$

now remove T_2 from consideration:

$$T_2 = \frac{e(W-T_1)}{d+e} = \frac{aw-bT_1}{b+c}. \qquad \textbf{3.4-15}$$

Solving for T_1, we find

$$\frac{eW}{d+e} - \frac{aw}{b+c} = \left(\frac{e}{d+e} - \frac{b}{b+c}\right)T_1,$$

$$T_1 = \frac{e(b+c)W - a(d+e)w}{e(b+c) - b(d+e)}. \qquad \textbf{3.4-16}$$

From Eq. 3.4-12, then,

$$\frac{e(b+c)W - a(d+e)w}{e(b+c) - b(d+e)} = \left(1 - \frac{x}{c+d}\right)W$$

and

$$w = \frac{e}{a}\left(\frac{b+c}{d+e}\right)W - \frac{e(b+c) - b(d+e)}{a(d+e)}\left[1 - \frac{x}{c+d}\right]W$$

$$= \frac{b}{a}W + \frac{x}{c+d}\left[\frac{e(b+c)}{a(d+e)} - \frac{b}{a}\right]W.$$

Therefore,

$$\frac{w}{W} = \frac{b}{a} + \frac{x}{a(c+d)}\left[\frac{ce - bd}{d+e}\right]. \qquad \textbf{3.4-17}$$

Therefore, if x is to disappear from the problem, the dimensions of the scale must be such that

$$ce = bd \quad \text{or} \quad \frac{b}{c} = \frac{e}{d}. \qquad \textbf{3.4-18}$$

Using this condition, we find that $w/W = a/b$ and

$$T_1 = W, \qquad B_y = w + W = W\left(1 + \frac{b}{a}\right), \qquad T_2 = G_y = H_y = 0.$$

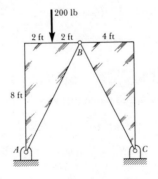

Fig. 3.4-8

Example **3.4-4**

An arch is constructed of two identical 90 lb uniform rigid plates. It supports a 200 lb load as shown in Fig. 3.4-8. Find the forces on the plates at the smooth pins A, B, and C.

Solution: In Fig. 3.4-9, we show free-body diagrams of the whole structure and each part. The c.m. of each plate has been located from the fact that each plate is uniform in its mass distribution, so that the c.m. coincides with the centroid of area, and from the fact that the medians of

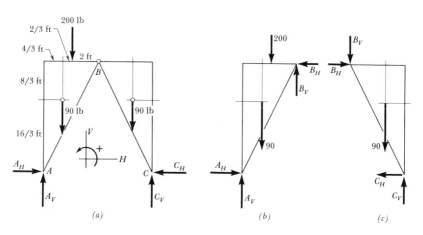

Fig. 3.4-9

a triangle intersect at the centroid at distances one-third of the altitude from the base on which the altitude is dropped. Equilibrium of the whole arch is governed by the equations

$$\sum M_A = 8C_V - \left(\frac{4}{3}\right)(90) - (2)(200) - \left(\frac{20}{3}\right)(90) = 0,$$

$$\sum M_C = -8A_V + \left(\frac{4}{3}\right)(90) + (6)(200) + \left(\frac{20}{3}\right)(90) = 0,$$

$$\sum R_H = A_H - C_H = 0,$$

from which we find

$$C_V = 140 \text{ lb}, \qquad A_V = 240 \text{ lb}, \qquad A_H = C_H. \qquad \textbf{3.4-19}$$

For plate BC (Fig. 3.4-9c), the equations are

$$\sum R_H = B_H - C_H = 0$$

$$\sum M_B = 4C_V - \left(\frac{8}{3}\right)(90) - 8C_H = 0,$$

$$\sum R_V = C_V - 90 - B_V = 0,$$

from which

$$B_V = 50 \text{ lb}, \qquad C_H = B_H = A_H = 40 \text{ lb}. \qquad \textbf{3.4-20}$$

All of the forces are thus determined.   Since all answers are positive, the directions shown in Fig. 3.4-9 are all correct.

Example 3.4-5

A windlass used to hoist a 100 lb weight consists of a 20 lb cylindrical drum of radius 2 ft and a crank AOBDE that is light; the drum is rigidly keyed to the shaft that passes through the geometric center O of the drum.

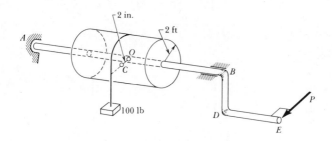

Fig. 3.4-10

The shaft is supported horizontally in a step bearing at A and a sleeve bearing at B.   In the position shown in Fig. 3.4-10, the handle BDE is in the vertical plane through AB and the eccentric c.m., C, of the drum is 2 inches off the center line horizontally to the left as one looks from B to A.   The cord and weight lie in the vertical plane through OC.   What horizontal force, P, must be applied perpendicular to the handle in the given position to lift the weight slowly?   What are the bearing reactions at A and B?   Dimensions are AO = 4 ft, OB = 3 ft, BD = DE = 1 ft.

Solution: Before we formulate this three-dimensional mechanism problem, we note three things.   First, the smooth sleeve bearing (which we have encountered before in Chapter II) is represented by a force normal to its axis; the step bearing also can sustain thrust along the line *AB*. Second, this is a mechanism; the hoist itself is a rigid body that can rotate about the horizontal axis *AB*.   Third, we are introducing a new area of application of the equilibrium equations here, i.e., to a machine that is actually moving, but "slowly."   The effect of "slowly" is not only to require a very small, i.e., negligible, angular acceleration—the phrase "slowly varying angular velocity" would do that—but also to require that the rotational angular velocity itself be small.   The full dynamical theory of such fixed-axis rotation problems shows that couples proportional to the square of the angular speed (which tend to rock the rotating body on its supports) can be present even if the angular acceleration vanishes.

We take as our system the hoist; Fig. 3.4-11 is a free-body diagram complete with axis system with origin A. Taking moments about A, we have (since equilibrium of the weight requires $T = 100$ lb)

$$\sum \mathbf{M}_A = \left(4\mathbf{k} + \frac{1}{6}\mathbf{i}\right) \times 20\mathbf{j} + (4\mathbf{k} + 2\mathbf{i}) \times 100\mathbf{j}$$
$$+ 7\mathbf{k} \times (B_x\mathbf{i} - B_y\mathbf{j}) + (8\mathbf{k} + \mathbf{j}) \times P\mathbf{i}$$
$$= (7B_y - 480)\mathbf{i} + (7B_x + 8P)\mathbf{j} + \left(\frac{610}{3} - P\right)\mathbf{k} = \mathbf{0},$$

from which we find

$$P = 203.3 \text{ lb}, \qquad B_x = -232.4 \text{ lb}, \qquad B_y = 68.6 \text{ lb}. \qquad \textbf{3.4-21}$$

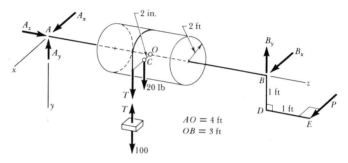

Fig. 3.4-11

We may now write the equations of moment equilibrium about B to determine A_x and A_y independently of B_x and B_y; in this simple problem, force equilibrium serves equally well:

$$\sum \mathbf{R} = P\mathbf{i} + (B_x\mathbf{i} - B_y\mathbf{j}) + 20\mathbf{j} + 100\mathbf{j} + (A_x\mathbf{i} - A_y\mathbf{j} + A_z\mathbf{k})$$
$$= (P + B_x + A_x)\mathbf{i} + (120 - B_y - A_y)\mathbf{j} + A_z\mathbf{k} = \mathbf{0}.$$

We find $A_z = 0$, as we expect, since there is no applied thrust in the z-direction. Further, we have that

$$A_y = B_y - 120 = -51.4 \text{ lb},$$
$$A_x = -(P + B_x) = 29.1 \text{ lb}. \qquad \textbf{3.4-22}$$

The signs of the answers tell us that we have shown the right directions for P, A_x, and B_y and the wrong directions for A_y and B_x in Fig. 3.4-11. The answers should not be given by tampering with the free-body diagram at this stage but, probably best, in vector form relative to the chosen axis system:

$$\mathbf{A} = A_x\mathbf{i} - A_y\mathbf{j} + A_z\mathbf{k} = 29.1\mathbf{i} + 51.4\mathbf{j} \text{ lb},$$
$$\mathbf{B} = B_x\mathbf{i} - B_y\mathbf{j} = -232.4\mathbf{i} - 68.6\mathbf{j} \text{ lb}, \qquad \textbf{3.4-23}$$
$$\mathbf{P} = 203.3\mathbf{i} \text{ lb}.$$

Example **3.4-6**

A *wall bracket frame* (*Fig.* 3.4-12) *of light rigid bars supports a* 5 *lb pulley of* 5 *in. radius at its center of gravity C and a* 50 *lb weight by a light inextensible cable, which is fastened to pin A and which passes over the pulley. All pins are smooth.   Find the forces on the pulley and on bars CF and AC.*

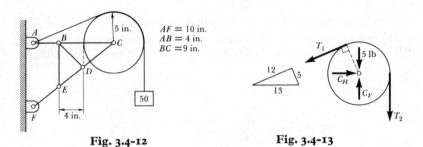

$AF = 10$ in.
$AB = 4$ in.
$BC = 9$ in.

Fig. 3.4-12   **Fig. 3.4-13**

Solution: Isolate the pulley as system, or rather the pulley and the portion of cable resting against the pulley (Fig. 3.4-13).   The forces acting are the weight of the pulley, 5 lb down at C; the two cable tensions, T_1 and T_2, tangent to the pulley; and the pin force at C on the pulley, represented by its horizontal and vertical components, C_H and C_V.   The basic effect of

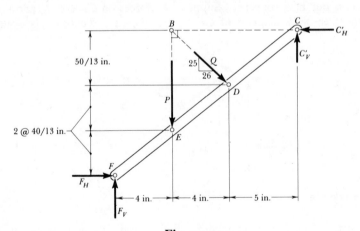

Fig. 3.4-14

the pulley, of course, is to cause a change in the direction of the cable, and hence of the tension force, around the pulley (and, if friction is present, sometimes a change in tension magnitude).   Moment equilibrium about C requires that $T_1 = T_2$.   Equilibrium of the 50 lb weight requires that

$T_2 = 50$ lb; therefore, $T_1 = T_2 = 50$ lb. The pin reaction on the pulley is then determined:

$$\sum R_H = C_H - \frac{12}{13} T_1 = 0, \qquad C_H = \frac{600}{13} \cong 46.2 \text{ lb};$$

$$\sum R_V = C_V - 5 - T_2 - \frac{5}{13} T_1 = 0, \qquad C_V = \frac{965}{13} \cong 74.2 \text{ lb}. \quad \textbf{3.4-24}$$

The forces for the equilibrium of the pulley are now completely determined.

Turning now to bar CF, we first recognize that the light bars BE and BD are loaded only at their ends, so that they are two-force members.

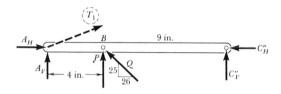

Fig. 3.4-15

Suppose BE carries a compressive load P; BD, a compressive load Q. The pin at F exerts a force with components F_H and F_V on the bar. The pin at C is our next concern. Suppose the forces on CF are C'_H and C'_V; then the free-body diagram of CF is Fig. 3.4-14. We have six scalar

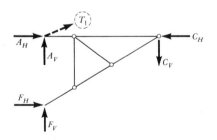

Fig. 3.4-16

unknowns and only three equations. Before writing any equations it is best to go on to some other system to see whether the problem is statically determinate. We have used the two-force members completely. We have only three other choices: AC, the whole system, or the frame without the pulley. Since the pulley has been considered completely, let us look at bar AC (Fig. 3.4-15) and at the frame without the pulley (Fig. 3.4-16). On bar AC, the forces P and Q due to the cross-members appear at B.

So does a reaction (C_H'', C_V'') due to the pin at C. At A, there is also a pin reaction force (A_H, A_V). If the cable is attached to the pin, no force T_1 should be shown. If the cable is attached to the bar, T_1 should be shown. We will not consider it in our equations, but will put it in as dotted in Figs. 3.4-15 and 3.4-16 to show how it would appear. If it is considered to be there, the only effect is to change the values of A_H and A_V; the total resultant force at point A will be the same either way. Four more unknowns have been introduced, and three equations: a total of ten unknowns, and only six equations.

On the whole frame, we have the forces at A and F and the reverse of the pulley reaction at the pin. It would seem wise to determine A_H, F_H, and a relation between A_V and F_V from this system before considering either of the separate bars.

Finally, we note that all of the forces due to the pin at C are not independent. We have three members—two bars and the pulley—coming together at C. For equilibrium of the pin (Fig. 3.4-17), we must have $C_H'' = C_H - C_H'$, $C_V'' = -(C_V + C_V')$. The important thing to note here, and to watch in one's own work, is the proper use of the action-reaction law at

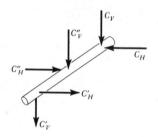

Fig. 3.4-17

a point where three or more members come together. It is worthwhile to examine the pin at B to see how the two-force members simplify the analysis.

At this point our unknowns are A_H, A_V, F_H, F_V, P, Q, and one pair of forces at C, say C_H', C_V': eight in number. We have used up all the information that equilibrium of the pulley, the pin at C, and the two bars BD and BE can give us. The three equations on the whole frame (Fig. 3.4-16), with C_H and C_V known, will determine F_H, A_H, and a relation between F_V and A_V. Expressing F_V in terms of A_V, we have left five unknowns. The three equations for AC (Fig. 3.4-15) can be written, with C_H'' and C_V'' expressed in terms of C_H' and C_V'. Now we must be cautious. Three more equations can be written for CF, but we cannot expect all three to be independent. Indeed, if they were, we would have more equations than unknowns. Moreover, we have put the whole system in equilibrium as well as each part except CF. Since the system must "fit together" we cannot expect any fresh information from these equations and should not be surprised if the system has two degrees of redundancy—that it is statically indeterminate.

Let us write the equations. For the free-body diagram of Fig. 3.4-16, we have

$$\sum M_A = 10F_H - 13C_V = 0, \qquad F_H = \frac{13}{10}C_V = 96.5 \text{ lb};$$

$$\sum R_H = A_H + F_H - C_H = 0, \qquad A_H = -50.3 \text{ lb}; \qquad \textbf{3.4-25}$$

$$\sum R_V = A_V + F_V - C_V = 0, \qquad F_V = C_V - A_V = 74.2 - A_V \text{ lb}.$$

Turning to bar AC (Fig. 3.4-15), we may write

$$\sum M_C = -13A_V - 9\left(P + \frac{25}{\sqrt{25^2 + 26^2}} Q\right) = 0,$$

$$\sum M_B = -4A_V + 9C_V'' = -4A_V - 9(C_V + C_V') = 0, \qquad \textbf{3.4-26}$$

$$\sum R_H = A_H - \frac{26}{\sqrt{25^2 + 26^2}} Q - C_H''$$

$$= A_H - \frac{26}{\sqrt{25^2 + 26^2}} Q - (C_H - C_H') = 0,$$

wherein the equilibrium equations for pin C have been utilized. From these, we find

$$C_V' = -C_V - \frac{4}{9} A_V = -74.2 - \frac{4}{9} A_V,$$

$$P + \frac{25}{\sqrt{1301}} Q = -\frac{13}{9} A_V, \qquad \textbf{3.4-27}$$

$$C_H' - \frac{26}{\sqrt{1301}} Q = C_H - A_H = 96.5.$$

For bar CF (Fig. 3.4-14), we have

$$\sum M_B = -4F_V + 10F_H + 9C_V' = 0,$$

$$\sum R_H = F_H + \frac{26}{\sqrt{1301}} Q - C_H' = 0, \qquad \textbf{3.4-28}$$

$$\sum R_V = F_V + C_V' - P - \frac{25}{\sqrt{1301}} Q = 0.$$

From these, we obtain

$$\sum M_B = -4(C_V - A_V) + 13C_V - 9C_V' - 4A_V \equiv 0, \qquad \textbf{3.4-29}$$

that is, the first equation is satisfied identically;

$$\sum R_H = 96.5 + \frac{26}{\sqrt{1301}} Q - C'_H = 0, \qquad \textbf{3.4-30}$$

which is the same as the third of Eqs. 3.4-27; and

$$\sum R_V = (C_V - A_V) + \left(-C_V - \frac{4}{9} A_V\right) - P - \frac{25}{\sqrt{1301}} Q = 0, \qquad \textbf{3.4-31}$$

which is the same as the second of Eqs. 3.4-27. There are two redundancies, all other unknown forces being expressible in terms of, say, A_V and Q:

$$F_V = 74.2 - A_V,$$

$$C'_V = -74.2 - \frac{4}{9} A_V, \qquad \textbf{3.4-32}$$

$$P = -\frac{13}{9} A_V - \frac{25}{\sqrt{1301}} Q.$$

The structure may be made statically determinate if the pin at A or F is replaced by a roller, in which case A_V or F_V will be zero; and if brace BE is removed, in which case P will be zero, or brace BD is removed, so that Q does not appear in the problem.

We have used this statically indeterminate problem to show two things: that the solution methods of rigid-body statics are still applicable as far as they will take us, and that the partial solution of a statically indeterminate problem may indicate what must be done to make a structure just determinate.

Exercises

3.2-1: A uniform L-section of weight 75 lb is pinned smoothly at the elbow P so that the body may rotate in a vertical plane. Its motion is further restrained by a vertical cable attached to end A of the 6 ft arm PA and to a ceiling so that arm PA makes a $35°$ angle with the horizontal. Find the cable tension and the pin force on the body for equilibrium.

Ans.: $T = 15.5$ lb, $P_z = 0$, $P_y = 59.5$ lb.

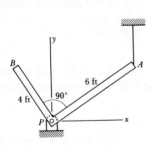

Exer. 3.2-1

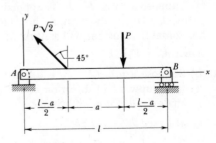

Exer. 3.2-2

3.2-2: Find the reactions at the pin A and the roller support B on the light beam loaded as shown.

Ans.: $A_x = P$, $A_y = -Pa/l$, $B_y = Pa/l$.

3.2-3: What horizontal force, P, is required to hold the 10 lb, 4 in. by 8 in. uniform block shown on the smooth 30° incline? What is the normal reaction, N, at the slope? What is the distance along the slope from the lowest corner to the line of action of N?

Ans.: $P = 5.77$ lb, $N = 11.5$ lb, $x = 1.5$ in.

3.2-4: A flat triangular plate of plan area A is to be cut from a sheet of thickness t and mass density ρ. The plate is to be supported on spring mounts at its vertices so that a horizontal position is the position of equilibrium. We should like to use three identical spring mounts of known properties. Does it make any difference in what way the triangular area is cut? That is, must we choose an equilateral triangle or some other special shape if identical mounts are used?

3.2-5: A rocker arm can be treated as a uniform rigid bar of mass m and length l pinned smoothly at its c.m. Its motion is restrained by an ideal torsional spring of constant K (moment/radian) which is undeformed when the bar is horizontal. (That is, the spring provides a restoring torque of K moment units per radian of angular deformation.)

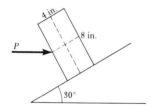

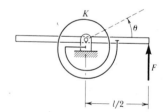

Exer. 3.2-3   **Exer. 3.2-5**

(a) Suppose a force $F=F_1$ is applied to the end of the arm and remains perpendicular to the arm as it rotates; find the angle $\theta=\theta_1$ with the horizontal that the bar will assume when it is in equilibrium.

Ans.: $\theta_1 = F_1 l/2k$.

(b) Suppose a force $F=F_2$ is applied to the end of the arm and remains vertically upward in direction as the arm rotates; what equation governs the angle $\theta=\theta_2$ for equilibrium?

Ans.: $\theta_2 \sec \theta_2 = F_2 l/2k$.

(c) If $F_1=F_2$, which is larger, θ_1 or θ_2? If $\theta_1=\theta_2$, which is larger, F_1 or F_2?

3.2-6: A 500 lb, 4 ft by 4 ft horizontal uniform slab is being slowly lifted in a triangular sling as shown. Find the tensions in the cables AP, BP, and CP.

Ans.: $T_B = 2T_A = 224$ lb;
$\qquad T_C = 229$ lb.

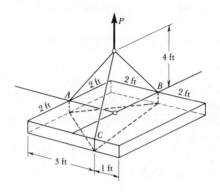

Exer. 3.2-6

3.2-7: A uniform semicircular arch of weight W and mean radius R is supported by a smooth pin at one end and by a smooth roller at the other. It supports two normal loads 90° apart, each equal to the weight of the arch in magnitude. Find the support reactions as functions of the angle θ shown, $0° < \theta < 90°$.

Ans.: $B = A_y = W(1 + \sin\theta + \cos\theta)/2$, $A_x = W(\cos\theta - \sin\theta)$.

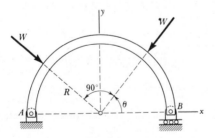

Exer. 3.2-7

3.2-8: A smooth ring weighing 1 lb is threaded on a light cord, the ends of which are attached to the ceiling of a room at points A and B. A horizontal force acts on the ring. Find the magnitude of this force if the plane of the string makes an angle of 45° with the vertical and the bisector of the angle subtended by the string at the ring makes an angle of 60° with AB.

Ans.: 1.29 lb.

3.2-9: The figure shows a plan view of a bent shaft held in smooth bearings at A and B. A couple of magnitude 277 lb-in. is applied to BC in a clockwise direction looking from B to C. A force of 50 lb acts at C at right angles to the plane of ABC and is directed so as to produce a clockwise moment about AB looking from B to A. What torque about AB and what bearing reactions are required to maintain equilibrium?

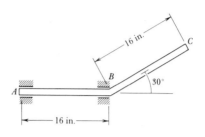

Exer. 3.2-9

Ans.: 160 lb-in., clockwise viewing from A to B; reaction at $A = 52$ lb in same direction as 50 lb force and reaction at $B = 102$ lb, opposite to direction of 50 lb force.

3.2-10: A particle weighing 10 lb is suspended from a point A on the ceiling by means of a cord 6 in. long. What is the greatest distance it can be pushed from the vertical through A by a force having a magnitude of 5 lb?

Ans.: 3 in.

3.2-11: The cord attached to the sphere has a length equal to the radius of the sphere. If the pull on the other cord is n times the weight of the sphere, what is the angle between the vertical and the cord attached to the sphere?

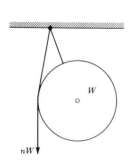

Exer. 3.2-11

Ans.: arcsin $\left(\dfrac{n}{2+2n}\right)$.

3.2-12: A pipe ABC has a 90° bend at B; $AB = 3$ ft, $BC = 4$ ft. Two machinists, one at each end, thread the pipe, each exerting a 24 lb-ft clockwise torque on the 9 in. long handles of a die holder. At the moment of interest, the pipe and die handles are horizontal. A support at B provides a vertical constraint force there. From above, the direction BC is 90° counterclockwise from AB. What forces must the man at A exert on the die handles?

Ans.: Left hand: 20 lb up; right hand: 12 lb down.

3.2-13: A uniform light rod ABC is freely pivoted at B (0, 0, 0) and held by cables AD and CE attached to A (-3, 0, 0) and C (4, 0, 0) and the fixed points D (0, -2, -6) and E (0, 4, -2). A load of 10 lb acts at C in the direction of the negative *y*-axis. Find the tensions in the strings and the magnitude of the reaction at *B*.

Ans.: $T_{AD} = 20/3$ lb; $T_{CE} = 90/7$ lb; $|\mathbf{B}| = 11.99$ lb.

3.2-14: The tail-gate of a truck may be regarded as a uniform rectangular plate *ABCD* weighing 50 lb. It is held in an inclined position by hinges at *C* and *D* and by a chain connecting *B* to a point 5 ft above *D*. The chain is 6.3 ft long and *AB*=4 ft, *BC*=3 ft. What is the load carried by the chain ?

Ans.: 31.5 lb.

3.2-15: A rectangular picture of width 2*w* and depth *d* is hung from a smooth peg by means of a cord attached to the two upper corners of the picture frame. The length of the cord is 2*l*. Show that if the depth of the picture is less than $2w^2/(l^2 - w^2)^{1/2}$, the picture can hang at an oblique angle to the horizontal.

3.3-1: The diagram shows a Howe truss, a common type for timber roof construction. Find the reactions and the loads carried by members *a*, *b*, *c*, and *d*. Are these loads tensile or compressive ? Which members obviously carry no stress for the loading shown ?

Ans.: $G_y = 2230$ lb; $C_y = 4910$ lb; $C_x = -3570$ lb; *a*: 4000 lb (*C*); *b*: 2230 lb (*T*); *c*: 0; *d*: 4460 lb (*T*); members *e* and *k*: 0.

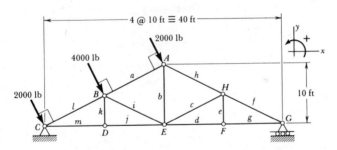

Exer. 3.3-1

3.3-2: The diagram shows a Warren truss. Find the load carried by members *a*, *b*, and *c*. Are they tensile or compressive ?

Ans.: *a*: 3.33 k (*C*); *b*: 1.08 k (*T*); *c*: 2.91 k (*T*).

3.3-3: The diagram shows a Warren truss with verticals. Find the load carried by members *a*, *b*, *c*, *d*, *e*. All upper chord forces are 600 lb and all lower chord forces are 2100 lb.

Ans.: *a*: 600 lb (*C*); *b*: 4360 lb (*C*); *c*: 8100 lb (*T*); *d*: 600 lb (*C*); *e*: 8640 lb (*C*).

3.3-4: Because of a rise in temperature, the arch shown expands and develops a reaction at *A* whose horizontal component is 60 k acting to the

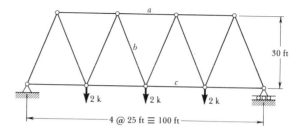

Exer. 3.3-2

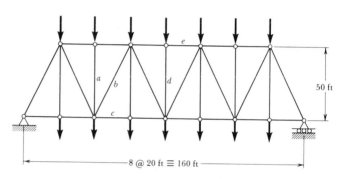

Exer. 3.3-3

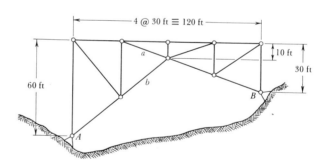

Exer. 3.3-4

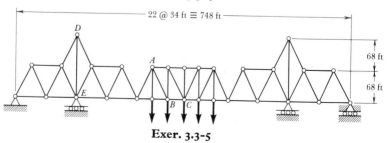

Exer. 3.3-5

right. Calculate the other reactions and the tensile or compressive loads carried by members *a* and *b*.

Ans.: $H_B = 60$ k left; $V_B = 15$ k down; $V_A = 15$ k up; *a*: 190 k (*C*); *b*: 117 k (*C*).

3.3-5: The cantilever bridge shown is symmetrical about its centerline. The suspended span is known as a Pratt truss. Its dead weight is 120,000 lb and may be considered divided into 5 equal loads as shown. Find the loads carried by members *AB* and *BC*. Tension or compression?

Ans.: *AB*: 40,200 lb (*T*); *BC*: 48,000 lb (*T*).

3.3-6: In Exercise 3.3-5, what is the load carried by the member *DE*? Is it tension or compression? Do you think that the design of this member would present any difficulty?

Ans.: *DE*: 240,000 lb (*C*).

3.3-7: Each lower chord panel point of the *K*-truss shown carries a load of 5000 lb and each upper panel point carries 2000 lb. Find the tensile or compressive loads carried by members *a*, *b*, *c*, and *d*.

Ans.: $a = 12{,}450$ lb (*C*); $b = 2350$ lb (*C*); $c = 2350$ lb (*T*); $d = 12{,}450$ lb (*T*).

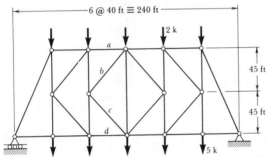

Exer. 3.3-7

3.3-8: Find the loads, tensile or compressive, carried by members *a*, *b*, *c*, *d* of the truss shown.

Ans.: $a = 7.5$ k (*T*); $b = 42.8$ k (*T*); $c = 5.5$ k (*C*); $d = 15$ k (*T*).

3.3-9: Find the loads carried by members *a*, *b*, *c*, and *d* of the truss shown.
Ans.: $a = 225$ k (*C*); $b = 75$ k (*C*); $c = 125$ k (*C*); $d = 0$.

3.3-10: Design your own truss to carry a downward load of 30,000 lb at the center of a 250 ft span. For ease of handling, no member is to exceed 40 ft in length. Find the greatest load carried by any member.

3.3-11: Show that a statically determinate planar truss with the usual three-foundation constraint quantities (*C*=3) must have at least one joint at which only two bars are connected or else one joint where only three bars are connected.

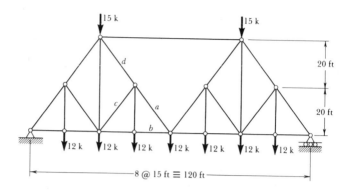

Exer. 3.3-8

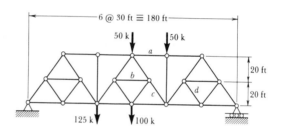

Exer. 3.3-9

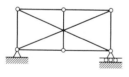

Exer. 3.3-12

3.3-12: Show that the truss pictured is a critical form. The bars are not connected at the center where they overlap.

3.3-13: The hexagonal truss shown is made of bars 6 ft long. Find the loads carried by members *AB* and *CD*. Would the truss be statically determinate if there were a bar connecting *F* and *G*?

Ans.: $F_{AB} = 25$ lb compression; $F_{CD} = 32.7$ lb tension.

3.3-14: Show that the hexagonal truss pictured is a critical form. There is no joint at the center; the bars merely overlap.

3.3-15: A regular tetrahedral truss is subject to the parallel loads shown. Show that the truss as a whole is in equilibrium and find the loads carried by all six members.

Ans.: $AB = AC = AD = P\sqrt{6}/6$ compression; $BC = CD = DB = P\sqrt{6}/18$ tension.

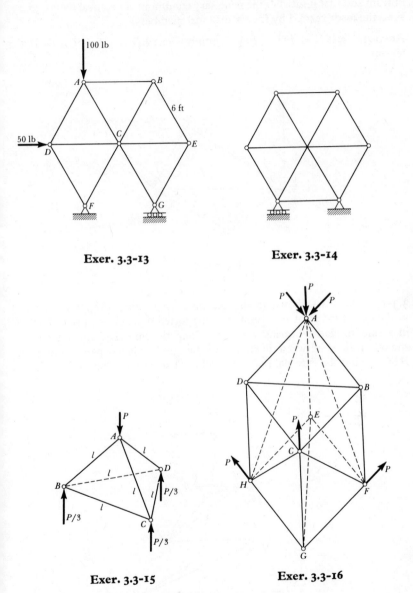

Exer. 3.3-13

Exer. 3.3-14

Exer. 3.3-15

Exer. 3.3-16

3.3-16: A spatial truss *ABCDEFGH* has the form of a cube. It is made of 12 bars of length l and six of length $l\sqrt{2}$. ("Hidden" bars are shown by broken lines.) It is subjected to 6 forces of magnitude P directed along the edges of the cube as shown.   Show that the truss as a whole is in equilibrium and that it satisfies the necessary conditions for statical determinacy. Find the loads carried by the six diagonal members.

Ans.: $AF = AH = EG = P/\sqrt{2}$ compression; $BD = CF = CH = P/\sqrt{2}$ tension.

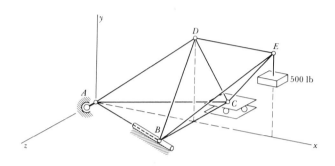

Exer. 3.3-17

3.3-17: The truss shown in the accompanying figure supports a vertical load of 500 lb at joint E.   Joint A is supported in a smooth pivot; joint B, in a smooth sleeve bearing with axis along the line AB; and joint C, on smooth rollers between fixed horizontal guide planes parallel to plane ABC.   Find the external reactions and the bar forces.   Bars AB, BC, AC,

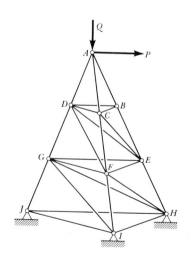

Exer. 3.3-18

BD, *CD*, and *DE* are each 6 ft long; joints *A*, *D*, and *E* are in the same vertical plane, with *D* above the midpoint of *BC*.

Ans.: A $= -577\mathbf{j}$ lb; **B** = **C** $= 539\mathbf{j}$ lb; *BE* = 408 lb (*C*); *BD* = 333 lb (*C*); *AD* = 816 lb (*T*).

3.3-18: (a) State precisely the conditions under which one can conclude that one or more bars meeting at an unloaded joint in a space truss carry no load.

(b) Apply one or both of these basic theorems step by step to the loaded truss of the accompanying figure to show that only the slant legs, and not the horizontal or diagonal cross-bracing, of the tower are carrying load.

3.4-1: Three masses are connected by light inextensible cords, which pass over small smooth pulleys distant $2a$ apart on the same horizontal level. Find the sag b for equilibrium of the central mass. For what ratios M/m of the mass of the center body to the mass of either of the other bodies is equilibrium possible?

Ans.: $\dfrac{b}{a} = \dfrac{M/2m}{[1-(M/2m)^2]^{1/2}}; \dfrac{M}{m} < 2.$

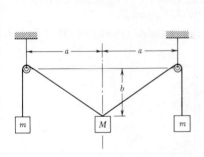

Exer. 3.4-1

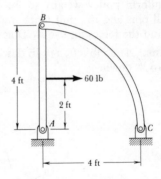

Exer. 3.4-2

3.4-2: The smoothly pinned arch shown consists of a 30 lb vertical bar *AB* and a light quarter-circle *BC*. Find the forces acting on member *AB* when the 60 lb horizontal load is applied at its center.

Ans.: at *A*: 30 lb to left; at *B*: $30\sqrt{2}$ lb up and to the left at 45°.

3.4-3: The rhomboidal frame *ABCD* consists of light rigid bars pinned smoothly together. The foundation pin at *A* is smooth, as are the rollers in the two-sided guide at *D*. A torque of 100 lb-ft is applied to member *AB*. Find the support reactions and the forces on each member.

Ans.: Support reactions: 25 lb up at *A*, 25 lb down at *D*; bars *BC* and *CD* carry $50\sqrt{3}/3$ lb tensile load; bar *AD* carries a $25\sqrt{3}/3$ lb tensile load; bar

AC carries a 50 lb compressive load; bar *AB* is subject to a $50\sqrt{3}/3$ lb force to the right at *B* and a resultant $50\sqrt{3}/3$ lb force to the left at *A*, besides the 100 lb-ft torque.

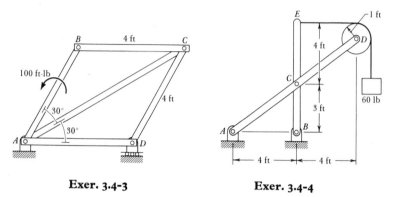

Exer. 3.4-3   Exer. 3.4-4

3.4-4: The vertical plane frame shown supports the 60 lb weight. The uniform pulley weighs 50 lb, while the bars *BE* and *AD* weigh 10 lb/ft. All pins and the pulley are smooth, and the cord is light and inextensible. Find the forces on bar *ACD* at the pins *A*, *C*, and *D*.

Ans.: *A*: 80 lb left, 115 lb down; *C*: 140 lb right, 335 lb up; *D*: 60 lb left, 110 lb down.

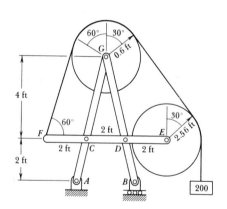

Exer. 3.4-5

3.4-5: The symmetrical *A*-frame, pulleys, and cord shown support a 200 lb load. Dimensions are as shown, all contacts are smooth, and all weights may be ignored except the 200 lb load. Find the forces on the horizontal member *FCDE*.

Ans.:

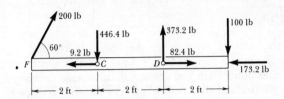

3.4-6: The weight of the study lamp shown is held in equilibrium by the spring. The tension of the spring is k multiplied by the length of the spring. Show that, if the designer makes the proper choice of k, the lamp will be balanced for all angles θ, and find what this value of k should be in terms of W, a, b, and h.

Ans.: $k = Wb/ah$.

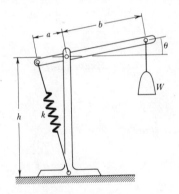

Exer. 3.4-6

3.4-7: The crankshaft of a single-cylinder engine is shown in outline.
(a) What horizontal force P must be applied to the handle in order to produce a compression force C of 100 lb in the cylinder?
(b) Determine the bearing reaction at B when this force is applied.

Ans.: (a) $P = 40.7$ lb; (b) $B_y = 45.3$ lb; $B_z = 82.1$ lb.

3.4-8: A circular table weighing 50 lb stands on a horizontal floor, supported by four equal legs placed symmetrically around its edge. What is the largest weight that can safely be placed on the table?

Ans.: 120 lb.

3.4-9: (a) In a so-called four-ball testing rig, three smooth, light ball bearings are placed, just touching, inside a cylinder and a fourth ball is placed symmetrically on top of them, touching all three as shown. A vertical load is then applied to the upper ball. What is the force exerted by any one of the lower ball bearings on the cylinder wall?

Ans.: $P\sqrt{18}/18$.

(b) This is the starting pressure in the test. As the test proceeds, the cylinder is spun about a vertical axis. What effect do you think this has on the force in question? Do you see any disadvantage to using four or five balls in the cylinder and thus testing a larger number at once?

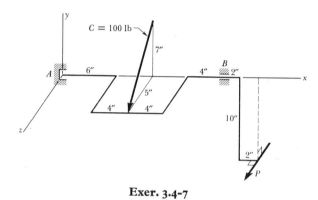

Exer. 3.4-7

Exer. 3.4-9

3.4-10: Here we show two smooth spheres of weight w and radius r placed inside a cylinder of radius R and weight W which is open at both ends and rests on a horizontal plane (see text Example 3.2-6). Of course $2r > R$.
(a) What is the pressure exerted by either one of the spheres on the cylinder?

(b) What is the smallest value of W allowable if the cylinder is not to tip over?

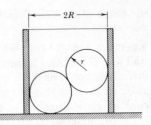

Ans.: $P = \dfrac{w(R-r)}{[R(2r-R)]^{\frac{1}{2}}}$;

$$(b)\ \ W = 2w\left(1 - \frac{r}{R}\right).$$

Exer. 3.4-10

3.4-11: Generalize part (b) of Exercise 3.4-10 to the case in which there are $2n$ spheres in the cylinder. Show that under these circumstances $W_{\min} = 2nw(1 - r/R)$.

3.4-12: Solve Exercise 3.4-10 for a cylinder having a solid bottom. Now what is the pressure exerted by either of the spheres on the cylinder? Can the cylinder possibly tip?

3.4-13: A flat-bottomed cup of radius R and weight nW stands on a table. A uniform rod of length $2L$ and weight W rests over the rim of the cup and presses against its smooth vertical interior. (a) Find the angle θ for which rod and cup can be in equilibrium. (b) Show that if this angle is smaller than the angle whose cosine is $(n+2)R/L$ the cup will tip over.

Ans.: $\theta = \arccos\left(\dfrac{2R}{L}\right)^{\frac{1}{3}}$.

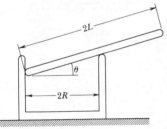

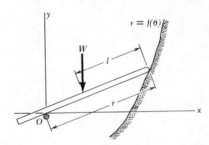

Exer. 3.4-13

Exer. 3.4-15

3.4-14: In the situation described in Exercise 3.4-13 find the length of the longest rod that can possibly be in equilibrium with one end pressing against the smooth vertical interior wall.

Ans.: $L = R(n+2)^{\frac{3}{2}}/\sqrt{2}$.

3.4-15: A rod of weight W rests on a smooth peg at O with one end pressing on a surface whose equation is $r = f(\theta)$. Show that the rod will be in equilibrium provided $dr/d\theta = -(r-l)\cot\theta$. Here l denotes the distance from one end of the rod to the center of gravity.

3.4-16: Use the results of Exercise 3.4-15 to show that, if the equation of the surface is $r = l + C \csc\theta$, the rod will be in equilibrium for any angle θ. Here C is a constant of integration and may have any value. Sketch the shape of the curve for $\theta = 0°$ to $\theta = -90°$ when C is such that $r = 2l$ at $\theta = -90°$.

3.4-17: A uniform rod AB rests in equilibrium with A touching a smooth wall and B touching a smooth floor. B is attached by a cord to a point C directly below A at the intersection of wall and floor. The cord makes an angle of 60° with that intersection and with AB. A is held by a horizontal cord which is attached to the wall. Find the tensions in the two cords if the rod weighs 100 lb.

Ans.: 14.5 lb at A; 29 lb at B.

3.4-18: The figure shows plan and elevation of a shaft with two cranks. One crank is subjected at C to a single force of 112 lb directed as shown in the figure (note that neither view looks perpendicular to this force). The shaft is kept in equilibrium by a vertical force R applied at D, an end thrust T, and bearing reactions having components H_A, V_A, H_B, V_B as shown. Find their magnitudes.

Ans.: 12, 50, -100, 52, 13.5, 10 lb.

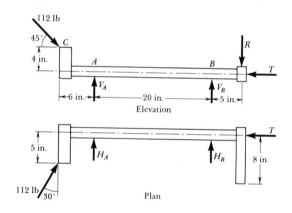

Exer. 3.4-18

CHAPTER **IV**

Equilibrium under

Distributed Forces

4.1 Introduction

The analysis of equilibrium of systems subjected to distributed loads parallels that of systems subjected to concentrated loads insofar as finding external constraint forces is concerned. The distributed load may be replaced by an equipollent resultant force set and the equations of equilibrium for the system can be written. If the problem is statically indeterminate, however, or if, for some reason, we need to know the details of the internal force distribution in a member that is statically determinate over-all, we must take into account the true external force distribution in determining the internal force distribution. A complete solution of such a problem—particularly statically indeterminate problems for deformable bodies—requires the introduction of displacement and strain analysis. The solution also requires that the strain quantities be related to the load quantities through the properties of the material of which the body is fashioned. We shall not be concerned with such questions here, but will consider only those that admit of a solution in terms of external load quantities alone, with a minimum assumption about deformation, such as the assumption of inextensibility for a cable.

In Section 2.7, the meaning of the equivalence of distributed loads to concentrated loads was discussed. For instance, the distribution of internal forces over the area of a beam cross-section was replaced by an equipollent resultant force, with axial and shear components, and a couple. In some problems, "partial" resultants may be the quantities of importance. For example, in the theory of thin plates, integrals of distributed forces per unit area are used as the fundamental quantities, much as in beam theory—but only integrals through the thickness of the plate, i.e., forces and moments per unit length of edge, not integrals over a whole area. Whatever type of internal force distribution is considered—the actual forces per unit area of some equipollent set of partial or total resultants—the equilibrium equations to be solved must generally be formulated as differential equations of equilibrium.

In this chapter, we shall treat a sequence of questions in which the internal forces to be found become successively of more complex types—although the problems solved may be more difficult for some of the simpler forces than for some of the more complex. First, the inextensible cable loaded along its length will be considered. The theory of the cable in a plane will be developed, and the problems of the suspension bridge cable, the belt on a smooth pulley, and the cable hanging under its own weight will be solved. Next, the distribution of internal shear force and bending moment in a statically determinate beam will be considered. The concept of pressure and the equations of fluid statics will lead to the general equilibrium equations governing internal force distributions and the concept of the stress tensor. Distributed forces of a frictional nature will be treated in Chapter V.

4.2 The Loaded Cable

The light cable treated so far has been considered to be a straight two-force member; the only forces of concern have been the tensile forces of equal magnitude applied to the cable at its ends, and hence applied by the cables to the bodies at either end. The cable supporting the deck of a suspension bridge, or a transmission line hanging under its own weight, assumes a sagging curved shape under the load distributed along the cable length and the tensile loads at the ends. In order to find the end tensions exerted by the cable on its supports, we must determine the equilibrium shape assumed by the cable. For a belt wrapped around a smooth pulley, we can often find the tensions at either end; however, to compute the pressure distribution between pulley and cable from the equilibrium equations, we must make use of the known shape of the belt.

The geometry of the curve assumed by the cable is, therefore, of fundamental importance. We shall treat only those problems in which the cable and all loads upon it can be considered to be in a plane; the geometry of space curves has more complexity than we care to introduce at this point. We shall begin by summarizing some results from the calculus about the properties of plane curves before formulating the problem of the loaded cable.

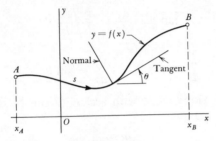

Fig. 4.2-I

Suppose a smooth curve between points A and B is given in a plane, and x-, y-axes are chosen so that the equation of the curve is $y = f(x)$. We suppose $f(x)$ to have at least two continuous derivatives. The tangent line to the curve at any point has *slope* $dy/dx = f'(x)$, with the *slope angle* θ from the x-axis to the tangent line determined by the relation

$$\frac{dy}{dx} = \tan \theta. \qquad\qquad \textbf{4.2-I}$$

The angle θ is, of course, a function of position. The *arclength s* along the curve is defined through the differential relation

$$(ds)^2 = (dx)^2 + (dy)^2, \qquad\qquad \textbf{4.2-2a}$$

or by

$$\left(\frac{ds}{dx}\right)^2 = 1 + \left(\frac{dy}{dx}\right)^2. \qquad\qquad \textbf{4.2-2b}$$

If we decide upon an orientation for the curve, i.e., decide in which sense along the curve the arclength increases, we may integrate

Eq. 4.2-2b for s as a function of x. Suppose that $s=0$ at A and increases as the curve is traversed toward B; then

$$s = \int_{x_A}^{x} \left[1 + \left(\frac{dy}{dx}\right)^2\right]^{½} dx, \qquad \text{4.2-3}$$

with the total length L of the curve being given by

$$L = \int_{x_A}^{x_B} \left[1 + \left(\frac{dy}{dx}\right)^2\right]^{½} dx. \qquad \text{4.2-4}$$

Once the arclength has been introduced, we may consider the equation of the curve to be given parametrically in the form $x=x(s), y=y(s)$. Then the slope angle $\theta = \theta(s)$ is determined by

$$\tan \theta = \frac{dy}{dx} = \frac{dy}{ds}\bigg/\frac{dx}{ds}, \qquad \text{4.2-5a}$$

or by

$$\frac{dx}{ds} = \cos \theta, \qquad \frac{dy}{ds} = \sin \theta. \qquad \text{4.2-5b}$$

The change in the slope angle with arclength can be determined by differentiating Eq. 4.2-5a:

$$\frac{d}{ds}(\tan \theta) = \sec^2 \theta \frac{d\theta}{ds} = \frac{d}{ds}\left(\frac{dy}{dx}\right) = \frac{d^2y}{dx^2}\frac{dx}{ds},$$

or

$$\frac{d\theta}{ds} = \cos^3 \theta \frac{d^2y}{dx^2}.$$

This is one form of the expression for the *curvature* of the curve; for, since $\cos \theta = 1/\sec \theta = \pm[1+\tan^2 \theta]^{-½}$, we have

$$\frac{d\theta}{ds} = \frac{\pm \frac{d^2y}{dx^2}}{\left[1+\left(\frac{dy}{dx}\right)^2\right]^{3/2}} = \pm\frac{1}{\rho} = \pm\kappa$$

where κ is the curvature and ρ is the radius of curvature. The choice of sign depends upon the sign convention selected for curvature. Since we shall not need to use the curvature formally, we shall not pursue this question further.

It will be helpful to establish formal coordinates tangent and normal to the curve. At any point on the curve, the direction tangent to the curve in the sense of increasing arclength is called the *tangential direction*, and a *unit tangent vector* $\mathbf{e}_t$ in that direction can be constructed. The direction 90° counterclockwise from the tangential direction is the *normal direction,* and the *unit normal vector* is denoted by $\mathbf{e}_n$. Since the slope angle θ is the angle between the x-axis and the tangential direction, the vectors $\mathbf{e}_t$ and $\mathbf{e}_n$ can be written down in cartesian components:

$$\mathbf{e}_t = \cos\theta\mathbf{i} + \sin\theta\mathbf{j}, \qquad \mathbf{e}_n = -\sin\theta\mathbf{i} + \cos\theta\mathbf{j}. \qquad \textbf{4.2-6}$$

These can be solved for $\mathbf{i}$ and $\mathbf{j}$:

$$\mathbf{i} = \cos\theta\mathbf{e}_t - \sin\theta\mathbf{e}_n, \qquad \mathbf{j} = \sin\theta\mathbf{e}_t + \cos\theta\mathbf{e}_n. \qquad \textbf{4.2-7}$$

The reader may compare these unit vector relations with those developed for polar coordinates in Section 1.5. The normal and tangential *intrinsic* coordinates are also of fundamental importance in the study of the motion of a particle along a curved path.

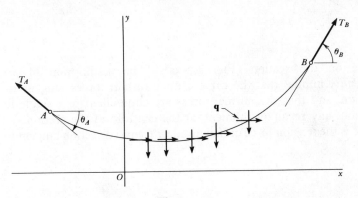

Fig. 4.2-2

We turn now to the formulation of the equilibrium equations for the loaded cable. Suppose a cable of length L is supported at two points, A and B, and subjected to a distributed load $\mathbf{q} = q_x\mathbf{i} + q_y\mathbf{j}$ (in units of force/length) in its plane. The load $\mathbf{q}$ may be regarded as known for the present, although there are questions where $\mathbf{q}$ is an unknown. A free-body diagram of the whole cable appears in Fig. 4.2-2, with the end reactions represented as tension forces of magnitudes T_A and T_B in directions determined by the slope angles θ_A and θ_B of the tangents to the curve at the endpoints. The problem is statically indeterminate, since there are four unknowns, T_A, T_B, θ_A, and θ_B, and only three non-trivial equilibrium equations. We expect, therefore, that we must add some statement about the cable geometry to the equations of equilibrium in order to obtain a solution. This statement will derive from the assumption of *inextensibility*;

i.e., the cable will be assumed to remain unchanged in length under load.

In order to proceed further, we examine the relations between the changing shape of the cable and the changing tension along the cable under the applied loads. Suppose we make a cut normal to the cable at some typical point $s = s_0$, and examine the distribution of

Fig. 4.2-3

force on the section (Fig. 4.2-3a). The assumption of *perfect flexibility* implies that the cable cannot sustain forces tangent to the section, and that the normal forces are equipollent to a single force, without any resultant moment, at the centroid of the section. This force is the tension force of magnitude $T(s)$ and direction tangent to the

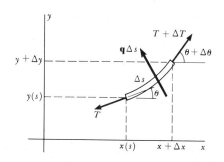

Fig. 4.2-4

center line of the cable. We replace the cable, in fact, by its center line as our model for analysis. The distributed load is thought of as applied at the center line, and will be considered either as a force $\mathbf{q}(s)$ per unit length of arc or a force $\mathbf{q}(x)$ or $\mathbf{q}(y)$ per unit x- or y-distance.

Let us now isolate a small segment of cable of length Δs and draw a free-body diagram of it (Fig. 4.2-4). The forces acting on the segment are three in number: the tension force of magnitude $T = T(s)$ in the negative tangential direction at the end $[x(s), y(s)]$, the tension force of magnitude $T(s + \Delta s) = T + \Delta T$ in the positive tangential direction at the end $(x + \Delta x, y + \Delta y)$, and the resultant* $\mathbf{q}(s) \Delta s$ of the distributed load. The distributed force $\mathbf{q}(s)$ is assumed to be given per unit of arclength. To write the force equilibrium equations for the cable segment, we can use either the fixed x-, y-directions or the intrinsic tangential and normal directions. We shall do both, for both forms of the equations are useful and important. We shall begin with the cartesian x-, y-form of the equations.

As shown in Fig. 4.2-4, we denote the slope angle at (x, y) by $\theta(s)$ and the slope angle at $(x + \Delta x, y + \Delta y)$ by $\theta + \Delta\theta$. The distributed force is written in cartesian components: $\mathbf{q}(s) = q_x(s)\mathbf{i} + q_y(s)\mathbf{j}$. The equations of force equilibrium are

$$\sum R_x = (T + \Delta T)\cos(\theta + \Delta\theta) - T\cos\theta + q_x\,\Delta s = 0,$$

$$\sum R_y = (T + \Delta T)\sin(\theta + \Delta\theta) - T\sin\theta + q_y\,\Delta s = 0. \qquad \textbf{4.2-8a}$$

Using the trigonometric formulas for the sine and cosine of the sum of two angles, we can rewrite these equations:

$$\sum R_x = \Delta T\cos(\theta + \Delta\theta)$$
$$- T\sin\theta\sin\Delta\theta + T\cos\theta(\cos\Delta\theta - 1) + q_x\,\Delta s = 0,$$

$$\sum R_y = \Delta T\sin(\theta + \Delta\theta)$$
$$+ T\cos\theta\sin\Delta\theta + T\sin\theta(\cos\Delta\theta - 1) + q_y\,\Delta s = 0. \qquad \textbf{4.2-8b}$$

---

* Properly we should consider the resultant $\int_s^{s+\Delta s} \mathbf{q}(\sigma)\,d\sigma$ of the distributed load on a finite segment $(s, s + \Delta s)$, as well as the tensions. We should also write a moment equilibrium equation, as well as the force equations, divide by Δs, and examine the limiting forms as $\Delta s \to 0$. When this is done, we find that the moment equation becomes trivial, i.e., of the $0 = 0$ form, and gives us no information. Moreover, in dealing with the force and moment resultants of the distributed forces, it is convenient to use the mean-value theorem of the integral calculus, which states that integrals such as $\int_s^{s+\Delta s} \mathbf{q}(\sigma)\,d\sigma$ can be replaced by $\mathbf{q}(s + \epsilon\,\Delta s)\,\Delta s$, $0 \leq \epsilon \leq 1$, the number ϵ approaching zero as Δs approaches zero. It is implied in the main text development that all of these replacement and limiting operations can be performed rigorously. The model of the segment is, therefore, essentially a particle model for which force equations of equilibrium alone suffice.

We shall now divide by Δs and pass to the limit $\Delta s \rightarrow 0$. Of course, ΔT and $\Delta \theta$ approach zero with Δs. Also, we make use of the two fundamental limits

$$\lim_{\Delta\theta \to 0} \frac{\sin \Delta\theta}{\Delta\theta} = 1, \qquad \lim_{\Delta\theta \to 0} \frac{1 - \cos \Delta\theta}{\Delta\theta} = 0 \qquad \textbf{4.2-9}$$

by multiplying and dividing the second and third terms in both of Eqs. 4.2-8b by $\Delta\theta$ before passing to the limit. We find

$$\frac{dT}{ds} \cos \theta - T \sin \theta \frac{d\theta}{ds} + q_x(s) = 0,$$

$$\frac{dT}{ds} \sin \theta + T \cos \theta \frac{d\theta}{ds} + q_y(s) = 0 \qquad \textbf{4.2-10a}$$

as our differential equations of equilibrium in the x- and y- directions. A more compact form can be given to each equation:

$$\frac{d}{ds} (T \cos \theta) + q_x(s) = 0,$$

$$\frac{d}{ds} (T \sin \theta) + q_y(s) = 0. \qquad \textbf{4.2-10b}$$

Equations 4.2-10b may be interpreted in the following way. Since $T \cos \theta$ and $T \sin \theta$ are the x- and y-components of the cable tension, respectively, the equations state that the rate of change with arclength of the cable tension component in the x- or y-direction is the negative of the applied load (per unit arclength) in that direction.

As we have mentioned, the intrinsic coordinate form of the equations is useful. Suppose we solve Eqs. 4.2-10a for dT/ds by multiplying the first equation by $\cos \theta$, the second by $\sin \theta$, and adding:

$$\frac{dT}{ds} + q_x \cos \theta + q_y \sin \theta = 0.$$

Now $q_x \cos \theta + q_y \sin \theta$ is the component of $\mathbf{q}$ in the tangential direction. From Eqs. 4.2-6,

$$q_t = \mathbf{q} \cdot \mathbf{e}_t = q_x \cos \theta + q_y \sin \theta$$

and

$$q_n = \mathbf{q} \cdot \mathbf{e}_n = -q_x \sin \theta + q_y \cos \theta \qquad \textbf{4.2-11}$$

are the tangential and normal components* of the distributed load at any point. Therefore, the equation for dT/ds can be written

$$\frac{dT}{ds} + q_t(s) = 0, \qquad\qquad \textbf{4.2-12a}$$

and, similarly, an equation for the curvature $d\theta/ds$ can be found:

$$T\frac{d\theta}{ds} + q_n(s) = 0. \qquad\qquad \textbf{4.2-12b}$$

From Eq. 4.2-12a, we conclude that the tension changes magnitude along the curve only if there is a load tangent to the curve.

Finally, if the load **q** is considered to be a function of some other position variable, say x, instead of arclength, then all the integrations and limiting processes should be performed with respect to that variable instead of s. The equilibrium equations 4.2-10 are replaced by similar ones with derivatives with respect to x replacing derivatives with respect to s:

$$\frac{d}{dx}(T\cos\theta) + q_x(x) = 0,$$

$$\frac{d}{dx}(T\sin\theta) + q_y(x) = 0. \qquad\qquad \textbf{4.2-13}$$

We now have two differential equations in the two unknowns, T and θ. Our boundary conditions, however, are not on T and θ but rather on $y = f(x)$: $y_A = f(x_A)$, $y_B = f(x_B)$. Equation 4.2-1, $dy/dx = \tan\theta$ (or its equivalent), must be used. But now we have three equations and only two boundary conditions; the problem is still statically indeterminate. The third condition that shall be imposed,

---

* It should be emphasized that the sign conventions for positive q_t and q_n depend upon the choice we have made for the positive tangential and normal directions—that is, on the direction of increasing arclength and on the $90°$ counterclockwise rotation from that direction. In a particular problem, we may find it more convenient to use a $90°$ clockwise convention for the positive normal—in which case Eqs. 4.2-6, 11, and 12 should be suitably modified. Equation 4.2-12b, in particular, may cause difficulty; but an examination of the loading conditions and of the sense in which θ increases should let one decide in each case whether $T\,d\theta/ds$ equals $+q_n$ or $-q_n$. For examples of the direct derivation of normal and tangential equilibrium equations, the reader is referred to Section 5.4 on belt and cable friction.

as we have mentioned, is that of inextensibility: the length L of the cable is a constant, and the cable shape $y = f(x)$ must satisfy Eq. 4.2-4:

$$L = \int_{x_A}^{x_B} \left[1 + \left(\frac{dy}{dx} \right)^2 \right]^{\frac{1}{2}} dx.$$

Example 4.2-1

A belt passes around a smooth pulley of radius r, covering an arc of θ_0 radians (Fig. 4.2-5a). From equilibrium considerations, it is found that the tension in the belt is a constant T_0 at either end of the segment touching the pulley. What is the force exerted by the pulley on the belt?

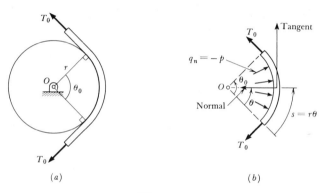

Fig. 4.2-5

Solution: The belt segment in contact with the pulley is circular in shape, so that here the equilibrium curve is known and the distributed loads are to be found. The free-body diagram of the segment is shown in Fig. 4.2-5b. The contact is smooth, so that no tangential loads q_t are exerted. The normal load q_n is of the form of a pressure per unit length, $q_n = -p(s)$. From Eq. 4.2-12a, we have

$$\frac{dT}{ds} + q_t = \frac{dT}{ds} = 0,$$

so that the tension is constant at any section: $T = T_0$. From the circular shape of the cable, we have $s = r\theta$, $d\theta/ds = 1/r$; the second of Eqs. 4.2-12 becomes

$$T \frac{d\theta}{ds} + q_n = \frac{T_0}{r} - p = 0,$$

and the pressure distribution is uniform in magnitude:

$$p = \frac{T_0}{r}.$$

Example 4.2-2

A suspension bridge deck of weight W is supported by vertical stringers from a light cable of length L which is supported at its ends by towers of equal height (Fig. 4.2-6). Assuming that the deck weight can be considered to be distributed uniformly along the horizontal span of length l, what is the tension on the cable at either support? What is the maximum sag of the cable?

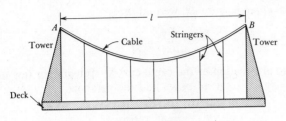

Fig. 4.2-6

Solution: The distributed load here is a constant $w = W/l$ in the vertically downward direction. The weight of the cable itself is neglected by comparison with this load. The uniformity of the load and the symmetry of the support conditions suggest that the equilibrium shape will be symmetrical, with a lowest point having horizontal tangent occurring at the midspan. A free-body diagram of the whole cable, with appropriate coordinates, is shown in Fig. 4.2-7. The sag is denoted by f; the supports are then at $x = \pm l/2$, $y = f$.

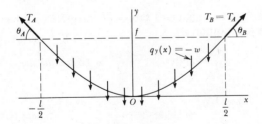

Fig. 4.2-7

Since the distributed load is given per unit horizontal span, Eqs. 4.2-13 with $q_x = 0$, $q_y = -w$ are used. The x-equation may be integrated immediately to obtain

$$T \cos \theta = H, \qquad\qquad 4.2\text{-}14$$

where H is a constant of integration. Here it may be interpreted as the tension in the cable at the lowest point O, since the tension there is the same as its horizontal component $T \cos \theta$. Solving Eq. 4.2-14 for $T(x)$, we find

$$T(x) = H \sec \theta(x),\qquad\qquad \textbf{4.2-15}$$

which, when substituted in the second of Eqs. 4.2-13, leads to an equation for $\theta(x)$:

$$\frac{d}{dx}(H \tan \theta) - w = 0.$$

Since (Eq. 4.2-1) $\tan \theta = dy/dx$, we find that

$$\frac{d^2y}{dx^2} = \frac{w}{H}\qquad\qquad \textbf{4.2-16}$$

is the differential equation of the cable curve. Integrating this under the conditions $y = dy/dx = 0$ at $x = 0$, we find the parabola

$$y = \frac{w}{2H}x^2 = \frac{W}{2Hl}x^2\qquad\qquad \textbf{4.2-17}$$

as the shape of the curve.

In order to select the correct parabola, we must determine H or some equivalent parameter. One such parameter which determines the shape and which is also easily measured is the sag f. The relation between f and H is

$$f = \frac{w}{2H}\left(\frac{l}{2}\right)^2 = \frac{Wl}{8H}.\qquad\qquad \textbf{4.2-18}$$

To find H, we must use the inextensibility condition Eq. 4.2-4:

$$L = \int_{-l/2}^{l/2}\left[1+\left(\frac{wx}{H}\right)^2\right]^{\frac{1}{2}}dx = 2\int_{0}^{l/2}\left[1+\frac{w^2x^2}{H^2}\right]^{\frac{1}{2}}dx.$$

This may be found in standard tables of integrals or integrated directly by use of the substitution

$$\frac{wx}{H} = \sinh u, \qquad \frac{w\,dx}{H} = \cosh u\,du.$$

Then

$$L = \frac{2H}{w}\int_{0}^{\operatorname{arcsinh}\left(\frac{wl}{2H}\right)}\cosh^2 u\,du = \frac{H}{w}\int_{0}^{\operatorname{arcsinh}\left(\frac{wl}{2H}\right)}(1+\cosh 2u)\,du$$

$$= \frac{H}{w}\left[u+\frac{1}{2}\sinh 2u\right]\Big|_{0}^{\operatorname{arcsinh}\left(\frac{wl}{2H}\right)}$$

$$= \frac{H}{w}\left[u+\sinh u \cosh u\right]\Big|_{0}^{\operatorname{arcsinh}\left(\frac{wl}{2H}\right)}$$

or

$$L = \frac{H}{w}\left\{\operatorname{arcsinh}\left(\frac{wl}{2H}\right)+\frac{wl}{2H}\left[1+\left(\frac{wl}{2H}\right)^2\right]^{\frac{1}{2}}\right\}.\qquad\qquad \textbf{4.2-19}$$

This equation defines H in terms of the known quantities w, l, and L implicitly, and must be solved by numerical means. Dividing both sides of 4.2-19 by l, we may put the equation in a more convenient form in terms of non-dimensional parameters L/l (length-to-span ratio) and W/H:

$$\frac{2L}{l} = \left[1 + \left(\frac{W}{2H}\right)^2\right]^{1/2} + \left(\frac{W}{2H}\right)^{-1} \operatorname{arcsinh}\left(\frac{W}{2H}\right). \qquad \textbf{4.2-20}$$

Since the sag f is related to H through Eq. 4.2-18, we can also find the sag, or rather the ratio f/l of the sag to the span, directly from the length-to-span ratio:

$$\frac{2L}{l} = \left[1 + \left(\frac{4f}{l}\right)^2\right]^{1/2} + \left(\frac{4f}{l}\right)^{-1} \operatorname{arcsinh}\left(\frac{4f}{l}\right). \qquad \textbf{4.2-21}$$

When the span and cable length are of the same order of magnitude, the sag can be expected to be small. In this case, when f/l is small compared to unity, power series expansion of the right-hand side of Eq. 4.2-21 leads to an approximate result. Since

$$\left[1 + \left(\frac{4f}{l}\right)^2\right]^{1/2} = 1 + \frac{1}{2}\left(\frac{4f}{l}\right)^2 - \frac{1}{8}\left(\frac{4f}{l}\right)^4 + \cdots,$$

$$\frac{\operatorname{arcsinh}(4f/l)}{(4f/l)} = 1 - \frac{1}{6}\left(\frac{4f}{l}\right)^2 + \frac{3}{40}\left(\frac{4f}{l}\right)^4 + \cdots,$$

we have (neglecting terms of order four)

$$\frac{2L}{l} \cong 2 + \frac{1}{3}\left(\frac{4f}{l}\right)^2.$$

Therefore, for small sag ratios, we have

$$\frac{4f}{l} \cong \left[6\left(\frac{L}{l} - 1\right)\right]^{1/2} \qquad \textbf{4.2-22a}$$

and

$$\frac{2H}{W} = \left(\frac{4f}{l}\right)^{-1} \cong \left[6\left(\frac{L}{l} - 1\right)\right]^{-1/2}. \qquad \textbf{4.2-22b}$$

Having found both exact and approximate expressions for determining the sag, we turn now to the other question asked: what is the tension $T_A = T_B$ at either support, which from Eq. 4.2-15 is the maximum tension in the parabolic cable? Since (from 4.2-17)

$$\left.\frac{dy}{dx}\right|_{x=l/2} = \tan\theta_B = \left(\frac{W}{Hl}\right)\left(\frac{l}{2}\right) = \frac{W}{2H},$$

we find

$$\sec\theta_B = [1 + \tan^2\theta_B]^{1/2}$$

$$= \left[1 + \left(\frac{W}{2H}\right)^2\right]^{1/2} = \left[1 + \left(\frac{4f}{l}\right)^2\right]^{1/2}.$$

The maximum tension, therefore, is given by

$$\frac{2T_{max}}{W} = \frac{2H}{W}\sec\theta_B$$

$$= \frac{2H}{W}\left[1+\left(\frac{W}{2H}\right)^2\right]^{\frac{1}{2}} = \left[\left(\frac{2H}{W}\right)^2+1\right]^{\frac{1}{2}} \qquad \textbf{4.2-23a}$$

$$= \left(\frac{4f}{l}\right)^{-1}\left[1+\left(\frac{4f}{l}\right)^2\right]^{\frac{1}{2}} = \left[\left(\frac{l}{4f}\right)^2+1\right]^{\frac{1}{2}}. \qquad \textbf{4.2-23b}$$

Any number of special problems can now be solved. For instance, suppose we are given the span and weight to be carried and the maximum allowable cable tension, and we ask for the least length of cable necessary to support the weight. From 4.2-23b we can compute the allowable sag ratio and then compute the cable length needed from 4.2-21 or the approximate relation 4.2-22a.

Example 4.2-3

What shape does a uniform cable hanging under its own weight assume in equilibrium? The supports are at equal height.

Solution: From uniformity of load and symmetry of the external geometry of support, Fig. 4.2-7 can again serve as the free-body diagram of the whole cable, provided that we now take $q_y = -w = -W/L$ to be the distributed weight per unit length of cable as a function of the arclength s. The fundamental equations are now Eqs. 4.2-10, the first of which again integrates immediately to the result that the x-component of the tension is constant, or, paralleling Eq. 4.2-15,

$$T(s) = H\sec\theta(s). \qquad \textbf{4.2-24}$$

The second of Eqs. 4.2-10b becomes

$$\frac{d}{ds}(H\tan\theta) - w = 0,$$

so that

$$H\tan\theta = ws + V.$$

If we measure arclength s from the lowest point O of the curve, with increasing s agreeing with increasing x, the constant of integration $V = 0$. Therefore,

$$\frac{dy}{dx} = \tan\theta = \frac{ws}{H}. \qquad \textbf{4.2-25}$$

To integrate this, we must use Eqs. 4.2-5b. Since $1+\tan^2\theta = \sec^2\theta$ and $\sin\theta = \tan\theta\cos\theta$, we find

$$\frac{dx}{ds} = \cos\theta = [1+\tan^2\theta]^{-\frac{1}{2}} = \left[1+\left(\frac{ws}{H}\right)^2\right]^{-\frac{1}{2}},$$

$$\frac{dy}{ds} = \sin\theta = \frac{ws}{H}\left[1+\left(\frac{ws}{H}\right)^2\right]^{-\frac{1}{2}}. \qquad \textbf{4.2-26}$$

Again, we may refer to tables of elementary integrals or else integrate directly (with $x = y = 0$ at $s = 0$ as conditions) by substituting

$$\frac{ws}{H} = \sinh u, \qquad \frac{w\,ds}{H} = \cosh u\,du.$$

We obtain:

$$x = \int_0^s \left[1 + \left(\frac{ws}{H}\right)^2 \right]^{-\frac{1}{2}} ds = \frac{H}{w} \int_0^{\operatorname{arcsinh}\left(\frac{ws}{H}\right)} \frac{\cosh u}{\cosh u}\,du$$

$$= \frac{H}{w} \operatorname{arcsinh}\left(\frac{ws}{H}\right); \qquad\qquad \textbf{4.2-27a}$$

$$y = \int_0^s \frac{ws}{H} \left[1 + \left(\frac{ws}{H}\right)^2 \right]^{-\frac{1}{2}} ds = \frac{H}{w} \int_0^{\operatorname{arcsinh}\left(\frac{ws}{H}\right)} \sinh u\,du$$

$$= \frac{H}{w} \left[\cosh u\right] \Big|_0^{\operatorname{arcsinh}\left(\frac{ws}{H}\right)} = \frac{H}{w} \left\{ \cosh\left[\operatorname{arcsinh}\left(\frac{ws}{H}\right)\right] - 1 \right\}. \;\textbf{4.2-27b}$$

These are the parametric equations of the curve. Since s may be expressed as a function of x easily from 4.2-27a, we can find the $y = f(x)$ form of the curve equation:

$$y = \frac{H}{w} \left\{ \cosh\left(\frac{wx}{H}\right) - 1 \right\}. \qquad\qquad \textbf{4.2-28}$$

Such a curve is called a *catenary*.

The condition that the curve pass through points A and B again relates the sag f to the constant H:

$$f = \frac{H}{w} \left\{ \cosh\left(\frac{wl}{2H}\right) - 1 \right\}. \qquad\qquad \textbf{4.2-29}$$

The determination of H follows from the inextensibility condition. Rather than perform the integration, however, we can find the appropriate relation from Eq. 4.2-27a, since $s = L/2$ when $x = l/2$:

$$\frac{wL}{2H} = \sinh\left(\frac{wl}{2H}\right), \qquad\qquad \textbf{4.2-30a}$$

or (with $wL = W$),

$$\frac{W}{2H} = \sinh\left[\frac{W}{2H}\left(\frac{l}{L}\right)\right]. \qquad\qquad \textbf{4.2-30b}$$

Again, this must be solved numerically in general. For small sag ratios ($f/l \ll 1$), i.e., for $l \cong L$, approximations based on series expansions may be used in Eqs. 4.2-29 and 4.2-30. From Eq. 4.2-29, we have

$$\frac{2f}{l} = \frac{2H}{wl} \left[\cosh\left(\frac{wl}{2H}\right) - 1 \right]$$

$$\cong \frac{1}{2}\left(\frac{wl}{2H}\right) = \frac{W}{4H}\left(\frac{l}{L}\right), \qquad\qquad \textbf{4.2-31a}$$

neglecting terms of order $(wl/2H)^3$; using this in 4.2-30, we find

$$\frac{W}{2H} \cong \sinh\left(\frac{4f}{l}\right), \qquad\qquad \textbf{4.2-31b}$$

or

$$\frac{L}{l} \cong \frac{\sinh\left(\dfrac{4f}{l}\right)}{\left(\dfrac{4f}{l}\right)} \cong 1 + \frac{1}{6}\left(\frac{4f}{l}\right)^2. \qquad\qquad \textbf{4.2-31c}$$

Solving for the sag ratio, we find

$$\frac{4f}{l} \cong \left[6\left(\frac{L}{l} - 1\right)\right]^{1/2}, \qquad\qquad \textbf{4.2-32}$$

which should be compared with Eq. 4.2-22 for some idea of the degree to which the parabola approximates the catenary for small sag ratios. The minimum tension H, as determined from 4.2-31a or 4.2-22b, is somewhat different for the same l, L, f, and W.

Example 4.2-4

A cable of length L hangs under its own weight over a span l. For what range of vertical distance h between supports does the cable not sag below the lowest support?

Solution: The maximum vertical distance between supports possible for a given length L and given span l occurs, of course, when the cable is along the straight line joining the supports: $h_{\max}^2 = L^2 - l^2$. As h decreases from this value, the cable hanging under its own weight will assume the shape of a piece of a catenary until, when $h = 0$, the symmetrical catenary of the last example is attained. For some range $h^* \leq h \leq h_{\max}$, no lowest point with horizontal tangent will occur between the supports. The value h^* is determined by the condition that the slope of the curve is just horizontal at one support.

Under such conditions, when no external geometric symmetry is imposed, the x-, y-coordinates may as well be chosen with origin at one support, say the lower one. Indeed, in the previous two examples, where the distributed loads are constant in magnitude and direction, one need not use the full differential equations of equilibrium but can write algebraic equations for a finite segment of cable. Take a segment between the lowest point, where the tension is H, and a general point $x(s)$, $y(s)$, where the tension is T, and replace the distributed load $-w\mathbf{j}$ by an equipollent concentrated load $-wx\mathbf{j}$ or $-ws\mathbf{j}$ passing through the point of concurrence on the x-axis of $-H\mathbf{i}$ and $T\mathbf{e}_t$. This finite segment is then equivalent to the three-force member of Example 2.4-2, and we have effectively performed one integration of the equations of equilibrium.

In this example, however, or any example wherein geometrical symmetry cannot be assumed to occur, whether due to load distribution or external support geometry, we must use the full differential equations. The free-body diagram of the full cable appears in Fig. 4.2-8. Since $q_x = 0$ again, the first of Eqs. 4.2-10b integrates to

$$T(s) = H \sec \theta(s)$$

as before (Eq. 4.2-24); and the second equation will integrate to

$$H \tan \theta = ws + V. \qquad \textbf{4.2-33}$$

Now, in general, V does not vanish when $s = 0$ at support A, for $\theta = \theta_A$ is not zero. Since, however, we want to determine the limits on h so that no relative minimum point occurs in $0 \le x \le l$, we may take the limiting

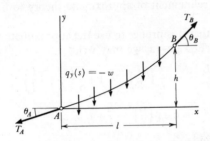

Fig. 4.2-8

condition $h = h^*$ for which $\theta_A = 0$. Then $V = 0$, and the integration of 4.2-33 proceeds as in the last example, with $x = y = s = 0$, to give Eqs. 4.2-27 and 4.2-28. The solution to our problem, therefore, is that the cable with the just-horizontal tangent at the support looks like the right half of the cable of the last example; now the end condition at B, however, is $x = l$ and $y = h^*$ when $s = L$. That is, substituting in Eqs. 4.2-27a and 4.2-28, we find

$$\frac{wL}{H} = \sinh\left(\frac{wl}{H}\right) \qquad \textbf{4.2-34a}$$

and

$$h^* = \frac{H}{w}\left[\cosh\left(\frac{wl}{H}\right) - 1\right]. \qquad \textbf{4.2-34b}$$

These differ from 4.2-30a and 4.2-29 of the previous example. The first of 4.2-34 is to be solved (numerically) for H in terms of l, L, and $w = W/L$; the second then determines h^*.

Example 4.2-5

A 50 ft cable weighing 10 lb/ft hangs between two supports on the same level. The observed central sag is 15 ft. How far apart are the supports? What are the minimum and maximum tensions in the cable?

Solution: Here we show how numerical results are obtained from the equations that have been derived. The problem is a particular example of the symmetrical catenary for which the general solution was derived in Example 4.2-3. We are given $L = 50$ ft, $f = 15$ ft, $-q_y = w = 10$ lb/ft, $W = wL = 500$ lb; we wish to find l, H, and T_{max}, the tension at either support.

The first decision that should be made is whether the approximate or exact theory should be used. We note that, if the 50 ft cable were simply supporting a concentrated 500 lb load at its center, so that the two 25 ft halves were straight, then a 15 ft sag would give a half-span of $(25^2 - 15^2)^{1/2} = 20$ ft or a total span of $l = 40$ ft. Thus a first rough approximation to the span is forty feet, and whether or not an apparent $f/l \cong 3/8$ is "small" compared with unity, or a possible $l/L \cong 4/5$ is "close enough" to one, for the next refinement of approximate theory to be used depends upon judgment.

Let us suppose that it is proper to use the approximate theory. Then, from Eq. 4.2-31c or Eq. 4.2-32, we may write

$$\frac{L}{l} = 1 + \frac{1}{6}\left(\frac{4f}{l}\right)^2 = 1 + \frac{1}{6}\left(\frac{4f}{L}\right)^2\left(\frac{L}{l}\right)^2,$$

$$0.24\left(\frac{L}{l}\right)^2 - \frac{L}{l} + 1 = 0.$$

Solving for L/l, we find

$$\frac{L}{l} = \frac{1 \pm \sqrt{1 - 0.96}}{2(0.24)} = \frac{1 \pm 0.2}{0.48}. \qquad\qquad \textbf{4.2-35}$$

Both roots are larger than two in value, and certainly do not appear close to one. The approximate theory should, therefore, be discarded.

We turn to the exact equations 4.2-29 and 4.2-30a and form their ratio:

$$\frac{2f}{L} = \frac{\cosh\left(\dfrac{wl}{2H}\right) - 1}{\sinh\left(\dfrac{wl}{2H}\right)} = \tanh\left(\frac{wl}{4H}\right). \qquad\qquad \textbf{4.2-36}$$

This is a transcendental equation for the quantity $\alpha = wl/4H$. If α can be found, then we can compute H from Eq. 4.2-30a:

$$\frac{wL}{2H} = \frac{W}{2H} = \sinh 2\alpha, \qquad\qquad \textbf{4.2-37}$$

and then l from α:

$$l = \frac{4H\alpha}{w}. \qquad\qquad \textbf{4.2-38}$$

Our whole problem, therefore, rests on the solution of

$$\tanh \alpha = \frac{2f}{L} = 0.6. \qquad\qquad \textbf{4.2-39}$$

Reference to tables of the hyperbolic tangent shows that $0.69 < \alpha < 0.70$. If a more accurate answer is desired than can be obtained from such a table and if tables of natural logarithms are available, then the definition of the hyperbolic tangent proves useful:

$$\tanh \alpha = \frac{e^\alpha - e^{-\alpha}}{e^\alpha + e^{-\alpha}} = 0.6;$$

$$0.4e^\alpha = 1.6e^{-\alpha}, \qquad e^{2\alpha} = 4, \qquad e^\alpha = 2;$$

$$\alpha = \log 2 = 0.69315. \qquad\qquad \textbf{4.2-40}$$

Therefore,

$$\sinh 2\alpha = (e^{2\alpha} - e^{-2\alpha})/2 = 15/8,$$

and

$$H = \frac{W}{2 \sinh 2\alpha} = \frac{400}{3} \text{ lb}, \qquad\qquad \textbf{4.2-41a}$$

$$l = \frac{4H\alpha}{w} = 36.968 \text{ ft}; \qquad\qquad \textbf{4.2-41b}$$

further, using Eqs. 4.2-24, 4.2-25, and 4.2-37, we find

$$T_{\max} = H \sec\left(\theta\left(\frac{L}{2}\right)\right) = H\left[1 + \left(\frac{wL}{2H}\right)^2\right]^{1/2}$$

$$= H \cosh 2\alpha = \left(\frac{400}{3}\right)\left(\frac{17}{8}\right)$$

$$= \frac{850}{3} \text{ lb} \simeq 283 \text{ lb}. \qquad\qquad \textbf{4.2-41c}$$

4.3   Statically Determinate Beams; Moment and Shear Diagrams

In Section 2.7, the beam subject to loads in a median plane was introduced and the resultant force set equipollent to the internal forces on a cross-section was defined (Fig. 2.7-4). In Example 2.7-5, the resultant set at one cross-section due to given loads on a particular simply-supported beam was found. Here we wish to consider the general problem of finding the resultant set at any cross-section by establishing the differential equations of equilibrium satisfied by the force and couple components of the resultant.

First, we describe the geometry of the straight beam of uniform cross-section and the coordinate system to be used (Fig. 4.3-1). The beam is a right cylinder of length l constructed on an area A, which we will take to be doubly symmetric. The center line of the beam passes through the centroids of the cross-sections, and will be taken as the x-axis; the y- and z-axes will be taken as shown at each section, along the lines of symmetry of the cross-section. (Removal of the symmetry condition will be discussed later.)

Let us isolate a length of the beam under load to the left of some cross-section normal to the center line, with the effect of the material removed being represented by a distribution of forces over the area

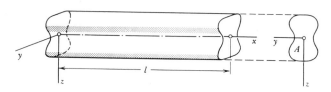

Fig. 4.3-1

of the cross-section (Fig. 4.3-2a). These are replaced by a resultant force **F** at the centroid of the section and a resultant couple **C**. The x-component of **F** is the axial force N of Section 2.7; the z-component is the shear force V of Section 2.7. The y-component of **F** is another shear force Q in the plane of the section; we shall consider for the present only those cases where we may set $Q=0$. Therefore, $\mathbf{F}=F_x\mathbf{i}+F_z\mathbf{k}=N\mathbf{i}+V\mathbf{k}$. The x-component of **C** is a torque about the axis of the cylinder and the z-component is a bending moment

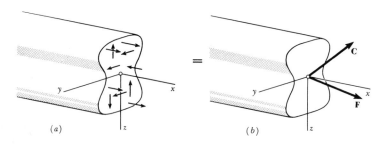

Fig. 4.3-2

about the z-axis; these torsional and bending moments will also be set equal to zero for the straight beam problem. The only resultant moment will then be the bending moment about the y-axis, which we shall denote by M as in Section 2.7: $\mathbf{C}=M\mathbf{j}$. If N and V are zero and only $M\neq0$ over a length of beam, that length is said to be in pure bending; if $N=0$ but M and $V\neq0$, the beam is in flexure with shear;

and, if M, V, and $N \neq 0$, we speak of a beam-column in combined flexure and tension or compression.

We shall now establish the differential equations of equilibrium of a beam-column subjected to distributed loads; the effect of concentrated loads will be considered later. Since the bending moment, shear force, and axial load depend upon the value of x, that is, upon which cross-section is being considered, we may expect the equations

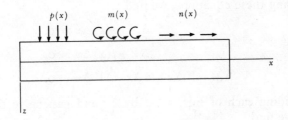

Fig. 4.3-3

to be ordinary differential equations with x as independent variable. The external loads will then be given as functions of the distance along the center line, i.e., will be forces and couples per unit length of beam. The distributed loads are considered to act in the xz-plane along the x-axis, and the distributed couples are due to forces in that plane such

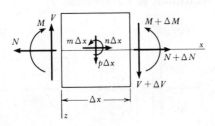

Fig. 4.3-4

that their resultant is a moment about the y-axis. Let $\mathbf{q}(x) = n(x)\mathbf{i} + p(x)\mathbf{k}$ be the force per unit length and $\mathbf{c}(x) = m(x)\mathbf{j}$ be the moment per unit length (Fig. 4.3-3). For the beam problem, we are, in technology, usually most concerned with the case $n(x) = m(x) = 0$.

Consider a small element of the beam of length Δx (Fig. 4.3-4). The forces and couples on the beam consist of (N, V, M) in the negative coordinate directions at the generic section x, $(N+\Delta N, V+\Delta V, M+\Delta M)$ in the positive senses at $x+\Delta x$, and the resultants

$(n \, \Delta x, p \, \Delta x, m \, \Delta x)$ of the distributed loads. The equilibrium equations for the segment are

$$\sum R_x = (N + \Delta N) - N + n(x) \, \Delta x = 0,$$

$$\sum R_z = (V + \Delta V) - V + p(x) \, \Delta x = 0,$$

$$\sum M_y = (M + \Delta M) - M - (V + \Delta V) \, \Delta x + m(x) \, \Delta x = 0.$$

     4.3-1

Simplifying these equations, we find

$$\Delta N + n(x) \, \Delta x = 0,$$

$$\Delta V + p(x) \, \Delta x = 0,$$

$$\Delta M - V \, \Delta x + m \, \Delta x - \Delta V \, \Delta x = 0.$$

     4.3-2

Dividing each of Eqs. 4.3-2 by Δx and passing to the limit as $\Delta x \rightarrow 0$, we find

$$\frac{dN}{dx} + n(x) = 0,$$

$$\frac{dV}{dx} + p(x) = 0,$$

$$\frac{dM}{dx} - V + m(x) = 0$$

     4.3-3

as the differential equations of equilibrium.

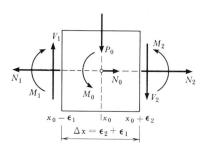

Fig. 4.3-5

Before discussing Eqs. 4.3-3, let us derive the "jump" conditions of equilibrium for concentrated loads. Suppose a concentrated load $N_0 \mathbf{i} + P_0 \mathbf{k}$ is applied at $x = x_0$, as is a concentrated couple $M_0 \mathbf{j}$. Isolate a segment of the beam which includes that section $x = x_0$, and suppose no other external loads act on the segment except the given ones and the resultants on the cross-sections (Fig. 4.3-5). The equilibrium equations are

$$N_2 - N_1 + N_0 = 0,$$

$$V_2 - V_1 + P_0 = 0,$$

$$M_2 - M_1 + M_0 - \epsilon_1 V_1 - \epsilon_2 V_2 = 0;$$

letting ϵ_1 and ϵ_2 approach zero, so that the segment approaches the cross-section $x = x_0$, we see that equilibrium requires that

$$[N(x_0)] = -N_0, \qquad [V(x_0)] = -P_0, \qquad [M(x_0)] = -M_0, \qquad \textbf{4·3-4}$$

where the notation $[f(x_0)]$ denotes a discontinuity, or "jump," in the value of the function $f(x)$ at $x = x_0$. That is,

$$[f(x_0)] = \lim_{\substack{\varepsilon_1 \to 0 \\ \varepsilon_2 \to 0}} \{f(x_0 + \epsilon_2) - f(x_0 - \epsilon_1)\} = f(x_0^+) - f(x_0^-). \qquad \textbf{4·3-5}$$

The equations of equilibrium 4.3-3 state that the axial force N and shear force V decrease along the length of the beam at a rate equal to the applied load per unit length in the axial or transverse directions. The bending moment M decreases with the applied couple and increases at a rate equal to the shear force on the section. The jump conditions 4.3-4 are equivalents to 4.3-3 when the applied loads are concentrated; note that the shear force effect does not appear in the jump condition for "concentrated" moment.

The shear force may be eliminated from the last two of Eqs. 4.3-3, resulting in a second-order differential equation for $M(x)$ in terms of the loads. Differentiate the moment equation and substitute for dV/dx from the shear equation:

$$\frac{d^2M}{dx^2} - \frac{dV}{dx} + \frac{dm}{dx} = 0,$$

so that

$$\frac{d^2M}{dx^2} + \frac{dm}{dx} + p(x) = 0. \qquad \textbf{4·3-6}$$

Let us now turn to the solution of the equations. We shall consider only transverse loadings $p(x)$ or P_0 in the z-direction, taking $m(x) = n(x) = N_0 = M_0 = 0$ and, in fact, $N(x) \equiv 0$. These effects are easily accounted for if necessary. To integrate the equations, we must adjoin boundary conditions. The boundary or support conditions for simple beams are usually taken to be one of the standard three: free, clamped, or simply-supported. Other end conditions are possible—an elastic constraint, for instance, that relates an end moment linearly to the slope of the (deformed) center line. Generally, the conditions set at the ends of the beam involve both applied forces and moments and possible deflections and slopes. The general beam problem is statically indeterminate, and, to the equilibrium equations, we must adjoin relations between the displacements and strains in the deformed beam and relations between the internal stress resultants, such as bending moment, and the strains, such as center-line curvature. The deformable beam is not of concern to us here; we shall consider only those statically determinate problems where the equations of equilibrium can be solved for the shear force and bending moment distributions in a rigid beam.

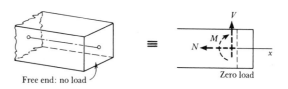

Free end: no load   Zero load

Fig. 4.3-6

The conditions at a *free* end of a beam express the fact that no load is applied: the bending moment and shear force (and axial load if considered) on any internal section must vanish as the free end is approached (Fig. 4.3-6). A simply-supported end may be pinned

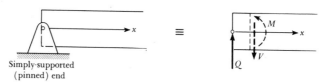

Simply-supported (pinned) end

Fig. 4.3-7

or on rollers; the conditions are that the center line has zero deflection in the z-direction transverse to the center line and that no moment can be transmitted. In Fig. 4.3-7, the representation of the effect of such a support is shown: an unknown z-reaction Q, zero moment, and no axial load. (Strictly, there will be no axial load only at the smooth roller type of simple support, but the possibility of one at a pinned joint should be considered.) The clamped or built-in joint was mentioned in Chapter II; the conditions at such a point are the vanishing of deflection and slope of the center line, so that unknown moment and transverse force reactions (and, again, an axial reaction in general) are exerted (Fig. 4.3-8). It should be noted that in the free-body diagrams of Figs. 4.3-7 and 4.3-8, the sign conventions for positive shear force and bending moment have been followed in drawing the reactions; these reactions are shown applied to a cross-section of the beam that has outward normal in the negative x-direction. The end conditions on M and V as we approach such a section from the positive x-direction are then $M = 0$, $V = Q$ for the simple support and $M = C$, $V = Q$ for the clamped end.

Fig. 4.3-8

Combinations of these end conditions, one at $x = 0$ and the other at $x = l$, then give the boundary conditions for integrating the equations. Some combinations lead to indeterminate problems. All of our examples will be determinate problems, for which the external reactions can be found from consideration of equilibrium of the beam as a whole.

A useful device for visualizing the shear and moment distribution along the beam is the construction of the *shear and bending moment diagrams*. These are simply plots of V and M against x as abscissa. Since (from Eqs. 4.3-3) the slope of the V-x curve is the negative of the applied load $p(x)$ and that of the M-x curve is V, the graphical construction of solutions for V, and then M, is not difficult. In the study of advanced beam theory, such diagrams are helpful in identifying critical sections subject to extremal values of bending moment.

We have developed the theory for doubly-symmetric cross-sections with loads in one principal plane of bending. But we have not explained why such planes are important. This is a task for deformable-body mechanics, where it is shown that, without this symmetry, loads in the xz-plane tend to produce torsion of the beam in addition to flexure.

Example 4.3-1

Find the bending moment and shear force distributions in a uniform beam of length l due to its own weight W distributed along the beam if the beam is (a) simply-supported at both ends, and (b) cantilevered at the left end.

Solution: The weight force is taken as a constant $w = W/l$ distributed along the center line. In Fig. 4.3-9, the simply-supported beam and the cantilevered beam together with complete free-body diagrams are shown. The support reactions are easily found in each case, with the distributed load replaced by the equipollent concentrated load W at the midpoint.

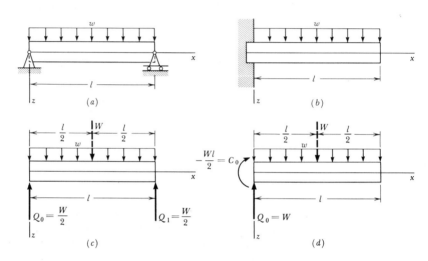

Fig. 4.3-9

The support reactions for the simply-supported beam are $Q_0 = Q_1 = W/2$, while the reactions at the built-in end of the cantilevered beam are $Q_0 = W$, $C_0 = -Wl/2$ (note the sign convention for the assumed direction of the couple in the free-body diagram 4.3-9d). In both cases, the transverse load $p(x)$ is the constant w. Let us integrate Eqs. 4.3-3, which here take the form

$$\frac{dV}{dx} + \frac{W}{l} = \frac{dV}{dx} + w = 0, \qquad \frac{dM}{dx} - V = 0.$$

In both cases, the shear force decreases linearly with x:

$$V = -wx + V_0; \qquad\qquad 4.3\text{-}7$$

the bending moment depends quadratically on x:

$$M = -\frac{wx^2}{2} + V_0 x + M_0. \qquad\qquad 4.3\text{-}8$$

The two cases differ in the evaluation of the constants of integration $V_0 = V(0)$ and $M_0 = M(0)$.

For the simply-supported beam, $V_0 = Q_0 = W/2$, $M_0 = 0$; therefore,

$$V(x) = -wx + \frac{W}{2} = \frac{W}{2}\left[1 - \frac{2x}{l}\right],$$

$$M(x) = -\frac{wx^2}{2} + \frac{Wx}{2} = \frac{Wx}{2}\left[1 - \frac{x}{l}\right]. \qquad \textbf{4.3-9}$$

Note that $V(x)$ vanishes at the midsection of the beam and equals $-W/2 = -Q_1$ at $x = l$, as it should; $M(x)$ vanishes at both ends and reaches a

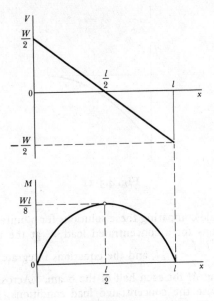

Fig. 4.3-10

maximum of $Wl/8$ at the midsection. The shear and bending moment diagrams are shown in Fig. 4.3-10.

For the cantilevered beam, $V_0 = Q_0 = W$, $M_0 = C_0 = -Wl/2$. Therefore,

$$V(x) = -wx + W = W\left(1 - \frac{x}{l}\right),$$

$$M(x) = -\frac{wx^2}{2} + Wx - \frac{Wl}{2} \qquad \textbf{4.3-10}$$

$$= -\frac{Wl}{2}\left(1 - \frac{x}{l}\right)^2.$$

Both $V(x)$ and $M(x)$ vanish, as they should, at the free end $x=l$. The shear and bending moment diagrams appear in Fig. 4.3-11.

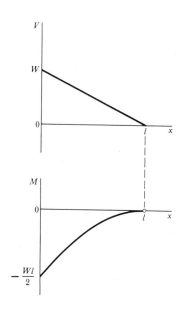

Fig. 4·3-11

It is worthwhile comparing these solutions for a uniformly distributed load to the solutions for a concentrated load W at the midpoint. Now $p(x)=0$ for $0 \leqq x < \dfrac{l}{2}, \dfrac{l}{2} < x \leqq l$, and the equations integrate to a constant V and linearly varying M for each half of the beam. Across the midsection $x=l/2$, we must use the concentrated load conditions (Eqs. 4.3-4) with $P_0=W$, M_0 (and $N_0)=0$. Therefore,

$$\left[V\left(\frac{l}{2}\right)\right] = -W, \qquad \left[M\left(\frac{l}{2}\right)\right] = 0. \qquad \textbf{4·3-11}$$

There is a discontinuity in V of magnitude W, while M is continuous. The analytical and graphical solutions follow.

For the simply-supported beam (Fig. 4.3-12),

$$\begin{aligned}
V(x) &= W/2, & 0 &\leqq x < l/2; \\
&= -W/2, & l/2 &< x \leqq l; \\
M(x) &= Wx/2, & 0 &\leqq x \leqq l/2; \\
&= W(l-x)/2, & l/2 &\leqq x \leqq l.
\end{aligned} \qquad \textbf{4·3-12}$$

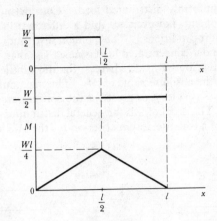

Fig. 4.3-12

For the cantilevered beam (Fig. 4.3-13),

$$V(x) = W, \quad 0 \le x < l/2;$$

$$= 0, \quad l/2 < x \le l;$$

$$M(x) = -\frac{Wl}{2}\left(1 - \frac{2x}{l}\right), \quad 0 \le x \le l/2;$$

$$= 0, \quad l/2 \le x \le l.$$

4.3-13

By comparing Eqs. 4.3-9 and 4.3-12 (or Figs. 4.3-10 and 4.3-12) for the simply-supported beam, and Eqs. 4.3-10 and 4.3-13 (Figs. 4.3-11 and 4.3-13) for the cantilever, we see that the concentrated load leads to a bending moment distribution that is algebraically larger than the bending

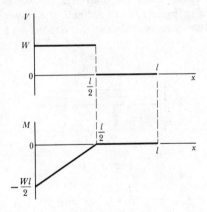

Fig. 4.3-13

moment for the uniformly distributed load. Considering absolute values of the bending moment, however, we find a difference in behavior for the two different support conditions. The moment distribution for the simply-supported beam under concentrated load is never less than that for the same beam under the distributed load, whereas, for the cantilevered beam, the reverse is true for the absolute value of M. The maximum absolute value $|M|_{max}$ in both cases is at least as great for the concentrated load as for the distributed load. The proof of this for general distributions is important for the development of a collapse design criterion for the safe loads that a beam may carry.

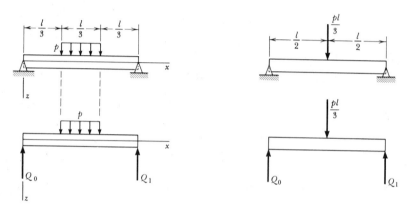

Fig. 4.3-14

Example 4.3-2

A simply-supported beam carries a uniform distributed load p over the middle third of its span. Find the shear and bending moment distributions. Compare with the distributions for an equipollent concentrated load. Neglect the weight of the beam by comparison with the applied load.

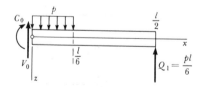

Fig. 4.3-15

Solution: In Fig. 4.3-14, the beam and its free-body diagram are shown for the two loading conditions. The beam under concentrated load has been solved already in the last example; simply replace W by $pl/3$ in Eqs. 4.3-12 and Fig. 4.3-12.

The beam under distributed load must be treated in three sections, $0 \leq x < l/3$, $l/3 < x < 2l/3$, and $2l/3 < x \leq l$. From the symmetry of both geometry and loading, we see that $Q_0 = Q_1 = pl/6$. Moreover, the symmetry permits the solution of the problem through consideration of half the beam only. Shift the origin of coordinates to the midsection. The free-body diagram of the right half of the beam is given in Fig. 4.3-15. The bending moment and shear force at the center are determined from equilibrium of the half beam:

$$R_z = \frac{pl}{6} - Q_1 - V_0 = -V_0 = 0, \qquad V_0 = 0;$$

$$M_y = \frac{l}{2} Q_1 - C_0 - \int_0^{l/6} xp\, dx = \frac{pl^2}{12} - C_0 - \frac{pl^2}{72} = 0, \qquad C_0 = \frac{5pl^2}{72}. \qquad \textbf{4.3-14}$$

The differential equation for the shear force is

$$\frac{dV}{dx} = -p, \qquad 0 \leq x < l/6;$$

$$= 0, \qquad l/6 < x \leq l/2. \qquad \textbf{4.3-15}$$

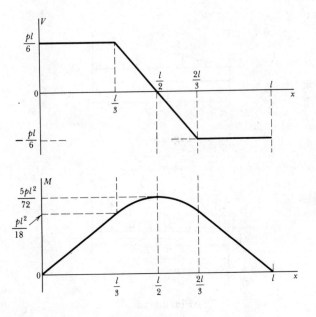

Fig. 4.3-16

Integrating subject to the conditions that $V(0)=0$ and $[V(l/6)]=0$ (since there is no concentrated load at $x=l/6$), we find

$$V(x) = -px, \qquad 0 \leq x \leq l/6;$$

$$= -pl/6, \qquad l/6 \leq x \leq l/2. \qquad \textbf{4.3-16}$$

From

$$dM/dx = V, \qquad M(0) = C_0, \qquad \left[M\!\left(\frac{l}{6}\right)\right] = 0,$$

we find

$$M(x) = -\frac{px^2}{2} + C_0 = \frac{pl^2}{72}\left[5 - 36\left(\frac{x}{l}\right)^2\right], \qquad 0 \leq x \leq l/6;$$

$$= -\frac{pl}{6}\left(x - \frac{l}{6}\right) + M\!\left(\frac{l}{6}\right)$$

$$= -\frac{plx}{6} + \frac{pl^2}{36} + \frac{pl^2}{18} = \frac{pl^2}{12}\left(1 - \frac{2x}{l}\right), \qquad l/6 \leq x \leq l/2. \qquad \textbf{4.3-17}$$

Remember that these hold for the right half of the beam only; they can be continued to the left half by recognizing that $V(-x) = -V(x)$, $M(-x) = M(x)$. The shear and bending moment diagrams are given in Fig. 4.3-16, with the origin shifted back to the left end for direct comparison with Fig. 4.3-12.

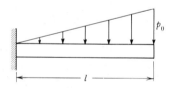

Fig. 4.3-17

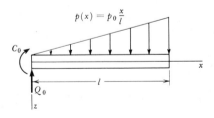

Fig. 4.3-18

Example **4.3-3**

A cantilevered beam (Fig. 4.3-17) *is subjected to a triangular load distribution. Find the shear and bending moment distributions.*

Solution: The free-body diagram of the whole beam is shown in Fig. 4.3-18. The applied load is $p(x) = p_0 x/l$. Equilibrium equations for the whole beam determine C_0 and Q_0:

$$R_z = -Q_0 + \int_0^l p(x)\,dx = -Q_0 + \frac{p_0 l}{2} = 0, \qquad Q_0 = \frac{p_0 l}{2};$$

$$M_y = -C_0 - \int_0^l x p(x)\,dx = -C_0 - \frac{p_0 l^2}{3} = 0, \qquad C_0 = -\frac{p_0 l^2}{3}.$$

4.3-18

Therefore, we wish to integrate

$$\frac{dV}{dx} = -\frac{p_0 x}{l}, \qquad V(0) = Q_0 = \frac{p_0 l}{2};$$

$$\frac{dM}{dx} = V, \qquad M(0) = C_0 = -\frac{p_0 l^2}{3}.$$

4.3-19

The solutions are

$$V(x) = \frac{p_0 l}{2}\left[1 - \left(\frac{x}{l}\right)^2\right];$$

$$M(x) = \frac{p_0 l}{2}\left[x - \frac{x^3}{3l^2}\right] - \frac{p_0 l^2}{3}$$

$$= -\frac{p_0 l^2}{6}\left(1 - \frac{x}{l}\right)^2\left(2 + \frac{x}{l}\right).$$

4.3-20

The shear and bending moment diagrams appear in Fig. 4.3-19.

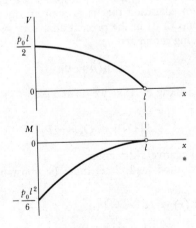

Fig. 4.3-19

Example 4·3-4

Suppose a beam is pinned at one end and supported on rollers at its middle, and a tip load of P is applied to the free end (Fig. 4.3-20). What are the shear and moment distributions?

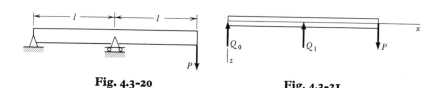

Fig. 4·3-20   **Fig. 4·3-21**

Solution: The whole beam is statically determinate. The free-body diagram appears in Fig. 4.3-21, and the equations of equilibrium are

$$Q_0 + Q_1 - P = 0,$$

$$lQ_1 - 2lP = 0. \tag{4·3-21}$$

Therefore, the reactions are

$$Q_1 = 2P, \qquad Q_0 = -P. \tag{4·3-22}$$

The application of the load P at the otherwise unconstrained end $x = 2l$ changes the free end boundary conditions $M = 0$, $V = 0$ to $M = 0$, $V = P$. The internal support at $x = l$ may be treated by noting the equivalence of the reaction Q_1 to a concentrated load at the point. The "jump" conditions of equilibrium 4.3-4 are appropriately used here. Besides the vanishing deflection condition that is present at any simple support (and which does not concern us in the present analysis), we have a condition of continuity of bending moment

$$[M(l)] = 0, \tag{4·3-23}$$

rather than the vanishing of M as we do at $x = 0$. The jump condition on the shear force is

$$[V(l)] = Q_1 = 2P, \tag{4·3-24}$$

since Q_1 is in the negative z-direction.

With no distributed load, $V(x)$ must be constant in each unloaded segment:

$$V(x) = Q_0 = -P, \qquad 0 \leqq x < l;$$

$$= Q_0 + [V(l)] = +P, \qquad l < x \leqq 2l. \tag{4·3-25}$$

The bending moment is

$$M(x) = -Px, \qquad 0 \leq x \leq l;$$
$$= P(x-2l), \qquad l \leq x \leq 2l. \qquad \textbf{4.3-26}$$

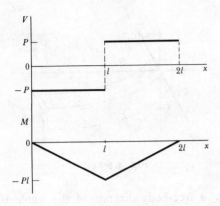

Fig. 4.3-22

Example **4.3-5**

A curved beam is formed in the shape of a circular quadrant of radius r, with cross-sections normal to the circular center line being rectangular in shape (Fig. 4.3-23). The beam is cantilevered at one end and subjected to a downward load P at the centroid of the other. The weight of the beam may be neglected. Find the reactions at the built-in end and the resultant force set at any section.

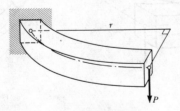

Fig. 4.3-23

Solution: Such curved beam problems can be solved in a manner analogous to that used for the straight beam. The analysis is generally more difficult, especially if the problem is statically indeterminate and the deformations of the beam must be taken into account. However, by considering the arclength along the beam and appropriate tangential and normal directions in the plane of the centerline (as well as a z-direction normal to the plane of the centerline), we can establish differential equations of equilibrium for the resultant force and moment components on any normal cross-section in terms of the distributed loads on the beam. Here, we may solve the problem without using differential equations.

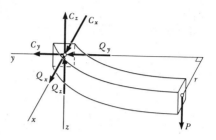

Fig. 4·3-24

In Fig. 4.3-24, a free-body diagram of the whole beam is shown. (Q_x, Q_y, Q_z) are the components of the resultant reaction force on the beam at the built-in end; (C_x, C_y, C_z) are the components of the reactive couple. The force equilibrium equations, when solved, result in

$$Q_x = Q_y = 0, \qquad Q_z = P. \hspace{3cm} \text{4·3-27}$$

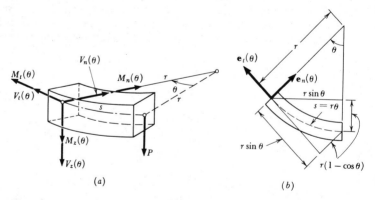

(a) $\hspace{5cm}$ (b)

Fig. 4·3-25

The moment equation about the centroid of the built-in end is

$$C_x\mathbf{i} + C_y\mathbf{j} + C_z\mathbf{k} + (-r\mathbf{j} + r\mathbf{i}) \times P\mathbf{k} = \mathbf{0},$$

from which we find

$$C_x = rP, \qquad C_y = rP, \qquad C_z = 0. \hspace{2.5cm} \text{4·3-28}$$

The C_y-component is a bending moment such as that found for the cantilevered straight beam; in addition, a torsional moment C_x about the center line is found.

A section of the beam from the loaded end to a general section is pictured in the free-body diagram of Fig. 4.3-25a. The angle θ or the arclength $s = r\theta$ may be used as the independent variable denoting the section. The force and moment components shown are in directions of positive tangential (agreeing with increasing θ and s), normal, and z-directions; these directions form a right-handed system at each section. A top view, looking in the positive z-direction, is given in Fig. 4.3-25b.

The equilibrium equations are:

$$P\mathbf{k} + [V_t(\theta)\mathbf{e}_t(\theta) + V_n(\theta)\mathbf{e}_n(\theta) + V_z(\theta)\mathbf{k}] = \mathbf{0},$$

$$[-r\sin\theta\,\mathbf{e}_t + r(1 - \cos\theta)\mathbf{e}_n] \times P\mathbf{k} + [M_t(\theta)\mathbf{e}_t + M_n(\theta)\mathbf{e}_n + M_z(\theta)\mathbf{k}] = \mathbf{0}.$$

$$\text{4.3-29}$$

Therefore,

$$V_t = V_n = 0, \qquad V_z(\theta) = -P \qquad\qquad \text{4.3-30}$$

and

$$M_t(\theta) = -rP(1 - \cos\theta), \qquad M_n(\theta) = -rP\sin\theta, \qquad M_z = 0. \quad \text{4.3-31}$$

As $\theta \to \pi/2$, i.e., as we approach the built-in end, we find $M_t(\pi/2) = M_n(\pi/2) = -rP$. At the built-in end, the tangential direction in the sense of increasing arclength is the negative of the x-direction of Fig. 4.3-24, and the normal direction there is the negative of the y-direction. Thus we have the proper agreement of these end values with the reactions 4.3-28: $M_t = -C_x$, $M_n = -C_y$ at $\theta = \pi/2$.

4.4   Hydrostatics and Aerostatics

So far, we have been replacing distributed forces over internal areas by equipollent concentrated resultants. We now turn to the study of the equilibrium of fluids, wherein we must examine the behavior of the distributed force itself.

A fluid can be differentiated mechanically from a solid by the statement that a tangential load increment, however small, applied to the surface of a fluid will cause it to move indefinitely as long as the load is applied. A solid, on the other hand, will have at most a perfectly definite additional deformation for a given additional increment of load. Fluids are classified as liquids or gases. A given mass of liquid occupies a definite volume under given conditions of temperature and external load; the boundary of the volume, however, is not of any definite shape but is formed by the solid container of the liquid. A given mass of gas does not have a definite volume, but will expand to fill its whole container. The equilibrium of liquids forms the study known as *hydrostatics*; the study of the equilibrium of gases is called *aerostatics*. Only a few of the principles and results of fluid statics will be treated here. The reader should note that there are no formal numbered "examples" in this section (or the next); the applications of the principles are worked into the general line of the textual development. The results on centers of pressure, the incompressible fluid under gravity, the isothermal atmosphere, and the hydraulic press may all be viewed as examples following from the theory that we now develop.

We proceed with the characterization of fluids. In Section 2.7, the replacement of the internal forces between parts of a body by an equipollent force set was discussed. Suppose we have a body,

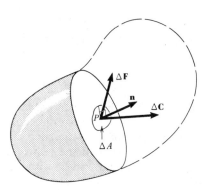

Fig. 4.4-1

either fluid or solid, and pick a point, P, in its interior (Fig. 4.4-1); as in Section 2.7, we pass a plane through P and replace one part of the body by the forces it exerts on the rest. These are distributed over the whole plane area. This time, rather than replace these forces by their full resultant set, we divide the total area into a number of parts and replace the forces on each part by their resultant. In particular, suppose that an element of area ΔA containing point P is chosen, and that the forces on ΔA are replaced by a resultant force $\Delta \mathbf{F}$ at P and a couple $\Delta \mathbf{C}$ (Fig. 4.4-1). We also draw the unit vector $\mathbf{n}$ at P perpendicular to the area ΔA and pointing away from the material we have retained as our system and into the part we have replaced. The average force per unit area, or *average traction*, at P on an area with normal $\mathbf{n}$ is then $\Delta \mathbf{F}/\Delta A$; the average moment is $\Delta \mathbf{C}/\Delta A$. The limiting process we are about to perform should now be obvious from our choice of notation: we let ΔA shrink to the point P and examine the limits of the average traction and average moment vectors. We suppose these limits to exist and to be independent of the shape of ΔA and of the way in which $\Delta A \to 0$. The limit of the average traction is the *traction vector* $\mathbf{T}^{(n)}$ at P associated with a unit plane area through P with normal $\mathbf{n}$:[*]

$$\mathbf{T}^{(n)} = \lim_{\Delta A \to 0} \frac{\Delta \mathbf{F}}{\Delta A}. \qquad \text{4.4-1}$$

Note that the normal $\mathbf{n}$ is held constant in the process. It is usually assumed that $|\Delta \mathbf{C}|$ is of the same order of magnitude as $|\Delta \mathbf{F}|$ multiplied by a moment arm whose length lies within the shrinking region ΔA. Therefore, even though $\Delta \mathbf{F}/\Delta A$ does not vanish as $\Delta A \to 0$,

$$\lim_{\Delta A \to 0} \frac{\Delta \mathbf{C}}{\Delta A} = 0. \qquad \text{4.4-2}$$

We shall pursue the consequences of these concepts further in the next section. Now we characterize fluids in terms of $\mathbf{T}^{(n)}$. The traction vector can be divided into two components, the *normal* or *direct stress* and the *tangential* or *shearing stress*. The normal stress component is

$$\mathbf{T}_\sigma^{(n)} = (\mathbf{T}^{(n)} \cdot \mathbf{n})\mathbf{n} = \sigma_n \mathbf{n}; \qquad \text{4.4-3}$$

the shearing stress component is

$$\mathbf{T}_\tau^{(n)} = \mathbf{T}^{(n)} - \mathbf{T}_\sigma^{(n)}. \qquad \text{4.4-4}$$

On the basis of experimental observations, all fluids at rest are characterized by the vanishing of shear stress, so that only a normal stress is exerted on any interior plane drawn in the fluid. Fluids in motion may exhibit a shear stress between neighboring layers; such fluids are said to be *viscous*. The assumption of vanishing shear stress is often made, whether or not the fluid is in motion; such fluids are termed *inviscid* or "*perfect*" fluids. Further, the normal stress in fluids is compressive in nature, resisting the interpenetration of the parts; for a fluid at rest,

$$\mathbf{T}^{(n)} = \mathbf{T}_\sigma^{(n)} = \sigma_n \mathbf{n} = -p\mathbf{n}, \qquad \text{4.4-5}$$

---

[*] The traction vector is often called the stress vector.

where $p = p(x, y, z)$ is the *pressure** at point P. One of the first theorems that we shall prove is that we can indeed speak of the pressure at a point, independently of our choice of the normal **n** to the area we imagine at P.

Let us now consider the equilibrium of a small mass of fluid surrounding the point P. We first introduce the density, ρ, of the fluid at any point, as we have done before, as the limit of the ratio of the mass, Δm, in a volume, ΔV, around the point as the volume approaches zero. If ρ remains a constant, whatever loads are applied, then the material is *incompressible*; if ρ changes with load, the material is *compressible*. Liquids have relatively low compressibility, and are often assumed to be strictly incompressible fluids; the compressibility of gases is an essential feature of their behavior.

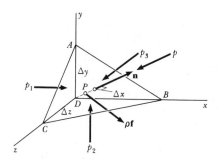

Fig. 4.4-2

Consider a small tetrahedron $ABCD$ of fluid surrounding point P, which may be taken at the centroid (Fig. 4.4-2); three faces of the tetrahedron are perpendicular to axes chosen as shown, while the fourth face ABC has outer normal $\mathbf{n} = n_x\mathbf{i} + n_y\mathbf{j} + n_z\mathbf{k}$. The outer normals to faces ACD, BCD, and ABD are $-\mathbf{i}$, $-\mathbf{j}$, and $-\mathbf{k}$, respectively. Let ΔA be the area of the slant face ABC; then the usual projection property enables us to write the areas of the other faces in terms of ΔA:

$$ACD: \frac{1}{2}\Delta y\,\Delta z = n_x\,\Delta A,$$

$$BCD: \frac{1}{2}\Delta x\,\Delta z = n_y\,\Delta A,$$ **4.4-6**

$$ABD: \frac{1}{2}\Delta x\,\Delta y = n_z\,\Delta A.$$

---

* A liquid carefully freed from dissolved gases can stand appreciable tension. In practice, however, p is normally a positive quantity.

The volume of the tetrahedron is

$$\Delta V = \frac{1}{6} \Delta x \, \Delta y \, \Delta z = \frac{1}{3} \Delta h \, \Delta A, \qquad \textbf{4·4-7}$$

where Δh is the length of the altitude dropped from vertex D on the slant face.

The forces acting on the tetrahedron are the pressure forces normal to the faces and body forces, such as gravity, acting on the volume. The pressure forces have resultant on each face equal to the integral of the pressure over the face; by the mean-value theorem, we replace this by the product of the pressure at some point on the face and the area of the face. Similarly, the body forces $\mathbf{f}$, which we take to be per unit mass, have force resultant equal to the integral over the volume of the product of the density ρ and $\mathbf{f}$. This we replace by the product of the volume and the value of $\rho\mathbf{f}$ at some interior point. The force equilibrium equation is

$$p_1(\tfrac{1}{2}\Delta y \, \Delta z)\mathbf{i} + p_2(\tfrac{1}{2}\Delta x \, \Delta z)\mathbf{j} + p_3(\tfrac{1}{2}\Delta x \, \Delta y)\mathbf{k} - p\,\Delta A\mathbf{n} + \rho\mathbf{f}\,\Delta V = \mathbf{0},$$
$$\textbf{4·4-8}$$

where p_1, p_2, p_3, and p are the pressures on the faces as shown in Fig. 4.4-2. Now, dividing by ΔA and using Eqs. 4.4-6, 4.4-7, we find

$$(p_1 - p)n_x\mathbf{i} + (p_2 - p)n_y\mathbf{j} + (p_3 - p)n_z\mathbf{k} + \rho\mathbf{f}\,\Delta h = \mathbf{0}. \qquad \textbf{4·4-9}$$

If the tetrahedron volume is now allowed to shrink to a point, so that $\Delta h \rightarrow 0$, the body force term vanishes; and, since the direction cosines (n_x, n_y, n_z) or the orientation $\mathbf{n}$ of ΔA was arbitrarily chosen, the only way the equilibrium equation can be satisfied is to have $p_1 = p_2 = p_3 = p$. Therefore, in a fluid at rest, the pressure on all planes through a point must be the same.

The same result holds for an inviscid fluid in motion. There are no tangential stresses on the faces in such a fluid, so that the surface force terms in Eq. 4.4-8 or 4.4-9 do not change. If the mass center of the tetrahedron has acceleration $\mathbf{a}^*$, then Newton's second law of motion requires a term $\rho\mathbf{a}^* \, \Delta V$ on the right side of 4.4-8 and hence a term $\rho\mathbf{a}^* \, \Delta h$ on the right side of 4.4-9. This term vanishes, like the body-force term, in the limiting process. For a viscous fluid, tangential stresses are present, and we cannot come to the same conclusion. However, in the usual theory, we still speak of the pressure at a point as the average of the normal compressive stresses over any three orthogonal planes through the point.

In order to find out how the pressure varies from point to point in a fluid, we must include the next higher order of pressure variation term in the equation of equilibrium 4.4-8. That is, we have established the equality of the pressure on any plane through the point P by keeping only those average pressure terms over the face areas that lead to forces proportional in magnitude to the area. To include the effect of the body forces, we must find the variation of pressure in the volume. It is easiest to do this if we drop our tetrahedron "particle" model and choose instead a rectangular parallelepiped "particle" (Fig. 4.4-3).

If we let $p = p(x, y, z)$ be the pressure at the center point P, then the pressures on the various faces are (approximately) as indicated in the figure; the partial derivatives are evaluated at the center P. Then the equation of equilibrium becomes (to within the first-order approximation ordinarily used)

$$\left[-p\left(x+\frac{\Delta x}{2}, y, z\right) \Delta y\, \Delta z + p\left(x-\frac{\Delta x}{2}, y, z\right) \Delta y\, \Delta z \right]\mathbf{i}$$

$$+ \left[-p\left(x, y+\frac{\Delta y}{2}, z\right) \Delta x\, \Delta z + p\left(x, y-\frac{\Delta y}{2}, z\right) \Delta x\, \Delta z \right]\mathbf{j}$$

$$+ \left[-p\left(x, y, z+\frac{\Delta z}{2}\right) \Delta x\, \Delta y + p\left(x, y, z-\frac{\Delta z}{2}\right) \Delta x\, \Delta y \right]\mathbf{k}$$

$$+ \rho\mathbf{f}\, \Delta x\, \Delta y\, \Delta z$$

$$= -\frac{\partial p}{\partial x} \Delta x\, \Delta y\, \Delta z\mathbf{i} - \frac{\partial p}{\partial y} \Delta x\, \Delta y\, \Delta z\mathbf{j} - \frac{\partial p}{\partial z} \Delta x\, \Delta y\, \Delta z\mathbf{k} + \rho\mathbf{f}\, \Delta x\, \Delta y\, \Delta z = \mathbf{0}.$$

Therefore, dividing by the volume and passing to the limit $\Delta V \to 0$, we find the vector equation of equilibrium*

$$\frac{\partial p}{\partial x}\mathbf{i} + \frac{\partial p}{\partial y}\mathbf{j} + \frac{\partial p}{\partial z}\mathbf{k} = \rho\mathbf{f}. \qquad \textbf{4.4-10}$$

If we neglect all body forces ($\mathbf{f}=\mathbf{0}$), then the pressure must be constant everywhere in a fluid in equilibrium. The most common non-zero body force considered in fluid statics is the gravitational force. Since the gravitational force per unit mass is simply the local gravitational acceleration, $\mathbf{f}$ is either $-g\mathbf{e}$, where $\mathbf{e}$ is the local upward

---

* The vector $\dfrac{\partial p}{\partial x}\mathbf{i} + \dfrac{\partial p}{\partial y}\mathbf{j} + \dfrac{\partial p}{\partial z}\mathbf{k}$ derived from the scalar field $p(x, y, z)$ is known as the *gradient* of p; Eq. 4.4-10 may be written grad $p = \rho\mathbf{f}$ or $\nabla p = \rho\mathbf{f}$, the *vector differential operator* $\mathbf{i}\dfrac{\partial}{\partial x} + \mathbf{j}\dfrac{\partial}{\partial y} + \mathbf{k}\dfrac{\partial}{\partial z}$ (in rectangular coordinates) being denoted by "grad" or ∇ (read "del" or "nabla").

vertical unit vector and g ($\cong 32.2$ ft/sec^2) is the constant gravitational acceleration near the earth, or $(-GM/r^2)\mathbf{e}$, from the full gravitational law. The latter expression is of use only if we wish to consider changes in pressure through large vertical distances in the earth's atmosphere.

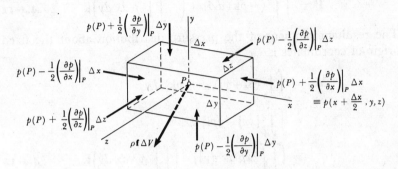

Fig. 4·4-3

The fundamental equilibrium problem of fluid statics is the solution of Eq. 4.4-10. Boundary conditions of an appropriate type must be adjoined. A distinction between liquid and gas, or at least between incompressible and compressible fluid, must be made in order to treat the relation between p and ρ properly. However, before examining some solutions, let us suppose that the pressure distribution $p(x, y, z)$ has been found in a fluid and let us then examine the resultant force due to fluid pressure on surfaces, real or imagined, acted upon by the fluid.

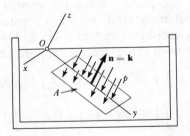

Fig. 4·4-4

Suppose that a plane area A bounds the fluid, or is imagined to be drawn in the fluid (Fig. 4.4-4). The fluid pressing on the plane boundary, or on one side of the imagined surface, gives rise to a pressure distribution of constant direction, even if of varying magnitude p, since the normal to the plane at every point is the same. Choose (x, y) axes in the plane and z in the positive normal direction. The resultant force is then

$$\mathbf{P} = \int\int_A (-p\mathbf{k})\, dA = \left(-\int\int_A p\, dx\, dy\right)\mathbf{k}. \qquad \textbf{4.4-11}$$

The resultant moment of the pressure distribution about the fixed origin of coordinates is

$$\mathbf{M}_O = \int\int_A (x\mathbf{i} + y\mathbf{j}) \times (-p\mathbf{k})\, dA$$

$$= \int\int_A [xp\mathbf{j} - yp\mathbf{i}]\, dA$$

$$= \left(\int\int_A xp\, dx\, dy\right)\mathbf{j} - \left(\int\int_A yp\, dx\, dy\right)\mathbf{i}. \qquad \textbf{4.4-12}$$

Since, after all, the pressure distribution is a parallel force system, we obtain the unsurprising result that the pressure distribution on a plane area may be replaced by a single force $\mathbf{P} = -P\mathbf{k}$ located at a point in the plane—the *center of pressure*—the coordinates $(\hat{x}, \hat{y})$ of which are given by

$$(\hat{x}\mathbf{i} + \hat{y}\mathbf{j}) \times (-P\mathbf{k}) = \mathbf{M}_O$$

or

$$\hat{x} = \frac{\int\int_A xp\, dx\, dy}{\int\int_A p\, dx\, dy}, \qquad \hat{y} = \frac{\int\int_A yp\, dx\, dy}{\int\int_A p\, dx\, dy}. \qquad \textbf{4.4-13}$$

We do not always find it convenient, of course, to choose such axes in and normal to the plane. Since the pressure distribution is a parallel force distribution $-p\mathbf{n}$, with $\mathbf{n}$ a constant unit vector, the result holds in any coordinate system. We find (with $\mathbf{r} = x\mathbf{i} + y\mathbf{j} + z\mathbf{k}$ the position vector from O to a general point in the plane)

$$\mathbf{P} = \int\int_A (-p\mathbf{n})\, dA = \left(-\int\int_A p\, dA\right)\mathbf{n},$$

$$\mathbf{M}_O = \int\int_A [\mathbf{r} \times (-p\mathbf{n})]\, dA = \left(-\int\int_A p\mathbf{r}\, dA\right) \times \mathbf{n},$$

so that the center of pressure is located at $\hat{\mathbf{r}}$ given by

$$\hat{\mathbf{r}} \times \mathbf{P} = \left(-\int\int_A p\, dA\right)(\hat{\mathbf{r}} \times \mathbf{n})$$

$$= \left(-\int\int_A p\mathbf{r}\, dA\right) \times \mathbf{n} = \mathbf{M}_O, \qquad \textbf{4.4-14}$$

or at $(\hat{x}, \hat{y}, \hat{z})$ given by

$$\hat{x} = \frac{\iint_A xp\,dA}{\iint_A p\,dA}, \qquad \hat{y} = \frac{\iint_A yp\,dA}{\iint_A p\,dA}, \qquad \hat{z} = \frac{\iint_A zp\,dA}{\iint_A p\,dA}. \qquad \textbf{4.4-15}$$

That the vector $\hat{\mathbf{r}}$ with these components satisfies Eq. 4.4-14 may be verified by substitution in that equation. As a final note on centers of pressure for the present, we see that Eqs. 4.4-13 and 4.4-15 follow the pattern for center of mass, centroid of area, and such other averaged quantities involving the first moment of a scalar. Indeed, if the pressure is constant, the center of pressure and centroid of area will coincide.

Suppose now that the surface we are considering is not plane but curved. We can no longer conclude in general that a resultant force set is a single force at a center of pressure. The force-and-couple resultant set must be used. Under certain circumstances, when there exists a plane of vertical symmetry of the surface and the pressure varies linearly with depth, a single resultant force may be found. Otherwise, the surface integrals—where **n** cannot now be removed from the integrand—for force and moment must both be evaluated and an appropriate couple kept, together with the force:

$$\mathbf{P} = -\int\int_S p\mathbf{n}\,dS, \qquad \mathbf{C} = -\int\int_S p(\mathbf{r} \times \mathbf{n})\,dS.$$

The line of action of the force is, of course, through the point from which **r** is measured.

Returning now to the solution of the equilibrium equation 4.4-10, let us see what the difficulties are. If $\mathbf{f} = \mathbf{0}$, then the pressure is constant—but what constant? If **f** is not zero, indeed if it is but a constant non-zero vector, then the density function must be prescribed. Conservation of mass in the equilibrium case tells us only that ρ is time-independent, as are all of our quantities. In order to solve our problem, we need an additional hypothesis about our fluid material that relates pressure and density. This is, in general, a *thermodynamic equation of state*

$$F(p, \rho, T) = 0 \qquad \textbf{4.4-16}$$

which also involves the temperature $T(x, y, z)$ of the fluid. This, in turn, requires that we know the temperature or that we can write an equation of thermal energy balance that will determine it. We shall not treat this question, for it is not our purpose to discuss the laws of thermodynamics in any detail. For *isothermal* processes, wherein the temperature at all points is the same, Eq. 4.4-16 becomes an equation in p and ρ alone.

For incompressible fluids, the equation of state is $\rho = $ constant. This we will take as characteristic of liquids for a wide range of temperature and pressure conditions. Suppose the body force per unit mass is due to gravity, and that the z-direction is the upward vertical. Then $\mathbf{f} = -g\mathbf{k}$, and Eq. 4.4-10 becomes

$$\frac{\partial p}{\partial x} = \frac{\partial p}{\partial y} = 0, \qquad \frac{\partial p}{\partial z} = -\rho g. \qquad \textbf{4·4-17}$$

The first two of Eqs. 4.4-17 say that the pressure is independent of the horizontal coordinates, and so must be the same at any given horizontal level; the last integrates to

$$p = p_0 - \rho g z. \qquad \textbf{4·4-18}$$

The pressure in an incompressible fluid subject to gravity decreases linearly with height. The pressure at all points in the same horizontal level is the same. The constant, p_0, is the pressure at the level $z = 0$. If $z = 0$ is taken at a free surface between air and the liquid, then p_0 is atmospheric pressure, with the fluid occupying a region in which $z < 0$. If we write $p_0 = \rho g z_0$, then 4.4-18 becomes $p = -\rho g (z - z_0)$; the level $z = z_0$ at which the pressure vanishes is the *effective surface* of the fluid, and the pressure due to a *head* of h feet means the pressure at a distance of h feet below the effective surface: $z = z_0 - h$, $p = +\rho g h$.

For gases, the assumption of incompressibility is generally no longer tenable. Aerostatics is based upon the additional assumption of the gas laws, usually those of the perfect gas. Boyle's law states that, if the temperature of a given mass of gas is constant, the pressure varies inversely as the volume:

$$pV = \text{const.}; \qquad \textbf{4·4-19}$$

and Charles' law states that, if the pressure in a given mass of gas is constant, the volume of the gas increases linearly with the temperature:

$$V = V_0(1 + \alpha T_c). \qquad \textbf{4·4-20}$$

Here V_0 is the volume at the zero point on the temperature scale. If T_c is measured in degrees Centigrade, then the coefficient of volume expansion α is approximately $1/273$ for many gases—leading to an "absolute zero" of $-273°$C at which V vanishes. Introducing the density by the conservation of mass equation $\rho V = $ constant, we may combine the laws into one of the two equivalent forms

$$p = R\rho T \qquad\qquad \textbf{4.4-21a}$$

or

$$pV = nRT \qquad\qquad \textbf{4.4-21b}$$

where R is a constant characteristic of the gas, $n = \rho V$ is the total mass, and T is the absolute temperature.

The gas laws, as stated, are for a total mass of gas in which the pressure is everywhere the same, so that $\mathbf{f}$ must be the zero vector in 4.4-10. If we wish to have $\mathbf{f} \neq \mathbf{0}$, say again the gravitational force $-g\mathbf{k}$ per unit mass, then we must modify these laws to ones valid point by point in the fluid. This is easily done by reinterpreting V as a specific volume, or volume per unit mass $(V = 1/\rho)$. In particular, 4.4-21a leads to a linear relation between p and ρ for an isothermal process:

$$\frac{p}{p_0} = \frac{\rho}{\rho_0} \qquad\qquad \textbf{4.4-22}$$

where (p_0, ρ_0) are the pressure and density at some particular point. Equilibrium of an isothermal gas under gravity is then governed by 4.4-10 and 4.4-22, resulting in the pressure equilibrium equation

$$\frac{\partial p}{\partial x}\mathbf{i} + \frac{\partial p}{\partial y}\mathbf{j} + \frac{\partial p}{\partial z}\mathbf{k} = -\frac{\rho_0}{p_0}\,pg\mathbf{k}. \qquad\qquad \textbf{4.4-23}$$

Again, p is independent of the horizontal coordinates x and y: $p = p(z)$; and 4.4-23 becomes the ordinary differential equation

$$\frac{dp}{dz} + \frac{\rho_0}{p_0}gp = 0. \qquad\qquad \textbf{4.4-24}$$

The solution is

$$p = p_0 e^{(-\rho_0/p_0)gz}, \qquad\qquad \textbf{4.4-25}$$

if we interpret p_0 and ρ_0 to be the pressure and density at $z = 0$. Thus, in an isothermal equilibrium atmosphere, the pressure (and density) decrease exponentially with altitude.

One important theorem that forms the basis for the design of the hydraulic press may be deduced from the general equilibrium equation 4.4-10. Suppose that we have found a solution $p = p_1(x, y, z)$ to the equation for a given $\mathbf{f}$, that is, for a given set of external forces. Then $p = p_1 + p_0$ is also a solution, where p_0 is an arbitrary constant that is the same at every point in the fluid. If this change of pressure

p_0 is somehow caused at any one point, it is immediately transmitted to every other point.   In Fig. 4.4-5, the application of this to the hydraulic press is sketched.   If the fluid in the press is in equilibrium, and a force F_1 is applied to the piston of area A_1, a constant pressure $p_0 = F_1/A_1$ is transmitted through the fluid to the piston of area A_2. The equilibrating force $F_2 = A_2 p_0 = A_2 F_1/A_1$ then acts to press body B between the piston and the upper wall of the container.   The so-called "hydrostatic paradox" finds its expression here: by adjusting

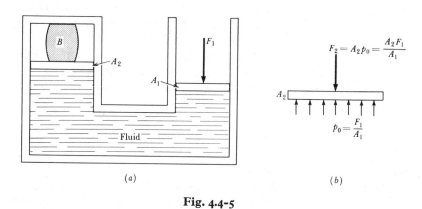

(a)   (b)

Fig. 4·4-5

the piston areas, any load F_2, however large, may be balanced by as small a load F_1 as desired.

Another class of equilibrium problems involving fluids are those involving floating or submerged bodies.   Solution of such problems depends upon *Archimedes' principle*:

A body wholly or partially immersed in a fluid at rest is subject to a resultant force due to fluid pressure which is the negative of the weight force vector of the displaced fluid and which has the same line of action, through the center of gravity of the displaced fluid.

This force is called the *buoyant force*, and the center of gravity of the displaced fluid is the *center of buoyancy*.   To prove Archimedes' principle, we first note that the resultant force, being the integral of the pressure distribution over the surface between body and fluid, depends only on the shape of that surface and its location in the fluid, and not on the material of which the body is made.   Imagine, then, that the body is removed and that the space which it occupied is filled with a mass of the same fluid that surrounds the body.   This additional mass of fluid—the "displaced mass"—is in equilibrium under its own weight and the resultant pressure of the surrounding fluid; if it were not, flow would start in it and in the surrounding fluid under an equilibrium pressure distribution. This cannot be. Thus the resultant of the pressure force, i.e., the buoyancy force, must be the negative of the weight of the displaced fluid and must act through its center of gravity.

There are many more problems of interest in aerostatics, hydrostatics, and the equilibrium of floating bodies. Among them may be mentioned capillarity and the hypothesis of *surface tension* to explain meniscus effects in tubes of small bore containing fluid; partial pressures in mixtures of fluids; and the equilibrium of stratified layers of immiscible fluids. For details of these and many others, reference should be made to a work on hydrostatics.*

4.5 The Stress Tensor; Equilibrium Equations for the Continuum

In the last section we defined the traction vector, its normal stress component, and its shearing stress component (Eqs. 4.4-2, 4.4-3, and 4.4-4) acting at a point in a continuous body on a unit area through the point having normal **n**. By assuming that the shearing stress on any plane vanished, we were able to derive the conditions of equilibrium at any point of the first two orders: that the normal stress—the pressure—on any plane through the point is the same, and that the rate of change of the pressure with position is proportional to the component of the body force per unit mass in the direction of the position coordinate. These two results were derived by consideration of the behavior of forces that vanished proportionally to area and volume, respectively.

For the general continuous distribution of matter, or *continuum*, corresponding results can be derived. Now we assume that the material can sustain shearing stress. The first results that we derive are *Cauchy's relations*; these express the traction vector on any plane through a point in terms of the traction vectors on three perpendicular planes through the point. The fact that the traction vector on any plane can be found from the three other vectors when the orientation of the plane is given leads us to the concept of the *state of stress* at a point and its representation by a mathematical entity, the *stress tensor*, that generalizes the vector concept. Our final result will be the derivation of the equations of equilibrium for a continuum in terms of body forces and the scalar components of the stress tensor in a rectangular cartesian coordinate system.

---

* For example, A. S. Ramsey, *Hydrostatics* (New York: Cambridge University Press, 1946).

As in Fig. 4.4-2, let us surround the point P by a tetrahedron $ABCD$ of material (Fig. 4.5-1), with three faces in the coordinate planes and the fourth slant face having unit normal vector $\mathbf{n} = n_x\mathbf{i} + n_y\mathbf{j} + n_z\mathbf{k}$. A body force $\mathbf{f}$ per unit mass is assumed to act. The traction vector on each face can have any direction; the notation given in the figure will be used. The area of the slant face will be denoted by ΔA once again, and the altitude

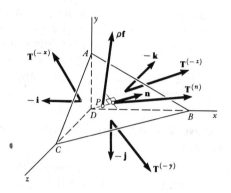

Fig. 4.5-1

from D to the face by Δh. With $BD = \Delta x$, $AD = \Delta y$, and $CD = \Delta z$, we have the relations 4.4-6 and 4.4-7 once again for the areas of the other faces and the volume of the tetrahedron:

$$\frac{1}{2}\Delta y\,\Delta z = n_x\,\Delta A, \qquad \frac{1}{2}\Delta x\,\Delta z = n_y\,\Delta A, \qquad \frac{1}{2}\Delta x\,\Delta y = n_z\,\Delta A,$$

$$\Delta V = \frac{1}{6}\Delta x\,\Delta y\,\Delta z = \frac{1}{3}\Delta h\,\Delta A. \qquad \text{4.5-1}$$

The average forces on each face and on the volume lead to the equilibrium equation

$$\mathbf{T}^{(-x)}n_x\,\Delta A + \mathbf{T}^{(-y)}n_y\,\Delta A + \mathbf{T}^{(-z)}n_z\,\Delta A + \mathbf{T}^{(n)}\,\Delta A + \rho\mathbf{f}\,\Delta V = 0,$$

which becomes, after division by ΔA,

$$\mathbf{T}^{(-x)}n_x + \mathbf{T}^{(-y)}n_y + \mathbf{T}^{(-z)}n_z + \mathbf{T}^{(n)} + \rho\mathbf{f}\,\Delta h = 0. \qquad \text{4.5-2}$$

Before letting the volume shrink to the point P, we replace $\mathbf{T}^{(-x)}$ by $-\mathbf{T}^{(x)}$, etc.; that is, the traction vector on each coordinate plane through D with normal in a negative coordinate direction must, by the third law of motion, be the negative of the traction vector on the same plane with positive orientation. Then, if the tetrahedron shrinks to the point P so that Δh approaches zero, the body force term vanishes and the traction vectors approach their values on the appropriate planes through P. Cauchy's relations in vector form are

$$\mathbf{T}^{(n)} = \mathbf{T}^{(x)}n_x + \mathbf{T}^{(y)}n_y + \mathbf{T}^{(z)}n_z. \qquad \textbf{4·5-3}$$

Equation 4.5-3 is valid in the dynamic case as well. Setting the forces equal to the mass of the tetrahedron multiplied by the acceleration of its mass center, $\rho \, \Delta V \, \mathbf{a}^*$, we see that this term also goes to zero with Δh if the acceleration is to remain finite.

Cauchy's relations may be written in scalar form by introducing the (x, y, z) components of the four vectors that occur in 4.5-3. A consistent notation is helpful here. Let us consider the vector $\mathbf{T}^{(x)}$, the force at P per unit area with normal in the positive x-direction. The normal stress is the component of $\mathbf{T}^{(x)}$ in the x-direction. Let us denote this component by σ_{xx}—the scalar component on a plane with normal in the positive x-direction (the first subscript, corresponding to the superscript x on $\mathbf{T}^{(x)}$) of the vector $\mathbf{T}^{(x)}$ in that normal x-direction (the second subscript). The normal component of the traction vector is, therefore, $\sigma_{xx}\mathbf{i}$. The remainder of $\mathbf{T}^{(x)}$ is the shear stress on that plane: $\mathbf{T}^{(x)} - \sigma_{xx}\mathbf{i}$. This shear stress can be resolved into y- and z-components, which we will denote by σ_{xy} and σ_{xz}—the components in the y- and z-directions (second subscripts) of the traction vector on a plane with normal in the positive x-direction (first subscripts). Thus

$$\mathbf{T}^{(x)} = \sigma_{xx}\mathbf{i} + \sigma_{xy}\mathbf{j} + \sigma_{xz}\mathbf{k}; \qquad \textbf{4·5-4a}$$

similarly,

$$\mathbf{T}^{(y)} = \sigma_{yx}\mathbf{i} + \sigma_{yy}\mathbf{j} + \sigma_{yz}\mathbf{k}, \qquad \textbf{4·5-4b}$$

$$\mathbf{T}^{(z)} = \sigma_{zx}\mathbf{i} + \sigma_{zy}\mathbf{j} + \sigma_{zz}\mathbf{k}. \qquad \textbf{4·5-4c}$$

The sign convention for positive scalar stress components is the same as for the components of any other vector; in particular, the normal stresses $(\sigma_{xx}, \sigma_{yy}, \sigma_{zz})$ are counted as positive if they are tensile. For the fluid at rest, we found that $\sigma_{xx} = \sigma_{yy} = \sigma_{zz} = -p$; all the shearing stresses were assumed to be zero.

The Cauchy relations 4.5-3 in scalar form are:

$$\begin{aligned}
T_x^{(n)} &= n_x\sigma_{xx} + n_y\sigma_{yx} + n_z\sigma_{zx}, \\
T_y^{(n)} &= n_x\sigma_{xy} + n_y\sigma_{yy} + n_z\sigma_{zy}, \qquad \textbf{4·5-5} \\
T_z^{(n)} &= n_x\sigma_{xz} + n_y\sigma_{yz} + n_z\sigma_{zz}.
\end{aligned}$$

The nine scalar quantities $\sigma_{xx}, \sigma_{xy}, \dots \sigma_{zz}$ are called the *components of stress*. They have the dimensions of force per unit area. In general, they are functions of position (x, y, z) and time.

The traction components on any plane through P are thus determined by the nine stress components $\sigma_{xx}, \sigma_{xy}, \dots \sigma_{zz}$. We can therefore speak of the *stress at a point* in a continuum, and say that this state of stress is known once the nine components of stress relative to any given set of cartesian axes are known. A very similar situation occurs with vector quantities: once the cartesian components (A_x, A_y, A_z) of a vector $\mathbf{A}$ are known with respect to one coordinate system, the component of the vector in any direction is known. If the arbitrary direction is prescribed by the unit vector $\mathbf{n} = n_x\mathbf{i} + n_y\mathbf{j} + n_z\mathbf{k}$, then the scalar component $A^{(n)}$ of $\mathbf{A}$ in the direction of $\mathbf{n}$ is computed by

$$A^{(n)} = \mathbf{A} \cdot \mathbf{n} = n_x A_x + n_y A_y + n_z A_z. \qquad \textbf{4.5-6}$$

The analogy between Eq. 4.5-6 and any one of the three Eqs. 4.5-5 is no coincidence. Just as we speak of a vector entity $\mathbf{A}$ and its representation (A_x, A_y, A_z) in some particular coordinate system, so may we speak of a new entity $\tilde{B}$ and its representation

$$\begin{pmatrix} B_{xx} & B_{xy} & B_{xz} \\ B_{yx} & B_{yy} & B_{yz} \\ B_{zx} & B_{zy} & B_{zz} \end{pmatrix} \qquad \textbf{4.5-7}$$

in a particular coordinate system. This new entity obeys certain rules of transformation (which can be derived from Eqs. 4.5-5) that relate its

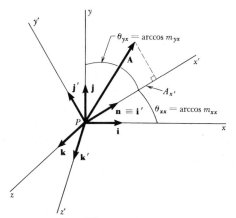

Fig. 4.5-2

components in any pair of coordinate systems. These rules of transformation are generalizations of those relating the scalar components of a vector in two different coordinate systems. Indeed, vectors and scalars are special cases of a more general concept, the *tensor*. In particular, the state of stress at a point is represented by a *second-order tensor*, each component of which depends upon two directions in space. Vectors are *first-order tensors*, involving one direction in space; and scalars, independent of spatial direction, are *zero-order tensors*. Higher-order tensors can be defined and are useful in various branches of mechanics and physics in general as well as being a study in themselves in mathematics. Besides the stress tensor, two other second-order tensors should be mentioned: the strain tensor, encountered in the study of deformable bodies, and the moment of inertia tensor, encountered in the dynamics of rigid bodies in three dimensions. We shall now derive the transformation rules for the components of a second-order tensor in two different coordinate systems and compare them to the rules for a vector. We are concerned with right-handed rectangular cartesian systems only, and with the transformation rules from one such system to another. The tensor quantities we define are not the most general possible but are known as cartesian tensors and, indeed, as oriented cartesian tensors.

In Fig. 4.5-2, two rectangular cartesian coordinate systems (x, y, z) and (x', y', z') with origin at P are shown. The unit vector $\mathbf{n}$, and the direction of that vector, have now been called $\mathbf{i}'$ and x'—one of our new coordinate directions. The other new directions are chosen perpendicular to x' in such a way that the primed coordinate system is right-handed. Rather than call the components of $\mathbf{n} \equiv \mathbf{i}'$ in the (x, y, z) system (n_x, n_y, n_z) as before, we introduce a new notation. Let $(\theta_{xx}, \theta_{yx}, \theta_{zx})$ be the direction angles between the x-axis and the x'-axis, y-axis and x'-axis, and z-axis and x'-axis, respectively. The *direction cosines* of x' with respect to (x, y, z) are, in fact, the components of the unit vector $\mathbf{i}'$ in the (x, y, z) system. We introduce the following notation for these direction cosines:

$$m_{xx} = \cos \theta_{xx}, \qquad m_{yx} = \cos \theta_{yx}, \qquad m_{zx} = \cos \theta_{zx}; \qquad \textbf{4.5-8a}$$

the first subscript refers to an axis of the (x, y, z) set, and the second to the x'-axis of the second set. Similarly, the direction cosines of the other primed axes are introduced:

$$m_{xy} = \cos \theta_{xy}, \qquad m_{yy} = \cos \theta_{yy}, \qquad m_{zy} = \cos \theta_{zy}; \qquad \textbf{4.5-8b}$$
$$m_{xz} = \cos \theta_{xz}, \qquad m_{yz} = \cos \theta_{yz}, \qquad m_{zz} = \cos \theta_{zz}. \qquad \textbf{4.5-8c}$$

It is worth noting that, although a double subscript notation has been used for the direction cosines, the array of nine direction cosines does *not* constitute a tensor. The subscripts refer to different axis systems, not to the same axis system as in the stress components of 4.5-5 or the components of $\tilde{B}$ in 4.5-7. The unit vectors $(\mathbf{i}', \mathbf{j}', \mathbf{k}')$ can be written in terms of the direction cosines and the vectors $(\mathbf{i}, \mathbf{j}, \mathbf{k})$:

$$\mathbf{i}' = m_{xx}\mathbf{i} + m_{yx}\mathbf{j} + m_{zx}\mathbf{k},$$
$$\mathbf{j}' = m_{xy}\mathbf{i} + m_{yy}\mathbf{j} + m_{zy}\mathbf{k}, \qquad \textbf{4.5-9}$$
$$\mathbf{k}' = m_{xz}\mathbf{i} + m_{yz}\mathbf{j} + m_{zz}\mathbf{k}.$$

With these results, we proceed to the transformation rules for vectors and second-order tensors. Suppose a vector $\mathbf{A}$ at point P is given (Fig. 4.5-2), with representations

$$\mathbf{A} = A_x\mathbf{i} + A_y\mathbf{j} + A_z\mathbf{k} = A_{x'}\mathbf{i}' + A_{y'}\mathbf{j}' + A_{z'}\mathbf{k}' \qquad \textbf{4.5-10}$$

in the two coordinate systems. We wish to express $(A_{x'}, A_{y'}, A_{z'})$ in terms of (A_x, A_y, A_z). We have already found $A_{x'}$ in Eq. 4.5-6; replacing $\mathbf{n}$ by $\mathbf{i}'$ and $A^{(n)}$ by $A_{x'}$, we have

$$A_{x'} = \mathbf{A} \cdot \mathbf{i}' = A_x \mathbf{i} \cdot \mathbf{i}' + A_y \mathbf{j} \cdot \mathbf{i}' + A_z \mathbf{k} \cdot \mathbf{i}'$$

$$= m_{xx} A_x + m_{yx} A_y + m_{zx} A_z;$$ **4.5-11a**

similarly,

$$A_{y'} = \mathbf{A} \cdot \mathbf{j}' = A_x \mathbf{i} \cdot \mathbf{j}' + A_y \mathbf{j} \cdot \mathbf{j}' + A_z \mathbf{k} \cdot \mathbf{j}'$$

$$= m_{xy} A_x + m_{yy} A_y + m_{zy} A_z,$$ **4.5-11b**

and

$$A_{z'} = \mathbf{A} \cdot \mathbf{k}' = A_x \mathbf{i} \cdot \mathbf{k}' + A_y \mathbf{j} \cdot \mathbf{k}' + A_z \mathbf{k} \cdot \mathbf{k}'$$

$$= m_{xz} A_x + m_{yz} A_y + m_{zz} A_z.$$ **4.5-11c**

Equations 4.5-11 are the transformation rules for vector components under the coordinate rotation 4.5-9.

The tensor transformation rules for any $\tilde{B}$ can be obtained from the rules for the special tensor $\tilde{\sigma}$ by computing (from Eqs. 4.5-5) the normal and shear stress components on the plane with normal $\mathbf{n}$—or, in our new notation, the normal stress $\sigma_{x'x'}$ and the shearing stresses $\sigma_{x'y'}$ and $\sigma_{x'z'}$ on the plane through P with normal in the x'-direction. In the new notation, the components of $\mathbf{n}$ in 4.5-5 are replaced by the appropriate direction cosines and the components in the (x, y, z) directions of the traction vector $\mathbf{T}^{(n)}$ are replaced by the (x, y, z) components of the traction vector $\mathbf{T}^{(x')}$. Rewriting Eqs. 4.5-5 in the new notation, we have:

$$T_x^{(x')} = m_{xx} \sigma_{xx} + m_{yx} \sigma_{yx} + m_{zx} \sigma_{zx},$$

$$T_y^{(x')} = m_{xx} \sigma_{xy} + m_{yx} \sigma_{yy} + m_{zx} \sigma_{zy},$$ **4.5-12**

$$T_z^{(x')} = m_{xx} \sigma_{xz} + m_{yx} \sigma_{yz} + m_{zx} \sigma_{zz}.$$

The normal stress $\sigma_{x'x'}$ is the component $T_x^{(x')}$ of the traction vector $\mathbf{T}^{(x')}$ in the direction of the normal to the plane:

$$\sigma_{x'x'} = T_{x'}^{(x')} = \mathbf{T}^{(x')} \cdot \mathbf{i}' = T_x^{(x')} \mathbf{i} \cdot \mathbf{i}' + T_y^{(x')} \mathbf{j} \cdot \mathbf{i}' + T_z^{(x')} \mathbf{k} \cdot \mathbf{i}'$$

$$= m_{xx} T_x^{(x')} + m_{yx} T_y^{(x')} + m_{zx} T_z^{(x')}.$$ **4.5-13**

Therefore, $\sigma_{x'x'}$ can be written in terms of $(\sigma_{xx}, \sigma_{xy}, \ldots \sigma_{zz})$; substituting 4.5-12 into 4.5-13, we obtain

$$\sigma_{x'x'} = m_{xx} m_{xx} \sigma_{xx} + m_{xx} m_{yx} \sigma_{xy} + m_{xx} m_{zx} \sigma_{xz}$$

$$+ m_{yx} m_{xx} \sigma_{yx} + m_{yx} m_{yx} \sigma_{yy} + m_{yx} m_{zx} \sigma_{yz}$$ **4.5-14a**

$$+ m_{zx} m_{xx} \sigma_{zx} + m_{zx} m_{yx} \sigma_{zy} + m_{zx} m_{zx} \sigma_{zz}.$$

The shear stress component in the y'-direction on the plane with normal x' is

$$\sigma_{x'y'} = \mathbf{T}^{(x')} \cdot \mathbf{j}' = m_{xy} T_x^{(x')} + m_{yy} T_y^{(x')} + m_{zy} T_z^{(x')},$$

or, if we use 4.5-12 again,

$$\sigma_{x'y'} = m_{xx}m_{xy}\sigma_{xx} + m_{xx}m_{yy}\sigma_{xy} + m_{xx}m_{zy}\sigma_{xz}$$
$$+ m_{yx}m_{xy}\sigma_{yx} + m_{yx}m_{yy}\sigma_{yy} + m_{yx}m_{zy}\sigma_{yz} \qquad \textbf{4.5-14b}$$
$$+ m_{zx}m_{xy}\sigma_{zx} + m_{zx}m_{yy}\sigma_{zy} + m_{zx}m_{zy}\sigma_{zz}.$$

The equations 4.5-14a and 4.5-14b are typical of the transformation rule for computing any component in the (x', y', z') system of a second-order tensor from the components in the (x, y, z) system. Let us state in words what the rule is. The typical term on the right is the product of two direction cosines and an (x, y, z) component of the tensor. The direction cosines are arranged so that the second subscripts, *taken in order*, are the same as the (x', y', z') subscripts on the component we are computing— (x', x') in 4.5-14a, (x', y') in 4.5-14b. The first subscripts on the direction cosines, again taken in order, are the same as those of the (x, y, z) component that the direction cosines multiply. Add up all nine possible terms in the (x, y, z) components; this sum is equal to the (x', y', z') component given by the second subscripts on the direction cosines. Following this rule, we can compute the other seven components in the (x', y', z') axes. We note that the vector component transformations 4.5-11 follow the same rule, with but one direction cosine involved in each term in the sum; and higher-order tensor transformations follow the same pattern, with direction cosines equal in number to the order in each term. Also, a much more efficient notation can be developed to make the expressions more compact and useful for theoretical and computational purposes.

Let us now derive the force equilibrium equations of the order of volume terms; we expect these to involve the partial derivatives of the stress components. The fluid equilibrium equation 4.4-10 is a special case of these general equations. Now, rather than replace the stress distribution on each face of the tetrahedron or parallelepiped by a mean stress over the face, we take into account the first variation of the stress

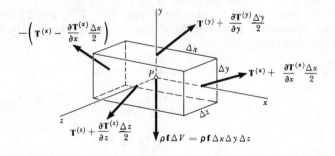

Fig. 4.5-3

components with distance. We take the parallelepiped of Fig. 4.4-3, with center at the point P and edges Δx, Δy, Δz, as shown here in Fig. 4.5-3. The body force per unit mass is again denoted $\mathbf{f} = f_x\mathbf{i} + f_y\mathbf{j} + f_z\mathbf{k}$. The stresses on the faces are taken to be the stresses at P plus the changes in stress, to first-order terms in the edge lengths, due to the distance of the face from P. Again, the variation in these stresses over the face is "averaged out," so that the stress is the same at each point of a given face. In Fig. 4.5-3, the traction vectors on the three faces with normals in the positive coordinate directions are shown, as is the body force $\rho\mathbf{f}\,\Delta V$. There are stresses on the other three faces as well. Only those on the face with unit normal $-\mathbf{i}$ are shown. Note the minus sign that appears for that traction vector (and for the other two similar traction vectors also); this sign occurs since $\mathbf{T}^{(x)}$ is the traction vector on a plane with unit normal $+\mathbf{i}$. The vectors $\mathbf{T}^{(x)}$, $\mathbf{T}^{(y)}$, $\mathbf{T}^{(z)}$ have cartesian components $(\sigma_{xx}, \sigma_{xy}, \sigma_{xz})$, $(\sigma_{yx}, \sigma_{yy}, \sigma_{yz})$, and $(\sigma_{zx}, \sigma_{zy}, \sigma_{zz})$, respectively; a partial derivative, such as $\partial\mathbf{T}^{(x)}/\partial x$, of a vector means the vector whose components are the partial derivatives of the components of the initial vector.

The force equilibrium equations are

$$\left[\left(\mathbf{T}^{(x)} + \frac{\partial\mathbf{T}^{(x)}}{\partial x}\frac{\Delta x}{2}\right) - \left(\mathbf{T}^{(x)} - \frac{\partial\mathbf{T}^{(x)}}{\partial x}\frac{\Delta x}{2}\right)\right]\Delta y\,\Delta z$$

$$+\left[\left(\mathbf{T}^{(y)} + \frac{\partial\mathbf{T}^{(y)}}{\partial y}\frac{\Delta y}{2}\right) - \left(\mathbf{T}^{(y)} - \frac{\partial\mathbf{T}^{(y)}}{\partial y}\frac{\Delta y}{2}\right)\right]\Delta x\,\Delta z$$

$$+\left[\left(\mathbf{T}^{(z)} + \frac{\partial\mathbf{T}^{(z)}}{\partial z}\frac{\Delta z}{2}\right) - \left(\mathbf{T}^{(z)} - \frac{\partial\mathbf{T}^{(z)}}{\partial z}\frac{\Delta z}{2}\right)\right]\Delta x\,\Delta y$$

$$+\rho\mathbf{f}\,\Delta x\,\Delta y\,\Delta z = \mathbf{0},$$

or (after division by $\Delta V = \Delta x\,\Delta y\,\Delta z$),

$$\frac{\partial\mathbf{T}^{(x)}}{\partial x} + \frac{\partial\mathbf{T}^{(y)}}{\partial y} + \frac{\partial\mathbf{T}^{(z)}}{\partial z} + \rho\mathbf{f} = \mathbf{0}. \qquad \textbf{4.5-15}$$

The "shrinking of the parallelepiped to the limit point P" has been carried out implicitly in this argument, with higher-order terms involving second derivatives of the stresses vanishing in the limit process.

If we now replace the traction vectors $\mathbf{T}^{(x)}$, $\mathbf{T}^{(y)}$, and $\mathbf{T}^{(z)}$ by their cartesian component representations, the vector equation 4.5-15 may be written in equivalent scalar form:

$$\frac{\partial\sigma_{xx}}{\partial x} + \frac{\partial\sigma_{yx}}{\partial y} + \frac{\partial\sigma_{zx}}{\partial z} + \rho f_x = 0,$$

$$\frac{\partial\sigma_{xy}}{\partial x} + \frac{\partial\sigma_{yy}}{\partial y} + \frac{\partial\sigma_{zy}}{\partial z} + \rho f_y = 0, \qquad \textbf{4.5-16}$$

$$\frac{\partial\sigma_{xz}}{\partial x} + \frac{\partial\sigma_{yz}}{\partial y} + \frac{\partial\sigma_{zz}}{\partial z} + \rho f_z = 0.$$

These are known as Navier's equations of equilibrium. They play a basic role in stress analysis.

To these three partial differential equations representing force equilibrium per unit volume we must adjoin moment equilibrium equations. Under the assumption that there are no surface or body moments, i.e., no couples per unit area or volume, the moment equations express a condition on the stress components themselves and not on the spatial derivatives of the stresses. The vectorial moment equilibrium equation about point P for the forces on the parallelepiped of Fig. 4.5-3 is:

$$\left(\frac{\Delta x}{2}\mathbf{i}\right) \times \left[\left(\mathbf{T}^{(x)} + \frac{\partial \mathbf{T}^{(x)}}{\partial x}\frac{\Delta x}{2}\right)\Delta y\,\Delta z\right]$$

$$+\left(-\frac{\Delta x}{2}\mathbf{i}\right) \times \left[-\left(\mathbf{T}^{(x)} - \frac{\partial \mathbf{T}^{(x)}}{\partial x}\frac{\Delta x}{2}\right)\Delta y\,\Delta z\right]$$

$$+\left(\frac{\Delta y}{2}\mathbf{j}\right) \times \left[\left(\mathbf{T}^{(y)} + \frac{\partial \mathbf{T}^{(y)}}{\partial y}\frac{\Delta y}{2}\right)\Delta x\,\Delta z\right]$$

$$+\left(-\frac{\Delta y}{2}\mathbf{j}\right) \times \left[-\left(\mathbf{T}^{(y)} - \frac{\partial \mathbf{T}^{(y)}}{\partial y}\frac{\Delta y}{2}\right)\Delta x\,\Delta z\right]$$

$$+\left(\frac{\Delta z}{2}\mathbf{k}\right) \times \left[\left(\mathbf{T}^{(z)} + \frac{\partial \mathbf{T}^{(z)}}{\partial z}\frac{\Delta z}{2}\right)\Delta x\,\Delta y\right]$$

$$+\left(-\frac{\Delta z}{2}\mathbf{k}\right) \times \left[-\left(\mathbf{T}^{(z)} - \frac{\partial \mathbf{T}^{(z)}}{\partial z}\frac{\Delta z}{2}\right)\Delta x\,\Delta y\right] = \mathbf{0},$$

which reduces to

$$(\Delta x \mathbf{i}) \times (\mathbf{T}^{(x)}\,\Delta y\,\Delta z) + (\Delta y \mathbf{j}) \times (\mathbf{T}^{(y)}\,\Delta x\,\Delta z) + (\Delta z \mathbf{k}) \times (\mathbf{T}^{(z)}\,\Delta x\,\Delta y) = \mathbf{0}.$$

4.5-17

Note that the body force $\rho \mathbf{f}\,\Delta V$ has been considered to act at P; if it does not, its moment will be of higher order in the edge lengths than those of the stress vectors and will vanish in the limiting process $\Delta V \to 0$. Dividing Eq. 4.5-17 by the volume $\Delta V = \Delta x\,\Delta y\,\Delta z$ of the parallelepiped and performing the limit process $\Delta V \to 0$, we find

$$\mathbf{i} \times \mathbf{T}^{(x)} + \mathbf{j} \times \mathbf{T}^{(y)} + \mathbf{k} \times \mathbf{T}^{(z)} = \mathbf{0} \qquad\qquad \text{4.5-18}$$

as the vector moment equilibrium equation. From this, we obtain

$$\mathbf{i} \times (\sigma_{xx}\mathbf{i} + \sigma_{xy}\mathbf{j} + \sigma_{xz}\mathbf{k}) + \mathbf{j} \times (\sigma_{yx}\mathbf{i} + \sigma_{yy}\mathbf{j} + \sigma_{yz}\mathbf{k}) + \mathbf{k} \times (\sigma_{zx}\mathbf{i} + \sigma_{zy}\mathbf{j} + \sigma_{zz}\mathbf{k}) = \mathbf{0},$$

or

$$(\sigma_{yz} - \sigma_{zy})\mathbf{i} + (\sigma_{zx} - \sigma_{xz})\mathbf{j} + (\sigma_{xy} - \sigma_{yx})\mathbf{k} = \mathbf{0}. \qquad\qquad \text{4.5-19}$$

Therefore, for moment equilibrium with no body or surface moments, we must have the shear stresses on orthogonal planes at a point equal in pairs:

$$\sigma_{xy} = \sigma_{yx}, \qquad \sigma_{yz} = \sigma_{zy}, \qquad \sigma_{zx} = \sigma_{xz}. \qquad\qquad \text{4.5-20}$$

The six equations of equilibrium 4.5-16 and 4.5-20 in nine unknowns—or the three equations in six unknowns resulting from the substitution of

4.5-20 in 4.5-16—are the only independent ones. Problems requiring the solution of these equations for the stress distribution are, therefore, statically indeterminate.

The dynamical equations of motion corresponding to 4.5-16 and 4.5-20 are simple to state, although we shall not derive them. Equations 4.5-16 are modified by the replacement of the right-hand side by the product of the density, ρ, and the appropriate component of the acceleration vector at point P. These equations are derived from the dynamical principle of motion of the mass center. The dynamical principle of moment of momentum, or angular momentum, leads to Eqs. 4.5-20 once again if there are no surface or body moments.

The relations 4.5-20 state that the stress tensor $\tilde{\sigma}$ is *symmetric*. That is, the component representation (in any rectangular cartesian coordinate system)

$$\tilde{\sigma} = \begin{pmatrix} \sigma_{xx} & \sigma_{xy} & \sigma_{xz} \\ \sigma_{yx} & \sigma_{yy} & \sigma_{yz} \\ \sigma_{zx} & \sigma_{zy} & \sigma_{zz} \end{pmatrix}$$

has equal-valued components in positions symmetrically placed with respect to the main diagonal formed by the normal stress components. This symmetry has important consequences for the development of the theory of stress analysis, perhaps the primary one being the existence at any point of three perpendicular planes on which there are no shearing stresses. Similar results hold for the symmetric strain tensor and the symmetric moment of inertia tensor.

Exercises

4.2-1: A cable in uniform tension fits tightly against a cam of arbitrary shape (except that there are no sharp corners). What is the tangential load, q_t, exerted by the cam on the cable?

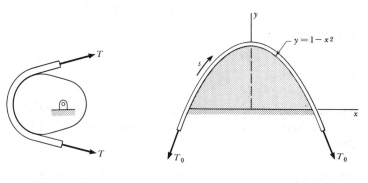

Exer. 4.2-1   **Exer. 4.2-2**

4.2-2: A cable subject to uniform tension T_0 lb passes around a parabolic cam, the equation of the boundary being $y = 1 - x^2$ (foot units are used). Measure arclength s in the sense shown; the slope angle θ is given by $\tan \theta = dy/dx$. By first finding ds/dx and $d\theta/ds = (d^2y/dx^2)/(ds/dx)^3$, find the normal load distribution q_n between cam and cable.

Ans.: $q_n(x) = 2T_0/[1+4x^2]^{3/2}$ lbs/ft (of arclength).

4.2-3: A cable weighing 5 lb/ft is 100 ft long. How far apart should the supports be (on the same horizontal level) if the cable is not to sag more than 12 ft at its center? What is the minimum tension H?

Ans.: Exact: $l = 96.12$ ft, $H = 490.8$ lb; Approx.: $l = 96$ ft, $H = 480$ lb.

4.2-4: Suppose a 100 ft cable is supporting a 5 lb load per foot of horizontal span, the weight of the cable being neglected. How far apart must the supports be if the cable is not to sag more than 12 ft? What are the maximum and minimum tensions in the cable? What is the total load carried by the cable? Compare the answer for the total span with the answer to the previous exercise.

Ans.: Approx: $l = 96$ ft, $H = W = 480$ lb, $T_{max} = 537$ lb.

4.2-5: The maximum tension permitted in a cable before it will snap is 1500 lb. A uniform load of 1000 lb per foot of horizontal span is to be carried over a 50 ft span. What is the minimum length of cable permissible? What will be the sag?

Ans.: $L = 51.0$ ft, $f = 4.42$ ft.

4.2-6: The maximum tension permitted in a cable before it will snap is T^* lb. It hangs under its own weight over a span of l ft. Find the relation between the length L of cable needed and its total weight W so that the maximum tension condition will be just satisfied.

Ans.: $\dfrac{L\sqrt{4T^{*2}-W^2}}{W} \operatorname{arcsinh}\left(\dfrac{W}{\sqrt{4T^{*2}-W^2}}\right) = l.$

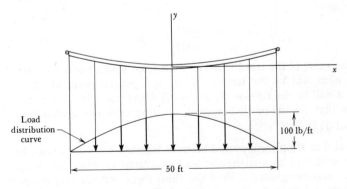

Exer. 4.2-7

4.2-7: A cable of negligible weight is supported with its ends at the same level 50 ft apart. A load is distributed along the span sinusoidally, vanishing at the ends and reaching a peak value of 100 lb/ft at the center. What is the shape of the cable if the maximum tension is $(15,000/\pi)$ lb?

Ans.: $y = \dfrac{25\sqrt{2}}{2\pi}\left[1 - \cos\left(\dfrac{\pi x}{50}\right)\right]$ ft.

4.2-8: A cable subject to uniform tension T_0 passes over half of a fixed elliptical bar as shown. The equation of the bar surface is

$$\frac{x^2}{a^2} + \frac{y^2}{b^2} = 1,$$

with $a > b$. Find the normal pressure $q_n(x, y)$ between bar and cable and determine the maximum value of the pressure.

Ans.: $q_n(x, y) = \dfrac{a^4 b^4 T_0}{(b^4 x^2 + a^4 y^2)^{3/2}}$ (per unit arclength).

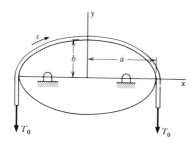

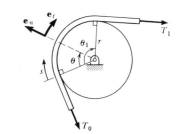

Exer. 4.2-8   Exer. 4.2-9

4.2-9: A cable passes around a fixed circular rough surface in such a way that the ratio of the tangential load (friction force) to the normal load is a constant:

$$\frac{q_t(s)}{q_n(s)} = -\mu.$$

If the value of the tension at the point from which s and θ are measured is T_0, what will be the tension, $T(\theta)$, at a general point along the cable? What will be the tension T_1 at $\theta = \theta_1$, where the cable leaves the surface? Note that, for the positive normal direction shown, $-T\, d\theta/ds + q_n = 0$.
Ans.: $T(\theta) = T_0\, e^{\mu\theta}$.

4.3-1: The simply-supported beam of Exercise 2.7-17 is shown here again. It is subjected to a triangular load compared to which the weight of the beam may be ignored. Find the shear force and bending moment distributions and draw the diagrams for them.

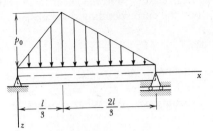

Exer. 4.3-1

Ans.: $M(x) = \dfrac{p_0 x}{18l}(5l^2 - 9x^2),\ 0 \le x \le l/3;$

$\qquad M(x) = \dfrac{p_0}{36l}(x-l)(9x^2 - 18lx + l^2),\ l/3 \le x \le l.$

4.3-2: Suppose the beam of Exercise 4.3-1 under the same load is clamped at the left and free at the right; what are the shear and moment distributions now? Draw the shear and bending moment diagrams.

Ans.: $M(x) = -\dfrac{p_0}{18l}(4l^3 - 9l^2 x + 9x^3),\ 0 \le x \le l/3;$

$\qquad M(x) = -\dfrac{p_0}{4l}(l-x)^3,\ l/3 \le x \le l.$

4.3-3: Suppose the beam of Exercise 4.3-1 under the same load is free at the left and clamped at the right; now what are the distributions of, and diagrams for, the shear force and bending moment?

Ans.: $M(x) = -\dfrac{p_0 x^3}{2l},\ 0 \le x \le l/3;$

$\qquad M(x) = -\dfrac{p_0}{36l}(l^3 - 9l^2 x + 27lx^2 - 9x^3),\ l/3 \le x \le l.$

4.3-4: The simply-supported beam of Exercise 2.7-16 is shown here again. It is subjected to the load $p(x) = p_0 \sin(\pi x/l)$ compared to which the weight

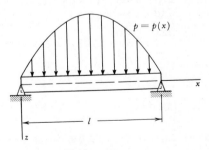

Exer. 4.3-4

of the beam may be neglected. Find the shear force and bending moment distributions and draw the corresponding diagrams.

Ans.: $V(x) = \dfrac{p_0 l}{\pi} \cos\left(\dfrac{\pi x}{l}\right)$; $M(x) = \dfrac{p_0 l^2}{\pi^2} \sin\left(\dfrac{\pi x}{l}\right)$.

4.3-5: (a) Suppose the beam of Exercise 4.3-4 under the same load is built-in at the left end and free at the right. Solve for the shear and bending moment distributions. (b) What changes occur if the free and fixed ends are interchanged?

Ans.: (a) $V(x) = \dfrac{p_0 l}{\pi} \left[\cos\left(\dfrac{\pi x}{l}\right) + 1\right]$; $M(x) = \dfrac{p_0 l^2}{\pi^2} \left[\sin\left(\dfrac{\pi x}{l}\right) - \pi\left(1 - \dfrac{x}{l}\right)\right]$.

(b) $V(x) = \dfrac{p_0 l}{\pi} \left[\cos\left(\dfrac{\pi x}{l}\right) - 1\right]$; $M(x) = \dfrac{p_0 l^2}{\pi^2} \left[\sin\left(\dfrac{\pi x}{l}\right) - \dfrac{\pi x}{l}\right]$.

4.3-6: A cantilevered beam of length l is loaded as shown with loads of magnitude p_0 lb/ft. Find the shear force and bending moment distributions.

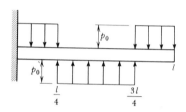

Exer. 4.3-6

Ans.: $M(x) = -\dfrac{p_0 x^2}{2}$, $0 \leq x \leq l/4$;

$M(x) = \dfrac{p_0}{16} (8x^2 - 8lx + l^2)$, $l/4 \leq x \leq 3l/4$;

$M(x) = -\dfrac{p_0}{2} (l-x)^2$, $3l/4 \leq x \leq l$.

4.3-7: Solve Exercise 4.3-1 if the two supports are not at the ends of the beam but are moved in to the points $x = l/3$, $x = 2l/3$.

Ans.: $M(x) = -\dfrac{p_0 l^2}{2} \left(\dfrac{x}{l}\right)^3$, $0 \leq x \leq l/3$;

$M(x) = -\dfrac{p_0 l^2}{36} \left[9\left(1 - \dfrac{x}{l}\right)^3 - 6\left(1 - \dfrac{x}{l}\right) + 2\right]$, $l/3 \leq x \leq 2l/3$;

$M(x) = -\dfrac{p_0 l^2}{4} \left(1 - \dfrac{x}{l}\right)^3$, $2l/3 \leq x \leq l$.

4.3-8: Solve Exercise 4.3-4 if the right-hand roller support is moved in to the center of the beam.

Ans.: $M(x) = \dfrac{p_0 l^2}{\pi^2} \left[\sin\left(\dfrac{\pi x}{l}\right) - \dfrac{\pi x}{l} \right], \ 0 \leqq x \leqq l/2;$

$$M(x) = \dfrac{p_0 l^2}{\pi^2} \left[\sin\left(\dfrac{\pi x}{l}\right) - \pi\left(1 - \dfrac{x}{l}\right) \right], \ l/2 \leqq x \leqq l.$$

4.3-9: An *L*-section is clamped at one end and loaded at the other as shown. By replacing the given load by an equipollent force set at the point *Q*, compute the axial force, shear force, and bending moment in the beam-column *OQ*.

Ans.: $N(x) = -P, \ V(x) = 0, \ M(x) = aP.$

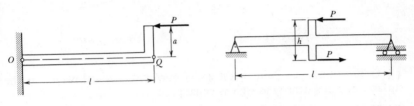

Exer. 4.3-9   **Exer. 4.3-10**

4.3-10: A simply-supported beam is loaded at its midsection effectively by a concentrated couple as shown. Find the shear and bending moment distributions. Solve the problem again with the beam cantilevered at the left.

Ans.: $V(x) = \dfrac{Ph}{l}; \ M(x) = \dfrac{Phx}{l}, \ 0 \leqq x < \dfrac{l}{2}; \ M(x) = \dfrac{Ph}{l}(x-l), \dfrac{l}{2} < x \leqq l.$

4.3-11: A uniform pole of length *l* ft and weight *W* lb is stuck in the ground at an angle θ to the vertical. Find the axial force, shear force, and bending moment distributions along the pole due to the distributed weight force.

Ans.: $N(x) = -W \cos\theta\left(1 - \dfrac{x}{l}\right); \ V(x) = W \sin\theta\left(1 - \dfrac{x}{l}\right);$

$$M(x) = -\dfrac{Wl \sin\theta}{2}\left(1 - \dfrac{x}{l}\right)^2.$$

4.3-12: If a circular cantilevered beam like that of Example 4.3-5 subtends an angle ϕ ($0 \leqq \theta \leqq \phi$) at the center, instead of 90°, what are the internal force set at any section and the reactions at the built-in end due to a downward load *P* at the free end? What happens as $\phi \to 360°$, i.e., as the beam approaches a split circular ring with one end clamped and the other free (except for the applied load *P*)?

Ans.: Forces and moments at any section θ from the loaded end are the same as in Example 4.3-5.

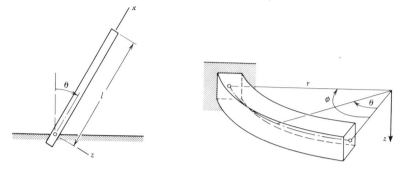

Exer. 4.3-11   **Exer. 4.3-12**

4.4-1: Show that, in a fluid at rest under gravity, horizontal planes are the surfaces of equal density as well as equal pressure.

4.4-2: Suppose that two fluids of different densities are poured in a container and come to rest under gravity. Suppose, further, that they do not mix. Using the result of the previous exercise, show that the surface separating the two fluids is a horizontal plane.

4.4-3: A plane area is immersed in an incompressible fluid at rest under gravity. Without changing the orientation of the area relative to fixed axes, it is lowered to greater and greater depths. Show that the center of pressure moves closer to the centroid of area as the depth is increased.

4.4-4: (a) An equilateral triangle of side s is submerged vertically in a fluid of constant density, with one vertex at depth h below the effective surface and the opposite (and lower) side horizontal. Find the distance from the effective surface to the center of pressure. (b) Reverse the triangle, putting the horizontal side at depth h and the vertex below it. Find the depth of the center of pressure. (c) Let h become large in each case and check the theorem of the last exercise.

Ans.: (a) $h+s\left(\dfrac{8\sqrt{3}h+9s}{24h+8\sqrt{3}s}\right)$; (b) $h+s\left(\dfrac{4\sqrt{3}h+3s}{24h+4\sqrt{3}s}\right)$.

4.4-5: A dam of concrete is built in the shape of an isosceles trapezoid, with the larger base up as shown. The wall is vertical, with the bases horizontal. Find the pressure distribution on the wall resulting only from water weighing 62.4 lb/ft³ completely filling the space behind the dam to the full height of 80 ft. Where is the center of pressure?

Ans.: $p = 62.4z$ lb/ft²; $\hat{z} = 50$ ft.

4.4-6: If the dam of the previous exercise makes an angle of $5°$ with the vertical, sloping out as shown, what is the pressure distribution? Where is the center of pressure?

Ans.: $p = 62.4z$ lb/ft^2; $\hat{x} = 50 \sin 5°$ ft; $\hat{z} = 50 \cos 5°$ ft.

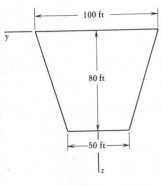

Exer. 4·4-5

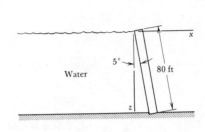

Exer. 4·4-6

4·4-7: Suppose we must take into account the variation of gravity with altitude in establishing the pressure distribution in an isothermal atmosphere. Let p_0 and ρ_0 be the values of pressure and density at the earth's surface, z be the altitude measured outward from the earth's surface, R_E the radius of the earth, and g the gravitational acceleration at the surface. The gravitational force per unit mass then has magnitude $gR_E^2/(R_E+z)^2$; the equation of state is $p/p_0 = \rho/\rho_0$. Find $p(z)$.

Ans.: $p(z) = p_0 e^{-\left(\frac{\rho_0 g R_E}{p_0}\right)\left(\frac{z}{R_E+z}\right)}.$

4·4-8: A process in which no heat exchange occurs is termed *adiabatic*, with equation of state $p/p_0 = (\rho/\rho_0)^\gamma$, where γ is the ratio of the specific heat at constant pressure to that at constant volume. Find the pressure and temperature distributions (under constant gravity) in an atmosphere subject to the adiabatic equation of state—an atmosphere in *convective equilibrium*.

Ans.: $\dfrac{p}{p_0} = \left[1 - \dfrac{(\gamma-1)\rho_0 g}{\gamma p_0} z\right]^{\frac{\gamma}{\gamma-1}}; \quad \dfrac{T}{T_0} = 1 - \dfrac{(\gamma-1)\rho_0 g}{\gamma p_0} z,$

where $p_0 = R\rho_0 T_0$ at $z = 0$.

CHAPTER V

Frictional Effects

in Statics

5.1 Sources of Friction in Technology

It will have been apparent to the reader that the mechanical analysis of structures and machine elements carried out in previous chapters has been greatly simplified by the assumption that the surfaces in contact were smooth. While the hypothesis of smoothness is closely approximated in a large number of engineering situations, and analyses are, in fact, often carried out on this basis, there are also many cases in which the presence of friction plays an essential role. Since frictional effects are always present to some extent whenever there is a tendency for one surface to move relative to another with which it is in contact, mechanical systems in which the presence of friction is taken into account are sometimes called "real" systems; those in which friction is neglected are termed "ideal" systems. The presence of friction in a machine entails an inevitable conversion of mechanical energy into heat. Although this energy "loss" can be considerable—amounting in the case of an automobile, for example, to about twenty per cent of the energy that would be available were there no friction in the moving parts—it is not the principal engineering objection to friction. The wear, rough operation, and premature failure of elements is ordinarily far more important. On the other hand, it must be recognized that were it not for the friction between tire and road the automobile would be unable to function at all, and that most holding and fastening devices rely on friction for their effectiveness.

Much progress has been made in recent years toward an understanding of frictional phenomena. In the first place it is necessary to distinguish between the friction of dry rubbing solids, rolling friction, and the friction of fully lubricated bearings. It is the first of these with which we shall be concerned. If a block of material in the form of a rectangular parallelepiped is placed on a horizontal surface, a horizontal force is needed to make the block move along the

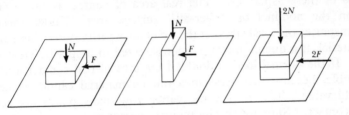

In each case the weight of a single block is N. The horizontal force shown is the minimum horizontal force which will produce sliding.

Fig. 5.1-1

surface. The magnitude of this force is independent of the surface area of apparent contact; if we turn the block on end the force required to initiate motion is not affected. Furthermore, the magnitude of the force is proportional to the weight of the block; when a second identical block is placed on top of the first, the horizontal force required to initiate motion is doubled. These facts, illustrated schematically in Fig. 5.1-1, appear to have been known to Leonardo da Vinci. They lay buried in his notebooks for many years. In 1699 they were independently rediscovered by the French engineer Amontons, who verified them experimentally. Coulomb in 1781 again independently discovered the law of rubbing friction. He further distinguished between the force necessary to initiate motion and the force needed to maintain motion, once begun. The latter, he found, was lower than the former and was, over a large speed range, independent of the relative velocities of the two surfaces. In statics we are interested primarily in the situation that exists before motion actually occurs and shall not be much concerned with this kinetic friction.

The ratio between the force component parallel to the contact surface (F in Fig. 5.1-1) and the component normal to the contact surface (N in Fig. 5.1-1) *when motion impends* is known as the coefficient of limiting friction, f, or simply as the *coefficient of friction*. According to the Amontons-Coulomb friction law, f is supposed to depend only on the smoothness and material of which the surfaces are made and not at all on the nominal area of the surfaces or on the normal force pressing them together. This friction law can be explained if we realize that at a microscopic level no surface is truly smooth and that contact between two bodies actually takes place at the tips of minute "high spots" or asperities. The normal load is carried on the tips of these asperities. The real area of contact is much smaller than the nominal or "over-all" surface area. Under these circumstances the local stress at the tip of an asperity is very high and the material, if a ductile metal, is soon stressed to its plastic yield stress, p. If the normal load is doubled the area of real contact must also double, because the stress in a ductile material cannot exceed the yield value. This is true no matter how many points are actually in contact. Suppose the individual contact areas are $a_1, a_2, \ldots a_n$; the load carried by each will be $N_1 = pa_1$, $N_2 = pa_2, \ldots N_n = pa_n$ and therefore

$$N = N_1 + N_2 + \ldots N_n = p(a_1 + a_2 + \ldots a_n) = pA. \qquad \textbf{5.1-1}$$

The area of real contact, A, is therefore proportional to the load, N, normal to the surface, and is independent of the shape, size, or nominal surface area of the bodies. Furthermore, on account of the high local pressures at the points of real contact, the bodies adhere at these locations; in metals an actual cold welding takes place. This adhesion is not ordinarily apparent upon removal of the normal load, N, because the release of the spring-like elastic stresses underlying the small plastic zone breaks the bond. But if, instead of removing the normal load, a tangential force, F, is applied so as to make the surfaces move relative to one another, the bonds will be sheared and we may write $F = As$, where s denotes the mean shear strength of the sheared material. Then

$$f = \frac{F}{N} = \frac{As}{Ap} = \frac{s}{p} \qquad \textbf{5.1-2}$$

and the coefficient of limiting friction is seen to be essentially a material property, independent of the normal load and the nominal surface area, as required by the Amontons-Coulomb friction law. Formulas such as 5.1-2, however, cannot be used to predict the magnitude of the coefficient of friction. They represent an oversimplification of the actual situation. The theory of plasticity shows that normal and tangential stresses cannot be treated as independent and that plastic flow is due to a combination of the two.

The foregoing explanation of the nature of the friction of rubbing solids is a restatement of the one advanced by Bowden and Tabor,[*] to whose work the student should refer for details of the supporting evidence. They give the representative values shown in Table 5.1 for the coefficient of limiting friction, determined by careful experiment on small specimens.

It may be seen from this table that the "constant", f, is one to which it is difficult for the designer to assign a precise value in advance of actual test. In cases of doubt, resort should be made to test results that duplicate the situation in question. Certain generalizations may, however, be made concerning the range of validity of the Amontons-Coulomb friction law. In the case of metals the presence of an oxide film is of prime importance. The extremely high values of f quoted for pure metals thoroughly denuded of surface films refer to the results of laboratory experiments performed in vacuum, where no oxide film can form. As has been noted, even a small tangential force produces a growth in junction area due to plastic yielding. For ordinary metals in air this surface oxide film shears easily, little junction growth takes place, and the elementary theory is satisfactory. But for laboratory-clean metals in vacuum, junction growth dominates; the real contact area bears no direct relation to the normal load and extremely high coefficients of friction are observed. On the other hand, in the case of materials that have a relatively large range of elastic behavior, such as diamond or rubber, the deformation is primarily elastic and the coefficient of friction decreases as the load is increased. This trend is also observed in plastics that deform viscoelastically.

Although we shall not be further concerned with them in the material of this text, it should be said that rolling friction and fully lubricated bearing friction differ fundamentally from the friction of

---

[*] F. P. Bowden and D. Tabor, *The Friction and Lubrication of Solids* (Oxford: The Clarendon Press, 1954). The student will find an excellent introduction to these ideas in the monograph *Friction and Lubrication* (London: Methuen; New York: Wiley, 1956) by the same authors.

Table 5-1: VALUES OF THE COEFFICIENT OF LIMITING STATIC FRICTION

Metals, pure, rubbing on themselves:

Thoroughly denuded of surface films	> 100
In air, unlubricated	1
Lubricated, mineral oil	0.2–0.4
Lubricated, animal, vegetable oil	0.1

Alloys rubbing on steel:

Copper-lead, unlubricated	0.2
Copper-lead, lubricated, mineral oil	0.1
White metal, Wood's alloy, unlubricated	0.7
White metal, Wood's alloy, lubricated, mineral oil	0.1
Phosphor bronze, brass, unlubricated	0.35
Phosphor bronze, brass, lub., mineral oil	0.15–0.2
Cast iron, unlubricated	0.4
Cast iron, lubricated, mineral oil	0.1–0.2

Hard steel surfaces with various lubricants:

Unlubricated	0.6
Mineral oils	0.14–0.2
Molybdenum disulphide	0.1

Non-metals:

Glass on glass, clean	1.0
Ice on self, below $-50°C$	0.5
Ice on self, between $0°$ and $-20°C$	0.05–0.1
Diamond on self, in air, clean	0.1
Rock salt on self, clean	0.8
Tungsten carbide on steel, clean	0.4–0.6
Nylon on self	0.5
Polytetrafluoroethylene (Teflon) on self	0.04–0.1
Polytetrafluoroethylene (Teflon) on steel	0.04–0.1
Brake material on cast iron, clean	0.4
Brake material on cast iron, wet	0.2
Brake material on cast iron, greasy	0.1
Leather on metal, clean, dry	0.6
Wood on self, clean, dry	0.25–0.5
Wood on metals, clean, dry	0.2–0.6

rubbing solids. In the case of the wheel of a heavy vehicle, large
tangential forces are indeed involved, but when a ball or disk rolls
freely on a horizontal surface the resistance to rolling corresponds
to a value of f of the order of 10^{-3}. To understand why there should,
in fact, be any resistance at all to rolling, we need to realize that all
materials are deformable to some extent. The rolling ball is in
contact with the bearing plate over a finite region called the contact
area, as pictured schematically in Fig. 5.1-2. Over the trailing part

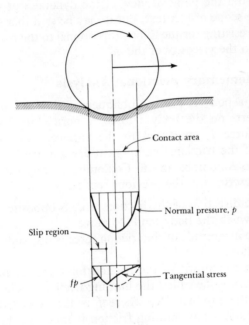

Fig. 5.1-2

of this region there is a local slip; the particle velocities of ball and
track differ and rubbing friction takes place. The slip region and the
relative motions are, however, small compared with what they would
be were the sphere in translational rather than in rolling motion.
There is a further source of energy loss arising from what is known as
"internal friction" or *"hysteresis,"* a name given to imperfect elasticity
in the material of ball and track. Which of the two influences, surface
or internal friction, is the more important would appear to depend
upon particular circumstances. The internal effect might be expected to dominate in the case of a rubber wheel on a flat track,
whereas surface effects would be more important in the case of a steel

ball rolling in a deep groove. In fully lubricated bearings, on the other hand, the surfaces in relative motion are separated by a continuous film of fluid and the resistance to motion arises from the viscosity of the fluid. A load-carrying shaft in a circular bearing will take up an eccentric position in the bearing. When the oil, dragged by the rotating shaft, is squeezed through the narrowest part of the gap between shaft and bearing, pressure builds up in the fluid. This pressure keeps the surfaces separated. A full examination of the situation from the point of view of the dynamics of viscous fluids is outside the scope of this text, but it may be said that such an analysis shows the resisting torque to be proportional to the rotation rate of the shaft and to the viscosity of the oil.

5.2 Elementary Frictional Analysis

When a body is pressed obliquely against a rough surface, the surface exerts on the body a force N normal to the surface and a frictional force F tangential to the surface. The magnitude and direction of the frictional component are governed by the following rules due to Amontons and to Coulomb, the physical basis of which has been described in the previous section.

1. The direction of the friction force is opposite to the direction in which the body tends to move.
2. The magnitude of the friction force is just sufficient to prevent motion.
3. The magnitude of the friction force cannot be larger than a certain value called the limiting friction. This value is given by the product fN, where f is the so-called coefficient of friction. The limiting friction is independent of the area of the body in contact with the rough surface.

These rules are supplemented by the statement that, when there is relative motion between the surfaces, the magnitude of the friction force is independent of the velocity, its direction opposes the relative motion, and its magnitude is $f'N$, where f', the so-called coefficient of kinetic friction, is, in general, less than f. As has been mentioned, we shall be concerned with the static situation and shall not make use of this supplement.

It is important to appreciate that the frictional force actually exerted is that required to satisfy the newtonian equations of equilibrium. Only when motion impends is the frictional force equal in magnitude to the product of the coefficient of friction and the normal component of force. Friction is one of that class of forces known as *resistances*; it operates to oppose motion, never to produce it. These points may be clarified by means of a very simple example. Consider a block resting on a plane inclined to the horizontal, as shown in Fig. 5.2-1. To fix ideas we may suppose that the block has a mass *m* (and therefore weight *mg*), that the plane is inclined at an angle θ to the horizontal, and that the coefficient of friction is *f*; we ask to know the magnitude of the friction force and whether or not the block will move. The analysis begins by supposing that the block does *not* move, but rests in equilibrium. Its free-body diagram is then as pictured in Fig. 5.2-1. Of course the forces *F* and *N* represent components of the resultant of distributed pressures and shears all along the base of the block (see Section 2.7). The exact distribution of these tractions cannot be found from rigid-body statics so that the

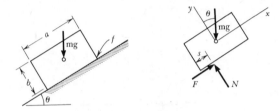

Fig. 5.2-1

point of application of the resultant pressure along the base must, temporarily, be regarded as unknown. This makes it impossible to begin by writing the moment equation of equilibrium. The other two equilibrium equations, however, take the form

$$\sum F_x = F - mg \sin \theta = 0, \qquad \sum F_y = N - mg \cos \theta = 0. \qquad \textbf{5.2-1}$$

We may at once conclude that $N = mg \cos \theta$ and that $F = mg \sin \theta$. This answers the question asked, on the supposition that the block does not move. No use has yet been made of the coefficient of friction. To see whether the block does or does not actually slide, we note that to maintain equilibrium we must have $F/N = \tan \theta$. Clearly, if *f* is greater than $\tan \theta$, we will be able to muster a friction force equal to $N \tan \theta$, but if *f* is less than $\tan \theta$ the block will slide downhill. In principle, *f* can be determined by increasing the angle θ until it reaches a critical value θ^* at which the block begins to slide. Then $f = \tan \theta^*$. The angle θ^* is known as the *angle of friction*.

    Knowing the normal and frictional components of the reaction of the plane on the block, it is simple to find the line of action of this resultant force. Of course the dimensions of the block (or at least the location of the mass center relative to the base) need to be known. Suppose that the block is homogeneous, that its breadth and depth are a and b, and that the reaction of the plane on the block intersects the base at a distance s from the lower end, as shown in Fig. 5.2-1. Then, taking moments about an axis through the mass center, we have

$$N\left(s - \frac{1}{2}a\right) + F\left(\frac{1}{2}b\right) = 0, \quad \text{or} \quad s = \frac{1}{2}(a - b\tan\theta). \qquad \textbf{5.2-2}$$

In the last step, use has been made of Eqs. 5.2-1 for F and N. Equation 5.2-2 locates the resultant pressure on the base. If θ is a small angle, this point on the line of action lies between the center of the base and the toe. But if θ is large enough the value of s given by Eq. 5.2-2 will be negative. This would imply that the reaction must

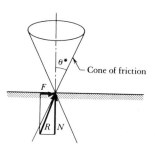

Fig. 5.2-2

fall outside the base in order to preserve rotational equilibrium. Since this is not possible, we conclude that tipping will occur if $\tan\theta$ exceeds a/b. If we think of θ as being increased gradually from zero, sliding will occur when $\theta = \arctan f$, tipping when $\theta = \arctan(a/b)$. If f is smaller than a/b sliding will occur first, otherwise tipping will occur first.

The idea of the angle of friction, θ^*, provides a geometric interpretation of the range of the frictional reaction which is often helpful. If we refer to Fig. 5.2-2 it may be seen that $F < N\tan\theta^*$ provided that the total reaction, R, of which F and N are components, falls within a cone of semivertical angle θ^*. If R were to fall outside this cone, F would have to exceed fN and sliding must ensue. This cone is sometimes termed the *cone of friction*.

A feature of interest in connection with the presence of friction is the possibility it offers the designer of producing what is known as *friction lock.* This condition arises when increase in load is automatically accompanied by increase in frictional capacity, so that a state of impending motion cannot be produced. Again, a simple example in the form of the block on an inclined plane may serve to illustrate the point. What horizontal force, for instance, will cause the block of Fig. 5.2-3a to slide up the plane? If we suppose that such a force exists, then, when it is applied and motion up the plane impends, the free-body diagram of the block is as shown in Fig. 5.2-3b. Since

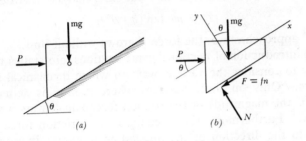

Fig. 5.2-3

motion of the block is supposed to impend, the frictional force on the block must, in view of rules 1 and 3, be directed down the plane and must be equal in magnitude to fN. When compared with Fig. 5.2-1, this free-body diagram has the same number of unknown elements, F being replaced by P as an unknown. Now the equations of translational equilibrium are

$$\sum F_x = P \cos \theta - mg \sin \theta - fN = 0,$$

and

$$\sum F_y = -P \sin \theta - mg \cos \theta + N = 0. \qquad \textbf{5.2-3}$$

On eliminating N and solving for P, we have

$$P = mg \, \frac{\tan \theta + f}{1 - f \tan \theta}. \qquad \textbf{5.2-4}$$

It follows from this result that as f or θ increases until $f \tan \theta = 1$, the force P required to produce impending motion uphill will increase without bound. For values of $f \tan \theta \geq 1$, no horizontal force to the right, however great, will push the block uphill; the situation of impending uphill motion originally hypothesized cannot, in fact, be created. What is happening is that the horizontal force P has two components, one normal to the friction surface and one tangential to it. When P is increased, both these components increase. If the normal component, multiplied by f, grows as rapidly as the tangential component, increasing P will not produce motion. Friction locking may be a desirable effect, as in the case of many gripping and lifting devices, or it may be quite undesirable, as in the case of a poorly designed drawer that will not open. It may be noted, finally, that expressions such as Eq. 5.2-4 may be put in a compact form through the introduction of the friction angle, $\theta^* = \arctan f$. Since $\tan (A + B) = (\tan A + \tan B)/(1 - \tan A \tan B)$, Eq. 5.2-4 may be rewritten as

$$P = mg \tan (\theta + \theta^*). \qquad 5.2\text{-}5$$

As $\theta + \theta^*$ approaches $\pi/2$, the force P grows without limit.

The introduction of frictional considerations into statics makes it necessary to consider the various ways in which mechanical systems can move. Only on those surfaces where motion is actually impending is the magnitude of the friction force equal to its maximum value, fN. Furthermore, the direction of the friction force is then opposite to the direction of the impending motion. In elementary mechanical analysis this direction is usually obvious, but there are cases where it is not. These cases are treated in Section 5.3. The student must beware of the false assumption that the friction force is equal in magnitude to fN. The friction law is essentially an inequality: $F \leqq fN$, and only when words such as "impending motion," "just moving," "just slips," or "just slides" are appropriate does the equality sign hold.

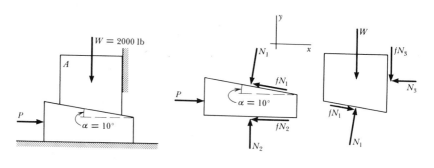

Fig. 5.2-4   **Fig. 5.2-5**

Example 5.2-1

A load of 2000 lb is to be raised by means of a wedge, as shown in Fig. 5.2-4. Ignoring the weight of the wedge, and assuming that on all contact *surfaces the coefficient of friction is $f = 0.2$, what is the minimum force, P, needed to lift the load? If P is removed will the weight remain in its raised position?*

Solution: We picture the situation when P is just large enough to cause motion of the wedge to the right to impend. But if motion of the wedge to the right impends, it follows logically that upward motion of the block A also impends. The free-body diagrams of wedge and block at this instant are shown in Fig. 5.2-5. The student should note the *directions* of the frictional forces. The frictional force exerted by the wedge on the heavy block, for example, is directed to the right because the block is about to move to the left with respect to the wedge. Notice that the forces N_1 and fN_1 which appear in both diagrams conform to Newton's third law. There are four unknowns, N_1, N_2, N_3, and P, so that the equations of equilibrium will enable us to find them all.

For the wedge,

$$\sum F_x = P - fN_1 \cos \alpha - N_1 \sin \alpha - fN_2 = 0,$$

$$\sum F_y = -N_1 \cos \alpha + fN_1 \sin \alpha + N_2 = 0.$$

For the block,

$$\sum F_x = N_1 \sin \alpha + fN_1 \cos \alpha - N_3 = 0,$$

$$\sum F_y = N_1 \cos \alpha - fN_1 \sin \alpha - fN_3 - W = 0.$$

To solve these equations, multiply the second by f and add it to the first to get

$$P = N_1[2f \cos \alpha + (1 - f^2) \sin \alpha].$$

Multiply the third equation by $-f$ and add it to the fourth to get

$$W = N_1[(1 - f^2) \cos \alpha - 2f \sin \alpha].$$

The ratio of these expressions gives

$$P = W \frac{2f \cos \alpha + (1 - f^2) \sin \alpha}{(1 - f^2) \cos \alpha - 2f \sin \alpha}.$$

This answers the first part of the question asked. The student may check that this expression can be put in the form

$$P = W \tan (2\theta^* + \alpha).$$

With $W = 2000$ lb, $f = 0.2$, and $\alpha = 10°$, these expressions indicate that the required value of P is

$$P = 2000 \frac{(0.4)(0.985) + (0.96)(0.174)}{(0.96)(0.985) - (0.4)(0.174)} = 1280 \text{ lb.}$$

Although it is counsel of perfection, we should now check to see that the corresponding values of N_1, N_2, and N_3 are positive, since, presumably, the surfaces in contact must be in compression, as drawn in the free-body diagram. In the present case we find

$$N_1 = W/[(1-f^2)\cos\alpha - 2f\sin\alpha] = 2280 \text{ lb,}$$
$$N_2 = N_1(\cos\alpha - f\sin\alpha) = 2170 \text{ lb,}$$
$$N_3 = N_1(\sin\alpha + f\cos\alpha) = 850 \text{ lb.}$$

What will happen if the force P is now removed? Two possibilities present themselves: either the system moves or it does not. If motion ensues, the question ceases to be one in statics; on the other hand, if the system remains in equilibrium there is no reason for assuming that motion will impend. The frictional forces fN_1, fN_2, and fN_3 become simply unknowns F_1, F_2, and F_3. But this means that even with $P=0$ there will

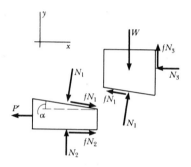

Fig. 5.2-6

be six unknowns in the free-body diagrams and only four equations of equilibrium. The system is statically indeterminate. To avoid this dilemma we suppose that a force, P', to the left, is required in an amount just sufficient to produce motion of the block A down the wedge. Then the free-body diagram is as shown in Fig. 5.2-6. If, on analysis, P' turns out to be positive, we can conclude that in the absence of the force P', motion to the left will not occur. The free-body diagrams now are as shown in Fig. 5.2-6. The equations of equilibrium are

$$-P' + fN_1\cos\alpha - N_1\sin\alpha + fN_2 = 0$$
$$-N_1\cos\alpha - fN_1\sin\alpha + N_2 = 0$$
$$N_1\sin\alpha - fN_1\cos\alpha - N_3 = 0$$
$$N_1\cos\alpha + fN_1\sin\alpha + fN_3 - W = 0.$$

We solve for P', exactly as before, to find

$$P' = W\frac{2f\cos\alpha - (1-f^2)\sin\alpha}{2f\sin\alpha + (1-f^2)\cos\alpha} = W\tan(2\theta^* - \alpha) = 450 \text{ lb.}$$

Our conclusion, therefore, is that, in order to make the wedge slide to the left, a leftward force of 450 lb must be applied to the wedge; in the absence of such a force the wedge and block will remain stationary.

Another way of regarding the situation would be to say that, as regards vertical load alone, the arrangement of wedge and block is self-locking. This is manifestly desirable from a practical engineering point of view; one would not want the raised weight to be continually slipping back. So that this self-locking effect will be achieved, the numerator of the expression for P' must be positive. That is, we must have

$$\frac{f}{1-f^2} > \frac{1}{2}\tan\alpha, \quad \text{or} \quad \theta^* > \frac{1}{2}\alpha.$$

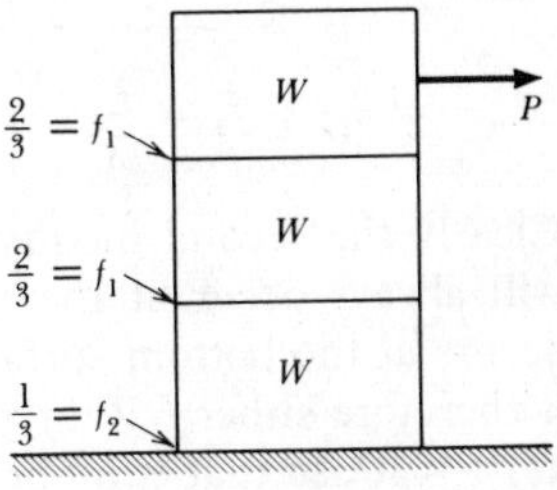

Fig. 5.2-7

Example 5.2-2

Three boxes, each of weight W, are stacked on the floor, as shown in Fig. 5.2-7. The coefficient of friction between boxes is $f_1 = \frac{2}{3}$ and between box and floor is $f_2 = \frac{1}{3}$. A horizontal force P is applied to the top box and gradually increased. What is the maximum P? How will equilibrium be broken?

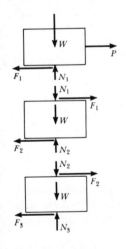

Fig. 5.2-8

Solution: The directions of the friction forces at each contact are known from equilibrium considerations; the only real problem is to find where slip will start. In Fig. 5.2-8 the free-body diagrams of the three boxes are given. Notice that the direction of the friction force acting on the uppermost block must be to the left; hence, from the third law, the friction force exerted by the uppermost block on the middle one must act to the right. It follows that the friction force exerted on the middle block by the lowest block must act to the left so that the equilibrium of the middle block will be maintained, and so on. Since the friction forces on the middle and bottom boxes must be opposite in direction, neither the middle nor the bottom box can possibly slip out by itself from the other two. Equilibrium can only be broken if the top box slides off the others or the whole group slides on the floor. The equilibrium equations are

$$
\begin{aligned}
F_1 &= P, & N_1 &= W, \\
F_2 &= F_1, & N_2 &= N_1 + W, \\
F_3 &= F_2, & N_3 &= N_2 + W,
\end{aligned}
$$

whence

$$F_1 = F_2 = F_3 = P \quad \text{and} \quad N_1 = W, \quad N_2 = 2W, \quad N_3 = 3W.$$

The system will be in equilibrium for P small enough; the limiting inequalities are

$$\frac{F_1}{N_1} = \frac{P}{W} \leq f_1 = \frac{2}{3}, \quad \frac{F_2}{N_2} = \frac{P}{2W} \leq f_1 = \frac{2}{3}, \quad \frac{F_3}{N_3} = \frac{P}{3W} \leq f_2 = \frac{1}{3}.$$

Clearly the second inequality will always be satisfied if the first is. Slip will always occur at the bottom surface of the uppermost box before it occurs at the bottom surface of the middle box. The limiting value of P is therefore either $f_1 W$ or $3f_2 W$. In the present case, $f_1 W = (\frac{2}{3})W$, whereas $3f_2 W = W$, so that equilibrium will be broken when the top box slides over the other two as soon as $P = (\frac{2}{3})W$.

The student may wish to work this example for the case in which the force P is applied to the middle box.

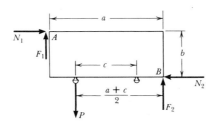

Fig. 5.2-9

Example 5.2-3

A drawer of width a and depth b has two symmetrically placed handles distant c apart. If the coefficient of friction of the drawer against the sides of the case is f, what should the dimensions be so that the drawer will not jam when it is pulled out by one handle?

Solution: Suppose that the drawer is pulled out by a force P exerted on the left-hand handle, as shown in Fig. 5.2-9. It will come in contact with the case at points A and B. We see that $N_1 = N_2$. Taking moments about B, we have

$$-aF_1 - bN_1 + \frac{1}{2}P(a+c) = 0,$$

and if there is to be motion in the direction of P we must have

$$P \geq F_1 + F_2.$$

Now the maximum value of F_1 is fN_1 and the maximum value of F_2 is fN_2. To assure outward motion of the drawer we must have

$$P \geq f(N_1 + N_2)$$

or, in view of the equality of N_1 and N_2,

$$P \geq 2fN_1.$$

But with $F_1 = fN_1$ the moment equation yields

$$N_1 = P\frac{a+c}{2(fa+b)}.$$

We must therefore have

$$P \geq 2fP\frac{a+c}{2(fa+b)}.$$

This inequality will be satisfied, for any P, provided

$$fa + b \geq f(a+c)$$

or

$$b \geq fc.$$

Example 5.2-4

A cylinder of radius a and weight W is wedged between a vertical wall and a light hinged bar, as shown in Fig. 5.2-10. The coefficient of friction between cylinder and wall is 0.2, and between bar and cylinder is 0.4. What

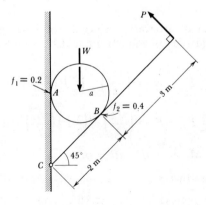

Fig. 5.2-10

is the force, P, which, when applied at the end of the bar and at right angles to the bar, is just sufficient to cause the cylinder to slip upward? The dimensions of the bar are given in the figure.

Solution: The essential point of this example is that if motion impends at the point of contact with the wall, A, it does not necessarily impend at the point of contact with the bar, B, and vice versa. This example therefore differs fundamentally from Example 5.2-1 in which, from the geometry of the question, motion had to impend simultaneously at all surfaces. Another way of putting this is to say that, in the present case, motion can begin with slipping at either A or B and rolling (without slip) at the other contact. We must therefore begin by making an assumption about the nature of the impending motion. Analysis will show whether or not this assumption is correct. Suppose, then, that when motion impends, slipping occurs at B and not at A. An elementary analysis of the equilibrium of the bar, taking moments about C, shows that the normal force exerted by the bar on the cylinder must be $(\frac{5}{2})P$. The free-body diagram of the cylinder is shown in Fig. 5.2-11. Note that the direction and magnitude of the

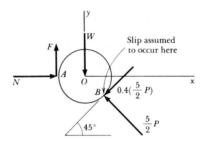

Fig. 5.2-11

friction force at A are arbitrary. Since no slip is assumed to impend at A, we rely on the equations of equilibrium to determine F completely. These equations are:

$$\sum F_x = N - P\left(\frac{\sqrt{2}}{2}\right) - \left(\frac{5}{2}P\right)\left(\frac{\sqrt{2}}{2}\right) = 0,$$

$$\sum F_y = F - P\left(\frac{\sqrt{2}}{2}\right) + \left(\frac{5}{2}P\right)\left(\frac{\sqrt{2}}{2}\right) - W = 0,$$

$$\sum M_O = -aF - aP = 0.$$

We see from these that

$$F = -16.5W, \quad N = 40.8W, \quad \text{and} \quad P = 16.5W.$$

How shall we interpret these results? The negative sign on F means simply that the actual direction of the friction force acting on the cylinder at A is downward, not upward. There is no inconsistency in this, and an experienced hand would have foreseen from the outset that F must in fact be downward. But is our assumption that there is no slip at A a valid one? We find $|F|/N = 16.5/40.8 = 0.40$, whereas the maximum F that can be mustered is $0.2N$ since the coefficient of friction at A is 0.2. We conclude that slip will occur at A before it occurs at B.

It is now necessary to repeat the analysis using this alternative assumption. The free-body diagram is as shown in Fig. 5.2-12. Note that the

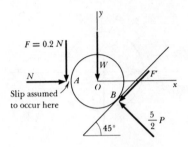

Fig. 5.2-12

friction force at B is now completely unknown and that the friction force at A must be drawn downward since upward slip of the disk impends at A. The equations of equilibrium now read:

$$\sum F_x = N - \left(\frac{5}{2}P\right)\left(\frac{\sqrt{2}}{2}\right) - F'\left(\frac{\sqrt{2}}{2}\right) = 0,$$

$$\sum F_y = -0.2N - W - F'\left(\frac{\sqrt{2}}{2}\right) + \left(\frac{5}{2}P\right)\left(\frac{\sqrt{2}}{2}\right) = 0,$$

$$\sum M_O = 0.2Na - F'a = 0$$

whence we conclude that

$$F' = 0.39W, \quad N = 1.94W, \quad \text{and} \quad P = 0.94W.$$

This answers the question raised; a force $P = 0.94W$ will cause the cylinder to slip upwards. We see that the ratio of frictional to normal force at point B, where motion was assumed not to impend, is

$$\frac{F'}{\left(\frac{5}{2}P\right)} = \frac{0.39}{(2.5)(0.94)} = 0.17,$$

and this is certainly less than the limiting value of 0.4; thus we have checked our assumption that motion would not impend at B.

There is an alternative way of looking at questions of this sort that is often instructive. Suppose we draw the limiting cones of friction at A and B, as shown in Fig. 5.2-13. These have semivertical angles of $11°$ and $22°$, respectively. The reactions at A and B must lie within these cones. But the cylinder is acted on by three forces, W and the forces at A and B. These must intersect at some point if there is to be equilibrium, and that point must lie on the line of action of W, i.e., on the vertical through the center of the cylinder. If slipping impends at B,

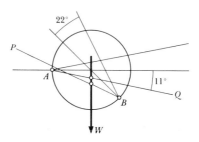

Fig. 5.2-13

the reaction at B will lie along the edge of the cone BP. But this intersects the line of action of W at a point outside the friction cone at A. Hence it is not possible to have motion impend at B. On the other hand, if upward motion impends at A, the reaction at A will lie along the line AQ. This line intersects the vertical through the mass center at a point within the friction cone at B, so that motion can impend at A without violating the friction laws at A. The intersection of AQ and the vertical also locates the line of action of the force at B and makes it simple to complete the analysis graphically.

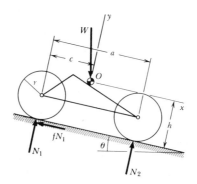

Fig. 5.2-14

Example 5.2-5

What is the steepest slope on which a bicycle can rest without slipping? Assume that only the uphill wheel is braked, that $f = 0.25$, that the axles of the bicycle are 48 in. apart, and that its mass center is 20 in. from the uphill wheel and 32 in. from the ground.

Solution: The free-body diagram of the bicycle, when slipping downhill impends, is shown in Fig. 5.2-14 together with a suggested nomenclature for the dimensions. Notice that there is no frictional force at the lower wheel because that wheel is neither powered nor braked in this example. The equations of equilibrium are

$$\sum F_x = W \sin \theta - f N_1 = 0,$$

$$\sum F_y = N_1 + N_2 - W \cos \theta = 0,$$

$$\sum M_O = N_2(a-c) - f N_1 h - N_1 c = 0.$$

We solve the first two of these equations for the unknowns N_1 and N_2, then substitute in the third equation to find the last unknown, θ.

$$N_1 = \left(\frac{W}{f}\right) \sin \theta, \qquad N_2 = W \cos \theta - \left(\frac{W}{f}\right) \sin \theta;$$

$$\left(\cos \theta - \frac{1}{f} \sin \theta\right)(a-c) - (fh+c)\left(\frac{1}{f} \sin \theta\right) = 0,$$

$$\tan \theta = \frac{f(a-c)}{a+fh}.$$

For $f = \frac{1}{4}$, $a = 48$ in., $c = 20$ in., $h = 32$ in., we obtain

$$\theta = \arctan\left(\frac{\frac{1}{4}(48-20)}{48+8}\right) = \arctan\left(\frac{1}{8}\right) = 7.125°.$$

The student may find it interesting to consider whether it would be a better design to have the brake on the other wheel.

Example 5.2-6

A simple friction grip has the general shape and dimensions shown in Fig. 5.2-15a. The designer wishes it to be used to pick up boxes of various sizes, with coefficients of friction that may be as low as 0.2. How should the dimensions a and c be chosen if the parcels are not to slip?

Solution: The free-body diagram of one of the two members that compose the grip is shown in Fig. 5.2-15b. The fact that the device is symmetrical and that the vertical and horizontal forces must add to zero implies that the vertical forces will each be $W/2$, half the weight of the box, and that the horizontal forces, N, will be equal. To find N, take moments about the origin of coordinates:

$$\sum M_O = Nc - \frac{1}{2} Wb - \frac{1}{2} Wa = 0,$$

$$N = \frac{1}{2} W\left(\frac{a+b}{c}\right).$$

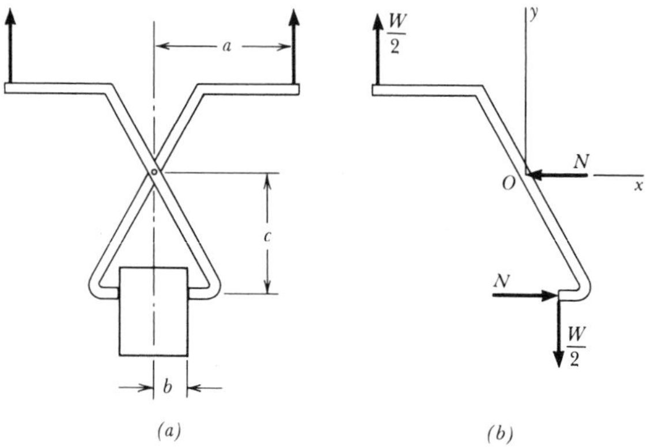

Fig. 5.2-15

It follows that the ratio of frictional to normal force at the contact between grip and box is $c/(a+b)$. If the coefficient of friction may be as low as 0.2 we must have $c/(a+b) < 0.2$ in order for the device to function with complete effectiveness. If the boxes are of various sizes, b may be small. For complete safety c should be kept to no more than one-fifth of a.

5.3 Further Aspects of Frictional Analysis

The logical structure of mechanics is so highly developed that additions to it, even when apparently well justified by experiment and physical theory, require careful consideration. In the case of the friction law, no conflict with the principles of mechanics arises provided the deformability of the parts in contact is taken into account where necessary.★ We can see that deformability will affect matters if we

---

★ If deformability is completely excluded, pathological situations can arise in dynamics when friction enters. [For further references see E. T. Whittaker, *Analytical Dynamics*, 4th ed. (Cambridge: Cambridge University Press, 1952), p. 227.] These are not of importance in engineering because no engineer would imagine his materials to be perfectly rigid.

consider the case of a body resting on a rough horizontal plane, on several supports. The loads, W_1, W_2, ... W_n, at each support may be regarded as known. Suppose a horizontal force, **P**, or a couple, is applied to the body at a point A. As this force is gradually increased in magnitude, the friction at the point of support nearest A—say, F_s—will gradually increase, so as to balance **P**. When the magnitude of the friction at this point has reached its limiting value, fW_s, the next point of support will begin to develop a frictional reaction, and so on. Another way of looking at the situation is to say that from the point of view of rigid-body mechanics there are $2n$ unknown frictional reaction components and only three equations of equilibrium in the plane. The situation that presents itself when the applied load **P** is less than that required to produce over-all motion is therefore statically indeterminate. All we can say about the frictional reactions under these circumstances, without a knowledge of the elastic properties of the body, is that they are less in magnitude than the limiting value and that there are many possible different arrangements that satisfy both the friction law and the equations of over-all statical equilibrium. The analysis of such situations— which arise, as has been mentioned, in connection with the contact stresses in ball and roller bearings—requires the resources of continuum mechanics, including the theories of elasticity and plasticity.

On the other hand, when the force **P** is great enough to make motion impend, a more complete analysis can be made within the framework of rigid-body mechanics. Unlike the frictional analysis of Section 5.2, however, the directions of the n frictional forces are now unknown. In order to reduce the number of unknowns to three, we note that the body described in the previous paragraph as resting on supports on a rough horizontal plane will, when it begins to move, turn about some axis perpendicular to the plane. This follows from the geometrical theorem that when a lamina is moved from one position to another in its own plane there is always one point, C, rigidly connected to the lamina, whose position in space is unchanged. The lamina can therefore be brought from its initial to its final position by a rotation about C through some appropriate angle. To prove this theorem we need only suppose that A, B are two points fixed on the lamina and that they move to A', B', as shown in Fig. 5.3-1. If A, B can be brought to A', B' by rotation about some point, the whole lamina will be in its proper final position. The perpendicular bisectors of AA' and BB' intersect at a point C. Since $AC = A'C$ and $BC = B'C$ (and, of course, $AB = A'B'$) it follows that the triangles ACB and $A'CB'$ are congruent. The angles subtended at C by AB and $A'B'$

are therefore equal. If we rotate AB about C through the angle ϕ shown, A will be carried to A' and B will also be carried to B'. It follows that there is always—and therefore initially—a unique point C about which the body may be considered to be rotating. In

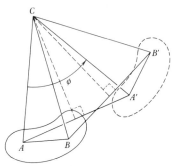

Fig. 5.3-1

dynamics the angle ϕ is taken vanishingly small and C is called the instantaneous center of zero velocity. Of course, if the lamina is in pure translation, C is infinitely distant. With the knowledge that there is a point, C, about which the body starts to rotate when motion impends, the analysis is reduced to finding the two coordinates of this point. These, together with the unknown limiting force magnitude, P, form the three unknowns of the analysis. Once C is found, the direction of the frictional force at any point of support must be at right angles to the line connecting that point to C and the magnitude of the frictional force at any point of support must be the normal load carried there multiplied by the coefficient of limiting friction. An exceptional case arises when C coincides with one of the points of support; this point cannot then be said to be on the verge of motion. In that special case the coordinates of C are replaced as unknowns by the components of the frictional reaction at C. These are subject to the limitation that their resultant is less than the limiting value.

Example 5.3-1

A small block of weight W rests on a rough plane which is inclined to the horizontal at an angle θ; a taut cord parallel to the plane passes over a pulley and supports the weight P, as shown in Fig. 5.3-2. The coefficient of limiting friction is f. Discuss equilibrium of the block. What weight P^* will cause it to slide?

Solution: In this case the body resting on the plane is a particle; it has, therefore, only one "point of contact" and the situation is statically determinate. Since the system is in equilibrium the cord tension will be

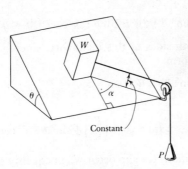

Fig. 5.3-2

P in magnitude.   A free-body diagram (Fig. 5.3-3) of the block shows P, the weight W, the normal force N, and a friction force having two components, F_x and F_y, tangent to the plane.   The equilibrium equations are

$$\sum R_x = P \cos \alpha + W \sin \theta - F_x = 0,$$
$$\sum R_y = P \sin \alpha - F_y = 0,$$
$$\sum R_z = N - W \cos \theta = 0.$$

We conclude that

$$N = W \cos \theta,$$
$$F_x = W \sin \theta + P \cos \alpha,$$
$$F_y = P \sin \alpha.$$

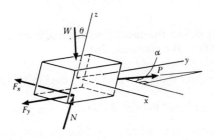

Fig. 5.3-3

Notice that the direction of the resultant friction force is neither along the cord nor straight down the plane.   The magnitude of the total friction force is

$$F = (F_x^2 + F_y^2)^{\frac{1}{2}} = (W^2 \sin^2 \theta + 2WP \sin \theta \cos \alpha + P^2)^{\frac{1}{2}}.$$

Since equilibrium is only possible when $F/N \leqq f$ it follows that, for equilibrium,

$$(W^2 \sin^2 \theta + 2WP \sin \theta \cos \alpha + P^2)^{\frac{1}{2}} \leqq fW \cos \theta.$$

We can square both sides of this inequality, since both sides are positive, and put it in the form

$$W^2 \sin^2 \theta + 2WP \sin \theta \cos \alpha + P^2 \leqq f^2 W^2 \cos^2 \theta,$$

or

$$\left(\frac{P}{W}\right)^2 + 2 \sin \theta \cos \alpha \left(\frac{P}{W}\right) + \sin^2 \theta - f^2 \cos^2 \theta \leqq 0.$$

The limiting conditions for slip occur when equality first becomes possible. Then $P = P^*$ and we have a quadratic equation for P^*/W. The roots of this equation are

$$\frac{P^*}{W} = -\sin \theta \cos \alpha \pm (\sin^2 \theta \cos^2 \alpha - \sin^2 \theta + f^2 \cos^2 \theta)^{\frac{1}{2}}.$$

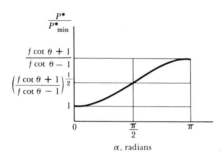

Fig. 5.3-4

The minus sign before the radical would make P^* negative, a physically meaningless result. We conclude that

$$\frac{P^*}{W} = (\sin^2 \theta \cos^2 \alpha - \sin^2 \theta + f^2 \cos^2 \theta)^{\frac{1}{2}} - \sin \theta \cos \alpha$$

$$= (f^2 \cos^2 \theta - \sin^2 \theta \sin^2 \alpha)^{\frac{1}{2}} - \sin \theta \cos \alpha.$$

P^* has its smallest value when $\alpha = 0$ (the cord straight down the plane). This value, denoted $P^*_{\min}$, equals $(f \cos \theta - \sin \theta)W$. To see how P^* varies with the angle α, we may conveniently divide P^* by $P^*_{\min}$:

$$\frac{P^*}{P^*_{\min}} = \frac{(f^2 \cos^2 \theta - \sin^2 \theta \sin^2 \alpha)^{\frac{1}{2}} - \sin \theta \cos \alpha}{f \cos \theta - \sin \theta}$$

$$= \frac{(f^2 \cot^2 \theta - \sin^2 \alpha)^{\frac{1}{2}} - \cos \alpha}{f \cot \theta - 1}.$$

Fig. 5.3-4 shows, schematically, the variation of P^* as a function of α in the range $0 \leqq \alpha \leqq \pi$.

Example 5.3-2

A uniform rod of weight W and length l lies on a rough table, the coefficient of limiting friction being f. If the rod exerts a uniform pressure on the table, what force directed at right angles to the rod at one end will cause it to move?

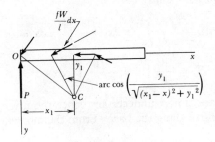

Fig. 5.3-5

Solution: Suppose that, initially, the rod breaks equilibrium by rotating about the point C whose coordinates are x_1, y_1, as shown in Fig. 5.3-5. Just before equilibrium is broken, there will be at each element, dx, of the bar a normal force on the bar $W\,dx/l$ exerted by the table and a frictional force $fW\,dx/l$. These frictional forces will act at right angles to the radius

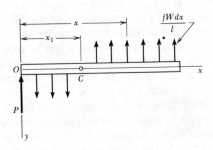

Fig. 5.3-6

vector from C, as shown. Since they all have negative x-components, and since there is no external force in the x-direction to balance, it is obvious that y_1 must be zero and the point C must lie on the x-axis. This also emerges from the first of the equations of equilibrium:

$$\sum F_x = -\frac{fW}{l} y_1 \int_0^l \frac{dx}{\sqrt{(x-x_1)^2 + y_1^2}} = 0.$$

We need not bother to work out the integral; it must be a positive number since the integrand is positive over the entire range of integration. The summation of forces in the x-direction can be zero only if $y_1 = 0$. An experienced hand would have started with this understanding. At any rate, the free-body diagram can now be redrawn, for the sake of simplicity, as shown in Fig. 5.3-6. The equation of equilibrium which asserts that the sum of the external forces in the x-direction must vanish is now identically satisfied. The other two equations of equilibrium determine x_1 and P when slipping impends.

$$\sum M_0 = \frac{fW}{l} \int_0^{x_1} x\, dx - \frac{fW}{l} \int_{x_1}^{l} x\, dx = 0,$$

$$\sum F_y = \frac{fW}{l} \int_0^{x_1} dx - \frac{fW}{l} \int_{x_1}^{l} dx - P = 0.$$

The integrations are almost unnecessary, since the magnitude of the frictional force is uniform along the bar. From the moment equation

$$-x_1^2 + (l^2 - x_1^2) = 0, \qquad x_1 = \frac{l}{\sqrt{2}}.$$

From the force equation

$$P = \frac{fW}{l}[x_1 - (l - x_1)] = \frac{fW}{l}(2x_1 - l)$$

$$= fW(\sqrt{2} - 1).$$

This completes the analysis. It is interesting to note that the force required to start motion in this way is only about $0.41fW$—that is, about 41 per cent of what would be needed to make the bar move in simple translation. The point C about which the bar starts to rotate is about 71 per cent of the way along the bar from the end at which P is applied. In dynamics we treat the case that is, in a manner of speaking, the opposite of this one: the case in which P instead of being applied slowly is applied very rapidly, as a sharp blow or "impulse". It is found in the dynamical case that the bar begins to move about a point two-thirds of the way along the bar from the struck end. There is surprisingly little difference in the results for the two extreme cases, and in each the location of C is independent of the magnitude of the friction present.

Example 5.3-3

A uniform 100 lb beam 12 ft long rests on pads at each end. The horizontal surface on which it rests has a coefficient of friction of one-half. One end of the bar is restrained by a horizontal cable extending at right angles to the bar. Initially the cable is just taut. A force P is applied to the bar at a point 8 ft from the end at which the cable is attached, in a direction away *from the cable at an angle of* 45° *with the bar, as shown in Fig.* 5.3-7a. *If P is gradually increased from zero, how large must it become before the bar moves?*

Solution: The point C about which the bar will begin to move must be somewhere along the line of the cable (the y-axis in Fig. 5.3-7b). This follows from the fact that, since the cable is taut, equilibrium must be broken by motion of point A at right angles to the cable (i.e., along the x-axis). This means that the frictional force at A must, when motion impends, be in the negative x-direction; and, since this friction force must be at

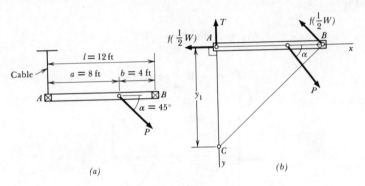

(a)   (b)

Fig. 5.3-7

right angles to the line AC, it follows that C must be on the y-axis. We denote the distance from the origin of coordinates at A to the point C by the symbol y_1, and the weight of the bar by the symbol W. Then the free-body diagram of the bar when motion impends is as shown in Fig. 5.3-7b. The equations of equilibrium are

$$\sum F_x = P \cos \alpha - \frac{1}{2} fW \frac{y_1}{\sqrt{y_1^2 + l^2}} - \frac{1}{2} fW = 0,$$

$$\sum F_y = -T - \frac{1}{2} fW \frac{l}{\sqrt{y_1^2 + l^2}} + P \sin \alpha = 0,$$

$$\sum M_A = -\frac{1}{2} fW \frac{l^2}{\sqrt{y_1^2 + l^2}} + Pa \sin \alpha = 0.$$

The second of these equations determines T, the tension in the cable—a quantity not of direct interest. We solve the first and third equations for the wanted quantities P and y_1:

$$y_1 = \frac{l^2 \cot^2 \alpha - a^2}{2a \cot \alpha}, \qquad P = \frac{1}{2} fW \frac{l^2}{a \sqrt{y_1^2 + l^2}} \csc \alpha.$$

In the present case, $l = 12$ ft, $\cot \alpha = 1$, $a = 8$ ft, $f = \frac{1}{2}$, and $W = 100$ lb, so that

$$y_1 = \frac{144 - 64}{16} = 5 \text{ ft},$$

$$P = \frac{(25)(12)^2}{(8)\sqrt{169}} \sqrt{2} = 49 \text{ lb}.$$

Finally, we must check the possibility that C coincides with one of the points of support, A. If this happens, the free-body diagram is as shown in Fig. 5.3-8.

$$\sum M_A = P'a \sin \alpha - \frac{1}{2} fWl = 0,$$

$$P' = \frac{1}{2} fW \frac{l}{a} \operatorname{cosec} \alpha.$$

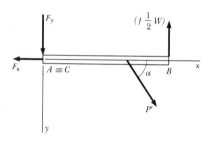

Fig. 5.3-8

We see from the general expression given above that this value of P can never exceed the one obtained previously. Also, if we solve for F_x we find

$$F_x = P' \sin \alpha = \frac{1}{2} fW \frac{l}{a},$$

which exceeds the largest permissible value of F_x, $\frac{1}{2} fW$.

5.4 Cable Friction

It is a common observation that by wrapping a rope around a post a man can hold in check a much larger force than he would ordinarily be able to exert. To see why this device is so effective, consider the case of a flexible cable carrying a force T_0 at one end and a force $T_1 > T_0$ at the other end, the cable being pressed for part of its length against a post. We suppose that T_1 is just large enough to produce impending motion. Then every point in contact with the post is in a state of impending motion. The free-body diagram of a typical element of the cable where it is in contact with the post is shown in Fig. 5.4-1. The post exerts on the cable a distributed normal pressure, p, and a distributed frictional tangential force, fp, units of force per unit of length. In general p must be regarded as a function of position along the cable. The equations of equilibrium

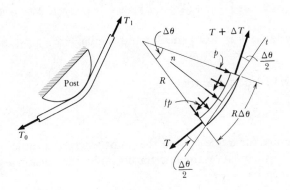

Fig. 5·4-1

for the typical element shown are found by summing forces in the normal and tangential directions. The normal equation of equilibrium is

$$\sum F_n = T \sin\left(\frac{\Delta\theta}{2}\right) + (T+\Delta T)\sin\left(\frac{\Delta\theta}{2}\right) - p(R\Delta\theta) = 0 \quad \textbf{5·4-1a}$$

or

$$2T \sin\left(\frac{\Delta\theta}{2}\right) + \Delta T \sin\left(\frac{\Delta\theta}{2}\right) - pR\,\Delta\theta = 0. \quad \textbf{5·4-1b}$$

If the element is taken to be very small, then $\sin(\Delta\theta/2)$ is approximately equal to $\Delta\theta/2$, and $\Delta T \sin(\Delta\theta/2)$ will be negligible compared to the other terms. Therefore, if Eq. 5.4-1 is to hold for *any* $\Delta\theta$, however small (i.e., hold in the limit as $\Delta\theta\to0$), we must have

$$T = pR. \quad \textbf{5·4-2}$$

Precisely the same conclusion can be reached from Eq. 4.2-12b if we recall that $d\theta/ds = 1/R$, the reciprocal of the radius of curvature, and that $q_n = -p$. Indeed, the situation pictured in Fig. 5.4-1 is only a special case of the flexible cable carrying a distributed load.

Equation 5.4-2, however, is an interesting result in its own right. It implies that for any given pull, T, the pressure, p, will be large if the radius of curvature, R, is small. No wonder that a cord tends to bite into a parcel where it goes round a corner! For a circular post R will be a constant, but there is nothing in the analysis that would prevent R from being a function of position along the curve. Turning now to the equation of tangential equilibrium, we have

$$\sum F_t = -T \cos \left(\frac{\Delta\theta}{2}\right) + (T+\Delta T) \cos \left(\frac{\Delta\theta}{2}\right) - fp(R \, \Delta\theta) = 0. \quad \text{5·4-3}$$

In the limit, as $\Delta\theta$ is taken smaller and smaller, Eq. 5.4-3 implies that

$$dT = fpR \, d\theta \quad \text{5·4-4}$$

or, in view of Eq. 5.4-2, that

$$\frac{dT}{T} = f \, d\theta. \quad \text{5·4-5}$$

If we measure the angle θ from the point where the cable first makes contact with the post on the low-tension side, the tension at any other point is given by

$$\int_{T_0}^{T} \frac{dT}{T} = f \int_{0}^{\theta} d\theta, \qquad \log \left(\frac{T}{T_0}\right) = f\theta,$$
$$T = T_0 e^{f\theta}. \quad \text{5·4-6}$$

Here θ is the angle through which the tangent to the post has turned in going from the element where the tension is T_0 to the element where the tension is T. This angle is measured in radians. In the case of a circular post, which is the one usually encountered in technology, θ is the same as the angle subtended at the center of the circle. Equation 5.4-4 is, of course, a special case of Eq. 4.2-12a with $ds = R \, d\theta$ and $q_t = -fp$. We see that T is a function of θ, growing exponentially with θ. It follows from Eq. 5.4-2 that if R is constant, p also increases exponentially with θ or with arclength, s. In the case of a smooth pulley, on the other hand, it was shown in Example 4.2-1 that $p =$ constant.

If the cable loses contact with the post at a point where $\theta = \theta_1$, we have

$$T_1 = T_0 e^{f\theta_1} \quad \text{5·4-7}$$

or

$$T_1 - T_0 = T_0(e^{f\theta_1} - 1). \quad \text{5·4-8}$$

Now we see why the load that can be held in this way is so large. The exponent $f\theta_1$ increases with the wrap angle θ_1 (once around the post, whatever its shape, makes $\theta_1 = 2\pi$) and, even if f is small, several complete circuits will make $e^{f\theta_1}$ a large number.

Example 5.4-1

A brake band consists of a wire band wound over half the circumference of a rotating drum and capable of being tightened by a force P, as shown in Fig. 5.4-2a. For the dimensions a, b, and R shown and with $f = 0.12$, how

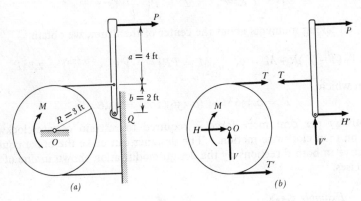

Fig. 5.4-2

large a force, P, is required to prevent the drum from rotating when a clockwise torque, M, of 100 lb-ft is applied to it?

Solution: The free-body diagrams of drum and brake lever are shown in Fig. 5.4-2b. Taking moments about the point, Q, at which the brake lever is hinged, we have

$$T = P\left(\frac{a+b}{b}\right).$$

Since T is on the "slack" or less taut side of the brake band and since rotation of the drum is impending, we have, from Eq. 5.4-7,

$$T' = Te^{0.12\pi} = P\left(\frac{a+b}{b}\right)e^{0.12\pi}.$$

The angle of wrap in this case is $\theta_1 = \pi$ radians. Now, on taking moments about the center, O, of the drum, we find

$$(T' - T)R - M = 0,$$

or

$$M = PR\left(\frac{a+b}{b}\right)(e^{0.12\pi} - 1)$$

$$= P(3)\left(\frac{6}{2}\right)(1.457 - 1) = 4.11P.$$

Therefore, with M given as 100 lb-ft, we find the necessary P to be

$$P = (0.243)(100) = 24.3 \quad \text{lb.}$$

It is interesting to note, before leaving the example, that this design is poorer in resisting counterclockwise torque than in resisting clockwise torque. If M is counterclockwise, T will be the tight and T' the slack side of the band. Then

$$T = T'e^{0.12\pi}, \qquad T' = P\left(\frac{a+b}{b}\right)e^{-0.12\pi},$$

and, on taking moments about the center of the drum, we obtain

$$-(T-T')R+M = 0, \qquad M = PR\left(\frac{a+b}{b}\right)(1-e^{-0.12\pi}) = 2.81P,$$

from which

$$P = 0.356M = (0.356)(100) = 35.6 \quad \text{lb.}$$

About 47 per cent more force is required to restrain counterclockwise motion than clockwise motion. The designer can make the brake equally effective in both directions by the design modification shown in one of the exercises.

Example 5.4-2

A light belt is used to transmit power from a 4-ft diameter driving pulley to a 2-ft diameter driven pulley, the angles of wrap being 210° and 150°, respectively, as shown in Fig. 5.4-3. If the coefficient of limiting friction is 0.25, and the ultimate tensile strength of the belt is 500 lb, how much torque can be transmitted to the smaller pulley before slip occurs?

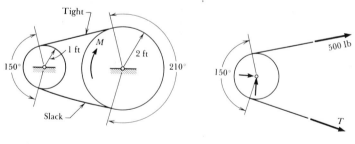

Fig. 5·4-3   Fig. 5·4-4

Solution: In this instance the upper side of the belt will be taut and the lower side will be under relatively less tension. To achieve the greatest possible torque, the tension in the taut side should be 500 lb. Slip will occur first on the smaller pulley since the angle of wrap is smaller

there.   The free-body diagram for the smaller pulley is shown in Fig.
5.4-4.   Since slip impends, we have

$$500 = Te^{(0.25)(5\pi/6)} = Te^{0.654},$$

$$T = \frac{500}{1.92} = 260 \quad \text{lb},$$

and the torque transmitted to the pulley cannot exceed

$$(500)(1) - (260)(1) = 240 \quad \text{lb-ft}.$$

In order to transmit this torque, a moment of $(500-260)(2)=480$
lb-ft must be applied to the driven pulley.   If more than this torque is
applied the belt will slip.   The designer who wishes to increase the amount
of torque transmitted, without changing the radii of the pulleys (which
controls the rotational speed of the smaller pulley), may introduce an idler
pulley, as shown in Fig. 5.4-5, which serves to increase the angle of wrap.

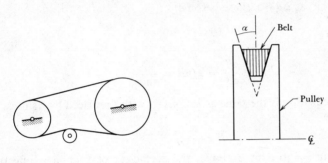

Fig. 5.4-5   **Fig. 5.4-6**

Example **5.4-3**

*Explain the effectiveness of the commercial Vee-belt design used for
power-transmission pulleys.*

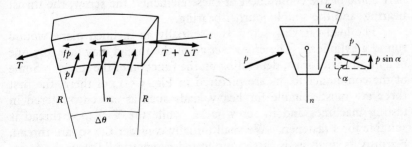

Fig. 5.4-7

Solution: For this pulley, the cross-section of the groove has the shape of a flat-bottomed *V*, as shown in Fig. 5.4-6. The belt need not have a trapezoidal cross-section—it could just as well be circular in cross-section—though the form shown is somewhat better adapted to reduce wear. We isolate an element of belt and draw its free-body diagram as shown in Fig. 5.4-7. The analysis now follows closely the lines of the text of Section 5.4, except that there are now two contact surfaces instead of one as in the case of the flat-faced pulley, and these faces are inclined to the vertical by an angle α. Resolving forces along the normal and tangential directions, we have

$$\sum F_n = T \sin\left(\frac{\Delta\theta}{2}\right) + (T+\Delta T)\sin\left(\frac{\Delta\theta}{2}\right) - (p\sin\alpha)(2R\,\Delta\theta) = 0,$$

$$\sum F_t = (T+\Delta T)\cos\left(\frac{\Delta\theta}{2}\right) - T\cos\left(\frac{\Delta\theta}{2}\right) - fp(2R\,\Delta\theta) = 0.$$

In the limit, as $\Delta\theta \to 0$, these become

$$T - 2pR\sin\alpha = 0$$

and

$$\frac{dT}{d\theta} = 2fpR = \frac{f}{\sin\alpha}\,T.$$

The last equation is the same as Eq. 5.4-5, with f replaced by $f/\sin\alpha$. We shall have

$$T = T_0 e^{(f\,\mathrm{cosec}\,\alpha)\theta}.$$

By making $\alpha = 30°$, for example, the coefficient of friction is effectively increased by a factor of 2. Of course the pressure p is also increased.

5.5 Friction in Machine Elements

For many of the fundamental machine elements the Amontons-Coulomb friction law provides a satisfactory estimate of the principal frictional effects encountered in engineering practice. We discuss here some of the commonest of these elements: the screw, the thrust bearing, and the simple journal bearing.

The load-carrying screw is essentially an inclined plane wound round a cylinder. The cross-section of the thread may take any one of a number of forms, depending on the function of the screw. Some of the commoner forms are pictured in Fig. 5.5-1; of these, the first three are most suitable for heavy loads such as are encountered in testing machines and in screw-jacks, while the V-shaped thread is suitable for a fastener. We shall initially consider the square thread, because its analysis is less complicated geometrically than the treatment of the others.

We suppose, then, that the screw is carrying an axial load W, which is balanced by a normal pressure p exerted by the nut on the underside of the threads. The units of p are force per unit length, length being measured along the thread. The screw is also subjected

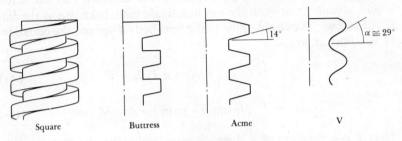

Square   Buttress   Acme   V

Fig. 5.5-1

to a torque, M, about its longitudinal axis, which is resisted partly by p and partly by a frictional shear stress exerted on the threads by the nut. When M is just sufficient to produce motion of the screw

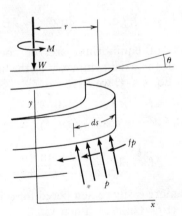

Fig. 5.5-2

in a direction opposite to that of the load W, this frictional effect is fp units of force per unit of thread length. The free-body diagram of the screw is as shown schematically in Fig. 5.5-2. Notice that in this figure only a small length of thread, ds, is shown loaded so as to avoid cluttering the figure unnecessarily. The angle of the inclined plane, sometimes termed the *screw angle*, is denoted by the symbol θ. If we follow a thread round the circumference of the screw we find, after the tangent to the thread has turned through $360°$, that we have moved a distance l along the axis from the point at which we started. Then $\theta = \arctan(l/2\pi r)$, where r is the radius of the screw. The distance l, which is the distance that the screw would advance relative to the nut in a single turn, is known as the *lead* of the screw. Returning now to the free-body diagram, the equations of equilibrium are

$$\sum F_y = \int_0^S (p \cos \theta - fp \sin \theta) \, ds - W = 0, \qquad \text{5.5-1}$$

$$\sum M_y = \int_0^S (fp \cos \theta + p \sin \theta) r \, ds - M = 0. \qquad \text{5.5-2}$$

Here p is a function of s, distance measured along the thread. The limits of integration are $s = 0$, where the thread first makes contact with the nut, and $s = S$, where the thread emerges from the nut. Since p is the only quantity in the integrand that depends on the variable of integration, s, these equations may be written

$$\left(\int_0^S p \, ds \right)(\cos \theta - f \sin \theta) = W, \qquad \text{5.5-3}$$

$$\left(\int_0^S p \, ds \right)(f \cos \theta + \sin \theta) r = M. \qquad \text{5.5-4}$$

The other equations of equilibrium are, of course, automatically satisfied on account of the axial symmetry of the screw. Taking the ratio of Eq. 5.5-4 to Eq. 5.5-3, we have

$$\frac{M}{W} = \frac{r(f \cos \theta + \sin \theta)}{\cos \theta - f \sin \theta} \qquad \text{5.5-5a}$$

or

$$M = rW \frac{f \cos \theta + \sin \theta}{\cos \theta - f \sin \theta}. \qquad \text{5.5-5b}$$

This can be put in a more easily remembered form if we introduce the angle of friction. Let $f = \tan \theta^*$. Then

$$M = rW \frac{\tan \theta^* \cos \theta + \sin \theta}{\cos \theta - \tan \theta^* \sin \theta}$$

$$= rW \frac{\sin \theta^* \cos \theta + \cos \theta^* \sin \theta}{\cos \theta^* \cos \theta - \sin \theta^* \sin \theta} = rW \frac{\sin(\theta + \theta^*)}{\cos(\theta + \theta^*)}$$

or

$$M = rW \tan(\theta + \theta^*). \qquad \text{5.5-6}$$

This is the torque required to raise the weight W. Of course, $\theta \le (\pi/2) - \theta^*$ for the torque to be positive.

The equations of equilibrium also fix the average normal pressure, p_{av}, exerted on the threads. This is rather important from a practical point of view because the threads will be stripped off if they are not strong enough to carry the load. Since

$$p_{av} = \frac{1}{S} \int_0^S p \, ds,$$

it follows at once from Eq. 5.5-4 that

$$p_{av} = \frac{M}{rS}(f \cos \theta + \sin \theta)^{-1} = \frac{M}{rS} \cos \theta^* \operatorname{cosec}(\theta + \theta^*). \quad \textbf{5.5-7}$$

Should the designer feel that this load per inch of thread is too great, he may increase the size of the thread so as to make it stronger, he may increase the length of the nut so as to increase S, or he may call for a reduced lead, also increasing S. Alternatively, a second spiral thread of the same lead may be cut on the cylindrical body of the screw with its threads half way between those of the first set. This doubles S while leaving the other quantities of the analysis unchanged. Such a screw is said to be *double-threaded*. When load-carrying capacity is essential, double- and even triple-threaded screws can be used. They are, of course, more expensive than the ordinary single-threaded screw. The *pitch* of a screw is the axial distance between successive threads; for a single-threaded screw, pitch and lead are identical; for a double-threaded screw the pitch is half the lead.[*]

What is known as the *efficiency* of a screw is the ratio of the force or torque which would be required in the complete absence of friction to the force or torque actually required to produce motion. In the case of a load-raising square screw it can be seen from Eq. 5.5-6 that this ratio is

$$\frac{\tan \theta}{\tan(\theta + \theta^*)}. \quad \textbf{5.5-8}$$

It follows that if the efficiency is to be a maximum we must choose θ so that

$$\frac{d}{d\theta}\left[\frac{\tan \theta}{\tan(\theta + \theta^*)}\right] = 0.$$

---

[*] This nomenclature is unfortunate. The thread of a screw is a helix, and the mathematical definition of the pitch of a helix is what is known as the lead of the screw.

To solve this equation, we perform the indicated differentiation of a quotient and then multiply both numerator and denominator of the resulting fraction by $2 \cos^2 \theta \cos^2 (\theta + \theta^*)$:

$$\frac{d}{d\theta}\left[\frac{\tan \theta}{\tan (\theta + \theta^*)}\right] = \frac{\tan (\theta + \theta^*) \sec^2 \theta - \tan \theta \sec^2 (\theta + \theta^*)}{\tan^2 (\theta + \theta^*)}$$

$$= \frac{2 \sin (\theta + \theta^*) \cos (\theta + \theta^*) - 2 \sin \theta \cos \theta}{2 \sin^2 (\theta + \theta^*) \cos^2 \theta}.$$

This last expression may be rewritten:

$$\frac{d}{d\theta}\left[\frac{\tan \theta}{\tan (\theta + \theta^*)}\right] = \frac{\sin 2(\theta + \theta^*) - \sin 2\theta}{2 \sin^2 (\theta + \theta^*) \cos^2 \theta}.$$

Setting this last expression for the derivative equal to zero, we find that the value of θ for maximum efficiency is determined by the trigonometric equation

$$\sin 2(\theta + \theta^*) - \sin 2\theta = 0$$

or [from $\sin A - \sin B = 2 \cos \frac{1}{2}(A + B) \sin \frac{1}{2}(A - B)$]

$$2 \cos (2\theta + \theta^*) \sin \theta^* = 0.$$

Since $\theta^* \neq 0$, the first root of this equation is given by $2\theta + \theta^* = \pi/2$, or

$$\theta = \frac{\pi}{4} - \frac{\theta^*}{2}. \qquad \textbf{5·5-9}$$

This value of θ is half of the permissible maximum value $(\pi/2) - \theta^*$ of θ found above. This value of θ substituted in 5.5-8 indicates that the maximum possible efficiency of a screw is

$$\frac{\tan \left(\dfrac{\pi}{4} - \dfrac{\theta^*}{2}\right)}{\tan \left(\dfrac{\pi}{4} + \dfrac{\theta^*}{2}\right)} = \frac{1 - \sin \theta^*}{1 + \sin \theta^*}. \qquad \textbf{5·5-10}$$

If $f = 0.20$, θ^* will be arctan $(0.2) = 11.3°$. It follows that the maximum efficiency of the screw will be 67.2 per cent. To attain this efficiency, θ should have the value $45° - 5.6° = 39.4°$. This means that for a one-inch radius screw the lead would have to be $2\pi r \tan \theta = 5.15$ inches. Most screw designs are not, in practice, intended to achieve maximum efficiency.

Rather more important than efficiency is the question of whether the release of the torque, M, which lifts the weight W, will result in the weight forcing the screw down again. To see whether or not this will happen we suppose that the moment, M', has the proper value to make downward motion impend.   Then if the M' required turns out to be negative we can conclude that in the absence of any torque no motion will occur.   The free-body diagram is the same as that shown in Fig. 5.5-2 except that the symbol M is replaced by the symbol M' and the directions of the frictional tractions are reversed. The equations of equilibrium are then the same as 5.5-1 and 5.5-2, except that M is replaced by M' and f by $-f$.   From Eq. 5.5-5b we conclude that for downward motion

$$M' = rW \frac{-f \cos\theta + \sin\theta}{\cos\theta + f \sin\theta} = rW \tan(\theta - \theta^*). \qquad \textbf{5.5-11}$$

M' will be zero, or the screw will be on the verge of slipping back, when $f = \tan\theta$ or $\theta = \theta^*$.   This result might have been anticipated from the fact that the screw is a form of inclined plane.   It follows from Eq. 5.5-8 that if a load-bearing screw is to be non-reversible the efficiency cannot exceed $\tan\theta^*/\tan 2\theta^*$, a value never greater than 50 per cent.

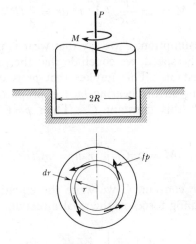

Fig. 5.5-3

Another common machine element in which friction plays an important role is the ordinary flat-collar thrust bearing or friction clutch.   The simplest possible example of such a bearing is shown in Fig. 5.5-3.   The shaft is supposed to be rotating at a constant rate so that an equilibrium treatment is appropriate.

Taking moments of the friction forces about the axis of the shaft, we have

$$M = 2\pi \int_0^R rfp(r\ dr).$$

5.5-12

Here p is the intensity of normal pressure on the base of the shaft (note that its dimensions are force per unit area). Lacking further information, all we can really assert with regard to p is that it is radially symmetric. At any value of r it seems reasonable to say that p will have the same magnitude all round. Use has been made of this presumption in writing Eq. 5.5-12. It is painfully obvious, however, that progress in the analysis depends on a knowledge of the distribution of the pressure over the surface. This can really only be derived from deformable-body mechanics. Two assumptions are, however, common in machine design: (1) the normal pressure is uniform over the contact region, and (2) the wear is uniform over the contact region. On the first assumption p is a constant equal to the load carried by the shaft divided by the area of the bearing: $p = P/\pi R^2$. Then the required torque is given by the expression

$$M = 2\pi \frac{P}{\pi R^2} f \int_0^R r^2\ dr = \frac{2}{3} fPR.$$

5.5-13

On the second assumption, if we say that wear is proportional to the pressure and to the speed, we conclude that the product of pressure and speed is constant. This implies that pr is constant, since the speed at any point on the bearing face is proportional to the radial distance, r. Call this constant C. Then $p = C/r$ and, from Eq. 5.5-12,

$$M = 2\pi Cf \int_0^R r\ dr = \pi CfR^2.$$

5.5-14

To determine the constant C we write the equation of equilibrium obtained by summing forces in the axial direction.

$$-P + 2\pi \int_0^R p(r\ dr) = 0,$$

$$C \int_0^R dr = \frac{P}{2\pi}, \qquad C = \frac{P}{2\pi R}.$$

5.5-15

It follows that

$$M = \frac{1}{2} fPR.$$

5.5-16

Neither of these two common assumptions is exactly correct and the truth is probably somewhere between them. The torque M generally is less on the second assumption than on the first. The power required to rotate the shaft at a constant rate of ω radians per second is $M\omega$. This is also the rate at which heat is generated by friction at the bearing.

Another common machine element that can be analyzed with the aid of the friction law is the plain axle and bearing. When an axle turns in a very slightly larger cylindrical cavity it makes line contact with the hole along a generator of the cylinder. To fix ideas, let us compute the friction needed to restrain a body from

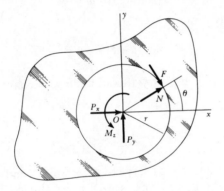

Fig. 5·5-4

rotating about a fixed axle. We suppose that the axle is in the z-direction and that the forces which act on the body, other than those exerted by the axle, can be reduced to an equipollent system consisting of a force $\mathbf{P} = P_x\mathbf{i} + P_y\mathbf{j}$ acting at O, the center of the axle, together with a couple, M_z, about the z-axis. The force exerted by the axle on the body will consist of a normal and a frictional reaction at the point, Q, where the axle presses on the circumference of the bearing. The free-body diagram is shown in Fig. 5·5-4. The point Q is located by the polar angle θ. The radius of the hole is denoted r; this is essentially the same as the radius of the axle. Now the equations of equilibrium are

$$P_x + F \sin \theta + N \cos \theta = 0,$$

$$P_y - F \cos \theta + N \sin \theta = 0, \qquad\qquad \textbf{5·5-17}$$

$$M_z - rF = 0.$$

These equations determine F, N, and θ, on the assumption that the friction is great enough to preserve equilibrium. To discover how much friction is actually needed to preserve equilibrium we suppose that counterclockwise rotation about the axle impends. Then $F = fN$ and is clockwise, as shown in Fig. 5.5-4. The first two of Eqs. 5.5-17 become

$$N(\cos \theta + f \sin \theta) = -P_x,$$

$$N(\sin \theta - f \cos \theta) = -P_y. \qquad \textbf{5.5-18}$$

Taking the ratio of these two expressions, we have

$$\frac{\sin \theta - f \cos \theta}{\cos \theta + f \sin \theta} = \frac{P_y}{P_x} \qquad \textbf{5.5-19}$$

or, what is equivalent,

$$\tan (\theta + \theta^*) = \frac{P_y}{P_x}. \qquad \textbf{5.5-20}$$

On squaring each of Eqs. 5.5-18 and adding, we have

$$(1 + f^2)N^2 = P_x^2 + P_y^2$$

or

$$N = \sqrt{P_x^2 + P_y^2} \cos \theta^*. \qquad \textbf{5.5-21}$$

Equations 5.5-20 and 5.5-21 serve to determine N and θ for this limiting case. But the last of Eqs. 5.5-17 must also be satisfied. This means that f must be such as to satisfy the equation

$$M_z - fr\sqrt{P_x^2 + P_y^2} \cos \theta^* = 0$$

or

$$\sin \theta^* = \frac{M_z}{r\sqrt{P_x^2 + P_y^2}}. \qquad \textbf{5.5-22}$$

The value of θ^* given by the last expression, then, is the smallest value of friction that will prevent rotation about the axle with the given set of forces, **P** and M_z.

As is so often the case, it is instructive to look at the situation from another point of view. The force components F and N are equivalent to a single force of magnitude $(P_x^2 + P_y^2)^{1/2}$ applied at a point on the rim of the bearing. The moment of this force about the center of the axle, when motion impends, is fNr, which, substituting for N from Eq. 5.5-21, is equal to $fr(P_x^2 + P_y^2)^{1/2} \cos \theta^*$. This means that the resultant of F and N has a moment arm about the center of the axle of magnitude $fr \cos \theta^*$, or, since $f = \tan \theta^*$, a moment arm $r \sin \theta^*$. To summarize: if we draw a circle with center at the center of the axle and radius $r \sin \theta^*$, the reaction at the rim of the axle must be tangent to this circle when motion impends. The circle of radius $r \sin \theta^*$ is known as the friction circle. Its use is usually the most expedient way to cope with axle friction analysis.

Many other instances of machine-element combinations could be adduced for which the effect of friction on behavior can be anticipated with the aid of the Amontons-Coulomb friction law. Some of these are best understood by means of particular examples, such as the ones which follow. The reader should be alert to recognize that in many cases an inherently statically indeterminate situation is made amenable to analysis either by the fact that motion impends or by that species of reasonable approximation to the existing pressure distribution which is so common in engineering.

Example 5·5-1

A screw jack is to be used to raise a load of 1500 lb. The user of the jack is to exert a force of 20 lb at the end of a 1 ft handle. If a single-threaded square screw of 1 in. radius is used, what should its pitch be? What will be the efficiency of the screw? Will the weight slip down when the force is released from the handle? Take $f = 0.10$.

Solution: For raising the load we have (Eq. 5.5-6)

$$M = rW \tan(\theta + \theta^*).$$

In the present case $M = 240$ lb-in., $r = 1$ in., and $W = 1500$ lb, so that

$$\tan(\theta + \theta^*) = \frac{240}{(1)(1500)} = 0.16 \quad \text{or} \quad \theta + \theta^* = 9.1°.$$

Since $\theta^* = \arctan(0.10) = 5.7°$ we must have a screw angle $\theta = 3.4°$. This implies that the pitch (or lead) of the screw will be given by

$$\tan \theta = \frac{l}{2\pi r}, \qquad l = 2\pi r \tan \theta,$$

$$l = (2\pi)(1)(0.059) = 0.37 \text{ in.}$$

We will therefore have about 3 threads per inch along the body of the screw. Before leaving this part of the question we note that if f were 0.16 or more, no pitch, however small, would serve to make this jack function. A higher torque would be needed. We also note that for design purposes $l = 0.37$ in. is a maximum value. We could make l smaller and the screw jack would still function properly; in fact it would require even less torque. It would, however, be slower in raising the weight.

The efficiency of the screw is given by Eq. 5.5-8.

$$\text{Efficiency} = \frac{\tan \theta}{\tan(\theta + \theta^*)} = \frac{0.059}{0.16} = 0.37.$$

Finally, we note that the weight W will not slip down when the force is released from the handle, because $f > \tan \theta$.

Although it is not a part of the question asked, a designer would have to examine the load carried by the thread so as to be certain that it was not excessive. We see from Eq. 5.3-7 that

$$p_{av} = \frac{M}{rS} \frac{\cos \theta^*}{\sin (\theta + \theta^*)} = \frac{240}{(1)(S)} \frac{0.9953}{0.158} = \frac{1580}{S} \text{ lb/in.}$$

Since there are about three threads per inch on screw and nut, each thread will have a thickness of no more than 0.16 in. at the root. The average shear stress at the root of the thread will be about $1580/(0.16S) = 9880/S$ pounds per square inch when S is measured in inches. The allowable shear stress, if steel is used, is about 10^4 lb/in.^{2}, so that only a short engagement with the nut, say $S = 1$ in., is required for a safe design from this point of view.

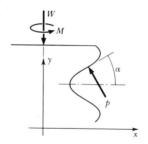

Fig. 5.5-5

Example 5.5-2

Find the torque required to exert a force W when a V-shaped screw thread is used.

Solution: We take the cross-section to be defined by the angle α, the semi-vertical angle of the V, as shown in Fig. 5.5-5. Now the normal pressure p per unit length of thread has a y-component $p \cos \alpha \cos \theta$ and a z-component $p \cos \alpha \sin \theta$. The frictional shear (directed out of the figure, toward the reader) has a y-component $-fp \sin \theta$ and a z-component $fp \cos \theta$. The equations of equilibrium analogous to Eqs. 5.5-1,2 are

$$\sum F_y = \int_0^S (p \cos \theta \cos \alpha - fp \sin \theta) \, ds - W = 0,$$

$$\sum M_y = \int_0^S r(p \sin \theta \cos \alpha + fp \cos \theta) \, ds - M = 0.$$

Just as in the case of Eqs. 5.5-3,4 we separate out $\int_0^S p\, ds$ and take the ratio of these expressions to find

$$\frac{M}{rW} = \frac{f\cos\theta + \cos\alpha\sin\theta}{\cos\theta\cos\alpha - f\sin\theta},$$

$$M = rW\frac{(f\sec\alpha)\cos\theta + \sin\theta}{\cos\theta - (f\sec\alpha)\sin\theta}.$$

This is the same as Eq. 5.5-5b, with f replaced by $f\sec\alpha$. It follows that all the conclusions previously reached for the case of a square thread apply to a V-shaped thread if we replace f by $f\sec\alpha$. In other words, the influence of the V-shape is to make friction more effective. The moment required to exert a force W is

$$M = rW\frac{\tan\theta + \sec\alpha\tan\theta^*}{1 - \sec\alpha\tan\theta\tan\theta^*}.$$

We see why, apart from cost, V-shaped threads are preferred for fasteners while square threads are preferred for power screws. In most commercial V-screws $\alpha \cong 29°$ so that friction is effectively increased by a factor 1.14.

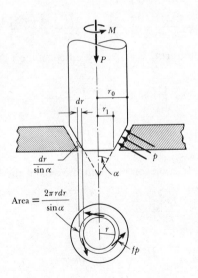

Fig. 5.5-6

Example **5.5-3**

    Find the torque required to rotate a conical pivot bearing of semi-vertical angle α, outer radius r_0, inner radius r_1, carrying a load P if the coefficient of *friction is f. Do this on the assumption* (1) *that the normal pressure is uniform;* (2) *that the wear is uniformly distributed.*

Solution: (1) The surface area of the bearing is

$$\frac{\pi(r_0^2 - r_1^2)}{\sin \alpha}.$$

Summing forces vertically, we have

$$p \sin \alpha \frac{\pi(r_0^2 - r_1^2)}{\sin \alpha} = P,$$

$$p = \frac{P}{\pi(r_0^2 - r_1^2)}.$$

The moment of the frictional forces carried on any ring element of the bearing extending from r to $r+dr$ is

$$\frac{rfp(2\pi r\, dr)}{\sin \alpha},$$

so, taking moments about the vertical axis, we have

$$\left(\frac{2\pi f}{\sin \alpha}\right) \frac{P}{\pi(r_0^2 - r_1^2)} \int_{r_1}^{r_0} r^2\, dr - M = 0,$$

$$M = \frac{2fP}{3 \sin \alpha} \frac{r_0^3 - r_1^3}{r_0^2 - r_1^2} = \frac{2fP}{3 \sin \alpha} \frac{r_0^2 + r_0 r_1 + r_1^2}{r_0 + r_1}.$$

(2) If wear is uniform, $p = C/r$. We determine C by summing forces vertically:

$$P = \int_{r_1}^{r_0} p \sin \alpha \frac{2\pi r\, dr}{\sin \alpha} = 2\pi C(r_0 - r_1)$$

or

$$C = \frac{P}{2\pi(r_0 - r_1)}.$$

The moment of the friction forces about the axis of the bearing is

$$M' = \int_{r_1}^{r_0} rfp \frac{2\pi r\, dr}{\sin \alpha} = \frac{2\pi fC}{\sin \alpha} \int_{r_1}^{r_0} r\, dr = \frac{\pi fC}{\sin \alpha}(r_0^2 - r_1^2).$$

Substituting for C, we obtain

$$M' = \frac{fP}{2 \sin \alpha}(r_0 + r_1).$$

It is interesting to note that if we take $\alpha = \pi/2$ and $r_1 = 0$ these results for M and M' reduce to the previous case of a flat-ended bearing.

Now let us compare the torques for uniform pressure and uniform wear:

$$\frac{M}{M'} = \frac{4}{3} \frac{r_0^2 + r_0 r_1 + r_1^2}{(r_0 + r_1)^2} = \frac{4}{3}\left[1 - \frac{r_0 r_1}{(r_0 + r_1)^2}\right].$$

Since the geometric mean of two different positive numbers is always less than their arithmetic mean, it follows that $(r_0 r_1)^{1/2} < \frac{1}{2}(r_0 + r_1)$ and hence that $(r_0 r_1)/(r_0 + r_1)^2 < \frac{1}{4}$. We conclude that M is always greater than M', i.e., the torque requirement is reduced when the bearing is "run in," or worn.

Example 5.5-4

A friction clutch (Fig. 5.5-7) connecting two coaxial shafts consists of two circular plates, which, when pressed together, can exert a force of up to 400 lb on one another. The plates have an annulus of brake lining of inside

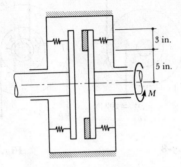

3 in.

5 in.

M

Fig. 5.5-7

radius $r_1 = 5$ in., outside radius $r_0 = 8$ in., and $f = 0.25$. For this material, how much torque can be transmitted before the clutch slips?

Solution: Assuming that p is uniform over the friction material, we have $p = 400/\pi (64 - 25) = 3.27$ lb/in^2.
Therefore,

$$M = 2\pi \int_{r_1}^{r_0} fpr^2 \, dr = \frac{2\pi f p}{3} (r_0^3 - r_1^3)$$

$$= \left(\frac{1}{3}\right)(6.28)(0.25)(3.27)(512 - 125) = 660 \text{ lb-in.}$$

On the other hand, when the clutch is worn we have $p = C/r$ so that

$$P = 2\pi \int_{r_1}^{r_0} pr \, dr = 2\pi C \int_{r_1}^{r_0} dr = 2\pi C(r_0 - r_1),$$

$$C = \frac{P}{2\pi(r_0 - r_1)};$$

$$M' = 2\pi \int_{r_1}^{r_0} fpr^2 \, dr = 2\pi f \frac{P}{2\pi(r_0 - r_1)} \int_{r_1}^{r_0} r \, dr = \frac{1}{2} fP(r_0 + r_1),$$

$$M' = \left(\frac{1}{2}\right)\left(\frac{1}{4}\right)(400)(8 + 5) = 650 \text{ lb-in.}$$

and there is a slight drop in the torque which can be transmitted.

Example **5.5-5**

   A 200 *lb weight hangs from a cable wound on a* 10 *in. radius drum.   The drum can rotate on a horizontal axle of* 3 *in. radius, the coefficient of friction at the bearing being* 0.10.   *On the same axle is a wheel of* 20 *in. radius around which another cable is fastened.   Find the minimum force P needed to raise the weight in each of the two cases shown in Fig.* 5.5-8a *and* b.

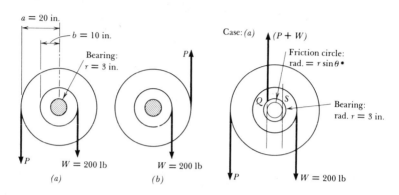

Fig. 5.5-8   **Fig. 5.5-9**

   Solution: For case (a), we draw the free-body diagram of the drum and wheel as shown in Fig. 5.5-9.   Notice the friction circle (which is drawn to an enlarged scale).   The force exerted by the axle on the drum must be vertical and directed upward so as to balance P and W.   In fact we can see that its magnitude must be $P + W$.   It can have no horizontal component since there is no other external force to balance such a component. This force exerted by the axle on the drum must act at a point on the rim of the bearing and must be tangent to the friction circle.   It must therefore act either at point Q or at point S.   To see which of these points gives us the correct tangent we note that the drum is on the point of rotating counterclockwise.   The friction force acting on the drum must therefore produce a clockwise moment about the geometrical center.   This means that the force exerted by the axle on the wheel must act at Q and not at S. Now it is a simple matter to take moments about Q:

$$P(a - r \sin \theta^*) - W(b + r \sin \theta^*) = 0,$$

$$P = W \frac{b + r \sin \theta^*}{a - r \sin \theta^*} = 200 \, \frac{10 + (3)(0.1)}{20 - (3)(0.1)} = (200)(0.523) = 105 \text{ lb.}$$

If the weight were being lowered, the axle would bear on the drum at S.
   For case (b), the free-body diagram is as shown in Fig. 5.5-10.   Since $W > P$, it follows that the bearing reaction on the drum is upward and of magnitude $W - P$.   It must again act at point Q in order to be tangent

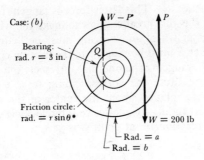

Case: (b)

Bearing:
rad. $r = 3$ in.

Friction circle:
rad. $= r \sin \theta^*$

$W - P$ P

Q

$W = 200$ lb

Rad. $= a$
Rad. $= b$

Fig. 5.5-10

to the friction circle, bear against the drum, and have a frictional component which opposes upward motion of W. Now taking moments about Q, we obtain

$$P(a + r \sin \theta^*) - W(b + r \sin \theta^*) = 0,$$

$$P = W \frac{b + r \sin \theta^*}{a + r \sin \theta^*} = 200 \frac{10 + 0.3}{20 + 0.3} = (200)(0.507) = 101 \text{ lb.}$$

Of course if friction were neglected we should have $P = 100$ lb. The arrangement (b) requires less force to raise the weight than does (a) because the reaction at the bearing is smaller ($W - P$ rather than $W + P$) and this implies a smaller frictional component.

Example 5.5-6

A railway freight car has journal bearings of radius 2.5 in. and coefficient of friction 0.10. If the wheels themselves have a radius of 22 in., how much pull is needed to move a 20,000 lb load ?

Solution: The freight car is shown schematically in Fig. 5.5-11 and a free-body diagram of one of the wheels in Fig. 5.5-12. The friction circle is shown enlarged for clarity. Two forces act on the wheel, one at S where the wheel is in contact with the rail and one at a point on the bearing

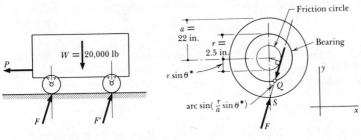

Fig. 5.5-11   **Fig. 5.5-12**

where the axle touches it. This latter force is tangent to the friction circle when the traction P is just great enough to make the wheel roll to the left. But the two forces at wheel and bearing must be "equal and opposite"; therefore the force at S must be tangent to the friction circle also, as shown. Of the two possible tangents the one that intersects the bearing circle at Q is the proper one because the corresponding force exerted by the axle produces a clockwise rotation about the center of the wheel as it should, since the wheel is about to rotate counterclockwise. The horizontal component of the reaction, F, at point S is

$$F \frac{r}{a} \sin \theta *$$

and the vertical component is

$$F\left(1 - \frac{r^2}{a^2} \sin^2 \theta *\right)^{1/2}.$$

The situation at the other wheel is the same, except that the reaction is not necessarily the same. Call it F'. We have

$$(F+F')\left(1 - \frac{r^2}{a^2} \sin^2 \theta *\right)^{1/2} = W$$

and

$$(F+F')\frac{r}{a} \sin \theta * = P,$$

so that

$$P = W \frac{\frac{r}{a} \sin \theta *}{\left(1 - \frac{r^2}{a^2} \sin^2 \theta *\right)^{1/2}}.$$

It appears from this result that it is desirable to have large wheels and small axles. With the numerical values of this example, $\theta * = 5.7°$ and

$$P = 20,000 \frac{\left(\frac{2.5}{22}\right)(0.1)}{\left[1 - \left(\frac{2.5}{22}\right)^2 (0.1)^2\right]^{1/2}} = (20,000)(0.011) = 220 \text{ lb.}$$

This is equivalent to an over-all coefficient of friction of 0.011. We see why it is much easier to pull a load in a wagon than to slide it along the ground.

Exercises

5.2-1: (a) A 30 lb block is placed on a plane inclined at an angle of 30° to the horizontal. The coefficient of limiting static friction is 0.30 and of kinetic friction is 0.25. Will the block be in equilibrium? What is the magnitude of the friction force acting on the block?

Ans.: 6.49 lb.

(b) If the slope angle is halved, to 15°, what are the answers to the questions of part (a)?

Ans.: 7.76 lb.

5.2-2: A force, P, making an angle, ϕ, with the inclined plane is applied to the 30 lb block of the previous exercise. For each of the two slope angles, (i) what is the minimum value of P and (ii) what is the corresponding ϕ to initiate motion of the block up the plane?

Ans.: For both slope angles, $\phi = 16.7°$; for case (a), $P_{min} = 21.8$ lb; for case (b), $P_{min} = 15.8$ lb.

5.2-3: The 30 lb uniform block on the 15° slope of Exercise 5.2-1b has dimensions 2.5 in. by 5 in. by 10 in. It is placed on the slope in each of the three positions shown. Will the block be in equilibrium for all three positions? Compute the distance from the lower corner of the block to the resultant normal reaction if the block is in equilibrium.

Ans.: (a) 4.66 in.

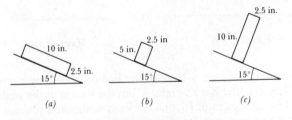

(a)   (b)   (c)

Exer. 5.2-3

5.2-4: The three boxes of Example 5.2-2 are shown here again, with an additional vertical load $Q = kW$ applied to the top box. Show that this load may be made so large that slipping can occur only at the floor, and

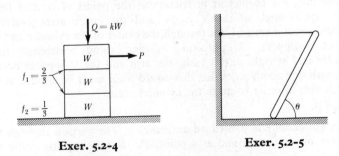

Exer. 5.2-4   **Exer. 5.2-5**

find the critical value of k. If $k=3$, what force P is needed to slip the stack of boxes?

Ans.: $P = 2W$ when $k = 3$.

5.2-5: The uniform rod is supported by the horizontal cable and the rough floor (coefficient of limiting friction 0.5). What is the smallest angle θ at which the rod can be in equilibrium?

Ans.: 45°.

5.2-6: A light wedge is used to raise a 2500 lb weight, as shown. The coefficient of friction at all contact surfaces is 0.5. What is the minimum force, P, needed to raise the weight?

Ans.: 6230 lb.

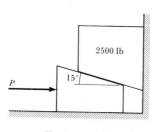

Exer. 5.2-6

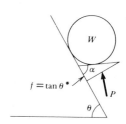

Exer. 5.2-7

5.2-7: The cylinder shown is held on the inclined plane by a wedge and a force, P. The cylinder has a weight W but the weight of the wedge may be ignored. The coefficient of friction between wedge and plane is $f = \tan \theta^*$ but all other contacts may be regarded as smooth. Supposing that the angle of inclination of the plane, θ, is less than θ^* and that θ^* is less than the wedge angle, α, find the smallest value of P which will prevent the cylinder and wedge from sliding down the plane. (Note that P is not necessarily parallel to the inclined plane.)

Ans.: $P = W \sin \theta \sin (\alpha - \theta^*)/\sin \alpha$.

5.2-8: A horizontal rod of 1 in. radius and weighing 50 lb rests on a V-shaped support, the coefficient of friction at the points of contact being 0.1. The apical angle of the V is 90° and the entire arrangement is symmetrical about a vertical line through the center of the cylinder and the apex of the V-support. A light arm 2 in. long extends horizontally from the cylinder and at right angles to it; the arm and the V-support do not interfere with one another. What downward force must be applied at the end of this arm in order to make the cylinder rotate?

Ans.: 2.45 lb.

5.2-9: An automobile is parked on an incline. The vertical through the mass center meets the ground at a point, P. Supposing that either the front wheels or the rear wheels (but not both sets) can be braked, show that it is best to brake the set closest to the point P.

5.2-10: The pin connections between the 13 in. light connecting rod and both the 5 in. radius flywheel and the small 3 lb piston are smooth, as is the shaft bearing at the center of the flywheel. The coefficient of limiting

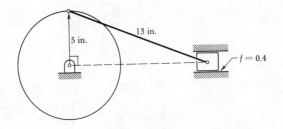

Exer. 5.2-10

static friction between the piston and the rough wall of the horizontal cylinder is $f = 0.4$.

(a) What counterclockwise torque M_1 supplied to the flywheel is needed to cause motion to impend?

Ans.: $M_1 = 5.14$ lb-in.

(b) What clockwise torque M_2 is needed for impending motion?

Ans.: $M_2 = 7.2$ lb-in.

5.2-11: A load W is to be raised by two light wedges, each of angle α. Which of the pictured arrangements, (a) or (b), is to be preferred? Consider both the load, P, required on each wedge for raising W and the self-locking characteristics of each mechanism. What would happen in case (b) if there were no vertical guide for W?

Ans.: System (a) is to be preferred for lifting the weight.

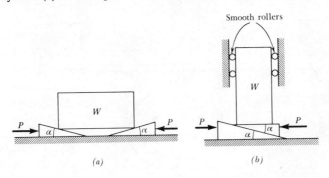

Exer. 5.2-11

5.2-12: The lifting device shown is to be designed so that the load will not slip, however heavy it may be. Show that this design criterion will be satisfied provided the dimensions are such that the angle α is less than the friction angle θ^*. Ignore friction at the pivot joints.

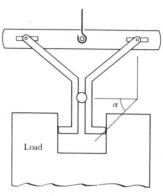

Exer. 5.2-12

5.2-13: What load, P, on the handle of the light brake lever is required to prevent rotation of the flywheel under the applied counterclockwise torque, M? The coefficient of friction is f. Can friction locking occur for proper choices of the system parameters? What happens if the direction of the torque is reversed?

Ans.: $P = \dfrac{M}{r} \dfrac{(a-fd)}{cf}$; locking occurs when $a = fd$; for clockwise M,

$$P = \dfrac{M}{r} \dfrac{(a+fd)}{cf}.$$

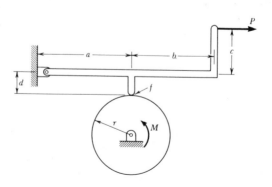

Exer. 5.2-13

5.2-14: A light collar 4 in. long slides on a vertical 3 in. diameter rod, the coefficient of friction at all points of contact being 0.2. Show that if the dimension c is greater than 8.5 in. the collar will not slip down, no matter how heavy the weight W.

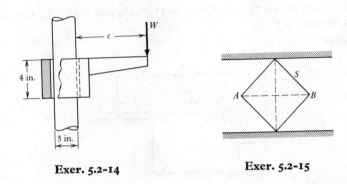

Exer. 5.2-14   Exer. 5.2-15

5.2-15: A light square block of side s is clamped tightly at two corners in the jaws of a vise, as shown. The coefficient of friction is f at each contact. If the clamping force is N, what force, P, along the diagonal AB is necessary to cause the block to slip? What torque, M, about an axis perpendicular to the plane is needed to cause slipping?

5.2-16: Body A weighs 200 lb, body B weighs 300 lb, and the weight of the brake may be ignored. The coefficients of friction are 0.30 between brake and A; 0.20 between A and B; and 0.10 between B and the plane. Find the minimum force, P, that will cause B to have impending motion to the right.

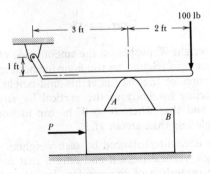

Exer. 5.2-16

Ans: 111 lb.

5.2-17: The force P applied to the bottom block is increased until motion of that block impends.

(a) What is the relationship between the coefficients of friction, the dimensions a and b, and the weights of the blocks that determines whether motion impends at contacts 1 and 3 or contacts 2 and 3?

Ans.: Motion impends at 1 and 3 if $bf_2 > af_1$.

(b) If $W = 2500$ lb, $w = 1500$ lb, $f_1 = 2f_2 = 3f_3 = 0.6$, and $b/a = 3/2$, what is P for slip impending?

Ans.: 1050 lb.

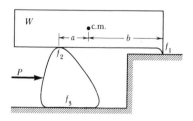

Exer. 5.2-17

5.2-18: A tapered cotter pin holds two rods which carry a tension, T. If the friction angle is θ^*, what is the largest taper angle, α, permissible?

Ans.: $\alpha = 2\theta^*$.

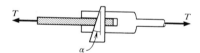

Exer. 5.2-18

5.2-19: A man of weight W pushes on the smooth side of a crate of weight W'. If the coefficient of friction on the floor for both man and crate is f, and if the mass-center of the man is at his mid-height, show that when $W > W'$ he can incline his body to the vertical by any angle less than arctan $(2fW'/W)$ and that when $W' > W$ he can incline his body to the vertical by any angle less than arctan $2f$.

5.2-20: A window is counterbalanced by sash weights. Show that it can be raised by a single vertical force if and only if that force is applied at a distance from the centerline of the window less than the height of the window divided by twice the coefficient of friction between window and moulding.

5.2-21: A uniform rod of length $2a$ and weight W rests on a horizontal cylinder of radius r, the axis of the rod being at right angles to the axis of the cylinder. If the angle of friction is θ^* and if the rod is initially horizontal, what is the largest weight that can be placed on the end of the rod without causing it to slip?

Ans.: $Wr\theta^*/(a-r\theta^*)$.

5.3-1: A beam rests on supports at its midpoint and at two equidistant points, their distances from the center support being chosen so that each of the three points of support carries a load of 100 lb (the total weight of the beam being, of course, 300 lb). The three points of support are at the same horizontal level. The coefficient of friction at each point of support is $\frac{1}{4}$. If a horizontal force, gradually increasing from zero, is applied to the beam at right angles to its length at one of the outer points of support, how large can this force grow before equilibrium becomes impossible?

Ans.: 37.5 lb.

5.3-2: A heavy circular disk is supported on three bosses, A, B, and C, which form an equilateral triangle as shown. The weight of the disk is W and the coefficient of friction at each boss is f. A gradually increasing horizontal force is applied to one of the bosses in a direction parallel to the

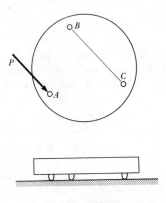

Exer. 5.3-2

line joining the other two. (a) How large can P become before equilibrium is broken? (b) Locate the axis about which the disk begins to rotate.

Ans.: (a) $P = \frac{2}{3}fW$; (b) initial rotation is about axis through the angle bisectors.

5.3-3: A horizontal cylinder of weight W rests in a V-shaped groove whose sides are inclined at $45°$ to the vertical. The coefficient of friction between groove and cylinder is 0.6. What is the minimum force, P, that will disturb equilibrium, when applied to the cylinder?

Ans.: 0.35W.

5.3-4: Two identical uniform rods, AB and BC, of weight W, are smoothly pinned at B and are laid in a straight line on a rough horizontal table. The length of each rod is l and the coefficient of friction is f. A gradually increasing force, P, is applied to point A at right angles to the bars. Show that equilibrium will be broken when $P = fW[\sqrt{4\sqrt{2}-2} - \sqrt{2}]$.

5.3-5: A particle is held on a rough inclined plane by a smooth light rod which is smoothly pivoted at a point of the plane. The acute angle, α, between this rod and the line of steepest slope on the plane is so large that, in the absence of any further constraint, the particle would not be in

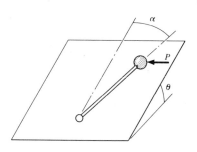

Exer. 5.3-5

equilibrium. Let W be the weight of the particle, f be the coefficient of friction between it and the plane, and θ be the angle of inclination of the plane to the horizontal. Show that the minimum additional horizontal force, P, needed to preserve equilibrium is given by the expression $W(\sin \theta \sin \alpha - f \cos \theta)/\cos \alpha$.

5.3-6: A uniform rod of length $3l$ and weight W rests on a rough horizontal table, being supported at one end, A, and at a point distant $2l$ from A by small projections. At the end of the rod remote from A it is subjected to a gradually increasing force, P. When equilibrium is broken the rod begins to rotate about a point distant $2l$ from the points of support. Find (a) the magnitude of P at this instant and (b) the angle it makes with the bar.

Ans.: (a) $P = 0.9fW$; (b) $16°$.

5.3-7: The rod of the previous problem is subjected to a couple about a vertical axis through the end of the rod remote from A. How large can this couple become before equilibrium is broken? How does the rod begin to move?

Ans.: $M = \frac{1}{2}fWl$.

5.3-8: A square table of weight W with a leg at each corner stands on a horizontal floor whose coefficient of friction is f. Find the minimum horizontal force which, applied at a corner, will make the table slip.

Ans.: $\frac{1}{4}(1 + \sqrt{2})fW$.

5.4-1: A pulley of 9 in. diameter drives a second pulley of 25 in. diameter in the same plane, their centers being 4 ft apart, by means of a flat belt. (a) If the minimum tension is 100 lb, what is the maximum tension when the belt is on the point of slipping? (b) How much torque can be transmitted in this way? Take $f = 0.3$ and assume that the belt is arranged as in the figure.

Ans.: (a) 232 lb; (b) 595 lb-in.

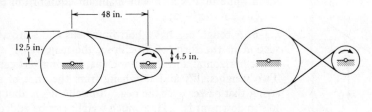

Exer. 5.4-1   **Exer. 5.4-2**

5.4-2: If, in Exercise 5.4-1, the belt is crossed, as in the revised figure, but all other conditions remain the same, answer the same questions.

Ans.: (a) 313 lb; (b) 960 lb-in.

5.4-3: The band brake shown is a modification of one described in the text. It is designed to be equally effective in resisting counterclockwise and clockwise torque applied to the drum. Find the maximum torque that can be restrained by this arrangement and verify that this value is in fact independent of the direction of rotation which impends.

Ans.: $M = \dfrac{Pr(a+b)}{b}\left(\dfrac{1 - e^{-\frac{3}{2}\pi f}}{1 + e^{-\frac{3}{2}\pi f}}\right).$

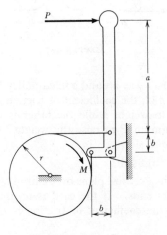

Exer. 5.4-3

5.4-4: How large a load can be restrained by a man exerting a pull of 100 lb on a rope wrapped for one and one-half turns around a post if $f = 0.4$?
Ans.: 4320 lb.

5.4-5: A circular disk of weight W is pressed against a perfectly rough wall by a cord attached to the wall and carrying a weight P. The cord makes an angle α with the wall. The coefficient of friction between cord and disk is f. Show that the minimum value of P which will maintain equilibrium is $W/[(1 + \cos \alpha)e^{\alpha f} - 2]$.

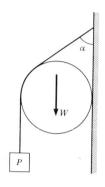

5.4-6: A rough peg has a horizontal axis and a cross-section in the form of an ellipse, the major axis, a, being horizontal and the minor axis, b, being vertical. Two weights, W_1 and W_2, hang from the ends of a string that passes over the peg. Initially W_1 is about to slip downwards. How much weight can be added to W_2 before it begins to descend?
Ans.: $(W_1^2 - W_2^2)/W_2$.

Exer. 5.4-5

5.4-7: A flexible steel wire is threaded around three posts of radius $r = 1.5$ in., spaced as shown. (a) What tension, T, is needed to overcome a resistance of 100 lb at the end of the wire if $f = 0.32$? (b) What is the maximum pressure exerted by the wire on the post?
Ans.: (a) $T = 272$ lb; (b) $p_{max} = 181$ lb/in.

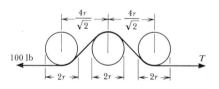

Exer. 5.4-7

5.4-8: A belt wraps half way around a fixed pulley having a 45° total apical angle V-groove in which the coefficient of friction is 0.3. One end of the belt carries a 1000 lb weight while the other is pulled with a force, P. (a) What is the minimum P to raise the weight? (b) At what value of P will the weight descend slowly?
Ans.: (a) 11,740 lb; (b) 85 lb.

5.4-9: A cord hangs in a vertical plane over a fixed horizontal peg and carries weights W, W' at its ends. If the cord is on the point of slipping and $W' > W$, show that the coefficient of friction is given by the expression
$$f = \frac{1}{\pi} \log (W'/W).$$

5.4-10: A device for applying torque to a shaft of radius r consists of a bar, AC, to which is attached a strap, BDA. The bar AC is normal to the surface of the cylinder, on which it bears at A. Show that no matter how large is the force P applied at C at right angles to the bar, no slipping will occur, provided f exceeds the value determined by the equation

$$4e^{-(5\pi f)/3} - 2\sqrt{3}f = 1.$$

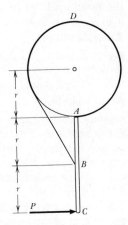

5.5-1: A screw jack has a square-threaded screw of mean diameter 2 in. and pitch 0.5 in. If the coefficient of friction between screw and nut is 0.15, what force must be exerted at the end of a lever 25 in. long in order to raise a 4000 lb load?

Ans.: 38 lb.

5.5-2: What force is necessary to lower the load of the previous problem, and what is the efficiency of the screw jack?

Ans.: 11 lb in direction opposite to that used in raising load.

Exer. 5.4-10

5.5-3: A square-threaded screw is tightened by a moment of 1500 in-lb to a tension, T. The screw has a diameter of 1.5 in. and a pitch of 0.3 in. The base of the nut has an outside diameter of 3.2 in. and an inside diameter of 1.6 in. Find the pull, T, (a) on the assumption that all friction is negligible, (b) on the assumption that $f = 0.2$ for the contact of screw in nut,

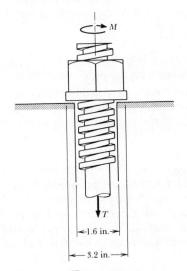

Exer. 5.5-3

but can be neglected elsewhere, and (c) on the assumption that $f = 0.2$ at all surfaces where motion impends.

Ans.: (a) 31,400 lb; (b) 7470 lb; (c) 3400 lb.

5.5-4: If the nut in the previous problem has a depth of 1 in., what will be the mean load per in. on the threads when they are tightened to an axial load $T = 2000$ lb?

Ans.: 130 lb/in.

5.5-5: Estimate the tension in a quarter-inch screw having 32 V-shaped threads per in. when a torque of 50 lb-in. is applied. Take $f = 0.15$ and the semi-apical angle as 29°.

Ans.: 1840 lb.

5.5-6: Criticize the logical structure of the following line of reasoning: A machine is used to raise a weight, W, through a height of 1 ft by means of an applied force. Suppose the work put in is cW. Then the forward efficiency is $1/c$. The energy lost in friction is $cW - W = (c-1)W$. When the machine runs freely back under gravity to its original position, the work done by the weight is W and the work lost in friction is again $(c-1)W$. The surplus energy is $W - (c-1)W = (2-c)W$. If $c = 2$ there is no surplus energy and so the machine will not automatically run back when the applied force is removed. Therefore if the forward efficiency is less than 50 per cent a machine will not automatically run back when the applied load is removed. Why is the argument only approximately true?

5.5-7: The tapered shank of a drill has a total apical angle of 12° and a mean diameter of $\frac{3}{4}$ in. It is entered lightly in the chuck and the drill is then operated with an axial force of 50 lb. If the coefficient of friction is 0.17, how much torque can the drill exert on the workpiece before it begins to slip in the chuck? Assume that the bearing of the drill in the chuck is "worn."

Ans.: 30.5 lb-in.

5.5-8: When a ball bearing is pressed into a steel plate by a force, P, it deforms and makes contact with the plate over a circle of radius a. Within this circle the normal pressure is governed by the law $p = (3P/2\pi a^3)\sqrt{a^2 - r^2}$, where r denotes distance from the center of the contact circle. Using this expression for p, estimate the torque required to spin such a ball bearing about a vertical axis.

Ans.: $3\pi f P a/16$.

5.5-9: When a hard steel, flat-ended circular shaft is pressed axially into a somewhat softer elastic material, the pressure exerted on the base of the cylinder is given by the expression $p = (P/2\pi a)(a^2 - r^2)^{-\frac{1}{2}}$. Assuming this distribution of pressure and a coefficient of friction f, find the torque required to rotate the shaft of a plain-thrust bearing. Compare your results with the text expressions for p constant and for p proportional to r^{-1}.

Ans.: $(\pi/4)fPa$.

5.5-10: A marine propulsion shaft carries a thrust of 6700 lb. This load is held by collars on which the pressure may be considered uniform. The collars are 8 in. *OD* and 5 in. *ID*. For $f = 0.08$ compute the torque and horsepower lost in friction when the shaft rotates at 120 rpm.

Ans.: 1740 lb-in; 3.3 hp.

5.5-11: A plain thrust bearing is recessed as shown. Find expressions for the torque required to produce uniform rotation if the friction coefficient is f. Assume (a) uniform pressure and (b) uniform wear.

Ans.: (a) $M = \dfrac{2fP}{3}\left(\dfrac{r_0^3 - r_1^3}{r_0^2 - r_1^2}\right)$; (b) $M' = \dfrac{1}{2}fP(r_0 + r_1)$.

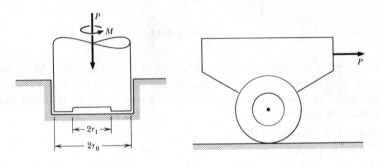

Exer. 5.5-11   **Exer. 5.5-12**

5.5-12: A two-wheeled cart carries a load, W, centered over the axle. (a) If the wheels are of 2.5 ft radius, if the axle is of 2 in. radius, and if the coefficient of friction at the journal bearing is 0.05, how heavy a load can be pulled by a horizontal force $P = 100$ lb? (b) How large must the coefficient of friction be so that the wheel will not slip where it is in contact with the road?

Ans.: (a) 30,000 lb; (b) 0.0033.

5.5-13: A light cord passes over a wheel mounted on a bearing carried on a horizontal axle. The cord carries weights W and W', which are so related that the wheel is on the point of turning around the axle. Assuming the cord does not slip, show that the friction angle of the bearing is given by the expression $\theta^* = \arcsin\left(\dfrac{W - W'}{W + W'}\dfrac{R}{r}\right)$, where R and r are the radii of the wheel and axle, respectively. Compare this result with that for Exercise 5.4-9.

5.5-14: A shaft 6 in. in diameter carries a vertical load of 10,000 lb and a horizontal load of 15,000 lb. For $f = 0.04$ find the horsepower lost in friction at the journals when the shaft is driven at 120 rpm by a torque.

Ans.: 4.31 hp.

5.5-15: The bell-crank shown is carried in a fixed axle at O, the radius of the axle being 2 in. and the coefficient of friction being 0.3. Arm OA is 10 in. long and makes an angle of 45° with the horizontal. Arm OB is 2 ft long and makes an angle of 30° with the horizontal. A 100 lb downward

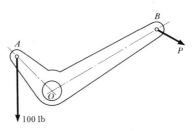

Exer. 5.5-15

force acts at A. (a) What force, P, acting at B in a direction at an angle of 60° with the vertical, is needed to make the bell-crank rotate in a clockwise direction? (b) Compare this with the force that would be required in the absence of friction.

Ans.: (a) 37 lb; (b) 34 lb.

Centers of Mass

A.1 Definition of the Mass Center of a Body

In this appendix we summarize the results of Section 2.7 on mass centers, discuss methods of locating them, and provide a table of positions of the mass centers of some uniform bodies.

(a) *System of Discrete Particles.* Suppose, for each of a system of N particles, we know the mass m_i, $i = 1, 2, 3, \ldots N$, and the position vector $\mathbf{r}_i$ with respect to a fixed point O. The mass center of the system is the point in space with position vector $\mathbf{r}^*$ defined by

$$\mathbf{r}^* = \frac{\sum\limits_{i=1}^{N} m_i \mathbf{r}_i}{\sum\limits_{i=1}^{N} m_i} = \frac{\sum\limits_{i=1}^{N} m_i \mathbf{r}_i}{m}, \qquad \textbf{A.1-1}$$

where

$$m = \sum_{i=1}^{N} m_i \qquad \textbf{A.1-2}$$

is the total mass of the system. If a particular cartesian coordinate system (x, y, z) with origin at O is introduced, so that the i-th particle has position coordinates (x_i, y_i, z_i), i.e., $\mathbf{r}_i = x_i \mathbf{i} + y_i \mathbf{j} + z_i \mathbf{k}$, then the mass center has position coordinates (x^*, y^*, z^*)—or $\mathbf{r}^* = x^*\mathbf{i} + y^*\mathbf{j} + z^*\mathbf{k}$—given by the scalar equivalents to Eq. A.1-1:

$$x^* = \frac{\sum\limits_{i=1}^{N} m_i x_i}{\sum\limits_{i=1}^{N} m_i}, \qquad y^* = \frac{\sum\limits_{i=1}^{N} m_i y_i}{\sum\limits_{i=1}^{N} m_i}, \qquad z^* = \frac{\sum\limits_{i=1}^{N} m_i z_i}{\sum\limits_{i=1}^{N} m_i}. \qquad \textbf{A.1-3}$$

(b) *Continuous Systems.* Suppose a body with distributed mass is given. The mass center position $\mathbf{r}^*$ is then defined by an integral equivalent to Eq. A.1-1. Formally, we divide the body into N parts, denoting the mass of the i-th part by Δm_i, $i = 1, 2, \ldots N$, and the position vector to an arbitrary point in the i-th part by $\mathbf{r}_i$, $i = 1, 2, \ldots N$. We then form the Riemann sums

$$\sum_{i=1}^{N} \Delta m_i, \qquad \sum_{i=1}^{N} \mathbf{r}_i \, \Delta m_i,$$

and consider the limit processes

$$\lim_{\substack{N \to \infty \\ \Delta m_i \to 0}} \left(\sum_{i=1}^{N} \Delta m_i \right), \qquad \lim_{\substack{N \to \infty \\ \Delta m_i \to 0}} \left(\sum_{i=1}^{N} \mathbf{r}_i \, \Delta m_i \right).$$

If these limits exist whatever the mode of subdivision may be and whatever the choice of the points $\mathbf{r}_i$ may be, then the Riemann integrals

$$m = \int dm \quad \text{and} \quad \int \mathbf{r} \, dm$$

exist, with m being the total mass of the body again. The mass center has position vector

$$\mathbf{r}^* = \frac{1}{m} \int \mathbf{r} \, dm \qquad \textbf{A.1-4}$$

with respect to the origin O.

If a cartesian coordinate system (x, y, z) is introduced, with $\mathbf{r} = x\mathbf{i} + y\mathbf{j} + z\mathbf{k}$, then the scalar equivalents to A.1-4 give the position coordinates (x^*, y^*, z^*) of the mass center:

$$x^* = \frac{1}{m} \int x \, dm, \qquad y^* = \frac{1}{m} \int y \, dm, \qquad z^* = \frac{1}{m} \int z \, dm. \qquad \textbf{A.1-5}$$

The integrals of Eqs. A.1-4 and A.1-5 are evaluated usually as line, surface, or volume integrals over the spatial region occupied by the body. A mass density function is introduced in order to transform the integrals into the desired form. If the body is curvilinear in form (thin rods or beams, for example), a line density

$\lambda(s)$ with dimensions mass per unit length may be defined: $\lambda = \lim_{\Delta s \to 0} (\Delta m/\Delta s)$, where Δm is the mass of a length Δs of the body. Similarly, surface and volume densities $\sigma = \lim_{\Delta A \to 0} (\Delta m/\Delta A)$ and $\rho = \lim_{\Delta V \to 0} (\Delta m/\Delta V)$ may be defined for bodies having the appropriate shapes: thin plates and shells are examples of the former, solid cylinders and thick slabs are examples of the latter. The integrals A.1-5 then become of the form, say for the case of a volume density,

$$x^* = \frac{1}{m} \int \int \int_V x\rho \, dV, \qquad y^* = \frac{1}{m} \int \int \int_V y\rho \, dV,$$

$$z^* = \frac{1}{m} \int \int \int_V z\rho \, dV, \qquad\qquad \textbf{A.1-6}$$

where the total mass m is given by

$$m = \int \int \int_V \rho \, dV. \qquad\qquad \textbf{A.1-7}$$

The mass center is of importance in statics primarily because of its usual identification with the center of gravity and hence with a point on the line of action of the resultant weight force on a body. In dynamics, it appears as the favored point in many ways: as the point which has known acceleration when the external forces are known (principle of motion of the mass center), as an appropriate base point for the principle of moment of momentum, and as the fundamental base point for moment of inertia computations.

The form of the computation for the position of the mass center is one of common occurrence in mathematics and physics. The integrals $\int x \, dm$, etc., are examples of the concept of the *first moment* of a scalar quantity, in this case mass. In general, $\int x \, df$ is the first moment of f with respect to the yz-plane. If f is, say, volume, then the computation leads to the coordinates (x^*, y^*, z^*) of the *centroid* of the volume. If $df = p \, dA$, where p is the pressure on the plane area dA, then we obtain first moment integrals of the density form—with the pressure p replacing the surface mass density σ—and the resulting point coordinates are those of the *center of pressure* (Section 4.4). In particular, if the mass density of a body is constant, then it disappears from the computations of Eqs. A.1-6, since it is a common factor in both the numerator and the denominator (m) of each equation. In this circumstance, the mass center and the geometrical centroid of the body are the same point. Such a body of constant density is said to be *uniform*.

A.2 Translation and Rotation of Axes

In this section we shall compute the position of the mass center with respect to another coordinate system, given its position with respect to one coordinate system. This computation is straightforward, involving no more than vectorial addition and the scalar product for finding components of vectors.

Suppose we are given one set of cartesian axes with origin O: $Oxyz$, and a parallel set with origin P: $Pxyz$ (Fig. A.2-1). The latter

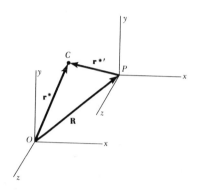

Fig. A.2-1

set is said to be translated with respect to the first (and conversely); that is, there has been a simple shift of origin from O to P, with no change in the coordinate directions. Let $\mathbf{R} = X\mathbf{i} + Y\mathbf{j} + Z\mathbf{k}$ denote the position of P relative to O, $\mathbf{r}^* = x^*\mathbf{i} + y^*\mathbf{j} + z^*\mathbf{k}$ denote the position of the mass center C of a system relative to O, and $\mathbf{r}^{*\prime} = x^{*\prime}\mathbf{i} + y^{*\prime}\mathbf{j} + z^{*\prime}\mathbf{k}$ denote the position of the mass center C relative to P. The triangle law of addition results in

$$\mathbf{r}^* = \mathbf{r}^{*\prime} + \mathbf{R} \qquad\qquad \textbf{A.2-1}$$

or

$$x^* = x^{*\prime} + X, \qquad y^* = y^{*\prime} + Y, \qquad z^* = z^{*\prime} + Z. \qquad \textbf{A.2-2}$$

Given $\mathbf{R}$ and either $\mathbf{r}^*$ or $\mathbf{r}^{*\prime}$, these serve to compute the third vector.

Suppose we are given the two sets of cartesian coordinates $Oxyz$ and $Ox'y'z'$ with the same origin, and the position vectors $\mathbf{r}^* = x^*\mathbf{i} + y^*\mathbf{j} + z^*\mathbf{k}$ and $\mathbf{r}^{*\prime} = x^{*\prime}\mathbf{i}' + y^{*\prime}\mathbf{j}' + z^{*\prime}\mathbf{k}'$ of the mass center C of the system in the two sets (Fig. A.2-2). In fact, $\mathbf{r}^* \equiv \mathbf{r}^{*\prime}$, since the vector from O to the mass center C is a given directed line segment; only its *representation* in scalar components differs. Either set of axes is said to be rotated from the other, or to be obtainable by a rotation (see *Dynamics*, Chapter VI). Since $x^{*\prime}$ is the x'-component of $\mathbf{r}^*$, we must have $x^{*\prime} = \mathbf{r}^* \cdot \mathbf{i}'$, where $\mathbf{i}'$ is the unit vector in the x'-direction. The (x, y, z) components of $\mathbf{i}'$ are the direction cosines of the x'-direction with respect to the (x, y, z) axes; therefore,

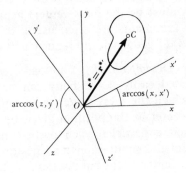

Fig. A.2–2

$$x^{*\prime} = x^* \cos(x, x') + y^* \cos(y, x') + z^* \cos(z, x'),$$

and, similarly,

$$y^{*\prime} = x^* \cos(x, y') + y^* \cos(y, y') + z^* \cos(z, y'), \qquad \textbf{A.2-3}$$

$$z^{*\prime} = x^* \cos(x, z') + y^* \cos(y, z') + z^* \cos(z, z').$$

Indeed, these typify the transformation of the components (A_x, A_y, A_z) into $(A_{x'}, A_{y'}, A_{z'})$ of any vector $\mathbf{A}$ under such a rotational transformation of coordinates (see Section 4.5).

A.3 Further Methods of Locating the Mass Center

(a) *Bodies with a Plane of Mass Symmetry.* If a body has a plane of mass symmetry, then the mass center must lie in that plane. A plane of mass symmetry is one such that the mass density is the same at points which are mirror images of one another in the plane. A plane of geometrical symmetry is not necessarily a plane of mass symmetry; it will be also a plane of mass symmetry for uniform bodies, however.

(b) *Bodies with Multiple Symmetries.* If a body has two planes of mass symmetry, then the mass center must lie on their line of intersection; if a body has three or more planes of mass symmetry, then their common point of intersection is the mass center. The case when three or more planes of symmetry intersect along a common line, of course, leads only to the conclusion that the mass center lies on that line. If every plane through such a line is a plane of mass symmetry, then the axis is an axis of symmetry and the body is axially symmetric —a uniform circular cylinder, for example. A uniform sphere is an example of a radially symmetric body, with every plane through a single point (which must be the mass center) being a plane of symmetry. Symmetry arguments are often useful in locating the mass center (and centroid) of geometrically regular uniform bodies.

(c) *Method of Decomposition.* The mass center of complex bodies may be located easily if the body can be decomposed into parts, for each of which the mass center is known. The composite body has its mass center at the position given by treating the body as a system of discrete particles, each particle having mass equal to the mass of one of the subdivisions and position the same as the position of the mass center of the subdivision.

For example, the uniform isosceles trapezoid of base angle $60°$, base lengths l and L, and total mass m shown in Fig. A.3-1a, has an x-coordinate of mass center given by $x^* = L/2$, by symmetry. The

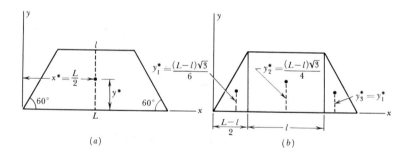

Fig. A.3-1

y-coordinate may be found by decomposing the trapezoid into two triangles and a rectangle, as in Fig. A.3-1b. The altitude of the trapezoid is $h = (L-l)\tan 60°/2$; the y-coordinates of the mass centers of the parts are, therefore, as given in the figure. Since the trapezoid is uniform, the mass of each part is equal to the total mass, m, multiplied by the ratio of the area of the part to the total area:

$$m_1 = m_3 = \left(\frac{L-l}{L+l}\right)\left(\frac{m}{2}\right), \qquad m_2 = \left(\frac{2l}{L+l}\right)m.$$

Therefore,

$$my^* = m_1 y_1^* + m_2 y_2^* + m_3 y_3^* = 2m_1 y_1^* + m_2 y_2^*$$

$$= \left(\frac{L-l}{L+l}\,m\right)\left(\frac{L-l}{6}\,\sqrt{3}\right) + \left(\frac{2l}{L+l}\,m\right)\left(\frac{L-l}{4}\,\sqrt{3}\right)$$

$$= \frac{m(L-l)\sqrt{3}}{12(L+l)}\,[2L - 2l + 6l],$$

or

$$y^* = \frac{(L-l)(L+2l)\sqrt{3}}{6(L+l)}.$$

The same conclusion can be reached in another way, by using a "negative" mass and removing part of a larger body to obtain the one we wish to consider. The trapezoid considered before is part of a large equilateral triangle of side L, obtained by cutting off a triangle of side l (Fig. A.3-2).

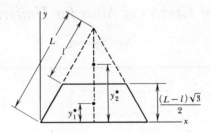

Fig. A.3-2

If the large triangle is body 1 and the small triangle is body 2, we have:

$$m_1 = \frac{L^2}{L^2 - l^2}\,m, \qquad m_2 = \frac{l^2}{L^2 - l^2}\,m, \qquad m = m_1 + (-m_2);$$

$$y_1^* = \frac{L\sqrt{3}}{6}, \qquad y_2^* = \frac{(L-l)\sqrt{3}}{2} + \frac{l\sqrt{3}}{6};$$

$$my^* = m_1 y_1^* + (-m_2)y_2^* = \frac{mL^3\sqrt{3}}{6(L^2 - l^2)} - \frac{ml^2(3L - 2l)\sqrt{3}}{6(L^2 - l^2)}$$

$$= \frac{m(L^3 - 3Ll^2 + 2l^3)\sqrt{3}}{6(L^2 - l^2)} = \frac{m(L-l)^2(L+2l)\sqrt{3}}{6(L^2 - l^2)}.$$

Therefore,

$$y^* = \frac{(L-l)(L+2l)\sqrt{3}}{6(L+l)},$$

the same, of course, as the previous result.

A.4 Center of Mass of Uniform Bodies

The table contains the following information for uniform mass distributions:

(1) Name of body, picture relative to a coordinate system $Oxyz$.

(2) The length (L), area (A), and volume (V) of one-, two-, and three-dimensional mass distributions, respectively; the total mass is the appropriate constant mass density multiplied by L, A, or V.

(3) The position $\mathbf{r}^* = x^*\mathbf{i} + y^*\mathbf{j} + z^*\mathbf{k}$ of the mass center relative to the given origin O and the given axis system.

Table of Centers of Mass for Uniform Bodies

Body	Axis System	$L - A - V$ $\mathbf{r}^*$
Thin Rod, Straight		$L = l$ $x^* = \dfrac{l}{2}$ $y^* = z^* = 0$
Thin Rod, Circular Arc		$L = 2r\theta$ $x^* = \dfrac{r \sin \theta}{\theta}$ $y^* = z^* = 0$

Body	Axis System	$L-A-V$ $\mathbf{r}^*$
Thin Rod, Circular Hoop		$L = 2\pi r$ $x^* = y^* = r$ $z^* = 0$
Isosceles Triangular Plate		$A = \frac{1}{2} bh$ $x^* = \frac{b}{2}$ $y^* = \frac{h}{3}$ $z^* = 0$
Square Plate		$A = a^2$ $x^* = y^* = \frac{a}{2}$ $z^* = 0$

Body	Axis System	$L - A - V$ $\mathbf{r}^*$
Rectangular Plate		$A = bh$ $x^* = \dfrac{b}{2}$ $y^* = \dfrac{h}{2}$ $z^* = 0$
Circular Disk		$A = \pi r^2$ $x^* = y^* = r$ $z^* = 0$
Circular Ring (Annulus)		$A = \pi(r_2^2 - r_1^2)$ $x^* = y^* = r_2$ $z^* = 0$

Body	Axis System	$L-A-V$ $\mathbf{r}^*$
Circular Sector		$A = r^2\theta$ $x^* = \dfrac{2r \sin \theta}{3\theta}$ $y^* = z^* = 0$
Elliptical Disk		$A = \pi ab$ $x^* = a$ $y^* = b$ $z^* = 0$
Cube		$V = a^3$ $x^* = y^*$ $\quad = z^* = \dfrac{a}{2}$

Body	Axis System	$L-A-V$ $\mathbf{r}^*$
Rectangular Parallelepiped		$V = abc$ $x^* = \dfrac{a}{2}$ $y^{*\cdot} = \dfrac{b}{2}$ $z^* = \dfrac{c}{2}$
Right Circular Cone		$V = \dfrac{1}{3}\pi r^2 h$ $x^* = z^* = 0$ $y^* = \dfrac{h}{4}$
Right Circular Cylinder, Solid		$V = \pi r^2 h$ $x^* = z^* = 0$ $y^* = \dfrac{h}{2}$

Body	Axis System	$L - A - V$ $\mathbf{r}^*$
Right Circular Cylinder, Hollow		$V = \pi h(r_2^2 - r_1^2)$ $x^* = z^* = 0$ $y^* = \dfrac{h}{2}$
Sphere, Solid		$V = \dfrac{4}{3}\pi r^3$ $x^* = y^* = z^*$ $= 0$
Sphere, Hollow		$V = \dfrac{4}{3}\pi(r_2^3 - r_1^3)$ $x^* = y^* = z^*$ $= 0$
Hemisphere, Solid		$V = \dfrac{2}{3}\pi r^3$ $x^* = z^* = 0$ $y^* = \dfrac{3r}{8}$

Body	Axis System	$L - A - V$ $\mathbf{r}^*$
Ellipsoid		$V = \dfrac{4}{3}\pi abc$ $x^* = y^* = z^*$ $= 0$

INDEX

INDEX

DYNAMICS

PREFACE

This book is intended to accompany the first course in dynamics for engineering students who have previously studied elementary calculus and either statics or elementary physics. We believe that a course in dynamics treating three-dimensional motion is a proper and necessary part of such students' professional training. The approach adopted is "vectorial," so that the full three-dimensional theory may be presented with reasonable completeness and rigor. This book, the result of three years of trial in classroom use, is designed to place the student at a satisfactory professional level from which he may proceed to technological applications or to advanced aspects of dynamical theory.

We have followed a pattern of presenting the pertinent theoretical treatment of a mechanical model system completely, before dealing with technological applications involving that model. The examples in the theory chapters thus tend to be somewhat more academic in nature than the ones in the physical application chapters. This division enables us, however, to discuss the technical applications against the background of various possible methods of analysis and to show how one chooses an appropriate method. The treatment of kinematics has been split up, and the necessary parts are presented just prior to their applications in kinetics. The idea of a coherent single treatment has its logical attractions, but our teaching experience has shown us that the present approach is a better one. The inclusion of the principle of virtual work in the dynamics course, rather than in its traditional place in statics, has been motivated primarily by similar considerations. An understanding of kinematics seems to us an essential prerequisite for an understanding of any work-energy relation.

The text is intended to be reasonably self-contained. With the appendix on vector algebra, it may be used by students who have not had a prior statics course using vectorial notation. Sections and paragraphs not essential to the main development have been set in smaller type. Instructors will in any case wish to select the application sections they prefer to consider. The solved examples are an integral part of the development and, we trust, illuminate the theory. A conventional numbering system has been used for easy cross-reference; for example, Eq. 2.4-5 is the fifth equation in Section 4 of Chapter II. The exercises are graded in difficulty somewhat, most, we feel, being of moderate difficulty. No real originality can be claimed for the exercises or for the presentation of the theory; elementary mechanics, and textbooks on the subject, have a long and honorable history, and we cannot help being influenced by the books we have read and taught from. This book is a reflection of our teaching experience and of the spirit in which we were taught.

Any book of this nature is in many ways a cooperative effort involving the work and ideas of others as well as of the authors. We are happy to acknowledge the help and thoughtfulness of many people: The staff members of the Wadsworth Publishing Company; the instructors who have taught from our notes in recitation sections; the secretarial staff of the Department of Aeronautics and Engineering Mechanics who have typed version after version, especially Mrs. Jeanne Ince, Mrs. Kathleen Webers, and Miss Ann Mitchell; Professor B. J. Lazan, department head, who has encouraged our intentions and provided us with the time and opportunity to complete our work; our colleagues who regularly teach the courses in mechanics and who have helped us clarify our thinking in many discussions, especially Professors P. R. Sethna, T. J. Mentel, and A. R. Robinson (now of the University of Illinois); Professors George Leitmann and R. M. Rosenberg, University of California, Berkeley; Richmond C. Neff, University of Arizona; and Robert J. Zaworski, Oregon State

College, who provided helpful comments and suggestions during the preparation of the manuscript; and the hundreds of engineering students of the University of Minnesota, who, by their reactions in and out of class, have helped us to find our way to a point that we feel is pedagogically sound and that we hope is professionally satisfactory.

L.E.G.

W.H.W.

CONTENTS

Contents

Contents

Contents

Contents

Introduction to
the Calculus of Vectors

1.1 Fundamental Ideas

Dynamics is concerned with the prediction of the motions of the widest possible variety of objects and with the computation of the effects that these motions entail. Its basic principles are linked to those of electrodynamics and thermodynamics. Its logical structure has long been a model for other branches of science. In technology, dynamics forms the basis for the design of high-speed vehicles, rotating and reciprocating machinery, structures subject to wind and earthquake effects, fluid flow devices, and electromechanical systems. Engineers, today increasingly confronted with the design of structural elements subject to large accelerations, require a thorough understanding of dynamical principles. Apart from utilitarian considerations, moreover, there has always been an element of delight in the mastery of a tool of the intellect that from a modest number of principles draws explanations of phenomena as diverse as the tipping of a boy's sled rounding a curve and the way in which a gyrocompass can be made to align itself with the earth's axis of rotation.

Modern dynamics is based upon Newton's laws of motion. Before these can be introduced and discussed effectively, it is necessary to describe some of the underlying concepts of mechanics. Words like "time interval," "velocity," and "acceleration" are part of everyday speech. Their technical meanings, however, embody subtle ideas. In this chapter we discuss those terms that refer to the mathematical description of motion—reserving others such as "force," "mass," and "momentum" for Chapter II.

The description of motion is based upon length measurements— that is, ultimately, upon comparison of distances with marks on a hard, straight rod known as a scale. If the direction of the rod is altered, it is assumed that the distance between two marks on it does not change. We express this by saying that space is *isotropic*; that is, its properties are independent of direction. The distance between marks does not change if the rod is placed in another location; we express this by saying that space is *homogeneous*. Since we do not wish to suppose that length measurements are limited to a surface or to particular locations, we say that space is *three-dimensional* and *continuous*. The attribution of these properties is a convention, but it is one that appears indispensable to any theory that is to be confirmed by experiment.

We also wish to make use of geometry and trigonometry in connection with the description of motion. Mathematics recognizes a variety of geometries and their corresponding "spaces," each kind having its own set of postulates from which its theorems follow. One geometry whose postulates satisfy the requirements of the preceding paragraph is that of Euclid. In classical mechanics the postulates of Euclidean geometry are taken as properties of space. All the wealth of geometric and trigonometric propositions learned in first courses in mathematics thereby become available for use in describing motion. Modern analysis has shown that this is not the sole possible choice. Euclid's fifth postulate asserts, in effect, that through a point not on a given straight line one and only one straight line parallel to the given line can be drawn. By denying this assertion and substituting others for it, a limited number of geometries can be constructed that still permit objects to be moved about freely without a change of dimensions. The preference for Euclidean geometry—like the statement that space is homogeneous, isotropic, three-dimensional, and continuous—is, therefore, a convention. But these are not arbitrary conventions. They are chosen because they are fruitful and consistent. If they did not lead to the applications of mechanics in technology and science, they would be abandoned; in fact, the

Euclidean convention is called into question in connection with the general theory of relativity.

Time is the second fundamental notion in the description of motion. It is commonly said that time flows evenly or uniformly, independent of events. This will hardly serve as a definition of time, however, since terms such as "evenly" or "uniformly" have no meaning independent of the quantity being described. The present point of view is that the symbol t, which appears in equations of motion, is simply a useful independent variable. It takes on all the values of the real number continuum. Every time interval corresponds to the interval between two real numbers. When the equations of motion are solved, and spatial position is known as a function of t, we wish to use the results of the analysis to predict the performance of actual mechanical systems. This is accomplished by identifying t with time measured on a clock. Essentially, we are here comparing the performances of two mechanical systems—the one we are interested in and a standard one. The standard clock to which other clocks are adjusted is the rotating earth.

It remains to describe the units of time and length. These are the *mean solar second* (sec), which is one part in $(60)(60)(24) = 86{,}400$ of the mean solar day, and the meter (m), which is the distance between two marks on a particular piece of metal.* The meter may be subdivided into one hundred parts, each of which is known as a centimeter (cm); or multiples of the meter may be used. The most common of these is the kilometer (km), which is equal to one thousand meters. English-speaking writers, addressing an audience of mixed background, use the inch (in), foot (ft), mile (mi), or yard (yd) as units of length. The British and United States inch are, however, officially defined in terms of the centimeter: one inch is the same as 2.54 cm. This makes one foot the same as 30.48 cm, one yard the same as 91.44 cm, and one mile the same as 1.609344 km.

It is important to recognize that lengths and time intervals are completely specified on a uniform scale by a single number known as the *measure*. Furthermore, there is a physical meaning to the sum of two lengths. It is a length whose measure is the sum of the measures of the two original lengths. If A, B, C are three points in order on a straight line, the length AC is the sum of the lengths AB and BC. Physical addition here corresponds to arithmetic addition. Quantities

---

* The International Prototype Meter has also been calibrated as a multiple of the wave-length of light of a particular frequency.

such as length and time intervals that have the property of adding in this simple way are known as *scalars*. Volume is a scalar quantity. So are mass, work, and energy, which will be encountered later.

1.2 Vectors

The position of a point, P, in space may be specified with reference to a set of three perpendicular axes by the coordinates (x_P, y_P, z_P) of the point. These are defined as the orthogonal projections on the axes of the line segment joining the origin to the point in question. This directed line segment is shown as OP in Fig. 1.2-1. Alternatively, the position P may be located by giving r_P, the magnitude of the distance from O to P, and the direction cosines of the line OP. These four quantities are not independent. Since

$$x_P = r_P \cos \alpha, \qquad y_P = r_P \cos \beta, \qquad z_P = r_P \cos \gamma \qquad \textbf{1.2-1}$$

and since

$$r_P^2 = x_P^2 + y_P^2 + z_P^2 \qquad \textbf{1.2-2}$$

it follows, by squaring and adding the Eqs. 1.2-1, that

$$\cos^2 \alpha + \cos^2 \beta + \cos^2 \gamma = 1. \qquad \textbf{1.2-3}$$

Whatever the preferred method of specification, it will entail giving three numbers. We call the directed line segment OP, the *position vector* of the point P, and denote it by the symbol $\mathbf{r}_P$. This symbol represents a triad of real numbers that collectively describe the magnitude and direction of the directed line segment OP in terms of the particular coordinate system used. The vector is independent of the particular coordinate system, but the description of the vector is not. The vector is distinguished from the symbol that represents its magnitude by the use of boldface type for the vector, ordinary type for its magnitude.* The notation $|\mathbf{r}_P|$ is also used to designate the magnitude of $\mathbf{r}_P$. The numbers (x_P, y_P, z_P) are known as the rectangular components of $\mathbf{r}_P$.

Now suppose that the position of the point under examination changes from P to Q, as shown in Fig. 1.2-2. We refer to the directed line segment PQ as the *displacement* of the moving point and denote it by the vector symbol $\mathbf{q}$. Of course $\mathbf{q}$ is only the position

---

* Several devices are available to maintain the distinction in manuscript. Perhaps the simplest is the use of a superposed bar to call attention to the vector symbol; e.g., $\bar{\mathbf{r}}_P$ is the same as $\mathbf{r}_P$.

vector of Q referred to P as origin, just as $\mathbf{r}_P$ could be regarded as the displacement vector of a motion from O to P. Now point Q has a position vector $\mathbf{r}_Q$. From point O a moving point may reach point Q either by successive displacements $\mathbf{r}_P$ and $\mathbf{q}$ or by a single displacement $\mathbf{r}_Q$. Displacements combine according to the so-called triangle law (sometimes termed the parallelogram law because OQ is the diagonal of the parallelogram with sides parallel and equal to OP and PQ). This is what is meant by vectorial addition. Whenever a

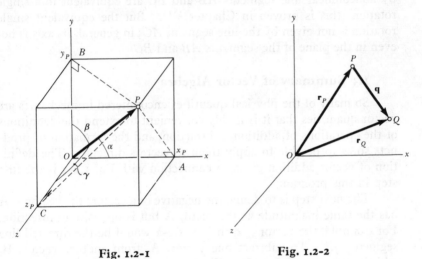

Fig. I.2-1   **Fig. I.2-2**

physical quantity can be represented by a directed line segment (*its vector*) and the physical sum of two such quantities is formed by vectorial addition, we say that the quantity in question is a *vector quantity*. We indicate that two vectors are to be added in this way by placing a + sign between the corresponding symbols. Two vectors are said to be equal if they have the same magnitude and direction; we indicate this by means of an = sign. Thus we write

$$\mathbf{r}_P + \mathbf{q} = \mathbf{r}_Q. \qquad \text{I.2-4}$$

The idea of vectorial addition is familiar to students of technology who meet it in their study of statics. In statics, the vectorial balance of forces plays a fundamental role. Among the many vectorial quantities encountered in dynamics are acceleration, angular velocity, momentum, and impulse. Indeed, so pervasive is the vector concept in mechanics that two words of caution are appropriate. First, not all the important properties of a vectorial quantity are necessarily given by its vector. Two forces having the same magnitude and direction will be represented by the same vector, but their effects will depend upon the points at which they are applied. Second, not every quantity that can be represented by a directed line segment is a vector quantity. The best-known exception is afforded by finite rotation of a rigid body. Rotation about an axis through an angle θ can be represented by a line segment AB having the direction of the axis and a length proportional to θ. Successive rotations represented by noncollinear line segments AB and BC are equivalent to a single rotation (this is proven in Chapter VI). But the equivalent single rotation is not given by the line segment AC; in general, its axis is not even in the plane of the segments AB and BC.

1.3 Summary of Vector Algebra

So many of the physical quantities encountered in mechanics are vector quantities that it is highly convenient to extend the definitions of the operations of addition, subtraction, and the formation of products so as to be able to apply them to vectors directly. The definition of vector addition given in connection with Eq. 1.2-4 is the first step in this program.

The next step is to define the negative of a vector; the vector $-\mathbf{A}$ has the same magnitude as the vector $\mathbf{A}$ but is opposite in direction. For example, the vector $-\mathbf{q}$ in Fig. 1.2-2 would be the directed line segment QP. To subtract one vector, $\mathbf{A}$, from another vector, $\mathbf{B}$, add the negative of $\mathbf{A}$ to $\mathbf{B}$. The product of a vector $\mathbf{A}$ and a scalar quantity n (i.e., one that has the properties of an ordinary number) is a vector whose magnitude is $|n|$ times the magnitude of $\mathbf{A}$ and whose direction is the same as that of $\mathbf{A}$ if n is positive, opposite to that of $\mathbf{A}$ if n is negative.

These are definitions. They are useful because they are consistent and because they lead to the same fundamental laws that govern ordinary arithmetic:

$$\mathbf{A} + \mathbf{B} = \mathbf{B} + \mathbf{A} \qquad\qquad \textbf{1.3-1a}$$

$$\mathbf{A} + (\mathbf{B} + \mathbf{C}) = (\mathbf{A} + \mathbf{B}) + \mathbf{C} \qquad\qquad \textbf{1.3-1b}$$

$$n(m\mathbf{A}) = m(n\mathbf{A}) = (mn)\mathbf{A} \qquad\qquad \textbf{1.3-1c}$$

$$(m + n)\mathbf{A} = m\mathbf{A} + n\mathbf{A} \qquad\qquad \textbf{1.3-1d}$$

$$m(\mathbf{A} + \mathbf{B}) = m\mathbf{A} + m\mathbf{B}. \qquad\qquad \textbf{1.3-1e}$$

The fact that these laws are valid justifies the use of the same $+$ and $=$ symbols in vector equations as in ordinary numerical equations.

Equations 1.3-1 are not definitions or conventions but theorems. The proofs of these theorems are given in Appendix I. Students who have not encountered vector algebra in connection with their study of statics should refer to this appendix for a detailed discussion of vector algebra. For the purposes of the present section we note simply that the laws governing addition and subtraction of vectors and multiplication of vectors by scalars are the same as the laws governing these operations in ordinary algebra and arithmetic. The *zero* or *null vector* is introduced to make these vector operations complete; that is, always possible. The null vector, written either **0** or o, may be regarded as one whose magnitude is zero; its direction is immaterial. In view of Theorems 1.3-1 and the definition of the null vector we may infer, for example, that, if two vectors **X** and **Y** are related to a vector **A** by the equations

$$\mathbf{X} - \frac{1}{2}\mathbf{Y} = 4\mathbf{A}$$

and

$$-3\mathbf{X} + 4\mathbf{Y} + 17\mathbf{A} = 0, \qquad \qquad \textbf{1.3-2}$$

it must follow that $\mathbf{X} = 3\mathbf{A}$ and $\mathbf{Y} = -2\mathbf{A}$. The vectors **X** and **Y** are parallel to **A** but **Y** is oppositely directed to **A**. The first has a magnitude $3A$; the second, a magnitude $2A$.

As a rule, in technological applications, we wish to specify a vector not in terms of some other vector but with reference to a convenient set of axes. This representation is effected by means of unit vectors. A unit vector is simply a vector whose magnitude is 1. The most commonly encountered unit vectors are those in the directions of (x, y, z) axes. They are usually denoted by the symbols **i**, **j**, **k** or $\mathbf{i}_1$, $\mathbf{i}_2$, $\mathbf{i}_3$ and are pictured in Fig. 1.3-1. Referring to Fig. 1.2-1, it may be seen that the directed line segment OA is the vector $x_P\mathbf{i}$, the directed line segment OB is the vector $y_P\mathbf{j}$, and the directed line segment OC is the vector $z_P\mathbf{k}$. These three components, added vectorially, form the directed line segment OP, which was denoted $\mathbf{r}_P$. In symbols,

$$\mathbf{r}_P = x_P\mathbf{i} + y_P\mathbf{j} + z_P\mathbf{k}. \qquad \qquad \textbf{1.3-3}$$

When a vector has been expressed in this form, its magnitude and direction cosines are easily found by means of the Eqs. 1.2-1, 2.

The basic ideas of vector algebra are completed by the introduction of two further operations, the scalar or "dot" product of two vectors, and the vector or "cross" product of two vectors. The creation of the first of these operations stems from our desire for a convenient formulation of the projection or *component* of a vector in any direction. The magnitude of this projection is proportional to the cosine of the interior angle between the vectors when their origins coincide. We therefore define an operation on a pair of vectors **A**, **B** by the formula

$$\mathbf{A} \cdot \mathbf{B} = AB \cos \theta. \qquad \textbf{1.3-4}$$

The notation is straightforward; A and B are the magnitudes of the corresponding vectors; θ is the angle mentioned. To find the component of **A** in the direction of **B**, it is only necessary to replace **B**

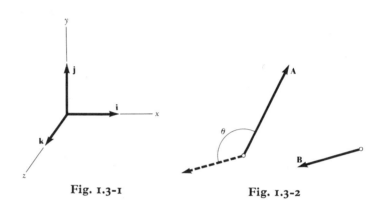

Fig. 1.3-1   **Fig. 1.3-2**

in Eq. 1.3-4 by a unit vector in the same direction. This unit vector is the vector **B** multiplied by the scalar $1/B$. It is easy to show (see Appendix I) that if

$$\mathbf{A} = A_x\mathbf{i} + A_y\mathbf{j} + A_z\mathbf{k} \quad \text{and} \quad \mathbf{B} = B_x\mathbf{i} + B_y\mathbf{j} + B_z\mathbf{k},$$

then

$$\mathbf{A} \cdot \mathbf{B} = A_x B_x + A_y B_y + A_z B_z. \qquad \textbf{1.3-5}$$

The scalar product, as its name implies, is itself a scalar quantity having the properties of a single ordinary number. It may be positive or negative.

The second product form, the so-called vector or "cross" product of two vectors, arises from the need for a convenient representation of the moment of a vector about a point. We define $\mathbf{A} \times \mathbf{B}$ as a vector whose magnitude is given by the expression

$$|\mathbf{A} \times \mathbf{B}| = AB \sin \theta, \qquad \textbf{1.3-6}$$

whose direction is at right angles to the plane passing through **A** and **B**, and whose sense is determined by the right-hand rule (i.e., when the tips of the fingers of the right hand pass from the terminus of the first-named vector, **A**, to the terminus of the second-named vector, **B**, the thumb of the right hand is directed along vector **A** × **B**). The relation of the vector **A** × **B** to the vectors **A** and **B** is illustrated in Fig. 1.3-3. The use of the right-hand rule to determine the sense of **A** × **B** implies that

$$\mathbf{A} \times \mathbf{B} = -\mathbf{B} \times \mathbf{A}. \qquad \textbf{1.3-7}$$

This is the only exception to the operations of ordinary algebra that arises in connection with the use of the vector symbolism. The representation of the vector product in cartesian form is shown in Appendix I to take the form

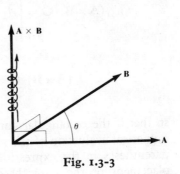

Fig. 1.3-3

$$\mathbf{A} \times \mathbf{B} = \begin{vmatrix} \mathbf{i} & \mathbf{j} & \mathbf{k} \\ A_x & A_y & A_z \\ B_x & B_y & B_z \end{vmatrix}$$

$$= (A_y B_z - A_z B_y)\mathbf{i} + (A_z B_x - A_x B_z)\mathbf{j} + (A_x B_y - A_y B_x)\mathbf{k}. \qquad \textbf{1.3-8}$$

In view of the use of the right-hand rule in defining the sense of **A** × **B**, it is essential that the orthogonal triad of axes (x, y, z) also be right-handed. It is also shown in Appendix I that the scalar product satisfies the commutative and distributive laws

$$\mathbf{A} \cdot \mathbf{B} = \mathbf{B} \cdot \mathbf{A} \quad \text{and} \quad \mathbf{A} \cdot (\mathbf{B} + \mathbf{C}) = \mathbf{A} \cdot \mathbf{B} + \mathbf{A} \cdot \mathbf{C}. \qquad \textbf{1.3-9}$$

The proofs of Eqs. 1.3-9, like those of Eqs. 1.3-1, follow directly from the definitions of the operations together with simple geometrical considerations. The proof of the distributive law for vector products is less obvious. It is shown in Appendix I that

$$\mathbf{A} \times (\mathbf{B} + \mathbf{C}) = \mathbf{A} \times \mathbf{B} + \mathbf{A} \times \mathbf{C}. \qquad \textbf{1.3-10}$$

Of course the order of the terms must not be altered since, in view of Eq. 1.3-7, the commutative law is not satisfied.

Since the vector product is itself a vector, it may be combined with a third vector to form a so-called triple product. The scalar triple product, which is a number, is a convenient and compact way of expressing the moment of a vector about a line. In view of Eqs. 1.3-5, 8,

$$(\mathbf{A} \times \mathbf{B}) \cdot \mathbf{C} = \begin{vmatrix} \mathbf{i} & \mathbf{j} & \mathbf{k} \\ A_x & A_y & A_z \\ B_x & B_y & B_z \end{vmatrix} \cdot (C_x\mathbf{i} + C_y\mathbf{j} + C_z\mathbf{k}) \qquad \textbf{1.3-11}$$

$$(\mathbf{A} \times \mathbf{B}) \cdot \mathbf{C} = \begin{vmatrix} A_x & A_y & A_z \\ B_x & B_y & B_z \\ C_x & C_y & C_z \end{vmatrix} \qquad \textbf{1.3-12}$$

so that if the rectangular components of the vectors are known, the numerical evaluation of the scalar triple product is elementary. The parentheses in the expression $(\mathbf{A} \times \mathbf{B}) \cdot \mathbf{C}$ are unnecessary; no other placement of the parentheses will yield a meaningful expression. Since the numerical value of a determinant is not affected by interchanging adjacent rows an even number of times but is reversed in sign by an odd number of interchanges, it follows that the scalar triple product depends only on the cyclic order of the vectors $\mathbf{A}$, $\mathbf{B}$, $\mathbf{C}$ and not on the symbols $\cdot$ and $\times$;

and
$$(\mathbf{A} \times \mathbf{B}) \cdot \mathbf{C} = \mathbf{A} \cdot (\mathbf{B} \times \mathbf{C})$$

$$(\mathbf{A} \times \mathbf{B}) \cdot \mathbf{C} = (\mathbf{B} \times \mathbf{C}) \cdot \mathbf{A} = (\mathbf{C} \times \mathbf{A}) \cdot \mathbf{B} \qquad \textbf{1.3-13}$$

but
$$(\mathbf{A} \times \mathbf{B}) \cdot \mathbf{C} = -(\mathbf{A} \times \mathbf{C}) \cdot \mathbf{B}. \qquad \textbf{1.3-14}$$

It also follows that if any two of the vectors $\mathbf{A}$, $\mathbf{B}$, $\mathbf{C}$ are identical $(\mathbf{A} \times \mathbf{B}) \cdot \mathbf{C} = 0$.

The repeated vector product is itself a vector and is known as the *vector triple product*, $(\mathbf{A} \times \mathbf{B}) \times \mathbf{C}$. Here the parentheses are indispensable. The vector $\mathbf{A} \times \mathbf{B}$ is perpendicular to the plane of $\mathbf{A}$ and $\mathbf{B}$. The second cross product provides a second ninety-degree rotation so that the vector $(\mathbf{A} \times \mathbf{B}) \times \mathbf{C}$ lies in the plane of $\mathbf{A}$ and $\mathbf{B}$. This suggests that $(\mathbf{A} \times \mathbf{B}) \times \mathbf{C}$ ought to be expressible as the sum of components proportional to $\mathbf{A}$ and to $\mathbf{B}$. The essence of the method by which this important resolution is effected lies in resolving $\mathbf{C}$ into the sum of components in directions perpendicular to $\mathbf{A}$, to $\mathbf{B}$ and to the plane of $\mathbf{A}$ and $\mathbf{B}$. Let $\mathbf{e}$ denote a unit vector normal to the plane of $\mathbf{A}$ and $\mathbf{B}$. Then $\mathbf{e}$ is parallel to $\mathbf{A} \times \mathbf{B}$. We express this fact by writing

$$\mathbf{A} \times \mathbf{B} = a\mathbf{e} \qquad \textbf{1.3-15}$$

where a denotes some number. Now the vectors $\mathbf{e}$, $\mathbf{e} \times \mathbf{A}$, and $\mathbf{e} \times \mathbf{B}$ are a set that do not all lie in the same plane, and no two of which are parallel (unless **A** and **B** are parallel). They form an oblique set of three-dimensional axes. Any vector, in particular the vector **C**, can be expressed in the form

$$\mathbf{C} = b\mathbf{e} + c(\mathbf{e} \times \mathbf{A}) + d(\mathbf{e} \times \mathbf{B}) \qquad \textbf{1.3-16}$$

where b, c, d, like a, are three as yet undetermined numbers. Now, in view of Eq. 1.3-15,

$$(\mathbf{A} \times \mathbf{B}) \times \mathbf{C} = a\mathbf{e} \times [b\mathbf{e} + c(\mathbf{e} \times \mathbf{A}) + d(\mathbf{e} \times \mathbf{B})]. \qquad \textbf{1.3-17}$$

But $\mathbf{e} \times \mathbf{e} = 0$ and, as may be seen by inspection of Fig. 1.3-4,

$$\mathbf{e} \times (\mathbf{e} \times \mathbf{A}) = -\mathbf{A} \quad \text{and} \quad \mathbf{e} \times (\mathbf{e} \times \mathbf{B}) = -\mathbf{B}. \qquad \textbf{1.3-18}$$

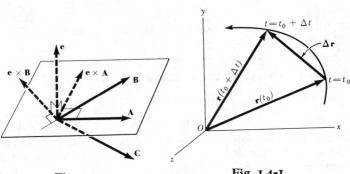

Fig. 1.3-4   **Fig. 1.4-1**

It follows that

$$(\mathbf{A} \times \mathbf{B}) \times \mathbf{C} = -ac\mathbf{A} - ad\mathbf{B}. \qquad \textbf{1.3-19}$$

The vector triple product has been expressed in the wanted form. It remains to determine the numbers ac and ad. From Eq. 1.3-16, we see that

$$\mathbf{B} \cdot \mathbf{C} = c[\mathbf{B} \cdot (\mathbf{e} \times \mathbf{A})] = c[(\mathbf{A} \times \mathbf{B}) \cdot \mathbf{e}] = ca\mathbf{e} \cdot \mathbf{e} = ca$$

$$\textbf{1.3-20}$$

and

$$\mathbf{A} \cdot \mathbf{C} = d[\mathbf{A} \cdot (\mathbf{e} \times \mathbf{B})] = -da. \qquad \textbf{1.3-21}$$

On substituting these expressions into Eq. 1.3-19, we have

$$(\mathbf{A} \times \mathbf{B}) \times \mathbf{C} = (\mathbf{A} \cdot \mathbf{C})\mathbf{B} - (\mathbf{B} \cdot \mathbf{C})\mathbf{A}. \qquad \textbf{1.3-22}$$

This result finds application in later development of the theory of our subject. An alternative proof is given in Appendix I. Verification of the result in the special case in which **A** and **B** are parallel may serve as an exercise to check the student's understanding of the operations of vector algebra.

I.4 Velocity and Acceleration

In dynamics, the position vector of a moving point is a function of time. We indicate this by writing $\mathbf{r}(t)$. The functional relationship is *continuous*. By this we mean that if t_0 is any particular instant of time, the magnitude of the vector difference $|\mathbf{r}(t) - \mathbf{r}(t_0)|$ can be made as small as desired by taking t sufficiently close to t_0. In symbols, if

$$\lim_{t \to t_0} |\mathbf{r}(t) - \mathbf{r}(t_0)| = 0 \quad \text{then } \mathbf{r}(t) \text{ is continuous at } t_0.$$

I.4-1

Now consider a moving point that at time t_0 has a position vector $\mathbf{r}(t_0)$, as shown in Fig. I.4-1. At a later time, $t_0 + \Delta t$, its position vector is $\mathbf{r}(t_0 + \Delta t)$. The change in $\mathbf{r}$ is the vector $\Delta \mathbf{r}$, which is the difference between these two values of $\mathbf{r}$.

$$\Delta \mathbf{r} = \mathbf{r}(t_0 + \Delta t) - \mathbf{r}(t_0).$$

I.4-2

We wish to make precise our intuitive notion that the velocity of the moving point is the rate at which its position vector is changing. To do this we define the time-average velocity of the moving point during the time interval Δt to be the product of the vector $\Delta \mathbf{r}$ and the scalar $1/\Delta t$. The *instantaneous velocity* of the moving point at time t_0 is defined as the limit that this average velocity approaches as the time interval, Δt, is taken shorter and shorter. By analogy with the ordinary differential calculus, this limit is called the derivative of the vector $\mathbf{r}$ with respect to the scalar variable t. In symbols,

$$\mathbf{v} = \lim_{\Delta t \to 0} \frac{\Delta \mathbf{r}}{\Delta t} = \frac{d\mathbf{r}}{dt}.$$

I.4-3

It has been assumed that this limit exists. If it does not, the function $\mathbf{r}$ has no derivative with respect to t at t_0. Instantaneous velocity finds such wide application in mechanics that the term is generally used without the qualifying adjective "instantaneous," and we speak simply of the *velocity*. The units of velocity are determined by the units chosen for distance and time. For this reason they are known as *derived* or *secondary* units. If distances are measured in meters and time intervals in seconds, the unit of velocity, to be consistent, should be the meter-per-second (m/sec). Similarly, the foot-per-second corresponds to measurement of distances in feet and time in seconds.

It should be noted that whereas the position vector, **r**, depends upon the choice of a reference point, O, the displacement vector does not.   Velocity is a path-dependent quantity.   That velocity is indeed a vector quantity follows from the fact that if we think of **r** as experiencing two independent component increments $\Delta\mathbf{r}_1$ and $\Delta\mathbf{r}_2$ in the time interval Δt, we shall have $(\Delta\mathbf{r}/\Delta t)=(\Delta\mathbf{r}_1/\Delta t)+(\Delta\mathbf{r}_2/\Delta t)$.   In the limit as $\Delta t \to 0$, these terms become derivatives.   Since the limit of a sum of two vector functions is the sum of their separate limits, it follows that the velocity is the vector sum of its components.   That the direction of this velocity vector is actually tangent to the path is shown in Section 1.9.   The magnitude of the velocity is called the *speed*.

The foregoing discussion, although it has been keyed to the position vector, may serve to define the derivative of any vector quantity that is a function of a scalar variable.   Time, however, is so commonly the scalar variable of interest in dynamics that derivatives with respect to time have come to be denoted simply by superscript dots.   For $d\mathbf{r}/dt$ we write simply $\dot{\mathbf{r}}$.   Finally, since the velocity is itself a vector function of time, it may be differentiated again.   The vector quantity $\mathbf{a}=\dot{\mathbf{v}}=\ddot{\mathbf{r}}$ is the *acceleration* of the moving point.

The analogy between the differentiation of a vector with respect to a scalar variable and the ideas of the ordinary differential calculus is a close one.   The rules for the differentiation of sums and products of two vectors are the same as those of elementary calculus:

$$\frac{d}{dt}\,(\mathbf{A}+\mathbf{B}) = \frac{d\mathbf{A}}{dt}+\frac{d\mathbf{B}}{dt} \qquad\qquad \textbf{1.4-4a}$$

$$\frac{d}{dt}\,(n\mathbf{A}) = \frac{dn}{dt}\,\mathbf{A}+n\,\frac{d\mathbf{A}}{dt} \qquad\qquad \textbf{1.4-4b}$$

$$\frac{d}{dt}\,(\mathbf{A}\cdot\mathbf{B}) = \frac{d\mathbf{A}}{dt}\cdot\mathbf{B}+\mathbf{A}\cdot\frac{d\mathbf{B}}{dt} \qquad\qquad \textbf{1.4-4c}$$

$$\frac{d}{dt}\,(\mathbf{A}\times\mathbf{B}) = \frac{d\mathbf{A}}{dt}\times\mathbf{B}+\mathbf{A}\times\frac{d\mathbf{B}}{dt}\cdot \qquad\qquad \textbf{1.4-4d}$$

The proofs of these statements are all quite similar and may be exemplified by that for Eq. 1.4-4b.   If n and **A** take on increments in time Δt,

$$\Delta(n\mathbf{A}) = (n+\Delta n)(\mathbf{A}+\Delta\mathbf{A})-n\mathbf{A},$$

$$\Delta(n\mathbf{A}) = \Delta n\mathbf{A}+n\,\Delta\mathbf{A}+\Delta n\,\Delta\mathbf{A},$$

and

$$\frac{\Delta(n\mathbf{A})}{\Delta t} = \frac{\Delta n}{\Delta t}\,\mathbf{A}+n\,\frac{\Delta\mathbf{A}}{\Delta t}+\frac{\Delta n}{\Delta t}\,\frac{\Delta\mathbf{A}}{\Delta t}\,\Delta t.$$

As $\Delta t \to 0$, the last term vanishes and the other terms approach the corresponding members of Eq. 1.4-4b. Equation 1.4-4b provides the basis of a practical way of computing the magnitude and direction of the derivative. If $(\mathbf{i}, \mathbf{j}, \mathbf{k})$ are vectors of unit magnitude directed along rectangular axes (x, y, z) and $\mathbf{r}$ is expressed as the sum of components

$$\mathbf{r} = f(t)\mathbf{i} + g(t)\mathbf{j} + h(t)\mathbf{k},$$

then it follows from Eq. 1.4-3 and 1.4-4b that

$$\mathbf{v} = \frac{df}{dt}\mathbf{i} + f\frac{d\mathbf{i}}{dt} + \frac{dg}{dt}\mathbf{j} + g\frac{d\mathbf{j}}{dt} + \frac{dh}{dt}\mathbf{k} + h\frac{d\mathbf{k}}{dt}.$$

Since the (x, y, z) axes are fixed in direction, $\mathbf{i}, \mathbf{j}, \mathbf{k}$ must be constant both in magnitude and direction. The derivative of a constant vector is zero so that

$$\mathbf{v} = \frac{df}{dt}\mathbf{i} + \frac{dg}{dt}\mathbf{j} + \frac{dh}{dt}\mathbf{k}. \qquad \text{1.4-5}$$

Higher derivatives may be calculated in the same way.

Example **1.4-1**

A vector has constant magnitude but varies in direction. Show that its time derivative at any instant is perpendicular to the vector itself at that instant.

Solution: Denote the vector by the symbol $\mathbf{A}$. We express the fact that the magnitude of $\mathbf{A}$ is constant by saying that the right-hand side of the equation

$$\mathbf{A} \cdot \mathbf{A} = A^2$$

is a constant. Differentiating both sides and using Eq. 1.4-4c, we have

$$\frac{d\mathbf{A}}{dt} \cdot \mathbf{A} + \mathbf{A} \cdot \frac{d\mathbf{A}}{dt} = 0.$$

But the order of terms in the scalar product is immaterial so that

$$\mathbf{A} \cdot \frac{d\mathbf{A}}{dt} = 0.$$

It follows from the definition of the scalar product (Eq. 1.3-4) that $\mathbf{A}$ and $d\mathbf{A}/dt$ must be at right angles to one another (unless one of them is zero). This result implies that the rate of change of a constant-magnitude vector must be perpendicular to the vector itself. In application, $\mathbf{A}$ might be the velocity of a point moving with constant speed; the acceleration would be at right angles to the velocity. Alternatively, $\mathbf{A}$ might be the position vector of a point on a rod, the end of which is held in a universal joint. In this case, the origin of the position vector would be at the joint, and we should conclude that the velocity vector of the point is at right angles to the rod.

Example 1.4-2

Investigate the time derivative of $(1/2)\mathbf{v} \cdot \mathbf{v}$.

Solution: We may treat this question in two ways. Starting from Eq. 1.4-4c, we see that

$$\frac{d}{dt}\left(\frac{1}{2}\mathbf{v} \cdot \mathbf{v}\right) = \frac{1}{2}\frac{d}{dt}(\mathbf{v} \cdot \mathbf{v}) = \frac{1}{2}\dot{\mathbf{v}} \cdot \mathbf{v} + \frac{1}{2}\mathbf{v} \cdot \dot{\mathbf{v}} = \mathbf{v} \cdot \dot{\mathbf{v}}$$

or

$$\frac{d}{dt}\left(\frac{1}{2}\mathbf{v} \cdot \mathbf{v}\right) = \mathbf{v} \cdot \mathbf{a} \qquad \textbf{1.4-6}$$

where $\mathbf{a} = \dot{\mathbf{v}}$. A second approach starts from the relation

$$\frac{1}{2}\mathbf{v} \cdot \mathbf{v} = \frac{1}{2}v^2.$$

The right-hand side of this expression is an ordinary scalar quantity, the square of the magnitude of $\mathbf{v}$. Differentiating,

$$\frac{d}{dt}\left(\frac{1}{2}\mathbf{v} \cdot \mathbf{v}\right) = v\frac{dv}{dt}. \qquad \textbf{1.4-7}$$

Both forms are interesting. If Eq. 1.4-6, 7 are combined, we have

$$v\frac{dv}{dt} = \mathbf{v} \cdot \mathbf{a}. \qquad \textbf{1.4-8}$$

Up to this point in the discussion, $\mathbf{v}$ has represented any vector; $\mathbf{a}$, its time derivative. If we interpret $\mathbf{v}$ as the velocity and $\mathbf{a}$ as the acceleration of a moving point, dv/dt is the rate at which the speed is changing. In view of the definition of the scalar product (Eq. 1.3-4), we have

$$\frac{dv}{dt} = a \cos \theta \qquad \textbf{1.4-9}$$

where θ denotes the angle between the velocity and acceleration vectors. The magnitude of the acceleration vector, a, is always greater than or equal to the rate at which speed is changing. As we shall see in Section 1.9, the reason for this is that part of the acceleration arises from a change in the direction of the velocity vector.

Example 1.4-3

The position vector of a moving point is given by the expression

$$\mathbf{r} = (R \cos \omega t)\mathbf{i} + (R \sin \omega t)\mathbf{j}.$$

Describe the motion.

Solution: The coordinates of this moving point at any time are $x = R \cos \omega t$, $y = R \sin \omega t$, $z = 0$. The point is moving in the xy-plane.

To find the equation of the path, eliminate t from the first two equations. In the present case, this is most easily done by squaring each and adding. Then

$$x^2 + y^2 = R^2 \cos^2 \omega t + R^2 \sin^2 \omega t,$$
$$x^2 + y^2 = R^2.$$

The point moves in a circle of radius R. Initially ($t = 0$), the point is located at $x = R$, $y = z = 0$. It returns to this place at $t = 2\pi/\omega$, $t = 4\pi/\omega$, $t = 6\pi/\omega$, etc. The motion is said to be *periodic* because it repeats itself. Since the moving point goes through a complete cycle of motion, returning to its original position every $2\pi/\omega$ sec, it is said to have a period of $2\pi/\omega$ seconds per cycle. The velocity and acceleration of the moving point are

$$\mathbf{v} = \dot{\mathbf{r}} = (-R\omega \sin \omega t)\mathbf{i} + (R\omega \cos \omega t)\mathbf{j}$$

and

$$\mathbf{a} = \dot{\mathbf{v}} = -(R\omega^2 \cos \omega t)\mathbf{i} - (R\omega^2 \sin \omega t)\mathbf{j}.$$

The speed of the moving point is

$$v = [(-R\omega \sin \omega t)^2 + (R\omega \cos \omega t)^2]^{1/2} = R\omega.$$

In this example the speed is constant. The acceleration vector, however, is not zero. It is equal to the negative of the radius vector multiplied by ω^2; that is,

$$\ddot{\mathbf{r}} = -\omega^2 \mathbf{r}.$$

We infer that in this example, where the speed is constant, the acceleration vector is always directed from the moving point toward the center of the circular path. The student should verify that this special case agrees with the general results reached in Examples 1.4-1, 2.

Example 1.4-4

An insect moves along a diameter of a turntable that is rotating at a uniform rate of p radians per second. The insect has a constant speed, s, relative to the turntable. What is its acceleration as it passes through the center?

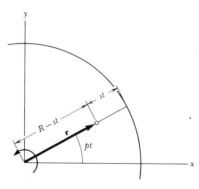

Fig. 1.4-2

Solution: This question is one of a type that can best be handled by a method to be developed in a later chapter. It is worth studying now because the result is not intuitively obvious, and because it provides a link between the ideas of this section and the ones developed later in connection with kinematics. In Fig. 1.4-2 the insect is shown in a typical position, at time t. If at time zero the insect started at a distance R from the center, it will have moved through a distance st measured on the turntable. The radius along which it is moving will have turned through an angle pt relative to the fixed x, y axes. The position vector is

$$\mathbf{r} = [(R-st)\cos pt]\mathbf{i} + [(R-st)\sin pt]\mathbf{j}.$$

If this is differentiated twice with respect to time,

$$\mathbf{v} = [-s\cos pt - (R-st)p\sin pt]\mathbf{i} + [-s\sin pt + (R-st)p\cos pt]\mathbf{j},$$

$$\mathbf{a} = [2sp\sin pt - (R-st)p^2\cos pt]\mathbf{i} + [-2sp\cos pt - (R-st)p^2\sin pt]\mathbf{j},$$

and

$$\mathbf{a} = 2sp[(\sin pt)\mathbf{i} - (\cos pt)\mathbf{j}] - p^2\mathbf{r}.$$

As the particle passes through the center of the turntable, $\mathbf{r}=\mathbf{o}$ and the acceleration has a magnitude $2sp$. It is interesting that even though the insect is traveling with constant speed relative to the turntable and has reached a point on the turntable which is at rest, its acceleration does not vanish. We shall later see that this acceleration term is what is known as the Coriolis component of acceleration. In the present example the direction of the acceleration vector when $\mathbf{r}=\mathbf{o}$ is at right angles to the radius along which the insect is crawling, pointed to the insect's left. The insect moving along the diameter of a rotating turntable is analogous to a fluid element moving along the vanes of a turbine or impeller (except that these vanes may be curved). Its acceleration is a measure of the force exerted on it by the vane.

1.5 Integration of Vector Functions

In vector calculus, just as in the ordinary calculus, the concept of the integral of a function presents two aspects. The integral may be introduced first as the antiderivative; that is, we call $\mathbf{F}(t)$ an integral of $\mathbf{f}(t)$ if $(d\mathbf{F}/dt)=\mathbf{f}$ and we write

$$\mathbf{F}(t) = \int \mathbf{f}(t)\, dt.$$

This is the indefinite integral, so termed because an arbitrary constant vector may be added to $\mathbf{F}$. For example,*

$$\int (6t^2\mathbf{i} - at^{-1}\mathbf{j})\, dt = 2t^3\mathbf{i} - a(\log t)\mathbf{j} + \mathbf{C}$$

---

* Throughout this book, "log" will stand for the natural logarithm function, or logarithm based on the number e; no other bases for logarithmic computation will be used.

and

$$\int (\sin \omega t \mathbf{i} + 2t\mathbf{k}) \, dt = (-\omega^{-1} \cos \omega t)\mathbf{i} + t^2 \mathbf{k} + \mathbf{C}.$$

Integrations of this type reduce at once to ordinary integrations because the vectors $(\mathbf{i}, \mathbf{j}, \mathbf{k})$, being constant in magnitude and direction, can be taken outside the integral sign. Similarly, if $\mathbf{A}$ is a constant and $\mathbf{F}$ a variable vector,

$$\int (\mathbf{A} \times \dot{\mathbf{F}}) \, dt = \mathbf{A} \times (\int \dot{\mathbf{F}} \, dt) = \mathbf{A} \times \mathbf{F} + \mathbf{C}.$$

A more sophisticated example is provided by

$$\int (\mathbf{r} \times \ddot{\mathbf{r}}) \, dt.$$

Here we seek a function whose derivative is the integrand $\mathbf{r} \times \ddot{\mathbf{r}}$. Now

$$\frac{d}{dt} (\mathbf{r} \times \dot{\mathbf{r}}) = \dot{\mathbf{r}} \times \dot{\mathbf{r}} + \mathbf{r} \times \ddot{\mathbf{r}}. \qquad \textbf{1.5-1}$$

The cross product of parallel vectors is zero so that the first term on the right-hand side of Eq. 1.5-1 vanishes. We have, therefore,

$$\int (\mathbf{r} \times \ddot{\mathbf{r}}) \, dt = \mathbf{r} \times \dot{\mathbf{r}} + \mathbf{C}. \qquad \textbf{1.5-2}$$

It is worthwhile to form the habit of checking integrations by a differentiation of the final result.

Linear differential equations in which the independent variable is a scalar and the wanted quantity is a vector may be treated in much the same way as differential equations in which the variables are ordinary numbers. It is important to remember, however, that the so-called constants of integration will be vectors. If, for example, acceleration is given by the expression

$$\frac{d^2 \mathbf{r}}{dt^2} = 6\mathbf{A}t + 2\mathbf{B}$$

where $\mathbf{A}$ and $\mathbf{B}$ are constant vectors, it follows that

$$\frac{d\mathbf{r}}{dt} = 3\mathbf{A}t^2 + 2\mathbf{B}t + \mathbf{C}_1$$

and

$$\mathbf{r} = \mathbf{A}t^3 + \mathbf{B}t^2 + \mathbf{C}_1 t + \mathbf{C}_2.$$

The constant vectors $\mathbf{C}_1$ and $\mathbf{C}_2$ require additional information for their determination. This information usually takes the form of *initial conditions* that specify the position vector, $\mathbf{r}_0$, and the velocity vector, $\mathbf{v}_0$, at the initial instant, $t=0$. Then $\mathbf{C}_1 = \mathbf{v}_0$ and $\mathbf{C}_2 = \mathbf{r}_0$.

In contrast to the antiderivative, the definite integral is defined as the limit of a sum. It is related to the indefinite integral by the fundamental theorem of integral calculus. This theorem,[*] in vector form, asserts that if $(d\mathbf{F}/dt) = \mathbf{f}$ for all values of t in the interval t_1, t_2, then

$$\int_{t_1}^{t_2} \mathbf{f}(t) \, dt = \mathbf{F}(t_2) - \mathbf{F}(t_1).$$

Example 1.5-1

A point moves with a constant acceleration. When observed, its velocity has components v_1 in the direction of the acceleration and v_2 at right angles to it. Find the position at any time after the observation.

Solution: Take an x-axis in the direction of the acceleration and a y-axis in the direction of v_2. The origin is at the position of the point when its velocity is observed, and we measure time from that instant.

$$\ddot{\mathbf{r}} = a\mathbf{i} \quad \text{whence} \quad \dot{\mathbf{r}} = at\mathbf{i} + \mathbf{C}_1 \qquad\qquad \textbf{1.5-3}$$

and

$$\mathbf{r} = \frac{1}{2} at^2\mathbf{i} + \mathbf{C}_1 t + \mathbf{C}_2. \qquad\qquad \textbf{1.5-4}$$

At $t = 0$, $\mathbf{r} = 0$ so that $\mathbf{C}_2 = 0$.

At $t = 0$, $\dot{\mathbf{r}} = v_1\mathbf{i} + v_2\mathbf{j}$ so that $\mathbf{C}_1 = v_1\mathbf{i} + v_2\mathbf{j}$.

The position at any time is therefore given by the expression

$$\mathbf{r} = \left(\frac{1}{2} at^2 + v_1 t\right)\mathbf{i} + (v_2 t)\mathbf{j}.$$

The x- and y-coordinates of the moving point are

$$x = \frac{1}{2} at^2 + v_1 t, \qquad y = v_2 t.$$

On eliminating t, we find the path equation:

$$x = \left(\frac{a}{2v_2^2}\right) y^2 + \left(\frac{v_1}{v_2}\right) y.$$

This is a parabola. Note that the analysis is greatly facilitated by the choice of axes.

---

[*] See, for example, Angus E. Taylor, *Calculus with Analytic Geometry* (Englewood Cliffs, N. J.: Prentice-Hall, Inc., 1959), p. 242.

1.6 Vector Fields

The vectors that we have considered thus far have all been constants or functions of a scalar variable. In mechanics, this scalar variable is usually time or distance along a path. There is no difficulty, however, in imagining a vector that is a function of another vector. The gravitational force exerted on an object depends both in magnitude and in direction upon the position of the object in space; so does the velocity of a fluid element in a moving body of liquid and so also does the force exerted on a charged particle near a current-carrying coil. When the vector in which we are interested is a function of position as well as time, we speak of a *vector field*. This may be, for example, a gravitational field or a velocity field or an electromagnetic field. Clearly the calculus of vector functions of several variables is more complex than is that of a vector function of a single scalar variable. We defer until later the discussion of vector fields.

1.7 Elements of Particle Kinematics

Emphasis so far in this chapter has been placed on the calculus of vectors, with the concepts of position, velocity, and acceleration of a moving point used as examples of vector procedures. We now wish to examine these concepts more closely. We shall be concerned with the motion of a point through space and want to describe its position, velocity, and acceleration as functions of time. The study of the geometry of motion without regard for the causes of the motion is called *kinematics*; here we are concerned with particle kinematics; i.e., with the study of the motion of objects that, insofar as their motion is concerned, can be represented by a moving point.

The precise description of motion is a necessary preliminary to the study of dynamics. Indeed, the purely kinematical relations strongly suggest the forms of the principles of dynamics. Teaching experience shows that inadequate understanding of kinematics is the most common single source of students' errors.

Let us first summarize what has been done so far. The position of a moving point is prescribed by a vector **r** from a point O in space to the moving point, and thus depends on the choice of O. Displacement, which we shall now denote by $\Delta\mathbf{r}$, is any change in position. If the position vector **r** is a twice differentiable function of the scalar time variable t, the velocity and acceleration of the particle are

$$\mathbf{v} = \frac{d\mathbf{r}}{dt} \equiv \dot{\mathbf{r}}, \qquad \mathbf{a} = \frac{d\mathbf{v}}{dt} = \frac{d^2\mathbf{r}}{dt^2} \equiv \ddot{\mathbf{r}}. \qquad \textbf{1.7-1}$$

The companion integral relations are

$$\Delta \mathbf{v} \equiv \mathbf{v}(t) - \mathbf{v}(t_0) = \int_{t_0}^{t} \mathbf{a}(\tau)\, d\tau, \qquad \textbf{1.7-2}$$

$$\Delta \mathbf{r} \equiv \mathbf{r}(t) - \mathbf{r}(t_0) = \int_{t_0}^{t} \mathbf{v}(\tau)\, d\tau.$$

Here $\mathbf{v}(t_0)$ and $\mathbf{r}(t_0)$ are vector constants of integration; and τ is a "dummy" variable of integration, replacing t in the functional forms $\mathbf{a}(t)$ and $\mathbf{v}(t)$. Two more relations, which we shall find of use in the next chapter, have been proved in the examples of previous sections; they are repeated here for convenience of reference:

$$\frac{d}{dt}\left(\frac{1}{2}\,\mathbf{v}\cdot\mathbf{v}\right) = \mathbf{v}\cdot\mathbf{a} \qquad \textbf{1.7-3}$$

$$\frac{d}{dt}(\mathbf{r}\times\mathbf{v}) = \mathbf{r}\times\mathbf{a}. \qquad \textbf{1.7-4}$$

In the solution of problems, the use of the vector relations 1.7-1 and 1.7-2 requires the representation of the vector quantities in terms of scalar functions. Three important methods of doing this are described in the next three sections. The student must realize, however, that the vectors have meaning independent of the manner in which we choose to describe them: the theory of particle and rigid-body mechanics can be developed entirely in vector symbolism. To solve specific problems we need specific scalar representations; but different representations of a vector are just different ways of looking at the same physical or geometric entity.

1.8 Rectangular Cartesian Coordinates

Suppose that a particle or point traverses a path C in space (Fig. 1.8-1). Its motion is to be described relative to a fixed point O. Such a description, as though it were by an observer at O standing outside of the moving system, is called *extrinsic*.

The ordinary rectangular cartesian component method of representing vectors is perhaps the simplest way of expressing $\mathbf{r}$, $\mathbf{v}$, and $\mathbf{a}$. As in Section 1.2, introduce a right-handed coordinate system $Oxyz$ at O with corresponding unit vectors $(\mathbf{i}, \mathbf{j}, \mathbf{k})$ fixed in spatial direction as well as in magnitude. When the point is at a typical position P on its path, its position vector $\mathbf{r} \equiv \overline{OP}$ can then be given in terms of (**i**, **j**, **k**) and the projections, or scalar components, of $\overline{OP}$ on the coordinate directions:

$$\mathbf{r} = x\mathbf{i} + y\mathbf{j} + z\mathbf{k}. \qquad \text{1.8-1}$$

As t changes, P moves along the path C; the equations of the path C are then given in parametric form by

$$x = x(t), \qquad y = y(t), \qquad z = z(t). \qquad \text{1.8-2}$$

The velocity has been defined in 1.4 as the derivative of the position vector; the acceleration, as the derivative of the velocity. Since the

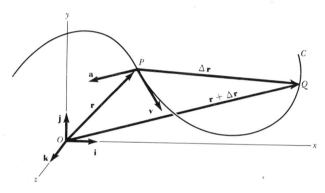

Fig. 1.8-1

unit vectors (**i**, **j**, **k**) do not change in magnitude or direction, following Eq. 1.4-5 we have

$$\mathbf{r} = x(t)\mathbf{i} + y(t)\mathbf{j} + z(t)\mathbf{k}$$
$$\Delta\mathbf{r} = \Delta x\mathbf{i} + \Delta y\mathbf{j} + \Delta z\mathbf{k}$$
$$\mathbf{v} = \dot{\mathbf{r}} = \dot{x}\mathbf{i} + \dot{y}\mathbf{j} + \dot{z}\mathbf{k} = v_x\mathbf{i} + v_y\mathbf{j} + v_z\mathbf{k} \qquad \text{1.8-3}$$
$$\mathbf{a} = \ddot{\mathbf{r}} = \ddot{x}\mathbf{i} + \ddot{y}\mathbf{j} + \ddot{z}\mathbf{k} = a_x\mathbf{i} + a_y\mathbf{j} + a_z\mathbf{k}.$$

Here superscript dots have been used to indicate differentiation with respect to time (as in 1.4) and $v_x(t)$, $v_y(t)$, ... $a_x(t)$ ... have been introduced to denote the components of velocity and acceleration.

Some further discussion of these relations and terms is pertinent here; also, there are some other important relations that the student should know. The displacement vector $\Delta\mathbf{r}$ is the change in position from one point on the path to another. From another point of view, it is no different than the position vector itself. It is simply the position vector of a point on the path with respect to an origin that happens to be on the path also. We use the terms position and displacement in the sense indicated: *position* as an "absolute" position with respect to a fixed origin O, whether or not the path ever goes through O, and *displacement* as a change in "absolute" position or as position relative to a point actually on the path.

The next concept of importance is that of the magnitude of the velocity vector, or *speed*:

$$v = |\mathbf{v}| = (v_x^2 + v_y^2 + v_z^2)^{\frac{1}{2}} = (\dot{x}^2 + \dot{y}^2 + \dot{z}^2)^{\frac{1}{2}}. \qquad \textbf{1.8-4}$$

In colloquial speech, we use the terms speed and velocity interchangeably; in technical work, a precise distinction between the vector and scalar concepts is often necessary. One situation in which this distinction must be made is in the discussion of *displacement* and *distance traveled*. From the integral relations, 1.7-2, the displacement vector from time t_0 to time t is the integral of the velocity vector

$$\Delta\mathbf{r} = \int_{t_0}^{t} \mathbf{v}(\tau)\,d\tau; \qquad \textbf{1.8-5}$$

the distance traveled, on the other hand, is the integral of the speed function

$$D = \int_{t_0}^{t} |\mathbf{v}(\tau)|\,d\tau. \qquad \textbf{1.8-6}$$

This distinction will be brought out more fully in the examples and problems of this section. Colloquially, we also use the term *deceleration* to denote a "negative acceleration" or negative rate of change of speed. Technically, acceleration is a vector quantity and the term deceleration is not necessary at all. The vector equation 1.8-5 and the corresponding expression for $\Delta\mathbf{v}$ are each equivalent to three scalar equations involving the coordinates $[x(t), y(t), z(t)]$ and the velocity and acceleration components $(v_x, v_y, v_z, a_x, a_y, a_z)$:

$$x(t) = x(t_0) + \int_{t_0}^{t} v_x(\tau)\,d\tau \qquad v_x(t) = v_x(t_0) + \int_{t_0}^{t} a_x(\tau)\,d\tau$$

$$y(t) = y(t_0) + \int_{t_0}^{t} v_y(\tau)\,d\tau \qquad v_y(t) = v_y(t_0) + \int_{t_0}^{t} a_y(\tau)\,d\tau \qquad \textbf{1.8-7}$$

$$z(t) = z(t_0) + \int_{t_0}^{t} v_z(\tau)\,d\tau \qquad v_z(t) = v_z(t_0) + \int_{t_0}^{t} a_z(\tau)\,d\tau.$$

The student should also be cautioned about the use of the simple integral formulas for constant acceleration such as we all learn in elementary physics; remember that formulas like $x = \frac{1}{2}at^2 + v_0 t$ hold *only if the acceleration is constant*. If the acceleration is not constant the full integrals 1.8-7 must be computed.

Example **I.8-1**

A particle travels on a plane path given by $x = 3 \sin 5t$, $y = 3 \cos 5t$, $z = 0$. Here (x, y, z) are measured in feet and t in seconds (and hence the multiplier 5 of t in the argument of the trigonometric functions has dimensions sec^{-1} or rad/sec). Compute the velocity and acceleration.

Solution: We are given

$$\mathbf{r} = x\mathbf{i} + y\mathbf{j} + z\mathbf{k} = 3 \sin 5t\mathbf{i} + 3 \cos 5t\mathbf{j} \quad ft;$$

thus

$$\mathbf{v} = \dot{\mathbf{r}} = 15 \cos 5t\mathbf{i} - 15 \sin 5t\mathbf{j} \quad ft/sec,$$

$$\mathbf{a} = \ddot{\mathbf{r}} = -75 \sin 5t\mathbf{i} - 75 \cos 5t\mathbf{j} \quad ft/sec^2.$$

Comments: The path is obviously a circle of radius $r = (x^2 + y^2)^{1/2} = 3 \ ft$ (see Example 1.4-3). The speed is a constant: $|\mathbf{v}| = (v_x^2 + v_y^2)^{1/2} = 15 \ ft/sec$; the acceleration is always directed toward the center of the circle. For any circular motion at constant speed, the acceleration is so directed, as the student should have no difficulty showing. The student may also show that the velocity and position vectors are orthogonal, and hence that the velocity is tangent to the circle.

Example **I.8-2**

Suppose a second particle moves with an acceleration equal to that of the particle of the previous example. This particle has initial position $\mathbf{r}_0 = 3\mathbf{j} \ ft$, as does the particle of the first example, but its initial velocity is different: $\mathbf{v}_0 = 15\mathbf{i} + 15\mathbf{k} \ ft/sec$. The path will not be a circle; what will it be?

Solution: The acceleration is

$$\mathbf{a} = -75 \sin 5t\mathbf{i} - 75 \cos 5t\mathbf{j} \quad ft/sec^2.$$

To compute the velocity, we must integrate the acceleration:

$$\mathbf{v} - \mathbf{v}_0 = \int_0^t \mathbf{a}(\tau) \, d\tau$$

$$= +15 \cos 5\tau \Big|_0^t \mathbf{i} - 15 \sin 5\tau \Big|_0^t \mathbf{j}$$

$$= (15 \cos 5t - 15)\mathbf{i} - 15 \sin 5t\mathbf{j}$$

$$\therefore \ \mathbf{v} = \mathbf{v}_0 + \int_0^t \mathbf{a}(\tau) \, d\tau,$$

$$\mathbf{v} = 15 \cos 5t\mathbf{i} - 15 \sin 5t\mathbf{j} - 15\mathbf{k} \quad ft/sec.$$

Similarly,

$$\mathbf{r} - \mathbf{r}_0 = \int_0^t \mathbf{v}(\tau) \, d\tau = 3 \sin 5t\mathbf{i} + 3(\cos 5t - 1)\mathbf{j} + 15t\mathbf{k}$$

and

$$\mathbf{r} = \mathbf{r}_0 + \int_0^t \mathbf{v}(\tau) \, d\tau = 3 \sin 5t\mathbf{i} + 3 \cos 5t\mathbf{j} + 15t\mathbf{k} \quad ft.$$

The path is thus the circular path of the first example with a z-component superimposed on it; the path is in fact the circular spiral or helix of Fig. 1.8-2, with constant *pitch* 6π ft—i.e., the distance traveled in the z-direction during one complete revolution about the z-axis is 6π ft.

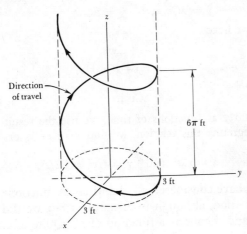

Direction of travel

6π ft

3 ft

3 ft

Fig. 1.8-2

Example **1.8-3**

   A pin P is forced to move in a slot having the shape of the parabola $y = Cx^2$; *its motion is controlled by that of the yoke A, which moves to the right at constant speed* v_0. *Find the velocity and acceleration of P in terms of C*, v_0, *and the position coordinate x (Fig. 1.8-3). Also, find x and y as functions of time if* $x = 0$ *at* $t = 0$.

   Solution: The general relations for motion on a plane path are

$$\mathbf{r} = x\mathbf{i} + y\mathbf{j}, \qquad \mathbf{v} = \dot{x}\mathbf{i} + \dot{y}\mathbf{j}, \qquad \mathbf{a} = \ddot{x}\mathbf{i} + \ddot{y}\mathbf{j}.$$

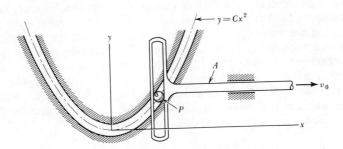

$y = Cx^2$

A

v_0

P

x

Fig. 1.8-3

Since the velocity of A is $v_0\mathbf{i}$ and is constant,

$$\dot{x} = v_0; \qquad \ddot{x} = 0.$$

Since $y = Cx^2$,

$$\dot{y} = 2Cx\dot{x}, \qquad \ddot{y} = 2C\dot{x}^2 + 2Cx\ddot{x};$$

hence

$$\dot{y} = 2Cv_0x, \qquad \ddot{y} = 2Cv_0^2$$

and therefore we have

$$\mathbf{r} = x\mathbf{i} + Cx^2\mathbf{j},$$
$$\mathbf{v} = v_0\mathbf{i} + 2Cv_0x\mathbf{j},$$

and

$$\mathbf{a} = 2Cv_0^2\mathbf{j}.$$

To obtain x and y as functions of time, we use the result that $\dot{x} = v_0$, a constant. Integrating this relation, we find $x = v_0t + x_0$ or, since $x = 0$ at $t = 0$,

$$x = v_0t \quad \text{and} \quad y = Cx^2 = Cv_0^2t^2.$$

So far we have considered all quantities as functions of the single scalar variable time, although in Example 1.8-3 we did have y as a function of x and then x as a function of t. Quite often direct integration with respect to time is not possible. Example 1.8-3—in which the equation of the path is given as $y = Cx^2$, $z = 0$—is a very simple example of relations stated explicitly as functions of position and only implicitly as functions of time. Similarly, time may be eliminated from the equations of the spiral in Example 1.8-2 by setting $t = z/15$; then the spiral is given in a different parametrization by $x = 3\sin z/3$, $y = 3\cos z/3$. In general, a path will be prescribed by two relations of the form $f(x, y, z) = 0$, $g(x, y, z) = 0$, and we must determine from other information what the explicit $x = x(t)$, $y = y(t)$, $z = z(t)$ relations are.

A more difficult case arises when, instead of working with implicit relations among the position functions, we must work with force and velocity functions that are not given explicitly as functions of time, but of position instead. For instance, the force exerted by a spring on a body depends on the extension of the spring and hence on the difference in position between the ends of the spring. The acceleration and velocity components must be then considered as functions of position. The formal differential relations are still easily found. For instance, suppose v_x is given as a function of (x, y, z) and $t: v_x = v_x(x, y, z, t)$. The acceleration component a_x is still found by differentiating v_x with respect to time; however, as the time changes, so do (x, y, z) so that

$$\Delta v_x = \frac{\partial v_x}{\partial x}\Delta x + \frac{\partial v_x}{\partial y}\Delta y + \frac{\partial v_x}{\partial z}\Delta z + \frac{\partial v_x}{\partial t}\Delta t$$

to terms of the first order in Δx, Δy, Δz, and Δt.   Computing the derivative, we find

$$a_x = \frac{dv_x}{dt} = \frac{\partial v_x}{\partial x}\frac{dx}{dt} + \frac{\partial v_x}{\partial y}\frac{dy}{dt} + \frac{\partial v_x}{\partial z}\frac{dz}{dt} + \frac{\partial v_x}{\partial t}$$

or

$$a_x = v_x\frac{\partial v_x}{\partial x} + v_y\frac{\partial v_x}{\partial y} + v_z\frac{\partial v_x}{\partial z} + \frac{\partial v_x}{\partial t}.$$

This, and the two similar relations for a_y and a_z, are of great importance in fluid mechanics; we shall not need them for our purposes.

We close this section by noting that the general relations 1.8-3 and 1.8-7 take special forms for motion on a plane curve and on a straight line, and by giving the first simple extension to motion of systems.   If the particle moves on a plane curve, we can—by suitable choice of coordinates—take the $z = 0$ plane to be the plane of motion. Then we simply drop the z-component from consideration, dealing only with $x(t)$ and $y(t)$.   For straight-line motion, we may choose the x-axis along the path; then $\mathbf{r} = x\mathbf{i}$, $\mathbf{v} = v\mathbf{i} = \dot{x}\mathbf{i}$, and $\mathbf{a} = a\mathbf{i} = \ddot{x}\mathbf{i}$, and we may drop vector considerations altogether and deal with the scalar kinematic functions $x(t)$, $v(t)$, and $a(t)$.   For such *rectilinear motion*, we have, in addition to the time relations

$$x(t) = x_0 + \int_{t_0}^{t} v(\tau)\,d\tau, \qquad v = \frac{dx}{dt}$$

and   1.8-8

$$v(t) = v_0 + \int_{t_0}^{t} a(\tau)\,d\tau, \qquad a = \frac{dv}{dt},$$

the additional important equations

$$\frac{1}{2}\{[v(x)]^2 - [v(x_0)]^2\} = \int_{x_0}^{x} a(\xi)\,d\xi, \qquad a = v\frac{dv}{dx}. \qquad \textbf{1.8-9}$$

These last are easily proved.   Consider v to be a function of position, x, only.   Then*

$$a = \frac{dv}{dt} = \frac{dv}{dx}\frac{dx}{dt} = v\frac{dv}{dx} = \frac{d}{dx}\left(\frac{1}{2}v^2\right)$$

---

* This proof, using the ordinary chain rule of differentiation, is valid only if $v \neq 0$; where $v = 0$, dv/dx is undefined and a more elaborate proof is required.   The final result is still valid, however, even in this case.   For details see L. A. Pars, *Introduction to Dynamics* (Cambridge University Press, 1953), p. 52.   Also, see text Example 1.4-2 for a similar computation.

and

$$\int_{x_0}^{x} a(\xi)\, d\xi = \int_{v_0}^{v} v\, dv = \frac{1}{2}\{[v(x)]^2 - [v(x_0)]^2\}.$$

The student should note that the functional form of the acceleration in 1.8-8 and 1.8-9 is different. As evidenced by the limits on the integrals, the acceleration is regarded as a function of time in 1.8-8 and as a function of position in 1.8-9. To emphasize this difference further, we have used different dummy variables of integration. In the next example, we shall integrate an acceleration proportional to displacement, and so will use 1.8-9; if we knew that acceleration as a function of time, we would use 1.8-8. The two functional forms for the a of the next example are quite different: linear in x but sinusoidal in t.

The description of rectilinear particle motion embodied in Eqs. 1.8-8 and 1.8-9 can be extended immediately to the description of that motion of any collection of particles, continuous or discrete, called *rectilinear translation*. If a system moves in such a way that the relative position vector from any point in the system to any other point, also in the system, does not change either in magnitude or direction when referred to fixed coordinate axes, then the system is said to be *translating* or to have a motion of *pure translation*. This means, as we shall see later, that every point has the same velocity and acceleration. If, moreover, the velocity and acceleration vectors are always parallel to a fixed direction, then the system is in a state of *rectilinear translation*. Since all points have the same **v** and **a**, we may choose the x-axis along any line parallel to the direction of motion and compute the velocity, acceleration, and position change of the system as though it were a particle in rectilinear motion. Usually, for reasons that will appear later, the typical path is chosen to be that of the mass center of the system, and (x, v, a) can be taken to refer to the motion of that point; the important fact is, however, that *the v and a relations* (1.8-8) *and* (1.8-9) *for the motion of one point hold for every point in a system in rectilinear translation.*

Example 1.8-4

A particle moves in a straight line, with its acceleration proportional to its distance from a fixed point on the line and oppositely directed to the displacement from the point. If the particle is moved out a distance x_0 from the fixed point and released from rest, find x and v at all time t.

Solution: In Fig. 1.8-4, the particle is shown at a typical position along its line of motion, at displacement x units from the neutral point O. A positive sense for measuring x along the line has been picked. The acceleration must then be proportional to x in magnitude and always directed to O from the position of the particle. We can ensure this by choosing the scalar acceleration function a to be of the form

$$a = -p^2 x.$$

With a given as a function of x, it is natural to integrate once using Eq. 1.8-9:

$$\frac{1}{2}(v^2 - v_0^2) = \int_{x_0}^{x} (-p^2\xi)\, d\xi,$$

or (with $v_0 = 0$ at $x = x_0$)

$$\frac{1}{2}v^2 = -\frac{p^2}{2}(x^2 - x_0^2).$$

Thus

$$v^2 = \left(\frac{dx}{dt}\right)^2 = p^2(x_0^2 - x^2).$$

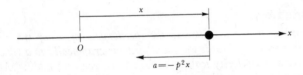

Fig. 1.8-4

Since $v^2 \geq 0$, we see that x can never be greater than x_0 in absolute value. To integrate this once more, we use Eq. 1.8-8. We must consider what sign to give to the square root in solving the above equation for v. For some time after release, the particle will move to the left. Thus, for a little while after motion starts,

$$v = \frac{dx}{dt} = -p(x_0^2 - x^2)^{1/2}, \qquad \text{where} \quad p > 0.$$

Separating variables,

$$\frac{dx}{(x_0^2 - x^2)^{1/2}} = -p\, dt$$

$$\int_{x_0}^{x} \frac{d\xi}{(x_0^2 - \xi^2)^{1/2}} = -p \int_{0}^{t} d\tau = -pt.$$

The integral on the left is easily evaluated, and may be written as

$$-\arccos \frac{\xi}{x_0}\Bigg|_{x_0}^{x} = -\arccos \frac{x}{x_0} + \arccos 1 = -\arccos \frac{x}{x_0};$$

then

$$\arccos \frac{x}{x_0} = pt,$$

$$x = x_0 \cos pt, \quad \text{and} \quad v = \dot{x} = -x_0 p \sin pt.$$

The formal derivation was good for $v < 0$; i.e., until $t = \pi/p$. We should then use $v = +p(x_0^2 - x^2)^{1/2}$; computation will show that the given expressions hold for all time t.

This is an elementary example of *simple harmonic motion*. From the formula for $x(t)$, we see that the particle moves to the left until it is x_0 units to the left of the equilibrium position, then moves to the right again; the particle oscillates periodically every $2\pi/p$ sec between $-x_0$ and $+x_0$.

In real problems, information is often given in the form of experimental data presented as tables or graphs. The next examples emphasize the geometrical meanings of the derivative and integral as slope of line and area under a curve respectively; these are the basis of much of the simple interpretation of experimental data.

Example 1.8-5

A recording device attached to the speedometer of a car traveling on a straight east–west road records the speed of a car graphically to a time scale of 1 in. to 60 sec and a velocity scale of 1 in. to 22 ft/sec ($= 15$ mph). Moreover, the direction of motion is also taken into account by the recording device—in this case, positive v corresponds to motion to the east. For the graph given, compute the distance traveled and the distance from the starting point after 6 min (Fig. 1.8-5).

Solution: The displacement, or change in position, being the integral of the velocity function, is the area between the velocity curve and the t-axis, areas below the axis being counted as negative. By some process, the areas have been determined as shown. For the scales used, 1 in$^2 \simeq$ (22 ft/sec) (60 sec) = 1320 ft. Thus the displacement is

$$\Delta x = 1320 \, (1.125 - 4.20 + 2.70)$$

$$= 1320 \, (-0.375) = -495 \text{ ft};$$

i.e., the final position is 495 ft to the west of the initial position. During this interval, the car has actually traveled a distance given by the integral of the speed—the area under the curve giving the absolute value of the velocity function. This curve is represented by v itself where $v > 0$ and by the dotted line shown in Fig. 1.8-5 over that time interval when $v < 0$. The distance traveled, D, is thus given by the area under the $|v|$-curve, all areas being positive:

$$D = 1320 \, (1.125 + 4.20 + 2.70) = 10{,}593 \text{ ft}.$$

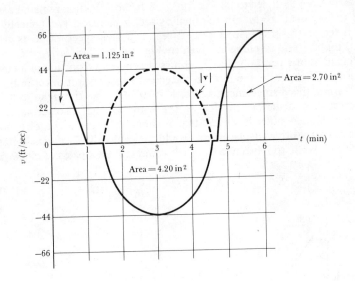

Fig. 1.8-5

Example 1.8-6

Suppose an automobile traveling at 60 mph on a level road accelerates at the rate of −2 ft/sec² for half a minute, goes at constant speed for half a minute, and then accelerates linearly for a quarter minute to a maximum acceleration of 2.5 ft/sec². The acceleration-time curve is given in Fig. 1.8-6. Draw the velocity-time and displacement-time curves and determine the speed and distance traveled at the end of the 1¼ min period.

Solution: The initial speed is 60 mph or 88 ft/sec. Since the change in velocity is the area under the at-curve, and the acceleration is the slope of the velocity curve, we see that for the first 30 sec the velocity decreases

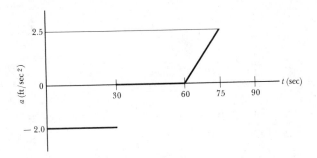

Fig. 1.8-6

linearly from 88 ft/sec to $88-(2)(30)=28$ ft/sec. It then remains constant for 30 sec, since $a=0$. In the final 15 sec, it increases parabolically from 28 ft/sec to $28+[(75-60)(2.5)/2]$ ft/sec, or a final speed of 46.75 ft/sec $=$ 31.9 mph. The vt-curve is given in Fig. 1.8-7. Similarly, the xt-curve will consist of a parabolic piece, a line segment, and a portion of a cubic, as shown in Fig. 1.8-8—the final displacement being 3094 ft or 0.586 mi.

Since the displacement function is of one sign throughout the time interval, the distance traveled is the same as the displacement. The student should note, however, that a simple change in the direction for measuring positive displacement would make the displacement a negative 0.586 mi, while the distance traveled would still be a positive 0.586 mi.

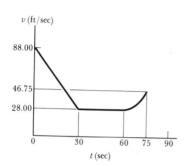

Fig. 1.8-7   **Fig. 1.8-8**

The analytical solution of this example follows. We have

$$a = -2 \text{ ft/sec}^2 \qquad\qquad 0 \leqq t \leqq 30$$

$$a = 0 \qquad\qquad 30 < t \leqq 60$$

$$a = \frac{t}{6} - 10 \text{ ft/sec}^2 \qquad\qquad 60 \leqq t \leqq 75;$$

integrating,

$$v = 88 - 2t \text{ ft/sec} \qquad\qquad 0 \leqq t \leqq 30$$

$$v = 28 \text{ ft/sec} \qquad\qquad 30 \leqq t \leqq 60$$

$$v = \frac{1}{12} t^2 - 10t + 328 \text{ ft/sec} \qquad\qquad 60 \leqq t \leqq 75,$$

and

$$x = 88t - t^2 \text{ ft} \qquad\qquad 0 \leqq t \leqq 30$$

$$x = 28t + 900 \text{ ft} \qquad\qquad 30 \leqq t \leqq 60$$

$$x = \frac{1}{36} t^3 - 5t^2 + 328t - 5100 \text{ ft} \qquad\qquad 60 \leqq t \leqq 75.$$

The constant of integration for each part is determined so that the function matches in value the value of the part from the previous time interval at the common time value; for instance, for $60 \leq t \leq 75$, we have

$$v - v(60) = \int_{60}^{t} \left(\frac{1}{6} \tau - 10 \right) d\tau$$

with $v(60)$ determined from the time interval $30 \leq t \leq 60$, namely $v(60) = 28$ ft/sec.

1.9 Normal and Tangential Coordinates

Another very natural way of describing motion is that which we use when we travel in a car or ship—we observe the motion from where we are at the moment. Describing the motion of a particle as would an observer moving with it is the *intrinsic* method of description—in contradistinction to the extrinsic, outside observer, method of the previous section. There is a natural coordinate system useful for representation of vector quantities when we regard the motion in this fashion. This coordinate system is based on the direction of the velocity vector.

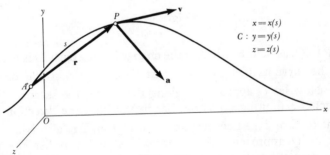

Fig. 1.9-1

Once again let us consider a particle traveling along a curve, C. Now, however, we do not deal with the equation of the curve in the form $x = x(t)$, $y = y(t)$, $z = z(t)$. Rather, we pick some arbitrary, but fixed, point A on the curve as an origin and select some positive sense along the curve for measurement of the *arclength* s, just as we select an origin O and a positive x-direction on the x-axis (Fig. 1.9-1). If we select some (x, y, z) coordinate system with origin O, we can think of the equation of the curve as given parametrically in the form $[x(s), y(s), z(s)]$. When the particle is at point P, it has velocity

v and acceleration **a**; the position vector may be taken to be the vector **r**, the position of P with respect to A. Under the action of an appropriately directed resultant force **F**, the particle will traverse the curve C more or less rapidly depending on the variation of the magnitude of **F** with time; then the arclength s will be determined as a function of time. Let us consider the intrinsic properties of motion along curves without regard for the forces causing the motion or for the time scale involved; that is, let us regard everything as functions of arclength and bring in the time dependence later.

Suppose the particle moves from point P to point Q on the curve C (Fig. 1.9-2); the displacement vector $\Delta\mathbf{r}$ is the directed line segment

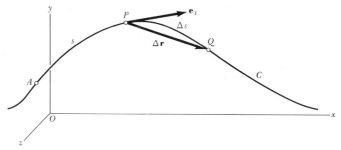

Fig. 1.9-2

from P to Q, as before; whereas the change in arclength Δs is measured along the curve itself. The vector $\Delta\mathbf{r} \equiv \overline{PQ}$ is a *secant* line, or chord, of C. Now let Q approach P along the curve; the secant $\overline{PQ}$, if it approaches a limiting direction, has in the limit the direction of the tangent to C at P. The magnitude of $\overline{PQ}$, or $\Delta\mathbf{r}$, also is expressed easily: as Q approaches P it approaches Δs, or rather the vector $\Delta\mathbf{r}/\Delta s$ has magnitude that approaches unity in the limit. We may formulate this analytically in the following way. If $\Delta\mathbf{r}/\Delta s$ has a limit when Δs has limit zero, then that limit is the *unit tangent vector* $\mathbf{e}_t$ to the curve C at P, in the sense of increasing arclength:

$$\lim_{\Delta s \to 0} \frac{\Delta\mathbf{r}}{\Delta s} = \frac{d\mathbf{r}}{ds} = \mathbf{e}_t. \qquad \text{1.9-1}$$

The velocity vector can now be found. If $\Delta\mathbf{r}$ or Δs is considered as a function of time, we have

$$\lim_{\Delta t \to 0} \frac{\Delta\mathbf{r}}{\Delta t} = \lim_{\Delta t \to 0} \frac{\Delta\mathbf{r}}{\Delta s}\frac{\Delta s}{\Delta t} = \frac{d\mathbf{r}}{ds}\frac{ds}{dt};$$

the velocity vector is given by

$$\mathbf{v} = \frac{d\mathbf{r}}{dt} = \frac{ds}{dt} \mathbf{e}_t. \qquad \text{1.9-2}$$

The fundamental result is that *the velocity is always tangent to the path,* and that the speed is the absolute value of the time derivative of the arclength:

$$|\mathbf{v}| = v = |\dot{s}|.$$

To compute the acceleration, we must differentiate the velocity. Since $\mathbf{v}$ is given as the product of a scalar function and a vector function, by Eq. 1.4-4b

$$\mathbf{a} = \frac{d\mathbf{v}}{dt} = \frac{d^2 s}{dt^2} \mathbf{e}_t + \frac{ds}{dt} \frac{d\mathbf{e}_t}{dt}.$$

The vector $d\mathbf{e}_t/dt$, being the rate of change of a unit vector, must, as was shown in Example 1.4-1, be at right angles to $\mathbf{e}_t$. There are, of course, any number of normal directions to a space curve; which is the proper direction of $d\mathbf{e}_t/dt$?

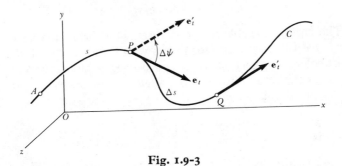

Fig. 1.9-3

Some geometric insight into the problem can be gained by seeing how $\mathbf{e}_t$ changes as C is traversed. Denote the unit tangent vector at P, a distance s from A along the curve, by $\mathbf{e}_t$ and that at Q, at $s + \Delta s$, by $\mathbf{e}_t'$ (Fig. 1.9-3). The lines of action of $\mathbf{e}_t$ and $\mathbf{e}_t'$ do not in general intersect. Moving $\mathbf{e}_t'$ parallel to itself, we can draw the parallel unit vector at P. The vectors $\mathbf{e}_t$ and $\mathbf{e}_t'$ at P then determine the angle $\Delta\psi$ between them: $\cos \Delta\psi = \mathbf{e}_t \cdot \mathbf{e}_t'$. We can now set out the separate vector sum triangle (Fig. 1.9-4), showing the change in $\mathbf{e}_t$ given by $\Delta\mathbf{e}_t =$

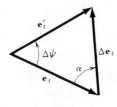

Fig. 1.9-4

$\mathbf{e}'_t - \mathbf{e}_t$, and determine the magnitude and direction (relative to $\mathbf{e}_t$) of $\Delta\mathbf{e}_t$.

Since $\mathbf{e}_t$ and $\mathbf{e}'_t$ are unit vectors, the triangle is isosceles with the equal sides of unit magnitude. The direction of $\Delta\mathbf{e}_t$ relative to $\mathbf{e}_t$ is then given by the interior angle α, where

$$\alpha = \frac{\pi}{2} - \frac{\Delta\psi}{2}.$$

The magnitude of $\Delta\mathbf{e}_t$ is that of the third side of the triangle; by the law of cosines,

$$|\Delta\mathbf{e}_t|^2 = 1^2 + 1^2 - 2\cos\Delta\psi = 2(1 - \cos\Delta\psi) = 4\sin^2\frac{\Delta\psi}{2}$$

or

$$|\Delta\mathbf{e}_t| = 2\sin\frac{\Delta\psi}{2}.$$

(Equivalently,

$$|\Delta\mathbf{e}_t|^2 = \Delta\mathbf{e}_t \cdot \Delta\mathbf{e}_t = (\mathbf{e}'_t - \mathbf{e}_t) \cdot (\mathbf{e}'_t - \mathbf{e}_t)$$

$$= \mathbf{e}_t \cdot \mathbf{e}_t + \mathbf{e}'_t \cdot \mathbf{e}'_t - 2\mathbf{e}_t \cdot \mathbf{e}'_t = 1 + 1 - 2\cos\Delta\psi.)$$

The natural variable to use in discussing the change in $\mathbf{e}_t$ is the angle ψ that the tangent vector makes with some line fixed in space.* In particular, we see that as Q approaches P along the curve, $\Delta\psi$ approaches the limit zero, and the angle α approaches $\pi/2$; the ratio $|\Delta\mathbf{e}_t|/\Delta\psi$ has the limit one:

$$\lim_{\Delta\psi \to 0} \frac{|\Delta\mathbf{e}_t|}{\Delta\psi} = \lim_{\Delta\psi \to 0} \frac{\sin(\Delta\psi/2)}{\Delta\psi/2} = 1.$$

Thus the vector $d\mathbf{e}_t/d\psi$ is a vector of magnitude one which is perpendicular to $\mathbf{e}_t$; it is the *unit principal normal vector* $\mathbf{e}_n$:

$$\frac{d\mathbf{e}_t}{d\psi} = \mathbf{e}_n. \qquad\qquad \textbf{I.9-3}$$

This result tells us what type of geometric changes and variables to use, but still does not tell us much about $\mathbf{e}_n$. What more can we

---

* Parallel translation of the vector is necessary in general to make the lines intersect and to actually draw the angle; this procedure is of course never really carried out, the angle being determined by $\cos\psi = \mathbf{e}_t \cdot \mathbf{e}$ where $\mathbf{e}$ is a unit vector in the fixed direction.

say ? As we can see from Fig. 1.9-3, the change in direction of e_t is related to the way the curve bends—that is, the direction of e_n should be determined by the *curvature* of C. The proper result is easy to establish for a *plane curve*. For such a curve, if the tangents at P and Q include the angle $\Delta \psi$, so do the normals to the curve at P and Q. Moreover, these normals will intersect at some point R (Fig. 1.9-5). As Q approaches P, QR approaches PR, with the position of R itself changing; the limiting position of R is the *center of curvature* at P and the limiting length of PR is the *radius of curvature* ρ at P. The fundamental relation between arclength and the angle ψ, where ψ is

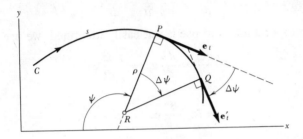

Fig. 1.9-5

the angle from some fixed direction to the radius of curvature now, is then

$$ds = \rho \, d\psi. \qquad \qquad \textbf{1.9-4}$$

This relation, and the terms center and radius of curvature, point up the true nature of this limiting process. We are really asking for the best approximation to the curve C at point P, using a circular arc as the approximating curve. The full circle is called the circle of curvature at P, with ρ as its radius and the center of curvature as the center of the circle. Then $ds = \rho \, d\psi$ is the element of arclength on the circle.

It is this concept of approximating the curve in the "best" way by a circular arc that enables us to handle space curves as well as plane curves. Another way of getting the circle of curvature in the plane is to choose three points P, Q, Q′ on the curve. Since a circle can be drawn through three points, each set of three points determines a circle in the xy-plane. Now let Q and Q′ approach P along the curve in any way; the circle, its center, and its radius will, if they approach limits at all, approach the circle, center, and radius of curvature at P. Do the same thing in three dimensions: P, Q, Q′

determine a plane, and a circle can be drawn in that plane through the points. Let Q and Q' approach P; the limiting position of the plane is called the *osculating plane*; the limiting circle is the *principal circle of curvature*, with the principal center and principal radius of curvature also defined in this way. As is shown in differential geometry, the proper unit normal vector—the *principal normal*—*points in toward the principal center of curvature*. Equation 1.9-4 holds in three dimensions as well as two, with ρ as the principal radius of curvature.

We are now ready to return to the computation of $d\mathbf{e}_t/dt$. We have

$$\frac{d\mathbf{e}_t}{dt} = \frac{d\mathbf{e}_t}{d\psi}\frac{d\psi}{dt} = \frac{d\psi}{dt}\mathbf{e}_n.$$ **1.9-5**

Since a proper angle ψ to use is not easily identified, we use 1.9-4:

$$\frac{d\mathbf{e}_t}{dt} = \frac{d\psi}{dt}\mathbf{e}_n = \frac{1}{\rho}\frac{ds}{dt}\mathbf{e}_n$$ **1.9-6**

and

$$\mathbf{a} = \ddot{s}\mathbf{e}_t + \frac{\dot{s}^2}{\rho}\mathbf{e}_n = \ddot{s}\mathbf{e}_t + \frac{v^2}{\rho}\mathbf{e}_n.$$ **1.9-7**

The quantity $a_t = \ddot{s}$ is the scalar *tangential acceleration*; $a_n = v^2/\rho$ is the *normal acceleration*, always positive by our definition of $\mathbf{e}_n$ and ρ.[*]

Equations 1.9-2 and 1.9-7, repeated here, are the fundamental kinematic relations in tangential and normal coordinates:

$$\mathbf{v} = \dot{s}\mathbf{e}_t$$

$$\mathbf{a} = \ddot{s}\mathbf{e}_t + \frac{\dot{s}^2}{\rho}\mathbf{e}_n.$$ **1.9-8**

For straight-line motion, these reduce to the proper form: for motion on the x-axis, $s = x$, $\mathbf{e}_t = \mathbf{i}$, and ρ is infinite. *There is always an*

---

[*] Note that we always take $\mathbf{e}_n$ in towards the center of curvature, and therefore ρ is always positive. In the study of plane curves, the following formula is developed for the curvature κ (Kappa) of $y = f(x)$:

$$\kappa = \frac{1}{\rho} = \frac{-\dfrac{d^2y}{dx^2}}{\left[1 + \left(\dfrac{dy}{dx}\right)^2\right]^{3/2}}.$$

Here κ and ρ can be positive or negative, depending on the sign of d^2y/dx^2. *We will not use this expression;* the ρ that we do use will correspond to the absolute value of the given formula.

acceleration if the path is curved; if the motion is at constant speed, $\dot{s}$ is constant, $a_t = \ddot{s} = 0$, but $\mathbf{a} = a_n \mathbf{e}_n \neq 0$. Relations of the form 1.8-8 and 1.8-9 for rectilinear motion hold here for s, $v = \dot{s}$, and $a_t = \ddot{s}$ (here v is used for $\dot{s}$, *not* for the speed $|\dot{s}|$):

$$v = \frac{ds}{dt} \qquad s - s_0 = \int_{t_0}^{t} v(\tau)\, d\tau$$

$$a_t = \frac{dv}{dt} \qquad v - v_0 = \int_{t_0}^{t} a_t(\tau)\, d\tau \qquad \textbf{1.9-9}$$

$$a_t = v\frac{dv}{ds} \qquad \frac{1}{2}(v^2 - v_0^2) = \int_{s_0}^{s} a_t(\sigma)\, d\sigma.$$

Equation 1.9-5 expresses a fundamental result that will be of use later. We find that $d\mathbf{e}_t/dt$ is the product of rate of change of angle, or *angular velocity*, into a unit vector perpendicular to $\mathbf{e}_t$. This is true for any unit vector. The derivative of any vector of constant magnitude must be perpendicular to the vector, or zero, as we have seen in Example 1.4-1. Considering the geometry of a change in a unit vector, as in Fig. 1.9-4, and the computations that follow, we see that the rate of change of the unit vector with an angle gives another unit vector. The only question will be: what angle and what angular velocity are the proper ones?

In the plane, $\mathbf{e}_t$ and $\mathbf{e}_n$ are orthogonal unit vectors and the tangential and normal directions are geometrically similar to the x- and y-axes. In three dimensions, for completeness, we should have a third direction and a third unit vector by analogy with the three (x, y, z) axes and the *unit orthogonal triad* $(\mathbf{i}, \mathbf{j}, \mathbf{k})$. This third direction is called the *binormal* direction and its unit vector is denoted by $\mathbf{e}_b$; its sense can be determined by $\mathbf{e}_b = \mathbf{e}_t \times \mathbf{e}_n$ so that $(\mathbf{e}_t, \mathbf{e}_n, \mathbf{e}_b)$ form a right-handed unit triad. The vector $\mathbf{e}_b$ would appear if we had to find $d\mathbf{e}_n/dt$; another number—the *torsion* of the curve—which measures the bending of the curve out of the osculating plane, would then enter the computations, much as the curvature enters in $d\mathbf{e}_t/dt$. In some problems, such as the study of vibrations of twisted propeller blades, the binormal vector is useful. We shall not encounter it, however, in this book.

For systems, immediate application of normal and tangential coordinates can be made if the motion is one of curvilinear translation. Here again all relative positions between parts of the system do not change either in magnitude or direction relative to fixed axes, all points having the same velocity and acceleration. The path of a typical point is, in general, curved—but all paths have the same radius of curvature at the same instant. The equations of motion can be written in $\mathbf{e}_t$ and $\mathbf{e}_n$ coordinates, the principal path usually being taken as the path of the mass center.

Example 1.9-1

A particle moves in the xy-plane in a circle of radius three feet about the origin at a constant speed of 15 feet per second. What is the acceleration?

Solution: This is Example 1.8-1 again. We have $\mathbf{v} = 15\mathbf{e}_t$ ft/sec always; thus $\dot{s} = 15$, and $\ddot{s} = 0$. The acceleration is then

$$\mathbf{a} = \frac{v^2}{\rho} \mathbf{e}_n = \frac{225}{3} \mathbf{e}_n \text{ ft/sec}^2.$$

Here $\mathbf{e}_n$ points toward the center of the circle always.

Example 1.9-2

At some instant of time, a particle has speed of 5 ft/sec, acceleration magnitude 10 ft/sec², and the angle between the acceleration and velocity vectors is 30°. Find a_t, a_n, and ρ at that instant.

Solution: Here $\mathbf{v} = 5\mathbf{e}_t$, $\mathbf{a} = 10\mathbf{e}$, where $\mathbf{e}$ is the unit vector in the direction of the acceleration. Since the angle between the vectors is 30°, $\mathbf{e} \cdot \mathbf{e}_t = \cos 30°$. (Draw a picture.) Hence,

$$a_t = \mathbf{a} \cdot \mathbf{e}_t = 10\mathbf{e} \cdot \mathbf{e}_t = 10 \cos 30° = 5\sqrt{3} \text{ ft/sec}^2$$

$$a_n = (a^2 - a_t^2)^{1/2} = (100 - 75)^{1/2} = 5 \text{ ft/sec}^2$$

$$\rho = \frac{v^2}{a_n} = \frac{25}{5} = 5 \text{ ft.}$$

Example 1.9-3

At some instant of time, a particle has acceleration $\mathbf{a} = 3.5\mathbf{e}_t + 4.5\mathbf{e}_n$ ft/sec². Its speed is 6 ft/sec. What is ρ?

Solution:

$$\rho = \frac{v^2}{a_n} = \frac{36}{4.5} = 8 \text{ ft.}$$

Example 1.9-4

Suppose that the velocity and acceleration of a particle are known at some instant in (x, y, z) coordinates: $\mathbf{v} = 2\mathbf{i} - 3\mathbf{j} + 4\mathbf{k}$ in/sec, $\mathbf{a} = -3\mathbf{i} - 2\mathbf{j}$ in/sec². What is ρ?

Solution: From the fundamental definition, $\mathbf{v}$ must be tangent to the path. Dividing the velocity by the speed, we obtain a unit tangent vector $\mathbf{e}_v$ in the direction of the velocity [which may be opposite to the $\mathbf{e}_t$ in the direction of increasing arclength (Why?)]:

$$\mathbf{e}_v = \frac{\mathbf{v}}{v} = \frac{2\mathbf{i} - 3\mathbf{j} + 4\mathbf{k}}{\sqrt{29}}.$$

The tangential acceleration is $a_t = \mathbf{a} \cdot \mathbf{e}_v = (-6+6)/\sqrt{29} = 0$; hence $a_n^2 = a^2 - a_t^2 = a^2 = 13$. Thus

$$\rho = \frac{v^2}{a_n} = \frac{29}{\sqrt{13}} = \frac{29}{13} \sqrt{13} \text{ inches.}$$

(Of course, a_t will not always be zero.)

Example 1.9-5

Find a formula for ρ in terms of vector operations.

Solution: Here we want a way of computing ρ that will be independent of the coordinate system used. Since $\rho = v^2/a_n$ we must find v^2 and a_n in a general way. For v^2, this is simple: $v^2 = \mathbf{v} \cdot \mathbf{v} = |\mathbf{v}|^2$. For a_n, we use the fact that the normal acceleration is what is left over when the tangential acceleration is removed: $a_n \mathbf{e}_n = \mathbf{a} - a_t \mathbf{e}_t$. Then

$$\mathbf{v} \times \mathbf{a} = \mathbf{v} \times (\mathbf{a}_t + \mathbf{a}_n) = \mathbf{v} \times \mathbf{a}_n$$

since $\mathbf{v}$ and $\mathbf{a}_t$ are in the tangential direction. Thus

$$|\mathbf{v} \times \mathbf{a}| = |\mathbf{v} \times \mathbf{a}_n| = |\mathbf{v}| \, |\mathbf{a}_n| \sin 90° = |\mathbf{v}| a_n$$

and

$$a_n = \frac{|\mathbf{v} \times \mathbf{a}_n|}{|\mathbf{v}|} = \frac{|\mathbf{v} \times \mathbf{a}|}{|\mathbf{v}|}.$$

Finally,

$$\rho = \frac{|\mathbf{v}|^3}{|\mathbf{v} \times \mathbf{a}|}.$$

This is often a useful way of computing ρ directly. The student should be careful to find the magnitudes indicated and not leave any vector symbols in the resulting expressions.

Example 1.9-6

Find the normal acceleration of the particle of Example 1.8-2, which travels on the helical path $3 \sin 5t\mathbf{i} + 3 \cos 5t\mathbf{j} + 15t\mathbf{k}$ ft, at time $t = \pi/5$ sec.

Solution: From Example 1.8-2, or by direct computation from the given position vector, we find that the position, velocity, and acceleration vectors at $t = \pi/5$ sec are

$$\mathbf{r}\,|_{t=\pi/5} = -3\mathbf{j} + 3\pi\mathbf{k} \text{ ft}$$

$$\mathbf{v}\,|_{t=\pi/5} = -15\mathbf{i} + 15\mathbf{k} \text{ ft/sec}$$

$$\mathbf{a}\,|_{t=\pi/5} = +75\mathbf{j} \text{ ft/sec}^2.$$

Clearly, $\mathbf{a}$ is perpendicular to $\mathbf{v}$ at this time: $\mathbf{a} \cdot \mathbf{v} = 0$. Thus the tangential acceleration is zero, and the normal acceleration $a_n = 75$ ft/sec^2.

In fact, $\mathbf{a} \cdot \mathbf{v} = 0$ at any time for this motion; there is never any tangential acceleration, and the particle traverses the helix at constant speed $|\mathbf{v}| = 15\sqrt{2}$ ft/sec.

Example 1.9-7

A particle moves on a path C, with its position vector with respect to fixed cartesian axes at point O being $\mathbf{r} = x\mathbf{i} + y\mathbf{j} + z\mathbf{k}$. *What are the direction cosines of the unit tangent vector with respect to the cartesian axes?*

Solution: This problem deals with the fundamental relations between the intrinsic normal and tangential coordinates and the extrinsic cartesian coordinates. Regarding the curve C as given by three scalar functions $x(u), y(u), z(u)$ of a scalar variable u, then the basic relation derives from the fact that the velocity is tangent to the path:

$$\mathbf{v} = \frac{ds}{dt}\mathbf{e}_t = \frac{d\mathbf{r}}{dt} = \frac{d\mathbf{r}}{du}\frac{du}{dt} = \frac{du}{dt}\left(\frac{dx}{du}\mathbf{i} + \frac{dy}{du}\mathbf{j} + \frac{dz}{du}\mathbf{k}\right).$$

Usually u is identified with the time t or the arclength s; i.e., the unit tangent vector is $(u \equiv s)$:

$$\mathbf{e}_t = \frac{dx}{ds}\mathbf{i} + \frac{dy}{ds}\mathbf{j} + \frac{dz}{ds}\mathbf{k}$$

or $(u \equiv t)$

$$\mathbf{e}_t = \left(\frac{ds}{dt}\right)^{-1}\left(\frac{dx}{dt}\mathbf{i} + \frac{dy}{dt}\mathbf{j} + \frac{dz}{dt}\mathbf{k}\right)$$

$$= \pm(v_x^2 + v_y^2 + v_z^2)^{-\frac{1}{2}}[v_x\mathbf{i} + v_y\mathbf{j} + v_z\mathbf{k}].$$

The sign in the last relation depends on the sign of ds/dt. In any case, a unit tangent vector is given by $\mathbf{e}_t = \mathbf{v}/|\mathbf{v}|$.

The direction cosines of $\mathbf{e}_t$ (in the sense of increasing arclength) are thus

$$\cos\theta_x = \frac{dx}{ds}, \qquad \cos\theta_y = \frac{dy}{ds}, \qquad \cos\theta_z = \frac{dz}{ds}.$$

1.10 Plane and Cylindrical Polar Coordinates

In solving particular problems, we often find that special coordinate systems, usually curvilinear, simplify the solution process. Only one of these systems will be of direct use to us in the developments presented in this text: cylindrical polar coordinates.

We start with the kinematics of a particle moving on a plane curve C, with the curve equations given in *plane polar coordinates* (r, ϕ) by functions $r(t), \phi(t)$. Here r is the distance to the particle from the origin or pole O, a fixed point in the plane of motion, and ϕ is the angle from some line fixed in the plane to the position vector of the particle (Fig. 1.10-1). A positive sense is assigned to ϕ, usually the counterclockwise sense.

Two unit vectors are introduced. The *unit radial vector* $\mathbf{e}_r$ points from O along the position vector OP; the direction OP is called the radial direction at P. The *unit transverse vector* $\mathbf{e}_\phi$ is perpendicular to $\mathbf{e}_r$ in the sense of increasing ϕ; in Fig. I.10-1, where ϕ increases in the counterclockwise sense, $\mathbf{e}_\phi$ is $90°$ counterclockwise from $\mathbf{e}_r$. This direction, perpendicular to the radial direction, is called the transverse or circumferential direction at P.

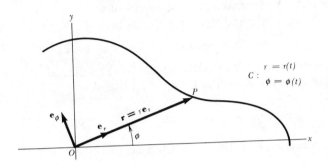

Fig. I.10-1

In terms of these vectors and coordinates, the position vector OP is

$$\mathbf{r} = r\mathbf{e}_r; \qquad\qquad \text{I.10-1}$$

the velocity vector is

$$\mathbf{v} = \frac{d\mathbf{r}}{dt} = \frac{dr}{dt}\,\mathbf{e}_r + r\,\frac{d\mathbf{e}_r}{dt}.$$

Again, we are concerned with the derivative of a unit vector that is not constant in direction. As P moves, the radial direction changes—unless P moves straight out the ray OP. That is, $\mathbf{e}_r$ will not change unless ϕ changes. From the discussion of the derivative of $\mathbf{e}_t$ in the last section, we can predict the result here. We know that $\dot{\mathbf{e}}_r$ should be of the form rate-of-change of angle times a unit vector orthogonal to $\mathbf{e}_r$. Since $\mathbf{e}_r$ stays in the plane of the curve C, $\mathbf{e}_\phi$ is the appropriate orthogonal unit vector; indeed, by substituting $\mathbf{e}_r$ for $\mathbf{e}_t$ and ϕ for ψ in the argument of the last section (see Fig. 1.9-4), we have

$$\frac{d\mathbf{e}_r}{d\phi} = \mathbf{e}_\phi \qquad\qquad \text{I.10-2}$$

and

$$\frac{d\mathbf{e}_r}{dt} = \frac{d\mathbf{e}_r}{d\phi}\frac{d\phi}{dt} = \dot{\phi}\mathbf{e}_\phi. \qquad\qquad \text{I.10-3}$$

The velocity vector becomes

$$\mathbf{v} = \dot{\mathbf{r}} = \dot{r}\mathbf{e}_r + r\dot{\phi}\mathbf{e}_\phi;$$ **1.10-4**

the scalar components,

$$v_r = \dot{r} \quad \text{and} \quad v_\phi = r\dot{\phi},$$ **1.10-5**

are the radial and transverse components of **v**.

A second differentiation of **r** results in

$$\mathbf{a} = \ddot{\mathbf{r}} = \ddot{r}\mathbf{e}_r + \dot{r}\dot{\mathbf{e}}_r + (\dot{r}\dot{\phi} + r\ddot{\phi})\mathbf{e}_\phi + r\dot{\phi}\dot{\mathbf{e}}_\phi.$$

We now need $\dot{\mathbf{e}}_\phi$. The student should have no difficulty showing, by an argument parallel to that for $\mathbf{e}_t$ or $\mathbf{e}_r$, that

$$\frac{d\mathbf{e}_\phi}{d\phi} = -\mathbf{e}_r \quad \text{or} \quad \frac{d\mathbf{e}_\phi}{dt} = -\dot{\phi}\mathbf{e}_r.$$ **1.10-6**

The acceleration can then be written as

$$\mathbf{a} = \ddot{\mathbf{r}} = (\ddot{r} - r\dot{\phi}^2)\mathbf{e}_r + (r\ddot{\phi} + 2\dot{r}\dot{\phi})\mathbf{e}_\phi,$$ **1.10-7**

with the scalar radial and transverse components of acceleration being

$$a_r = \ddot{r} - r\dot{\phi}^2 \quad \text{and} \quad a_\phi = r\ddot{\phi} + 2\dot{r}\dot{\phi}.$$ **1.10-8**

Example 1.10-1

Discuss the circular motion of Examples 1.8-1 and 1.9-1 again, this time in plane polar coordinates.

Solution: At any point on the circular path of radius 3 ft, the radial direction is outward from the center of the circle and the transverse direction is tangent to the circle. The position vector is $\mathbf{r} = 3\mathbf{e}_r$ ft. Since $r = 3$ ft is constant, $\dot{\mathbf{r}} = \ddot{\mathbf{r}} = 0$, and

$$\mathbf{v} = r\dot{\phi}\mathbf{e}_\phi, \qquad \mathbf{a} = -r\dot{\phi}^2\mathbf{e}_r + r\ddot{\phi}\mathbf{e}_\phi.$$

Since the speed $v = 15$ ft/sec is constant, and $v = (v_r^2 + v_\phi^2)^{1/2} = v_\phi = r\dot{\phi}$, $\dot{\phi} = 5$ rad/sec, $\ddot{\phi} = 0$. Therefore,

$$\mathbf{v} = 15\mathbf{e}_\phi \text{ ft/sec}, \qquad \mathbf{a} = -75\mathbf{e}_r \text{ ft/sec}^2.$$

These are the same results as before, of course. Comparing with Example 1.9-1, we see that $\mathbf{e}_r$ and $\mathbf{e}_n$ are oppositely directed unit vectors, while $\mathbf{e}_\phi$ and $\mathbf{e}_t$ are the same. Circular motion is the only motion for which normal and tangential and radial and transverse directions essentially correspond.

Example 1.10-2

A particle travels on the spiral path $r = 2e^{-0.3\phi}$ ft such that ϕ is a constant 1.5 rad/sec. Find the velocity and acceleration when $\phi = 210°$; find the radius of curvature of the path (Fig. 1.10-2).

Solution: We have $\dot{\phi}=1.5$ rad/sec, $\ddot{\phi}=0$; thus

$$r = 2e^{-0.3\phi} \quad \text{ft}$$

$$\dot{r} = 0.6\dot{\phi}e^{-0.3\phi} = -0.9e^{-0.3\phi} \quad \text{ft/sec}$$

$$\ddot{r} = 0.27\dot{\phi}e^{-0.3\phi} = 0.405e^{-0.3\phi} \quad \text{ft/sec}^2.$$

Hence

$$a_r = \ddot{r}-r\dot{\phi}^2 = (0.405-4.5)e^{-0.3\phi} = -4.095e^{-0.3\phi},$$

$$a_\phi = r\ddot{\phi}+2\dot{r}\dot{\phi}= -2.7e^{-0.3\phi},$$

with

$$\mathbf{v} = \dot{r}\mathbf{e}_r+r\dot{\phi}\mathbf{e}_\phi = -0.9e^{-0.3\phi}\mathbf{e}_r+3e^{-0.3\phi}\mathbf{e}_\phi,$$

$$\mathbf{a} = (\ddot{r}-r\dot{\phi}^2)\mathbf{e}_r+(r\ddot{\phi}+2\dot{r}\dot{\phi})\mathbf{e}_\phi = -4.095e^{-0.3\phi}\mathbf{e}_r-2.7e^{-0.3\phi}\mathbf{e}_\phi.$$

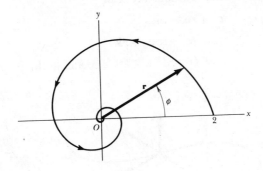

Fig. 1.10-2

When $\phi=210°=7\pi/6$ radians,

$$e^{-0.3\phi} = e^{-7\pi/20} = e^{-1.10} = 0.333.$$

Thus, at $\phi=210°$,

$$\mathbf{v} = -0.30\mathbf{e}_r+0.99\mathbf{e}_\phi \quad \text{ft/sec},$$

$$\mathbf{a} = -1.36\mathbf{e}_r-0.899\mathbf{e}_\phi \quad \text{ft/sec}^2.$$

To compute ρ, we may use the fact that $\mathbf{e}_t=\mathbf{v}/|\mathbf{v}|$ as in Example 1.9-4 or use the result of Example 1.9-5. Here we note that, if $\mathbf{e}_r\times\mathbf{e}_\phi=\mathbf{k}$, a unit vector perpendicular to the plane, then $\mathbf{e}_\phi\times\mathbf{e}_r=-\mathbf{k}$.

Then

$$\mathbf{v}\times\mathbf{a} = (-0.3)(-0.899)\mathbf{k}+(0.99)(-1.36)(-\mathbf{k}) = 1.63\mathbf{k}$$

so that

$$|\mathbf{v}\times\mathbf{a}| = 1.63, \qquad |\mathbf{v}| = [(0.3)^2+(0.99)^2]^{\frac{1}{2}} = 1.088$$

and

$$\rho = \frac{(1.088)^3}{1.63} = 0.79 \quad \text{ft.}$$

As indicated in the last example, the extension of plane polar coordinates to three dimensions can be accomplished simply by adding a third coordinate z with unit vector $\mathbf{k}$ perpendicular to the plane of $\mathbf{e}_r$ and $\mathbf{e}_\phi$. *Cylindrical polar coordinates* (r, ϕ, z) are often useful for problems involving motion around an axis of symmetry. In this context, the z-direction is called the *axial* direction. The results obtained already are still valid; we need only add that

$$\mathbf{e}_r \times \mathbf{e}_\phi = \mathbf{k}, \qquad \mathbf{e}_\phi \times \mathbf{k} = \mathbf{e}_r, \qquad \mathbf{k} \times \mathbf{e}_r = \mathbf{e}_\phi$$

and that $d\mathbf{k}/dt = 0$, of course. The coordinates are shown in Fig. 1.10-3; the kinematic relations are now

$$\mathbf{r} = r\mathbf{e}_r + z\mathbf{k}$$
$$\mathbf{v} = \dot{r}\mathbf{e}_r + r\dot{\phi}\mathbf{e}_\phi + \dot{z}\mathbf{k} \qquad \textbf{1.10-9}$$
$$\mathbf{a} = (\ddot{r} - r\dot{\phi}^2)\mathbf{e}_r + (r\ddot{\phi} + 2\dot{r}\dot{\phi})\mathbf{e}_\phi + \ddot{z}\mathbf{k}.$$

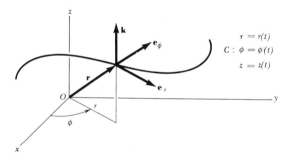

Fig. 1.10-3

Integration of vectors given in polar coordinates is difficult, in general, with no simple formulas corresponding to Eqs. 1.8-7 existing. For instance, the integral of the radial acceleration is *not* the radial velocity, since $dv_r/dt \neq a_r$. There is one relation that is often useful. Since $a_\phi = r\ddot{\phi} + 2\dot{r}\dot{\phi}$, we find that

$$ra_\phi = r^2\ddot{\phi} + 2r\dot{r}\dot{\phi} = \frac{d}{dt}(r^2\dot{\phi});$$

thus

$$a_\phi = \frac{1}{r}\frac{d}{dt}(r^2\dot{\phi}) = \frac{1}{r}\frac{d}{dt}(rv_\phi), \qquad rv_\phi = \int ra_\phi \, dt. \qquad \textbf{1.10-10}$$

The student should note that, in cylindrical polar coordinates, there is one variation from standard notation. That is the use of the symbol r to represent the plane polar or radial distance, rather than as the magnitude of the position vector. The use of (r, ϕ, z) as cylindrical polars is so standard that we hesitate to suggest any change—particularly since we will not often use them. If it is necessary to avoid this confusion, we can keep r as the magnitude of the position vector and introduce R or ρ as the plane radial coordinate. A three-dimensional generalization of plane polar coordinates that preserves the $\mathbf{r} = r\mathbf{e}_r$ form of the position vector is provided by spherical polar coordinates. Particle kinematics in these coordinates is discussed in the next section.

Proper choice of coordinates simplifies the computational work and aids one's insight into the significance of the answer. Such a choice is sometimes dictated by the statement of a problem, but often it is not. We shall show how coordinate systems are picked by example. The student should pay particular attention to those examples worked in alternative ways.

The study of motion in cylindrical polar coordinates raises a number of important questions that must be answered in the theoretical development of dynamics. We see that polar coordinates have many of the properties of rectangular coordinates. If we superpose the two coordinate systems with common origin O and common z-axis, measuring ϕ from the x-axis—as in Fig. I.10-3—we see that the polar coordinates, if they remained fixed, would be just another rectangular system rotated through angle ϕ about the z-axis from the given (x, y, z) system. Both systems can be considered as extrinsic systems based on O. Both are orthogonal systems, with the unit coordinate vectors $(\mathbf{e}_r, \mathbf{e}_\phi, \mathbf{k})$ related to one another just as $(\mathbf{i}, \mathbf{j}, \mathbf{k})$ are. Now, with ϕ changing, we can think of the polar coordinates as a rectangular coordinate system rotating with respect to the fixed system. We are thus led to the consideration of the treatment of the principles of kinematics and dynamics so that they will be properly stated for coordinate systems that rotate relative to one another. This is not just a theoretical question. We use the laws of motion to describe behavior of machines here on the earth's surface as though the laws were valid for measurements made with respect to the earth. The earth rotates—how good an approximation is the assumption that Newton's laws hold relative to the earth? What are the limitations on such an assumption? We shall return to such questions in the subsequent development of the theory.

Example **1.10-3**

A particle travels on a path $\mathbf{r} = 3\mathbf{e}_r + 15t\mathbf{k}$ ft, t in seconds. Find the acceleration if ϕ is a constant 5 rad/sec.
Solution:

$$\mathbf{r} = 3\mathbf{e}_r + 15t\mathbf{k}$$

$$\mathbf{v} = \dot{\mathbf{r}} = 3\dot{\mathbf{e}}_r + 15\mathbf{k} = 15\mathbf{e}_\phi + 15\mathbf{k}$$

$$\mathbf{a} = \ddot{\mathbf{r}} = 15\dot{\mathbf{e}}_\phi = -75\mathbf{e}_r \quad \text{ft/sec}^2.$$

This is the helix of Example 1.8-2.

Example **1.10-4**

Find the scalar tangential acceleration a_t in terms of the components of velocity and acceleration in cylindrical polar coordinates.

Solution: The solution is easily derived from the fact that the velocity is tangent to the path and the fact that cylindrical polar coordinates are orthogonal coordinates. That is, since

$$\mathbf{v} = v_r\mathbf{e}_r + v_\phi\mathbf{e}_\phi + v_z\mathbf{k},$$

the speed is

$$v = (v_r^2 + v_\phi^2 + v_z^2)^{1/2}$$

and a unit vector tangent to the path is

$$\mathbf{e}_t = \frac{\mathbf{v}}{v} = \frac{v_r\mathbf{e}_r + v_\phi\mathbf{e}_\phi + v_z\mathbf{k}}{(v_r^2 + v_\phi^2 + v_z^2)^{1/2}}.$$

The scalar tangential acceleration is

$$a_t = \mathbf{a} \cdot \mathbf{e}_t = \frac{a_r v_r + a_\phi v_\phi + a_z v_z}{(v_r^2 + v_\phi^2 + v_z^2)^{1/2}}.$$

In terms of r, ϕ, z and their derivatives,

$$a_t = \frac{\dot{r}\ddot{r} + r\dot{r}\dot{\phi}^2 + r^2\dot{\phi}\ddot{\phi} + \dot{z}\ddot{z}}{(\dot{r}^2 + r^2\dot{\phi}^2 + \dot{z}^2)^{1/2}}.$$

Example **1.10-5**

From the expressions for $\mathbf{e}_\phi$ and $\mathbf{e}_r$ in terms of $\mathbf{i}$ and $\mathbf{j}$, prove the result of Eq. 1.9-6: $\dot{\mathbf{e}}_\phi = -\dot{\phi}\mathbf{e}_r$.

Solution: Taking the x-axis as the base line from which ϕ is measured, as in Fig. 1.10-1, we see that:

$$\mathbf{e}_r = \cos\phi\,\mathbf{i} + \sin\phi\,\mathbf{j}$$

$$\mathbf{e}_\phi = -\sin\phi\,\mathbf{i} + \cos\phi\,\mathbf{j}.$$

Thus:

$$\dot{\mathbf{e}}_\phi = -\cos\phi\dot{\phi}\mathbf{i} - \sin\phi\dot{\phi}\mathbf{j} - \sin\phi\,\mathbf{i} + \cos\phi\,\mathbf{j}$$

$$= -\dot{\phi}(\cos\phi\,\mathbf{i} + \sin\phi\,\mathbf{j}) = -\dot{\phi}\mathbf{e}_r$$

since $\mathbf{i}$ and $\mathbf{j}$ are constant vectors.

I.II Spherical Polar Coordinates

One description of three-dimensional motion of a point that takes the direction of the position vector as a fundamental coordinate direction—as the plane polar description does in plane motion—is that in spherical polar coordinates. Spherical polars are often useful for describing motion about a fixed point when information about the motion is given in terms of distance or direction from the point. Motion on the surface of a given sphere is the most obvious example.

To describe the basic coordinates and coordinate directions, we must introduce an auxiliary line and plane through the fixed point, or *pole*. We select some line through the pole and a positive direction along the line; this is the (directed) *polar axis*. Through the polar axis, we choose a fixed plane; this is the base meridional plane. Let the position vector of the particle with respect to the pole be $\mathbf{r}$ (Fig. I.II-I). Write this as its magnitude multiplied into a unit vector:

$$\mathbf{r} = r\mathbf{e}_r. \qquad\qquad \text{I.II-I}$$

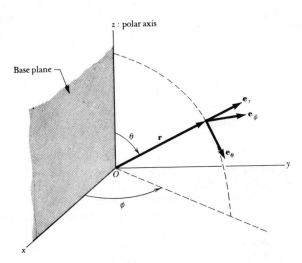

Fig. I.II-I

The scalar function r is the *radial* coordinate, and has range of values $0 \leq r < \infty$; the unit vector $\mathbf{e}_r$ is the *unit radial vector*. The second and third coordinates are defined by passing the meridional plane through the position vector and the polar axis. The angle θ from the positive direction of the polar axis to the position vector is the *colatitude* or azimuthal angle. The associated coordinate direction is then given by the unit vector $\mathbf{e}_\theta$ perpendicular to $\mathbf{e}_r$ in the meridional plane in the sense of increasing θ. The coordinates (r, θ) thus appear as plane polar coordinates for the plane of $\mathbf{r}$ and the polar axis. The third coordinate, the *longitude*, is the angle ϕ from the base meridional plane to the plane through $\mathbf{r}$, measured positively by the right-hand rule for rotations about the polar axis. The associated unit vector $\mathbf{e}_\phi$ is then taken perpendicular to the meridional plane through $\mathbf{r}$ (and hence orthogonal to $\mathbf{e}_r$ and $\mathbf{e}_\theta$), in the sense of increasing ϕ. The ranges of values on θ and ϕ are

$$0 \leqq \theta \leqq \pi, \qquad 0 \leqq \phi < 2\pi.$$

The coordinate vectors $(\mathbf{e}_r, \mathbf{e}_\theta, \mathbf{e}_\phi)$ form a right-handed unit orthogonal triad:

$$\mathbf{e}_r \times \mathbf{e}_\theta = \mathbf{e}_\phi, \qquad \mathbf{e}_\theta \times \mathbf{e}_\phi = \mathbf{e}_r, \qquad \mathbf{e}_\phi \times \mathbf{e}_r = \mathbf{e}_\theta$$

$$\mathbf{e}_r \cdot \mathbf{e}_r = \mathbf{e}_\theta \cdot \mathbf{e}_\theta = \mathbf{e}_\phi \cdot \mathbf{e}_\phi = 1 \qquad \text{I.II-2}$$

$$\mathbf{e}_r \cdot \mathbf{e}_\theta = \mathbf{e}_\theta \cdot \mathbf{e}_\phi = \mathbf{e}_\phi \cdot \mathbf{e}_r = 0.$$

We may relate the coordinates (r, θ, ϕ) to rectangular coordinates based on the pole, polar axis, and base meridional plane in a simple way. Take the pole O as origin, the positive direction of the polar axis as the positive z-direction, and the x-axis in the base plane so that the rotation from x to y about z corresponds to increasing ϕ (Fig. I.II-I). Then the coordinate transformation is

$$\begin{cases} r = (x^2 + y^2 + z^2)^{\frac{1}{2}} \\[2mm] \theta = \arctan \dfrac{(x^2 + y^2)^{\frac{1}{2}}}{z} \\[3mm] \phi = \arctan \dfrac{y}{x} \end{cases} \qquad \begin{cases} x = r \sin \theta \cos \phi \\[2mm] y = r \sin \theta \sin \phi \\[2mm] z = r \cos \theta \end{cases} \qquad \text{I.II-3}$$

To find the velocity and acceleration vectors in spherical polars from the position vector $\mathbf{r} = r\mathbf{e}_r$, we must differentiate the unit vectors $(\mathbf{e}_r, \mathbf{e}_\theta, \mathbf{e}_\phi)$ as well as the scalar functions $r(t)$, $\theta(t)$, $\phi(t)$. The derivatives of the unit vectors may be computed by expressing them in terms of θ, ϕ and the constant vectors $(\mathbf{i}, \mathbf{j}, \mathbf{k})$ or, as we shall do here, directly by consideration of the effects of changing position. As in Sections I.9 and I.10, the directions of the unit vectors depend primarily on the position coordinates and only secondarily on time.

Regarding the unit vectors as functions of the coordinates (r, θ, ϕ), we have by the usual formula for the differential of a function of several variables:

$$d\mathbf{e}_r = \frac{\partial \mathbf{e}_r}{\partial r} dr + \frac{\partial \mathbf{e}_r}{\partial \theta} d\theta + \frac{\partial \mathbf{e}_r}{\partial \phi} d\phi,$$

$$d\mathbf{e}_\theta = \frac{\partial \mathbf{e}_\theta}{\partial r} dr + \frac{\partial \mathbf{e}_\theta}{\partial \theta} d\theta + \frac{\partial \mathbf{e}_\theta}{\partial \phi} d\phi, \qquad \text{I.II-4}$$

$$d\mathbf{e}_\phi = \frac{\partial \mathbf{e}_\phi}{\partial r} dr + \frac{\partial \mathbf{e}_\phi}{\partial \theta} d\theta + \frac{\partial \mathbf{e}_\phi}{\partial \phi} d\phi.$$

Evaluate the partial derivatives by seeing what happens when each co-ordinate changes in value by itself. For a change in r only, the point moves along a ray $\theta =$ constant, $\phi =$ constant. The triad $(\mathbf{e}_r, \mathbf{e}_\theta, \mathbf{e}_\phi)$ then moves parallel to itself, with $\mathbf{e}_r$ sliding along the ray. Thus, since none of the three changes direction,

$$\frac{\partial \mathbf{e}_r}{\partial r} = \frac{\partial \mathbf{e}_\theta}{\partial r} = \frac{\partial \mathbf{e}_\phi}{\partial r} = \mathbf{0}. \qquad \text{I.II-5}$$

For a change in θ alone, the point moves along a meridional circle $r =$ constant in the plane $\phi =$ constant through $\mathbf{r}$ and the polar axis. Thus $\mathbf{e}_\phi$ remains constant, while $\mathbf{e}_r$ and $\mathbf{e}_\theta$ behave like plane polar coordinate vectors:

$$\frac{\partial \mathbf{e}_r}{\partial \theta} = \mathbf{e}_\theta, \qquad \frac{\partial \mathbf{e}_\theta}{\partial \theta} = -\mathbf{e}_r, \qquad \frac{\partial \mathbf{e}_\phi}{\partial \theta} = \mathbf{0}. \qquad \text{I.II-6}$$

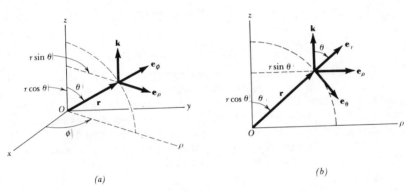

(a)

(b)

Fig. I.II-2

A change in ϕ only causes a change in all three directions. However, the plane polar coordinate results may be used again, once we recognize that the point again travels in a circle if ϕ alone changes. This is a circle of latitude of radius $r \sin \theta$ in the plane $z = r \cos \theta =$ constant (Fig. I.II-2a). Introduce local cylindrical coordinates $(\rho \equiv r \sin \theta, \phi, z)$ and the associated unit vectors $(\mathbf{e}_\rho, \mathbf{e}_\phi, \mathbf{e}_z \equiv \mathbf{k})$; the relations between $(\mathbf{e}_\rho, \mathbf{k})$ and $(\mathbf{e}_r, \mathbf{e}_\theta)$ are (Fig. I.II-2b):

$$\mathbf{e}_r = \sin \theta \, \mathbf{e}_\rho + \cos \theta \, \mathbf{k}, \qquad \mathbf{e}_\theta = \cos \theta \, \mathbf{e}_\rho - \sin \theta \, \mathbf{k}. \qquad \text{I.II-7}$$

As the angle ϕ changes, and the point moves around the circle of latitude, we know from our study of cylindrical coordinates that

$$\frac{\partial \mathbf{e}_\rho}{\partial \phi} = \mathbf{e}_\phi, \qquad \frac{\partial \mathbf{e}_\phi}{\partial \phi} = -\mathbf{e}_\rho, \qquad \frac{\partial \mathbf{k}}{\partial \phi} = \mathbf{0}. \qquad \text{I.II-8}$$

Differentiating I.11-7 with respect to ϕ and using I.11-8, we see that

$$\frac{\partial \mathbf{e}_r}{\partial \phi} = \sin \theta \frac{\partial \mathbf{e}_\rho}{\partial \phi} + \cos \theta \frac{\partial \mathbf{k}}{\partial \phi} = \sin \theta \mathbf{e}_\phi,$$

$$\frac{\partial \mathbf{e}_\theta}{\partial \phi} = \cos \theta \frac{\partial \mathbf{e}_\rho}{\partial \phi} - \sin \theta \frac{\partial \mathbf{k}}{\partial \phi} = \cos \theta \mathbf{e}_\phi, \qquad \textbf{I.11-9}$$

$$\frac{\partial \mathbf{e}_\phi}{\partial \phi} = -\mathbf{e}_\rho = -\sin \theta \mathbf{e}_r - \cos \theta \mathbf{e}_\theta.$$

Substitution of Eqs. I.11-5, 6, and 9 into I.11-4 results in

$$d\mathbf{e}_r = \mathbf{e}_\theta \, d\theta + \sin \theta \mathbf{e}_\phi \, d\phi$$

$$d\mathbf{e}_\theta = -\mathbf{e}_r \, d\theta + \cos \theta \mathbf{e}_\phi \, d\phi \qquad \textbf{I.11-10a}$$

$$d\mathbf{e}_\phi = -(\sin \theta \mathbf{e}_r + \cos \theta \mathbf{e}_\theta) \, d\phi$$

or, for the time derivatives,

$$\dot{\mathbf{e}}_r = \qquad\qquad \dot\theta \mathbf{e}_\theta + \dot\phi \sin \theta \mathbf{e}_\phi$$

$$\dot{\mathbf{e}}_\theta = -\dot\theta \mathbf{e}_r \qquad + \dot\phi \cos \theta \mathbf{e}_\phi \qquad \textbf{I.11-10b}$$

$$\dot{\mathbf{e}}_\phi = -\dot\phi \sin \theta \mathbf{e}_r - \dot\phi \cos \theta \mathbf{e}_\theta.$$

These results conform to the expected pattern. The derivative of each unit vector is orthogonal to that vector, as it should be. Each component of the time derivative has dimensions $(\text{time})^{-1}$. The student may compare these results with those of the previous two sections and see, in particular, that these follow the pattern discussed just after Eq. 1.9-9.★

We are now prepared to compute the velocity and acceleration vectors by differentiation of $\mathbf{r}$. The results of the computation are (as the student should verify):

$$\mathbf{r} = r\mathbf{e}_r;$$

$$\mathbf{v} = v_r\mathbf{e}_r + v_\theta\mathbf{e}_\theta + v_\phi\mathbf{e}_\phi$$

$$= \dot r\mathbf{e}_r + r\dot\theta\mathbf{e}_\theta + r\dot\phi \sin \theta \mathbf{e}_\phi;$$

$$\mathbf{a} = a_r\mathbf{e}_r + a_\theta\mathbf{e}_\theta + a_\phi\mathbf{e}_\phi \qquad \textbf{I.11-11}$$

$$= [\ddot r - r\dot\theta^2 - r\dot\phi^2 \sin^2 \theta]\mathbf{e}_r$$

$$+ [r\ddot\theta + 2\dot r\dot\theta - r\dot\phi^2 \sin \theta \cos \theta]\mathbf{e}_\theta$$

$$+ [(r\ddot\phi + 2\dot r\dot\phi) \sin \theta + 2r\dot\phi\dot\theta \cos \theta]\mathbf{e}_\phi.$$

★ One may show that each of the derivatives of I.11-10b may be computed by taking the vector product of a vector

$$\boldsymbol{\omega} = \dot\phi \cos \theta \mathbf{e}_r - \dot\phi \sin \theta \mathbf{e}_\theta + \dot\theta \mathbf{e}_\phi$$

into each of the unit vectors in turn: $\dot{\mathbf{e}}_r = \boldsymbol{\omega} \times \mathbf{e}_r$, etc. The significance of this result will be discussed in Chapter VI.

Exercises

In this set of exercises $\mathbf{r}$, $\mathbf{v}$, $\mathbf{a}$ denote the position, velocity, and acceleration vectors, respectively, of a moving point. $\mathbf{A}$, $\mathbf{B}$, $\mathbf{C}$ represent constant vectors.

1.2-1: Identify as vectors, scalars, or neither any of the following quantities that you may have encountered in previous study: (a) volume, (b) electrical potential, (c) area of a plane figure, (d) electric intensity, (e) pressure in a fluid, (f) magnetic intensity, (g) electric induction, (h) stress, (i) heat content, (j) magnetic permeability.

1.4-1: Find the time derivatives of (a) $r^2\mathbf{r} + \mathbf{A} \times \mathbf{v}$, (b) $\mathbf{r} \cdot \mathbf{r} + \mathbf{A}(\mathbf{r} \cdot \mathbf{r})^{-1}$.
Ans.: $2r\dot{r}\mathbf{r} + r^2\mathbf{v} + \mathbf{A} \times \mathbf{a}$, $2\dot{r}(r - Ar^{-3})$.

1.4-2: If $\mathbf{P}$ is a function of t, find $\dfrac{d}{dt}[(\mathbf{P} \times \dot{\mathbf{P}}) \cdot \ddot{\mathbf{P}}]$.

Ans.: $\mathbf{P} \times \dot{\mathbf{P}} \cdot \dddot{\mathbf{P}}$.

1.4-3: Prove that $\mathbf{r} \cdot \mathbf{v} = r\dfrac{dr}{dt}$.

1.4-4: Show that if a point moves on the surface of a sphere its velocity will always be tangent to the sphere.

1.4-5: The position vector of a moving point is
$$\mathbf{r} = (A \cos \omega t)\mathbf{i} + (B \sin \omega t)\mathbf{j}.$$

(a) Describe the path.
Ans.: Ellipse.
(b) Show that the magnitude of the acceleration is proportional to the distance of the point from the origin.
(c) Is the acceleration vector directed toward the origin or away from it?
Ans.: Toward.
(d) Show that $\mathbf{r} \times \mathbf{v}$ is a constant vector.
(e) Is the motion periodic?
Ans.: Yes.

1.4-6: The position vector of a moving point is
$$\mathbf{r} = (A \cosh \omega t)\mathbf{i} + (B \sinh \omega t)\mathbf{j}.$$

Answer parts (a) to (e) of the preceding question.
Ans.: Hyperbola; away; no.

1.4-7: Suppose that $\mathbf{r} = \mathbf{A} \cos \omega t + \mathbf{B} \sin \omega t$; answer parts (a) to (e) of question 1.4-5.
Ans.: Same as 1.4-5.

1.4-8: At a particular instant, a moving point has a velocity $4\mathbf{i} - 3\mathbf{j}$ ft/sec and an acceleration $\mathbf{i} + \mathbf{j} + \mathbf{k}$ ft/sec². What is the speed? How rapidly is it increasing?
Ans.: 5 ft/sec; $\frac{1}{5}$ ft/sec².

1.4-9: Find a complete solution for $\mathbf{r}$ if $\ddot{\mathbf{r}} = \mathbf{A}t$.
Ans.: $\mathbf{r} = \frac{1}{6}\mathbf{A}t^3 + \mathbf{B}t + \mathbf{C}$.

1.4-10: Show that if $\mathbf{r} \times \mathbf{A} = \mathbf{B}$ then $\mathbf{r} = -\dfrac{\mathbf{B} \times \mathbf{A}}{A^2} + C\mathbf{A}$ where C is an arbitrary constant.

1.4-11: Show that $\int \mathbf{A} \cdot \mathbf{v} \, dt = \mathbf{A} \cdot \mathbf{r} + C.$

1.4-12: Find (a) $\int 2\mathbf{v} \cdot \mathbf{a} \, dt$; (b) $\int \mathbf{r} \times \mathbf{a} \, dt.$
Ans.: $v^2 + C$; $\mathbf{r} \times \mathbf{v} + \mathbf{C}.$

1.4-13: An impeller of radius a has a hub of radius b. Water moves outward from the perimeter of the hub at A to the perimeter of the impeller at B along a straight vane which is tangent to the hub. The impeller rotates at a constant rate, ω rad/sec. The speed of the fluid relative to the impeller vane is constant at v in/sec.

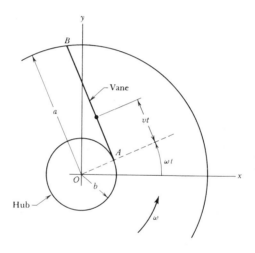

(a) Taking fixed xy-axes with x parallel to the radius OA at $t=0$, show that the position vector of a fluid element that enters the vane at A at $t=0$ is given by the expression

$$\mathbf{r} = (b \cos \omega t - vt \sin \omega t)\mathbf{i} + (b \sin \omega t + vt \cos \omega t)\mathbf{j}.$$

(b) Find the velocity of the fluid particle as it enters the vane at A if $a = 8$ in, $b = 3$ in, $v = 100$ in/sec, $\omega = 140$ rad/sec.
(c) Find its velocity as it leaves the vane. What is the angle between this vector and the vane?
Ans.: 520**j** in/sec; 1012**i** + 569**j** in/sec; 63°.

1.8-1: A particle moves along the x-axis such that the displacement x (in feet) is given by $x = (t^4/4) - 2t^2$, t in seconds. Find the following at $t = 3$ sec: (a) velocity, (b) acceleration, (c) distance traveled since $t = 0$.
Ans.: (b) 23 ft/sec²; (c) 10.25 ft.

1.8-2: The velocity of a particle in rectilinear motion changes from 30 ft/sec to the right to 12 ft/sec to the left; the acceleration is a constant 8 ft/sec^2 to the left. Determine the total time interval required for this change in velocity. Find the displacement and the distance traveled during this interval.

Ans.: 47.2 ft to right; 65.2 ft.

1.8-3: The pin, Q, is fixed on the rim of the 3-in disk that can rotate about its center, O. The pin is forced to move in the slot of the yoke P that moves upward at a constant speed of 6 in/sec. Find the velocity and acceleration of Q at a time when $\theta = 53°$. Sketch these vectors to show their relation to the line OQ. (Hint: use the method of Example 1.8-3 at this time.)

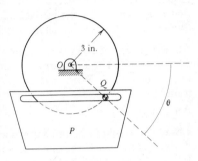

Ans.: $\mathbf{v} = 8\mathbf{i} - 6\mathbf{j}$, $\mathbf{a} = -55.5\mathbf{i}$ (in, sec); x^+ to right, y^+ down.

1.8-4: An electron moves in an electric field such that its displacement is given by $x = 0.08 \sin 5t$, $y = 0.06 \cos 5t$, $z = 0$, where distances are in meters and time in seconds. Find the maximum and minimum acceleration magnitudes.

Ans.: $a_{max} = 2$ m/sec^2; $a_{min} = 1.5$ m/sec^2.

1.8-5: A particle moves on the path $x = 3 \sin 5t$, $y = \dfrac{3\sqrt{3}}{2} \cos 5t$, $z = \dfrac{3}{2} \cos 5t$ ft when t is in seconds. Find the acceleration and show that it has constant magnitude. How is the path of this problem related to that of Example 1.8-1?

Ans.: Same motion, referred to new axes.

1.8-6: The velocity of a particle is given by

$$\dot{\mathbf{r}} = \mathbf{v} = 12t^2\mathbf{i} + 16t^3\mathbf{j} + \sin(\pi t)\mathbf{k} \quad \text{(v in m/sec, } t \text{ in sec).}$$

The displacement vector $\mathbf{r}_0$ at time $t = 0$ is given by $\mathbf{r}_0 = 4\mathbf{j} + 3\mathbf{k}$ m.
   (a) Find the acceleration vector as a function of time.
   (b) Find the position vector as a function of time.

Ans.: (b) $\mathbf{r} = 4t^3\mathbf{i} + 4(t^4 + 1)\mathbf{j} + \left(3 + \dfrac{1}{\pi} - \dfrac{1}{\pi} \cos \pi t\right)\mathbf{k}$ m.

1.8-7: A particle moves in the xy-plane according to the law $v_x = 2t - 6$, $v_y = 3t^2 - 18t + 27$. If the particle is at $(9, -27)$ when $t = 0$, determine the equation of its path.

Ans.: $y^2 = x^3$.

1.8-8: The magnitude of the acceleration of a particle moving along a straight line is given by $a = 12x^{1/2}$. When $x = 16$ ft, $v = 25$ ft/sec. Find the velocity of the particle when $x = 25$ ft.

Ans.: 40 ft/sec.

1.8-9: Explain what is meant by the mean velocity of a particle in rectilinear motion: (a) with respect to time and (b) with respect to distance. Show that if v_0 and v_1 are the initial and final velocities, the difference between these two means, for constant acceleration, is $(v_1 - v_0)^2/6(v_1 + v_0)$.

1.8-10: A freight train is traveling with speed V when the caboose of mass M is uncoupled and brought to a stop by uniform application of the brakes in a distance D. When the caboose comes to rest, how far is it from the train?

Ans.: D.

1.8-11: A weight is dropped down a mine shaft and is heard striking bottom T seconds later. If the speed of sound is c, find the depth, h, of the shaft. If $c = 1100$ ft/sec and $T = 7$ sec what is this depth? If the finite velocity of sound were ignored would the depth be overestimated or underestimated and by how much? Take the acceleration of gravity to be $g = 32.2$ ft/sec² during free fall of the weight.

Ans.: $h = (c^2/g)[1 + gT/c - (1 + 2gT/c)^{1/2}]$; 600 ft, 190 ft overestimate.

1.8-12: A particle moves in the xy-plane with the velocity components given by the accompanying graphs. At time $t = 0$ the particle is at the origin of coordinates, $x = y = 0$.

(a) Find the y-coordinate after 30 sec.
(b) Find the magnitude of the velocity at $t = 30$ sec.
(c) Find the magnitude and direction of the acceleration of the particle at $t = 30$ sec.
(d) Find the largest acceleration magnitude of the particle during the first 30 sec.

Ans.: (a) 9000 ft; (b) 390 ft/sec.

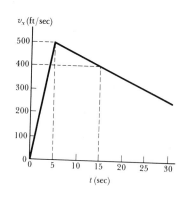

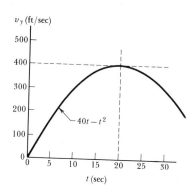

1.8-13: We wish to design the foundation for a heavy machine located in an earthquake-sensitive region. The records of the U.S. Coast and Geodetic Survey show that the predominant horizontal motion of the ground is east-west and one of their strong-motion accelerometers has shown a graphical record as follows in a recent destructive earthquake.

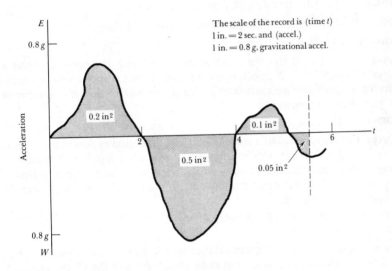

The scale of the record is (time t)
1 in. = 2 sec. and (accel.)
1 in. = 0.8 g, gravitational accel.

(a) What is the speed of the ground at 5.5 sec?
(b) What is the maximum speed during the first 5.5 sec?

Ans.: (a) 12.9 ft/sec west; (b) 15.5 ft/sec west.

1.8-14: The maximum velocity of a point moving with simple harmonic motion is 10 ft/sec. When the point is 3 in. from the position of maximum velocity the magnitude of the acceleration is 2.50 ft/sec². Determine (a) the period of the motion and (b) the magnitude of the maximum acceleration of the point.

Ans.: (a) 1.98 sec; (b) 31.8 ft/sec².

1.8-15: A piston rests on a circular cam of radius a mounted eccentrically at a distance e from its geometric center. Show that, if the cam rotates at a uniform rate ω rad/sec, the piston will execute simple harmonic motion of amplitude e and frequency ω in the vertical direction.

Ans.: $y = a + e \sin \omega t$.

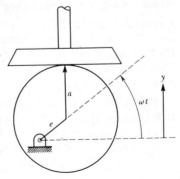

1.9-1: Find the scalar tangential acceleration of the pin Q of Exercise 1.8-3 for the conditions of that exercise.
Ans.: $a_t = 44.4$ in/sec².

1.9-2: For the motion of Exercise 1.8-6, find the normal and tangential components of acceleration and the radius of curvature of the path at $t = 1$ sec.
Ans.: $a_t = 52.8$ m/sec²; $a_n = 10.1$ m/sec²; $\rho = 39.6$ m.

1.9-3: Find the radius of curvature of the path of Exercise 1.8-7 at $t = 0$.
Ans.: $\rho = 85\sqrt{85}/2$.

1.9-4: A baseball is thrown at an angle of $37°$ with the horizontal and a speed of 200 ft/sec. Neglecting air resistance what is the radius of curvature of its path two seconds later? Take the acceleration due to gravity as 32.2 ft/sec² downward.
Ans.: 940 ft.

1.9-5: The coordinates of a moving particle, expressed as functions of time, are $x = 7t$, $y = 3 + t^2$, $z = t^3/3$ m when t is in seconds. Find the normal and tangential components of velocity and acceleration, the principal radius of curvature, and the cartesian components of the unit normal and tangential vectors when $t = 3$ sec.
Ans.: $\mathbf{v} = 12.9\mathbf{e}_t$ m/sec; $\mathbf{a} = 5.12\mathbf{e}_t + 3.7\mathbf{e}_n$ m/sec²; $\rho = 45$ m; $\mathbf{e}_n = -0.75\mathbf{i} - 0.10\mathbf{j} + 0.66\mathbf{k}$.

1.9-6: Using normal and tangential components of velocity and acceleration find the maximum and minimum radii of curvature of the ellipse in which the electron of Exercise 1.8-4 moves.
Ans.: 0.107 m, 0.045 m.

1.10-1: A particle travels on a plane curve $r = 2t + 1$, $\phi = 3t$, where t is measured in seconds, r in cm, ϕ in radians. Find $\mathbf{v}$ and $\mathbf{a}$ at any time t.
Ans.: $\mathbf{a} = -(18t + 9)\mathbf{e}_r + 12\mathbf{e}_\phi$ cm/sec².

1.10-2: A particle travels on a plane curve $r = 4\cos(\phi/4)$ in, with $\dot{\phi} = 3$ rad/sec at all times. Find $\mathbf{r}$, $\mathbf{v}$, and $\mathbf{a}$ when $\phi = \pi$ radians and sketch these vectors.
Ans.: $\mathbf{a} = -27\mathbf{e}_r - 12.7\mathbf{e}_\phi$ in/sec².

1.10-3: A particle slides on a circular helix of radius r and vertical displacement $z = bt^2/2$ (see Example 1.8-2). The acceleration vector has constant magnitude a. Show that such a motion is possible with a constant value of $\dot{\phi}$ and find that value of $\dot{\phi}$ in terms of a, b, and r.
Ans.: $\dot{\phi} = [(a^2 - b^2)/r^2]^{1/4}$.

1.10-4: A particle slides down the helix of the previous exercise, but now at a constant speed v instead of a constant acceleration magnitude. (a) What is the acceleration? (b) What is the maximum time T for which such a motion is possible? Why does the analysis break down as $t \to T$?
Ans.: (a) $\mathbf{a} = -(v^2 - b^2t^2)\mathbf{e}_r/r - b^2t(v^2 - b^2t^2)^{-1/2}\mathbf{e}_\phi + b\mathbf{k}$; (b) $T = v/b$.

1.10-5: A particle moves in a plane path under the action of a central force; i.e., one that has only a radial component. Show that $r^2\dot\phi$ is constant. (Hint: see Eq. 1.10-10.)

1.10-6: A particle moves in a plane in such a way that the angle between the position and velocity vectors remains constant, say α. If $\alpha = 0$ the path is a straight line; if $\alpha = 90°$ the path is a circle. Show that for all other values of α the path is a logarithmic spiral

$$r = r_0 \exp \{\pm \cot \alpha(\phi - \phi_0)\}$$

where $r = r_0$ when $\phi = \phi_0$. (Hint: find $\cos \alpha$ by use of the scalar product.)

CHAPTER II

Theory of Particle Motion

2.1 Introduction

The engineer's study of dynamics has for one of its goals the acquisition of methods of computing the forces necessary to sustain a prescribed motion of a mechanical system. Such a computation is an essential step in the design of a structure that can support the required loads. In the analysis, we first isolate the system and describe by means of a mathematical model those features of the system, including the forces acting on it, that we consider essential. This model—commonly presented in the form of the free-body diagram—is then subjected to analysis, the results of which are used as a guide in the study of the real system.

In this chapter, we shall develop the basic newtonian theory governing the simplest of model systems: the particle or mass-point. Many of the results will be familiar ones of elementary mechanics. For this very reason, the material of this chapter should be examined with care; too often a remembered formula is used where it does not apply simply because a problem appears to be the same as one previously encountered.

The particle model is an appropriate one to use when we can neglect the size of the system under study compared to some other length in our problem or when certain rotational motion effects can be ignored. For example, the earth may be treated as a particle in finding a first approximation to its path around the sun. On the other hand, the earth is essentially treated as a large fixed body when we talk about the motion of an automobile along a road. The automobile is a "particle" for the discussion of some aspects of its motion—but cannot be so treated when, say, the rotary inertia of its wheels must be accounted for. In the examples of this chapter and in the applications of the next, many things will be called particles. The student should give some thought to the reasons why such models are appropriate.

2.2 Newton's Laws of Motion; Mass and Force

Dynamics is based upon Newton's laws of motion which, in modern language, take the form:

(1) A particle acted on by forces whose resultant always vanishes will move with constant velocity.

(2) A particle acted on by forces whose resultant is not zero will move in such a way that the time rate of change of its momentum will at any instant be proportional to the resultant force.

(3) If one particle, A, exerts a force on a second particle, B, then B exerts a collinear force of equal magnitude and opposite direction on A.

As has been remarked in Section 2.1 the word "particle" refers to any object that, with regard to its position and motion, may with sufficient accuracy be regarded as a moving point. The ideas underlying the description of motion have been developed. We now consider the ideas of force, which is related to the mechanical effect of one body on another, and mass, which is a property of each object.

Consider a hypothetical experiment in which two small objects, A and B, connected by a light spring, are removed from the influence of all other bodies and released from a stretched position of the spring. However we define force, the third law assures us that A and B will be acted upon by forces of equal magnitude. Their accelerations, however, will as a rule be quite different in magnitude. One of the particles will be more sluggish or inert than the other. We account for this by ascribing to each particle a property called *mass*, and we say that the more sluggish particle has a larger mass. To make this idea precise we may find the accelerations at a particular instant after the particles are released. Then, denoting the masses of the particles by m_A and m_B and their accelerations by $\mathbf{a}_A$ and $\mathbf{a}_B$,

$$\frac{m_A}{m_B} = \frac{|\mathbf{a}_B|}{|\mathbf{a}_A|}.$$

2.2-1

If one of the particles is taken as a standard of mass, this experiment serves to determine the mass of any other particle in terms of the standard.

In newtonian mechanics, the mass of an object is a fundamental property of the object. Mass does not change with time or location. So-called "variable mass" problems are actually ones in which an object comes in contact with other particles that adhere to it (raindrop falling through a cloud) or in which a multi-particle system spews off part of its content (rocket ejecting burnt fuel). These are treated in Section 5.4. It is also a fundamental postulate of newtonian mechanics that mass is a scalar quantity. If objects of mass m_1 and m_2 are glued together they form an object of mass $m_1 + m_2$. It follows that the mass of an extended system can be found by adding the masses of all its parts in the ordinary arithmetic way. The *momentum* of a particle is the product of its mass and its velocity. Momentum is a vector quantity.

It was stated that the idea of force is related to the mechanical effect of one body on another. The "mechanical effect" of interest in dynamics is motion. But how is force to be related to motion? The answer to this question is provided by the second law. Of all possible relations the correct one is

$$\mathbf{F} = \frac{d}{dt}(m\mathbf{v}).$$

Of course the second law asserts only the proportionality of the vectors $\mathbf{F}$ and $d(m\mathbf{v})/dt$; but, by proper choice of units (dynamically consistent units as described in 2.3), the constant of proportionality can always be made equal to unity. The utility of the force concept arises from three sources. First, the third law of motion makes it possible to simplify the analysis of complex systems by examining their separate parts without introducing completely new and unknown forces at each step of the analysis. It thus makes possible the extension of newtonian mechanics from particles to objects of finite size. Second, the vectorial character of force as defined by Eq. 2.2-2 makes it possible to add (vectorially) the forces arising from a number of sources. Finally, we have learned to recognize a variety of forces that occur in practice and for them have learned to write appropriate mathematical expressions for use in Eq. 2.2-2.

Among the forces commonly encountered in mechanics, contact forces, gravitational forces, electromagnetic forces, and viscous drag forces deserve special mention. The first-named arise whenever two objects are in contact. They may be distributed over an area or idealized as concentrated forces. A case commonly encountered in technology is that of massive objects connected by a relatively light spring or inextensible cable. Contact forces may be functions of time or of the difference between the position vectors of two points. Gravitational forces are introduced as a consequence of Newton's law of universal gravitation, which asserts that a particle of mass m_B exerts on a particle of mass m_A a force

$$\mathbf{F} = -Gm_Am_B \frac{\mathbf{r}_A - \mathbf{r}_B}{|\mathbf{r}_A - \mathbf{r}_B|^3} \qquad 2.2\text{-}3$$

where G is a constant and $\mathbf{r}_A$, $\mathbf{r}_B$ are the position vectors of the particles. Since $(\mathbf{r}_A - \mathbf{r}_B)$ divided by $|\mathbf{r}_A - \mathbf{r}_B|$ is a unit vector in the direction from B to A, this is the well-known inverse square relationship. Clearly gravitational forces are functions of the difference between the position vectors of two points. Coulomb's laws for the forces exerted on electrically charged bodies take the same mathematical form as the law of gravitation.* Mass is replaced by electrical charge and the constant G by the reciprocal of the dielectric constant. Charges, unlike masses, may be of opposite sign; and, since like charges repel, Coulomb's law for the force on A takes the form**

$$\mathbf{F} = +\frac{1}{D} q_Aq_B \frac{\mathbf{r}_A - \mathbf{r}_B}{|\mathbf{r}_A - \mathbf{r}_B|^3}. \qquad 2.2\text{-}4$$

These forces are also functions of the difference between the position vectors of two points. On the other hand, retardation forces such as the drag on an airplane in flight depend upon relative velocities of the fluid and the body with which it is in contact. Since the forces that we encounter in mechanics are functions of position, velocity, or time, the Eqs. 2.2-2 are differential equations for the position of the moving object.

The idea that positions, velocities, and accelerations can be measured implies the existence of a reference frame or set of axes. What is the appropriate reference frame for the purposes of newtonian mechanics? A clue to the answer to this question is provided by the first law, which asserts that a particle removed from the influences of all other particles will move at constant velocity. If we imagine that we can free a particle from all such influences, a reference frame can be checked for its suitability under this criterion. A set of axes

---

* Provided the bodies are not charged like a dipole.
** D is replaced by $4\pi k\epsilon_0$ in the "rationalized" *mks* system of units; k is the dielectric constant and ϵ_0 the permittivity of space.

that meets this test is called an *inertial, Newtonian,* or *Galilean frame of reference.* In practice, of course, we cannot apply the test. What we do is to use a convenient frame of reference and check the predictions of the second law of motion (Eq. 2.2-2) against the results of experiment. The enormous power and scope of newtonian mechanics is a result of the accurate agreement between predicted and measured effects in the widest range of situations. For most engineering problems, axes fixed in the earth, regarded as stationary, form a quite satisfactory inertial frame of reference. When we come to deal with the motion of a gyrocompass or the long-range trajectory of a projectile it is no longer possible to ignore the rotation of the earth. If still further accuracy is needed, as in celestial mechanics, an *astronomical* frame of reference is used. One such frame is that having its origin at the mass center of the solar system and its axes fixed in direction with respect to stars whose parallaxes are too small to be measured (the so-called fixed stars). This set of axes corresponds to an inertial frame of reference with a high degree of accuracy indeed.

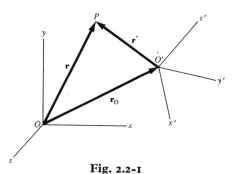

Fig. 2.2-1

We now show that, if $Oxyz$ is one inertial frame of reference, the equations of motion will be the same in any reference frame $O'x'y'z'$ having an origin that moves with constant velocity relative to $Oxyz$, provided that there is no rotation of the axes. The situation is pictured in Fig. 2.2-1. We may regard O as being at rest. Since $Oxyz$ is an inertial frame, Eq. 2.2-2 holds and

$$\mathbf{F} = m\ddot{\mathbf{r}} \qquad\qquad \textbf{2.2-5}$$

where $\mathbf{F}$ is the resultant force acting on a typical particle P of mass m. Now

$$\mathbf{r} = \mathbf{r}_O + \mathbf{r}', \qquad\qquad \textbf{2.2-6}$$

and, since O' is moving with constant velocity $\mathbf{V}$,

$$\mathbf{r}_O = \mathbf{V}t + \mathbf{C}. \qquad \text{2.2-7}$$

If we substitute from 2.2-7 in 2.2-6 and differentiate, we have

$$\dot{\mathbf{r}} = \mathbf{V} + \dot{\mathbf{r}}'. \qquad \text{2.2-8}$$

This equation tells us that the "absolute" velocity, $\dot{\mathbf{r}}$, of P is the vector sum of the "absolute" velocity, $\mathbf{V}$, of O' and $\dot{\mathbf{r}}'$. Now

$$\mathbf{r}' = x'\mathbf{i}' + y'\mathbf{j}' + z'\mathbf{k}' \qquad \text{2.2-9}$$

so that

$$\dot{\mathbf{r}}' = \dot{x}'\mathbf{i}' + \dot{y}'\mathbf{j}' + \dot{z}'\mathbf{k}' + (x'\dot{\mathbf{i}}' + y'\dot{\mathbf{j}}' + z'\dot{\mathbf{k}}'). \qquad \text{2.2-10}$$

But if the (x', y', z') axes do not rotate, $(\mathbf{i}', \mathbf{j}', \mathbf{k}')$ are constant in magnitude and direction so that the terms in parentheses are zero. Differentiating once again

$$\ddot{\mathbf{r}}' = \ddot{x}'\mathbf{i}' + \ddot{y}'\mathbf{j}' + \ddot{z}'\mathbf{k}'. \qquad \text{2.2-11}$$

Now, if we differentiate Eq. 2.2-8, we have $\ddot{\mathbf{r}} = \ddot{\mathbf{r}}'$, in view of the fact that $\mathbf{V}$ is constant. Eq. 2.2-5 then implies that

$$\mathbf{F} = m\ddot{\mathbf{r}}'. \qquad \text{2.2-12}$$

From Eq. 2.2-11 we see that $\ddot{\mathbf{r}}'$ is simply the acceleration of P measured in the $O'x'y'z'$ frame of reference. The forces with which we deal in newtonian dynamics depend upon relative position or velocity; i.e., if Q is another particle, the force $\mathbf{F}_{PQ}$ exerted on P by Q will be a function of $\mathbf{r}_P - \mathbf{r}_Q$ or $\dot{\mathbf{r}}_P - \dot{\mathbf{r}}_Q$. But $\mathbf{r}_P = \mathbf{r}_O + \mathbf{r}'_P$ and $\mathbf{r}_Q = \mathbf{r}_O + \mathbf{r}'_Q$ at all times, so that $\mathbf{r}_P - \mathbf{r}_Q = \mathbf{r}'_P - \mathbf{r}'_Q$ and $\dot{\mathbf{r}}_P - \dot{\mathbf{r}}_Q = \dot{\mathbf{r}}'_P - \dot{\mathbf{r}}'_Q$. We conclude that the force $\mathbf{F}$ in Eq. 2.2-12 will be the same function of the primed as of the unprimed coordinates. The axes $O'x'y'z'$ moving without rotation and at a constant velocity are termed a *secondary inertial frame* of reference. We have shown that the equations of motion are *invariant*; that is, they are the same in all frames of reference moving at constant velocity without rotation.

In vector symbols, the equation of motion of a single particle may be written in any of the equivalent forms:

$$\mathbf{F} = \frac{d}{dt}(m\mathbf{v}) \quad \text{or} \quad \mathbf{F} = m\mathbf{a} \quad \text{or} \quad \mathbf{F} = m\ddot{\mathbf{r}}. \qquad \text{2.2-13}$$

This equation expresses the key idea of particle dynamics: acceleration is proportional to force. It is equivalent to three scalar equations.

Where rectangular coordinates are convenient to describe the path or the forces, we write (utilizing the last of Eq. 1.8-3):

$$F_x = ma_x \qquad\qquad F_x = m\ddot{x}$$
$$F_y = ma_y \quad \text{or} \quad F_y = m\ddot{y} \qquad\qquad \textbf{2.2-14}$$
$$F_z = ma_z \qquad\qquad F_z = m\ddot{z}$$

When the path is known, it is often more convenient to use intrinsic coordinates. Then, from Eq. 1.9-8,

$$F_t = m\ddot{s}, \qquad F_n = m\frac{\dot{s}^2}{\rho}, \qquad F_b = 0. \qquad\qquad \textbf{2.2-15}$$

This form is especially useful when the motion is in a plane. Then the plane of motion is the osculating plane, and the normal and tangential axes lie in this plane. When cylindrical polar coordinates are well adapted to describe the forces or path we use Eqs. 1.10-8 and write

$$F_r = m(\ddot{r} - r\dot{\phi}^2), \qquad F_\phi = m(r\ddot{\phi} + 2\dot{r}\dot{\phi}), \qquad F_z = m\ddot{z}.$$
$$\textbf{2.2-16}$$

Intrinsic and polar coordinates are not secondary inertial axes because they rotate with the moving particle. That is why the term $\dot{s}^2/\rho$ appears in the second of Eq. 2.2-15 and the terms $-r\dot{\phi}^2$, $r\ddot{\phi}$ and $2\dot{r}\dot{\phi}$ appear in Eq. 2.2-16.

If we take the cross product of the position vector with the left- and right-hand sides of Eq. 2.2-13, we have

$$\mathbf{r} \times \mathbf{F} = \mathbf{r} \times \frac{d}{dt}(m\mathbf{v}). \qquad\qquad \textbf{2.2-17}$$

The left-hand side of this equation is the moment about the origin, O, of coordinates of the resultant force applied to the particle; we denote this moment by the symbol $\mathbf{M}_O$. Since the cross product of any two parallel vectors is zero,

$$\frac{d}{dt}(\mathbf{r} \times m\mathbf{v}) = \mathbf{v} \times m\mathbf{v} + \mathbf{r} \times m\dot{\mathbf{v}} = \mathbf{r} \times \frac{d}{dt}(m\mathbf{v}). \qquad\qquad \textbf{2.2-18}$$

Equation 2.2-17 may be rewritten

$$\mathbf{r} \times \mathbf{F} = \frac{d}{dt}(\mathbf{r} \times m\mathbf{v}). \qquad\qquad \textbf{2.2-19}$$

The quantity in parentheses is the moment of the momentum vector about the origin O. We denote this quantity by the symbol $\mathbf{H}_O$. Then Eq. 2.2-19 may be written simply

$$\mathbf{M}_O = \dot{\mathbf{H}}_O. \qquad\qquad \textbf{2.2-20}$$

The quantity $\mathbf{H}_O$ is known as the *angular momentum* or as the *moment of momentum* of the particle about the origin O. The term "angular" momentum is, perhaps, unfortunate in view of the fact that $\mathbf{H}_O$ is not zero when a particle travels in a straight line unless that line happens to intersect the origin. Eq. 2.2-20 is interesting because it fore-shadows the method by which the equations of motion are extended to rotating objects. It also proves of direct application in the theory of central force motion.

Example 2.2-1

In what is known as Atwood's machine, two heavy particles are attached together by a cord passing over a pulley. Find the acceleration with which the heavier particle descends.

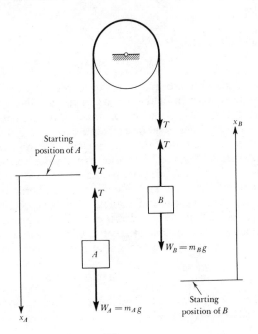

Fig. 2.2-2

Solution: We begin by isolating each of the particles, A and B, and drawing a sketch, Fig. 2.2-2, that shows the forces acting on them. This sketch is known as a free-body diagram. Its role in the analysis should not be underestimated. The forces are next labeled with appropriate symbols. In the present case, as is indicated by the symbolism, we assume that the tension in the cable is the same throughout. This is equivalent to neglect-ing the mass of the pulley and cord as well as friction at the pulley bearing and at the contact of pulley and cord. The downward forces, which are the weights of the two particles, may be written either w_A and w_B or $m_A g$ and $m_B g$, g denoting, as usual, the acceleration due to gravity. Notice that the vector **T** is represented in the free-body diagram by an arrow and a magnitude. Next, choose a set of axes for each of the isolated systems. In the present case, the motion is entirely vertical so we need label only the vertical axis. In the illustration, x_A has been chosen positive downward and x_B positive upward, measured from the starting positions of A and B. This choice of axes is arbitrary, in principle. In practice, a choice of axes that facilitate analysis is the hallmark of experience. At this point, the equations of motion for each of the isolated systems is written down. In the present case, the forces and motions being entirely vertical, only one of the three scalar equations implicit in the vector equation $\mathbf{F} = m\mathbf{a}$ is different from zero. We have, for particle A,

$$m_A g - T = m_A \ddot{x}_A \qquad \textbf{2.2-21}$$

and, for particle B,

$$-m_B g + T = m_B \ddot{x}_B. \qquad \textbf{2.2-22}$$

Note that the signs that are given to the forces in these equations are determined by the direction of the arrows in the free-body diagram with respect to the chosen directions of the axes. The weight force in Eq. 2.2-22 is entered as a negative force because it is directed downward, whereas the positive direction of the axes in which the motion of B is being described is upward. The acceleration of particle A is written $\ddot{x}_A$ because its position vector is $\mathbf{r} = x_A \mathbf{i}$. Equations 2.2-21, 22 are two equations in three unknowns—T, x_A, and x_B. We need a third relationship. This cannot come from the equations of motion; they have been fully utilized. It must be derived from some consideration based on physics or geometry. In the present case, this additional relation is simple. Since the cord does not stretch, B must move up just as far as A moves down. In symbols:

$$x_A = x_B. \qquad \textbf{2.2-23}$$

We note that Eq. 2.2-23 is true for all values of t, hence may be differentiated to yield the needed third relation:

$$\ddot{x}_A = \ddot{x}_B. \qquad \textbf{2.2-24}$$

Now the three Eqs. 2.2-21, 22, 24 may readily be solved:

$$\ddot{x}_A = \ddot{x}_B = \frac{m_A - m_B}{m_A + m_B} g. \qquad \textbf{2.2-25}$$

The acceleration is constant. If $m_A > m_B$, $\ddot{x}_A$ and $\ddot{x}_B$ are positive, indicating that A moves downward and B upward (starting from rest). But if B is heavier than A, these accelerations will be negative, indicating that in this case B moves downward and A upward. We may also find the tension in the cord

$$T = \frac{2m_A m_B}{m_A + m_B} g. \qquad \text{2.2-26}$$

Since T is positive, our assumption that the cord would be in tension is verified.

Example 2.2-2

A particle of unit mass moves on the positive x-axis under the influence of a force $\mathbf{F} = 6t\mathbf{i}$, which increases linearly with time. Initially the particle is at the origin and has zero velocity. Find the motion of the particle.

Solution: We have for the equation of motion

$$\ddot{x} = 6t. \qquad \text{2.2-27}$$

It follows that

$$\dot{x} = 3t^2 \qquad \text{2.2-28}$$

and

$$x = t^3. \qquad \text{2.2-29}$$

The constants of integration that would otherwise appear in Eqs. 2.2-28, 29 vanish because x and $\dot{x}$ are zero at $t = 0$. The motion given by Eq. 2.2-29 is not in any way remarkable. We see that $\mathbf{F} = 6t\mathbf{i} = 6x^{\frac{1}{3}}\mathbf{i}$.

Example 2.2-3

The same particle considered in the preceding example is subjected to a force $\mathbf{F} = 6x^{\frac{1}{3}}\mathbf{i}$. Investigate the motion.

Solution: The equation of motion is again given by the first of 2.2-14:

$$\ddot{x} = 6x^{\frac{1}{3}}. \qquad \text{2.2-30}$$

In contrast to Eq. 2.2-27, the acceleration is now given as a function of position. This suggests the use of Eq. 1.8-9:

$$\frac{1}{2}(\dot{x}^2 - \dot{x}_0^2) = \int_{x_0}^{x} 6\xi^{\frac{1}{3}} d\xi = \frac{9}{2}(x^{\frac{4}{3}} - x_0^{\frac{4}{3}}). \qquad \text{2.2-31}$$

As before, both x_0 and $\dot{x}_0$ are zero; they are the initial values of displacement and velocity. We have

$$\frac{dx}{dt} = 3x^{\frac{2}{3}}, \qquad \text{2.2-32}$$

an equation that is readily solved:

$$t = x^{\frac{1}{3}} \quad \text{or} \quad x = t^3, \qquad \text{2.2-33}$$

the constant of integration vanishing as before. This result seems entirely consistent with the result of the preceding problem, expressed in Eq. 2.2-29. There is, however, a difference. The equation of motion in the preceding example has only one solution consistent with the initial conditions, namely $x = t^3$. The equation of motion in the present example (Eq. 2.2-30) has, in addition to the solution $x = t^3$, the solution $x = 0$, which also satisfies the initial conditions. The first law of motion serves to discriminate between these possible solutions, both of which satisfy the second law. It tells us that the particle, being initially at rest with zero unbalanced force acting on it, will remain at rest. The alternative solution $x = t^3$ does have a physical significance. It represents the motion that would occur if the particle were slightly disturbed from its rest position. In the preceding example the possibility $x = 0$ did not arise, the exciting force being given as a function of time and not position.

Example 2.2-4

A particle of mass m moves at constant speed, v, over a curve lying in a vertical plane. What force is exerted on the particle by the curve at the instant when the particle passes a point where the radius of curvature is ρ and the normal to the curve make an angle α with the vertical?

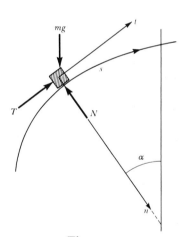

Fig. 2.2-3

Solution: The particle is shown at the instant in question in Fig. 2.2-3. The use of intrinsic coordinates is suggested by the fact that certain properties of the path—its radius of curvature and slope—are known. Notice that the positive direction of n is drawn towards the center of curvature while the positive direction of t is the direction of the velocity vector. The force exerted on the particle by the curve has been shown separated into normal and tangential components, N and T. Since these components are unknown, the directions in which we draw them are arbitrary guesses. Once these directions have been chosen and entered on the free-body diagram, however, they must be adhered to when the equations of motion are written. Furthermore, *all* the forces acting on the isolated system (in this case the particle) must appear in the free-body diagram. In addition to the force exerted by the curve, we therefore also show the weight force, mg. Now Eqs. 2.2-15 take the form

$$F_t = T - mg \sin \alpha = m\ddot{s}, \qquad F_n = mg \cos \alpha - N = m\frac{\dot{s}^2}{\rho}. \qquad \textbf{2.2-34}$$

Note that T has been entered as a positive and $mg \sin \alpha$ as a negative term in the first of Eqs. 2.2-34 because they are shown in the free-body diagram directed toward the positive and the negative tangential direction, respectively. For similar reasons, N has been entered as a negative and $mg \cos \alpha$ a positive term in the second of the equations of motion. We solve these equations in the present case by noting that the speed, $\dot{s}$, is a constant, v. This implies that $\ddot{s} = 0$. The first of Eqs. 2.2-34 predicts

$$T = mg \sin \alpha, \qquad\qquad \textbf{2.2-35}$$

and the second predicts

$$N = mg \cos \alpha - m \frac{v^2}{\rho}. \qquad\qquad \textbf{2.2-36}$$

We notice that, if $mg \cos \alpha$ exceeds mv^2/ρ, the component, N, given by Eq. 2.2-36 will be positive. This means that it will be in the direction assumed in Fig. 2.2-3. If $mg \cos \alpha$ is smaller than mv^2/ρ, N will be negative; i.e., opposite to the direction assumed. In this case the particle will leave the curve unless it is attached to it in some way that permits the curve to exert a force downward to the right in Fig. 2.2-3. The occupant of an airplane traveling this path may be taken as the particle. He would experience a sensation of "weightlessness" at a speed

$$v = (\rho g \cos \alpha)^{1/2} \qquad\qquad \textbf{2.2-37}$$

because N, the force exerted on him by the seat, would vanish. For most highways, α is a small angle. It may be concluded that an automobile traversing a vertical curve will lose contact with the pavement if the radius of curvature is less than v^2/g. On the other hand, for an airplane at the *bottom* of a loop, $\alpha = \pi$ radians and Eq. 2.2-36 becomes

$$N = -mg \left(1 + \frac{v^2}{\rho g} \right). \qquad\qquad \textbf{2.2-38}$$

The occupant of the airplane now feels a force equal to his normal weight, mg, multiplied by $1 + (v^2/\rho g)$ exerted on him by the seat. The minus sign indicates that the force is directed toward the center of curvature rather than away from it, as assumed in Fig. 2.2-3.

In this example, the acceleration is given and the force is computed from the equations of motion. Under these circumstances it is not necessary to solve a differential equation.

Example 2.2-5

A small object is placed on a smooth table at a distance r_0 from a hole in the table. A cord attached to the object passes through this hole. The object is set into motion with a velocity of magnitude v_0 at right angles to the cord and at the same time the cord is pulled through the hole at the uniform rate of c units of length per second. Find the force, T, that must be exerted on the cord and find the path of the moving object.

Solution: The free-body diagram of the particle is shown in Fig. 2.2-4. The weight, mg, acts in the z-direction and is balanced by the upward reaction of the table; these forces may be omitted, there being no motion in the z-direction. Since the path is unknown, intrinsic coordinates are of little value. Polar coordinates with origin at the hole are natural ones to use because r is known as a function of time: $r = r_0 - ct$. The free-body diagram shows the particle at a typical instant during its motion. Note that the tension, T, is not a constant. In view of Eq. 2.2-16 the equations of motion take the form

$$-T = m(\ddot{r} - r\dot{\phi}^2), \qquad 0 = r\ddot{\phi} + 2\dot{r}\dot{\phi}. \qquad \text{2.2-39}$$

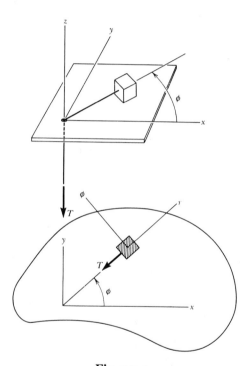

Fig. 2.2-4

There is no force in the transverse (ϕ) direction because the table is supposed smooth. The second of Eqs. 2.2-39 may be rewritten (see Eq. 1.10-10)

$$\frac{d}{dt}(r^2\dot{\phi}) = 0, \qquad \text{2.2-40}$$

which implies that $r^2\dot{\phi} = \text{constant}$. But initially, when the motion is started, $r = r_0$ and $\dot{\phi} = v_0/r_0$ so that

$$r^2\dot{\phi} = r_0 v_0. \qquad \text{2.2-41}$$

But we know that $r = r_0 - ct$ so that

$$\phi = \frac{r_0 v_0}{(r_0 - ct)^2} \qquad\qquad 2.2\text{-}42$$

Since $\ddot{r} = 0$, the first of Eq. 2.2-39 may be written

$$T = m(r_0 - ct)\,\frac{r_0^2 v_0^2}{(r_0 - ct)^4},$$

$$T = \frac{m r_0^2 v_0^2}{(r_0 - ct)^3}. \qquad\qquad 2.2\text{-}43$$

We see that the tension in the cord will increase with time. When $t = r_0/c$, the object reaches the central hole and the equations of motion are no longer realistic. The rate of rotation of the cord is given by Eq. 2.2-42. It too grows larger as the particle is pulled toward the central opening.

2.3 Units

In Section 1.1, the primary units of length and time were described and, in Section 1.4, it was noted that these determined the so-called "derived" units for velocity. The unit of mass is the mass of a particular piece of metal known as the International Prototype Kilogram (kg). Like the meter, it may be subdivided for convenience when dealing with small objects; the gram is one one-thousandth part of the kilogram. In English-speaking countries the pound-mass avoirdupois (lb-m) is the standard of mass. The two standards are, of course, related. An object of mass 2.2046 lb-m would also be described as having a mass of 1 kg.

The second law of motion asserts that force is proportional to the product of mass and acceleration. We wish to let the constant of proportionality have the value unity so that the law can be written simply $\mathbf{F} = m\mathbf{a}$. This implies, however, that the unit of force cannot be a primary standard. Like the units of velocity and acceleration, which are determined by the units used for $\mathbf{r}$ and t, the unit of force is determined by the units used for m, $\mathbf{r}$, and t. In the meter-kilogram-second (mks) system, unit force must be that force which, acting on a one-kilogram mass, will produce an acceleration of magnitude one meter per second per second. A force of this magnitude is called a *newton*. If centimeters, grams, and seconds (cgs) are being used, the unit force is that which will produce an acceleration of one centimeter per second per second when acting on a one-gram mass. This amount of force is called a *dyne*. Since there are 100 centimeters in a meter and 1000 grams in a kilogram, one newton must be the same as 10^5 dynes. If the pound-mass and foot per second per second are used, the unit of force (i.e., that force which will accelerate one pound-mass at the rate of one foot per second per second) is known as the *poundal*. One poundal is the same as 0.1383 newtons.

When the unit of mass is chosen as primary and the unit of force is derived through the equation $\mathbf{F} = m\mathbf{a}$, the resulting system is known as an *absolute* system of units, either metric or English. Instead of proceeding in this way, it is possible to construct what is known as a *gravitational* system. In gravitational systems, force is taken as primary and the unit of mass is a derived unit. In the British gravitational system, the unit of force is defined as the weight of a pound-mass avoirdupois. This unit of force is known as the pound-force. By weight, we understand the force which applied to one end of an equal-arm scales will balance a pound-mass avoirdupois at the other end. This definition, however, is open to the objection that the weight of the piece of metal known as the pound-mass avoirdupois will vary from place to place. True, the variation is slight. It is less than one half of one percent for points on the surface of the earth. This is smaller than the uncertainty that occurs in most engineering data. Nevertheless, the variation does exist and so the pound-force is defined as the weight of the pound-mass avoirdupois at a point where the acceleration due to gravity has a value of 32.174 ft/sec² (9.81146 m/sec²). The unit of mass in the British gravitational system is then derived from the equation $\mathbf{F} = m\mathbf{a}$. It is that mass which, when acted on by one pound-force, will have an acceleration of 1 ft/sec². This unit has no distinctive name, but it is sometimes termed the *slug* or *engineering unit of mass*. Conversion from the gravitational to the absolute system can be effected by considering a pound-mass falling in a standard gravitational field. It will have an acceleration of 32.174 ft/sec²; therefore, 32.174 poundals must be acting on it. This implies that 1 lb-force is the same as 32.174 poundals, which in turn corresponds to 4.44 newtons. Similarly, 1 slug corresponds to 32.174 lb-mass, which is the same as 14.594 kg. Whether absolute or gravitational, systems that employ three primary mechanical units of measure and derive the fourth by means of the equation $\mathbf{F} = m\mathbf{a}$ are known as dynamically consistent sets of units.

It may be recalled that the definition of mass adopted in 2.2 did not depend at all on the gravitational effect. Mass defined in this way is known as "inertial" mass. Mass determined by an experiment in which gravity plays a part is known as "gravitational" mass. The most refined experiments have failed to detect any difference between the two. The equivalence of "inertial" and "gravitational" mass is a fundamental postulate of relativistic mechanics.

In practice, when the British gravitational system is used, forces are given in pounds-force and the weight of the object under analysis is also given in pounds-force. The mass of this object is then found by dividing its weight by the local acceleration of gravity. (32.2 ft/sec^2 is accurate enough for most engineering purposes.)

Considering the simplicity of the absolute systems, it is natural to ask why the gravitational systems are still generally used by engineers and by the public. The explanation probably stems from the fact that technology has developed over centuries while dynamical questions have been of serious concern to engineers only relatively recently. In the statical analyses that were satisfactory for the design of slowly moving machinery, the concept of mass never arose. In statics, $\mathbf{a} = \mathbf{0}$, and the unit of force can be selected quite arbitrarily. One unit of force that gained popular acceptance was the pound-force. Even when dynamical considerations became important the engineer retained this unit of force in order to be able to communicate with the workmen and technicians who executed his designs. The morning newspaper reports that a rocket motor of one million pounds thrust is under development. It is doubtful that the general public would make much of a report of a rocket motor capable of producing 4.4 million newtons.

The need for effective communication with technicians on the one hand and scientists on the other imposes on the engineer the burden of acquiring familiarity with absolute and gravitational unit systems. In this task, the human tendency to abbreviate terms in widespread use sometimes creates confusion. The word "pound" is commonly used without indication whether it is the pound-mass or the pound-force to which reference is made. So long as we deal with events on the surface of the earth, the distinction may appear unimportant; after all a pound-mass of material weighs almost exactly one pound-force. A man may say he "weighs seventy kilograms"; it would be pedantic to insist he say he "has a mass of seventy kilograms." No difficulty arises until quantities involving force and mass appear in the same equation. Then we must use dynamically consistent units, as in this text, or tolerate the appearance of numerical factors. In chemical engineering and to some extent in mechanical engineering, for example, it is common to express flow rates in pounds per second and pressures in pounds per square foot. This is equivalent to writing $\mathbf{F} = m\mathbf{a}/g$, taking $\mathbf{F}$ in lb-force, m in lb-mass and $\mathbf{a}$ in ft/sec^2. The factor g must be given the numerical value 32.2 so that the conversion from lb-mass to slugs will be made in the process of using the equation. This particular set of non-consistent units must then be employed by all who use the equation, an awkward situation that, however, is not infrequently encountered. The use of dynamically consistent units is implied throughout theoretical mechanics so that the equations developed in that subject may be used by anyone anywhere employing whatever (consistent) set of units he prefers.

In electrical engineering, the mks system has found wide acceptance. This system should always be used when the situation under analysis involves both mechanical and electrical quantities (e.g. the dynamic response of a moving-coil voltmeter). The advantage of the mks system in these situations arises from the fact that the watt or volt-ampere is defined as one newton-meter per second. If the mks system is used for mechanical quantities, it is relatively simple to combine forces or moments arising from mechanical and electrical sources in the same equation.

In this text, the British gravitational system (lb-force, slug, foot, second) and the metric absolute system (mks) will be used for the bulk of the illustrative examples and problems. The unqualified word "pound" will always refer to a force and the word "kilogram" to a mass. Occasionally other systems will be used so that familiarity with them may be acquired.

Example 2.3-1

An automobile weighs 3000 lb; what force is required to make it reach a speed of 60 mph in 10 sec, starting from rest?
Solution:

$$m = \frac{3000}{32.2} = 93.2 \text{ slugs}$$

$$60 \frac{\text{mi}}{\text{hr}} = 60 \frac{\text{mi}}{\text{hr}} \left(\frac{5280 \text{ ft}}{1 \text{ mi}}\right)\left(\frac{1 \text{ hr}}{3600 \text{ sec}}\right) = 88 \frac{\text{ft}}{\text{sec}}.$$

Notice the arrangement of the computations. Each term in parentheses has a numerator and denominator that are equivalent. Literal factors (mi, hr) are cancelled like ordinary numbers. This is not an ordinary arithmetic operation, but its similarity to one makes it a useful memory aid.

$$a = \frac{88}{10} = 8.8 \text{ ft/sec}^2,$$

$$F = ma = (93.2)(8.8) = 820 \text{ lb}.$$

This force is that which the road exerts on the automobile.

It is instructive to work the example in the metric gravitational system as would a continental European or South American engineer. He would say that the automobile weighs 1360 kg (since 1 lb is equivalent to 0.453 kg) and that the required acceleration is 2.68 m/sec². Then

$$m = \frac{1360}{9.81} = 138.5 \text{ metric slugs}$$

$$F = (138.5)(2.68) = 371 \text{ kg-force}.$$

Of course 371 kg (force) is the same thing as 820 lb, as may be verified: $(820)(0.453) = 371$.

In the mks system, the automobile is said to have a mass of 1360 kg and

$$F = (1360)(2.68) = 3640 \text{ newtons}.$$

Again 3640 newtons is the same as $3640/4.44 = 820$ lb.

Example 2.3-2

The meteorologist expresses atmospheric pressure in bars (1 bar = 10^6 dynes/cm²). Laboratory pressures are generally reported in mm of mercury. What is the connection between these two? The density of mercury is 13.59 gm/cm³.

Solution:

$$13.59 \frac{\text{gm}}{\text{cm}^3} = 13.59 \frac{\text{gm}}{\text{cm}^3} \left(\frac{1 \text{ cm}}{10 \text{ mm}}\right)^3 = 13.59(10)^{-3} \frac{\text{gm}}{\text{mm}^3}.$$

A cubic mm of mercury will have a mass of $13.59(10)^{-3}$ gm. Its weight will be

$$13.59(10)^{-3} \text{ gm} \frac{981.1 \text{ cm}}{\text{sec}^2} = 13.33 \text{ dynes}.$$

It follows that a pressure of 1 mm of mercury corresponds to 13.33 dynes/mm².

$$1 \text{ mm Hg} = 13.33 \frac{\text{dynes}}{\text{mm}^2} \left(\frac{1 \text{ bar}}{10^6 \text{ dynes/cm}^2}\right)\left(\frac{10 \text{ mm}}{1 \text{ cm}}\right)^2$$

$$= 13.33(10)^{-4} \text{ bars}.$$

Atmospheric pressure corresponds to 760 mm of mercury:

$$1 \text{ atm} = 760 \text{ mm Hg} = 760(13.33)(10)^{-4} \text{ bar} = 1.013 \text{ bar}.$$

In British units,

$$1 \text{ atm} = 1.013(10)^6 \frac{\text{dynes}}{\text{cm}^2} \left(\frac{2.54 \text{ cm}}{1 \text{ in}}\right)^2\left(\frac{1 \text{ newton}}{10^5 \text{ dyne}}\right)\left(\frac{1 \text{ lb}}{4.44 \text{ newton}}\right)$$

$$= 14.7 \text{ lb/in}^2.$$

Example 2.3-3

An object is attracted to a fixed origin by a force proportional to the nth power of its distance from the origin. If the object is released from rest, how will the time required to reach the origin depend upon the initial separation, a?

Solution: An equation that relates physical quantities may be regarded as expressing a purely mathematical relationship between the measures of these quantities. It may also be thought of as one in which the terms retain their dimensional significance. Then these dimensions, reduced to primary ones, must be the same in every term. This point of view is of great value in engineering problems because it provides information as to the form of the solution without a complete analysis. The greatest contribution of this *dimensional analysis* lies in guiding experiment so that the results of tests may be given the widest possible range of utility.

In the present case, we have $F = kx^n$ where k is the proportionality factor and x the distance from the origin to the moving point. Notice that n must be a pure number, without dimensions. Since the dimensions of force are those of the product of mass and acceleration, which we indicate by writing MLT^{-2}, it follows that dimensional homogeneity requires k to have the dimensions $ML^{1-n}T^{-2}$. The equation of motion takes the form

$$m\ddot{x} = kx^n.$$

We see that the time interval of interest, T_0, must be a function of m, k, and a (which enters through the constants of integration). Tentatively, we write

$$T_0 = Cm^\alpha k^\beta a^\gamma \qquad \textbf{2.3-1}$$

where C is a dimensionless quantity, in general a function of n. Dimensional homogeneity now requires

$$T = (M)^\alpha (ML^{1-n}T^{-2})^\beta (L)^\gamma.$$

Since the dimensions in each of the primary units M, L, and T must be the same in each term, it follows that

$$0 = \alpha + \beta, \qquad 0 = \beta(1-n) + \gamma, \qquad 1 = -2\beta,$$

or

$$\alpha = \frac{1}{2}, \qquad \beta = -\frac{1}{2}, \qquad \gamma = \frac{1}{2}(1-n).$$

Returning now to Eq. 2.3-1,

$$T_0 = C\sqrt{\frac{m}{k}}\, a^{\frac{1}{2}(1-n)}. \qquad \textbf{2.3-2}$$

This answers the question originally raised: the time of fall is proportional to the separation raised to the power $(1-n)/2$. Note that the result is entirely consistent with that given in Eq. 2.2-30 for the case $n = 1/3$. Two other values of n are of special interest. If $n = 1$ the time is independent of the amplitude; this corresponds to a spring-like restoring force. If $n = -2$ the time is proportional to the three-halves power of the separation; this is an illustration of Kepler's law for free fall in a gravitational force field.

The weakness of dimensional analysis lies in the need to foresee all quantities that may affect the one that is of interest. In the present

xample, we were able to do this by inspection of the equation of motion.
t may also be said that, from a logical point of view, there is no reason for
presupposing the functional relationship between these quantities to be of a
simple form such as that of Eq. 2.3-1. What we have shown is that, if a
simple relation is possible, it must be the one given by Eq. 2.3-2.

Example 2.3-4

*An airfoil model is tested in a wind tunnel. The scale of the model is
1:10; density in the tunnel is 1/3 of air density at cruising altitude. If a lift
force of 100 lb is measured on the model at a wind speed of 300 knots what will be
the lift force on the prototype at a speed of 150 knots?*

Solution: We assume the force exerted by the fluid on the immersed
object to have magnitude dependent on relative velocity, v, density of fluid,
ρ, and size of object as represented by a typical dimension. We may take
the plan area A to represent the size. Then the lift force—which is the
force component at right angles to the upstream air velocity—may, following the line of reasoning of the previous example, be written

$$F_L = Cv^\alpha \rho^\beta A^\gamma.$$

For dimensional homogeneity,

$$MLT^{-2} = (LT^{-1})^\alpha (ML^{-3})^\beta (L^2)^\gamma$$

so that

$$1 = \beta, \qquad 1 = \alpha - 3\beta + 2\gamma, \qquad -2 = -\alpha$$

or

$$\alpha = 2, \qquad \beta = 1, \qquad \gamma = 1.$$

It follows that

$$F_L = C\rho v^2 A \qquad \qquad \text{2.3-3}$$

where C is a dimensionless coefficient. It is customary to insert a factor
$\frac{1}{2}$ and to write Eq. 2.3-3 in the form

$$F_L = C_L \frac{1}{2} \rho v^2 A. \qquad \qquad \text{2.3-4}$$

The coefficient C_L is known as the *lift coefficient.* There is, of course, a
corresponding "drag coefficient," $C_D = F_D / \frac{1}{2}\rho v^2 A$, for the component of
force parallel to the airstream. In the present example, we need not
actually compute C_L. The essential idea is that C_L, being dimensionless, is
the same for model and prototype. Using subscripts m and p to distinguish model and prototype, we have

$$\frac{(F_L)_p}{(F_L)_m} = \frac{\rho_p v_p^2 A_p}{\rho_m v_m^2 A_m}$$

$$\frac{(F_L)_p}{(F_L)_m} = \left(\frac{1}{3}\right)\left(\frac{300}{150}\right)^2 \left(\frac{10}{1}\right)^2 = 133$$

$$(F_L)_p = (100)(133) = 13{,}300 \text{ lb.}$$

The result is only an approximation because viscosity has been neglected. At high speeds comparable to the speed of sound, the fluid is no longer of approximately uniform density and this is an even more serious limitation on the foregoing analysis.

Example 2.3-5

Experiments are conducted to measure the drag force encountered by a sphere moving at constant speed through a viscous fluid. How should the experimental results be reported if they are to be of greatest utility ?

Solution: We begin by arguing that the drag force will be a function of the sphere radius R, fluid density ρ, viscosity μ, and speed v. Then, as before, we write

$$F_D = C\rho^\alpha v^\beta R^\gamma \mu^\delta.$$

The viscosity is the ratio between the shear stress and the velocity gradient in the fluid. Its dimensions are $ML^{-1}T^{-1}$. From a dimensional point of view,

$$MLT^{-2} = (ML^{-3})^\alpha (LT^{-1})^\beta (L)^\gamma (ML^{-1}T^{-1})^\delta.$$

$$1 = \alpha + \delta, \qquad 1 = -3\alpha + \beta + \gamma - \delta, \qquad -2 = -\beta - \delta.$$

There are three equations in four unknowns. The best we can do is to express α, β, γ, δ in terms of one of them, say δ.

$$\alpha = 1 - \delta, \qquad \beta = 2 - \delta, \qquad \gamma = 2 - \delta.$$

$$F_D = C\rho^{1-\delta} v^{2-\delta} R^{2-\delta} \mu^\delta = C\rho v^2 R^2 \left(\frac{\rho v R}{\mu}\right)^{-\delta}. \qquad \textbf{2.3-5}$$

Since δ may have any value, so far as our present analysis is concerned, the right-hand side of Eq. 2.3-5 may be taken to represent the typical term of a power series. Another way of expressing this is

$$F_D = \frac{1}{2}\rho v^2 R^2 f\left(\frac{\rho v R}{\mu}\right). \qquad \textbf{2.3-6}$$

The ratio $F_D/\frac{1}{2}\rho v^2 R^2$ is the drag coefficient C_D described in the previous example except that the area A, which in this case would be πR^2, has been replaced by R^2. The quantity $\rho v R/\mu$ is known as the Reynolds number of the flow. Equation 2.3-6 indicates that, for maximum utility, experimental results should be presented in the form of a graph or table giving the drag coefficient, C_D, as a function of Reynolds number. Then the results may be used to compute the drag force on a sphere of any specified size in a fluid of any specified density, viscosity, and speed. All that is required is to compute the Reynolds number of the flow, look up the corresponding drag coefficient and multiply it by $\frac{1}{2}\rho v^2 R^2$ or $\frac{1}{2}\rho v^2 A$.

2.4 Impulse and Momentum

If we are interested only in the resultant force and the acceleration at a particular instant of time, it is unnecessary to solve a differential equation. The relation between these quantities is given directly by the law of motion, $\mathbf{F} = m\mathbf{a}$. The fact that $\mathbf{a} = \ddot{\mathbf{r}}$ is immaterial. However, as soon as we become interested in a change in position or in finding how velocity or force change with time we must treat the equation $\mathbf{F} = m\mathbf{a}$ as a differential equation. This implies that, in addition to the equation itself, some initial conditions on the motion—say the velocity and position vectors at some particular time—must be specified.

Among all the methods for solving differential equations there are two fundamental methods for integrating the equation $\mathbf{F} = m\mathbf{a}$. Both of these provide *first integrals*; that is, they "integrate the equations once," leaving first-order differential equations in the position vector. These methods are based mathematically on the functional dependence of the forces and hence of the accelerations, and, for the particle, are immediately suggested by the basic kinematic relations. In this section, we shall consider the forces as functions of time, and derive the *impulse-momentum principles*; in the next, force will be considered as a function primarily of position, and the *work-energy principle* will be derived.

The impulse-momentum principles are based on the kinematic relation 1.7-2: $\int \mathbf{a}\, dt = \mathbf{v} - \mathbf{v}_0$. For any force $\mathbf{P}(t)$, we define the *linear impulse* of $\mathbf{P}$ over a time interval (t_1, t_2) to be the vector quantity

$$\hat{\mathbf{P}}(t_2, t_1) \equiv \hat{\mathbf{P}} = \int_{t_1}^{t_2} \mathbf{P}(\tau)\, d\tau. \qquad \textbf{2.4-1}$$

That linear impulse is a vector quantity follows from the general proposition of Chapter I that integrals of vector functions are themselves vectors. If $\mathbf{F}(t)$ is the resultant force on a particle, then the resultant linear impulse on the particle over a time interval (t_1, t_2) is

$$\hat{\mathbf{F}}(t_2, t_1) = \int_{t_1}^{t_2} \mathbf{F}(\tau)\, d\tau.$$

In Section 2.2, we have defined the *linear momentum* of a particle at any time to be the product of its mass and velocity, $m\mathbf{v}(t)$. Relative to an inertial frame of reference, then, we have

$$\mathbf{F} = m\mathbf{a} = m\frac{d\mathbf{v}}{dt},$$

$$\hat{\mathbf{F}}(t_2, t_1) = \int_{t_1}^{t_2} \mathbf{F}(\tau)\, d\tau = \int_{t_1}^{t_2} m\mathbf{a}(\tau)\, d\tau$$

$$= m\int_{t_1}^{t_2} \mathbf{a}(\tau)\, d\tau = m\mathbf{v}(t_2) - m\mathbf{v}(t_1). \qquad \textbf{2.4-2}$$

This last equation embodies the

Principle of Linear Impulse and Momentum for a Particle:

The resultant linear impulse of the forces acting on a particle over any time interval is equal to the change in linear momentum of the particle during that interval, where the momentum change is measured relative to an inertial frame of reference. If we wish to speak of the velocity at a general time, t, we only need replace the upper limit of integration t_2 in Eq. 2.4-2 by t, of course; then

$$\mathbf{v}(t) = \mathbf{v}(t_1) + \frac{1}{m}\,\hat{\mathbf{F}}(t, t_1) = \mathbf{v}(t_1) + \frac{1}{m}\int_{t_1}^{t} \mathbf{F}(\tau)\,d\tau.$$

We shall discuss the physical significance of the linear-impulse principle shortly; first, for completeness, we state the parallel angular-impulse principle and the corollaries to these—the conservation-of-momentum laws. In the last section, the principle of moment of momentum for a particle was derived:

$$\mathbf{M}_O = \dot{\mathbf{H}}_O.$$

Here $\mathbf{M}_O$ is the resultant moment vector of the forces with respect to a point O fixed in an inertial reference frame and $\dot{\mathbf{H}}_O$ is the time rate of change of the moment of momentum, or angular momentum, $\mathbf{H}_O = \mathbf{r} \times m\mathbf{v}$ of the particle with respect to O. For any force $\mathbf{P}(t)$ with moment $\mathbf{M}_O$ about point O, we define the *angular impulse* over a time interval (t_1, t_2) with respect to O by

$$\hat{\mathbf{M}}_O(t_2, t_1) = \int_{t_1}^{t_2} \mathbf{M}_O\,dt. \qquad \textbf{2.4-3}$$

If $\mathbf{M}_O$ is the resultant moment about O of the forces acting on a particle, then $\hat{\mathbf{M}}_O$ as given by 2.4-3 will be the resultant angular impulse with respect to O. Time integration of the angular-momentum equation over the interval (t_1, t_2) results in the angular-impulse, angular-momentum principle:

$$\hat{\mathbf{M}}_O(t_2, t_1) = \int_{t_1}^{t_2} \mathbf{M}_O\,d\tau = \mathbf{H}_O(t_2) - \mathbf{H}_O(t_1). \qquad \textbf{2.4-4}$$

Stated in words, this is the

Principle of Angular Impulse and Momentum for a Particle:

The resultant angular impulse of the forces acting on a particle with respect to a point fixed in an inertial reference frame over any time interval equals the change in angular momentum of the particle with respect to the same point over that time interval.

If the resultant force $\mathbf{F}(t)$ vanishes for all time t in the interval (t_1, t_2), then the resultant linear impulse $\hat{\mathbf{F}}(t)$ also vanishes, and the linear momentum remains constant, as we see from 2.4-2 with the upper limit of integration set equal to the general time variable t. This expresses the

Principle of Conservation of Linear Momentum for a Particle:

If the resultant force on a particle vanishes at every instant during a time interval, the linear momentum of the particle remains constant (is conserved) throughout the interval, relative to an inertial reference frame. Similarly, the vanishing of the resultant moment with respect to the base point O of the angular impulse-momentum principle at all times t in an interval ensures the constancy of the angular momentum of the particle throughout the interval; this is the

Principle of Conservation of Angular Momentum for a Particle:

If the resultant moment of the forces acting on a particle about a point fixed in an inertial reference frame vanishes at each instant of a time interval, then the angular momentum of the particle with respect to the fixed point remains constant during the time interval.

These momentum principles seem to be strictly mathematical formalisms, and to some extent this is true. Conservation of linear momentum for a particle appears to say nothing that the first law of motion does not say. It is fair to state that angular impulse-momentum and the two conservation principles are not of prime importance in the study of particle dynamics, although conservation of angular momentum is useful in one important case that will be treated in the examples. The momentum principles are of basic importance for systems, and the formal statement of them for the particle will help the student in his comparison of the theory of systems with the theory of the particle.

Besides this, however, there are a number of problems that can be treated by impulse-momentum methods but which, usually for lack of information about force distribution, cannot be solved by direct application of the equations of motion. Problems of impact wherein the details of the force distribution during the impact aren't known but for which change in momentum can be measured lead through the impulse-momentum principle to a time-average force distribution. The effects of different force distributions on the motion of systems can be compared under the condition that the total linear or angular impulse of the distributions be held constant. The concept of impulse also leads to the introduction of another mechanical concept, the *impulsive force*, which is closely related to our intuitive physical meaning of impulse as a comparatively large force acting over an extremely short time. The technical use of impulse implies no restriction on force magnitude nor on the duration of the time interval. Discussion of impulsive forces is contained in the next section; it may be omitted on a first reading.

Example 2.4-1

A particle of mass 3 slugs is moving at 5 ft/sec in the positive x-direction. A force 2i − 3j lb is applied to it for 2 sec. What is its velocity at the end of the 2-sec interval?

Solution: The linear impulse of the force is

$$\hat{\mathbf{F}} = \int_0^2 (2\mathbf{i} - 3\mathbf{j})\, dt = 4\mathbf{i} - 6\mathbf{j} \text{ lb-sec.}$$

The initial linear momentum is

$$(m\mathbf{v})|_{t=0} = (3)(5\mathbf{i}) = 15\mathbf{i} \text{ lb-sec;}$$

the change in linear momentum is

$$(m\mathbf{v})|_{t=2} - (m\mathbf{v})|_{t=0} = (3\mathbf{v}|_{t=2} - 15\mathbf{i}) \text{ lb-sec.}$$

By the linear impulse-momentum principle,

$$\hat{\mathbf{F}} = 4\mathbf{i} - 6\mathbf{j} = \Delta(m\mathbf{v}) = 3\mathbf{v}|_{t=2} - 15\mathbf{i},$$

$$\mathbf{v}|_{t=2} = \frac{19}{3}\mathbf{i} - 2\mathbf{j} \text{ ft/sec.}$$

Example 2.4-2

In 3 sec, a particle of mass 0.5 slugs changes velocity from −4i + 6j − 2k in/sec to −2j + k in/sec. What average force will produce this change?

Solution: The change in linear momentum is

$$\Delta(m\mathbf{v}) = 0.5(\mathbf{v}_2 - \mathbf{v}_1) = \frac{1}{2}\left[\frac{-2\mathbf{j} + \mathbf{k}}{12} - \frac{-4\mathbf{i} + 6\mathbf{j} - 2\mathbf{k}}{12}\right]$$

$$= \frac{1}{6}\mathbf{i} - \frac{1}{3}\mathbf{j} + \frac{1}{8}\mathbf{k} \text{ lb-sec.}$$

The total impulse in 3 sec must equal this. The average force is defined as

$$\mathbf{F}_{ave} = \frac{1}{t_2 - t_1}\int_{t_1}^{t_2} \mathbf{F}(\tau)\, d\tau = \frac{\hat{\mathbf{F}}(t_2, t_1)}{t_2 - t_1};$$

therefore,

$$\mathbf{F}_{ave} = \frac{1}{3}\left[\frac{1}{6}\mathbf{i} - \frac{1}{3}\mathbf{j} + \frac{1}{8}\mathbf{k}\right]$$

$$= \frac{1}{18}\mathbf{i} - \frac{1}{9}\mathbf{j} + \frac{1}{24}\mathbf{k} \text{ lb.}$$

Example 2.4-3

A billard ball banks off a cushion of a billiard table. It strikes the cushion at speed v_0 at angle ϕ_0 with the cushion and leaves at speed v_1 at angle ϕ_1. What is the impulse on the ball? Resolve the impulse into normal and frictional components perpendicular and tangent to the cushion.

Solution: Let the tangential direction along the cushion be the x-direction, the normal to the cushion in toward the table be the y-direction. Then the entering velocity is $\mathbf{v}_0 = v_0(\cos\phi_0\mathbf{i} - \sin\phi_0\mathbf{j})$, and the separation velocity is $\mathbf{v}_1 = v_1(\cos\phi_1\mathbf{i} + \sin\phi_1\mathbf{j})$. Taking the ball as a particle of mass m, its change in linear momentum is

$$\Delta(m\mathbf{v}) = m(v_1\cos\phi_1 - v_0\cos\phi_0)\mathbf{i} + m(v_1\sin\phi_1 + v_0\sin\phi_0)\mathbf{j}.$$

The impulsive force $\hat{\mathbf{P}}$ in normal and tangential coordinates is $\hat{\mathbf{P}} = \hat{F}\mathbf{i} + \hat{N}\mathbf{j}$; therefore, since $\hat{\mathbf{P}} = \Delta(m\mathbf{v})$,

$$\hat{F} = m(v_1\cos\phi_1 - v_0\cos\phi_0),$$

$$\hat{N} = m(v_1\sin\phi_1 + v_0\sin\phi_0).$$

Example 2.4-4

Show that a particle moving under a central force moves in a plane.

Solution: A central force is one that has line of action always passing through a fixed point. Let O be the fixed point, and let $\mathbf{r}$ be the position of the particle relative to O. The line of action of the central force $\mathbf{F}$ then is the same as that of $\mathbf{r}$, so that $\mathbf{M}_O = \mathbf{r} \times \mathbf{F} = \mathbf{0}$ always. By conservation of angular momentum, the angular momentum $\mathbf{H}_O$ of the particle is constant:

$$\mathbf{H}_O = \mathbf{r} \times m\mathbf{v} = \text{constant}.$$

Since $\mathbf{H}_O$ is a constant vector, its direction is constant. Since $\mathbf{r}$ is always perpendicular to $\mathbf{H}_O$, and $\mathbf{r}$ emanates from O, the position vector of the particle always lies in the plane through O perpendicular to $\mathbf{H}_O$. (If $\mathbf{H}_O$ vanishes, the motion degenerates to a rectilinear motion; prove this.) This result will find application in the next chapter in the discussion of orbital motion.

2.5*   Impulsive Forces

Suppose we wish to describe the motion of a ball bouncing on the floor. A detailed analysis of the "bounce" is complex, involving the deformation of the ball during the time of contact. If we model the ball as a particle to obtain a first approximation to its motion, we are led to an apparently

---

* This section may be omitted on a first reading without destroying the continuity of development.

discontinuous change in velocity. Even if the speed does not change as a result of the impact, the direction of the velocity changes from down to up while the particle appears to hold the same position. Certainly this is a situation not encompassed by Newton's laws, since we cannot define acceleration now. It is a difficulty introduced by our own model of a physical situation. It cannot be explained away entirely by saying that all we need to do is drop the particle model so that the details of the contact forces may be analyzed properly. Within the framework of particle mechanics, we wish to be able to handle the analysis of collision processes in a reasonable mathematical way. This can be done by introducing discontinuous velocities and the concept of impulsive force. In this way, we can treat problems of particle motion in which there are "corners" on the particle path, as opposed to the smooth paths with continuous tangents treated in the last sections of Chapter I.

Consider the impulse of a force over a time interval $t_1 \leq t \leq t_2$:

$$\hat{\mathbf{F}}(t_2, t_1) = \int_{t_1}^{t_2} \mathbf{F}(\tau) \, d\tau.$$

Suppose the time interval becomes shorter and shorter; i.e., suppose we examine the limit of the impulse as t_2 approaches the limit t_1. If the impulse possesses a derivative—the force $\mathbf{F}(t)$—at t_1, then that limit will be zero. But now suppose we change the force acting in such a way that the impulses of the sequence of different forces remain constant and different from zero as $t_2 \to t_1$. For instance, for a given time interval (t_1, t_2), the constant force $(t_2 - t_1)^{-1}$ leads to a unit impulse over the time interval. Letting t_2 approach t_1 *and* changing the force so that it remains of the form $(t_2 - t_1)^{-1}$, the impulse remains constant. In the limit, of course, the force itself does not exist. The student must realize that this has been only one example of how an instantaneous impulse, or *impulsive force*, can arise mathematically. If, for any impulse function $\hat{\mathbf{F}}(t_2, t_1)$, the limit of $\hat{\mathbf{F}}$ as t_2 approaches t_1 is different from zero, we say that an impulsive force (dimensionally an impulse, not a force) has been applied at time t_1, with the impulsive force $\hat{\mathbf{F}}(t_1)$ being given by

$$\hat{\mathbf{F}}(t_1) = \lim_{t_2 \to t_1} \hat{\mathbf{F}}(t_2, t_1).$$

We can now remove the formal limiting process, and speak directly of impulsive forces applied instantaneously to the particle. The fundamental principle governing these new quantities is the linear impulse-momentum principle, stated as

$$\hat{\mathbf{F}} = \Delta(m\mathbf{v}): \qquad \text{2.5-1}$$

the impulsive force applied to a particle equals the instantaneous change in linear momentum of the particle. Note that the theory of impulsive forces implies that no change of position occurs during the instantaneous, or discontinuous, change of velocity. This zero instantaneous displacement condition is consistent with the derivation of impulsive forces as limits of impulse functions. The displacement during any time interval will have zero limit if the time interval approaches zero, even if the impulse has a finite non-zero limit. Therefore, the position vectors considered in newtonian mechanics are always continuous even if impulsive motion is taken into account.

2.6 Power, Work, and Kinetic Energy

The impulse-momentum principles are derived by considering forces and accelerations as functions of time. The forces may depend explicitly on position and velocity, however, so that the formal impulse integral cannot be evaluated directly. Alternative methods of integrating the equations must be found. As stated in Section 2.4, there is a second fundamental method of finding a first integral of the equations. The mechanical *work-energy principle* is directly useful when the forces are functions of position. Such vector fields were mentioned briefly in Section 1.6. In this section, the principle will be derived formally; detailed discussion of force fields will be reserved for the next section.

Just as the linear impulse-momentum principle is suggested by the kinematical relation 1.7-2, so the form of the work-energy principle derives from the rectilinear motion relation 1.8-9, the tangential acceleration relation 1.9-9, and the more fundamental kinematical equation 1.7-3. The latter result,

$$\mathbf{a} \cdot \mathbf{v} = \frac{d}{dt} \left(\frac{1}{2} \mathbf{v} \cdot \mathbf{v} \right), \qquad \textbf{2.6-1}$$

is the essential step in the derivation of the work-energy principle.

Coupled with the equations of motion, Eq. 2.6-1 suggests the definition of a quantity $\mathbf{F} \cdot \mathbf{v}$ for any force $\mathbf{F}$, as the $\mathbf{a} = \dot{\mathbf{v}}$ or $\Delta \mathbf{v} = \int \mathbf{a} \, dt$ relation suggests the definition of the impulse integral. In discussing force and moment resultants, only the magnitude, direction, and line of action of the force vector are important. Now the point of application of the force enters our considerations. Suppose a force, $\mathbf{F}$, is applied at a moving point that instantaneously has velocity $\mathbf{v}$. The *power*, P, of the force is defined to be

$$P = \mathbf{F} \cdot \mathbf{v}; \qquad \textbf{2.6-2}$$

power is therefore a scalar quantity. If a number of forces $\mathbf{F}_i$, $i = 1, 2, \ldots, n$, act at the same point, the power of the resultant force is the algebraic sum of the powers of the separate forces:*

$$P = \mathbf{F} \cdot \mathbf{v} = \left(\sum_{i=1}^{n} \mathbf{F}_i \right) \cdot \mathbf{v} = \sum_{i=1}^{n} (\mathbf{F}_i \cdot \mathbf{v}) = \sum_{i=1}^{n} P_i.$$

From Eqs. 2.6-1 and 2.6-2 and $\mathbf{F} = m\mathbf{a}$, it follows that *the power of the resultant force on a particle equals the time rate of change of the kinetic energy of the particle*:

$$P = \mathbf{F} \cdot \mathbf{v} = m\mathbf{a} \cdot \mathbf{v} = \frac{d}{dt}\left(\frac{1}{2} m\mathbf{v} \cdot \mathbf{v} \right) = \frac{dT}{dt}.$$

The scalar function

$$T = \frac{1}{2} m\mathbf{v} \cdot \mathbf{v} = \frac{1}{2} mv^2 \qquad\qquad \textbf{2.6-3}$$

is called the *kinetic energy* of the particle. It is defined at each position of the particle, and is never negative. The power-time rate of kinetic energy principle is a scalar principle, in contrast to the vector principles developed so far, so that it cannot be expected to furnish as much information about the motion as the full vector equations.

The time integral of the power of any force acting on a moving particle is called the mechanical *work* done by the force on the particle:**

$$\Delta W \equiv \Delta W(t_2, t_1) = \int_{t_1}^{t_2} P \, dt = \int_{t_1}^{t_2} (\mathbf{F} \cdot \mathbf{v}) \, dt. \qquad \textbf{2.6-4}$$

Integrating the power principle with respect to time, we obtain the mechanical

Work-Energy Principle for a Particle:

The work done by the forces acting on a particle during any motion of the particle equals the change in value of the kinetic energy of the particle:

$$\Delta W = \Delta T = \Delta \left(\frac{1}{2} mv^2 \right). \qquad\qquad \textbf{2.6-5}$$

The work-energy integral of the equations of motion appears as

---

* The symbol $\sum_{i=1}^{n} \mathbf{F}_i$ means the same as $\mathbf{F}_1 + \mathbf{F}_2 + \mathbf{F}_3 + \cdots + \mathbf{F}_n$; that is, we are to add all terms of the type $\mathbf{F}_i$ where i takes on all values from 1 to n.
** The notation ΔW for the work should be thought of as a single symbol, and *not* as the change in value of a function W from a time t_1 to a time t_2. As we shall see, the work done by some forces can be computed as the change in value of a scalar function, but this is not true for all forces.

a mathematical formalism derived from the equations of motion and the rules of the vector calculus, much as the impulse-momentum principle does. If the principle were just a formalism, there would be little point in the introduction of such special terms as power, work, and energy. The student knows from his study of physics, and possibly of thermodynamics, that these concepts are important and help to provide unity between mechanics and other branches of physics. We shall look at various extensions of this mechanical work-energy principle, but shall not stray far away from mechanics proper.

So far, no restriction to position-dependent forces has been made. The first modification that we make brings the dependence of forces on position into prominence, and shows the identity of our definition of work with the elementary one of "force component in the direction of the displacement times displacement."

Since we are concerned with the forces acting on a moving particle, the velocity $\mathbf{v}$ referred to in 2.6-2 is the velocity of the particle and equals $d\mathbf{r}/dt$. The power is

$$P = \mathbf{F} \cdot \mathbf{v} = \mathbf{F} \cdot \frac{d\mathbf{r}}{dt};$$

therefore, the work done by $\mathbf{F}$ on the particle as it moves from position $\mathbf{r}_1 \equiv \mathbf{r}(t_1)$ to $\mathbf{r}_2 \equiv \mathbf{r}(t_2)$ along a path C may be written as

$$\Delta W = \int_{t_1}^{t_2} P \, dt = \int_{t_1}^{t_2} \mathbf{F} \cdot \frac{d\mathbf{r}}{dt} \, dt = \int_C \mathbf{F} \cdot d\mathbf{r}. \qquad \textbf{2.6-6}$$

The last integral form must be defined. Such integrals are known as *line integrals*, since the integration is to be carried out with respect to position variables that are restricted to lie on a line or curve, C, of space. It is a generalization of the ordinary definite integral of a scalar function of a single variable, $\int_a^b f(x) \, dx$, where the "path" of integration is along the x-axis. A formal definition of the line integral and some discussion of its properties will be given in the next section. Assuming for the moment that such mathematical matters can be disposed of properly, we turn to the question of the direct evaluation of 2.6-6 for a given path C.

Introducing the arclength s and the intrinsic path coordinates along C, we may write

$$\mathbf{F} \cdot d\mathbf{r} = \mathbf{F} \cdot \frac{d\mathbf{r}}{ds} \, ds = F_t \, ds;$$

this, in differential form, explicitly agrees with the elementary definition of work. If s_1 and s_2 are the values of s at $\mathbf{r}_1$ and $\mathbf{r}_2$, then the work integral becomes

$$\Delta W = \int_{C:s_1}^{s_2} F_t \, ds; \qquad \textbf{2.6-7}$$

the work done by $\mathbf{F}$ is the integral with respect to arclength of the tangential component of $\mathbf{F}$ along the particle path. To evaluate 2.6-7, we must know both the path and the form of the dependence of F_t on s.

Introducing a set of rectangular cartesian axes (x, y, z), we obtain another form of the work integral:

$$\mathbf{F} \cdot d\mathbf{r} \equiv F_x \, dx + F_y \, dy + F_z \, dz,$$

$$\Delta W = \int_{C:(x_1,y_1,z_1)}^{(x_2,y_2,z_2)} (F_x \, dx + F_y \, dy + F_z \, dz). \qquad \textbf{2.6-8}$$

Here the line integral is to be evaluated as the sum of the three separate integrals on x, y, and z, with the proviso that in $F_x \equiv F_x(x, y, z)$, the variables y and z are to be replaced by the path equations in the form $y = y(x)$, $z = z(x)$. Similar substitutions must be made in the other two integrals.

In the application of the work-energy principle to mechanical problems, work is most often computed by means of the position-dependent integral 2.6-6 rather than by the time-dependent integral 2.6-4. The objection that immediately arises to such a procedure is this: how can we perform an integration over a path, when the object of the solution of the equations of motion is in fact to find that path? There are two answers to this objection. Quite often we do know the path, or enough about the path to formulate an equation, due to constraints on the motion. For example, the bead sliding on a helical wire fixed in space travels on a curve for which we can write the equations. We may not know beforehand whether the bead slides up, then down, then up again under action of the forces on it; but we can formulate the integrals along the curve.*

———————

* There is a distinction that should be made between the path of the particle and the geometric curve along which the path lies. Given a geometric curve with a defined sense of increasing arclength along it from one end to the other, the curve will correspond to a particle's path only if the ds/dt for the particle is non-negative. If the particle moves along the curve in a positive sense, stops and moves back again, then turns around once more, the path of the particle is not simply the curve. Such turning points must be accounted for in setting up the work integral in the form 2.6-6.

The second answer to the objection is that, for many forces important in mechanics, the work integral depends only on the end-points and not on the path joining them. Such forces are called *conservative.* The evaluation of the work integral for conservative forces is discussed in the next section. All other forces that do work are nonconservative; the work done by these does depend on the path.

Let us now turn to some simple examples of the use of the work-energy principle and of the evaluation of the work integral.

Example **2.6-1**

A block weighing 20 *lb moves along a horizontal table, starting from rest at* $x=0$; *a* 50-*lb force is applied to the block as shown in Fig.* 2.6-1a. *The coefficients of static and kinetic friction are* 0.1. *Show that the block will slide and find its speed after it has moved* 3 *in to the right.*

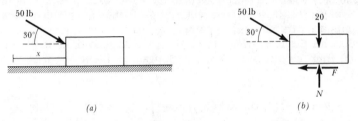

(a)   (b)

Fig. 2.6-1

Solution: A free-body diagram of the particle in general position is shown in Fig. 2.6-1b. The normal reaction is $N = 20 + 50 \sin 30° = 45$ lb; the frictional reaction is $F = 0.1N = 4.5$ lb. Since F is less than the x component of the 50-lb load ($4.5 < 50 \cos 30° = 43.3$), the block will slide.

Since a change in position is specified in the problem, it is natural to seek a work-energy solution. The weight force and the normal reaction force do no work in the motion, since the displacement is always at right angles to them. (The normal reaction is a *workless constraint* force.) The work done on the block is

$$\Delta W = \int_0^3 (50 \cos 30° - 4.5)\, dx = (38.8)(3) = 116.4 \text{ in-lb.}$$

The change in kinetic energy is

$$\Delta T = \frac{1}{2} mv_2^2 - \frac{1}{2} mv_1^2 = \frac{1}{2} mv_2^2 = \frac{1(20)}{(2)(32.2)(12)}\, v_2^2.$$

Note that in the numerical work, which should (as far as possible) be delayed to the end of the analysis, we write g as $(32.2)(12)$ because distances are being expressed in inches in this example.

Since $\Delta W = \Delta T$,

$$v_2^2 = \frac{(2)(32.2)(12)\,(116.4)}{20}\ (\text{in/sec})^2,$$

and the final speed is

$$v_2 = 67.1\ \text{in/sec}.$$

Example 2.6-2

Suppose the particle of the previous example is traveling at a rate $v_1 = 40$ in/sec to the left when the 50-lb force is applied to it. What will be its speed v_2 when it returns to its initial position? What will be its speed v_3 when it is 3 in to the right of its initial position, as in the previous example?

Solution: Now the fact that the direction of the friction force depends on relative velocity complicates matters. The free-body diagram 2.6-1b is valid only when the block travels to the right; while it is moving to the left, a proper free-body diagram will have the friction force (still of the same magnitude 4.5 lb) directed oppositely to that of Fig. 2.6-1b. Let b be the distance the block slides to the left; the total work done during the motion from $x = 0$ to $x = -b$ and back again is due to the friction force alone:

$$\Delta W = \int_0^{-b} (50 \cos 30^\circ + 4.5)\,dx + \int_{-b}^0 (50 \cos 30^\circ - 4.5)\,dx$$

$$= 2 \int_0^{-b} 4.5\,dx = -9b.$$

This will equal the change in kinetic energy ΔT during the motion:

$$-9b = \frac{1}{2}\,m(v_2^2 - v_1^2).$$

To determine v_2, we must determine b; to do this, we look at the first part of the motion as the speed decreases from v_1 to zero:

$$\Delta W = \int_0^{-b} (50 \cos 30^\circ + 4.5)\,dx = \frac{1}{2}\,m(0 - v_1^2).$$

Therefore, $-\frac{1}{2}mv_1^2 = (50 \cos 30^\circ + 4.5)(-b) = -47.8b$, and

$$\frac{1}{2}\,mv_2^2 = \frac{1}{2}\left[\frac{20}{32.2(12)}\right]v_2^2 = 38.8b = \frac{38.8}{47.8}\left(\frac{1}{2}\right)\left[\frac{20}{32.2(12)}\right]v_1^2,$$

or

$$v_2^2 = \frac{38.8}{47.8}\,v_1^2, \qquad v_2 = 36.0\ \text{in/sec}.$$

When the particle travels another 3 in to the right, the additional work done will be the same as in the last example:

$$\Delta W = 116.4 = \frac{1}{2} m(v_3^2 - v_2^2),$$

$$v_3^2 = v_2^2 + \frac{2(116.4)(32.2)(12)}{20} = 5796,$$

$$v_3 = 76.1 \text{ in/sec.}$$

Example 2.6-3

A bead of mass m slides on a smooth, circular wire of radius r that is fixed in a vertical plane. It starts from rest at position A [Fig. 2.6-2a]; find the angle, θ_B, determining the point, B, where it comes to rest again for the first time.

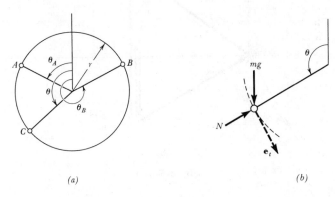

(a)   (b)

Fig. 2.6-2

Solution: Let point C in Fig. 2.6-2a represent a typical position, with θ being the general coordinate giving the position of C. Measure arclength s counterclockwise around the circle from the top, so that $s = r\theta$. A free-body diagram of the bead in general position is given in 2.6-2b. N is again a workless constraint; only the weight force does work. The tangential component of the weight is $mg \cos(\theta - \pi/2) = mg \sin \theta$; therefore the work done is

$$\Delta W = \int_{s_A}^{s_B} mg \sin \theta \, ds = \int_{\theta_A}^{\theta_B} mgr \sin \theta \, d\theta$$

$$= -mgr(\cos \theta_B - \cos \theta_A).$$

The change in kinetic energy is zero, so that $\Delta W = 0$; therefore, $\cos \theta_B = \cos \theta_A$, and the solution that we want is, from our picture, $\theta_B = 2\pi - \theta_A$. Point B is on the same horizontal level as point A.

Example **2.6-4**

Compute the work done by the force $\mathbf{F} = x^2\mathbf{i} + y^2\mathbf{j} + z^2\mathbf{k}$, given as a function of position, along a closed path consisting of straight line segments from $(0, 0, 0)$ to $(1, 1, 1)$ to $(1, 1, 0)$ to $(1, 1, \frac{1}{2})$ to $(1, 1, 0)$ to $(0, 0, 0)$ (*Fig.* 2.6-3).

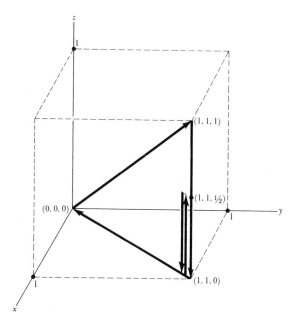

Fig. 2.6-3

Solution: The total work done by $\mathbf{F}$ over the whole path C is the sum of the five integrals over the five path segments. Call these segments C_1 to C_5 in order. The equations of these "curves," and the ranges of value of the variables along them, are:

$$C_1 : x = y = z; \quad 0 \le x \le 1, \quad 0 \le y \le 1, \quad 0 \le z \le 1$$
$$C_2 : x = y = 1; \quad 1 \ge z \ge 0$$
$$C_3 : x = y = 1; \quad 0 \le z \le \tfrac{1}{2}$$
$$C_4 : x = y = 1; \quad \tfrac{1}{2} \ge z \ge 0$$
$$C_5 : z = 0, \quad x = y; \quad 1 \ge x \ge 0, \quad 1 \ge y \ge 0.$$

The work integral along C_1 is

$$\Delta W_1 = \int_{C_1} \mathbf{F} \cdot d\mathbf{r} = \int_{C_1} (x^2 \, dx + y^2 \, dy + z^2 \, dz)$$
$$= \int_0^1 x^2 \, dx + \int_0^1 y^2 \, dy + \int_0^1 z^2 \, dz = \frac{1}{3} + \frac{1}{3} + \frac{1}{3} = 1.$$

This can also be evaluated using the equations of C_1, $x=y=z$, from which it follows that $dx=dy=dz$ along C_1; then

$$\int_{C_1} \mathbf{F} \cdot d\mathbf{r} = 3 \int_0^1 x^2\, dx = 1.$$

The other integrals are similarly evaluated. Along C_2, x and y are constant, so that $dx=dy=0$:

$$\Delta W_2 = \int_{C_2} (x^2\, dx + y^2\, dy + z^2\, dz) = \int_{C_2} z^2\, dz = \int_1^0 z^2\, dz = -\frac{1}{3}.$$

Also,

$$\Delta W_3 = \int_{C_3} (x^2\, dx + y^2\, dy + z^2\, dz) = \int_{C_3} z^2\, dz = \int_0^{1/2} z^2\, dz = \frac{1}{24},$$

$$\Delta W_4 = \int_{C_4} (x^2\, dx + y^2\, dy + z^2\, dz) = \int_{C_4} z^2\, dz = \int_{1/2}^0 z^2\, dz = -\frac{1}{24},$$

$$\Delta W_5 = \int_{C_5} (x^2\, dx + y^2\, dy + z^2\, dz) = \int_{C_5} (x^2\, dx + y^2\, dy)$$

$$= 2 \int_1^0 x^2\, dx = -\frac{2}{3}.$$

The total work done by $\mathbf{F}$ is

$$\Delta W = \int_C \mathbf{F} \cdot d\mathbf{r} = \sum_{i=1}^5 \int_{C_i} \mathbf{F} \cdot d\mathbf{r} = 1 - \frac{1}{3} + \frac{1}{24} - \frac{1}{24} - \frac{2}{3} = 0.$$

As we shall see in the next section, we can determine that $\mathbf{F}$ is a conservative force and write down the result immediately.

Example 2.6-5

Find the work done by the force $\mathbf{P} = y^2\mathbf{i} + z^2\mathbf{j} + x^2\mathbf{k}$ *around the path of the last example.*

Solution: The five work integrals are of the form

$$\Delta W_i = \int_{C_i} \mathbf{P} \cdot d\mathbf{r} = \int_{C_i} (y^2\, dx + z^2\, dy + x^2\, dz).$$

For segment C_1, to evaluate $\int_{x=0}^{x=1} y^2\, dx$, we use the fact that $y=x$ along C_1; then

$$\int_0^1 y^2\, dx = \int_0^1 x^2\, dx = \frac{1}{3}.$$

Similar substitutions lead to

$$\Delta W_1 = \int_0^1 (x^2\, dx + y^2\, dy + z^2\, dz) = 3 \int_0^1 x^2\, dx = 1.$$

For C_2, since $dx = dy = 0$,

$$\Delta W_2 = \int_{C_2} (y^2\,dx + z^2\,dy + x^2\,dz) = \int_{C_2} x^2\,dz = \int_1^0 dz = -1.$$

Also,

$$\Delta W_3 = \int_{C_3} x^2\,dz = \int_0^{1/2} dz = \frac{1}{2},$$

$$\Delta W_4 = \int_{C_4} x^2\,dz = \int_{1/2}^0 dz = -\frac{1}{2},$$

$$\Delta W_5 = \int_{C_5} (y^2\,dx + z^2\,dy + x^2\,dz) = \int_{C_5} (y^2\,dx + z^2\,dy) = \int_{C_5} y^2\,dx$$

$$= \int_1^0 x^2\,dx = -\frac{1}{3}.$$

Therefore,

$$\Delta W = \sum_{i=1}^5 \Delta W_i = 1 - 1 + \frac{1}{2} - \frac{1}{2} - \frac{1}{3} = -\frac{1}{3}.$$

For both the force **P** of this example and the force **F** of the last, the work done on segment C_4 is the negative of the work done on segment C_3 so that this jog can be neglected. The retracing of a curve will always contribute zero work for a conservative force such as **F** but not for a nonconservative force such as **P**. An example where a nonconservative force does non-zero work over such a path was given in Example 2.6-2, where the friction force did non-zero work from $x = 0$ to $x = -b$ and back again.

2.7 Force Fields and Potential Energy

The utility of the work-energy principle is limited by the work integral itself. The evaluation of the integral requires either a knowledge of the power as a function of time or a knowledge of the tangential force as a function of position along a path, C. In particular, we are concerned with the latter definition of work as a line integral. In this section, the development of some of the properties of such integrals will lead to a new and important relation between scalar functions and certain vector functions of position. This *gradient* relation or operation enables us to extend the definition of energy and restate the work-energy principle in a useful alternative form.

The evaluation of line integrals requires that we understand the meaning of such an integral. Let us start, therefore, with the definition of the line integral of a scalar function. We suppose that we are given a curve, C, in space with arclength s defined along C; each point with position vector **r** of C corresponds to a value of s in some range (s_1, s_2). C may be open $[\mathbf{r}(s_2) \neq \mathbf{r}(s_1)]$ or closed $[\mathbf{r}(s_2) = \mathbf{r}(s_1)]$. Along C, we are given a scalar function of position $f(s) \equiv f[\mathbf{r}(s)] \equiv f(x, y, z)$. The line integral of the function $f(s)$ along C is defined just as any definite integral is. Divide C in any fashion into N segments, of lengths Δs_i, $i = 1, 2, \ldots N$. In each of the N segments, choose a point $\mathbf{r}_i^* \equiv \mathbf{r}(s_i^*)$, $i = 1, 2, \ldots N$. Form the Riemann sum $\sum_{i=1}^{N} f(s_i^*) \Delta s_i$, and consider the limit of the sum as N increases without bound and all lengths Δs_i approach zero. If the limit exists independently of the choice of the values s_i^*, then the line integral is said to exist and equals the limit of the sum:

$$\int_C f(s)\, ds = \lim_{\substack{N \to \infty \\ \text{all } \Delta s \to 0}} \sum_{i=1}^{N} f(s_i^*)\, \Delta s_i. \qquad \textbf{2.7-1}$$

There are other forms in which the line integral may be cast. If the equations of the curve C are given in the form $y = y(x)$, $z = z(x)$, we may wish to integrate $f(x, y, z) \equiv f(x, y(x), z(x))$ with respect to x along the curve.

In our development of the work integral, we do not have a scalar function f defined along the path, but a vector function $\mathbf{F}$. The scalar product $\mathbf{F} \cdot d\mathbf{r} \equiv F_t\, ds$ that occurs in the work integral does give a scalar integrand of the line integral type. The important property that arises from this formation of a scalar integrand from the vector function $\mathbf{F}$ is, of course, the scalar property itself: $\mathbf{F} \cdot d\mathbf{r}$, and hence $\int_C \mathbf{F} \cdot d\mathbf{r}$, must be the same whatever coordinate system is used for writing the equations of the path.

A definite integral of the form $\int_a^b f(x)\, dx$ is usually evaluated in terms of an indefinite integral, say $F(x)$, of $f(x)$. The fundamental theorem of the integral calculus states that

$$\int_a^b f(x)\, dx = F(b) - F(a),$$

where $F(x)$ is any function such that $dF/dx = f(x)$. It is natural to wonder whether this same type of procedure can be extended for the evaluation of line integrals of functions $f(s) \equiv f(x, y, z)$. We must be careful here to state what we mean by extension. There are three important parts of the fundamental theorem. First, there is the relation between $f(x)$ and $F(x)$. Should we generalize this to a relation between $f(s)$ and $F(s)$ so that $dF/ds = f$, and what does this mean if we are given $f(x, y, z)$ instead of $f(s)$ directly? Second, there is the integration along the x-axis; is this to be replaced by the integration along one curve C? Finally, given f and F, there is the result that the value of the integral depends only on the choice of the interval of integration (a, b). This should go over into a dependence only on the endpoints $\mathbf{r}_1$ and $\mathbf{r}_2$ of C.

The fruitful extension of the theorem is based on the last statement, removing any mention of the particular curve C joining the points $\mathbf{r}_1$ and $\mathbf{r}_2$. If the integral from $\mathbf{r}_1$ to $\mathbf{r}_2$ is to have the same value whatever the curve C is, however, we must extend the definition of the functions involved. Instead of speaking about functions $f(x, y, z)$ or $\mathbf{F}(x, y, z)$ defined along a single curve, we must now regard these as defined throughout a region of space. A scalar function that assigns a number to each point $\mathbf{r}$ of a region of space is called a *scalar field*; a vector function that assigns a vector to each point $\mathbf{r}$ of a region of space is called a *vector field*.

The extension of the fundamental theorem we want to discuss is: given two points $\mathbf{r}_1$ and $\mathbf{r}_2$ in space, is the value of the line integral of a function along any curve joining the two points the same whatever the curve may be, at least for all curves in some region where the function field is defined? In particular, is this true for line integrals of tangential components of vector fields, $\int \mathbf{F} \cdot d\mathbf{r}$? As we have seen in the last section, such *path independence* of the integral is not in general true. For some vector fields, it is. We then have the further physical question: do any such fields represent physically meaningful force functions?

The answer, of course, is yes; there are many such force functions for which the work integral is path-independent. Such forces are called *conservative*. The newtonian gravitational force is one such. There are many, however, that do not give rise to such integrals— sliding friction, for example. Since the friction force depends on the direction of the relative velocity between two points or surfaces in contact, and velocities certainly depend on the tangential direction of the path, the work done by friction forces will in general be path-dependent. The first requirement for a force to be conservative is, therefore, that it cannot depend on time or velocity directly, but only on position; even then not all forces dependent on position are conservative.

Suppose that in some region, R, of space, which may be all of space, a vector field, $\mathbf{F}(\mathbf{r})$, is defined. Choose any two points, $\mathbf{r}_1$ and $\mathbf{r}_2$, in R and consider the line integral $\int \mathbf{F} \cdot d\mathbf{r}$ over any path C joining $\mathbf{r}_1$ and $\mathbf{r}_2$ and lying wholly in R (Fig. 2.7-1). If the value of the integral is the same for *all* paths C in R for all choices of $\mathbf{r}_1$ and $\mathbf{r}_2$, then $\mathbf{F}$ is a conservative field in R.   Alternatively, since the integral from $\mathbf{r}_2$ to $\mathbf{r}_1$ along any path must be the negative of the integral along the reversed path, the field will be conservative if the line integral around all closed loops in R vanishes.   We cannot check all such integrals over all paths joining all pairs of points; we need a simple criterion for a conservative field.

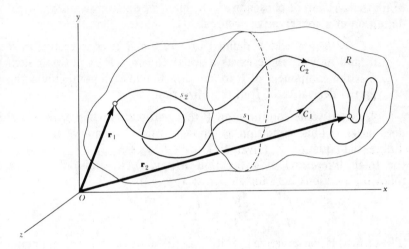

Fig. 2.7-1

If the line integral is to be path-independent, there should exist some scalar function $P(\mathbf{r})$ such that

$$\int_{C:\mathbf{r}_1}^{\mathbf{r}_2} \mathbf{F} \cdot d\mathbf{r} = P(\mathbf{r}_2) - P(\mathbf{r}_1);$$

that is, that for *any* path C

$$\int_{\mathbf{r}_1}^{\mathbf{r}_2} \mathbf{F} \cdot d\mathbf{r} = \Delta P \equiv \int_{\mathbf{r}_1}^{\mathbf{r}_2} dP. \qquad \textbf{2.7-2}$$

This means that $\mathbf{F}$ will be a conservative field if

$$\mathbf{F} \cdot d\mathbf{r} = dP; \qquad \textbf{2.7-3}$$

that is, if $\mathbf{F} \cdot d\mathbf{r}$ is the perfect differential at each point of R of some function P whatever the choice of the direction of $d\mathbf{r}$.   Introduce a rectangular cartesian coordinate system; then 2.7-3 becomes

$$\mathbf{F} \cdot d\mathbf{r} \equiv F_x \, dx + F_y \, dy + F_z \, dz = dP.$$

But the differential of $P(x, y, z)$ is given by

$$\frac{\partial P}{\partial x}\, dx + \frac{\partial P}{\partial y}\, dy + \frac{\partial P}{\partial z}\, dz = dP;$$

thus the components of the force must be the partial derivatives of P:

$$F_x = \frac{\partial P}{\partial x}, \qquad F_y = \frac{\partial P}{\partial y}, \qquad F_z = \frac{\partial P}{\partial z}. \qquad \textbf{2.7-4}$$

Since the axes can be chosen in any fashion, we obtain the more general definition of a conservative vector field:

> A vector field **F** defined in a region R is conservative in R if, and only if, there exists a scalar function P of position such that the component of **F** in any direction at each point equals the partial derivative of P in that direction.

We need some condition on **F** that will tell us whether or not P does exist. This condition is known from elementary theory of differential equations. Given **F**, $\mathbf{F} \cdot d\mathbf{r} \equiv F_x\, dx + F_y\, dy + F_z\, dz$ will be the total differential of a function $P(x, y, z)$, if, and only if, the following relations hold for all points x, y, z in R:

$$\frac{\partial F_x}{\partial y} = \frac{\partial F_y}{\partial x}, \qquad \frac{\partial F_x}{\partial z} = \frac{\partial F_z}{\partial x}, \qquad \frac{\partial F_y}{\partial z} = \frac{\partial F_z}{\partial y}. \qquad \textbf{2.7-5}$$

Thus a field is conservative in R if, and only if, its cartesian components satisfy Eqs. 2.7-5.

The general relation between the vector field **F** and the scalar function P (often called the scalar potential for the field) is known as the gradient relation; **F** is said to be the *gradient* of P. The operation of finding the gradient of a scalar field is denoted by the symbols *grad* or ∇ (read *nabla* or *del*):

$$\mathbf{F} = \operatorname{grad} P \equiv \nabla P. \qquad \textbf{2.7-6}$$

The name gradient for the operation comes from the analogy of measuring the slope or gradient of a hill. Most of us are familar with the representation of a hill on a flat map by drawing contour lines or lines of constant height $z(x, y) = C$ (Fig. 2.7-2). The slope of the hill can be estimated by looking at the distance Δn between neighboring contours along (approximately) the common normal to the two; the slope, going up hill, is then $\Delta z/\Delta n$. In the limit, we can show that the vector giving the magnitude and direction of the slope is the vector of magnitude dz/dn normal to the contour lines, viz., the vector grad z. In the same way, if the vector field $\mathbf{F} = \operatorname{grad} P$, and we are treating the two-dimensional case $[P = P(x, y)]$, then we can represent it by drawing the curves $P = \mathrm{const}$ and constructing the vectors **F** perpendicular to these curves and having magnitude dP/dn.

The vector operation 2.7-6 has the representation 2.7-4 in Cartesian components. For the sake of completeness, we give without proof the representation in cylindrical polars (r, ϕ, z) and spherical polars (r, θ, ϕ):

$$F_r = \frac{\partial P}{\partial r}, \qquad F_\phi = \frac{1}{r}\frac{\partial P}{\partial \phi}, \qquad F_z = \frac{\partial P}{\partial z},$$

$$F_r = \frac{\partial P}{\partial r}, \qquad F_\theta = \frac{1}{r}\frac{\partial P}{\partial \theta}, \qquad F_\phi = \frac{1}{r \sin \theta}\frac{\partial P}{\partial \phi}.$$

If we have a force field parallel to the xy-plane, then $F_z \equiv 0$. The proper relations in plane cartesian or polar coordinates can then be obtained from the general relations.

The ∇ form of the gradient operator is desirable for a symbolic vector calculus useful in fluid mechanics and other fields of study. The operation ∇P of Eq. 2.7-6 can be put in cartesian form by assigning the "cartesian" representation

$$\nabla \equiv \mathbf{i}\frac{\partial}{\partial x} + \mathbf{j}\frac{\partial}{\partial y} + \mathbf{k}\frac{\partial}{\partial z};$$

the interpretation of ∇P as the gradient vector

$$\mathbf{i}\frac{\partial P}{\partial x} + \mathbf{j}\frac{\partial P}{\partial y} + \mathbf{k}\frac{\partial P}{\partial z}$$

is then an almost obvious use of the symbolic representation for ∇. A further extension is made by introducing a symbolic vector product using ∇ and a vector: $\nabla \times \mathbf{F}$, read as *curl* of $\mathbf{F}$ and also denoted curl $\mathbf{F}$. Just as the ordinary vector product has a cartesian representation given by a symbolic determinant, so does the curl operation:

$$\nabla \times \mathbf{F} \equiv \text{curl } \mathbf{F} = \begin{vmatrix} \mathbf{i} & \mathbf{j} & \mathbf{k} \\ \dfrac{\partial}{\partial x} & \dfrac{\partial}{\partial y} & \dfrac{\partial}{\partial z} \\ F_x & F_y & F_z \end{vmatrix}$$

$$= \left(\frac{\partial F_z}{\partial y} - \frac{\partial F_y}{\partial z}\right)\mathbf{i} + \left(\frac{\partial F_x}{\partial z} - \frac{\partial F_z}{\partial x}\right)\mathbf{j} + \left(\frac{\partial F_y}{\partial x} - \frac{\partial F_x}{\partial y}\right)\mathbf{k}.$$

The conditions that a force field $\mathbf{F}$ be the gradient of a scalar field, as given by Eq. 2.7-5, are equivalent to the statement that $\mathbf{F}$ be a curl-free vector field: curl $\mathbf{F} = 0$.

A conservative field of force does zero work on a particle along any closed path, starting from and returning to a given point. Suppose that we compute the work done going from $\mathbf{r}_1$ to $\mathbf{r}_2$ along path C_1 (Fig. 2.7-1); this is equal to the change in the value of the function P between the two points. Since we are only interested in the change in

P, we can always add a constant to it or, equivalently, choose its value at some point. Suppose $\mathbf{r}_1$ is this *datum point*, and we choose $P = 0$ at $\mathbf{r} = \mathbf{r}_1$. Then the value of P at any point is the work that is done by the field on a particle moving from $\mathbf{r}_1$ to that point; $-P$ is the work that must be done by the field in moving a particle from the point back to $\mathbf{r}_1$. This measure of the work that must be done by a conservative field on a particle to move it from $\mathbf{r}$ to a standard position $\mathbf{r}_1$ is called the *potential energy*, $V(\mathbf{r})$, of the force field; notice that it, like P, is only defined to within an arbitrary constant. We have

$$\mathbf{F} = -\operatorname{grad} V; \qquad\qquad \textbf{2.7-7}$$

in cartesian form,

$$F_x = -\frac{\partial V}{\partial x}, \qquad F_y = -\frac{\partial V}{\partial y}, \qquad F_z = -\frac{\partial V}{\partial z}. \qquad \textbf{2.7-8}$$

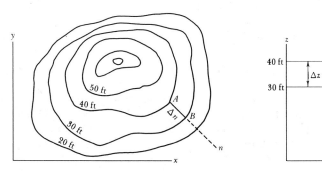

Fig. 2.7-2

There is a subtle shift of emphasis in the way forces are considered here that is worth discussing. We began by considering force as the mechanical interaction between material systems. By introducing the concept of the force field, we have suppressed the idea of the "cause" or "source" of the field and placed the force distribution itself in the spotlight. Once the field is prescribed, the particle moving in the field is thought of as being subjected to a force at each position without consideration of the other body or bodies producing the force. Then the special conservative force field is considered and the mechanical interaction is completely replaced by assigning a potential energy V such that the change in potential energy is the negative of the work done by the conservative field. Although we commonly speak of the potential energy of a particle or of a mechanical system in general, it must not be forgotten that this is not an inherent property of the system. Rather, it represents the effects of other bodies that give rise to the force field derivable from the potential energy function by Eq. 2.7-7.

Now let us consider some common conservative force fields and their associated potential energy functions.

(a) Constant force field

If the force $\mathbf{F} \equiv \mathbf{F}_0 = F_x\mathbf{i} + F_y\mathbf{j} + F_z\mathbf{k}$ is a constant at every point, then the components are constants, and the conditions 2.7-5 for a conservative field are satisfied. The associated potential energy function is

$$V = -\mathbf{F}_0 \cdot \mathbf{r} = -(xF_x + yF_y + zF_z). \qquad \textbf{2.7-9}$$

The reader may check that $\mathbf{F}_0 = -\mathrm{grad}\,V$. A more sophisticated proof may be based on the fact that the derivative of the position vector in any direction is the unit vector in that direction. This result is essentially the same as the result that the derivative of the position vector with respect to arclength along a curve is the unit tangent vector to the curve. That is, choose any direction with unit vector $\mathbf{e}$ and let s be the distance coordinate measured in that direction; then $\partial\mathbf{r}/\partial s = \mathbf{e}$. Using this result, we have that the directional derivative of V in any direction is

$$\frac{\partial V}{\partial s} = -\frac{\partial}{\partial s}(\mathbf{F}_0 \cdot \mathbf{r}) = -\mathbf{F}_0 \cdot \mathbf{e},$$

the negative of the component of $\mathbf{F}_0$ in the direction $\mathbf{e}$. Since $\mathbf{e}$ can be any direction, $\mathbf{F}_0$ is the negative of the gradient of V.

(b) Central force fields dependent on r only

A central force field, $\mathbf{F}$, is one such that the line of action of $\mathbf{F}$ is always the same as that of the position vector $\mathbf{r}$ of the point with respect to a fixed point O, the center of force. That is, if $\mathbf{r} = r\mathbf{e}_r$, then $\mathbf{F} = F_r\mathbf{e}_r$. If the scalar function F_r is a function of r only, then the central force field $\mathbf{F} = F_r(r)\mathbf{e}_r$ is conservative. The potential energy function is

$$V = -\int_{r_0}^{r} F_r(\rho)\,d\rho, \qquad \textbf{2.7-10}$$

where r_0 is a convenient datum-level distance from the center of force. We may check that $\mathbf{F} = -\mathrm{grad}\,V$:

$$F_r = -\frac{\partial V}{\partial r} = +F_r(r), \qquad F_\theta = F_\phi = 0.$$

In particular, the inverse square laws of the newtonian gravitational force and the Coulomb electrostatic or magnetostatic force (Section 2.2) are of this type, if we regard one particle or charge or magnetic pole as fixed at the center of force. An inverse square law of the form

$$\mathbf{F} = \frac{\mu m}{r^2} \, \mathbf{e}_r,$$ **2.7-11**

where m is the mass of the particle on which the force is acting and μ measures the strength or intensity of the center of force, corresponds to a potential energy

$$V = \frac{\mu m}{r};$$ **2.7-12**

here the zero level of potential energy—the value of r_0 in 2.7-10—has been taken infinitely far from the center of force.

(c) *Gravitational force near the earth's surface*

The weight of a body near the surface of the earth is treated as constant in magnitude and direction in most mechanical problems. As long as the distances traveled above the surface do not vary greatly, such an approximation for the magnitude of the gravitational attraction of the earth is an excellent one. For distance traveled along the surface, the direction change is small if the distance is small, and the magnitude may be considered constant unless measurements are to be made that are so precise as to require consideration of changing attraction with latitude or anomalous gravitational effects. We wish to show why such an approximation is a good one, at least for an idealized earth.

It will be shown in Chapter IV that the gravitational attraction of a sphere of uniform mass density or of a sphere with density varying only with the distance from the center of the sphere is the same at points outside of the sphere as that due to a single particle of mass equal to the total mass of the sphere located at the center of the sphere. Regard the earth as a fixed sphere of this sort. Let w be the magnitude of the attraction of the sphere of radius R and mass M on a particle of mass m placed on the surface of the sphere. By Newton's law of gravitation (Section 2.2), this magnitude will be

$$w = \frac{GMm}{R^2}.$$ **2.7-13**

The gravitational acceleration at the surface of the earth has magnitude

$$g = \frac{w}{m} = \frac{GM}{R^2} = \frac{\mu}{R^2},$$ **2.7-14**

and the magnitude of the attractive force at any distance $r = R + h$ (where h is the altitude above the surface) will be

$$w' = \frac{GMm}{r^2} = \frac{GMR^2m}{R^2r^2} = \frac{mgR^2}{r^2} = \frac{wR^2}{(R+h)^2}.$$

If the altitude is small (h/R much less than one), we may write

$$w' = \frac{w}{(1+h/R)^2} \cong w\left[1 - 2\left(\frac{h}{R}\right) + 3\left(\frac{h}{R}\right)^2 - \cdots\right]. \qquad \textbf{2.7-15}$$

Thus near the surface the magnitude of the gravitational force is approximately constant. Similarly, the gravitational potential is

$$V = -\frac{GMm}{r} = -\frac{wR^2}{R+h} = -\frac{wR}{1+h/R} \cong -wR\left[1 - \frac{h}{R} + \left(\frac{h}{R}\right)^2 - \cdots\right]. \qquad \textbf{2.7-16}$$

The potential near the surface is approximately $V = -wR + wh$; since V may be changed by a constant, we may take the surface (or any constant altitude near the surface) as the datum level, and let

$$V = wh = mgh, \qquad \textbf{2.7-17}$$

with h the height above datum level. This potential energy leads to a force field

$$\mathbf{F} = -\text{grad } V = -mg\mathbf{e}_h, \qquad \textbf{2.7-18}$$

where $\mathbf{e}_h$ is the unit normal vector outward from the surface at each point.

(d) Elastic strain energy and the ideal linear spring

An elastic body is, roughly, a deformable body that changes shape under load but resumes its initial shape when the loads are removed. The ideal elastic spring is a simple example of such a body. We neglect the mass of the spring, so that the forces acting on the ideal spring always constitute an equilibrium system. The spring has a natural or undeformed state, characterized by its undeformed length l_0. When a load, P, is applied along the length of the spring, an opposite load or reaction of equal magnitude must then be applied at the other end—the length of the spring changes to a value l. The quantity $e = l - l_0$ is the deformation or extension of the spring; if $e > 0$, the spring is in tension; and if $e < 0$, the spring is in compression. If, when the load P is removed, the spring returns at once to its undeformed length, the spring is said to be *elastic*.

A graph of the load P against the deformation e for various springs will result in curves like the three shown in Fig. 2.7-3. Curves

$A'OA$ and $C'OC$ represent the phenomena known as hardening and softening respectively; that is, as the deformation increases, a larger or smaller load is required to produce a further unit deflection than was required initially. Curve $B'OB$ is a linear load-deformation curve; the slope of the line, $k = P/e$, is the *spring constant* or characteristic.* We shall deal only with these ideal linear elastic springs, which are massless and are completely specified by the spring constant k and the unstretched length l_0. The force transmitted by such a spring is always proportional to its deflection and is always directed along the line, or axis, of the spring.

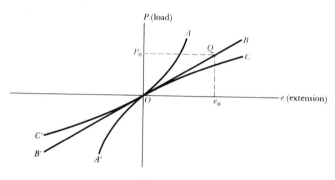

Fig. 2.7-3

Consider the work done on a spring as it is loaded. We shall show later on that the neglect of the mass implies that no work is done by the spring forces unless the spring changes length. Assuming this result for the present, we can consider the spring as fixed at one end and free at the other, with a load applied at the free end. Since one end is fixed, the reaction force at that end—equal to the negative of the applied force—does no work; its point of application does not move. The applied load does work. Suppose we extend the spring from zero extension to extension e_0 (Fig. 2.7-3). At each stage of the process, the applied load is in the direction of the extension with magnitude $P = ke$. The work done is

$$\Delta W = \int_0^{e_0} P\, de = \int_0^{e_0} ke\, de = \frac{1}{2} ke_0^2. \qquad \textbf{2.7-19}$$

---

* Some authors use the "modulus," $\lambda = kl_0$ in place of k, but the latter is much more common in technical literature.

When the load P is relieved, allowing the spring to resume its initial shape, negative work of this same amount will be done on the spring.

Suppose now a particle is attached to the free end of the spring, and we wish to compute the work done by the spring force on the body during some motion. Since the force exerted on the body by the spring is the negative of the force on the spring that deforms it, the work done by the spring force on the particle will be the negative of the work done on the spring. Moreover, it is clear that the work done on the spring during any deformation process that returns the spring to the same length will be zero; i.e., the spring force is conservative. We therefore may account for the work done by the spring force by assigning a potential energy function, the *elastic strain energy* due to elastic deformation or straining. Let us see what this potential energy function is.

Since the work done on the particle is the negative of that done on the spring, we see from 2.7-19 that the work done on the particle during any extension e is $\Delta W = -\frac{1}{2}ke^2$; since this is the work of a conservative field, the change in potential energy will be the negative of this: $\Delta V = \frac{1}{2}ke^2$. Taking the zero level of potential energy as any state in which the spring is undeformed, we may take the potential energy of strain as

$$V = \frac{1}{2}\,ke^2. \qquad\qquad \textbf{2.7-20}$$

Notice that the potential energy associated with strain is always a positive number, even when the spring is compressed.

Example 2.7-1

Show that the force field $\mathbf{F} = x^2\mathbf{i} + y^2\mathbf{j} + z^2\mathbf{k}$ of Example 2.6-4 *is conservative, and find a potential energy function V corresponding to* $\mathbf{F}$.

Solution: $\mathbf{F}$ is conservative since conditions 2.7-5 are satisfied. In fact, for any force function $\mathbf{F} = F_x\mathbf{i} + F_y\mathbf{j} + F_z\mathbf{k}$, where F_x is a function of x only, F_y of y only, and F_z of z only, all the partial derivatives in 2.7-5 vanish identically.

From $\mathbf{F} = -\operatorname{grad} V$, we then have

$$\frac{\partial V}{\partial x} = -x^2, \qquad \frac{\partial V}{\partial y} = -y^2, \qquad \frac{\partial V}{\partial z} = -z^2;$$

here $V = -\frac{1}{3}(x^3 + y^3 + z^3)$ is clearly a potential energy function.

Example 2.7-2

Show that $\mathbf{F} = yz\mathbf{i} + zx\mathbf{j} + xy\mathbf{k}$ *is conservative, and find the potential energy that has datum point* $(1, 1, -1)$.

Solution: We have $F_x = yz$, $F_y = zx$, $F_z = xy$; application of 2.7-5 leads to

$$\frac{\partial F_x}{\partial y} = \frac{\partial F_y}{\partial x} = z, \qquad \frac{\partial F_y}{\partial z} = \frac{\partial F_z}{\partial y} = x, \qquad \frac{\partial F_z}{\partial x} = \frac{\partial F_x}{\partial z} = y.$$

Therefore **F** is conservative. To find V, we integrate $\mathbf{F} = -\text{grad } V$.

From $\partial V/\partial x = -F_x = -yz$, integration with respect to x as an independent variable leads to

$$V = -xyz + f(y, z),$$

where f is a function to be determined. From $\partial V/\partial y = -F_y$ and from the computed form of V, we find that

$$\frac{\partial V}{\partial y} = -zx = -xz + \frac{\partial f}{\partial y};$$

therefore, f is not a function of y. Similarly,

$$\frac{\partial V}{\partial z} = -xy = -xy + \frac{\partial f}{\partial z},$$

so that f cannot depend on y or z but is at most a non-zero constant. For V to vanish at $(1, 1, -1)$, f must equal -1. Thus

$$V = -1 - xyz$$

is the desired potential energy function.

Example 2.7-3

Compute the work done by the force of the previous problem along a semicircular path from $(0, 0, 0)$ to $(2, -2, 1)$ lying in a plane containing the x-axis and thence to $(4, -7, 5)$ by a straight-line path.

Solution: Since **F** is conservative, the work done by **F** is independent of the path and equals the *negative* of the change of potential energy associated with **F**:

$$\begin{aligned}
\Delta W = -\Delta V &= -\{V(4, -7, 5) - V(0, 0, 0)\} \\
&= -\{[-1 - (4)(-7)(5)] - [-1 - (0)(0)(0)]\} \\
&= -140.
\end{aligned}$$

Example 2.7-4

A particle, P, slides on a circular wire of radius r (Fig. 2.7-4a). A light ideal linear spring is attached to a fixed point O of the wire at one end and to the particle at its other end. The spring has constant k and unstretched length r. Compute the work done by the spring on the particle (a) directly from the definition of work and (b) from the potential energy of strain, as the particle moves along the wire from A to B.

Solution: In Fig. 2.7-4b, the direction of the spring force **F** is shown at a general point along the wire where the spring is assumed to be in tension. The central angle ϕ shown may be taken as the basic coordinate governing position. The spring is unstretched when $\phi = 60°$. To compute the work done by **F**, we want the component of **F** tangent to the wire at each position ϕ.

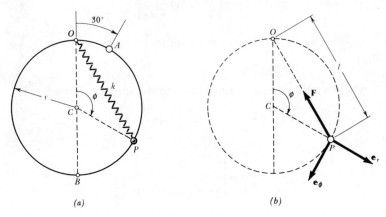

(a)   (b)

Fig. 2.7-4

The length of the spring in general position is

$$l = 2r \sin \frac{\phi}{2},$$

from the geometry of the isosceles triangle *PCO*. The extension e is then

$$e = l - l_0 = r \left[2 \sin \frac{\phi}{2} - 1 \right],$$

and the magnitude of the spring force is $ke = kr[2 \sin (\phi/2) - 1]$. If $e > 0$, $(\phi > 60°)$, the direction of the spring force is from *P* toward *O*; the force vector may be written in the polar coordinates shown as

$$\mathbf{F} = ke \left[-\cos \left(\frac{\pi}{2} - \frac{\phi}{2} \right) \mathbf{e}_r - \sin \left(\frac{\pi}{2} - \frac{\phi}{2} \right) \mathbf{e}_\phi \right]$$

$$= -ke \sin \frac{\phi}{2} \mathbf{e}_r - ke \cos \frac{\phi}{2} \mathbf{e}_\phi.$$

The differential $d\mathbf{r}$ of position may be written

$$d\mathbf{r} = d(r\mathbf{e}_r) = r \, d\mathbf{e}_r = r \, d\phi \mathbf{e}_\phi;$$

thus

$$\Delta W = \int_{\phi=\pi/6}^{\phi=\pi} \mathbf{F} \cdot d\mathbf{r} = -kr^2 \int_{\pi/6}^{\pi} \cos\frac{\phi}{2} \left[2\sin\frac{\phi}{2} - 1 \right] d\phi$$

$$= -kr^2 \int_{\pi/6}^{\pi} \left(\sin\phi - \cos\frac{\phi}{2} \right) d\phi,$$

$$\Delta W = -kr^2 \left[-\cos\phi \Big|_{\pi/6}^{\pi} - 2\sin\frac{\phi}{2} \Big|_{\pi/6}^{\pi} \right]$$

$$= -kr^2 \left[1 + \frac{\sqrt{3}}{2} - 2 + 2\sin 15° \right]$$

$$\cong -0.383kr^2.$$

The potential energy corresponding to the spring deformation is

$$V = \frac{1}{2} ke^2 = \frac{1}{2} kr^2 \left[2\sin\frac{\phi}{2} - 1 \right]^2$$

$$= \frac{1}{2} kr^2 \left[4\sin^2\frac{\phi}{2} - 4\sin\frac{\phi}{2} + 1 \right]$$

$$= \frac{1}{2} kr^2 \left[3 - 2\cos\phi - 4\sin\frac{\phi}{2} \right];$$

the change in potential energy from $\phi = \pi/6$ radians $\equiv 30°$ to $\phi = \pi$ radians $\equiv$ 180° is

$$\Delta V = \frac{1}{2} kr^2 [3 + 2 - 4] - \frac{1}{2} kr^2 [3 - \sqrt{3} - 4\sin 15°]$$

$$= \frac{1}{2} kr^2 [1 - (3 - \sqrt{3} - 4\sin 15°)]$$

$$= kr^2 \left[-1 + \frac{\sqrt{3}}{2} + 2\sin 15° \right]$$

$$\cong 0.383kr^2.$$

The work done is the negative of the change in potential energy:

$$\Delta W = -\Delta V \cong -0.383kr^2,$$

in agreement with the direct computation.

2.8 Mechanical Energy and Conservation of Energy

The introduction of the concept of the potential energy of a particle moving in a conservative force field leads to an alternate form of the work-energy principle 2.6-5. Consider all the forces acting on a particle. Some will be conservative, some will not. Split the total work done into two parts. The work done by the conservative forces is representable by the change in value of a scalar function $P(\mathbf{r})$.

The work done by the nonconservative forces is some quantity ΔW^*, where ΔW^* is a single symbol and not the change in value of a work function. The work-energy principle may be rewritten:

$$\Delta W^* = \Delta T - \Delta P = \Delta(T - P).$$

We introduce the potential energy $V = -P$ to remove the minus sign on the right-hand side. (This, of course, explains why we introduce the minus sign in the $\mathbf{F} = -\text{grad } V$ relation. It is a matter of choice that we wish to speak of $T + V$ rather than $T - P$.) Then

$$\Delta W^* = \Delta(T + V).$$

Finally, we introduce the *mechanical energy*, E, of the particle, defined as the sum of the kinetic and potential energies:

$$E = T + V. \qquad \text{2.8-1}$$

The work-energy principle is now formulated as:

The work done by the nonconservative forces on a particle equals the change in mechanical energy of the particle:

$$\Delta W^* = \Delta E. \qquad \text{2.8-2}$$

It should be noted that only changes in E are important. Since the work done by the conservative forces is equal to the change in value of P, the functions P, V, and E are defined only to within an arbitrary constant.

Finally, we may state our last mechanical energy principle, which follows as a corollary from 2.8-2:

Principle of Conservation of Mechanical Energy:

If only conservative forces do work on a particle, the mechanical energy remains constant throughout the motion of the particle:

$$E \equiv T + V = \text{constant}. \qquad \text{2.8-3}$$

The transformations made of the basic work-energy principle 2.6-5 thus far have introduced the concept of the work integral as a line integral along a curve in space and the concepts of conservative forces, potential energy, and mechanical energy. Even granting the usefulness of these concepts, there still remains the fact that these are mathematical consequences of Newton's laws.

Perhaps the greatest triumph of nineteenth-century physics was the demonstration that thermal and electromagnetic processes are equivalent to mechanical processes in many of their effects. In particular, the concepts of work and energy provide a connection between the various fields of physics and technology. The "mechanical equivalent of heat," for example, is a measure of energy equivalence. The mechanical work-energy principle 2.6-5 or 2.8-2, when extended to include the thermal energy change as well as the mechanical work and energy terms, becomes a new fundamental hypothesis, the First Law of Thermodynamics. Indeed, some authors on thermodynamics have been led to extend the concept of force to include thermomechanical forces, so that the change in thermal energy appears as the work done by such forces. Under such extended hypotheses, conservation of energy takes on a wider meaning, and the principle of conservation of energy becomes a foundation stone of classical physics.

Within the scope of the mechanics with which we are concerned, the extended concept of energy plays no part. That the dissipation of mechanical energy by friction can be accounted for by a change in thermal energy is immaterial for our purposes. Reference to conservation of energy will always mean conservation of mechanical energy. We are concerned only with those mechanical aspects of physical processes that may be treated by Newton's laws (and their extensions to systems) through the use of force functions of the type we have introduced in Section 2.2: those dependent on time, relative position, or relative velocity.

Example 2.8-1

A particle of mass m moves subject to the central force $\mathbf{F} = -(\mu m/r^2)\mathbf{e}_r$. *Write the energy conservation equation in appropriate coordinates.*

Solution: Since $\mathbf{F}$ is conservative and is the only force acting on the particle, mechanical energy is conserved. From the conservation of angular momentum (Example 2.4-4) we know that the path lies in a plane through the center of force. We choose cylindrical polar coordinates with origin at the center of force and axial direction z perpendicular to the plane of motion. Then

$$T = \frac{1}{2}mv^2 = \frac{1}{2}m(\dot{r}\mathbf{e}_r + r\dot{\phi}\mathbf{e}_\phi)\cdot(\dot{r}\mathbf{e}_r + r\dot{\phi}\mathbf{e}_\phi)$$

$$= \frac{1}{2}m(\dot{r}^2 + r^2\dot{\phi}^2);$$

$$V = -\frac{m\mu}{r};$$

and

$$E = T + V = \frac{1}{2}m(\dot{r}^2 + r^2\dot{\phi}^2) - \frac{m\mu}{r} = E_0,$$

where E_0 is a constant that may be evaluated from given initial position and velocity vectors.

Example **2.8-2**

Solve Example 2.6-3 of the bead sliding on a smooth vertical wire using the mechanical energy concept.

Solution: Referring to Fig. 2.6-2b, we have that the normal reaction does zero work and that the weight force, which is conservative, is the only force that does work. Taking the horizontal level through the center of the circle as the zero level of potential, the potential energy for the weight force can be written

$$V = wr \cos \theta = mgr \cos \theta.$$

Since E is conserved, $\Delta E = 0$; since the particle goes from rest to rest, $\Delta T = 0$; therefore

$$\Delta V = mgr(\cos \theta_B - \cos \theta_A) = 0.$$

Again, $\theta_B = 2\pi - \theta_A$ and B is on the same level as A.

An important consequence of the conservation-of-energy principle appears here. Once we have established that

$$E = T + V = T + mgh,$$

where h is the height above the fixed level, then the place the bead comes to rest again must be on the same horizontal level as A whatever the shape of the smooth wire. The *time* it takes to come to rest again will depend on the shape of the wire.

Exercises

2.2-1: The device pictured is similar to Atwood's machine described in Example 2.2-1. The masses of the pulleys, friction at the bearings, and extensibility of the cords may be neglected. The masses are released from rest. (a) Show that m_3 will remain at rest provided

$$\frac{4}{m_3} = \frac{1}{m_1} + \frac{1}{m_2}$$

and find the corresponding accelerations of m_2 and m_1.

Ans.: $a_2 = -a_1 = \dfrac{m_2 - m_1}{m_2 + m_1} g.$

(b) Show that if $m_3 = m_1 + m_2$, m_3 will move downward with an acceleration $(m_2 - m_1)^2 g / (m_1^2 + m_2^2 + 6m_1 m_2)$.

2.2-2: Show that the angular momentum of the particle in Example 2.2-5 is constant.

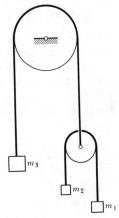

2.2-3: An object is placed on a plane inclined to the horizontal by an angle θ. The limiting coefficient of friction between the object and the plane is μ. We suppose that $\mu < \tan \theta$ so that the object cannot rest in static equilibrium. The particle is projected up the slope with speed v_0 and returns to its starting point with speed v_1. Express the ratio $(v_1/v_0)^2$ in terms of μ and θ.

Ans.: $(v_1/v_0)^2 = (1 - \mu \cot \theta)/(1 + \mu \cot \theta)$.

2.2-4: A block slides with constant speed down a plane inclined at an angle θ_0 to the horizontal. With what acceleration will it slide down the same plane if the angle of inclination is increased to θ_1?

Ans.: $\ddot{x} = g \sin \theta_1 (1 - \tan \theta_0 \cot \theta_1)$.

2.2-5: A golf ball leaves the tee with a velocity of 100 ft/sec directed at an angle of 15 degrees to the horizontal. What is the radius of curvature of its path at this instant? Does this radius increase or decrease as the ball approaches maximum altitude?

Ans.: 320 ft; decreases.

2.2-6: The velocity of a particle of mass $\frac{1}{2}$ is given by the expression

$$\mathbf{v} = 6 \cos 3t\mathbf{i} + 8t^3\mathbf{j} - 6 \sin 3t\mathbf{k}.$$

The displacement vector of the particle at time $t = 0$ was

$$\mathbf{r}(0) = 2\mathbf{i} + 2\mathbf{j} + 2\mathbf{k}.$$

(a) Find the position vector $\mathbf{r}(t)$.
(b) Find the resultant force $\mathbf{F}(t)$ on the particle.
(c) Find the angular momentum about the origin at $t = 0$.

Ans.: $\mathbf{r}/2 = (1 + \sin 3t)\mathbf{i} + (1 + t^4)\mathbf{j} + \cos 3t\mathbf{k}$;

$$\mathbf{F} = -9 \sin 3t\mathbf{i} + 12t^2\mathbf{j} - 9 \cos 3t\mathbf{k};$$

$$\mathbf{H}_o = 6(\mathbf{j} - \mathbf{k}).$$

2.2-7: A particle of unit mass moves on a spiral, the radius vector being given by the equation $\mathbf{r} = 2(1 + \phi)\mathbf{e}_r$. The angle $\phi = \frac{1}{2}t$. (a) Find the force acting on the particle when $t = 4$. Sketch this vector on a drawing of the path. (b) At another time the velocity and acceleration of the particle are $\mathbf{v} = \mathbf{e}_r + 2\mathbf{e}_\phi$ and $\mathbf{a} = -\mathbf{e}_r + \mathbf{e}_\phi$. Find the radius of curvature of the spiral at the point corresponding to this time.

Ans.: $\mathbf{F} = \mathbf{e}_\phi - 1.5\mathbf{e}_r$, $\rho = 3.73$.

2.2-8: A particle of unit mass moves along a circular arc of radius 2 with a speed $v = 3 + 2s/\pi$, where s denotes arc length. Find the force acting on the particle when it has traveled over one-quarter of the circle.

Ans.: $\mathbf{F} = -\dfrac{10}{\pi}\mathbf{i} - 12.5\mathbf{j}$.

2.2-9: A small object of mass m_1 is placed on a wedge of mass m_2 and inclination angle θ. If all surfaces are smooth what is the reaction of the fixed base on the wedge when the mass m_1 is released?

Ans.: $(m_1 + m_2)g \left[1 - \dfrac{1}{1 + \dfrac{m_2}{m_1} \operatorname{cosec}^2 \theta} \right].$

2.3-1: If the machine described in Exercise 1.8-13 weighs 16,500 lb and the bolts that hold it to its base can transmit a load of 1500 lb each, how many bolts will be required to hold this machine to its foundation during the first 5.5 sec of the earthquake?

Ans.: 10.

2.3-2: What is the shortest time in which a 10,000-lb weight can safely be lifted from rest to a height of 100 ft by a cable with a rated load-carrying capacity of 15,000 lb?

Ans.: 3.5 sec.

2.3-3: Suppose that in the preceding exercise the "weight" is an elevator that must be brought to rest at a height of 100 ft and that in the braking operation that brings it to rest the cable is not to become slack. What is now the minimum time for the ascent?

Ans.: 4.0 sec.

2.3-4: The unit of power in the mks system is the watt, which is one newton-meter per second. In the English gravitational system, it is the horsepower. One horsepower corresponds to 550 ft-lb/sec. How many watts correspond to 1 horsepower?

Ans.: 746.

2.3-5: How many ft-lb of work can be purchased for ten dollars if electric power costs three cents per kilowatt hour?

Ans.: $884(10)^6$ ft-lb.

2.3-6: Express the acceleration of gravity at the surface of the earth in kilometers per min^2.

Ans.: 35.3 km/min^2.

2.3-7: In the State of Nirvana they use the nert, stad, and tan as units of mass, length, and time. The acceleration of gravity is quoted as 10 stads per tan^2, the density of water as 4 nerts per cubic stad, and the day is divided into fifty thousand tans. How many grams correspond to one nert?

Ans.: 1 nert $= 6.38(10)^6$ gm.

2.3-8: Which of the terms in the equation $\ddot{x} + m\dot{x}^2 + \displaystyle\int_{x_0}^{x_1} F\,dx = mgx$ is dimensionally inconsistent with the other three? Here x denotes a length, m a mass, F a force, g an acceleration.

Ans.: $\ddot{x}$.

2.3-9: The stiffness of a shaft is given in a reference book by the formula $k = (\pi/32)GD^4/l$, where D is the diameter and l the length of the shaft and the units of k are twisting moment per unit angle. G has the units of a force per unit area. Is the equation dimensionally consistent? The same book says that for a steel shaft $G = 12(10)^6$ lb/in^2 and $k = 1.18(10)^6 D^4/l$. Can D and l now be expressed in meters or must some special unit be used for them; and, if so, in what units must they be expressed?
Ans.: Inches.

2.3-10: What are the dimensions of G in the expression (Eq. 2.2-3) for the gravitational force of attraction?
Ans.: $L^3 M^{-1} T^{-2}$.

2.3-11: A particle is placed at a distance h from an infinite thin sheet of material whose mass per unit area, σ, is uniform. Show by dimensional analysis that the gravitational attraction exerted on the particle by the sheet is independent of h. What is the corresponding result in electrostatics?

2.3-12: If all the dimensions of the solar system, including the radii of the planets, were half as large as they are, by what factor would the duration of the year be increased (or decreased)?
Ans.: The year would be unchanged.

2.3-13: A particle is placed at a distance h from a uniform thin wire. Predict, by dimensional analysis, how the gravitational attraction exerted by the wire on the particle will depend upon h. What is the corresponding result in electrostatics?
Ans.: The force will vary as h^{-1}.

2.3-14: Suppose air resistance at high speed to depend upon the size, l, and speed, v, of an airplane and upon the density, ρ, viscosity, μ, and sound velocity, c, of the air. Show that the resisting force $F_D = C_D \frac{1}{2} \rho v^2$ where C_D can be regarded as a function of the Mach number, v/c, and the Reynolds number $\rho v l/\mu$.

2.4-1: A particle of mass 0.5 slugs has velocity $-3\mathbf{i} + 7\mathbf{j}$ ft/sec at $t = 1$ sec. It is subjected to a force $\mathbf{F} = t^3\mathbf{i} - \sin \pi t\mathbf{j}$ lb. Find the impulse of the force over the interval $1 \leq t \leq 3$, and the velocity at $t = 3$ sec.
Ans.: $\mathbf{v}|_{t=3} = 37\mathbf{i} + 7\mathbf{j}$ ft/sec.

2.4-2: A particle of mass 3 kg has velocity $2\mathbf{i} - 3\mathbf{j}$ m/sec and position $\mathbf{i} + \mathbf{j} + \mathbf{k}$ m at time $t = 1$ sec. It has velocity $-\mathbf{k}$ m/sec and position $3\mathbf{i} - 2\mathbf{j}$ m at $t = 3$ sec.

(a) Find the resultant linear impulse over the time interval.
(b) Find the resultant angular impulse about the origin over the time interval.
(c) What time-average resultant force must act on the particle to produce the necessary change in linear momentum?

(d) If the resultant force on the particle is in fact the constant force computed in (c), will the particle have the final position given?

Ans.:
    (b) $-3\mathbf{i}+3\mathbf{j}+15\mathbf{k}$ newton-meter-seconds.
    (c) 5.6 newtons in magnitude.
    (d) Yes.

2.4-3: If the particle of the last exercise is subject to all the same conditions, except that the final position is $3\mathbf{i}+2\mathbf{j}$ m, answer the questions raised in the last problem.

2.6-1: How much work is done on the particle of Exercise 2.4-1 during the motion described there?
Ans.: $\Delta W = 340$ ft-lb.

2.6-2: A particle of mass m is constrained to move along the x-axis. The resultant force on the particle is $\mathbf{F} = -kx\mathbf{i}$. When $x=0$, $v=v_0>0$. Find the value of x at which the particle first comes to rest.
Ans.: $v_0\,(m/k)^{1/2}$.

2.6-3: A block weighing 64.4 lb is pulled along a rough horizontal table by a 25-lb force. If it starts from rest, how fast is it going when it has traveled 1.5 ft? The coefficient of friction, μ, is 0.2.
Ans.: 4.26 ft/sec.

2.6-4: If the block of the previous problem is traveling at 4 ft/sec in a direction opposite to that of the 25-lb force when the force is applied, how fast is it going when it has traveled 1.5 ft? Again $\mu=0.2$.
Ans.: 3.61 ft/sec.

2.6-5: Compute the work done by the following forces around the closed path consisting of straight line segments $(0, 0, 0)$ to $(1, 0, 0)$ to $(1, 1, 0)$ to $(0, 0, 0)$:

    (a) $\mathbf{F} = 3x^2\mathbf{i}+5y^2\mathbf{j}+7z\mathbf{k}$ newtons, x, y, z in meters.
    (b) $\mathbf{F} = yz\mathbf{i}+xz\mathbf{j}$ lb, x, y, z ft.
    (c) $\mathbf{F} = 3r\mathbf{e}_r+3z\mathbf{k}$ lb, r, z in.
    (d) $\mathbf{F} = A(y^2-z^2)\mathbf{i}+B(z^2-x^2)\mathbf{j}+C(x^2-y^2)\mathbf{k}$ lb,
        x, y, z ft, A, B, C constants.
    (e) $\mathbf{F} = -5\mathbf{r}$ lb, $\mathbf{r}$ ft.
    (f) $\mathbf{F} = Ax^3y\mathbf{i}+Bx^4\mathbf{j}$ dynes, x, y cm, A, B constants.

Ans.: (a), (b), (c), (e): 0; (d): $-(A+2B)/3$ ft-lb; (f): $(4B-A)/5$ dyne-cm.

2.6-6: Compute the work done by the forces (a)–(f) of the previous exercise around the closed path consisting of straight line segments $(0, 0, 0)$ to $(1, 0, 0)$ to $(1, 1, 0)$ to $(1, 1, 1)$ to $(0, 0, 0)$.
Ans.: The same as 2.6-5 except: (b) $-\frac{2}{3}$ ft-lb; (d) $-B$.

2.7-1: Which of the following force functions are conservative fields? Are there any points of space that must be excluded from the regions in which the fields are conservative? What is the potential energy associated with each of the conservative fields? Where constants A, B, C appear, how must these be chosen to make the fields conservative?

(a) $\mathbf{F} = 9\mathbf{i} - 10\mathbf{j} + 6\mathbf{k}$ lb at every point.

(b) $\mathbf{F} = 3x^2\mathbf{i} + 5y^2\mathbf{j} + 7z\mathbf{k}$ newtons.

(c) $\mathbf{F} = -5\dot{r}$.

(d) $\mathbf{F} = yz\mathbf{i} + xz\mathbf{j}$ lb.

(e) $\mathbf{F} = (3x^2 + \dot{x}^2)\mathbf{i} + 5y^2\mathbf{j} + 7z\mathbf{k}$ newtons.

(f) $\mathbf{F} = 3r\mathbf{e}_r + 3z\mathbf{k}$ lb, r, z in.

(g) $\mathbf{F} = (3/r)\mathbf{e}_r$ lb (spherical or cylindrical polars).

(h) $\mathbf{F} = A(y^2 - z^2)\mathbf{i} + B(z^2 - x^2)\mathbf{j} + C(x^2 - y^2)\mathbf{k}$ lb.

(i) $\mathbf{F} = 3 \sin 2t\mathbf{i} + 5 \cos 7t\mathbf{j} + 9t^2\mathbf{k}$.

(j) $\mathbf{F} = -5\mathbf{r}$.

(k) $\mathbf{F} = Ax^3y\mathbf{i} + Bx^4\mathbf{j}$.

Ans.: All nonconservative fields except the following:

(a) $V = -9x + 10y - 6z$ ft-lb.

(b) $V = -x^3 - \frac{5}{3}y^3 - \frac{7}{2}z^2$ newton-meters.

(f) $V = -\frac{3}{2}r^2 - 4z^2$ lb-in.

(g) $V = -3 \log r$; exclude $r = 0$.

(j) $V = \frac{5}{2}r^2$, $r = |\mathbf{r}|$.

(k) $V = -Bx^4y$ when field is conservative, which occurs if, and only if, $A = 4B$.

2.7-2: Compute the force field corresponding to the following potential energy functions. Are there any points at which the field is undefined?

(a) $V = -r^2 \cos 2\phi$ in-lb (cylindrical polars).

(b) $V = \frac{1}{2}k(r - r_0)^2$ ft-lb (spherical polars).

(c) $V = -\mu \log (x^2 + y^2 + z^2)$ newton-meters.

(d) $V = \frac{1}{2}k(\arctan y/x)^2$ ft-lb.

(e) $V = Axy/z + Byz/x + Czx/y$ in-lb.

Ans.:

(a) $\mathbf{F} = 2r \cos 2\phi\mathbf{e}_r - 2r \sin 2\phi\mathbf{e}_\phi$ lb.

(b) $\mathbf{F} = -k(r - r_0)\mathbf{e}_r$ lb.

(c) $\mathbf{F} = 2\mu(x\mathbf{i} + y\mathbf{j} + z\mathbf{k})/(x^2 + y^2 + z^2)$ newtons.

(d) $\mathbf{F} = (k \arctan y/x)(y\mathbf{i} - x\mathbf{j})/(x^2 + y^2)$ lb.

(e) $\mathbf{F} = [-Ay/z + Byz/x^2 - Cz/y]\mathbf{i}$
$+ [-Ax/z - Bz/x + Czx/y^2]\mathbf{j}$
$+ [+Axy/z^2 - By/x - Cx/y]\mathbf{k}$ lb.

2.7-3: A particle moves on a straight line from $(1, 1, 0)$ to $(-2, 3, 1)$ referred to an (x, y, z) coordinate system. Compute the work done on the particle by the force fields associated with the potentials of parts (a), (c), and (d) of the last exercise.

Ans.: (a) 5 in-lb; (c) $\mu \log (1/7)$ newton-meters; (d) $2.13k$ ft-lb.

2.7-4: Prove that grad $(\mathbf{r} \cdot \mathbf{r}) = 2\mathbf{r}$, where $\mathbf{r}$ has its usual meaning of position vector.

2.7-5: Prove that grad $(\mathbf{A} \cdot \mathbf{r}) = \mathbf{A}$, if $\mathbf{A}$ is a constant vector.

2.8-1: A particle of mass 3 slugs moves in a plane; the only force acting on the particle is due to a light ideal linear spring of constant $k = 15$ lb/in and undeformed length 0.25 ft. The other end of the spring is fixed at the origin of coordinates. The particle is observed to be at position $\mathbf{r}_1 = 3\mathbf{i} + 4\mathbf{j}$ in at one instant and at $\mathbf{r}_2 = \mathbf{i} - \mathbf{j}$ in at another.

    (a) What work is done on the particle during this motion?

    (b) What work is done on the spring?

    (c) What is the change in mechanical energy of the particle?

Ans.: (a) 11.0 in-lb; (c) 0.

2.8-2: Is the force field of Exercise 2.6-2 conservative? Solve that exercise using the concept of the mechanical energy of the particle.

2.8-3: A particle of mass 3 slugs has velocity $2\mathbf{i} + 4\mathbf{j} - 2\mathbf{k}$ ft/sec at position $\mathbf{i} + \mathbf{k}$ ft. What will be its speed at position $-\mathbf{j} - \mathbf{k}$ ft if it moves in the force field of 2.7-1 (a)? Of 2.7-1 (b)? Of 2.7-1 (j)? (Take the forms of the functions as given, but consider all force units as lb, all distance units as ft.)

Ans.:

    (a) 4.1 ft/sec.

    (b) 4.7 ft/sec.

    (j) 4.9 ft/sec.

CHAPTER **III**

Applications in

Particle Motion

3.1 Introduction

In this chapter, we consider some of the applications of the principles of particle motion. Naturally, the physical systems that can be represented by this simple model are limited. Yet the examples are not without technical interest and serve to present, in a simplified form, many of the concepts that reappear in the detailed study of specialized branches of technology.

Force functions of practical importance are discussed in order of complexity: uniform, linear, central, and dissipative. In each case, equations of motion are written for the particle—either in vectorial form or in terms of a specific set of coordinates—as seems most effective. The methods of solution, with the aid of the energy and angular momentum principles where appropriate, are then described. On a first reading, attention should be concentrated on the formulation of the equations of motion and on the interpretation of the results of the analysis. The intermediate mathematical steps in the analysis can often be managed in a variety of ways, but there is no substitute for correct formulation and correct interpretation.

3.2 The Uniform Force Field

The simplest dynamical questions of any technical importance are those concerned with the motion of a free particle in a uniform force field. Gravity provides an example of such a field as long as motion is restricted to a small region near the earth's surface, and an elementary theory of projectiles can be developed on the assumption that air resistance is negligible. If only the constant force **F** acts on the particle, the vector equation of motion is

$$m\ddot{\mathbf{r}} = \mathbf{F}. \tag{3.2-1}$$

This equation is easily integrated because **F** is a constant:

$$\mathbf{v} = \frac{\mathbf{F}}{m}t + \mathbf{v}_0 \tag{3.2-2}$$

$$\mathbf{r} = \frac{\mathbf{F}}{2m}t^2 + \mathbf{v}_0 t + \mathbf{r}_0. \tag{3.2-3}$$

Here $\mathbf{v}_0$ and $\mathbf{r}_0$ denote the velocity and displacement, respectively, of the particle at $t = 0$. If the origin of the position vector is taken at the initial position of the particle, $\mathbf{r}_0 = 0$ and

$$\mathbf{r} = \frac{\mathbf{F}}{2m}t^2 + \mathbf{v}_0 t. \tag{3.2-4}$$

The motion is seen to take place in the plane of the constant vectors **F** and $\mathbf{v}_0$.

It is customary to take rectangular axes with a y-axis directed opposite to **F** and an x-axis in the plane of **F** and $\mathbf{v}_0$. Then

$$\mathbf{F} = -F\mathbf{j} \quad \text{and} \quad \mathbf{v}_0 = \dot{x}_0\mathbf{i} + \dot{y}_0\mathbf{j}. \tag{3.2-5}$$

With this choice of axes, Eqs. 3.2-2, 4 become

$$\mathbf{v} = \dot{x}_0\mathbf{i} + \left(\dot{y}_0 - \frac{Ft}{m}\right)\mathbf{j}, \tag{3.2-6}$$

$$\mathbf{r} = \dot{x}_0 t\mathbf{i} + \left(\dot{y}_0 t - \frac{Ft^2}{2m}\right)\mathbf{j}. \tag{3.2-7}$$

The path of the particle, obtained by eliminating t from the equations

$$x = \dot{x}_0 t, \qquad y = \dot{y}_0 t - \frac{Ft^2}{2m},$$

is

$$\left(x - \frac{m\dot{x}_0\dot{y}_0}{F}\right)^2 = \frac{2m\dot{x}_0^2}{F}\left(\frac{m\dot{y}_0^2}{2F} - y\right). \tag{3.2-8}$$

This is the equation of a parabola with its axis in the direction of the force **F**. It is simplified if we take new axes with origin at the point whose coordinates are $m\dot{x}_0\dot{y}_0/F$, $m(\dot{y}_0^2 - \dot{x}_0^2)/2F$. Then, calling the new coordinates x', y' and letting $r' = (x'^2 + y'^2)^{\frac{1}{2}}$ we have

$$r' = \frac{m\dot{x}_0^2}{F} - y'. \qquad \text{3.2-9}$$

The two sets of axes and the path are shown in Fig. 3.2-1.

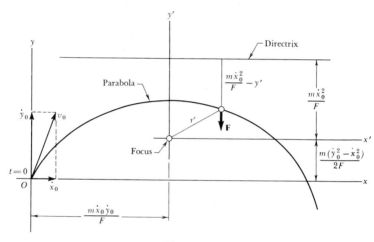

Fig. 3.2-1

Equation 3.2-9 tells us that the distance r' from the origin of the x', y'-coordinates to a point on the path is the same as the distance from that point to the line $y' = m\dot{x}_0^2/F$. The path is therefore the locus of points equidistant from a fixed point and a fixed line. Such a locus is known as a parabola and Eq. 3.2-9 is an alternative proof that the path is a parabola with axis parallel to the direction of the constant force. The origin of the x', y'-coordinates is known as the *focus* of the parabola and the line $y' = m\dot{x}_0^2/F$ or, what is the same, $y = mv_0^2/2F$ is known as the *directrix* of the parabola. The ordinate of the directrix is related to the total energy of the particle. The potential energy corresponding to the force $\mathbf{F} = -F\mathbf{j}$ is $V = Fy$. Since the only force acting on the system is conservative, the energy equation (2.8-3) takes the form

$$\frac{1}{2}mv^2 + Fy = \frac{1}{2}mv_0^2. \qquad \text{3.2-10}$$

We see that $v = 0$ at $y = mv_0^2/2F$. The directrix therefore passes through the point most remote from the origin that can be reached by projection from the origin in a direction opposite to that of the force.

When the particle is constrained so as to move along a curve that is not a parabola, forces other than the constant **F** act on it; indeed they must act on it. Under these circumstances, a representation of forces and accelerations in intrinsic coordinates is often of advantage. Where the forces of constraint do no work or have a potential, the use of the energy principle suggests itself.

Example **3.2-1**

Find the range of a projectile having an initial speed v_0 directed at an angle θ to a plane that is inclined at an angle β to the horizontal.

Solution: Choose xy-axes with origin at the point of projection, y positive upward. Then, neglecting air resistance, the equation $\mathbf{F} = m\mathbf{a}$ is written

$$-mg\mathbf{j} = m\mathbf{a} \qquad\qquad \textbf{3.2-11}$$

whence

$$\mathbf{a} = -g\mathbf{j}.$$

The negative sign appears in 3.2-11 because the force in question is directed toward the negative y-axis (see Fig. 3.2-2). The vector notation is

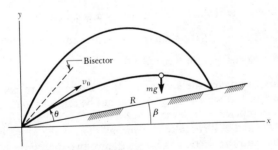

Fig. 3.2-2

convenient here for keeping account of the horizontal and vertical motions. Integrating,

$$\mathbf{v} = (-gt + c_1)\mathbf{j} + c_2\mathbf{i}.$$

The constants of integration are determined by the fact that, at $t = 0$,

$$\mathbf{v} = v_0 \cos(\beta + \theta)\mathbf{i} + v_0 \sin(\beta + \theta)\mathbf{j}.$$

This makes

$$\mathbf{v} = v_0 \cos(\beta + \theta)\mathbf{i} + [v_0 \sin(\beta + \theta) - gt]\mathbf{j}.$$

Integrating once again,

$$\mathbf{r} = v_0 t \cos (\beta + \theta)\mathbf{i} + \left[v_0 \sin (\beta + \theta) - \frac{1}{2} gt^2\right] \mathbf{j}.$$

We have made use of the condition $\mathbf{r}=0$ at $t=0$ to find the constants of integration. Next we find the path of the projectile by the same technique used in obtaining Eq. 3.2-8.

$$x = v_0 t \cos (\beta + \theta), \qquad y = v_0 t \sin (\beta + \theta) - \frac{1}{2} gt^2,$$

$$t = x[v_0 \cos (\beta + \theta)]^{-1},$$

$$y = x \tan (\beta + \theta) - \frac{1}{2} gx^2[v_0^2 \cos^2 (\beta + \theta)]^{-1}. \qquad \textbf{3.2-12}$$

The path is a parabola.

We wish to find the range. Since the equation of the incline is $y = x \tan \beta$, the projectile will strike when the value of x given by this formula and by Eq. 3.2-12 is the same; that is, when x satisfies the relationship

$$x \tan \beta = x \tan (\beta + \theta) - \frac{1}{2} gx^2[v_0^2 \cos^2 (\beta + \theta)]^{-1}. \qquad \textbf{3.2-13}$$

The solution $x=0$ represents the initial position. The other solution is

$$x = (2v_0^2/g) \cos^2 (\beta + \theta)[\tan (\beta + \theta) - \tan \beta].$$

The range along the incline, R, is given by $x \sec \beta$ so that

$$R = [2v_0^2/(g \cos^2 \beta)][\cos \beta \sin (\beta + \theta) - \sin \beta \cos (\beta + \theta)] \cos (\beta + \theta)$$

$$= [2v_0^2/(g \cos^2 \beta)] \sin \theta \cos (\beta + \theta). \qquad \textbf{3.2-14}$$

Formally this completes the solution. It is interesting to note that there are two values of θ at which the projectile can be released to achieve a given range. If we replace θ by $(\pi/2) - (\beta + \theta)$, the right-hand side of 3.2-14 remains unchanged. Physically this means that, if the angle between the inclined plane and the vertical is bisected, any two directions of projection making equal angles above and below the bisector will produce the same range. The two possible trajectories are sketched in Fig. 3.2-2. Since the range obviously increases as θ increases from zero and since it is symmetrical about the previously mentioned bisector, it follows that the maximum range is obtained, for a given v_0, by projection along the bisector.

In order to treat the case of a level range, we need only set $\beta=0$ in 3.2-14. Then

$$R = \frac{v_0^2}{g} \sin 2\theta.$$

It is easy to see that in this case R is a maximum when $\theta = 45°$.

Example 3.2-2

A proton (hydrogen atom stripped of its electron) moving in a horizontal path in a vacuum at a speed of $2(10)^6$ m/sec enters a uniform electric field that exerts a downward force of $5(10)^{-15}$ newtons on it. The mass of the atom is $1.66(10)^{-27}$ kg. The field extends over a region 0.25 m long. Through what angle is the particle deflected?

Solution: Choosing origin at the point of projection with x-axis horizontal and y-axis vertical upward we have

$$\ddot{\mathbf{r}} = \frac{-F_0}{m}\,\mathbf{j},$$

$$\dot{\mathbf{r}} = \frac{-F_0}{m}\,t\mathbf{j} + v_0\mathbf{i}. \qquad \text{3.2-15}$$

The direction of the velocity vector is the direction of the path. We have, from 3.2-15, $v_y = -(F_0/m)t$, $v_x = v_0$ and therefore

$$\tan\alpha = \frac{-v_y}{v_x} = \frac{F_0 t}{m v_0}. \qquad \text{3.2-16}$$

(We use $-v_y/v_x$ because it is convenient to find the angle included from the positive x-axis toward the negative y-axis, as shown in Fig. 3.2-3.) Since

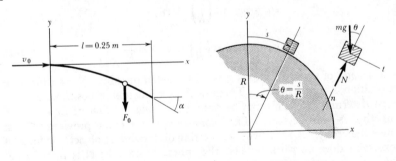

Fig. 3.2-3   **Fig. 3.2-4**

v_x is constant, the particle will reach the end of the region when $t = l/v_0$ so that

$$\alpha = \arctan\frac{F_0 l}{m v_0^2} = \arctan\frac{(5)(10)^{-15}(0.25)}{(1.66)(10)^{-27}(4)(10)^{12}}$$

$$= \arctan 0.1887 = 10°40'. \qquad \text{3.2-17}$$

We have neglected gravity in this analysis. If it had been included, Eq. 3.2-15 would have read

$$\ddot{\mathbf{r}} = -\left(\frac{F_0}{m} + g\right)\mathbf{j}. \qquad \text{3.2-18}$$

But for the data given, $F_0/m = 3.0(10)^{12}$ m/sec², whereas $g = 9.8$ m/sec², so that this neglect is quite reasonable. We can see from Eq. 3.2-16 that, if the particle had been an electron having a mass about one two-thousandth that of the hydrogen atom, its deflection—in addition to being in the opposite direction because of the charge sign—would have been much larger.

Example **3.2-3**

An object is projected horizontally from its position at the top of a smooth sphere. How far does it slide before losing contact with the sphere?

Solution: A free-body diagram of the object at a typical instant while it is still in contact with the sphere is shown in Fig. 3.2-4. This is no longer free motion since a variable force, N, is exerted on the object in addition to the force mg. Such a force is known as a *constraint*. In this case, the constraint is *one-sided*; that is, the sphere can push outward on the particle but not inward. Since the path during contact is known, intrinsic coordinates suggest themselves. They are shown in Fig. 3.2-4. Notice that the positive direction of the normal axis is *toward* the center of curvature. The positive direction of the tangential axis is in the direction of the velocity vector. Equations 2.2-12 take the form

$$F_t = mg \sin\left(\frac{s}{R}\right) = m\ddot{s},$$

$$F_n = mg \cos\left(\frac{s}{R}\right) - N = m\frac{\dot{s}^2}{R}. \qquad \textbf{3.2-19}$$

The second of these equations gives the wanted quantity, N, as a function of position, s, and speed, $\dot{s}$. To know N as a function of position alone we must determine $\dot{s}$. This can be done by solving the first of Eqs. 3.2-19, but this is unnecessary. The work-energy principle provides a first integral directly. Of the two forces acting on the sliding object, the force of constraint does no work because the sphere is smooth; N is therefore at right angles to the sphere, $\mathbf{N} \cdot \mathbf{v} = 0$ so that the power of N is zero and the work done by $\mathbf{N}$ vanishes. The constraint provided by any smooth guide is workless. The potential energy corresponding to the gravitational force field is mgy, where y is measured upward from the point of projection:

$$V = mgy = -mg\left(R - R\cos\frac{s}{R}\right). \qquad \textbf{3.2-20}$$

The work-energy principle asserts that the change in kinetic energy, as the object moves from its original to a typical position, added to the change in potential energy must be equal to the work done by the force $\mathbf{N}$. In symbols,

$$\left(\frac{1}{2}m\dot{s}^2 - \frac{1}{2}mv_0^2\right) + \left[-mgR\left(1 - \cos\frac{s}{R}\right)\right] = 0. \qquad \textbf{3.2-21}$$

Notice that *change* means final less initial value. Here v_0 denotes the velocity of projection from the top of the sphere. Equation 3.2-21 is easily solved for the speed:

$$\dot{s}^2 = v_0^2 + 2gR \left(1 - \cos \frac{s}{R}\right). \qquad \textbf{3.2-22}$$

This, substituted in the second of 3.2-19, yields

$$N = mg \left[3 \cos \theta - 2 - \frac{v_0^2}{Rg}\right] \qquad \textbf{3.2-23}$$

where s/R has been replaced by θ. Contact is lost when N vanishes; that is, when

$$\cos \theta = \frac{2}{3} + \frac{v_0^2}{3Rg}. \qquad \textbf{3.2-24}$$

If $v_0^2 > Rg$, the right-hand side of this expression is greater than 1; referring to Eq. 3.2-23, we see that this means that N is negative even when $\theta = 0$— implying that contact is lost immediately. But if $v_0^2 < Rg$, N will be positive (i.e., will be outward, as drawn in Fig. 3.2-4 and as assumed in setting up the equations of motion) for some range of values as θ increases from zero.

Finally, we note that, instead of using the work-energy principle, we could have integrated the first of Eqs. 3.2-19. There is a standard technique for doing this. Multiply both sides of the equation by $2\dot{s}$. Then

$$2\dot{s}\ddot{s} = 2g\dot{s} \sin \left(\frac{s}{R}\right),$$

$$\frac{d}{dt} (\dot{s}^2) = \frac{d}{dt} \left[-2gR \cos \left(\frac{s}{R}\right)\right],$$

$$\dot{s}^2 = -2gR \cos \left(\frac{s}{R}\right) + \text{constant}. \qquad \textbf{3.2-25}$$

The constant is evaluated by noting that $\dot{s} = v_0$ at $s = 0$, whereupon Eq. 3.2-25 becomes the same as Eq. 3.2-22. The attentive reader will appreciate that the steps in the solution of the differential equation follow the derivation of the mechanical work-energy principle.

Example **3.2-4**

A slider weighing 2 *lb moves on a smooth elliptical guide as shown in Fig.* 3.2-5. *The slider is connected to the center of the ellipse by a spring of unstretched length* 10 *in and modulus* 0.4 *lb/in. If started at A with a speed of* 5 *in/sec, what speed will the slider have when it reaches B?*

Solution: The forces acting on the slider are (1) a weight force, $\mathbf{F} = -mg\mathbf{j}$, the effect of which can be replaced by a potential energy $V = mgy$; (2) a spring force, ke, directed toward the origin O and replaceable by a potential energy $\frac{1}{2}ke^2$, e being the difference between the actual and the unstretched lengths of the spring; (3) a force, N, exerted by the guide. This force is at right angles to the smooth guide and therefore does no work. The fact that the effect of all the forces that do work can be replaced by potential energy expressions suggests writing the energy equation

$$E = \frac{1}{2} mv^2 + \frac{1}{2} ke^2 + mgy.$$

$$E_A = \frac{(2)(5)^2}{(2)(12)(32.2)} + \frac{(0.4)(-2)^2}{2} + (2)(8) = 16.9 \text{ in-lb};$$

$$E_B = \frac{2v^2}{(2)(12)(32.2)} + \frac{(0.4)(6)^2}{2} + 0 = 7.2 + \frac{v^2}{386}.$$

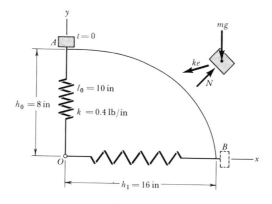

Fig. 3.2-5

Since all the forces that do work are conservative, $E_A = E_B$, and

$$7.2 + \frac{v^2}{386} = 16.9, \qquad v = 61 \quad \text{in/sec.}$$

Note that the shape of the guide between points A and B does not affect the result.

3.3 Simple Harmonic Motion

After the case of motion in a uniform force field, the simplest is that of motion in a field exerting a force proportional to the displacement. This is a case of great technical importance. All engineering structures deform when loaded; and, to a first approximation, they resist deformation with a proportional force. An elementary instance of an object subject to such forces is a mass, m, attached to a fixed point by means of a spring of constant k and unstretched length l_0.

This situation is pictured in Fig. 3.3-1. The position of the object is specified by a coordinate, x, measured from the unstretched position of the spring. Note that $x = 0$ corresponds to stable static equilibrium. We suppose the particle to be started at the coordinate $x = x_0$ with the speed $v = v_0$ and ask to know the position at any subsequent time. The free-body diagram of the particle is shown in Fig. 3.3-1. Notice that the particle is pictured as having a positive x

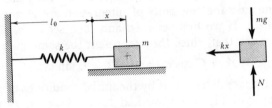

Fig. 3.3-1

position; then the force exerted on it by the spring acts to the left. The support of the object being supposed smooth, $N = mg$ and $F_x = ma_x$ is written

$$-kx = m\ddot{x} \qquad\qquad \textbf{3.3-1}$$

or

$$\ddot{x} + \omega_n^2 x = 0 \qquad\qquad \textbf{3.3-2}$$

where $\omega_n^2 = k/m$ in this example.

We may expect to encounter equations of the type 3.3-2 whenever we deal with a mechanical system in motion near a position of stable equilibrium and subject to restoring forces proportional to the displacement from that position. The quantity denoted by the symbol x in Eq. 3.3-2 may, in a different situation, be some other kind of coordinate; and the constant ω_n^2 need not always be the ratio of a spring constant to a mass. For example, in the case of the small vibrations of a pendulum, it is usually more convenient to define position by means of an angle, whereupon ω_n^2 turns out to be the ratio of the local acceleration of gravity to the pendulum length. In the following discussion, therefore, we interpret x simply as the coordinate defining the position and ω_n^2 as a constant. Then we enquire into the motion corresponding to any equation of the type 3.3-2.

This equation was examined in Example 1.8-4 for the special initial conditions $x = x_0$, $\dot{x} = 0$. The analysis, which was made from a purely kinematical point of view, showed that x was proportional to $\cos \omega_n t$. It is obvious from the form of Eq. 3.3-2 that $x(t)$ may be expressed as a sine or cosine function of $\omega_n t$ since such a function differentiated twice will recover the original function with a multiplier $(-\omega_n^2)$. For the general solution of Eq. 3.3-2, we write

$$x = A \cos \omega_n t + B \sin \omega_n t \qquad \qquad 3.3\text{-}3$$

or

$$x = C \cos (\omega_n t - \alpha). \qquad \qquad 3.3\text{-}4$$

The student should verify by direct substitution that these expressions do indeed satisfy Eq. 3.3-2 for all values of t. They are equivalent forms: in one case the constants of integration are A and B; in the other C and α. If we first set $t=0$ and then set $t=\pi/2\omega_n$ in these equations, we see that, since they represent the same motion,

$$A = C \cos \alpha \quad \text{and} \quad B = C \sin \alpha. \qquad \qquad 3.3\text{-}5$$

These constants are determined by the initial conditions of projection. In the example of Fig. 3.3-1 we had $x=x_0$, $\dot{x}=v_0$ at $t=0$. These imply

$$A = x_0, \qquad B = \frac{v_0}{\omega_n} \qquad \qquad 3.3\text{-}6$$

or, squaring and adding Eqs. 3.3-5,

$$C = [A^2+B^2]^{\frac{1}{2}} = [x_0^2+(v_0^2/\omega_n^2)]^{\frac{1}{2}}. \qquad \qquad 3.3\text{-}7$$

The angle α is determined by the pair of Eqs. 3.3-5:

$$\cos \alpha = \frac{A}{C} = \frac{x_0}{[x_0^2+(v_0^2/\omega_n^2)]^{\frac{1}{2}}}, \quad \sin \alpha = \frac{B}{C} = \frac{v_0}{\omega_n[x_0^2+(v_0^2/\omega_n^2)]^{\frac{1}{2}}}.$$
$$3.3\text{-}8$$

Motion of the type described by Eqs. 3.3-3, 4 is known as *simple harmonic motion*. This motion is periodic; the displacement at time t_0 is the same as the displacement at time $t_0+2\pi/\omega_n$, $t_0+4\pi/\omega_n$, $t_0+6\pi/\omega_n$, etc. Velocity and acceleration also are repeated with period

$$T_n = \frac{2\pi}{\omega_n} \text{ sec.} \qquad \qquad 3.3\text{-}9$$

T_n is called the *natural period of free vibration* because, left to itself, the particle moves with this period. Whereas periodicity is a feature of many types of motion, simple harmonic motion is remarkable in that the periodicity is independent of the initial conditions. In studying central force motion (Section 3.5), for example, we shall see that whether the motion is periodic (elliptic orbit) or nonperiodic (hyperbolic orbit) depends upon the initial energy content; in simple harmonic motion it depends only upon the properties of the system and is beyond our control. The reciprocal of the natural period is the *natural frequency*, the number of cycles executed each second;

$$f_n = \frac{1}{T_n} = \frac{\omega_n}{2\pi} \text{ cycles per second.}^\star \qquad \textbf{3.3-10}$$

The quantity ω_n itself is known as the *natural circular frequency*. Its units are radians per second. The quantity C in Eq. 3.3-4 is called

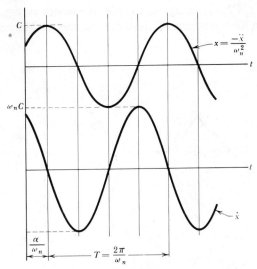

Fig. 3.3-2

the *amplitude* of the motion. It may be seen by reference to Eq. 3.3-7 that the amplitude does depend upon the circumstances with which the motion is started. Upon differentiating Eq. 3.3-3 or 3.3-4 we see that the velocity and acceleration are given by expressions of the same period, $2\pi/\omega_n$. Their amplitudes differ from that of the displacement by factors ω_n and ω_n^2 respectively:

$$\dot{x} = v = -C\omega_n \sin(\omega_n t - \alpha), \qquad \textbf{3.3-11}$$

and

$$\ddot{x} = a = -C\omega_n^2 \cos(\omega_n t - \alpha). \qquad \textbf{3.3-12}$$

These quantities are displayed graphically in Fig. 3.3-2.

An object that vibrates in simple harmonic motion is termed a *linear harmonic oscillator*.

The motion of a linear harmonic oscillator may be pictured in a number of ways. If a point, P, moves counterclockwise on the

---

$\star$ In the continental European literature, the unit of f_n, one cycle per second, is sometimes designated a Hertz (abbr. Hz).

circumference of a circle of radius C, the orthogonal projection of the radius vector OP on a horizontal diameter will be C multiplied by the cosine of the angle between OP and the horizontal. If the initial inclination of OP to the horizontal is $-\alpha$ and if OP rotates at the rate ω_n radians per second, the projection of OP on the horizontal axis will be $C \cos(\omega_n t - \alpha)$, which—according to Eq. 3.3-4—is the displacement x. The rotating vector OP is shown in Fig. 3.3-3. Its projection on the horizontal diameter is the displacement of the

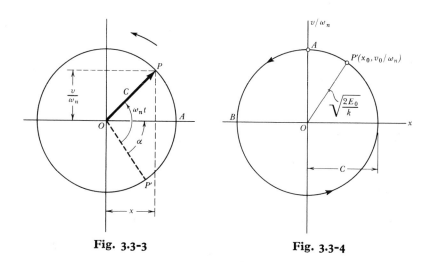

Fig. 3.3-3   **Fig. 3.3-4**

simple harmonic motion and its projection on the vertical diameter is the velocity divided by ω_n and reversed in sign. The angle POA is the *phase* of the motion; α is sometimes called the *initial phase*. This representation of the displacement in simple harmonic motion as the projection of the line segment OP on a horizontal diameter suggests by its similarity to the Argand diagram of complex number theory that we may think of the displacement as the real part of a complex number of modulus C and argument $\omega_n t - \alpha$.

$$x = C \cos(\omega_n t - \alpha) = Re\{Ce^{i(\omega_n t - \alpha)}\}, \qquad \textbf{3.3-13}$$

or simply*

$$x = Ce^{i(\omega_n t - \alpha)} \qquad \textbf{3.3-14}$$

---

* Electrical engineers write j instead of i for $\sqrt{-1}$ to avoid confusion with the symbol for current.

where it is understood that only the real part of the complex number is to be utilized in physical interpretations. Although this notation is of advantage in extensive computations where displacements arising from different sources are to be combined, we shall not have further need for it.

Another way of visualizing the motion of a linear harmonic oscillator is afforded by energy considerations. Referring to Fig. 3.3-1, we see that the only force acting on the particle that does work is the one exerted by the spring. This can be accounted for by a potential energy $V = \frac{1}{2}kx^2$. Then

$$T + V = \text{constant,} \qquad \textbf{3.3-15}$$

and

$$\frac{1}{2}mv^2 + \frac{1}{2}kx^2 = E_0 \qquad \textbf{3.3-16}$$

where E_0 is the constant initial energy of projection. In the example pictured in Fig. 3.3-1, E_0 is $\frac{1}{2}mv_0^2 + \frac{1}{2}kx_0^2$. Equation 3.3-16 may be rewritten

$$\left(\frac{v}{\omega_n}\right)^2 + x^2 = \frac{2E_0}{k}. \qquad \textbf{3.3-17}$$

If now a plot is made with x as abscissa and v/ω_n as ordinate, both drawn to the same scale, the graph will be a circle of radius $(2E_0/k)^{1/2}$. Such a plot is shown in Fig. 3.3-4. The motion starts at the point P' with coordinates x_0, v_0/ω_n and proceeds counterclockwise around the circle centered on the origin. After some time, the position and velocity of the particle are represented by point A. At this point the displacement is zero and the speed is a maximum. Later the motion is represented by point B where the speed is zero and the mass is (momentarily) at rest. Here the energy is entirely potential energy of strain. After a time $T_n = 2\pi/\omega_n$ the initial situation is restored, and the motion is again represented by point P'. A diagram such as that of Fig. 3.3-4 in which displacement is plotted as a function of velocity (rather than time) is known as a *phase-plane diagram*. By a natural generalization of the word "path," we speak of the path of the motion in the phase plane. For simple harmonic motion, position in the phase plane at any time is at once determined by a knowledge of the initial conditions and the period. We start at P' and move counterclockwise through an arc that is the same fraction of the circumference that t is of the natural period. Of course if the motion is not simple harmonic (e.g., if the restoring force is not proportional to the displacement), the path in the phase plane will not be a circle, and may not even be a closed figure. Under these circumstances there is no particular advantage to retaining a factor such as ω_n^{-1} in the ordinate.

Up to this point, the moving particle has been supposed to have a single degree of freedom, by which is meant that its position has been described by a single coordinate called $x(t)$. If the particle has two degrees of freedom, as the mass in Fig. 3.3-1 would if it were spring-restrained in the vertical as well as in the horizontal direction, its position is described by two coordinates—$x(t)$, $y(t)$. It is natural to generalize the idea of simple harmonic motion to the case in which

$$x = C_1 \cos(\omega_1 t - \alpha_1), \qquad y = C_2 \cos(\omega_2 t - \alpha_2). \qquad \textbf{3.3-18}$$

We notice first that the orbit or path of the particle will lie inside the rectangle bounded by $x = \pm C_1$ and $y = \pm C_2$. If ω_1/ω_2 is a rational number, the motion is periodic, repeating itself after an

$$\alpha_1 - \alpha_2 = 0 \qquad\qquad \alpha_1 - \alpha_2 = \frac{\pi}{2} \qquad\qquad \alpha_1 - \alpha_2 = \pi$$

Fig. 3.3-5

interval that is the smallest common multiple of $2\pi/\omega_1$ and $2\pi/\omega_2$. The paths that result from the elimination of t in Eqs. 3.3-18 are, in general, quite complex. They were first studied systematically by J. A. Lissajous and are known by his name. The simplest Lissajous figure is that corresponding to the case $\omega_1 = \omega_2$, the so-called two-dimensional *linear isotropic oscillator*. This case can be realized mechanically by the small oscillations of a spherical pendulum or by a particle restrained against motion in a plane by springs of equal stiffness in two orthogonal directions. When t is eliminated from Eqs. 3.3-18, we have for the case $\omega_1 = \omega_2$:

$$\frac{x^2}{C_1^2} - \frac{2xy}{C_1 C_2} \cos(\alpha_1 - \alpha_2) + \frac{y^2}{C_2^2} = \sin^2(\alpha_1 - \alpha_2). \qquad \textbf{3.3-19}$$

This is the equation of an ellipse, unless $\alpha_1 - \alpha_2 = 0$ or π, in which case it is the equation of a straight line. The paths are shown in Fig. 3.3-5 for various values of initial phase difference and $C_1 = C_2$.

If $\omega_1/\omega_2 = m/n$ where m and n are integers with no common factor, the curve will touch the edges of the bounding rectangle that are parallel to the x-axis m times and those parallel to the y-axis n times. For example, the paths corresponding to $m/n = 2$ are pictured in Fig. 3.3-6.   The paths for $\alpha_1 - \alpha_2 = 0$, π do not really contradict the rule; two points of tangency on one of the boundaries have coalesced. This property of Lissajous figures is most useful in experimental work.   The displacement at unknown frequency can, by means of a suitable transducer, be made to produce a proportional voltage. This is applied to one set of plates of a cathode ray tube while a signal of known but adjustable frequency is applied to the other set.   The known frequency is then adjusted until a simple Lissajous pattern, such as an ellipse, appears on the oscilloscope.

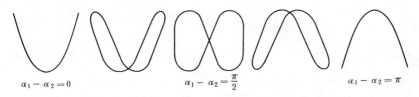

$\alpha_1 - \alpha_2 = 0$ $\qquad\qquad\qquad$ $\alpha_1 - \alpha_2 = \dfrac{\pi}{2}$ $\qquad\qquad\qquad$ $\alpha_1 - \alpha_2 = \pi$

Fig. 3.3-6

Example **3.3-1**

A hydrometer floats in a liquid.   Find the relationship between the submerged volume, cross-sectional area of the bore, and period of vertical oscillation.

Solution: Let V denote the submerged volume when the hydrometer floats undisturbed, A the area of the tube cross section, and x the distance from the "undisturbed" position of the tip to the actual position—as shown in Fig. 3.3-7.   The free-body diagram has been drawn for a positive

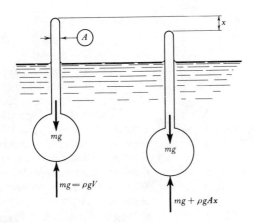

mg

$mg = \rho g V$

mg

$mg + \rho g A x$

Fig. 3.3-7

displacement, x, from the position of static equilibrium. The upward force exerted by the fluid is increased over its value in the static situation by an amount $\rho g A x$, the weight of the volume, Ax, of additional fluid displaced. We have

$$m\ddot{x} = mg - (mg + \rho g A x)$$

$$\ddot{x} + \left(\frac{\rho g A}{m}\right) x = 0. \qquad \textbf{3.3-20}$$

We recognize this as an equation of simple harmonic motion (Eq. 3.3-2). Its solution is $x = C \cos(\omega_n t - \alpha)$. The hydrometer will bob up and down with a natural circular frequency

$$\omega_n = \sqrt{\frac{\rho g A}{m}} \quad \text{or, from Eq. 3.3-9, a period} \qquad \textbf{3.3-21}$$

$$T_n = 2\pi \sqrt{\frac{m}{\rho g A}}. \qquad \textbf{3.3-22}$$

These expressions can be simplified if we recall that, at rest, the weight of the displaced volume of fluid must be the same as the weight of the hydrometer:

$$mg = \rho g V. \qquad \textbf{3.3-23}$$

With the aid of this relationship, the mass m may be eliminated from Eqs. 3.3-21 and 3.3-22 leaving the result in the form contemplated in the statement of the example:

$$\omega_n = \sqrt{\frac{gA}{V}}, \qquad T_n = 2\pi \sqrt{\frac{V}{gA}}. \qquad \textbf{3.3-24}$$

The expressions 3.3-21, 22 are in some respects preferable. They make it clear that the period depends upon properties of the fluid (ρ) as well as on those of the hydrometer (m, A).

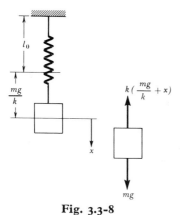

Fig. 3.3-8

Example **3.3-2**

Find the natural period of a mass hanging from a spring.

Solution: Teaching experience shows that many students who have no difficulty analyzing the spring-supported mass in horizontal motion (Fig. 3.3-1) encounter a mental block when the effect of gravity appears to enter. In reality the analysis is no more difficult. The system and its free-body diagram are shown in Fig. 3.3-8. When the mass is in static equilibrium the spring length is $l_0 + mg/k$: we measure x from this position. Then the length of the spring when the mass is in motion is

$l_0 + (mg/k) + x$. There is an upward force exerted on the mass by the spring of magnitude $k(mg/k + x)$, as shown. The equation of motion is

$$m\ddot{x} = mg - k\left(\frac{mg}{k} + x\right)$$

$$\ddot{x} + \frac{k}{m}x = 0. \qquad\qquad \textbf{3.3-25}$$

This is exactly the same equation as 3.3-2. As in that case, $\omega_n^2 = k/m$ and $T_n = 2\pi(m/k)^{1/2}$. It may be noted that, if the origin of the coordinate x is not chosen so as to make x vanish in the position of static equilibrium, a constant term will appear in the equation of motion. Suppose we let y denote the distance from the fixed support of the spring to the moving mass. Then the force exerted by the spring is an upward force of magnitude $(y - l_0)k$. The equation of motion is

$$m\ddot{y} = mg - k(y - l_0)$$

$$\ddot{y} + \frac{k}{m}y = \left(g + \frac{k}{m}l_0\right). \qquad\qquad \textbf{3.3-26}$$

If we write $y = x + l_0 + mg/k$, this equation reduces at once to the previous form, Eq. 3.3-25. The particular integral of 3.3-26 is $y = l_0 + mg/k$ so that the solution of 3.3-26 is

$$y - \left(l_0 + \frac{mg}{k}\right) = A \cos \sqrt{\frac{k}{m}}\, t + B \sin \sqrt{\frac{k}{m}}\, t.$$

Physically, the result is exactly the same wherever we choose the origin of coordinates. It is, however, easier to visualize the nature of the motion when the origin is chosen at a point of static equilibrium.

Finally, it should be noted that when the motion of the system involves an interchange of kinetic energy and potential energy of strain, the natural period is a property of the mechanical system and is independent of gravity. The natural period of the mass-spring system would be the same on the moon as it is on earth.

Example **3.3-3**

A particle is attached to the midpoint of a cable stretched with a tension T between fixed points. Find the period of free lateral vibration.

Solution: We assume that the motions are so small that the additional stretching of the cable due to the vertical displacement x does not appreciably alter T. We also neglect the inertia of the cable. The free-body diagram of the particle is shown in Fig. 3.3-9. The equation of motion is

$$-2T \frac{x}{\sqrt{x^2 + l^2/4}} = m\ddot{x}. \qquad\qquad \textbf{3.3-27}$$

The motion is not, strictly speaking, of the simple harmonic type. For small values of x compared with l, however, we may write

$$\frac{x}{\sqrt{x^2+l^2/4}} = \frac{2x}{l}\left(1+\frac{4x^2}{l^2}\right)^{-\frac{1}{2}} = \frac{2x}{l}\left[1-\frac{2x^2}{l^2}+\cdots\right] \approx \frac{2x}{l}. \qquad \textbf{3.3-28}$$

This is equivalent to dropping the term x^2 in comparison with the term $l^2/4$ in the radical. With this approximation, Eq. 3.3-27 becomes

$$\ddot{x}+\frac{4T}{ml}x = 0 \qquad \textbf{3.3-29}$$

so that the period of small vibrations is

$$T_n = 2\pi\sqrt{\frac{ml}{4T}}. \qquad \textbf{3.3-30}$$

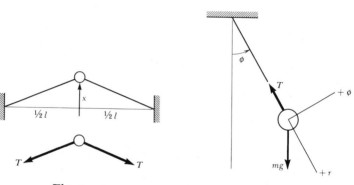

Fig. 3.3-9   **Fig. 3.3-10**

    The same principle of approximation is used in the conventional analysis of the pendulum. Here it is convenient to use as coordinate the angle ϕ between the vertical and the pendulum support string. The free-body diagram is shown in Fig. 3.3-10. If we use plane polar coordinates, the transverse component of force will be $-mg \sin \phi$ since ϕ increases counterclockwise. The equation of motion in the transverse direction will be (2.2-16)

$$-mg \sin \phi = ml\ddot{\phi} \qquad \textbf{3.3-31}$$

$$\ddot{\phi}+\frac{g}{l} \sin \phi = 0. \qquad \textbf{3.3-32}$$

If ϕ is a small angle,

$$\sin \phi = \phi-\frac{\phi^3}{3!}+\frac{\phi^5}{5!}-\cdots \approx \phi$$

so that we write, for small oscillations,

$$\ddot{\phi} + \frac{g}{l}\phi = 0$$

and

$$T_n = 2\pi\sqrt{\frac{l}{g}}.$$

3.4 Effect of a Periodic Disturbing Force

We have seen that a particle subject to a constraint that provides a linear restoring force will oscillate at its own natural frequency. What happens if we try to make it oscillate at some other frequency? The question is of great technological importance. Structures and machinery are subject to many periodic forces and their behavior in the presence of these disturbances may well limit their usefulness. Consider, for example, the mass-spring system of Fig. 3.3-1 subject to an exciting force of amplitude F_0 and circular frequency p. The free-body diagram is shown in Fig. 3.4-1. The equation of motion is

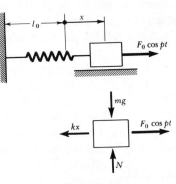

Fig. 3.4-1

$$m\ddot{x} = F_0 \cos pt - kx$$

or

$$\ddot{x} + \omega_n^2 x = \frac{F_0}{m}\cos pt.$$

3·4-1

We may anticipate that the effect of the excitation will be to produce a motion at the exciting frequency, p. Tentatively, therefore, we write

$$x = X \cos pt, \qquad\qquad \textbf{3·4-2}$$

and substitute this in Eq. 3.4-1 to see whether there is any constant value of X that will satisfy the equation of motion for all t. On making the substitution, we find that $\cos pt$ factors out of every term leaving the expression:

$$-p^2 X + \omega_n^2 X = \frac{F_0}{m} \qquad\qquad \textbf{3·4-3}$$

$$X = \frac{F_0/m}{\omega_n^2 - p^2} \qquad\qquad \textbf{3·4-4}$$

$$\frac{X}{F_0/k} = \frac{1}{1 - \dfrac{p^2}{\omega_n^2}}. \qquad\qquad \textbf{3·4-5}$$

A motion of the type

$$x = \frac{F_0/k}{1 - \dfrac{p^2}{\omega_n^2}} \cos pt$$

    3.4-6

may occur.   The complete solution of Eq. 3.4-1 is

$$x = \frac{F_0/k}{1 - \dfrac{p^2}{\omega_n^2}} \cos pt + A \cos \omega_n t + B \sin \omega_n t.$$

    3.4-7

This simply tells us that a free oscillation at the natural frequency may be superposed upon the forced oscillation of frequency p.   For our present purposes, it is the forced motion of Eq. 3.4-6 that is of interest.   The free oscillation will, at all events, die out with time if damping is taken into consideration.

Examination of Eq. 3.4-5 shows that, if p is very small, $X = F_0/k$. This is the displacement that would occur if the system had no inertia ($m = 0$) or if the force were applied very slowly.   It is sometimes known as the "static" deflection.   As p/ω_n increases, the amplitude of the forced oscillation increases until, at $p = \omega_n$, it grows without limit.   This condition in which exciting frequency matches natural frequency is known as *resonance*.   Of course the displacement does not become infinite; usually some agency intervenes to destroy the linearity of restoring force after the displacement exceeds moderate bounds.   But it does become large, and this destructively large response can be most embarrassing to the designer if it is not properly anticipated.   As the excitation becomes more rapid, p/ω_n increases. The denominator of the fraction in Eq. 3.4-6 becomes negative. This simply means that there is a 180° phase difference between exciting force and displacement; $\cos pt = -\cos(pt - \pi)$.   The amplitude of the response dies out as p increases until, at extremely high frequencies of excitation, the displacement $x \to 0$.   In Fig. 3.4-2, the amplitude of the displacement x_{max}, divided by the static displacement F_0/k, is plotted as a function of p/ω_n.   As is conventional in resonance diagrams, only the absolute value of x_{max} is plotted.   The sign, which depends upon the previously mentioned phase shift, is not usually of engineering importance.   This curve is a plot of $|(1 - p^2/\omega_n^2)^{-1}|$, a quantity which is known as the dynamic *magnification factor*.   The response of a structure or machine element to a periodic disturbing force, then, depends upon the amplitude of the force and the closeness with which its period matches the natural period of the structure.

If the support of the structure vibrates with a periodic motion, the effect is much the same as if a periodic disturbing force were present. Denote position of the support of the mass in Fig. 3.4-3 by the coordinate $x_1(t)$. The position in which x and x_1 are both zero is a position of static equilibrium. The free-body diagram is shown in the figure. Notice that, if $x > x_1$, the spring force will act to the left. The diagram tells us in little space that the external force-to-the-left is of magnitude $k(x - x_1)$. Then

$$m\ddot{x} = -k(x - x_1),$$

$$\ddot{x} + \omega_n^2 x = \omega_n^2 x_1. \qquad \textbf{3.4-8}$$

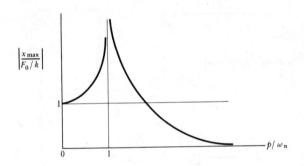

Fig. 3.4-2

If $x_1 = x_0 \cos pt$, this implies that

$$\ddot{x} + \omega_n^2 x = \omega_n^2 x_0 \cos pt, \qquad \textbf{3.4-9}$$

an equation that may be compared with 3.4-1. The steady-state response will be of the form $x = X' \cos pt$. On substituting this expression into 3.4-9, we have

$$-p^2 X' + \omega_n^2 X' = \omega_n^2 x_0,$$

$$X' = \frac{x_0}{1 - \dfrac{p^2}{\omega_n^2}}$$

so that the steady-state motion is

$$x = \frac{x_0}{1 - \dfrac{p^2}{\omega_n^2}} \cos pt. \qquad \textbf{3.4-10}$$

The dynamic magnification factor is the same for a periodic disturbing motion as for a periodic disturbing force.

Example 3.4-1

A weight is carried at the end of a light cantilevered beam. The natural frequency of the system is 30 cps. The support of the beam oscillates harmonically with an amplitude 1 cm; whereas the tip mass oscillates with an amplitude of 2 cm, 180° out of phase with the support. What is the frequency of the exciting motion?

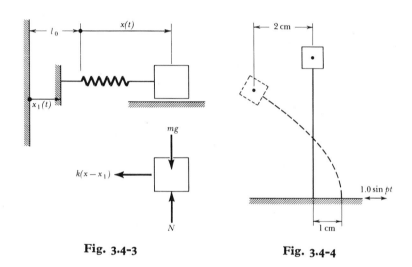

Fig. 3·4-3   **Fig. 3·4-4**

Solution: In this case, the dynamic magnification factor is given as 2. This means

$$\left| \frac{1}{1 - \dfrac{p^2}{\omega_n^2}} \right| = 2. \qquad\qquad \textbf{3·4-11}$$

There are two possible values for p^2/ω_n^2 corresponding to the two points at which a horizontal line at an ordinate greater than 1 intersects the graph of Fig. 3.4-2. The two possible values are

$$\frac{p^2}{\omega_n^2} = \frac{1}{2} \quad \text{and} \quad \frac{p^2}{\omega_n^2} = \frac{3}{2}. \qquad\qquad \textbf{3·4-12}$$

The decision as to which is correct is provided by the statement that the motion of the tip is 180° out of phase with the motion of the support, as shown in Fig. 3.4-4. This implies that $p/\omega_n > 1$, so we must use the second value.

$$p^2 = \frac{3}{2}\,\omega_n^2.$$

In the present case, $f_n = 30$ cycles/sec $= (2\pi)(30)$ rad/sec so that

$$\omega_n = 189 \text{ rad/sec}$$

$$p = 231 \text{ rad/sec} = 36.8 \text{ cps.}$$

Example 3.4-2

   A single-cylinder gas engine weighs 128 lb. As the piston moves up and down at 1200 rpm, a variable force of 48 lb amplitude is exerted on the frame. Design a spring support for the engine that will reduce the amplitude of the variable part of the load transmitted to the floor to 2 lb.

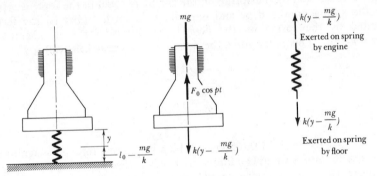

Fig. 3.4-5

   Solution: The engine is shown schematically in Fig. 3.4-5. When the engine is stationary, the spring is compressed an amount mg/k and its length is therefore $l_0 - mg/k$. We measure the coordinate y from the position of static equilibrium (that is, from a point $l_0 - mg/k$ above the floor) and positive upward. When the engine has moved to a point with co-ordinate y, the length of the spring will be $y + (l_0 - mg/k)$. The spring will therefore be stretched by an amount $y - mg/k$. It will therefore exert a downward force of magnitude $k(y - mg/k)$ on the engine. This is shown in the free-body diagram appended to Fig. 3.4-5. Of course it will very likely turn out, when the analysis is completed, that y will be smaller than mg/k so that the downward force exerted by the springs will be negative; i.e., the springs actually exert an upward force on the engine. But this is something that only the equations of motion can really tell us. The important thing to appreciate is that showing the force exerted by the spring on the engine as a downward force is consistent with saying that its magnitude is $k(y - mg/k)$ and that this in turn is dictated by our choice of y

as positive upward, measured from the position of static equilibrium. With this preamble, the rest of the analysis follows easily. The equation of motion is

$$m\ddot{y} = -k\left(y - \frac{mg}{k}\right) - mg + F_0 \cos pt,$$

$$\ddot{y} + \omega_n^2 y = \frac{F_0}{m} \cos pt, \qquad \omega_n^2 = k/m, \qquad \textbf{3.4-13}$$

of which the solution, in the form $y = X \cos pt$, is easily seen to be

$$y = \frac{F_0/k}{1 - \dfrac{p^2}{\omega_n^2}} \cos pt.$$

Here F_0 is known to be 48 lb, and p is known to be 1200 rpm = 126 rad/sec. The force exerted by the spring on the engine is equal to the force exerted by the spring on the floor and oppositely directed. That is, the force exerted by the spring on the floor is an *upward* force of magnitude $k(y - mg/k)$. This is the force the designer is interested in; call it P.

$$P = k(y - mg/k) \quad \text{upward},$$

$$P = \frac{F_0}{1 - \dfrac{p^2}{\omega_n^2}} \cos pt - mg.$$

We see that the load on the floor will be a downward force of magnitude $mg = 128$ lb with a variable additive part. It is this variable part that the designer wishes to minimize, or at least to reduce to a safe value of 2 lb. He wants

$$\left| \frac{F_0}{1 - \dfrac{p^2}{\omega_n^2}} \right| = 2 \qquad \textbf{3.4-14}$$

or, with $F_0 = 48$ lb, he wants a dynamic magnification factor of $1/24$. Eq. 3.4-14 implies

$$1 - \frac{p^2}{\omega_n^2} = \pm 24. \qquad \textbf{3.4-15}$$

The plus sign may be discarded since p^2/ω_n^2 must be a positive number (this is equivalent to the observation that a horizontal line with ordinate $1/24$ will have only one intersection with the curve of Fig. 3.4-2):

$$\frac{p^2}{\omega_n^2} = 25,$$

$$\omega_n^2 = \frac{p^2}{25} = \frac{(126)^2}{25} = 632 \ (\text{rad/sec})^2.$$

But ω_n^2 in this example is an abbreviation for k/m (see Eq. 3.4-13), so that

$$k = (632)\frac{128}{32.2} = 2520 \text{ lb/ft.}$$

By putting springs of this collective stiffness under the engine, the designer can keep the load transmitted to the floor to the dead weight of the machine plus an alternating component of magnitude 2 lb. This completes the analysis as far as we wish to go at present. The student may want to consider the following matters: Is there any danger of resonance as the machine is brought up to operating speed? Is there any danger of resonance if the operating speed is exceeded? What is the static deflection of the springs from their unloaded length? Why is it impractical to try to reduce the variable part of the transmitted force to, say, 0.1 lb using conventional springs? Why are we concerned about a variable force of 48 lb when the engine itself weighs 128 lb?

3.5 Central Force Motion

One of the most impressive achievements of newtonian mechanics was its prediction of the motion of a particle under the action of a force directed toward a fixed point. The analysis is of interest today as one of the intellectual achievements of science. It plays a basic role in celestial mechanics, in the guidance theory of earth satellite vehicles, and in the interpretation of the scattering cross section of charged particles repelled by a nucleus. Only the leading results of the so-called one-body problem are developed in this section; for a more detailed treatment reference should be made to a treatise on celestial mechanics.*

Consider a particle attracted to a fixed point called the *center of force* by a force that is a function of the distance between the particle and the fixed point. Take the center of force as the origin of coordinates. Then the only force acting on the particle has zero moment about the origin. We infer (2.4) that the angular momentum of the particle about the origin will be constant:

$$\mathbf{r} \times m\mathbf{v} = \text{constant} = \mathbf{H}_O. \qquad \textbf{3.5-1}$$

It is convenient to deal with the angular momentum per unit mass, $\mathbf{H}_O/m$:

$$\mathbf{r} \times \mathbf{v} = \mathbf{h}, \text{ a constant vector.} \qquad \textbf{3.5-2}$$

---

* e.g., J. M. A. Danby, *Fundamentals of Celestial Mechanics* (New York: The Macmillan Co., 1962).

If we take the scalar product of both sides of this expression with the vector $\mathbf{r}$, the left side, $\mathbf{r} \cdot (\mathbf{r} \times \mathbf{v})$, will be zero. The scalar triple product always vanishes if two terms are identical (1.3-12, 13). Hence

$$\mathbf{h} \cdot \mathbf{r} = 0. \qquad \text{3·5-3}$$

Since $\mathbf{h}$ is a constant vector, it follows from this equation that $\mathbf{r}$ lies in a fixed plane perpendicular to $\mathbf{h}$. The motion is therefore in a plane that we may take as the xy- or $r\phi$-plane (see also Example 2.4-4). Then $\mathbf{h}$ and $\mathbf{H}_O$ are directed along the z-axis. In rectangular coordinates,

$$\mathbf{r} \times \mathbf{v} = (x\mathbf{i} + y\mathbf{j}) \times (\dot{x}\mathbf{i} + \dot{y}\mathbf{j}) = (x\dot{y} - y\dot{x})\mathbf{k} = h\mathbf{k}$$

$$x\dot{y} - y\dot{x} = h. \qquad \text{3·5-4}$$

In cylindrical polar coordinates,

$$\mathbf{r} \times \mathbf{v} = (r\mathbf{e}_r) \times (\dot{r}\mathbf{e}_r + r\dot{\phi}\mathbf{e}_\phi) = r^2\dot{\phi}\mathbf{k} = h\mathbf{k}$$

$$r^2\dot{\phi} = h. \qquad \text{3·5-5}$$

This last equation has a simple physical interpretation. First, the particle can never reverse its direction of motion because the sign of $\dot{\phi}$ must always be the same as that of h. Second, the term $r^2\dot{\phi}$ is related to the rate at which the position vector $\mathbf{r}$ sweeps out area in the plane. Let A be the area swept out by $\mathbf{r}$. The increment in A as the particle moves from P to P' in time Δt will be the area of the triangle OPP' in Fig. 3.5-1, except for terms that depend upon the curvature of the arc PP'.

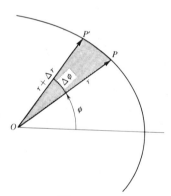

$$\Delta A = \frac{1}{2}(r + \Delta r)r \sin \Delta \phi. \qquad \text{3·5-6}$$

Fig. 3.5-1

Divide this expression by Δt and allow Δt, Δr, and $\Delta \phi$ to approach zero:

$$\frac{dA}{dt} = \frac{1}{2}r^2\dot{\phi} = \frac{1}{2}h. \qquad \text{3·5-7}$$

It follows that the *areal velocity*, or rate at which area is being swept out by the position vector, is constant. The fact that the position vector from the sun to any of the planets sweeps out equal areas in equal time intervals was discovered by Kepler and forms the substance of his second law of planetary motion. It is interesting to note that the law is true for any central force whatever.

We now specialize to the case of an inverse square law attraction,

$$\mathbf{F} = -\mu \frac{m}{r^2} \mathbf{e}_r = -\mu \frac{m}{r^2} \cos \phi \mathbf{i} - \mu \frac{m}{r^2} \sin \phi \mathbf{j}. \qquad \textbf{3.5-8}$$

The negative sign is needed because the positive radial direction is outward from the center of force. The quantity μ is the intensity of the center of force (see 2.7-11). For gravitational attraction, $\mu = Gm'$ where m' is the mass of the attracting body at the center of force and G is the universal constant of gravitation defined in 2.2. As we have seen (Eq. 2.7-14), if the attracting body is the earth of radius R, $\mu \simeq gR^2 = 39.89(10)^4$ km^3/sec^2.

The equations of motion are

$$m\ddot{x} = -\mu \frac{m}{r^2} \cos \phi, \qquad m\ddot{y} = -\mu \frac{m}{r^2} \sin \phi. \qquad \textbf{3.5-9}$$

In view of Eq. 3.5-5, these may be written

$$\ddot{x} = -\frac{\mu}{h} \dot{\phi} \cos \phi, \qquad \ddot{y} = -\frac{\mu}{h} \dot{\phi} \sin \phi. \qquad \textbf{3.5-10}$$

It follows that

$$\dot{x} = -\frac{\mu}{h} (\sin \phi + C_1), \qquad \dot{y} = \frac{\mu}{h} (\cos \phi + C_2) \qquad \textbf{3.5-11}$$

where C_1 and C_2 are constants of integration. Initially, at the instant of projection $\phi = 0$ and $\dot{x} = \dot{x}_0, \dot{y} = \dot{y}_0$ so that

$$C_1 = -\frac{h\dot{x}_0}{\mu}, \qquad C_2 = \frac{h\dot{y}_0}{\mu} - 1. \qquad \textbf{3.5-12}$$

With these values for C_1 and C_2, the expressions for $\dot{x}$ and $\dot{y}$ given by Eqs. 3.5-11 may be substituted into Eq. 3.5-4. The resulting equation is

$$x \cos \phi + y \sin \phi = \frac{h^2}{\mu} + x \left(1 - \frac{h}{\mu} \dot{y}_0\right) + y \left(\frac{h}{\mu} \dot{x}_0\right), \qquad \textbf{3.5-13}$$

or, since $\cos \phi = x/r$, $\sin \phi = y/r$, and $x^2 + y^2 = r^2$,

$$r = \frac{h^2}{\mu} + x \left(1 - \frac{h}{\mu} \dot{y}_0\right) + y \left(\frac{h}{\mu} \dot{x}_0\right). \qquad \textbf{3.5-14}$$

This is the equation of the orbit. The value of h is determined by the initial conditions; at $t = 0$, $x = x_0$, $y = 0$, and $\dot{x} = \dot{x}_0, \dot{y} = \dot{y}_0$. Since h is the moment of the velocity vector, $h = x_0 \dot{y}_0$.

Although the determination of the orbit is formally completed, the results require interpretation. Consider the distance d from a point x_1, y_1 on the orbit to the line

$$\frac{h^2}{\mu} + x\left(1 - \frac{h}{\mu}\dot{y}_0\right) + y\left(\frac{h}{\mu}\dot{x}_0\right) = 0. \qquad 3.5\text{-}15$$

This distance is given by the expression*

$$d = \frac{\left|\dfrac{h^2}{\mu} + x_1\left(1 - \dfrac{h}{\mu}\dot{y}_0\right) + y_1\left(\dfrac{h}{\mu}\dot{x}_0\right)\right|}{\left[\left(1 - \dfrac{h}{\mu}\dot{y}_0\right)^2 + \left(\dfrac{h}{\mu}\dot{x}_0\right)^2\right]^{\frac{1}{2}}}. \qquad 3.5\text{-}16$$

The distance of the point x_1, y_1 from the origin is $r = (x_1^2 + y_1^2)^{\frac{1}{2}}$. Eq. 3.5-14 tells us that for any point on the orbit

$$r = d\left[\left(1 - \frac{h}{\mu}\dot{y}_0\right)^2 + \left(\frac{h}{\mu}\dot{x}_0\right)^2\right]^{\frac{1}{2}}. \qquad 3.5\text{-}17$$

The orbit is therefore the locus of a point the ratio of whose distance from a fixed point to its distance from a fixed line is a constant. Such a path is known as a *conic section*.** The fixed point is the *focus* and the fixed line the *directrix* of the conic. The ratio r/d is known as the *eccentricity* of the conic; we denote it by the symbol e. If $e < 1$, the conic is an ellipse; if $e = 1$, it is a parabola; and if $e > 1$, it is a hyperbola.

$$e^2 = \left(\frac{r}{d}\right)^2 = 1 + \frac{h^2}{\mu^2}\left(\dot{x}_0^2 + \dot{y}_0^2 - \frac{2\mu}{x_0}\right). \qquad 3.5\text{-}18$$

This equation has a simple physical significance. The force field $\mathbf{F} = -(m\mu/r^2)\mathbf{e}_r$ has associated with it a potential energy, $V = -m\mu/r$ (see Section 2.7). The kinetic energy of the particle is $mv^2/2$. The *total energy per unit mass*, denoted by E, is

$$E = \frac{1}{2}v^2 - \frac{\mu}{r}. \qquad 3.5\text{-}19$$

---

* For this result, reference may be made to any text on analytic geometry; e.g., A. E. Taylor, *Calculus with Analytic Geometry* (Englewood Cliffs, N. J.: Prentice-Hall, Inc., 1959), p. 272.

** See, e.g., Taylor, pp. 401–404 or R. E. Johnson and F. L. Kiokemeister, *Calculus with Analytic Geometry*, 2nd ed. (Boston: Allyn and Bacon, Inc., 1960), pp. 170–180, 418. That the orbit is a conic is also evident from the fact that Eq. 3.5-14, on squaring and setting $r^2 = x^2 + y^2$, is seen to be a quadratic form.

This is a constant because there are no dissipative forces present. It follows that E, like h, is determined by the initial conditions.

$$E = \frac{1}{2}(\dot{x}_0^2 + \dot{y}_0^2) - \frac{\mu}{x_0}. \qquad \text{3.5-20}$$

Equation 3.5-18 can now be written in the physically suggestive form

$$e^2 = 1 + \frac{2h^2 E}{\mu^2}. \qquad \text{3.5-21}$$

We see that the orbit is an ellipse if $E < 0$, a parabola if $E = 0$, and a hyperbola if $E > 0$. The fact that the planets move in ellipses with the sun at a focus constitutes Kepler's first law of planetary motion. Unlike the motion in a field where the restoring force is proportional to the separation, motion in an inverse square law central field is periodic only for special initial conditions. The value of v that, for a given r and μ, makes $E = 0$ is known as the *escape velocity*. We see from Eq. 3.5-19 that

$$v_e = \sqrt{\frac{2\mu}{r}}. \qquad \text{3.5-22}$$

If the orbit is an ellipse, its dimensions and the orientation of its major axis may be found easily. The major axis passes through the origin and is perpendicular to the directrix. Since the equation of the directrix is 3.5-15, it follows that the equation of the major axis is

$$x\left(1 - \frac{h}{\mu}\dot{y}_0\right) - y\left(\frac{h}{\mu}\dot{x}_0\right) = 0, \qquad \text{3.5-23}$$

and hence that the major axis is inclined to the axis through the point of projection by an angle

$$\theta = \arctan\left[\dot{x}_0 \Big/ \left(\frac{\mu}{h} - \dot{y}_0\right)\right]. \qquad \text{3.5-24}$$

When the particle is closest to or farthest from the focus O, its velocity will be at right angles to the position vector. If we call either of these special values r^*, and the corresponding speed v^*, we have for the angular momentum and energy equations

$$v^* r^* = h, \qquad E = \frac{1}{2}v^{*2} - \frac{\mu}{r^*}. \qquad \text{3.5-25}$$

On eliminating v^*, we get a quadratic equation in r^*

$$r^{*2} + \frac{\mu}{E}r^* - \frac{h^2}{2E} = 0 \qquad \text{3.5-26}$$

whose roots are

$$r_1^* = \frac{-\mu}{2E}[1 - \sqrt{1+(2Eh^2/\mu^2)}],$$

$$r_2^* = \frac{-\mu}{2E}[1 + \sqrt{1+(2Eh^2/\mu^2)}].$$

3·5-27

Since E is negative for an elliptic orbit, these roots are both positive numbers. The radii r_1^*, r_2^* determine the dimensions OA and OA' shown in Fig. 3.5-2. The point A is the *pericentron* (if the attracting body is the earth, *perigee*; if the sun, *perihelion*; if another star,

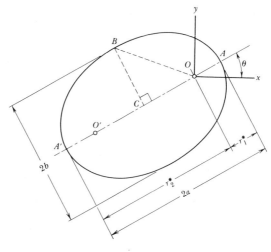

Fig. 3.5-2

periastron), and the point A' is the *apocentron* (or apogee, aphelion, apastron). These points are also apses, an *apse* being a point where the velocity is at right angles to the position vector from the center of force. The lines OA and OA' are called *apse lines*; and the angle between these lines, 180 degrees in the case of an elliptic orbit, is called an *apsidal* angle. Equation 3.5-26 is sometimes termed the *apsidal quadratic*. The major axis of the ellipse is the sum of the distances r_1^*, r_2^*; that is

$$a = \frac{1}{2}(r_1^* + r_2^*) = \frac{-\mu}{2E}.$$

3·5-28

The minor axis is also easily expressed in terms of the roots of the apsidal quadratic. We have only to recall that the sum of the distances to the two foci is the same for all points on a given ellipse.[*]

$$OA + AO' = OB + BO'$$

where O' is the unoccupied focus of the ellipse. But $O'A'$ is the same as OA, and OB is the same as BO' so that

$$OA = r_1^*, \qquad AO' = r_2^*, \qquad OB = \tfrac{1}{2}(r_1^* + r_2^*) = a.$$

The hypotenuse of the right triangle OCB is the length a, and its leg CO is the length $a - r_1^*$. The leg $CB = b$ is given by the expression

$$b^2 = a^2 - (a - r_1^*)^2 = r_1^*(2a - r_1^*),$$

$$b^2 = r_1^* r_2^* = \frac{-h^2}{2E}. \qquad\qquad \textbf{3·5-29}$$

The last step has been made through the substitution of Eqs. 3.5-27. We note that the length of the major axis depends only on the energy E; whereas the minor axis is sensitive to h as well. If we substitute from 3.5-28 and 3.5-21 into 3.5-27, we find that $r_1^* = a(1 - e)$ and $r_2^* = a(1 + e)$. Multiplying these and using 3.5-29, we recover the alternative definition of the eccentricity of an ellipse[**] as the ratio $(a^2 - b^2)^{1/2}/a$.

Finally we note that the period of the orbit is easily determined from the relation 3.5-7. The area of the ellipse, πab, is swept out in a time interval equal to the period, T_n.

$$\int_0^{\pi ab} dA = \frac{h}{2}\int_0^{T_n} dt, \qquad T_n = \frac{2\pi ab}{h}. \qquad\qquad \textbf{3·5-30}$$

This equation gives the period when a, b, and h have been computed. Since b/h and a depend only on the energy E, it should be possible to express the period in terms of E or a alone. From 3.5-29, $b/h = (-2E)^{-1/2}$ so that, in view of 3.5-28,

$$T_n = \frac{2\pi\mu}{(-2E)^{3/2}} \quad \text{or} \quad T_n = \frac{2\pi}{\mu^{1/2}} a^{3/2}. \qquad\qquad \textbf{3·5-31}$$

This last expression is Kepler's third law of planetary motion: the square of the period divided by the cube of the mean radius is a constant, the same for all planets. By "mean radius" is meant the

---

[*] Taylor, p. 140, or Johnson and Kiokemeister, pp. 170–180.

[**] Taylor, p. 141, or Johnson and Kiokemeister, p. 418.

average of perihelion and aphelion, i.e., the semi-axis major, a. The fact that this ratio is the same for every planet shows that the agency causing the motion is the same in each case.

Retrospect: In all this material what is important are the basic ideas and methods, not the various formulas. It is suggested that the student bear in mind the way in which the energy and angular momentum are determined so that he can write the apsidal quadratic equation. The arithmetic mean of its roots is the semi-axis major; the geometric mean is the semi-axis minor. The period is then expressed in terms of the area-angular momentum relation. Other relationships are not essential—except possibly for Eq. 3.5-24, which determines the orientation of the major axis.

We have treated the motion of a particle attracted to a fixed point. By implication, our results are applicable to planets circling the sun and to satellites of the planets. Curiously, the fact that these attracting bodies are of finite size has no effect at all on the motion. As we shall see in Section 4.8, the attraction of any body whose density is a function only of distance from its center is the same as if the entire mass of the body were concentrated at the center. Lack of perfect sphericity does have an effect upon central force motion. So does the fact that the attracting body is not fixed. These modifications of the theory are small because the earth and sun are nearly spherical and because the primary attracting body, in application, usually has a much larger mass than the secondary.

Example 3.5-1

A particle is projected with velocity v_0 at right angles to its position vector. Discuss the orbit.

Solution: In this case the point of projection is an apse. The energy per unit mass $E = (v_0^2/2) - (\mu/r_0)$. If $v_0^2 > 2\mu/r_0$, the orbit will be a hyperbola. If $v_0^2 = 2\mu/r_0$, the orbit will be a parabola. If $v_0^2 < 2\mu/r_0$, the orbit will be an ellipse.

We may profitably discuss the case $v_0^2 < 2\mu/r_0$ more fully. For a circular orbit, the attracting force must be equal to the mass multiplied by the radial acceleration:

$$-\frac{m\mu}{r_0^2} = ma_r = -m\frac{v_0^2}{r_0}$$

$$v_0^2 = \mu/r_0.$$

There is a distinction between the elliptic orbits in which $2\mu/r_0 > v_0^2 > \mu/r_0$ and those in which $v_0^2 < \mu/r_0$. We have from 3.5-28

$$a = \frac{-\mu}{2E} = \frac{-\mu}{v_0^2 - (2\mu/r_0)} = \frac{r_0}{2 - (v_0^2 r_0/\mu)}.$$

The larger range of v_0^2 will be associated with large values of a. This means that the other apse will be remote from the point of projection; i.e., the point of projection will be pericenter. But the smaller range of v_0^2 will be associated with small values of a; the ellipse will barely enclose the force center. For this range, the point of projection will be the apocenter. These orbits are illustrated in Fig. 3.5-3.

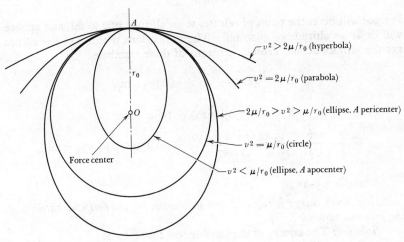

Fig. 3.5-3

Example 3.5-2

An artificial earth satellite is released at an altitude of 250 miles with a velocity of 5.50 mi/sec in a horizontal direction. Find apogee, perigee, and period. For the earth as force center, $\mu = 9.570(10)^4$ mi^3/sec^2.

Solution: First we find the angular momentum and the energy per unit mass. Since the radius of the earth is 4000 mi (nearly), release occurs at $x_0 = 4250$ mi.

$$h = \dot{y}_0 x_0 = (5.5)(4250) = 23{,}375 \quad \text{mi}^2/\text{sec}$$

$$E = \frac{1}{2}v_0^2 - \frac{\mu}{x_0} = \frac{1}{2}(5.5)^2 - \frac{(9.570)(10)^4}{4250} = -7.425 \quad \text{mi}^2/\text{sec}^2.$$

The orbit will be an ellipse because E is negative. The angular momentum and energy relations at an apse are

$$r^*v^* = h, \qquad \frac{1}{2}v^{*2} - \frac{\mu}{r^*} = E.$$

Eliminating v^* we get the apsidal quadratic

$$r^{*2} + \frac{\mu}{E} r^* - \frac{h^2}{2E} = 0$$

$$r^{*2} - 1.289(10)^4 r^* + 0.3679(10)^8 = 0$$

$$r_1^* = 4250 \quad \text{mi}$$

$$r_2^* = 8620 \quad \text{mi}.$$

Perigee will be at the point of release, at an altitude of 250 mi, and apogee will be at an altitude of 4620 mi. The dimensions a and b of the ellipse are the arithmetic and geometric means of these numbers:

$$a = \frac{1}{2}(4250 + 8620) = 6435 \quad \text{mi},$$

$$b = \sqrt{(4250)(8620)} = 6050 \quad \text{mi}.$$

$$T_n = \frac{\pi a b}{(h/2)} = \frac{(3.14)(6435)(6050)}{11,687} = 10,450 \text{ sec} = 175 \text{ min}.$$

Example **3·5-3**

How much energy is required, per unit mass, for the artificial satellite of the previous example?

Solution: The energy of the satellite was found to be

$$E = \frac{1}{2} v^2 - \frac{\mu}{r} = \frac{1}{2}(5.5)^2 - \frac{9.570(10)^4}{4250} = -7.425 \quad \text{mi}^2/\text{sec}^2$$

in the previous example. At the launching site,

$$E_0 = 0 - \frac{(9.570)(10)^4}{4000} = -23.92 \quad \text{mi}^2/\text{sec}^2.$$

Energy required $= E - E_0 = -7.425 - (-23.92) = 16.50 \text{ mi}^2/\text{sec}^2$

$$= 460(10)^6 \text{ ft}^2/\text{sec}^2 \quad \text{or} \quad \text{ft-lb/slug}.$$

Four hundred and sixty million ft-lb of energy must be expended to raise 32 lb to an altitude of 250 mi and give it a speed of 5.5 mi/sec. Of this amount, the part that is required to produce kinetic energy is

$$\frac{T}{m} = \frac{1}{2} v^2 = \frac{1}{2}(5.5)^2 = 15.125 \quad \text{mi}^2/\text{sec}^2$$

$$\frac{15.125}{16.50} = 0.92,$$

so that 92% of the required energy is used to provide velocity. Only 8% is needed to lift the mass to an altitude of 250 mi. This estimate, of course, does not include the effects of atmospheric resistance.

Example **3·5-4**

Due to slight inaccuracy of the guidance system, the artificial satellite of the previous two examples is released at an (upward) angle of 10 degrees with the horizontal. How will this affect the orbit?

Solution: We now have

$$h = (4250)(5.5) \cos 10° = 23,000 \text{ mi}^2/\text{sec};$$

whereas $E = -7.425 \text{ mi}^2/\text{sec}^2$ as before

so that the apsidal quadratic (see Example 3.5-2) becomes

$$r^{*2} - 1.289(10)^4 r^* + 0.356(10)^8 = 0$$

$$r_1^* = 8890 \quad \text{mi}$$

$$r_2^* = 4000 \quad \text{mi.}$$

This launching will not be successful since perigee is the same as the radius of the earth. The major axis of the orbit will be inclined to the vertical by an angle (see Eq. 3.5-24)

$$\theta = \arctan [\dot{x}_0/(\tfrac{\mu}{h} - \dot{y}_0)] = \arctan \left[\frac{5.5 \sin 10°}{(9.57/2.30) - 5.5 \cos 10°} \right]$$

$$= \arctan (-0.76) = 143°.$$

The orbit is shown in Fig. 3.5-4. The computation may serve to give some feeling for the degree of attitude control for which the guidance system must be designed.

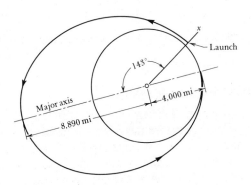

Fig. 3·5-4

Example **3·5-5**

A particle approaches a newtonian center of attraction from a remote point where its velocity is v_0 and its direction such that, were there no gravitation, it would miss the focus by a distance p. Find the actual distance by which the particle misses the focus.

Solution: The orbit must be hyperbolic since at $r=\infty$, $v=v_0$, and therefore $E=(v_0^2/2)>0$. There can be no "capture," although if the center of attraction has a finite size, impact may occur. The situation is as pictured in Fig. 3.5-5. Note that initially the moment of the velocity vector is $h=pv_0$. The point we are interested in is an apse where $r=r^*$ and $v=v^*$. Since energy and momentum are conserved,

$$\frac{1}{2}v_0^2 = \frac{1}{2}v^{*2}-\frac{\mu}{r^*} \quad \text{and} \quad pv_0 = r^*v^*.$$

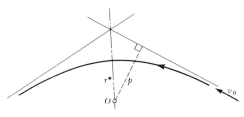

Fig. 3.5-5

After eliminating v^* we get the apsidal quadratic

$$r^{*2}+\frac{2\mu}{v_0^2}\,r^*-p^2 = 0. \tag{3.5-32}$$

This quadratic has only one positive root:

$$r^* = (\mu/v_0^2)[\sqrt{1+(p^2v_0^4/\mu^2)}-1], \tag{3.5-33}$$

which is the distance wanted. The corresponding value of v^* is easily computed.

3.6 Central Repulsive Force

Since the work of Rutherford and Wilson, the alpha-particle bombardment of atomic nuclei has been a fruitful tool of experimental physics. In this case, an inverse-square law repulsive force is operative. The analysis of the motion follows the same lines as that for the gravitational attraction of the previous section except that μ is now a negative quantity. It follows that the energy is always positive. Only hyperbolic orbits are possible. They are convex to the focus rather than concave to it. (The concave case is pictured in Fig. 3.5-5). The principal quantity of interest is the "scattering angle" through which the particle is deflected.

We suppose the particle to approach the scattering focus along a line that, in the absence of repulsion, would make it miss the focus by a distance p (the so-called impact parameter). Remote from the focus (point A in Fig. 3.6-1), the particle has a speed v_0. We choose the x-axis through the apse with origin at the focus, y, and ϕ, as shown. We want to determine the angle ψ shown in Fig. 3.6-1. The particle is deflected through the scattering angle $\pi - \psi$.

The particle is shown in a typical position. The free-body diagram shows an outward (repulsive) force vm/r^2 acting. The

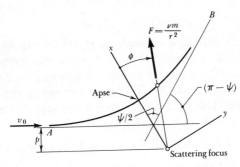

Fig. 3.6-1

symbol v is used instead of μ to avoid possible confusion with the gravitational case. Writing $F_x = ma_x$ we have, as in 3.5,

$$m\ddot{x} = vmr^{-2} \cos \phi.$$ **3.6-1**

As in 3.5, angular momentum is conserved:

$$r^2\dot{\phi} = h = pv_0.$$ **3.6-2**

Use this fact to eliminate r^2 from Eq. 3.6-1.

$$\ddot{x} = [v/(pv_0)]\dot{\phi} \cos \phi$$

whence

$$\dot{x} = [v/(pv_0)] \sin \phi.$$ **3.6-3**

The constant of integration vanishes because $\dot{x} = 0$ when $\phi = 0$. That is the advantage of choosing x to pass through the apse. When the particle swings around to B, it is again remote from the focus. Since it has not suffered any energy loss, its speed approaches v_0 again as ϕ approaches $\psi/2$. The x-component of its speed therefore approaches $v_0 \cos (\psi/2)$. On inserting these facts in Eq. 3.6-3 we have

$$v_0 \cos (\psi/2) = [v/(pv_0)] \sin (\psi/2),$$

$$\tan (\psi/2) = [(pv_0^2)/v].$$ **3.6-4**

The apsidal quadratic is the same as that for an attractive hyperbolic orbit (Eq. 3.5-32) discussed in Example 3.5-5 except that μ is replaced by $-\nu$. The pericentron distance is therefore the same as that given by Eq. 3.5-33, with the sign of the second term in brackets altered from negative to positive and with ν replacing μ. In conjunction with Eq. 3.6-4, this implies that the pericentron distance for Coulomb repulsive forces is

$$r^* = (\nu/v_0^2)[1 + \sqrt{1 + \tan^2 (\psi/2)}]$$
$$= (\nu/v_0^2)[1 + \sec (\psi/2)]. \qquad \textbf{3.6-5}$$

Rutherford's experiments were designed to estimate the dimensions of the atomic nucleus. He used α-particles traveling at $v_0 = 1.92(10)^6$ m/sec and a gold foil target. According to Coulomb's law (Eq. 2.2-4), $\nu = q_1 q_2/(4\pi m \epsilon_0)$. The mass appears in the denominator because the force law used in deriving 3.6-5 was $F = \nu m/r^2$ whereas Coulomb's law has $F = q_1 q_2/(4\pi \epsilon_0 r^2)$. With

$$q_1 = (2)(1.60)(10)^{-19} \text{ coulombs for } \alpha\text{-particle,}$$
$$q_2 = (79)(1.60)(10)^{-19} \text{ coulombs for gold,}$$
$$m = 6.67(10)^{-27} \text{ kg for } \alpha\text{-particles,}$$
$$\epsilon_0 = 8.854(10)^{-12} \text{ farad/m,}$$

we have

$$\nu = 0.0546 \text{ m}^3/\text{sec}^2.$$

The experiments showed the minimum value of ψ, presumably corresponding to the closest approach r^*, to be about 30 degrees. Accordingly the closest approach possible is

$$r^* = \frac{5.46(10)^{-2}}{[1.92(10)^6]^2} (1 + 1.035) \cong 3(10)^{-14} \text{ m.}$$

This provided an early estimate of the size of the nucleus. From the point of view of modern physics, the treatment of this problem along the lines of classical mechanics is open to some objection. It should be reexamined from the viewpoint of quantum mechanics. But that is another story.

3·7 Dissipative Forces

The situations treated in the preceding sections have been concerned with motion under the influence of conservative forces. Under these circumstances the velocity can usually be obtained in a fairly simple form either by integrating the equations of motion or by means of the principle of conservation of energy. On the other hand, when a body is subject to nonconservative forces, the analysis of its motion is more complex. These forces usually arise through the presence of solid or fluid friction. They are sometimes called velocity-dependent forces. The term, however, is somewhat misleading; the force exerted by a magnetic field on a charged particle is at right angles to the velocity vector of the particle and is therefore velocity dependent without being dissipative.

Consider, for simplicity, the case of rectilinear motion of a foreign particle immersed in a fluid and under the influence of no forces except the drag of the fluid. The equation of motion takes the form

$$m\ddot{x} = -F(v). \qquad \textbf{3·7-1}$$

This may be integrated in either of two ways. The most obvious is to write $\ddot{x} = dv/dt$ whereupon Eq. 3.7-1 becomes a first-order separable equation in v and t:

$$m \frac{dv}{dt} = -F(v), \qquad \textbf{3·7-2}$$

$$-m \int_{v_0}^{v} \frac{dv}{F(v)} = t - t_0. \qquad \textbf{3·7-3}$$

If the form of the resistance function, $F(v)$, is known, this expression relates the velocity at any time to the velocity, v_0, at some particular time, t_0. Alternatively, we may write

$$\ddot{x} = \frac{dv}{dt} = \frac{dv}{dx}\frac{dx}{dt} = v\frac{dv}{dx} \qquad \textbf{3·7-4}$$

whereupon Eq. 3.7-1 again becomes a first-order equation, now in v and x:

$$mv \frac{dv}{dx} = -F(v), \qquad \textbf{3·7-5}$$

$$-m \int_{v_0}^{v} \frac{v\,dv}{F(v)} \doteq x - x_0. \qquad \textbf{3·7-6}$$

One or the other of expressions 3.7-3 or 3.7-6 usually provides the wanted information concerning the motion. In those cases in which a complete solution for displacement as a function of time is wanted, it is generally simplest to solve either 3.7-3 or 3.7-6 for v and substitute in the other.

The foregoing discussion shows that, for rectilinear motion at least, a dynamic analysis can be carried out once the form of the resistance function is established. The prediction of the way in which the retarding force varies with speed is one of the chief objectives of aerodynamics and hydrodynamics, but, in the present state of development of these fields, such a prediction is possible only for very simple shapes immersed in fluids with somewhat idealized properties. Usually the engineer must rely on the results of wind-tunnel or towing-tank tests to provide quantitative information on the magnitude of the resisting force. In a general way it may be said that the resistance is due to the fact that the fluid is set into motion. At low speeds the dominant effect of this motion is frictional, due to the slipping of one fluid layer over its neighbor. At higher speeds a crude analysis shows that in time Δt an object of cross-sectional area A advancing with speed v will impart a velocity proportional to v to a volume of fluid of mass proportional to $\rho A v \Delta t$. Since force is proportional to rate of change of momentum, we should expect, at intermediate speeds, to encounter a resistance largely proportional to the square of the velocity. The reasoning, due originally to Newton, is only approximate because the geometry of the flow pattern changes with speed. As speed is further increased, the compressibility of the fluid tends to play an important role in the determination of the resistance.

Example **3.7-1**

A small sphere falls in a viscous fluid; discuss the motion.

Solution: We take y as position measured downward. Borrowing a result from hydrodynamics, we write the retarding force in the form

$$F(v) = -6\pi\mu r v \qquad \text{3.7-7}$$

where r and v are the radius and velocity of the sphere and μ is the viscosity of the fluid. For the present we regard μ simply as a material constant whose dimensions, since $F(v)$ is a force, are $ML^{-1}T^{-1}$ (gm/cm-sec). The other external forces are the downward gravitational pull on the sphere and the upward pressure that the fluid would exert even if the sphere were stationary. This resultant pressure is given by Archimedes' principle as the weight of a volume of fluid equal to the volume of the sphere. In terms of the densities ρ_1 for the sphere and ρ_0 for the fluid we have

$$\left(\frac{4}{3}\pi r^3 \rho_1\right)\ddot{y} = \left(\frac{4}{3}\pi r^3 \rho_1\right)g - \left(\frac{4}{3}\pi r^3 \rho_0\right)g - 6\pi\mu r v. \qquad \text{3.7-8}$$

The term $\frac{4}{3}\pi r^3$ is, of course, the volume of the sphere. Now, using the method of Eq. 3.7-3, we have

$$t - t_0 = \int_{v_0}^{v} \left[\frac{(\rho_1 - \rho_0)g}{\rho_1} - \frac{9}{2}\frac{\mu}{r^2\rho_1}v\right]^{-1} dv$$

$$= -\frac{2}{9}\left(\frac{r^2\rho_1}{\mu}\right)\log\left[\frac{(\rho_1 - \rho_0)g}{\rho_1} - \frac{9}{2}\frac{\mu v}{r^2\rho_1}\right]\bigg|_{v_0}^{v}. \qquad \text{3.7-9}$$

In the present instance, $v_0 = 0$ at $t_0 = 0$; the sphere is released from rest, so that

$$t = -\frac{2}{9}\frac{r^2\rho_1}{\mu} \log\left(1 - \frac{9}{2}\frac{\mu v}{(\rho_1 - \rho_0)gr^2}\right).$$

We solve for v to get

$$v = \frac{2}{9}\left(\frac{\rho_1 - \rho_0}{\mu}\right)gr^2\left[1 - e^{-\frac{9}{2}\frac{\mu}{r^2\rho_1}t}\right]. \qquad \textbf{3.7-10}$$

As t increases without limit, the velocity increases from zero to its terminal value v':

$$v' = \frac{2}{9}\frac{\rho_1 - \rho_0}{\mu}gr^2. \qquad \textbf{3.7-11}$$

The existence of a terminal velocity is typical of motion resulting from a constant force and a velocity-dependent retardation. It is the speed at which the retarding force is equal in magnitude to the constant force. In the present case, we note that larger and heavier spheres will have larger terminal velocities, other things being equal.

It is of some interest to find the magnitude of v', say in the case of a particle of clay falling in water. Taking

$$\rho_1 = 2.6 \text{ gm/cm}^3, \qquad \rho_0 = 1 \text{ gm/cm}^3, \qquad \mu = 0.01 \text{ gm/cm-sec,}$$

we find

$$v' = \frac{(2)(1.6)(980)}{(9)(0.01)}r^2 = 3.48(10)^4 r^2 \quad \text{cm/sec} \qquad \textbf{3.7-12}$$

when r is given in cm. It must be noted, however, that the hydrodynamic theory from which Eq. 3.7-7 was drawn is valid only for values of the dimensionless (Reynolds) number $v'r\rho_0/\mu$ less than 1. If we set

$$\frac{v'r\rho_0}{\mu} = 1$$

and take

$$v' = 3.48(10)^4 r^2, \qquad \rho_0 = 1, \qquad \mu = 0.01,$$

we can see that Eq. 3.7-12 will be valid only if r is less than 0.0066 cm. For a particle of this size, $v' = 1.51$ cm/sec.

Let us see how rapidly this velocity is approached. Referring to Eq. 3.7-10, we have

$$\frac{9}{2}\frac{\mu}{r^2\rho_1} = \frac{(9)(0.01)}{(2)(43.5)(10)^{-6}(2.6)} = 400/\text{sec}$$

so that Eq. 3.7-10 can be written

$$v = v'(1 - e^{-400t})$$

and, when $t = 0.01$ sec, $v = 0.98v'$. The terminal velocity is approached very rapidly indeed. For this reason applications of Eq. 3.7-7 in engineering practice are usually made on the further simplifying assumption that the particle falls with a constant velocity v' given by Eq. 3.7-11. Among these applications are the size analysis of silty and clayey soils in soil mechanics and the motion of droplets in a stream of gas.

Example 3.7-2

A 3500-lb automobile rolls down a 5 per cent grade. How far will it travel before it reaches a speed of 30 mph?

Solution: The retardation force on an object such as an automobile can often be approximated closely by an equation of the type

$$F(v) = A + Bv^2.\qquad\qquad \textbf{3·7-13}$$

A and B are constants determined by experiment. A is known as the "rolling resistance"; for a light automobile it is about 60 lb. B is known as the wind resistance coefficient. It is proportional to the cross-sectional area of the vehicle. For a light conventional automobile, B is approximately 0.011 lb-sec^2/ft^2.

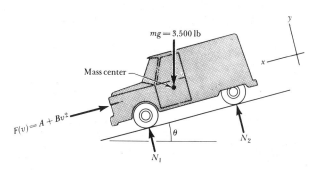

Fig. 3·7-1

We draw the free-body diagram as shown in Fig. 3.7-1. Friction forces at the wheels will be negligible because the automobile is rolling freely (strictly speaking, the motor should be disengaged from the transmission). Equating the x-components of $\mathbf{F}$ and $m\mathbf{a}$,

$$mg \sin \theta - (A + Bv^2) = m\ddot{x}.\qquad\qquad \textbf{3·7-14}$$

Since we now wish to find x as a function of v, it will be expedient to use the method of Eq. 3.7-6, obtained by replacing $\ddot{x}$ by $v(dv/dx)$. Then

$$v\frac{dv}{dx} = g \sin \theta - \frac{(A + Bv^2)}{m}$$

$$x - x_0 = m \int_{v_0}^{v} \frac{v\, dv}{mg \sin \theta - A - Bv^2} = \frac{-m}{2B} \log\left(mg \sin \theta - A - Bv^2\right)\Big|_{v_0}^{v}.$$

In this case, since the vehicle starts from rest, $x_0 = v_0 = 0$ and

$$x = \frac{-m}{2B} \log \left(1 - \frac{Bv^2}{mg \sin \theta - A} \right). \qquad \textbf{3·7-15}$$

We are now in a position to answer the question originally presented. Taking $v = 44$ ft/sec, $B = 0.011$ lb-sec^2/ft^2, $A = 60$ lb, $g = 32.2$ ft/sec^2, $\sin \theta = 0.05$, we have

$$x = \frac{-3500}{(64.4)(0.011)} \log \left(1 - \frac{(0.011)(44)^2}{175 - 60} \right) = -4950 \log 0.815$$

$$= (4950)(0.205) = 1000 \text{ ft.} \qquad \textbf{3·7-16}$$

We can see the effect of neglecting air resistance in this problem by allowing A and B in Eq. 3.7-15 to approach zero. Note that

$$\lim_{B \to 0} \frac{\log \left[1 - \dfrac{Bv^2}{mg \sin \theta} \right]}{B} = \frac{-v^2}{mg \sin \theta}.$$

For no air resistance, Eq. 3.7-15 reduces to $x = v^2/(2g \sin \theta)$, a result that could as easily have been reached from first principles. Setting $v = 44$ ft/sec, $g = 32.2$ ft/sec^2, $\sin \theta = 0.05$, we find $x = 600$ ft. The error due to neglect of air resistance would be considerable in this case.

The terminal velocity can be obtained directly from the equation of motion, 3.7-14, by setting $\ddot{x} = 0$.

$$mg \sin \theta - (A + Bv'^2) = 0$$

$$v' = [(mg \sin \theta - A)/B]^{1/2} = 102 \text{ ft/sec} = 70 \text{ mph.} \qquad \textbf{3·7-17}$$

Example 3·7-3

Discuss the effect of a retarding force proportional to speed and directed opposite to the velocity vector on the motion of a projectile.

Solution: Take origin at the point of release of the projectile, x-axis horizontal, y vertical upward. Then

$$m\dot{\mathbf{v}} = mg\mathbf{j} - k\mathbf{v}, \qquad \textbf{3·7-18}$$

$$\mathbf{v} = \mathbf{C}_1 e^{-(k/m)t} - \frac{mg}{k} \mathbf{j}, \qquad \textbf{3·7-19}$$

as may easily be verified by substitution. If $\mathbf{v} = \mathbf{v}_0$ at $t = 0$, the constant of integration $\mathbf{C}_1 = \mathbf{v}_0 + mg\mathbf{j}/k$,

$$\dot{\mathbf{r}} = \left(\mathbf{v}_0 + \frac{mg}{k} \mathbf{j} \right) e^{-(k/m)t} - \frac{mg}{k} \mathbf{j} \qquad \textbf{3·7-20}$$

$$\mathbf{r} = -\frac{m}{k} \left(\mathbf{v}_0 + \frac{mg}{k} \mathbf{j} \right) e^{-(k/m)t} - \frac{mg}{k} t\mathbf{j} + \mathbf{C}_2. \qquad \textbf{3·7-21}$$

At $t = 0$, $\mathbf{r} = 0$ so that

$$\mathbf{r} = \frac{m}{k}\left(\mathbf{v}_0 + \frac{mg}{k}\,\mathbf{j}\right)\left(1 - e^{-(k/m)t}\right) - \frac{mg}{k}\,t\mathbf{j}. \qquad \text{3.7-22}$$

The solution of the vector differential equation follows the solution of the scalar equation closely. In fact, in proceeding from Eq. 3.7-18 to 3.7-19 and from 3.7-20 to 3.7-21, the vectorial character of the variable may essentially be ignored provided we check the result after we have made the step.

The motion lies in the plane of the initial velocity vector $\mathbf{v}_0$ and the gravitational force. If we take an x-axis in that plane and write $\mathbf{v}_0 = \dot{x}_0\mathbf{i} + \dot{y}_0\mathbf{j}$,

$$\mathbf{r} = \frac{m\dot{x}_0}{k}\left(1 - e^{-(k/m)t}\right)\mathbf{i} + \left[\left(\frac{m\dot{y}_0}{k} + \frac{m^2 g}{k^2}\right)\left(1 - e^{-(k/m)t}\right) - \frac{mg}{k}\,t\right]\mathbf{j},$$

$$\mathbf{v} = (\dot{x}_0 e^{-(k/m)t})\mathbf{i} - \left[\frac{mg}{k}\left(1 - e^{-(k/m)t}\right) - \dot{y}_0 e^{-(k/m)t}\right]\mathbf{j}.$$

As t increases without limit, the displacement becomes asymptotic to the line $x = \dot{x}_0 m/k$. The path is shown in Fig. 3.7-2. The speed approaches a terminal value mg/k.

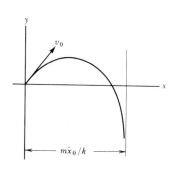

This example is one of the few cases of curvilinear motion under retardation forces that can be solved simply. It cannot be claimed, however, that the computation is of great utility so far as projectile motion is concerned because the linear resistance law is a gross oversimplification. In practice, the retarding force is tabulated as a function of altitude and speed and the equation of motion is solved by a numerical integration. This computation, though simple in principle, is time consuming when not performed by a high-speed electronic computer.

Fig. 3.7-2

Exercises

3.2-1: What is the maximum range of a projectile thrown in a horizontal tunnel 10 ft in diameter? The projectile is released from the bottom of the tunnel with a speed of 80 ft/sec.
Ans.: 104 ft.

3.2-2:   Swift of foot was Hiawatha;
          He could shoot an arrow from him,
          And run forward with such fleetness,
          That the arrow fell behind him!

Strong of arm was Hiawatha;
He could shoot ten arrows upward,
Shoot them with such strength and swiftness,
That the tenth had left the bow-string
Ere the first to earth had fallen!

Assuming Hiawatha could shoot arrows at the rate of two each second and that he tried for maximum range when he shot an arrow "from him," how swift of foot was he?
Ans.: 52 ft/sec.

3.2-3: A baseball is hit on a trajectory whose range is 350 ft and whose maximum height is 70 ft. Over what horizontal distance is the ball within 7 ft of the ground at the terminal end of its trajectory?
Ans.: 9 ft.

3.2-4: If a man can throw a ball 200 ft, how high can he throw it?
Ans.: 100 ft.

3.2-5: An object starting from rest at A slides down a straight chute inclined at an angle θ to the vertical. Show that the time required for it to reach the perimeter of a circle of radius R drawn through A and with center vertically below A is independent of θ and proportional to the square root of R. Neglect friction.

3.2-6: Consider the design of a package chute on which parcels slide from a point A to a lower point C on a ramp that is inclined to the horizontal. This ramp, if prolonged, would reach the same level as A at a point B, the horizontal distance AB being S. Use the result of the previous exercise to show that, for minimum travel time from A to C, the point C should be selected so as to be distant S from B. What is this minimum travel time from A to C if $S = 60$ ft and the ramp is inclined at an angle of $20°$ to the horizontal?
Ans.: 1.15 sec.

3.2-7: A box is placed on the flat bed of a truck at a distance s from the tailgate. The truck starts forward with an acceleration ng. Show that, if the coefficient of friction f is smaller than n, the package will fall off the truck after the truck has moved a distance $ns/(n-f)$.

3.2-8: A 16-lb collar on a smooth vertical shaft is connected by a spring of unstretched length 1.75 ft to a point 1.5 ft from the shaft. The collar is raised until the spring is horizontal and is then allowed to fall. Its motion reverses direction when it has dropped 2 ft. What is the modulus of the spring?
Ans.: 128 lb/ft.

3.2-9: Prove that for motion in a straight line under a constant force the time-average velocity in any time interval t_1, t_2 is the same as the velocity at $t = (t_1 + t_2)/2$ and the same as $[v(t_1) + v(t_2)]/2$.

3.2-10: For motion in a straight line, we define the distance-average velocity as the integral of $\dot{x}\, dx$ divided by the distance traversed. Show that the time-average velocity is always larger than the distance average for motion under constant force.

3.2-11: The cam shown below is cut so that $r = a + b \cos \theta$ where $a = 6$ in, $b = 3$ in. It rotates at the rate $\dot{\phi} = 12$ rad/sec. The contact follower weighs 4 lb, and its spring has a modulus of 0.2 lb/in. What is the minimum unstretched length of the spring if it is to prevent the follower from chattering on the cam? Neglect horizontal forces on the follower.
Ans.: 8.4 in.

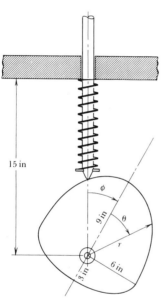

15 in

ϕ

9 in

θ

r

6 in

3 in

3.2-12: A vehicle travels in a straight path impelled by a constant thrust, F. After t_1 sec, starting from rest, it travels a distance x_1. Suppose the thrust had been controlled so as to keep the power at a constant value Fx_1/t_1; would the vehicle be traveling faster after t_1 sec than in the constant force case? What would be the speed ratio V_P/V_F in the two cases after traversing equal distances? What vehicle would you bet on in a race? Do you see any practical difficulty to keeping power constant?
Ans.: At corresponding times, $V_P = 2V_F$; at corresponding distances, $V_P = V_F$; $x_P/x_F = 4/3$; $P \to \infty$ as $t_1 \to 0$.

3.2-13: A particle of mass m is displaced from its position at the vertex of the parabola $x^2 = -4ay$. Show that the reaction of the smooth parabola on the particle is $mg[a/(a-y)]^{3/2}$ at any point y.

3.2-14: A particle moves in a straight line under the influence of a constant force. The velocities at times t_1, t_2 are v_1, v_2. Show that the time-average kinetic energy is $(m/6)(v_1^2 + v_1 v_2 + v_2^2)$.

3.3-1: Write the displacement $x = 5 \sin \left(2t - \dfrac{\pi}{4} \right)$ in the form

$$x = A \cos 2t + B \sin 2t.$$

Ans.: $-A = B = 5/\sqrt{2}$.

3.3-2: A particle moves with simple harmonic motion, its displacements at $t = 1, 2, 4$ sec being 2, 3.46, 3.46 cm respectively. Find the amplitude, period, and phase angle at time zero.
Ans.: $C = 4$ cm, $T_n = 12$ sec, $\alpha = \pi/2$.

3.3-3: Show that the phase-plane diagram for a mass connected to a fixed point by a spring and subject to a constant force F is a circle of radius $(2E_0/k)^{1/2}$ with center at $x = F/k$, $v = 0$. Here $2E_0 = (mv_0^2 + kx_0^2)$, v_0 and x_0 being the initial displacement and velocity.

3.3-4: A simple harmonic motion has an amplitude of 4 in and a period of 100 milliseconds (0.100 sec). What are the maximum velocity and acceleration?
Ans.: 251 in/sec; 15,800 in/sec².

3.3-5: A valve is controlled by an eccentric of radius R and eccentricity e, which rotates at the constant rate of p rad/sec. Show that the motion of the valve is simple harmonic.

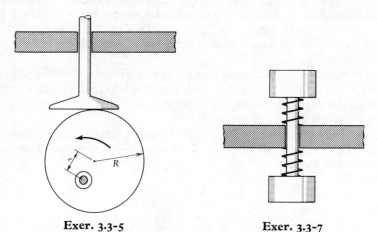

Exer. 3.3-5   Exer. 3.3-7

3.3-6: A mass of 5 kg is suspended from a spring of stiffness 30 newtons per meter, and this spring hangs from a second one whose stiffness is 20 newtons per meter. What is the natural frequency of the assembly?
Ans.: 0.25 cps.

3.3-7: The plunger shown weighs 16 lb. The springs have stiffnesses of 8 lb per foot each. What is the natural period of the system?
Ans.: 1.1 sec.

3.3-8: What is the natural frequency of the system shown? Ignore the mass of the pulley.

Ans.: $\omega_n = \dfrac{1}{2}\sqrt{\dfrac{k}{m}}.$

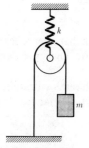

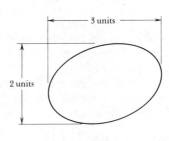

Exer. 3.3-8   Exer. 3.3-10

3.3-9: A ship whose volume below the water line is V and whose cross-sectional area at the water line is A floats in a canal lock of area B. Taking the sides of the ship at the water line to be vertical, compute the ship's natural period of vertical oscillation.

Ans.: $T_n = 2\pi \sqrt{\dfrac{V}{g}\left(\dfrac{1}{A} - \dfrac{1}{B}\right)}.$

3.3-10: The Lissajous figure for a simple harmonic motion with two degrees of freedom is as pictured. If the horizontal motion has a frequency of 60 cycles per second, what is the frequency of the vertical motion? What is the ratio of the amplitudes of horizontal and vertical motions?
Ans.: 60 cps, 3:2.

3.3-11: An accelerometer shows that a certain point on a vibrating body is moving at a frequency of 86 cps and a peak acceleration of 386 in/sec². What is the amplitude of the displacement?
Ans.: $1.32(10)^{-3}$ in.

3.3-12: The Lissajous figure for a simple harmonic motion with two degrees of freedom has the shape shown. What is the frequency ratio of vertical to horizontal motion?
Ans.: 1:5.

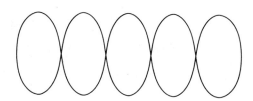

3.3-13: Draw the phase-plane diagram for free vibration of a single degree of freedom system whose equation of motion is $\ddot{x} + 36x = 0$ if $x_0 = 5$ ft and $v_0 = -18$ ft/sec. How long will it take the speed to reach its maximum value and what will this maximum value be?
Ans.: 35 ft/sec, 0.35 sec.

3.3-14: Show that if $m\ddot{x} + kx = 0$ then

$$\int_0^{2\pi/\omega_n} m\dot{x}^2 \, dt = \int_0^{2\pi/\omega_n} kx^2 \, dt.$$

This is sometimes paraphrased by the statement that over a complete cycle of simple harmonic motion the average kinetic energy is equal to the average potential energy.

3.3-15: Find the natural frequency of small lateral vibration of a cable stretched to a tension T and carrying a mass m at a distance a from one end and b from the other.

Ans.: $\omega_n^2 = (T/m)\left(\dfrac{1}{a} + \dfrac{1}{b}\right).$

3.4-1: The point of suspension of a simple pendulum is given a harmonic motion $x_0 = A \sin pt$ along a horizontal line. Derive the differential equation of motion for small amplitudes of oscillation using the coordinates shown and solve for x/x_0.

Ans.: $x/x_0 = (1 - p^2 l/g)^{-1}$.

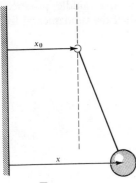

Exer. 3.4-1

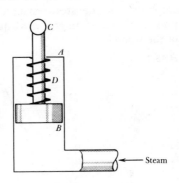

Exer. 3.4-2

3.4-2: A steam indicator consists of a cylinder, A, and a piston, B, acting against a spring, D, and carrying a rod that operates a recording pencil at C. The moving parts of the indicator weigh 2 lb and it takes 7.5 lb to compress the spring 1 in. The area of the piston is 0.6 in².

A record is made with the engine running at 180 rpm. It is found that the record is sinusoidal and has an amplitude of 2.5 in. Deduce the maximum value of the variable part of the steam pressure.

Ans.: 23.5 psi.

3.4-3: A sensitive instrument weighs 30 lb and is supported by 4 mounts each rated at 3/16 in per 20 lb. What percentage of the base vibration amplitude is the instrument vibration amplitude when the base vibrates at 40 cps?

Ans.: 9.5%.

3.4-4: A variable-speed electric motor is mounted on springs that have a total stiffness $k = 50$ lb/in. The weight of the assembly is 129 lb, and only vertical motion is possible. The rotor is slightly unbalanced. (a) At what speed will resonance occur? (b) If the unbalance produces a force whose magnitude at 100 rpm is 1.7 lb, what will be the amplitude of the motor vibration at that speed?

Ans.: 117 rpm, 0.13 in.

3.4-5: The needle shown is the recording element of an ammeter. It has a natural frequency of angular motion of 8.6 cps. If this instrument is calibrated by means of a steady signal and is then used to measure a signal that has a period of 0.4 sec, what will be the percentage error in the maximum reading? Will the instrument read too high or too low?

Ans.: 9.5% too high.

3.4-6: A simply supported horizontal beam under the action of a vertical force F applied at the middle deflects 1 in at the middle. What will be the amplitude of the steady-state deflection at the middle produced by a pulsating force $F \sin pt$ if p is equal to one-half the fundamental frequency of the beam?

Ans.: 1.33 in.

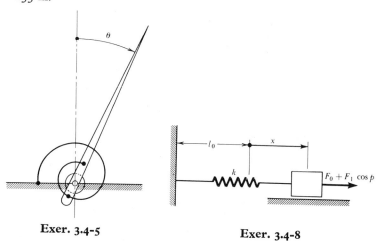

Exer. 3.4-5   **Exer. 3.4-8**

3.4-7: A 5000-lb machine, when bolted to the floor, produces a variable force of amplitude F at its operating frequency, 800 rpm. Design a vibration isolating mount that will reduce the amplitude of this transmitted force to 0.1 F.

Ans.: $k = 8100$ lb/in.

3.4-8: Write the complete solution for the displacement of the mass-spring system shown. Initially $x = x_0$ and $\dot{x} = v_0$.

Ans.: $x = x_0 \cos \omega_n t + (v_0/\omega_n) \sin \omega_n t + (F_0/k)(1 - \cos \omega_n t)$
$$+ (F_1/k)[1 - (p^2/\omega_n^2)]^{-1}[\cos pt - \cos \omega_n t].$$

3.4-9: Show that if the exciting frequency coincides with the natural frequency ($p = \omega_n$), the motion of a linear harmonic oscillator is given by $x = (F/2mp)t \sin pt$, and sketch the displacement as a function of time.

Note: *All problems of the next group on Section 3.5 refer to motion in an inverse square central force field.*

3.5-1: Show that at any point in an elliptic orbit $v^2 = \mu[(2/r) - (1/a)]$. (Hint: Use Eqs. 3.5-19 and 28.)

3.5-2: What is the minimum period of an artificial satellite that is to circle the earth?

Ans.: 85 min.

3.5-3: Show that the perpendicular to the major axis through the focus intersects an elliptic orbit at a   distance $q = h^2/\mu$ from the focus.   This distance is half the *latus rectum* of the ellipse.

3.5-4: Show that the equation of the orbit can be put in the form

$$r = q/[1 + e \cos(\phi - \alpha)]$$

where r and ϕ are polar coordinates.   (Hint: In Eq. 3.5-14, let $x = r \cos \phi$, $y = r \sin \phi$.)

3.5-5: What is the escape velocity from the surface of the earth?   What is the escape velocity from the solar system? $\mu_E = 39.89(10)^4$ km^3/sec^2, $\mu_S = 13.22(10)^{10}$ km^3/sec^2, radius of earth 6367 km, mean distance from sun $1.497(10)^8$ km.

Ans.: 11.2 km/sec, 42 km/sec.

3.5-6: The moon, which is distant 60.27 earth radii from us, has a period of 27 days 7 hrs 43 min.   The earth, which is $1.497(10)^8$ km from the sun, has a period of 365.26 days.   What is the ratio of the mass of the sun to the mass of the earth?

Ans.: 333,400.

3.5-7: Mars is at a mean distance from the sun 1.524 times the earth's mean distance, and Mercury is at a mean distance 0.387 that of the earth. What are the periods of Mars and Mercury?

Ans.: 687 days, 88 days.

3.5-8: A particle moves in an elliptic orbit about a gravitational force center at one focus.   If the greatest and least speeds of the particle are v_1 and v_2, find the eccentricity of the orbit.

Ans.: $e = (v_1 - v_2)/(v_1 + v_2)$.

3.5-9: An earth satellite is observed to have a speed of 5.5 mi/sec at its minimum altitude of 400 mi.   Take μ for the earth to be $9.6(10)^4$ mi^3/sec^2, and the mean radius of the earth as 3960 mi.

   (a) What is the angular momentum per unit mass (h) of the satellite?
   (b) What is the energy per unit mass (E)?
   (c) Explain how you can tell that the orbit is an ellipse, rather than a parabola or hyperbola.
   (d) Since h and E are constants of the orbit, what is the speed of the satellite at apogee?
   (e) What is the *altitude* of the satellite at apogee?

Ans.: (a) $h = 23,980$ mi^2/sec; (b) $E = -6.88$ mi^2/sec^2; (d) 2.6 mi/sec; (e) 5580 mi.

3.5-10: An earth satellite is to have an apogee of 6400 mi and a perigee of 4400 mi.   It is to be released at a distance of 5400 mi from the center of

the earth. What should be the velocity V_0, and the angle β with the horizontal; i.e., with the direction that is locally tangent to the earth's surface, at release? Take $\mu = 9.6(10)^4$ mi^3/sec^2.
Ans.: $V_0 = 4.22$ mi/sec; $\beta = 10.67°$.

3.5-11: An earth satellite is to have an apogee R_1 and a perigee R_2. It is to be released at a distance R_0, $R_2 \leqq R_0 \leqq R_1$, from the center of the earth. What should be the speed v_0 at release? What are the speeds v_1 and v_2 at apogee and perigee? What is h? What is the angle β between the initial velocity and the local horizontal at release? Check your answers for v_0 and β against those for the previous problem.

Ans.: $$v_0^2 = \frac{2\mu(R_1 + R_2 - R_0)}{R_0(R_1 + R_2)}; \qquad v_1^2 = \frac{2\mu R_2}{R_1(R_1 + R_2)};$$

$$h = \left[\frac{2\mu R_1 R_2}{R_1 + R_2}\right]^{\frac{1}{2}}; \qquad \beta = \arccos\left(\left[\frac{R_1 R_2}{R_0(R_1 + R_2 - R_0)}\right]^{\frac{1}{2}}\right).$$

3.5-12: A satellite weighing 250 lb at the earth's surface is to be put in orbit by taking it to an altitude of 200 mi above the surface and firing it with the velocity of magnitude V_0 and direction angle α_0 with its initial position vector. It is to come no nearer than 140 mi and go no farther than 260 mi from the surface. Find V_0, α_0, and the *total* energy, E_0, of the orbit. Take $\mu = 9.6(10)^4$ mi^3/sec^2, the radius of the earth as 3960 mi, and g at the surface as 32.2 ft/sec^2.
Ans.: $E_0 = -2.50(10)^9$ ft-lb, $\alpha_0 = 89^-$ degrees, $V_0 = 4.81$ mi/sec.

3.5-13: What will be the period of the satellite of Exercise 3.5-12?
Ans.: 90.5 min.

3.5-14: What energy E must be given to the satellite of Exercise 3.5-12 to take it from rest on the earth and establish it in orbit? Regard the earth as at rest.
Ans.: $E = 2.75(10)^9$ ft-lb.

3.5-15: A body is taken to a distance R_0 from the center of the earth and released with speed V_0 parallel to the earth's surface. We wish to investigate the degree of control that we must have on the launching speed V_0 in order to have the body move in an elliptical orbit outside the surface of the earth. Take the radius of the earth as R, and the force constant as μ.

(a) Let V^* be the escape speed for the distance R_0. What is V^*?

(b) The minimal orbit is one that just misses the earth's surface. What is the speed V^{**} for this grazing orbit? Neglect atmospheric effects.

(c) Compute the allowable velocity range (as a fraction of the escape velocity) as a function of the initial distance ratio, i.e., $(V^* - V^{**})/V^*$ as a function of R_0/R.

(d) Show that this ratio is smallest near the surface, largest far away; for what value of R_0/R is the ratio equal to 0.5? Does speed control seem particularly critical from this point of view?

(e) The results of parts (c) and (d) are based on computing the allowable speed range as a fraction of the escape speed at the initial altitude. Since this "local" escape speed decreases rapidly, this does not give a completely accurate picture of the allowable range. Suppose now that we refer the $V^* - V^{**}$ range to the escape speed at the surface, V^* (at $R_0 = R) = V_1^*$ and express the ratio $(V^* - V^{**})/V_1^*$ as a function of R_0/R. Show that the range is a maximum at a distance R_0 of approximately $1.62R$. Does speed control seem extremely critical from this point of view, at least in the distance range $1 \leqq R_0/R \leqq 3$?

Ans.:

(a) $V^{*2} = 2\mu/R_0$.

(b) $V^{**2} = 2\mu R/[R_0(R+R_0)]$.

(c) $(V^* - V^{**})/V^* = 1 - [1 + R_0/R]^{-\frac{1}{2}}$.

(d) $R_0/R = 3$.

(e) $(V^* - V^{**})/V_1^* = (R_0/R)^{-\frac{1}{2}}\{1 - [1 + (R_0/R)]^{-\frac{1}{2}}\}$.

3.5-16: Redo Exercise 3.5-15 in the context of a specific system of units—in particular, using miles and seconds as in other problems of this set. Use $R = 3960$ mi, $\mu = 9.6(10)^4$ mi^3/sec^2. What does the numerical solution do for your understanding of the problem? What do you think it conceals?

3.5-17: In Exercises 3.5-15, 16 we have been interested in the effect of changing initial speeds for a given launch angle on the possibility of an orbit. Now suppose that we are given v_0 as well as the initial distance R_0 from the center; v_0, of course, is less than the escape speed v^* for the distance. We wish to investigate the effect of the angle of launching. Instead of the angle α between $\mathbf{r}_0$ and $\mathbf{v}_0$ (angle with the local vertical), use the angle $\beta = (\pi/2) - \alpha$ (angle with the local horizontal). Take the radius of the earth $= R$, force law constant as μ.

(a) For given R_0 and v_0, compute the mean distance a of the satellite.

Ans.: $a = \mu R_0/(2\mu - R_0 v_0^2)$.

(b) From the general orbit relations (such as apogee and perigee distances and velocities), show that $h = [\mu a(1 - e^2)]^{\frac{1}{2}}$ and hence that the eccentricity is given in terms of the initial distance, speed, and angle by

$$e^2 = 1 - 2R_0 v_0^2 \mu^{-1} \cos^2 \beta + R_0^2 v_0^4 \mu^{-2} \cos^2 \beta.$$

(c) From the expressions for a and e, find the perigee distance in terms of the initial conditions. Since, for orbit, this must be at least as large as the radius of the earth, show that

$$\cos^2 \beta \geqq \frac{p + v^2 - 1}{p^2 v^2},$$

where

$$p = R_0/R \geqq 1 \quad \text{and} \quad v^2 = v_0^2/v^{*2}, \quad (1+p)^{-1} \leqq v^2 \leqq 1.$$

(The inequality governing ν arises from $v^{**2} \leq v_0^2 \leq v^{*2}$; see Exercise 3.5-15.)

(d) From part (c) show that the farthest that the launching angle can deviate from the horizontal (β deviate from $0°$) on either side without having the orbit hit the earth is under conditions of just about escape velocity for v_0 ($\nu \cong 1$); further, that then

$$-\arccos(p^{-\frac{1}{2}}) \leq \beta \leq \arccos(p^{-\frac{1}{2}}).$$

How big an angular deviation is this for launch at altitudes of 0.05, 0.10, 0.15, 0.20 of the earth's radius? Is angle of launch critical for satellites placed into orbit from positions near the earth?

3.5-18: What is the speed (in terms of μ and a) at perigee and at apogee of a particle in orbit about an inverse square center of force ($f = -\mu/r^2$) that is launched from an end of the semiminor axis of its orbit with speed two thirds of its maximum speed?

Ans.: perigee speed: $\dfrac{3}{2}\sqrt{\dfrac{\mu}{a}}$;   apogee speed: $\dfrac{2}{3}\sqrt{\dfrac{\mu}{a}}$.

3.5-19: In a book, *The System of the World*, attributed to Newton, the author—in an effort to explain why the mutual gravitational attraction of bodies is not noticed in everyday life—asserts that if two identical spheres of 1 ft diameter and density equal to the mean density of the earth were placed $\frac{1}{4}$ in apart "they would not, even in spaces of void of resistance, come together by the force of their mutual attraction in less than a month's time." The mean density of the earth is 5.5 times that of water (Newton knew this). Correct the computation.
Ans.: About 330 sec.

3.7-1: A ball is thrown vertically. Assuming air resistance proportional to the speed, will the resistance increase or decrease the total time in the air?
Ans.: Decrease; for small resistance coefficient k the ratio of the two times is $1 - (v_0 k/mg)$.

3.7-2: Clay particles are stirred up in a beaker of water 10 cm deep. Assuming the particles to be spherical, estimate the radius of the largest particle remaining in suspension after 24 hrs. Take the density of clay as 4 gm/cm³ and the viscosity of water as 0.010 poise (1 poise = 1 gm/cm-sec).
Ans.: $4.21(10)^{-5}$ cm.

3.7-3: An air bubble, radius 1 cm, rises through a column of oil at a steady rate 0.20 cm/sec. If the density of the oil is 1.5 gm/cm³, find its viscosity at the temperature of the experiment.
Ans.: $1.03(10)^3$ poise.

3.7-4: An automobile experiences resistance of $60 + (v^2/100)$ lb when v is in ft/sec. The rear wheels carry a load of 1500 lb, and the coefficient of friction under them is 0.5. What is the maximum speed of the vehicle? What horsepower must be available to reach this speed?
Ans.: 262 ft/sec; 357 hp.

3.7-5: A ship is propelled by a constant thrust, pm, where m is the mass of the ship. The water exerts a resistance cmv^2.

(a) What is the terminal velocity, V?

Ans.: $V = \sqrt{p/c}$.

(b) What is the distance traversed, starting from rest, in time t?

Ans.: $x = (V^2/2p) \log \cosh (pt/V)$.

(c) What is the distance traversed, starting from rest, when the speed is v?

Ans.: $x = (V^2/2p) \log [V^2/(V^2 - v^2)]$.

3.7-6: Suppose the ship of the previous problem is being brought to a stop and that p and c have the same meaning (but not necessarily the same magnitude) as before. Show that the ship, if traveling initially at speed v_0, will come to rest in a time $t = (V/p) \arctan (v_0/V)$ after traveling a distance $x = (V^2/2p) \log [1 + (v_0^2/V^2)]$.

3.7-7: Use the results of the previous problem to show that, if $v_0 = V$, the time required to stop the ship is $\pi V/4p$ and the distance is $0.347 V^2/p$. How much space is required to stop an 8000 HP ship weighing $5(10)^6$ lb traveling at top speed of 25 knots? One knot $= 1.69$ ft/sec. Assume, for this last part, that p and c are the same for reverse as for forward motion.

Ans.: 810 ft.

3.7-8: Suppose that the only force acting on a particle is the retarding force and that its magnitude is known as a function of time. It brings an object in rectilinear motion to rest in a time t_0. Show that the distance traversed is $\int_0^{t_0} \frac{1}{m} t F(t) \, dt$.

CHAPTER **IV**

Dynamics of Particle Systems
and Plane Rigid Bodies

4.1 Introduction

The particle model of a mechanical system is not sufficient for the description of most systems of engineering interest. Its use so far has enabled us to gain familiarity with the principles and methods of solution in situations where the geometry of motion is relatively simple.

We now wish to extend the particle principles to those for complex systems. We shall find that the principles for such systems can be phrased almost exactly like those for a single particle, with appropriate reinterpretations of terms such as linear momentum and kinetic energy. The geometry of motion—kinematics—becomes more complex now. For this reason, we shall limit the types of systems we are to consider.

The first generalization is from one to many particles. The full three-dimensional principles for a multiparticle system are not difficult to prove. The only additional kinematic concept we need is that of relative motion of two points, treated in the next section. The basic equations for multiparticle systems are then derived, and their extension to the next model—the body with continuously distributed mass—is discussed.

The continuous body model is, of course, the one most often used in engineering for a system, or a part of a system. In order to be able to treat a macroscopic system usefully, we do not consider its atomic structure but rather think of it as a distribution of mass through a region of space. The simplest model we can make of a continuous system is the *rigid body*. As we know from statics, a rigid body is one in which the distances between points of the body do not change during any motion or loading of the body. The rigid model leads to a mathematical description, both kinematical and dynamical, that is relatively easy to use. The complications that remain are still great enough to make it advisable to treat only two-dimensional motion of systems of rigid bodies in this chapter. Three-dimensional motion will be discussed in Chapter VI, where another important characteristic of the rigid model will be proved: the equations of dynamics are theoretically sufficient for the description of motion of a rigid body independent of the material of which it is made. Bodies of real materials, on the other hand, deform under load and indeed flow under certain circumstances. The analysis of such bodies requires statements about the properties of the materials of which they are made. Indeed, the solution of problems in statics of deformable media can be difficult, even without consideration of dynamic effects. The study of deformable solids and fluids is the province of elasticity, plasticity, viscous and compressible fluid flow, and other advanced fields of mechanics.

The rigid-body model is not simply a mathematical convenience. Most of the materials used in engineering fabrication and construction are stiff enough so that their local deformation can be neglected in comparison with their over-all motions. Under these circumstances a rigid-body analysis is usually accurate enough for the purpose of technology. Nor is the restriction to plane motion an artificial one; many important engineering devices can be replaced by a plane model. The applications of Chapter V illustrate this point more fully. The examples of this chapter, somewhat more academic in nature, are intended to bring out important features of the principles and of the methods of solution.

4.2 Relative Motion of Two Particles

Suppose two particles, P and Q, are moving in space, with their position vectors with respect to a fixed point O being $\mathbf{R}$ and $\mathbf{r}$ respectively (Fig. 4.2-1). The difference, $\mathbf{p} = \mathbf{r} - \mathbf{R}$, between the two position vectors is the position vector of Q with P taken as an origin. The vector $\mathbf{p}$ is called the *relative position vector* of Q with respect to P, and

$$\mathbf{r} = \mathbf{R} + \mathbf{p} \qquad\qquad 4.2\text{-}1$$

is the *relative position equation*. Regarding these vectors as twice-differentiable functions of a scalar time variable, we find the *relative velocity* and *relative acceleration equations*:

$$\dot{\mathbf{r}} = \dot{\mathbf{R}} + \dot{\mathbf{p}}, \qquad\qquad 4.2\text{-}2$$

$$\ddot{\mathbf{r}} = \ddot{\mathbf{R}} + \ddot{\mathbf{p}}. \qquad\qquad 4.2\text{-}3$$

The vectors $\dot{\mathbf{p}}$ and $\ddot{\mathbf{p}}$ are the *relative velocity* and *relative acceleration vectors* of Q with respect to P.

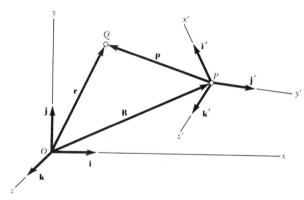

Fig. 4.2-1

There is an alternative notation useful in special problems where the derivative relations need not be emphasized by the dots. Use $\mathbf{r}$, $\mathbf{v}$, and $\mathbf{a}$ for all positions, velocities, and accelerations, differentiating between points by subscripts: e.g., $\mathbf{v}_P$ for the velocity of P. The relative motion quantities have two subscripts: $\mathbf{v}_{Q/P}$ for the velocity of Q relative to P. In this notation, 4.2-2 reads $\mathbf{v}_Q = \mathbf{v}_P + \mathbf{v}_{Q/P}$.

These three relative motion equations are so simple in form that it seems unnecessary to make special mention of them. As with many of our other equations and principles, the value of the relative motion equations comes from the interpretations that we are able to give to them and the applications we can make of them.

The simplest use of the relative-motion concept arises in problems in which the motion of a point, Q, is quite complex but can be resolved into two (or more) simpler motions. For example, if we can recognize the motion of Q as the combination of a circular motion of a point, P, about O and a circular motion of Q about P, we can form a description of Q's motion by compounding the two circular motions that we do know how to describe.

Information about a motion may be given in such a way that certain relative motion vectors are easier to write down directly than are the full "absolute" motion quantities. In such cases, it is natural to base the analysis on the relative motion equations. Also, as we shall see in the examples, conditions governing solutions may be expressed in terms of relative position or velocity vectors. The condition for collision of two particles, for instance, can be formulated as the vanishing of the relative position vector.

Proper development of the dynamical theory of systems requires the relative motion concept. The sections that follow on dynamics will make use of the vectorial relative motion equations over and over again for the simplification and extension of results. Indeed, we have used the relative motion concept already; in Section 2.2, conditions for the equality of absolute and relative acceleration vectors led to the identification of equivalent inertial frames of reference.

Introduction of specific coordinate systems permits us to write scalar equivalents to the vector equations. As we shall see in this chapter and in Chapter VI, careful consideration of the scalar forms of the relative motion equations will aid in our comprehension of the derivative of a vector and in the development of the dynamical theory, as well as in the direct calculation of velocities and accelerations.

Suppose that we introduce a cartesian coordinate system (x, y, z) with origin O and coordinate directions fixed in space so that the unit vectors $(\mathbf{i}, \mathbf{j}, \mathbf{k})$ are constant vectors (Fig. 4.2-1). Denoting the coordinates of Q with respect to O by (x, y, z), of P with respect to O by (X, Y, Z), and of Q with respect to P by (ξ, η, ζ), then the three vector equations (4.2-1, 2, 3) may be replaced by the three groups of three scalar equations, each obtained by projecting the vectors on the (x, y, z) axes in turn:

$$x = X + \xi, \qquad y = Y + \eta, \qquad z = Z + \zeta. \qquad \textbf{4.2-4}$$

$$\dot{x} = \dot{X} + \dot{\xi}, \qquad \dot{y} = \dot{Y} + \dot{\eta}, \qquad \dot{z} = \dot{Z} + \dot{\zeta}. \qquad \textbf{4.2-5}$$

$$\ddot{x} = \ddot{X} + \ddot{\xi}, \qquad \ddot{y} = \ddot{Y} + \ddot{\eta}, \qquad \ddot{z} = \ddot{Z} + \ddot{\zeta}. \qquad \textbf{4.2-6}$$

There is nothing new so far. If, in any one of these groups, we know six of the scalar functions, we may solve for the other three. The only feature of these equations that we wish to emphasize now is that, in the (x, y, z) coordinate system, the relative position vector and its derivatives are computed with $(\mathbf{i}, \mathbf{j}, \mathbf{k})$ fixed:

$$\mathbf{p} = \xi\mathbf{i} + \eta\mathbf{j} + \zeta\mathbf{k},$$

$$\frac{d\mathbf{p}}{dt} = \dot{\mathbf{p}} = \dot{\xi}\mathbf{i} + \dot{\eta}\mathbf{j} + \dot{\zeta}\mathbf{k}, \qquad \text{4.2-7}$$

$$\frac{d^2\mathbf{p}}{dt^2} = \ddot{\mathbf{p}} = \ddot{\xi}\mathbf{i} + \ddot{\eta}\mathbf{j} + \ddot{\zeta}\mathbf{k}.$$

It may happen that the relative motion of Q with respect to P is more easily described in a different set of coordinates. For instance, if the relative motion is a circular motion in a known plane inclined to the (x, y, z) axes, a second set of coordinates taken in and perpendicular to the plane will make the mathematical description of the motion simpler in form. Let us introduce a second set of coordinates (x', y', z') with unit vectors $(\mathbf{i}', \mathbf{j}', \mathbf{k}')$ and take the origin of these coordinates at P, since we shall use them for the relative motion with respect to P (Fig. 4.2-1). Projecting the relative position vector on these axes, we obtain a representation

$$\mathbf{p} = \xi'\mathbf{i}' + \eta'\mathbf{j}' + \zeta'\mathbf{k}'. \qquad \text{4.2-8}$$

The vector $\mathbf{p}$ is the same whether 4.2-8 or the first of 4.2-7 is used to represent it. There must then be some relation between the scalar functions (ξ', η', ζ') and (ξ, η, ζ). Using the *direction cosines* of the (x', y', z') axes with respect to the (x, y, z) axes, we can find these relations. The unit vectors $(\mathbf{i}', \mathbf{j}', \mathbf{k}')$ are given by

$$\mathbf{i}' = \cos(x, x')\mathbf{i} + \cos(y, x')\mathbf{j} + \cos(z, x')\mathbf{k},$$
$$\mathbf{j}' = \cos(x, y')\mathbf{i} + \cos(y, y')\mathbf{j} + \cos(z, y')\mathbf{k}, \qquad \text{4.2-9}$$
$$\mathbf{k}' = \cos(x, z')\mathbf{i} + \cos(y, z')\mathbf{j} + \cos(z, z')\mathbf{k},$$

where, for example, $\cos(z, y')$ is the cosine of the angle between the positive z-direction and the positive y'-direction. Then

$$\xi' = \mathbf{p} \cdot \mathbf{i}' = (\xi\mathbf{i} + \eta\mathbf{j} + \zeta\mathbf{k}) \cdot \mathbf{i}'$$

or

$$\xi' = \xi \cos(x, x') + \eta \cos(y, x') + \zeta \cos(z, x'). \qquad \text{4.2-10}$$

Similarly,

$$\eta' = \xi \cos(x, y') + \eta \cos(y, y') + \zeta \cos(z, y'), \qquad \text{4.2-11}$$

$$\zeta' = \xi \cos (x, z') + \eta \cos (y, z') + \zeta \cos (z, z'). \qquad \textbf{4.2-12}$$

The three relations 4.2-10, 11, 12 of course hold for the components of any vector in the two coordinate systems. That is, if $\mathbf{A} = A_x\mathbf{i} + A_y\mathbf{j} + A_z\mathbf{k} = A_x'\mathbf{i}' + A_y'\mathbf{j}' + A_z'\mathbf{k}'$, then (A_x', A_y', A_z') can be found from (A_x, A_y, A_z) by formulas analogous to 4.2-10, 11, 12 when the direction cosines are known. In Chapter VI, we shall see why the (x', y', z') axes can properly be said to be rotated from the (x, y, z) axes; the formulas 4.2-10, 11, 12 give the components of a vector under rotation of axes. These relations lie at the core of the proof that a vector equation is equivalent to at most three independent scalar equations.

Computation of the relative velocity vector by differentiation of the representation 4.2-8 results formally in

$$\frac{d\mathbf{p}}{dt} = \dot{\xi}'\mathbf{i}' + \dot{\eta}'\mathbf{j}' + \dot{\zeta}'\mathbf{k}' + \xi'\frac{d\mathbf{i}'}{dt} + \eta'\frac{d\mathbf{j}'}{dt} + \zeta'\frac{d\mathbf{k}'}{dt}. \qquad \textbf{4.2-13}$$

The first three terms of the right-hand side of 4.2-13 are analogous to the second of Eq. 4.2-7. Their sum is exactly the derivative of 4.2-8 if $\mathbf{i}'$, $\mathbf{j}'$, and $\mathbf{k}'$ are constant vectors. We introduce this as the formal concept of the derivative of a vector relative to, or in, a coordinate frame of reference or simply the *frame derivative* of a vector. Given the representation of a vector in a particular coordinate system, its frame derivative is the derivative computed as though the coordinate directions were fixed in space. The frame derivative can be denoted in a number of ways, among which are

$$\left(\frac{d\mathbf{p}}{dt}\right)_{(x', y', z')} \equiv \left(\frac{d\mathbf{p}}{dt}\right)' \equiv \frac{\delta\mathbf{p}}{\delta t}.$$

The first or second notation is helpful when one has to deal with a number of coordinate systems (x, y, z), (x', y', z'), (x'', y'', z''), and so forth. The last notation will be used here to save space when only two coordinate systems are involved. With

$$\frac{\delta\mathbf{p}}{\delta t} \equiv \dot{\xi}'\mathbf{i}' + \dot{\eta}'\mathbf{j}' + \dot{\zeta}'\mathbf{k}', \qquad \textbf{4.2-14}$$

we may rewrite 4.2-13 as

$$\frac{d\mathbf{p}}{dt} = \frac{\delta\mathbf{p}}{\delta t} + \xi'\frac{d\mathbf{i}'}{dt} + \eta'\frac{d\mathbf{j}'}{dt} + \zeta'\frac{d\mathbf{k}'}{dt}. \qquad \textbf{4.2-15}$$

We give the following interpretation to this equation. One observer measures the relative velocity of Q with respect to P by projecting it on axes parallel to (x, y, z), and says that it is $d\mathbf{p}/dt$. A second observer projects it on axes (x', y', z') and says that it is $\delta\mathbf{p}/\delta t$. These two observations do not agree unless both axis systems have fixed directions in space, the difference being the last three terms due to the change of one set of directions with respect to the other.

Just how these direction changes can be computed will be postponed until Chapter VI (although we could at this point say much about these derivatives of unit vectors, similar computations having been made in Sections 1.9–1.10). In this chapter, we shall consider only those cases for which

$$\frac{d\mathbf{p}}{dt} = \frac{\delta\mathbf{p}}{\delta t};$$ **4.2-16**

i.e., those for which the moving coordinate system does not rotate. So far, we have not really used the fact that the origin of (x, y, z) is O and the origin of (x', y', z') is P, and we have not needed to; the two systems could have the same origin, since only their relative directions are of importance. If we do consider them as having different origins but constant relative directions, then we say that the coordinate systems are in a state of relative *translation*—or, with (x, y, z) fixed and (x', y', z') moving,* the latter *translates* relative to the former. The velocity and acceleration of translation are the velocity $\dot{\mathbf{R}}$ and acceleration $\ddot{\mathbf{R}}$ of P.

Finally, a second differentiation of the relative position vector in each of the coordinate frames leads from 4.2-15 to a general relation between

$$\frac{d^2\mathbf{p}}{dt^2} \equiv \left(\frac{d^2\mathbf{p}}{dt^2}\right)_{(x,\,y,\,z)} \quad \text{and} \quad \frac{\delta^2\mathbf{p}}{\delta t^2} \equiv \left(\frac{d^2\mathbf{p}}{dt^2}\right)_{(x',\,y',\,z')},$$

where the second frame derivative is defined as

$$\frac{\delta^2\mathbf{p}}{\delta t^2} = \ddot{\xi}'\mathbf{i}' + \ddot{\eta}'\mathbf{j}' + \ddot{\zeta}'\mathbf{k}'.$$ **4.2-17**

The general relation will be treated in Chapter VI; for translating coordinates,

$$\frac{d^2\mathbf{p}}{dt^2} = \frac{\delta^2\mathbf{p}}{\delta t^2}.$$ **4.2-18**

The equality of the two frame derivatives in 4.2-16 and in 4.2-18 means that relations between their scalar components of the

---

* From the kinematical point of view, it does not matter which frame is regarded as fixed and which as moving. From the dynamical point of view, the special place held by the inertial frame selects the inertial frame as "fixed."

form 4.2-10, 11, 12 hold; for translating coordinates, the direction cosines are constants, independent of time.

The following examples illustrate some applications of the relative motion equations. The first three are properly not particle motion problems at all, but should be treated under kinematics of systems of rigid bodies. They can be adapted, however, as point motion problems and serve to illustrate some important features of the relative motion approach to problems.

Example **4.2-1**

A rod of length l rotates at a constant angular rate Ω in the (x, y) plane, with one end, O, fixed (Fig. 4.2-2). A turntable of radius r is pinned at the other end, P, of the rod. The turntable rotates freely about its center at constant rate ω. Find the acceleration of point Q on the rim of the turntable when it is in the general position shown.

Solution: Here the use of the relative motion equations is the natural approach to the problem. An attempt to write down the position vector **r** of Q with respect to O in terms of its magnitude and direction would lead to the use of the lengths and angles shown in Fig. 4.2-2 in any case. We consider the motion in two parts: the motion of P relative to O and the motion of Q relative to P.

Let θ be the angle from the x-axis to OP; the constant rotation rate of the rod means that $\dot\theta=\Omega$, $\ddot\theta=\dot\Omega=0$. Let ϕ be the angle from a line through P parallel to the x-axis to the radius line PQ; the turntable rotates at rate $\dot\phi=\omega$ with $\ddot\phi=\dot\omega=0$. We may approach the problem in two ways. First,

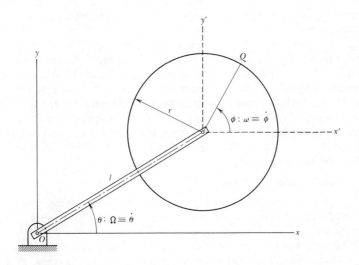

Fig. 4.2-2

we find the position $\mathbf{R}$ of P and the relative position $\mathbf{p}$ of Q with respect to P:

$$\mathbf{R} = l \cos \theta \mathbf{i} + l \sin \theta \mathbf{j},$$

$$\mathbf{p} = r \cos \phi \mathbf{i}' + r \sin \phi \mathbf{j}'$$

$$= r \cos \phi \mathbf{i} + r \sin \phi \mathbf{j}.$$

Using the relative position equation, we write the position vector $\mathbf{r}$ for Q, then differentiate twice to find $\ddot{\mathbf{r}}$:

$$\mathbf{r} = \mathbf{R} + \mathbf{p} = (l \cos \theta + r \cos \phi)\mathbf{i} + (l \sin \theta + r \sin \phi)\mathbf{j},$$

$$\dot{\mathbf{r}} = -(l\Omega \sin \theta + r\omega \sin \phi)\mathbf{i} + (l\Omega \cos \theta + r\omega \cos \phi)\mathbf{j},$$

$$\ddot{\mathbf{r}} = -(l\Omega^2 \cos \theta + r\omega^2 \cos \phi)\mathbf{i} - (l\Omega^2 \sin \theta + r\omega^2 \sin \phi)\mathbf{j}.$$

Second, we can compute the accelerations $\ddot{\mathbf{R}}$ and $\ddot{\mathbf{p}}$ first, then use the relative acceleration equation to find $\ddot{\mathbf{r}}$:

$$\ddot{\mathbf{R}} = -l\Omega^2(\cos \theta \mathbf{i} + \sin \theta \mathbf{j}) = -\Omega^2 \mathbf{R}$$

$$\ddot{\mathbf{p}} = -r\omega^2(\cos \phi \mathbf{i} + \sin \phi \mathbf{j}) = -\omega^2 \mathbf{p}$$

$$\ddot{\mathbf{r}} = \ddot{\mathbf{R}} + \ddot{\mathbf{p}} = -\Omega^2 \mathbf{R} - \omega^2 \mathbf{p}.$$

There is not much difference between these two approaches. The first is the direct approach that one would probably use without formal knowledge of the relative motion equations: find the position vector and differentiate it. The second procedure brings out the fact that the motion of Q is a vectorial compounding of two circular motions, each at constant speed. This way of thinking about the motion gives us insight into the motion of Q, to be sure, but it can lead to a serious misinterpretation in more difficult problems.

In this problem, we can compute the motion of Q with respect to P without regard for the motion of P itself. That is, if P were not moving ($\Omega = 0$), we would still have the same $\ddot{\mathbf{p}}$. The form of the relative motion equations suggests that this is generally true: the motion of P is accounted for in $\mathbf{R}, \dot{\mathbf{R}}, \ddot{\mathbf{R}}$; the relative motion is therefore computed as though P were not moving but fixed. *This is a false conclusion.* The choice of P influences the form of $\mathbf{p}$ generally. Since $\mathbf{p}$ depends on the coordinates of $\mathbf{R}$, the derivatives of $\mathbf{p}$ will depend on the derivatives of $\mathbf{R}$. This will be clarified in the next two examples.

Example 4.2-2

Suppose that the turntable of the last problem cannot freely rotate about the pin at P, but is welded to the rod so that the radius PQ makes an angle of $30°$ with OP. Find the acceleration of Q.

Solution: Again we may split the motion of Q into two parts, the motion of P and the relative motion. The motion of P is still the same, so that

$$\ddot{\mathbf{R}} = -l\Omega^2(\cos \theta \mathbf{i} + \sin \theta \mathbf{j}) = -\Omega^2 \mathbf{R}.$$

The angle ϕ shown in Fig. 4.2-2 is not now free to change independently of θ, but is given by

$$\phi = \theta + \frac{\pi}{6} \text{ radians};$$

thus

$$\mathbf{p} = r(\cos\phi\mathbf{i} + \sin\phi\mathbf{j}) = r\left[\cos\left(\theta + \frac{\pi}{6}\right)\mathbf{i} + \sin\left(\theta + \frac{\pi}{6}\right)\mathbf{j}\right],$$

and

$$\ddot{\mathbf{p}} = -r\Omega^2\left[\cos\left(\theta + \frac{\pi}{6}\right)\mathbf{i} + \sin\left(\theta + \frac{\pi}{6}\right)\mathbf{j}\right] = -\Omega^2\mathbf{p}.$$

The acceleration of Q is then

$$\ddot{\mathbf{r}} = \ddot{\mathbf{R}} + \ddot{\mathbf{p}} = -\Omega^2(\mathbf{R} + \mathbf{p}) = -\Omega^2\mathbf{r}.$$

Note that the relative motion is still a circular motion at constant speed $(r\Omega)$, but that now $\ddot{\mathbf{p}}$ does in fact depend on the motion of P: if $\ddot{\mathbf{R}} = \mathbf{0}$, so does $\ddot{\mathbf{p}}$.

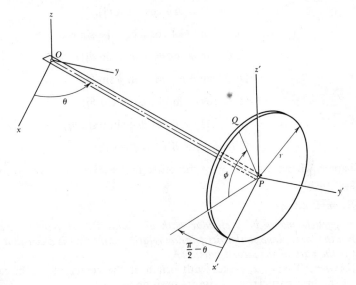

Fig. 4.2-3

Example 4.2-3

Suppose the turntable of Example 4.2-1 is mounted orthogonally on the rod, like a flywheel on a shaft (Fig. 4.2-3). The rod still rotates at constant rate Ω in the plane. The disk can rotate freely about the shaft at rate ω. Find the acceleration of Q.

Solution: Again, we split the motion into two parts, with the motion of P as before: $\ddot{\mathbf{R}} = -\Omega^2\mathbf{R} = -l\Omega^2(\cos\theta\mathbf{i} + \sin\theta\mathbf{j})$. The plane of the disk is now perpendicular to the shaft and hence to the xy-plane. Choosing (x', y', z') axes at P as shown, parallel to (x, y, z), the z'-axis is always in the plane of the disk, which is rotated at angle $(\pi/2) - \theta$ back from the $x'z'$-plane. The angle ϕ measuring the rotation of the disk about the rod (so that $\dot{\phi} = \omega$) is now measured from a line in the xy-plane and in the plane of the disk, which does not have constant direction in space.

The relative position vector is given by

$$\mathbf{p} = r\sin\phi\mathbf{k}' + r\cos\phi\left[\cos\left(\frac{\pi}{2} - \theta\right)\mathbf{i}' - \sin\left(\frac{\pi}{2} - \theta\right)\mathbf{j}'\right]$$

$$= r\cos\phi\sin\theta\mathbf{i} - r\cos\phi\cos\theta\mathbf{j} + r\sin\phi\mathbf{k}.$$

If we attempt an analysis on the basis that the motion of Q is still compounded of two simple circular motions at constant speed, we are led to the wrong answer; $\ddot{\mathbf{p}} \neq -\omega^2\mathbf{p}$. In fact,

$$\dot{\mathbf{p}} = r\omega(-\sin\phi\sin\theta\mathbf{i} + \sin\phi\cos\theta\mathbf{j} + \cos\phi\mathbf{k})$$

$$+ r\Omega(\cos\phi\cos\theta\mathbf{i} + \cos\phi\sin\theta\mathbf{j}),$$

$$\ddot{\mathbf{p}} = r\omega^2(-\cos\phi\sin\theta\mathbf{i} + \cos\phi\cos\theta\mathbf{j} - \sin\phi\mathbf{k})$$

$$+ r\omega\Omega(-\sin\phi\cos\theta\mathbf{i} - \sin\phi\sin\theta\mathbf{j})$$

$$+ r\Omega\omega(-\sin\phi\cos\theta\mathbf{i} - \sin\phi\sin\theta\mathbf{j})$$

$$+ r\Omega^2(-\cos\phi\sin\theta\mathbf{i} + \cos\phi\cos\theta\mathbf{j})$$

$$= -\omega^2\mathbf{p} - 2r\omega\Omega(\sin\phi\cos\theta\mathbf{i} + \sin\phi\sin\theta\mathbf{j})$$

$$- r\Omega^2(\cos\phi\sin\theta\mathbf{i} + \cos\phi\cos\theta\mathbf{j}).$$

In Chapter VI, we will see why the other terms arise and how we may interpret them.

Example 4.2-4

A particle moves in a circular path of radius R. A second particle moves in the same plane so that its position relative to the first is a constant $\mathbf{p}_0$. What is the path of the second particle?

Solution: Taking x, y-axes with origin at the center of the circular path of the first particle, we write its position as

$$\mathbf{R} = x_1\mathbf{i} + y_1\mathbf{j} = R(\cos\theta\mathbf{i} + \sin\theta\mathbf{j}).$$

The position of the second particle is then given by

$$\mathbf{r} = \mathbf{R} + \mathbf{p}$$

$$= (R\cos\theta + p_x)\mathbf{i} + (R\sin\theta + p_y)\mathbf{j},$$

where $\mathbf{p}_0 = p_x\mathbf{i} + p_y\mathbf{j}$. The second particle thus travels in a circle of radius

R with center at the point $\mathbf{p}_0$ from the origin:

$$x = R \cos \theta + p_x, \qquad y = R \sin \theta + p_y,$$
$$(x - p_x)^2 + (y - p_y)^2 = R^2.$$

Example 4.2-5

A particle moves in a straight line at constant speed V. A second particle, moving with constant speed v, starts at position $\mathbf{p}_0$ relative to the first. The velocity of the second particle is always directed toward the first. Formulate the differential equations governing the position vector $\mathbf{r}$ of the second particle.

Solution: This is a pursuit-curve problem in a simple form; the path $\mathbf{r}$ is the path of pursuit of one body after another, say one airplane "particle" pursuing another, both at constant speed and with no evasive action. Choose the origin of coordinates at the initial position of the first particle and the x-axis in the direction of its motion. Then its velocity and position are $\dot{\mathbf{R}} = V\mathbf{i}$, $\mathbf{R} = Vt\mathbf{i}$.

Let $\mathbf{r}$ be the position of the second particle at any time t; the conditions of the problem lead to the vector differential equation

$$\mathbf{v} = \frac{d\mathbf{r}}{dt} = -v\,\frac{\mathbf{p}}{|\mathbf{p}|} = -v\,\frac{(\mathbf{r} - \mathbf{R})}{|\mathbf{r} - \mathbf{R}|},$$

which is to be solved with the initial condition $\mathbf{r}(0) = \mathbf{p}_0$. Now reformulate the equations, recognizing that the motion must always lie in the plane of the x-axis and the initial position vector $\mathbf{p}_0$. Then

$$\mathbf{r} = x\mathbf{i} + y\mathbf{j}, \qquad \mathbf{v} = \dot{x}\mathbf{i} + \dot{y}\mathbf{j}, \qquad \mathbf{p}_0 = x_0\mathbf{i} + y_0\mathbf{j},$$

and

$$\mathbf{p} = \mathbf{r} - \mathbf{R} = (x - Vt)\mathbf{i} + y\mathbf{j}.$$

Then the vector differential equation can be replaced by the equivalent scalar equations

$$\dot{x} = -v(x - Vt)[(x - Vt)^2 + y^2]^{-\frac{1}{2}},$$
$$\dot{y} = -vy[(x - Vt)^2 + y^2]^{-\frac{1}{2}},$$

subject to the initial conditions

$$x(0) = x_0, \qquad y(0) = y_0.$$

4.3 Dynamics of Multiparticle Systems

Consider an isolated system of mass particles moving with respect to an inertial frame under the influence of some force system (Fig. 4.3-1). Suppose that there are N particles. The typical particle is called the "i-th" particle, its mass being denoted by m_i and its position relative to the origin O of the inertial frame being $\mathbf{r}_i$. The subscript i ranges over the values $1, 2, 3, \ldots N$. The forces acting on each particle can be divided into two groups—the *external* and *internal* forces. As the words imply, the internal forces are those forces exerted by other parts of the same system on the particle, whereas the external forces are any forces exerted on the particle by bodies not considered as part of the system. This distinction points up the necessity of the clear, explicit selection of the particular system to be considered and the identification and classification of the forces acting on it by means of the free-body diagram. The importance of this becomes clear with the final statement of the governing principles for systems. Let the resultant of the external forces on the *i*-th particle be denoted by $\mathbf{F}_i$. The internal force on the *i*-th particle due to another typical particle, the *j*-th particle, is denoted by $\mathbf{f}_{ij}$. The forces acting on the *i*-th particle are shown in Fig. 4.3-1; for each particle in the system we have a similar picture. For each particle, the second law of motion holds:

$$\mathbf{F}_i + \sum_{\substack{j=1 \\ j \neq i}}^{N} \mathbf{f}_{ij} = m_i \mathbf{a}_i = \frac{d}{dt}(m_i \mathbf{v}_i), \qquad i = 1, 2, 3, \ldots N.$$

We may eliminate the restriction that $j \neq i$ in the sum representing the resultant of the internal forces if we define the symbol $\mathbf{f}_{ii}$ as equal to

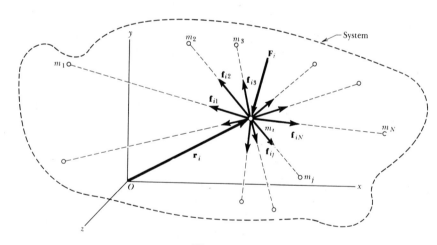

Fig. 4.3-1

the zero vector, $i = 1, 2, 3, \ldots N$. Then the equations of motion for each particle of the system, representing in all $3N$ scalar equations, are

$$\mathbf{F}_i + \sum_{j=1}^{N} \mathbf{f}_{ij} = \frac{d}{dt}(m_i \mathbf{v}_i), \qquad i = 1, 2, 3, \ldots N. \qquad \textbf{4.3-1}$$

Seeking a closed-form analytic solution to Eqs. 4.3-1 is at best a thankless, at worst a hopeless, task; even when such a solution exists, its interpretation in terms of simple statements about the motion of each point becomes much too complex as the number of particles increases. For instance, in celestial mechanics, we are interested in the N-body problem for the sun and planets, where the particles move under their mutual gravitational attractions. The equations are of the type 4.3-1 with $\mathbf{F}_i = \mathbf{0}$, and the internal forces are of the newtonian gravitational type. The solution for the two-body problem can be written down in relatively simple mathematical form for any set of initial positions and velocities. For three or more bodies, no complete analytic solution for arbitrary initial conditions is known, though many special cases have been solved. This does not mean that the three-body problem is insoluble or that the equations are insufficient for the determination of the motion. The problem can be solved to whatever accuracy desired by numerical means. What we are saying is that for multi-body problems there is no relatively simple mathematical solution for the motion of all particles that enables us to gain a clear picture of what the subsequent motion will be.

Rather than treat all of the Eqs. 4.3-1, we settle for something less than complete knowledge of the motion of the system. We use the third law of motion to eliminate the internal forces from consideration. By Newton's third law, to each of the forces $\mathbf{f}_{ij}$ there corresponds a collinear force of equal magnitude but opposite direction $\mathbf{f}_{ji}$, the force on the j-th particle due to the i-th particle:

$$\mathbf{f}_{ji} = -\mathbf{f}_{ij}. \qquad \textbf{4.3-2}$$

If we add the N vector Eqs. 4.3-1, we obtain the single vector equation

$$\sum_{i=1}^{N} \mathbf{F}_i + \sum_{i=1}^{N} \sum_{j=1}^{N} \mathbf{f}_{ij} = \sum_{i=1}^{N} \frac{d}{dt}(m_i \mathbf{v}_i). \qquad \textbf{4.3-3}$$

The first term on the left is the resultant, $\mathbf{F}$, of the external forces only: $\mathbf{F} = \sum_{i=1}^{N} \mathbf{F}_i$. The second term, the double sum, is the resultant of the internal forces—and this vanishes:

$$\sum_{i=1}^{N} \sum_{j=1}^{N} \mathbf{f}_{ij} = \mathbf{0}.$$

For, if $i = j$, $\mathbf{f}_{ii} = \mathbf{0}$ by hypothesis; and, if $i \neq j$, to the term $\mathbf{f}_{ij}$ there is added its negative $\mathbf{f}_{ji}$. Thus the sum of all internal forces vanishes.

Our result can be stated as

The resultant force sum of all forces, external and internal, is equal to the sum of the external forces on the system only.

The right-hand side of Eq. 4.3-3 can be rewritten, using the fact that the sum of the derivatives of vectors equals the derivative of the sum of the vectors, as

$$\sum_{i=1}^{N} \frac{d}{dt} (m_i \mathbf{v}_i) = \frac{d}{dt} \left(\sum_{i=1}^{N} m_i \mathbf{v}_i \right).$$

Just as $m_i \mathbf{v}_i$ is the linear momentum of the i-th particle, we define $\sum_{i=1}^{N} m_i \mathbf{v}_i$ to be the total *linear momentum of the system*.   Equation 4.3-3 expresses the generalization of Newton's second law to systems:

> In an inertial frame of reference, a system of particles moves under all forces acting on it in such a way that the resultant of the external forces alone is equal to the time rate of change of the linear momentum of the system (measured in consistent dynamical units):

$$\mathbf{F} = \frac{d}{dt} \sum_{i=1}^{N} (m_i \mathbf{v}_i). \qquad \textbf{4.3-4}$$

By analogy with particle motion, we say a system behaves as though it were a particle in the sense that the above principle indicates—the resultant force on the system as a whole causes a change in the momentum of the system.   We may make the analogy more complete by imagining a single particle of mass m equal to the total mass of the system moving on a path.   What should the path be so that the motion of the model particle under the resultant of the external forces on the system may represent the average motion of the system?   Such a particle must have momentum equal to the momentum of the system; denoting the velocity of the particle by $\mathbf{v}^*$, we have

$$m\mathbf{v}^* = \sum_{i=1}^{N} m_i \mathbf{v}_i, \qquad \textbf{4.3-5}$$

where

$$m = \sum_{i=1}^{N} m_i. \qquad \textbf{4.3-6}$$

Integration of 4.3-5 gives

$$m\mathbf{r}^* = \sum_{i=1}^{N} m_i \mathbf{r}_i + \mathbf{C}.$$

Taking the constant of integration $\mathbf{C} = \mathbf{0}$, we have

$$m\mathbf{r}^* = \sum_{i=1}^{N} m_i \mathbf{r}_i. \qquad \text{4·3-7}$$

The point at position $\mathbf{r}^*$ is the *center of mass*, C, of the system and will be so denoted on free-body diagrams in this text. Its coordinates (x^*, y^*, z^*) are defined by the equation just written. In the calculus, the concept of the *first moment* of a scalar quantity with respect to a line or plane is defined. Sums like $\sum m_i x_i$ are the first moments of mass—this particular sum being the first moment of the mass system with respect to the yz-coordinate plane. The number $x^* = \sum m_i x_i / \sum m_i \equiv \sum m_i x_i / m$ is then the x-coordinate of the point where a single mass m must be located to give the same first moment with respect to the yz-plane. The process of finding the centroid of a volume or area is an example of the use of the first-moment concept, with area or volume being the quantity whose moment is being found. The vector moment $\mathbf{r} \times \mathbf{F}$ of a vector $\mathbf{F}$ is also directly related to the first-moment concept; here again we have a "multiplication" of a length into a quantity.

Differentiating 4·3-7, we of course obtain 4·3-5; a second differentiation defines the acceleration of the mass center:

$$m\mathbf{a}^* = \sum_{i=1}^{N} m_i \mathbf{a}_i. \qquad \text{4·3-8}$$

The first basic dynamical principle governing motion of a system can then be restated in the form in which it is most often given:

The Principle of Motion of the Mass Center:

Relative to an inertial frame of reference, the mass center C of a system of particles moves as though the system were a single particle of mass equal to the total mass of the system moving under the external forces according to Newton's second law:

$$\mathbf{F} = m\mathbf{a}^* = \frac{d}{dt}(m\mathbf{v}^*). \qquad \text{4·3-9}$$

The second basic principle is the angular-momentum principle. Write the moment-of-momentum equation for each particle by taking the moments with respect to the origin of the inertial frame. From Eq. 4·3-1 and the basic vector relation $\mathbf{r} \times \mathbf{a} = d(\mathbf{r} \times \mathbf{v})/dt$, we have

$$\mathbf{r}_i \times \mathbf{F}_i + \mathbf{r}_i \times \sum_{j=1}^{N} \mathbf{f}_{ij} = \mathbf{r}_i \times \frac{d}{dt}(m_i \mathbf{v}_i)$$

$$= \frac{d}{dt}(\mathbf{r}_i \times m\mathbf{v}_i), \qquad i = 1, 2, 3, \ldots N. \qquad \text{4·3-10}$$

The left-hand side is the resultant moment about O of all the forces acting on the i-th particle; the right-hand side is the time rate of change of its moment of momentum. Now add the N vector equations 4.3-10:

$$\sum_{i=1}^{N} (\mathbf{r}_i \times \mathbf{F}_i) + \sum_{i=1}^{N} \left(\mathbf{r}_i \times \sum_{j=1}^{N} \mathbf{f}_{ij}\right) = \sum_{i=1}^{N} \frac{d}{dt} (\mathbf{r}_i \times m_i \mathbf{v}_i). \qquad \textbf{4.3-11}$$

The right-hand side of this equation is, by the theorem that the sum of the derivatives equals the derivative of the sum of the vectors, just the time rate of change of the moment of momentum of the system:

$$\sum_{i=1}^{N} \frac{d}{dt} (\mathbf{r}_i \times m_i \mathbf{v}_i) = \frac{d}{dt} \sum_{i=1}^{N} \mathbf{r}_i \times m_i \mathbf{v}_i = \frac{d\mathbf{H}_O}{dt},$$

where $\mathbf{H}_O$ is defined by

$$\mathbf{H}_O = \sum_{i=1}^{N} \mathbf{r}_i \times m_i \mathbf{v}_i. \qquad \textbf{4.3-12}$$

The first term on the left of Eq. 4.3-11 is the resultant moment $\mathbf{M}_O$ about O of the external forces acting on the system. Let us show that the second term,

$$\sum_{i=1}^{N} \left(\mathbf{r}_i \times \sum_{j=1}^{N} \mathbf{f}_{ij}\right) = \sum_{i=1}^{N} \sum_{j=1}^{N} (\mathbf{r}_i \times \mathbf{f}_{ij}),$$

vanishes. Each term in the sum for which $i = j$ vanishes automatically, of course, since $\mathbf{f}_{ii} = \mathbf{0}$ by definition. If $i \neq j$, consider the sum of the two terms

$$\mathbf{r}_i \times \mathbf{f}_{ij} + \mathbf{r}_j \times \mathbf{f}_{ji}.$$

By Eq. 4.3-2, this sum equals

$$\mathbf{r}_i \times \mathbf{f}_{ij} + \mathbf{r}_j \times \mathbf{f}_{ji} = \mathbf{r}_i \times \mathbf{f}_{ij} + \mathbf{r}_j \times (-\mathbf{f}_{ij}) = (\mathbf{r}_i - \mathbf{r}_j) \times \mathbf{f}_{ij}.$$

But $\mathbf{r}_i - \mathbf{r}_j$ is the relative position vector $\mathbf{r}_{ij}$ of the i-th particle with respect to the j-th particle. By Newton's third law, we know that $\mathbf{f}_{ij}$ has line of action along the line joining m_i and m_j, and so has the same (or opposite) direction as $\mathbf{r}_{ij}$. Since the vector product of parallel vectors vanishes,

$$\mathbf{r}_i \times \mathbf{f}_{ij} + \mathbf{r}_j \times \mathbf{f}_{ji} = \mathbf{r}_{ij} \times \mathbf{f}_{ij} = \mathbf{0}.$$

Since the sum of the moments of the internal forces thus vanishes by pairs, the whole sum vanishes. (The student should draw a picture showing $\mathbf{r}_i$, $\mathbf{r}_j$, $\mathbf{f}_{ij}$, $\mathbf{f}_{ji}$ and the appropriate moment vectors—the result is clearly indicated by such a picture.)

We have shown that the resultant moment about a fixed point of all forces is equal to the moment of the external forces only. We have further shown that the following principle holds:

Principle of Moment of Momentum (for a system of particles):

Relative to the fixed origin of an inertial frame of reference, the resultant moment of the external forces acting on a system of particles equals the time rate of change of the moment of momentum of the system about the origin:

$$\mathbf{M}_O = \dot{\mathbf{H}}_O. \qquad\qquad 4\cdot3\text{-}13$$

The fact that these principles involve the external forces only explains why we usually show only such forces on the free-body diagram we make of the isolated system.

There are two things to be done next. One is the extension of these principles, and those derivable from them, so that they—or properly modified forms—hold with respect to points not fixed in an inertial frame or with respect to frames of reference moving with respect to the base inertial frame. The other is the immediate extension of these principles to so-called continuous mass distributions—those systems where we regard the mass as given by some density distribution, ρ, throughout the volume of a body (or along a curve or on a surface). The final result is the same as that given in Eqs. 4.3-9 and 4.3-13; the same principles hold for continuous systems, so the restriction to systems of discrete particles can be eliminated from the statement of the principles. In the definition of the mass center and of $\mathbf{H}_O$, the sums are replaced by definite integrals in the usual manner of the calculus.

Consider a body and divide it into N sections; the i-th section has mass Δm_i. Let $\mathbf{r}_i$ be the position vector to any point in Δm_i, and $\mathbf{v}_i$ be its derivative. Form the sums

$$\sum_{i=1}^{N} \Delta m_i, \qquad \sum_{i=1}^{N} \mathbf{r}_i \, \Delta m_i, \qquad \sum_{i=1}^{N} \mathbf{r}_i \times (\mathbf{v}_i \, \Delta m_i).$$

Now find the limits of these as N becomes large without limit and each Δm approaches zero; if these limits exist, however $\mathbf{r}_i$ is chosen and whatever the method of subdivision is, then we say that the definite integrals exist, and are—respectively—the total mass, the mass times the position vector of the mass center, and the moment of momentum of the body:

$$m = \int dm, \qquad m\mathbf{r}^* = \int \mathbf{r} \, dm, \qquad \mathbf{H}_O = \int (\mathbf{r} \times \mathbf{v}) \, dm. \qquad 4\cdot3\text{-}14$$

If the mass distribution has a density function ρ so that $dm = \rho \, dV$

then these become triple integrals over the volume of the body:

$$m = \int\int\int_V \rho \, dV, \qquad m\mathbf{r}^* = \int\int\int_V \mathbf{r}\rho \, dV,$$

$$\mathbf{H}_O = \int\int\int_V (\mathbf{r} \times \mathbf{v})\rho \, dV.$$

Equations 4.3-14 thus define the quantities m, $\mathbf{r}^*$, and $\mathbf{H}_O$ for continuous distributions. The assertion that the equations $\mathbf{F} = m\mathbf{a}^*$ and $\mathbf{M}_O = \dot{\mathbf{H}}_O$ hold for a continuous body as well as for a system of discrete particles embodies a physical hypothesis. We must assume that the internal forces in such a body obey the third law of motion and are of finite magnitude so that they cancel in the same way for continuous systems as for discrete particles.

Example 4.3-1

Find the location of the mass center and the linear momentum of the system of four particles shown. Also find the angular momentum with respect to O of the system (Fig. 4.3-2).

Solution:

$$m = \sum_{i=1}^{4} m_i = 5 \text{ slugs};$$

$$m\mathbf{r}^* = \sum_{i=1}^{4} m_i \mathbf{r}_i$$

$$= 2(\mathbf{i}+\mathbf{j}+\mathbf{k}) + 1(4\mathbf{j}+3\mathbf{k}) + 1.5(2\mathbf{i}+2\mathbf{k}) + 0.5(4\mathbf{k})$$

$$= 5\mathbf{i} + 6\mathbf{j} + 10\mathbf{k};$$

$$\mathbf{r}^* = \mathbf{i} + 1.2\mathbf{j} + 2\mathbf{k} \text{ ft.}$$

$$m\mathbf{v}^* = \sum_{i=1}^{4} m_i \mathbf{v}_i = 14\mathbf{i} - 6\mathbf{j} - 4.5\mathbf{i} + 6\mathbf{i} + 2.5\mathbf{k}$$

$$= 15.5\mathbf{i} - 6\mathbf{j} + 2.5\mathbf{k},$$

$$\mathbf{v}^* = 3.1\mathbf{i} - 1.2\mathbf{j} + 0.5\mathbf{k} \text{ ft/sec.}$$

$$\mathbf{H}_O = \sum_{i=1}^{4} (\mathbf{r}_i \times m_i \mathbf{v}_i)$$

$$= \begin{vmatrix} \mathbf{i} & \mathbf{j} & \mathbf{k} \\ 1 & 1 & 1 \\ 14 & 0 & 0 \end{vmatrix} + \begin{vmatrix} \mathbf{i} & \mathbf{j} & \mathbf{k} \\ 0 & 4 & 3 \\ 0 & -6 & 0 \end{vmatrix} + \begin{vmatrix} \mathbf{i} & \mathbf{j} & \mathbf{k} \\ 2 & 0 & 2 \\ -4.5 & 0 & 0 \end{vmatrix} + \begin{vmatrix} \mathbf{i} & \mathbf{j} & \mathbf{k} \\ 0 & 0 & 4 \\ 6 & 0 & 2.5 \end{vmatrix}$$

$$= 18\mathbf{i} + 29\mathbf{j} - 14\mathbf{k} \text{ lb-ft-sec.}$$

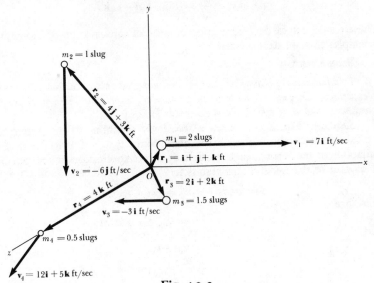

Fig. 4.3-2

Example 4.3-2

If the initial positions and velocities of a system of four particles are as given in the previous problem, and if the only forces acting are the internal forces between particles—whatever the connections between them are—what can be said about the subsequent motion of the system?

Solution: Since there are no external forces on the system, Fig. 4.3-2 can serve as a free-body diagram if we imagine the position vector to each as quite general rather than the particular numbers given. The motion of the mass center is determined by

$$\mathbf{F} = \mathbf{0} = 5\mathbf{a}^*,$$

or $\mathbf{a}^* = \mathbf{0}$; thus the mass center moves with constant velocity

$$\mathbf{v}^* = 3.1\mathbf{i} - 1.2\mathbf{j} + 0.5\mathbf{k} \text{ ft/sec.}$$

Integrating,

$$\mathbf{r}^* = \mathbf{v}^* t + (\mathbf{r}^*)|_{t=0}$$
$$= (3.1t+1)\mathbf{i} + 1.2(1-t)\mathbf{j} + (0.5t+2)\mathbf{k} \text{ ft.}$$

Thus the mass center moves on a straight line at constant velocity.

Similarly, $\mathbf{M}_O = \mathbf{0}$; thus $\dot{\mathbf{H}}_O = \mathbf{0}$ and $\mathbf{H}_O$ is a constant:

$$\mathbf{H}_O = 18\mathbf{i} + 29\mathbf{j} - 14\mathbf{k} \text{ lb-ft-sec.}$$

Thus, however the individual particles may move, they must do so in such a way that

$$\sum m_i \mathbf{r}_i = 5\mathbf{r}^* = 5[(3.1t+1)\mathbf{i} + 1.2(1-t)\mathbf{j} + (0.5t+2)\mathbf{k}],$$

$$\sum m_i \mathbf{r}_i \times \frac{d\mathbf{r}_i}{dt} = 18\mathbf{i} + 29\mathbf{j} - 14\mathbf{k}.$$

These results can be derived as consequences of conservation-of-momentum principles that we derive later.

Example 4.3-3

Two particles of masses m_1 and m_2 are subjected only to the forces of mutual interaction. Discuss the motion; in particular, show that there is an inertial coordinate system in which the mass center is fixed.

Solution: Fig. 4.3-3 shows a free-body diagram of the system at a typical instant; only internal forces act. Since $\mathbf{f}_{21} = -\mathbf{f}_{12}$, addition of the equations of motion for each particle or direct application of the principle of motion of the mass center results in

$$\mathbf{0} = m_1\ddot{\mathbf{r}}_1 + m_2\ddot{\mathbf{r}}_2 = (m_1 + m_2)\ddot{\mathbf{r}}^*;$$

therefore,

$$\ddot{\mathbf{r}}^* = \mathbf{0}, \qquad \dot{\mathbf{r}}^* = \mathbf{v}_0, \text{ a constant,}$$

and

$$\mathbf{r}^* = \mathbf{v}_0 t + \mathbf{r}_0.$$

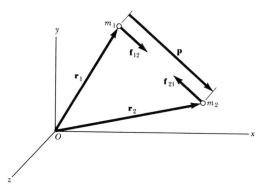

Fig. 4.3-3

The mass center moves at constant velocity relative to O. Since (Section 2.2) a coordinate frame translating at constant velocity relative to an inertial frame is also inertial, we may choose an inertial frame in which the mass center is fixed, and indeed choose the origin at the mass center. Since

$$\mathbf{r}^* = \frac{m_1\mathbf{r}_1 + m_2\mathbf{r}_2}{m_1 + m_2},$$

by taking $\mathbf{r}^* = \mathbf{0}$, we have

$$\mathbf{r}_1 = -\frac{m_2}{m_1}\mathbf{r}_2 \qquad \text{and} \qquad \mathbf{p} = \mathbf{r}_2 - \mathbf{r}_1 = \frac{m_1 + m_2}{m_1}\mathbf{r}_2.$$

Thus, in the inertial system based on the mass center as fixed, we may express the positions of the two particles in terms of their relative position:

$$\mathbf{r}_1 = -\frac{m_2}{(m_1+m_2)}\,\mathbf{p}, \qquad \mathbf{r}_2 = +\frac{m_1}{(m_1+m_2)}\,\mathbf{p}.$$

The angular-momentum principle $\dot{\mathbf{H}}^*=\mathbf{M}^*$ leads to a constant $\mathbf{H}^*$, since $\mathbf{M}^*$ vanishes. Now

$$\mathbf{H}^* = \mathbf{r}_1 \times m_1\mathbf{v}_1 + \mathbf{r}_2 \times m_2\mathbf{v}_2$$

$$= -\frac{m_2}{m_1+m_2}\,\mathbf{p} \times m_1 \left(\frac{-m_2}{m_1+m_2}\,\dot{\mathbf{p}}\right)$$

$$+\frac{m_1}{m_1+m_2}\,\mathbf{p} \times m_2 \left(\frac{m_1}{m_1+m_2}\,\dot{\mathbf{p}}\right)$$

$$= \frac{m_1m_2}{m_1+m_2}\,\mathbf{p} \times \dot{\mathbf{p}};$$

a constant $\mathbf{H}^*$ implies $\mathbf{p}$ lies always in a fixed plane perpendicular to $\mathbf{H}^*$ through the fixed mass center. The motion of the two bodies is thus seen to be a plane motion about the mass center, coupled with (at most) a constant translation with the velocity of the mass center.

Finally, if m_1 is very much bigger than m_2, we see that the mass center is very close to m_1. The limit $m_1 \to \infty$ gives $\mathbf{r}^*=\mathbf{r}_1$ as a fixed point, and $\mathbf{r}_2=\mathbf{p}$; i.e., we have the fixed-center-of-force, single-particle motion problem discussed in Chapters II and III.

This example has discussed some general results for a special case of the *two-body problem*.

After stating the angular momentum principle, we said there were two things to be done. We have considered the extension of the basic principles to continuous distributions by means of an additional hypothesis on the nature of internal forces. The continuous-system model of a physical body is the one we are most interested in; before going on to discuss it, however, still further extension of the basic principles for particle systems will help us understand what we must do for continuous systems. This is the second task mentioned earlier: what are the forms of the principles referred to coordinates moving with respect to an inertial frame? After all, it would be very inconvenient to refer the motion of an airplane to a coordinate frame a thousand miles away at an airport, when we are not even sure that such a frame is an inertial one.

Consider the particle system of Fig. 4.3-1 once again, moving with respect to an inertial frame with origin at the fixed point O. Choose any point P with position vector $\mathbf{R}(t)$ relative to O. Let $\mathbf{p}_i$ be the relative position vector of the i-th particle relative to P; the relative motion equations are then

$$\mathbf{r}_i = \mathbf{R} + \mathbf{p}_i, \qquad \mathbf{v}_i = \dot{\mathbf{R}} + \dot{\mathbf{p}}_i, \qquad \mathbf{a}_i = \ddot{\mathbf{R}} + \ddot{\mathbf{p}}_i. \qquad \textbf{4.3-15}$$

The position of the mass center C relative to P is given by $\mathbf{p}^*$, where $\mathbf{r}^* = \mathbf{R} + \mathbf{p}^*$. We can rewrite the principle of motion of the mass center (Eq. 4.3-9):

$$\mathbf{F} = m\mathbf{a}^* = m(\ddot{\mathbf{R}} + \ddot{\mathbf{p}}^*),$$

or, alternatively,

$$\mathbf{F} - m\ddot{\mathbf{R}} = m\ddot{\mathbf{p}}^*.$$

We see that, if we measure accelerations with respect to P, the principle of motion of the mass center holds ($\mathbf{F} = m\ddot{\mathbf{p}}^*$) if, and only if, P is not accelerating with respect to the base inertial frame of reference. This parallels the developments of Section 2.3 for single particle. Formally,

(1) If the mass-center principle holds in a given coordinate system, it does not hold—that is, does not preserve its form—in any translating system based on a point having non-zero acceleration with respect to the given system:

$$m\ddot{\mathbf{p}}^* = \mathbf{F} - m\ddot{\mathbf{R}}. \qquad \textbf{4.3-16}$$

(2) If the principle of motion of the mass center holds in a given reference frame, it also holds in any frame (and only those frames) that translates with constant velocity with respect to the given system; moreover, the two frames of reference are indistinguishable insofar as measurements of acceleration are concerned:

$$\mathbf{F} = m\ddot{\mathbf{r}}^* = m\ddot{\mathbf{p}}^*. \qquad \textbf{4.3-17}$$

The first statement is the basis for the use of *D'Alembert's principle*, or the method of "reversed effective force," for translational motion. If we measure accelerations in a coordinate system translating with acceleration $\ddot{\mathbf{R}} = \ddot{\mathbf{r}}^*$ with respect to the given inertial frame, then in the new coordinate system $m\ddot{\mathbf{p}}^* = \mathbf{0}$. Thus, if we imagine that a "force"—the *reversed effective force* or *inertia force*—equal to $-m\ddot{\mathbf{r}}^*$ is imposed on our system in the original frame of reference, equations of force equilibrium will be satisfied: $\mathbf{F} + (-m\ddot{\mathbf{r}}^*) = \mathbf{0}$. The second statement tells us again that we cannot distinguish between two inertial frames of reference by the measurement of accelerations.

In order to derive useful alternative forms of the principle of angular momentum, we must derive first a formula relating the angular momentum vectors computed with respect to different base points.

The vector symbols used so far will still be used, but with slightly different meanings in this paragraph; see Fig. 4.3-4. Take any two points, Q and P, in space; let $\mathbf{r}_i$ and $\mathbf{p}_i$ now be the positions of the i-th particle relative to Q and P respectively, and let $\mathbf{R}$ be the position of P relative to Q. The fundamental definition of angular momentum for a particle leads to $\mathbf{H}_Q = \mathbf{r}_i \times m_i \dot{\mathbf{r}}_i$, $\mathbf{H}_P = \mathbf{p}_i \times m_i \dot{\mathbf{p}}_i$ as the angular momentum vectors based on Q and P for the i-th particle, and (following Eq. 4.3-12) to

$$\mathbf{H}_Q = \sum_{i=1}^{N} \mathbf{r}_i \times m_i \dot{\mathbf{r}}_i, \qquad \mathbf{H}_P = \sum_{i=1}^{N} \mathbf{p}_i \times m_i \dot{\mathbf{p}}_i$$

for the angular momentum of the whole system of particles. Use the relative motion equations (Eqs. 4.3-15) to transform $\mathbf{H}_P$:

$$\mathbf{H}_P = \sum_{i=1}^{N} \mathbf{p}_i \times m_i \dot{\mathbf{p}}_i = \sum_{i=1}^{N} (\mathbf{r}_i - \mathbf{R}) \times m_i (\dot{\mathbf{r}}_i - \dot{\mathbf{R}})$$

$$= \sum_{i=1}^{N} \mathbf{r}_i \times m_i \dot{\mathbf{r}}_i - \sum_{i=1}^{N} \mathbf{r}_i \times m_i \dot{\mathbf{R}} - \sum_{i=1}^{N} \mathbf{R} \times m_i \dot{\mathbf{r}}_i + \sum_{i=1}^{N} \mathbf{R} \times m_i \dot{\mathbf{R}}.$$

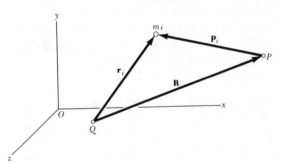

Fig. 4.3-4

But $\mathbf{R}$ and $\dot{\mathbf{R}}$ refer to the position and velocity of the specific point P relative to Q, and hence may be factored out of the summation operation:

$$\mathbf{H}_P = \sum_{i=1}^{N} \mathbf{r}_i \times m_i \dot{\mathbf{r}}_i - \left(\sum_{i=1}^{N} m_i \mathbf{r}_i \right) \times \dot{\mathbf{R}}$$

$$- \mathbf{R} \times \left(\sum_{i=1}^{N} m_i \dot{\mathbf{r}}_i \right) + \left(\sum_{i=1}^{N} m_i \right) \mathbf{R} \times \dot{\mathbf{R}}.$$

The first term is $\mathbf{H}_Q$. Introducing the total mass m of the system and the position $\mathbf{r}^*$ and velocity $\dot{\mathbf{r}}^*$ of the mass center relative to Q, we can replace the sums in the last three terms by $m\mathbf{r}^*$, $m\dot{\mathbf{r}}^*$, and m

respectively. We can then write the first form of the fundamental change of base point formula for angular momentum:

$$\mathbf{H}_P = \mathbf{H}_Q - \mathbf{r}^* \times (m\dot{\mathbf{R}}) - \mathbf{R} \times (m\dot{\mathbf{r}}^*) + \mathbf{R} \times (m\dot{\mathbf{R}}). \qquad \textbf{4.3-18a}$$

Two alternative forms result from grouping the second and fourth and the third and fourth terms, and recognizing that the position and velocity of the mass center relative to P are given by $\mathbf{p}^* = \mathbf{r}^* - \mathbf{R}$, $\dot{\mathbf{p}}^* = \dot{\mathbf{r}}^* - \dot{\mathbf{R}}$:

$$\mathbf{H}_P = \mathbf{H}_Q - \mathbf{p}^* \times m\dot{\mathbf{R}} - \mathbf{R} \times m\dot{\mathbf{r}}^*, \qquad \textbf{4.3-18b}$$

$$\mathbf{H}_P = \mathbf{H}_Q - \mathbf{r}^* \times m\dot{\mathbf{R}} - \mathbf{R} \times m\dot{\mathbf{p}}^*. \qquad \textbf{4.3-18c}$$

(These are not the kinds of formulas worth remembering; rather, one should know about them, their significance, and where to find them.)

We can now go on to the alternative forms of the angular-momentum principle. We start by identifying the point Q of the last development with the origin O of an inertial frame of reference, and the time derivative (indicated by the dot over the vectors as usual) with the time derivative in the inertial frame. Then $\mathbf{r}_i$ and $\dot{\mathbf{r}}_i \equiv \mathbf{v}_i$, $\mathbf{r}^*$, and $\dot{\mathbf{r}}^* \equiv \mathbf{v}^*$ have their ordinary meanings relative to the inertial frame; also, the angular momentum principle, in its simplest form, holds with respect to O: $\mathbf{M}_O = \dot{\mathbf{H}}_O$.

Differentiating 4.3-18a, we find

$$\dot{\mathbf{H}}_P = \mathbf{M}_O - m\mathbf{v}^* \times \dot{\mathbf{R}} - m\mathbf{r}^* \times \ddot{\mathbf{R}} - m\dot{\mathbf{R}} \times \mathbf{v}^*$$
$$- m\mathbf{R} \times \mathbf{a}^* + m\dot{\mathbf{R}} \times \dot{\mathbf{R}} + m\mathbf{R} \times \ddot{\mathbf{R}},$$

or

$$\dot{\mathbf{H}}_P = \mathbf{M}_O - \mathbf{R} \times m\mathbf{a}^* - m(\mathbf{r}^* - \mathbf{R}) \times \ddot{\mathbf{R}}.$$

But the principle of motion of the mass center holds in the reference frame based on O, so that $m\mathbf{a}^* = \mathbf{F}$. In the study of resultant force systems in statics, the general result is derived that a force system having resultant force $\mathbf{F}$ and resultant moment $\mathbf{M}_O$ about O must have resultant moment

$$\mathbf{M}_P = \mathbf{M}_O + \mathbf{r}_{PO} \times \mathbf{F} \qquad \textbf{4.3-19}$$

about any other point P. Since the position vector from P to O is $-\mathbf{R}$ in our notation, we see that

$$\dot{\mathbf{H}}_P = \mathbf{M}_P - m\mathbf{p}^* \times \ddot{\mathbf{R}}. \qquad \textbf{4.3-20}$$

Thus, if $\dot{\mathbf{H}}_O = \mathbf{M}_O$, then $\dot{\mathbf{H}}_P$ is in general not equal to $\mathbf{M}_P$ for any other point P moving with respect to O. Only if the vector $m\mathbf{p}^* \times \ddot{\mathbf{R}} = \mathbf{0}$ will $\mathbf{M}_P = \dot{\mathbf{H}}_P$. This can occur if, and only if, one of three conditions holds:

     1. $\ddot{\mathbf{R}} = \mathbf{0}$: P moves at constant velocity relative to O. This is the same condition as that derived for the mass-center principle, and includes points fixed in the inertial frame.

     2. $\mathbf{p}^* = \mathbf{0}$: the position of the mass center C relative to P vanishes; i.e., P is the mass center C.

     3. $\mathbf{p}^*$ and $\ddot{\mathbf{R}}$ are parallel: the acceleration of P lies along the line joining the mass center and P.

The simple form of the angular-momentum principle holds if, and only if, P is one of these three kinds of points. In particular, we have the important result that the angular-momentum principle based on the mass center has the form

$$\dot{\mathbf{H}}^* = \mathbf{M}^*. \qquad\qquad \textbf{4.3-21}$$

If P does not satisfy one of these three conditions, Eq. 4.3-20 is the proper form of the angular-momentum principle.

     It should be noted here that, in the extension of both the mass-center and moment-of-momentum principles, we are concerned usually with new coordinate systems based on the new origin P for the simplest representation of the relative motion vectors. If, as we have seen in Section 4.2, the new coordinates at P do not rotate with respect to the ones at O, but translate with the velocity of P, then we may use either coordinate system for representation of the vectors with equal validity.

     Finally, we note two matters of importance. The extensions of the moment-of-momentum principle were derived for particle systems, but the conclusions expressed in Eqs. 4.3-18, 20, 21, and in the three conditions for the choice of auxiliary base points hold for any continuous system as well. Integrals with respect to mass replace the sums leading to 4.3-18, but otherwise the derivations are the same. The second important fact is that Eq. 4.3-18 gives the relation between the angular momenta based on any two points, Q and P, and its derivation does not require that Q be fixed in an inertial system. We can use this to derive the relation between the angular momentum $\mathbf{H}^*$ based on the mass center and the angular momentum based on any other point P. Take Q as the mass center C; then the position and velocity $\mathbf{r}^*$ and $\mathbf{v}^*$ of the mass center C with respect to Q

will be the position and velocity of C with respect to itself and hence must vanish. Thus

$$\mathbf{H}_P = \mathbf{H}^* + m\mathbf{R} \times \dot{\mathbf{R}}, \qquad 4.3\text{-}22$$

where $\mathbf{R}$ is the position of P relative to C.

4.4 Kinematics of Plane Rigid Bodies

The development so far of the vector principles of dynamics for systems provides the theoretical foundations for applications to systems of engineering interest. The difficulty in application lies in the representation of the vectors appropriately. In particular, the vectors expressing basically kinematic concepts, $\mathbf{a}^*$ and $\mathbf{H}$, need interpretation; the computation of force and moment sums is straight-forward.

We shall be concerned in the rest of this chapter with the theory of the rigid body, and systems of rigid bodies, in plane motion, although we shall not hesitate to state general three-dimensional results for systems where they can be derived easily. We start with a kinematical study. Our point of departure is the relative motion equations 4.2-1, 2, 3, and we wish to find the form of the relative motion vectors that hold for two points on the same plane rigid body.

A system is said to be in (general) *plane motion* if every point in the system moves on a plane path parallel to some fixed base plane. The plane of motion of the mass center is called the *principal plane of motion*. If all of the mass of the system and the forces acting on the system can be considered to be in the principal plane of motion, then the system is in *strictly plane motion*. Throughout the rest of this chapter, the words "plane motion" will be used in this latter restric-tive sense. Pick any two points P and Q on the rigid body L (called a *lamina*) in plane motion (Fig. 4.4-1). Let $\mathbf{R}$ and $\mathbf{r}$ be the position vectors of these points with respect to O at any time t, and let $\mathbf{p}$ be the relative position vector. Since L is rigid, the distance between points on L never changes: $|\mathbf{p}| = p$ is a constant. Let θ_{PQ} be the angle from some fixed direction in the plane, say Ox, to $\mathbf{p}$.

As L moves in its plane, point Q must describe a circle about point P of radius p; that is, to an observer at P, point Q would appear to move on a circular arc. But we know how to describe circular motion, with either plane polar or intrinsic coordinates as natural ones for its description. In particular, we use what may be called relative intrinsic coordinates $\mathbf{e}'_t$ and $\mathbf{e}'_n$. Here $\mathbf{e}'_n$ is the relative unit normal vector of Q with respect to P, pointing from Q toward P; $\mathbf{e}'_t$ is the relative unit tangent vector perpendicular to the relative position vector and in the sense of increasing θ_{PQ}. Then for two points on the same rigid body,

$$\mathbf{p} = p(-\mathbf{e}_n') = -p\mathbf{e}_n';$$
$$\dot{\mathbf{p}} = p\dot{\theta}_{PQ}\mathbf{e}_t';$$
$$\ddot{\mathbf{p}} = p\dot{\theta}_{PQ}^2\mathbf{e}_n' + p\ddot{\theta}_{PQ}\mathbf{e}_t'.$$

4.4-1

The relative acceleration components are called the relative normal and relative tangential components, respectively.

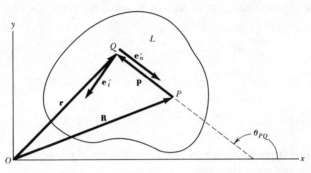

Fig. 4.4-1

In this form, the relations—while useful—would still not tell us much about the motion of the lamina as a whole. One of the most important consequences of the assumption of rigidity simplifies the discussion of rigid-body motion greatly—that is the fact that the quantities $\dot{\theta}_{PQ}$ and $\ddot{\theta}_{PQ}$ are not merely the rates of angle change for the line $\mathbf{p}$, *but are the same for all lines in the body.* This is easy to show. Consider any two lines in the lamina, making angles θ and ϕ with the positive x-axis. Extend the two lines until they intersect, including between them a third angle, ψ: $\phi = \theta + \psi$ (Fig. 4.4-2). Since

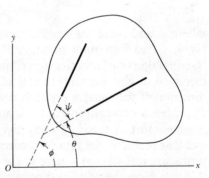

Fig. 4.4-2

the body is rigid, ψ must be a constant as the body moves; otherwise two points, one on each line, would have changing distance between them. Thus $\dot\phi = \dot\theta + \dot\psi = \dot\theta$, $\ddot\phi = \ddot\theta$. The special case $\psi = 0$—parallel lines—of course leads to $\dot\phi = \dot\theta$, since ψ must then always vanish. The quantity $\dot\theta = \omega$ is the *angular velocity* of the rigid body; $\ddot\theta = \dot\omega = \alpha$ is the *angular acceleration* of the rigid body. It is important that these are properties of the body as a whole; for a nonrigid system moving in a plane, the angular velocities of different relative position vectors are different, and we cannot speak of *the* angular velocity. As defined here, ω and α are scalar functions. We may define a third scalar function, θ, the *angular displacement* of the body in the plane, as the time integral of the angular velocity; then (θ, ω, α) are related in the same way as the (x, v, a) and (s, v, a_t) of Sections 1.8 and 1.9 are:

$$\omega = \frac{d\theta}{dt}, \qquad \theta - \theta_0 = \int_{t_0}^{t} \omega(\tau)\, d\tau,$$

$$\alpha = \frac{d\omega}{dt}, \qquad \omega - \omega_0 = \int_{t_0}^{t} \alpha(\tau)\, d\tau, \qquad \textbf{4.4-2}$$

$$\alpha = \omega\, \frac{d\omega}{d\theta}, \qquad \frac{1}{2}(\omega^2 - \omega_0^2) = \int_{\theta_0}^{\theta} \alpha(\phi)\, d\phi.$$

The relative motion equations for a plane rigid body can be then written in the following way:

If two points on the same rigid body are distance p apart, then the relative position, velocity, and acceleration vectors are

$$\mathbf{p} = -p\mathbf{e}'_n,$$

$$\dot{\mathbf{p}} = p\omega\mathbf{e}'_t, \qquad \textbf{4.4-3}$$

$$\ddot{\mathbf{p}} = p\omega^2\mathbf{e}'_n + p\alpha\mathbf{e}'_t,$$

where ω and α are the angular velocity and acceleration of the rigid body. Two important points that the student must remember are the direction of $\mathbf{e}'_n$ and the sign convention for ω and α, and hence the direction of $\mathbf{e}'_t$. Remember that $\mathbf{e}'_n$ is the unit vector *opposed* to the direction of the relative position vector, always *from* point Q *to* point P. Also, a sign convention for ω and α establishing a positive *sense of rotation* must be used. In any given problem, this may be chosen to suit that problem; for general theoretical development and for complex problems, it is wise to adhere to the standard *right-hand rule*. Just as this rule gives the positive direction of the z-axis by the sense of rotation of the x- into y-axes, or the direction of the cross product of two vectors $(\mathbf{i} \times \mathbf{j} = \mathbf{k})$, so it establishes for the usual x, y-axes in the plane of Fig. 4.4-1 that counterclockwise rotations are positive, clockwise rotations negative. Thus, if $\omega = -2$ rad/sec, every line in the body is turning at a rate of 2 rad/sec in a clockwise sense. The direction of $\mathbf{e}'_t$ is then determined by the perpendicular to $\mathbf{p}$ in the direction of positive rotation of $\mathbf{p}$. Note that this means that, if we talk of the relative motion of P with respect to Q, both the relative normal and relative tangential unit vectors change direction, while the numbers p, ω, and α remain the same.

Let us consider the use of the plane relative motion equations for a rigid body. If we know the velocity and acceleration of one point on a rigid body at some instant of time, and if we know the ω and α of the body at that time, then we know the velocity and acceleration of every point on the body. For, combining the rigid-body relations 4.4-3 with the general relative motion equations, we see that $\dot{\mathbf{r}} = \dot{\mathbf{R}} + p\omega\mathbf{e}'_t$, $\ddot{\mathbf{r}} = \ddot{\mathbf{R}} + p\omega^2\mathbf{e}'_n + p\alpha\mathbf{e}'_t$ where the directions $\mathbf{e}'_t$ and $\mathbf{e}'_n$ are known when the position of Q relative to P is known. These are then two vector equations for the two unknowns $\dot{\mathbf{r}}$ and $\ddot{\mathbf{r}}$. Other combinations of information about accelerations and velocities permit us to compute the motion of any point on a rigid body in similar ways, using the relative motion equations. The application of equations requires, of course, that the equivalent scalar equations be written down. This means that we must express $\dot{\mathbf{r}}$ and $\dot{\mathbf{R}}$ in terms of $\mathbf{e}'_n$ and $\mathbf{e}'_t$ or else express $\mathbf{e}'_n$ and $\mathbf{e}'_t$ in terms of the x,y-coordinates used for $\dot{\mathbf{r}}$.

Example 4·4-1
The 12-ft rigid ladder AB slips along the wall and floor as shown in Fig. 4.4-3. In the position shown, B has the velocity $3\mathbf{i}$ ft/sec and acceleration

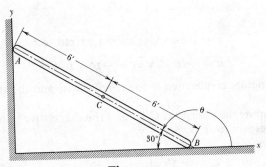

Fig. 4·4-3

$8\mathbf{i}$ ft/sec². *Find ω and α for the ladder, the velocity and acceleration of A, and the velocity of the midpoint C.*

Solution: We use the alternative notation mentioned in Section 4.2.

We have $\mathbf{v}_A = v\mathbf{j}$, $\mathbf{v}_B = 3\mathbf{i}$, $\mathbf{a}_A = a\mathbf{j}$, $\mathbf{a}_B = 8\mathbf{i}$ since A must move along the wall. The relative velocity equation states that

$$\mathbf{v}_A = \mathbf{v}_B + \mathbf{v}_{A/B}$$

where $\mathbf{v}_{A/B} = -12\omega(\sin 30°\mathbf{i} + \cos 30°\mathbf{j})$. Note that the unit vector $\mathbf{e}'_t = -\sin 30°\mathbf{i} - \cos 30°\mathbf{j}$ is the unit vector perpendicular to BA in the sense of increasing θ, as if we considered B as fixed and A moving about B in a circle of radius 12 ft. Then

$$v\mathbf{j} = 3\mathbf{i} - (6\omega\mathbf{i} + 6\sqrt{3}\omega\mathbf{j})$$

or, in component form,

$$0 = 3 - 6\omega,$$

$$v = -6\sqrt{3}\omega.$$

Solving, $\omega = 0.5$ rad/sec, $v = -3\sqrt{3}$ ft/sec. The bar at this instant is rotating counterclockwise at 0.5 rad/sec; the end A is moving downward at $3\sqrt{3}$ ft/sec.

The relative acceleration is

$$\mathbf{a}_{A/B} = r\omega^2(\cos 30°\mathbf{i} - \sin 30°\mathbf{j}) + r\alpha(-\sin 30°\mathbf{i} - \cos 30°\mathbf{j}).$$

The relative acceleration equation can be written:

$$\mathbf{a}_A = \mathbf{a}_B + \mathbf{a}_{A/B}$$

$$a\mathbf{j} = 8\mathbf{i} + 12(0.5)^2 \left(\frac{\sqrt{3}}{2}\mathbf{i} - \frac{1}{2}\mathbf{j}\right) + 12\alpha \left(\frac{-1}{2}\mathbf{i} - \frac{\sqrt{3}}{2}\mathbf{j}\right),$$

or

$$0 = 8 + 1.5\sqrt{3} - 6\alpha$$

$$a = 1.5 - 6\sqrt{3}\alpha.$$

Solving,

$$\alpha = (16 + 3\sqrt{3})/12 = 1.77 \text{ rad/sec}^2$$

$$a = -(6 + 8\sqrt{3}) = -19.9 \text{ ft/sec}^2.$$

Hence the angular acceleration is counterclockwise and the acceleration of A is downward.

To compute the velocity of C, let us write the relative velocity equation for C with respect to A: $\mathbf{v}_C = \mathbf{v}_A + \mathbf{v}_{C/A}$.

We have

$$\mathbf{v}_A = -3\sqrt{3}\mathbf{j};$$

$$\mathbf{v}_{C/A} = r_{A/C}\omega\mathbf{e}''_t = (6)\left(\frac{1}{2}\right)(\sin 30°\mathbf{i} + \cos 30°\mathbf{j})$$

$$= \frac{3}{2}\mathbf{i} + \frac{3}{2}\sqrt{3}\mathbf{j}.$$

Note that the unit vector $\mathbf{e}_t''$ here is the negative of the unit vector used in computing $\mathbf{v}_{A/B}$. We need the unit vector perpendicular to AC, pointing in the direction of increasing θ as if A were fixed and C rotating about A— the unit vector opposite in direction to the one used for $\mathbf{v}_{A/B}$. Therefore,

$$\mathbf{v}_C = -3\sqrt{3}\mathbf{j} + \frac{3}{2}\mathbf{i} + \frac{3}{2}\sqrt{3}\mathbf{j}$$

$$= \frac{3}{2}\mathbf{i} - \frac{3}{2}\sqrt{3}\mathbf{j} \ \text{ft/sec}.$$

This result is easily checked. The x-component of the velocity of C must be the average of the x-components of the velocities of A and B (Why?), and similarly v_y must be the average of the y-components. (Is this also true for the acceleration of C?)

The motion of a plane lamina about a fixed point, or *pure rotation*, is particularly important. Suppose a plane body is pinned at a

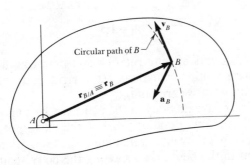

Fig. 4.4-4

point A in such a way that it is free to rotate about A (Fig. 4.4-4). In this case, since A never moves, $\mathbf{v}_A = \mathbf{a}_A = \mathbf{0}$. Then any other point, such as B, on the rigid body can move only on a circular path about A, with $\mathbf{r}_B = \mathbf{r}_{B/A}$, $\mathbf{v}_B = \mathbf{v}_{B/A}$, $\mathbf{a}_B = \mathbf{a}_{B/A}$. On Fig. 4.4-4, the velocity and acceleration vectors are sketched for a counterclockwise (positive) angular velocity ω and a clockwise (negative) angular acceleration α. If the body rotates with constant angular velocity, then the acceleration vector $\mathbf{a}_B$ points directly toward A.

If, for a rigid system, $\omega = 0$ always, then the relative velocity and acceleration vectors vanish and the velocity and acceleration of any two points are always the same. If the body moves in this way, it is said to be *translating*. The points of the system travel on parallel paths having the same radius of curvature at corresponding points.

We usually consider the path of the mass center as the typical path; when we write the equations of motion for curvilinear translation, we write them in terms of the normal and tangential components of acceleration of the mass center. In Fig. 4.4-5, two positions of a rigid body in curvilinear translation are sketched; note that the vector **r** does not change direction.

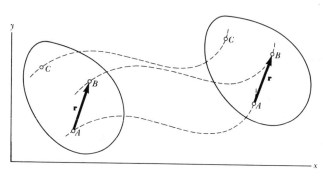

Fig. 4.4-5

With the concepts of pure rotation and pure translation, we can state the relative motion equations for a rigid body in words that clearly point out what we are doing:

Any motion of a rigid body in the plane can be considered to be a translation followed by a rotation; that is, the motion of any point in the rigid body is found by giving that point the translational motion of any other point in the body, then rotating the body about the second point as though it were a fixed point. (This statement holds true in three dimensions also; our problem will later be to describe three-dimensional rotations properly.)

Example 4.4-2

A rigid circular shaft of radius 4 in rotates about its own axis, the α-t curve for it being given graphically as in Fig. 4.4-6. The scales along the axes are 1 in $\cong$ 2 rad/sec^2 and 1 in $\cong$ 3 sec, respectively. Find the angular velocity of the shaft after 15 sec if the initial angular velocity is $+5$ rad/sec. Also find the velocity and acceleration of a point on the lateral surface of the shaft at that time.

Solution: Since $\omega - \omega_0 = \int \alpha \, dt$, the change in ω is given by the area under the α-curve; from the scale, an area of 1 in^2 represents 6 rad/sec. Thus

$$\omega - \omega_0 = (6)(0.67 - 0.33 + 0.4 - 0.75 + 0.125)$$
$$= (6)(0.115) = 0.690 \text{ rad/sec,}$$

the final ω being 5.69 rad/sec in the same sense as the initial ω_0. The speed of a point on the rim is $(4)(5.69) = 22.76$ in/sec, so the velocity is tangent to the rim in the positive ω sense. The acceleration has components $(4)(3/4) = 3$ in/sec^2 tangent to the shaft and $(4)(5.69)^2 = 129.5$ in/sec^2 in toward the axis of the shaft.

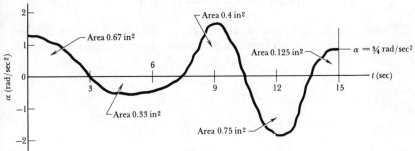

Fig. 4.4-6

Example 4.4-3

A rigid bar of length 8 in rotates about one of its ends in such a way that its $\alpha = -5\theta$, where θ is the bar's angular displacement from its initial position. If the bar has initial angular velocity $\omega_0 = 2$ rad/sec, what is ω at any θ? What will be the tip acceleration when $\theta = 30°$?

Solution: Using the last of Eqs. 4.4-2 we have

$$\frac{1}{2}\left(\omega^2 - (2)^2\right) = \int_0^\theta (-5\phi)\, d\phi = -\frac{5}{2}\theta^2$$

or

$$\omega^2 = 4 - 5\theta^2, \qquad \omega = \pm(4 - 5\theta^2)^{1/2}.$$

For $\theta = 30° = \pi/6$ rad, $\alpha = -5\pi/6$, $\omega^2 = 4 - (5\pi^2/36)$; the tip acceleration has components $r\omega^2 = 21.0$ in/sec^2 in toward the fixed end and $r\alpha = -20.9$ in/sec^2 perpendicular to the bar in the sense of increasing θ, or $+20.9$ in/sec^2 in the direction of decreasing θ.

This type of θ-ω-α relation corresponds to the x-v-a relations of a spring-mass system. It can be produced by a torsional spring attached to the bar, one that produces a restoring torque or moment proportional to the angular displacement—just as a linear spring produces a restoring force proportional to its extension.

Example 4.4-4

A rigid triangular plate of side 4 ft moves in a plane with two vertices constrained to move in grooves as shown (Fig. 4.4-7). Corner B has speed

3 ft/sec upward in its slot and acceleration 4 ft/sec² downward at this instant. What is the acceleration of A ?   The velocity of C ?

Solution: The axes and positive sense of rotation are shown in the figure. We are given $\mathbf{v}_B = 3\mathbf{j}$, $\mathbf{a}_B = -4\mathbf{j}$ and that A is constrained to move horizontally: $\mathbf{v}_A = v_A\mathbf{i}$, $\mathbf{a}_A = a_A\mathbf{i}$. The relative acceleration equation $(\mathbf{a}_A = \mathbf{a}_B + \mathbf{a}_{A/B})$ gives

$$a_A\mathbf{i} = -4\mathbf{j} + 4\omega^2\left(-\frac{\sqrt{2}}{2}\mathbf{i} + \frac{\sqrt{2}}{2}\mathbf{j}\right) + 4\alpha\left(\frac{\sqrt{2}}{2}\mathbf{i} + \frac{\sqrt{2}}{2}\mathbf{j}\right).$$

This contains three unknowns, and a_A can not be found; this is a common occurrence in relative acceleration problems. Even though we wish only

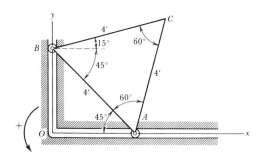

Fig. 4.4-7

an acceleration, we must solve a velocity problem first. In particular, to find ω, we only need that component of the $A - B$ relative velocity equation perpendicular to $\mathbf{v}_A$; i.e.,

$$(\mathbf{v}_A)_y = 0 = (\mathbf{v}_B + \mathbf{v}_{A/B})_y = 3 + 4\omega\left(\frac{\sqrt{2}}{2}\right).$$

Then

$$\omega = -\frac{3}{4}\sqrt{2} \text{ rad/sec}, \qquad \omega^2 = \frac{9}{8} \text{ (rad/sec)}^2$$

and

$$a_A = -\frac{9\sqrt{2}}{4} + 2\sqrt{2}\alpha,$$

$$0 = -4 + \frac{9}{4}\sqrt{2} + 2\sqrt{2}\alpha.$$

Solving,

$$\alpha = \frac{16 - 9\sqrt{2}}{8\sqrt{2}} = 0.289 \text{ rad/sec}^2,$$

$$a_A = \frac{8 - 9\sqrt{2}}{2} = -2.36 \text{ ft/sec}^2$$

Thus A is accelerating to the left, the plate is rotating clockwise at rate ω, and the angular acceleration is counterclockwise.

The velocity of C is given by

$$\mathbf{v}_C = \mathbf{v}_B + \mathbf{v}_{C/B} = 3\mathbf{j} + (4)\left(-\frac{3}{4}\sqrt{2}\right)(-\sin 15°\mathbf{i} + \cos 15°\mathbf{j})$$

$$= 1.098\mathbf{i} - 1.097\mathbf{j} \text{ ft/sec.}$$

Example 4.4-5

Find the acceleration of A in the previous example directly, using the fact that r_{AB} is constant.

Solution: By *directly*, we mean find the acceleration by differentiating the position vector of A twice. This requires that we know $\mathbf{r}_A$ for any position of the plate. Introducing the angle θ from the negative y-axis to the line BA (Fig. 4.4-8), we see that $\mathbf{r}_A = x_A\mathbf{i} = 4\sin\theta\mathbf{i}$, $\mathbf{r}_B = 4\cos\theta\mathbf{j}$, or that x_A and y_B are related by $x_A^2 + y_B^2 = 16$. Then $\mathbf{v}_A = \dot{x}_A\mathbf{i} = 4\cos\theta\dot\theta\mathbf{i}$,

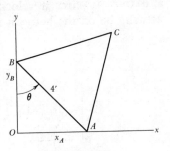

Fig. 4.4-8

$$\mathbf{a}_A = \ddot{x}_A\mathbf{i} = (-4\sin\theta\dot\theta^2 + 4\cos\theta\ddot\theta)\mathbf{i}.$$

The values of $\dot\theta$ and $\ddot\theta$ (ω and α) can be found for $\theta = 45°$ from the known results for B. We may also proceed by differentiating the *constraint condition* $x_A^2 + y_B^2 = 16$:

$$x_A\dot{x}_A + y_B\dot{y}_B = 0,$$

$$x_A\ddot{x}_A + \dot{x}_A^2 + y_B\ddot{y}_B + \dot{y}_B^2 = 0.$$

With $x_A = 2\sqrt{2}$, $y_B = 2\sqrt{2}$, $\dot{y}_B = 3$, the first equation gives

$$\dot{x}_A = -y_B\dot{y}_B/x_A = -3 \text{ ft/sec;}$$

with $\ddot{y}_B = -4$, the second equation gives

$$\ddot{x}_A = -\frac{1}{x_A}(\dot{x}_A^2 + y_B\ddot{y}_B + \dot{y}_B^2) = 4 - \frac{9}{2}\sqrt{2}$$

$$= -2.36 \text{ ft/sec}^2$$

as before.

The student should note the difference between this approach and that of the previous example. The present method requires that we be able to write the position vector for an arbitrary configuration of the body and also write down any constraint conditions that exist; the relative motion equations require only that the instantaneous configuration be known. In the present case, the computation from the constraint condition was simple—perhaps even simpler than that based on the relative motion equations. But now imagine that both constraints are removed— that the plate is free to move anywhere in its plane—but that, at the instant when AB makes 45° with the axes, $\mathbf{v}_B$, $\mathbf{a}_B$ are as given, and A is known to have horizontal $\mathbf{v}_A$ and $\mathbf{a}_A$. The relative-motion solution is the same; the "absolute" or "direct" solution involves the four coordinates x_A, y_A, x_B, y_B constrained by $(x_A - x_B)^2 + (y_A - y_B)^2 = 4^2$ and satisfying the given conditions at one instant only.

One of the remarkable conclusions that can be drawn about two-dimensional rigid-body motion is that there is always a point in the plane such that, for computing velocities, we can consider the body to be in pure rotation about an axis through that point. This point, called the *instantaneous center* of zero velocity for the body, is not always the same point in the plane; if it is, then we have the case of fixed-point rotation discussed before. In general, the instantaneous center (regarded as rigidly attached to the body) has an acceleration and thus acquires a velocity. The instantaneous center may not actually be on the body; it is, at the one instant of time considered,

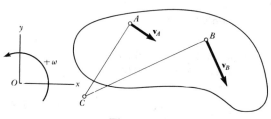

Fig. 4.4-9

a point that, if it were rigidly attached to the body and moving with it, would have zero velocity. Its importance arises from the simplicity of constructing the velocity vector of any point on a rigid body from the relative velocity equation when we know the velocity of the base point to be zero: this velocity is then equal in magnitude to the product of the distance between the points and the absolute value of the angular velocity and is given in direction by that perpendicular to the line joining the two points which agrees with the sense of rotation given by the angular velocity.

Let us show the existence of the instantaneous center when $\omega \neq 0$. Suppose that a rigid body moves in the plane, and that the velocity of point A on the body is known, $\mathbf{v}_A = v_A \mathbf{e}_A$, $v_A > 0$. Now if such a point as the instantaneous center exists, A must behave as though A were traveling in a circle about it, and thus it must be on the perpendicular to $\mathbf{v}_A$. Draw that perpendicular, 90° counterclockwise from $\mathbf{v}_A$ if $\omega > 0$ and 90° clockwise from $\mathbf{v}_A$ if $\omega < 0$. In Fig. 4.4-9, we draw the case $\omega < 0$. Locate the point C at a distance $r_{AC} = v_A/|\omega|$ from A, and compute its velocity as though it were moving with the body:

$$\mathbf{v}_C = \mathbf{v}_A + \mathbf{v}_{C/A} = v_A\mathbf{e}_A - r_{AC}|\omega|\mathbf{e}_A = \mathbf{0}.$$

This shows that there is a point that can serve as a center of rotation for A. To show that it is unique, we consider any other point B on the body but not on the line AC, the velocity of which is known: $\mathbf{v}_B = v_B\mathbf{e}_B$. Now, $\mathbf{v}_A \neq \mathbf{v}_B$ if $\omega \neq 0$, since the relative velocity term $\mathbf{v}_{A/B}$ will then be non-zero. If B can be considered to move in a circle about some point, that point must lie on the perpendicular to $\mathbf{v}_B$. Since $\mathbf{v}_A \neq \mathbf{v}_B$, and A and B are not on the same perpendicular to $\mathbf{v}_A$,

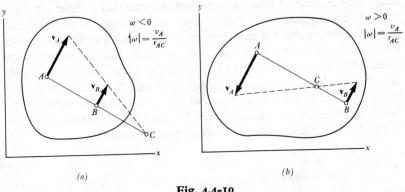

(a)   (b)

Fig. 4.4-10

the perpendiculars to $\mathbf{v}_A$ and $\mathbf{v}_B$ cannot be parallel but must intersect at some point C'. This point C' is the same as the point C obtained above; for

$$\mathbf{v}_{C'} = v_A\mathbf{e}_A - r_{AC'}|\omega|\mathbf{e}_A = (v_A - r_{AC'}|\omega|)\mathbf{e}_A$$

$$= v_B\mathbf{e}_B - r_{BC'}|\omega|\mathbf{e}_B = (v_B - r_{BC'}|\omega|)\mathbf{e}_B.$$

Since $\mathbf{e}_A \neq \mathbf{e}_B$, the only way these two forms of $\mathbf{v}_{C'}$ can be equal is for $\mathbf{v}_{C'} = \mathbf{0}$. But then

$$r_{AC'} = v_A/|\omega| = r_{AC}$$

so that C' and C coincide—and there is a unique point at each instant of time that can be considered to have zero velocity.

In the above derivation, we were careful to choose B so that the line AB was not the common normal to $\mathbf{v}_A$ and $\mathbf{v}_B$. If we do so choose, we get one of the constructions shown in Fig. 4.4-10 for the instantaneous center; again it is evident from the geometry of similar triangles that $|\omega| = v_A/r_{AC} = v_B/r_{BC}$, and from the relative velocity equation that $\mathbf{v}_C = \mathbf{0}$.

If $\omega = 0$, the body is not rotating but is translating instantaneously. We can still keep the idea of instantaneous center by admitting the "point at infinity" to the plane. Consider what happens as the velocity of B becomes parallel to the velocity of A (Fig. 4.4-9); the instantaneous center C moves farther and farther away from the lamina, in the limit approaching the point at infinity. When $\mathbf{v}_B$ is parallel to $\mathbf{v}_A$, but these vectors are not perpendicular to the line AB, consistency requires $\mathbf{v}_A = \mathbf{v}_B$; i.e., the relative velocity vanishes, $\omega = 0$, and the velocity of every point is the same.

Remember that C, considered as a point moving with the rigid body, will in general have an acceleration, and that a different point will be the instantaneous center later on. If we try to locate an instantaneous center for acceleration in the same way that we locate the instantaneous center for velocity, we find that our attempts are defeated by the presence of the $r\omega^2$ term, the relative normal acceleration in the relative motion equation. It is true that for plane motion there is, at any instant, a point whose acceleration is zero. This point, however, is not easily located for the reason mentioned above. It has found little application in engineering design.

Example 4.4-6

The 12-ft ladder of Example 4.4-1 is shown here again (Fig. 4.4-11), with $\mathbf{v}_B = 3\mathbf{i}$ *fps and* $\mathbf{v}_A$ *along the wall as before. Find the angular velocity, the velocity of A, and the velocity of C by the instantaneous-center method.*

Solution: Drawing the perpendiculars to $\mathbf{v}_A$ and $\mathbf{v}_B$, we find the instantaneous center, D, as shown in Fig. 4.4-11. From the geometry, $r_{BD} = 12 \sin 30° = 6$ ft, and

$$|\omega| = v_B/r_{BD} = 0.5 \text{ rad/sec.}$$

To agree with the direction of motion of B, ω must be counterclockwise; hence $\omega = 0.5$ rad/sec. Then $v_A = r_{AD}|\omega| = 3\sqrt{3}$ ft/sec; again, to agree with the sense of rotation, A must be moving down. Thus $\mathbf{v}_A = -3\sqrt{3}\mathbf{j}$ ft/sec.

Similarly,

$$v_C = r_{DC}|\omega| = 3 \text{ ft/sec,}$$
$$\mathbf{v}_C = 3(\cos 60°\mathbf{i} - \sin 60°\mathbf{j})$$
$$= \frac{3}{2}\mathbf{i} - \frac{3}{2}\sqrt{3}\mathbf{j} \text{ ft/sec.}$$

One particularly important case where the instantaneous center can be determined (and hence the velocity pattern of the rigid body)

is that of the motion of one rigid body with respect to another fixed
body known as *rolling without slipping*. We are all familiar with the
notion of rolling—a billiard ball on a table or a wheel on a road or a
roller bearing in the bearing race; rolling without slipping is the
particularly important case in which there is no relative motion
between the two bodies at their common points of contact.

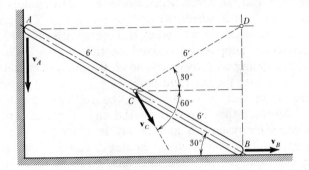

Fig. 4.4-11

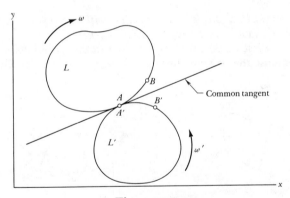

Fig. 4.4-12

Consider two rigid laminas, L and L', in motion in a plane, moving so that there is always a single point on each body in contact
(Fig. 4.4-12); we say that L rolls on L' or vice versa. Since there is
always but one point on each body, say A on L and A' on L', in contact,
we can draw a common tangent to the bodies. The rigidity of the
lamina implies that the two bodies cannot penetrate each other, so
that, if they are to remain in contact, the velocity components of A

and A' normal to the common tangent must be the same. If the components of velocity along the tangent are different, then the bodies *roll and slip* on one another; if they are the same, then the bodies *roll without slipping* on one another. Thus the condition of rolling without slipping can be expressed in terms of the velocities of the points of contact; $\mathbf{v}_A = \mathbf{v}_{A'}$, or no relative velocity between the two. Also, if the velocities are always the same, the speeds are the same; and hence the scalar tangential accelerations of the two points must be the same. *The total accelerations are not the same.* The points do separate; they are on different bodies and move with those bodies.

In particular, suppose L' is fixed, so that $\mathbf{v}_{A'} = \mathbf{0}$. Then, if L rolls without slipping on L', $\mathbf{v}_A = \mathbf{0}$; and A, the point of contact, is the instantaneous center for the rigid body L.

There is another way of stating the rolling-without-slipping criterion. Suppose that at one instant A and A' are in contact and that at some later instant B and B' are in contact. Measure the distances s_{AB} and s'_{AB} rolled off on bodies L and L' respectively; if these are the same for all time intervals, however small, then the bodies are rolling without slipping on one another.

Example **4.4-7**

Let us consider the simplest case of rolling without slipping, that of a rigid circular disk of radius a on a fixed line (Fig. 4.4-13).

Solution: First we take the point of view of the second definition given above. Suppose that at some instant of time C is in contact with the line

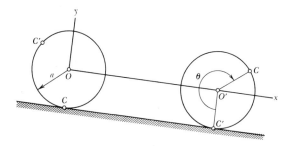

Fig. 4.4-13

and at a later instant C' is in contact, the wheel having turned through an angle θ. Then the arc length rolled off on the wheel is the distance CC', and this must be equal to the corresponding distance along the fixed line. Now consider the motion of the center of the wheel, taking x- and y-axes based on its initial position as shown. In the later position, the center has been displaced to point O'; clearly the x-displacement of the center of the wheel is equal to the distance CC' along the fixed line.   If, in the usual way, θ is measured positive in a counterclockwise sense, the angular displacement here is negative; thus the arc length CC' on the wheel is $s = -a\theta$, and $x_O = -a\theta$.   Since the center O moves along the x-axis, its velocity and acceleration vectors point in that direction, so that we have the following relations for a wheel of radius a, center O, rolling without slipping along a fixed line:

$$\mathbf{r}_O = x_O\mathbf{i} = -a\theta\mathbf{i},$$

$$\mathbf{v}_O = \dot{x}_O\mathbf{i} = -a\omega\mathbf{i}, \qquad\qquad \text{4.4-4}$$

$$\mathbf{a}_O = \ddot{x}_O\mathbf{i} = -a\alpha\mathbf{i}.$$

Now compute the velocity and acceleration of the point of contact C at any time t:

$$\mathbf{v}_C = \mathbf{v}_O + \mathbf{v}_{C/O} = -a\omega\mathbf{i} + a\omega\mathbf{i} = \mathbf{0},$$

$$\mathbf{a}_C = \mathbf{a}_O + \mathbf{a}_{C/O} = -a\alpha\mathbf{i} + a\alpha\mathbf{i} + a\omega^2\mathbf{j} = a\omega^2\mathbf{j}. \qquad \text{4.4-5}$$

The point of contact is the instantaneous center for the wheel and has acceleration directed toward the wheel's center.

If we take the first definition of rolling without slipping, since the line is fixed, $\mathbf{v}_C = \mathbf{0}$; then if O moves in the positive x-direction, $\mathbf{v}_O = a|\omega|\mathbf{i}$. Since the angular velocity is clockwise when $\mathbf{v}_O$ is in the $+\mathbf{i}$ direction, $|\omega| = -\omega$ and $\mathbf{v}_O = -a\omega\mathbf{i}$.   Hence the displacement of O is $-a\theta\mathbf{i}$, and the acceleration of O is $-a\alpha\mathbf{i}$.   Similarly, if O moves in the negative x-direction, $\mathbf{v}_O = -a|\omega|\mathbf{i}$; but then $\omega = |\omega|$, since the body rotates counterclockwise, and again $\mathbf{v}_O = -a\omega\mathbf{i}$.

Example. 4.4-8

As a more complicated example of rolling without slipping, let us consider the cylindrical roller of radius r rolling inside the fixed circular race of radius R (Fig. 4.4-14).

Solution: The center P of the roller travels in a circle of radius $(R-r)$ about O, the center of the race; thus, in polar coordinates based on O as shown, we must have

$$\mathbf{v}_P = (R-r)\dot{\phi}\mathbf{e}_\phi,$$

$$\mathbf{a}_P = -(R-r)\dot{\phi}^2\mathbf{e}_r + (R-r)\ddot{\phi}\mathbf{e}_\phi.$$

But, since the outer circle is fixed, the point C must be the instantaneous center and

$$\mathbf{v}_P = -r\dot{\theta}\mathbf{e}_\phi,$$

where θ is the angular velocity of the

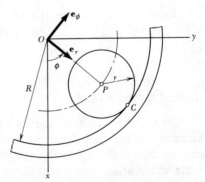

Fig. 4.4-14

cylinder.   The negative sign arises from the fact, obvious from Fig. 4.4-14, that if the velocity is to be in the $+\mathbf{e}_\phi$ direction, the angular velocity of the wheel must be clockwise.   Hence

$$(R-r)\dot{\phi} = -r\dot{\theta}$$

or

$$\dot{\theta} = -\left(\frac{R}{r}-\mathbf{1}\right)\dot{\phi}.$$

We can obtain the same result from the second definition of rolling without slipping.   Suppose we start rolling the disk inside the circle from the standard position shown in Fig. 4.4-15a up to the position shown in Fig. 4.4-15b.   The arclength CC' along the fixed circle is then $R\phi$; what is the arclength CC' on the moving circle? As indicated in Fig. 4.4-15, if we merely translated the body along the circle, then PC' would be along the line PQ, and the angle between PC' and PC would be ϕ.   Thus the actual angle θ through which the roller has turned is the (negative) angle from PQ to PC'.   Thus the arclength rolled through on the disk is $s = r(\phi - \theta)$,

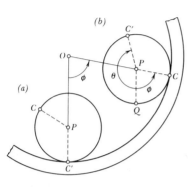

Fig. 4.4-15

taking into account that θ is negative.   Hence

$$R\phi = r(\phi - \theta),$$

$$\theta = -\frac{(R-r)}{r}\,\phi,$$

and

$$\dot{\theta} = -\left(\frac{R}{r}-\mathbf{1}\right)\dot{\phi}.$$

Finally, let us compute the acceleration of the instantaneous center.

$$\mathbf{a}_C = \mathbf{a}_P + \mathbf{a}_{C/P} = -(R-r)\dot{\phi}^2\mathbf{e}_r + (R-r)\ddot{\phi}\mathbf{e}_\phi + r\ddot{\theta}\mathbf{e}_\phi - r\dot{\theta}^2\mathbf{e}_r$$

or

$$\mathbf{a}_C = -\frac{rR}{R-r}\,\dot{\theta}^2\mathbf{e}_r$$

directed toward point P.

In the discussion of the rolling problem, we found one type of kinematic connection between two rigid bodies—that the two points in contact, one on each body, must have the same total velocity and the same acceleration component along the common tangent to the bodies. Similar kinematic conditions arise between parts of other systems that are not single rigid bodies; we consider a few simple examples in order to show how such kinematic conditions can be determined. These examples include some of the most common types of systems.

Example 4.4-9

In Fig. 4.4-16, *we show a cylindrical drum supported on a shaft at its center. A cable wrapped around the drum supports a load, W. By applying a torque to the shaft, we rotate the drum, wrapping or unwrapping cable from it, thereby raising or lowering the load. We ask for the relations between the kinematic variables describing the motion of the drum and the motion of the load.*

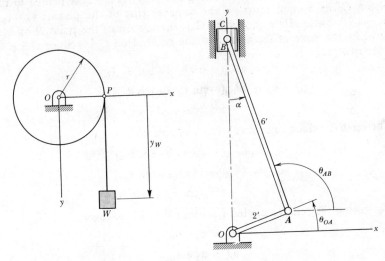

Fig. 4.4-16   **Fig. 4.4-17**

Solution: We consider the drum as rigid, the cable as flexible and inextensible, and the load as a particle. The connection between the drum and load variables is given by the inextensibility of the cable: if the load rises a distance Y, then a length of cable equal to Y must wrap around the drum. Hence the drum turns through an angle $\theta = Y/r$, where r is the radius of the drum. The particle has rectilinear motion; its velocity and acceleration are $\mathbf{v}_W = \dot{y}_W \mathbf{j}$, $a_W = \ddot{y}_W \mathbf{j}$. The velocity and acceleration of point P are

$$\mathbf{v}_P = r\dot{\theta}\mathbf{j} = \dot{y}_W\mathbf{j}, \qquad \mathbf{a}_P = -r\dot{\theta}^2\mathbf{i} + \ddot{y}_W\mathbf{j}.$$

The kinematic relations between two points connected by an inextensible cord or cable are:

(a) the velocity component in the direction of the cord at the two points must be the same;

(b) the acceleration component in the direction of the cord at the two points must be the same.

Example 4.4-10

The rigid crank rod, OA (Fig. 4.4-17), *rotates about the fixed point, O; at A it is pinned to the rigid connecting rod, AB, which is in turn pinned at B to the piston, C, which can slide in the cylinder along the y-axis. If, when the crank is in the position shown, its angular velocity and acceleration are θ_{OA}, $\ddot{\theta}_{OA}$, find the velocity and acceleration of the piston.*

Solution: Write the relative motion equations for the two points A and B at the ends of the rigid connecting rod AB. Since B is pinned to the piston C, its motion must be the same as that of the piston: $\mathbf{v}_B = v_B\mathbf{j}$, $\mathbf{a}_B = a_B\mathbf{j}$. Since AB is pinned to OA, the motion of the point A on AB must be the same as the motion of the point A on OA. Since OA is in pure rotation,

$$\mathbf{v}_A = 2\dot{\theta}_{OA}(-\sin\theta_{OA}\mathbf{i} + \cos\theta_{OA}\mathbf{j}),$$
$$\mathbf{a}_A = 2\ddot{\theta}_{OA}(-\sin\theta_{OA}\mathbf{i} + \cos\theta_{OA}\mathbf{j})$$
$$-2\dot{\theta}_{OA}^2(\cos\theta_{OA}\mathbf{i} + \sin\theta_{OA}\mathbf{j}).$$

The relative velocity and acceleration vectors are

$$\mathbf{v}_{B/A} = 6\dot{\theta}_{AB}(-\sin\theta_{AB}\mathbf{i} + \cos\theta_{AB}\mathbf{j}),$$
$$\mathbf{a}_{B/A} = 6\ddot{\theta}_{AB}(-\sin\theta_{AB}\mathbf{i} + \cos\theta_{AB}\mathbf{j})$$
$$-6\dot{\theta}_{AB}^2(\cos\theta_{AB}\mathbf{i} + \sin\theta_{AB}\mathbf{j}).$$

Now using the relative motion equations for AB, we have

$$\mathbf{v}_B = \mathbf{v}_A + \mathbf{v}_{B/A},$$
$$\mathbf{a}_B = \mathbf{a}_A + \mathbf{a}_{B/A},$$

which represent four scalar equations in the four scalar unknowns v_B, a_B, $\dot{\theta}_{AB}$, $\ddot{\theta}_{AB}$; the angle θ_{AB} can be determined from the geometry.

In particular, suppose that $\theta_{OA} = \pi/3$ radians, $\dot{\theta}_{OA} = 2$ rad/sec, $\ddot{\theta}_{OA} = 0$. Set angle OBA equal to α; then, by the law of sines,

$$\frac{\sin\alpha}{2} = \frac{\sin(\pi/6)}{6} \quad \text{or} \quad \sin\alpha = \frac{1}{6}, \quad \cos\alpha = \frac{\sqrt{35}}{6}.$$

Angle

$$\theta_{AB} = \alpha + \frac{\pi}{2} \quad \text{so} \quad \sin\theta_{AB} = \cos\alpha = \frac{\sqrt{35}}{6}, \quad \cos\theta_{AB} = -\frac{1}{6}.$$

Then

$$0 = -2\sqrt{3} - \sqrt{35}\dot{\theta}_{AB},$$
$$v_B = 2 - \dot{\theta}_{AB},$$
$$0 = -4 - \sqrt{35}\ddot{\theta}_{AB} + \dot{\theta}_{AB}^2,$$
$$a_B = -4\sqrt{3} - \ddot{\theta}_{AB} - \sqrt{35}\dot{\theta}_{AB}^2,$$

the solutions being

$$\dot{\theta}_{AB} = \frac{-2}{35} \sqrt{105} = -0.584 \text{ rad/sec (a clockwise rate of rotation)}$$

$$v_B = 2.58 \text{ ft/sec}$$

$$\ddot{\theta}_{AB} = -0.618 \text{ rad/sec}^2 \quad \text{and} \quad a_B = -8.33 \text{ ft/sec}^2.$$

The velocity portion of the problem may also be solved by locating the instantaneous center of bar *AB*.

Example 4·4-11

Consider the four-bar linkage of three rigid bars, AB, BC, CD, pinned together at B and C and to a fixed foundation (the "fourth bar") at A and D (Fig. 4.4-18).

Solution: Much as in the previous example, we can determine the motion of the whole system knowing its configuration and the angular velocity and acceleration of bar *CD* alone. That is, for the given position,

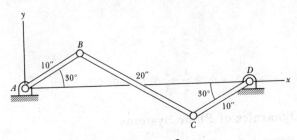

Fig. 4·4-18

we wish to find the angular velocity and acceleration of bars *BC* and *AB*, knowing them for bar *CD*. Suppose $\omega_{CD} = 1$ rad/sec, $\alpha_{CD} = -1/2$ rad/sec²; then

$$\mathbf{v}_C = 10 \left(\frac{1}{2}\mathbf{i} - \frac{\sqrt{3}}{2}\mathbf{j} \right) \text{ in/sec}$$

$$\mathbf{a}_C = -5 \left(\frac{1}{2}\mathbf{i} - \frac{\sqrt{3}}{2}\mathbf{j} \right) - 10 \left(-\frac{\sqrt{3}}{2}\mathbf{i} - \frac{1}{2}\mathbf{j} \right) \text{ in/sec}^2.$$

Similarly,

$$\mathbf{v}_B = 10\omega_{AB} \left(-\frac{1}{2}\mathbf{i} + \frac{\sqrt{3}}{2}\mathbf{j} \right) \text{ in/sec,}$$

$$\mathbf{a}_B = 10\alpha_{AB} \left(-\frac{1}{2}\mathbf{i} + \frac{\sqrt{3}}{2}\mathbf{j} \right) - 10\omega_{AB}^2 \left(\frac{\sqrt{3}}{2}\mathbf{i} + \frac{1}{2}\mathbf{j} \right) \text{ in/sec}^2,$$

and

$$\mathbf{v}_{B/C} = 20\omega_{BC} \left(-\frac{1}{2}\mathbf{i} - \frac{\sqrt{3}}{2}\mathbf{j} \right) \quad \text{in/sec,}$$

$$\mathbf{a}_{B/C} = 20\alpha_{BC} \left(-\frac{1}{2}\mathbf{i} - \frac{\sqrt{3}}{2}\mathbf{j} \right) - 20\omega^2_{BC} \left(-\frac{\sqrt{3}}{2}\mathbf{i} + \frac{1}{2}\mathbf{j} \right) \quad \text{in/sec}^2.$$

Relative velocity states $\mathbf{v}_B = \mathbf{v}_C + \mathbf{v}_{B/C}$:

$$-5\omega_{AB} = 5 - 10\omega_{BC},$$

$$5\sqrt{3}\omega_{AB} = -5\sqrt{3} - 10\sqrt{3}\omega_{BC}.$$

Hence, $\omega_{BC} = 0$, $\omega_{AB} = -1$ rad/sec.

Relative acceleration states that $\mathbf{a}_B = \mathbf{a}_C + \mathbf{a}_{B/C}$:

$$-5\alpha_{AB} - 5\sqrt{3} = 5\sqrt{3} - \frac{5}{2} - 10\alpha_{BC},$$

$$5\sqrt{3}\alpha_{AB} - 5 = 5 + 5\left(\frac{\sqrt{3}}{2} \right) - 10\sqrt{3}\alpha_{BC}.$$

Solving,

$$\alpha_{BC} = \frac{2}{3}\sqrt{3} \quad \text{rad/sec}^2,$$

$$\alpha_{AB} = \frac{1}{2} - \frac{2}{3}\sqrt{3} \quad \text{rad/sec}^2.$$

4.5 Dynamics of Plane Systems

The general dynamical equations of Section 4.3 take special forms for systems, and particularly the rigid body, in strictly plane motion. The principle of motion of the mass center causes no difficulty. Isolating our system, we identify the external forces, which all lie in the plane of motion; we also describe the acceleration of the mass center in coordinates appropriate for motion on a plane curve. The vector principle then reduces to two scalar equations for plane motion.

For plane motion, the angular-momentum principle is expressed by a single scalar equation. All forces and couples lie in the plane of motion, so that the resultant moment vector has direction perpendicular to the plane of motion. All position and velocity vectors also lie in the plane; the moment-of-momentum vector is perpendicular to the plane. Once a sign convention has been established for positive moments, the vector principle can be replaced by a scalar one.

Since all parts of the system are now constrained to move in a plane, the position and velocity vectors of a typical point can be written in one of the forms

$$\mathbf{r} = x\mathbf{i} + y\mathbf{j} = r\mathbf{e}_r,$$
$$\mathbf{v} = \dot{x}\mathbf{i} + \dot{y}\mathbf{j} = \dot{r}\mathbf{e}_r + r\dot{\phi}\mathbf{e}_\phi.$$

For a particle in a plane motion, the moment-of-momentum vector is

$$\mathbf{H}_O = H_O\mathbf{k} = \mathbf{r} \times m\mathbf{v} = m(x\dot{y} - y\dot{x})\mathbf{k} = mr^2\dot{\phi}\mathbf{k};$$

the scalar moment-of-momentum function

$$H_O = m(x\dot{y} - y\dot{x}) = mr^2\dot{\phi} \qquad \textbf{4.5-1}$$

is all we need, with the moment-of-momentum principle for a particle becoming

$$M_O = xF_y - yF_x = rF_\phi = \dot{H}_O. \qquad \textbf{4.5-2}$$

For a *system* in plane motion, we have the similar scalar principles

$$M_O = \dot{H}_O \quad \text{or} \quad M^* = \dot{H}^*, \qquad \textbf{4.5-3}$$

where

$$H_O = \sum_{i=1}^{N} m_i(x_i\dot{y}_i - y_i\dot{x}_i) = \sum_{i=1}^{N} m_i r_i^2 \dot{\phi}_i \qquad \textbf{4.5-4a}$$

for discrete systems, and

$$H_O = \int (x\dot{y} - y\dot{x})\, dm = \int r^2\dot{\phi}\, dm \qquad \textbf{4.5-4b}$$

for a continuous body.

For a *rigid body* moving in a plane, the angular-momentum function is even simpler, provided the base point for computation is a point of the body or a point considered to be moving with the body. Let P be any point on a plane rigid body or moving with it, and let (r, ϕ) be plane polar coordinates emanating from P. Then H_P has the form given in relation 4.5-4b:

$$H_P = \int r^2\dot{\phi}\, dm.$$

But $\dot{\phi}$ is the angular velocity of the line from P to a typical point in the rigid body—and we know that this is the same for all lines joining two points on the same rigid body, the angular velocity function ω of the body. Since ω does not depend on the position of any point in the body, it may be factored from the integrand and placed outside the integral sign:

$$H_P = \omega \left(\int r^2\, dm \right).$$

The integral that remains is the *polar moment of inertia of the body with respect to P* and is denoted by I_P:

$$I_P = \int r^2 \, dm.$$

The student should recall from his study of the calculus that this is usually evaluated by introducing a surface density $\sigma = \sigma(x, y)$ (mass per unit area) and evaluating the double integral

$$I_P = \iint_A r^2 \sigma \, dA$$

over the area of the body—usually by introducing (x, y) coordinates with origin at P, so that $r^2 = x^2 + y^2$, and selecting proper limits of integration so that the integral is given by the iterated integral

$$I_P = \iint (x^2 + y^2) \sigma(x, y) \, dx \, dy.$$

As we can see from the definition, I_P is always positive (except if the mass is concentrated at P; then $I_P = 0$).

There are a few properties of polar moments of inertia that the student must know in order to solve plane-motion problems. First, there is the property of *composition*: if a body is regarded as composed of a number of parts, then the moment of inertia of the whole body is the sum of the moments of the parts. Second, there is the *change-of-base-point theorem*, a special case of the general parallel axes transfer theorems. We need not recompute the basic integral whenever we change origins for moments to a new base point, Q, but need the computation with respect to one point only. Let $\mathbf{R}$ be the position of Q with respect to P, and let $\mathbf{p}$ be the position of a typical point in the body with respect to Q, so that the relative position equation $\mathbf{p} = \mathbf{r} - \mathbf{R}$ holds (Fig. 4.5-1). By definition, $I_P = \int r^2 \, dm$, $I_Q = \int p^2 \, dm$. But

$$p^2 = \mathbf{p} \cdot \mathbf{p} = (\mathbf{r} - \mathbf{R}) \cdot (\mathbf{r} - \mathbf{R}) = r^2 - 2\mathbf{R} \cdot \mathbf{r} + R^2;$$

hence

$$I_Q = \int p^2 \, dm = \int r^2 \, dm - 2\mathbf{R} \cdot \int \mathbf{r} \, dm + R^2 \int dm,$$

in which we have used the fact that $\mathbf{R}$ is a fixed vector independent of the integration. Therefore, since $\int dm = m$ and $\int \mathbf{r} \, dm = m\mathbf{r}^*$,

$$I_Q = I_P - 2m\mathbf{R} \cdot \mathbf{r}^* + mR^2. \qquad \text{4.5-5}$$

This is the general transfer of base point theorem for any two points in the plane, where $\mathbf{R}$ is the position of Q relative to P and $\mathbf{r}^*$ is, as usual, the position of the mass center C relative to P. If we take $P \equiv C$, then $\mathbf{r}^* = \mathbf{0}$, and

$$I_Q = I^* + mR^2. \tag{4.5-6}$$

This basic transfer theorem is the one most used, so that a table of moments of inertia need list the moments of inertia I^* at the mass center only. In words, Eq. 4.5-6 states that the polar moment of inertia about any point Q in the plane is equal to the polar moment of inertia at the mass center C plus the product of the mass of the body and the square of the distance between C and Q. A consequence of the theorem is the result that, of all moments of inertia about points in

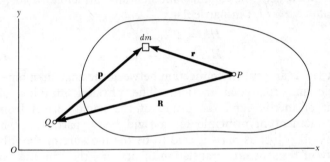

Fig. 4.5-1

the plane, the moment of inertia about the mass center C is the smallest. This fact is often of use in checking possible errors in numerical computation.

Allied to the concept of moment of inertia is that of the *radius of gyration* of a body. The distance k_P defined by the relation

$$I_P = mk_P^2 \tag{4.5-7}$$

is the radius of gyration of the body about P; it is the distance from P that a single particle of mass m must be placed in order to have the same moment of inertia as the body. Nonuniform bodies or composite bodies, for which I is not easily expressed in terms of over-all dimensions, usually have their moments of inertia prescribed indirectly by means of the centroidal radius of gyration k^*: $I^* = mk^{*2}$.

The moment of inertia is an example of the second moment of a quantity, just as the centroid and mass center are examples of the concept of a first moment. The polar moment of inertia, in particular, is an example of the second moment of mass with respect to an axis or line—in the case discussed, the z-axis through P. The notation I_P and the terms "polar moment" or "moment with respect to P" are sufficient in the discussion of plane motion; as we shall see later, this is not adequate in three dimensions. Alternative notations are I_z^P and I_{zz}^P; in referring to the table of moments of inertia in Appendix II, the student should look for the last notation, or I_{zz}^*, for the polar moments of plane distributions of mass.

Finally, we return to the plane angular momentum principle and the physical meaning of I_P. We have shown that for a plane rigid body in plane motion

$$H_P = I_P \omega \qquad\qquad \textbf{4.5-8}$$

where P is any point on the rigid body. If P is also a point with respect to which the angular-momentum principle holds, then $\dot{H}_P = I_P \dot{\omega} = I_P \alpha = M_P$; in particular,

$$H^* = I^* \omega, \qquad\qquad \textbf{4.5-9a}$$
$$\dot{H}^* = I^* \alpha = M^*. \qquad\qquad \textbf{4.5-9b}$$

Here at last is an explicit connection between the angular-momentum principle and rotational motion. The physical meaning of the moment of inertia—and the origin of the name—arises from the angular-momentum principle for a rigid body, particularly in the form 4.5-9b. Just as mass is said to be the measure of the inherent property of resistance to translation of matter—the "inertia" of the matter—so the "moment of inertia" measures its resistance to rotational motion. This vague statement about inherent tendency to resist motion is made precise in the formulation of the laws of motion of a particle and their generalization to systems. That is, for given external forces, all systems having the same mass have the same mass-center acceleration; all rigid plane systems having the same centroidal moment of inertia have the same angular acceleration for given moments about the mass center. Such systems are called dynamically equivalent in plane motion.

Summary. For systems in strictly plane motion, there are three independent scalar equations of motion, which may be taken from the mass-center principle and a scalar angular-momentum principle:
Mass Center:

$$\mathbf{F} = m\mathbf{a}^*, \qquad\qquad \textbf{4.5-10}$$

$$F_x = m\ddot{x}^*, \qquad F_y = m\ddot{y}^*, \qquad\qquad \textbf{4.5-10a}$$

$$F_t = m\ddot{s}^*, \qquad F_n = m\frac{(\dot{s}^*)^2}{\rho^*} \qquad\qquad \textbf{4.5-10b}$$

$$F_r = ma_r^*, \qquad F_\phi = ma_\phi^*. \qquad\qquad \textbf{4.5-10c}$$

Angular Momentum:

$$M_O = \dot{H}_O, \qquad O \text{ fixed.} \qquad\qquad \textbf{4.5-11a}$$

$$M^* = \dot{H}^*. \qquad\qquad \textbf{4.5-11b}$$

If the system is a single rigid body, then

$$H_P = I_P \omega \qquad\qquad \textbf{4.5-12}$$

if P moves with the body; in particular, 4.5-11b takes the form for a rigid body

$$M^* = \dot{H}^* = I^*\alpha. \qquad\qquad \textbf{4.5-13}$$

We remind the student that the force system called a *couple* can be applied to a continuous body. For plane motion, we only consider couples in the plane of motion. A couple, of course, contributes nothing to the resultant force sums but does to the moment sums; the moment of the couple must be added to all other moments whatever the base point for moments is.

Example 4.5-1

Find the centroidal radius of gyration, and the radius of gyration with respect to a point A on the rim, of a uniform disk of mass m and radius r.

Solution: Since $I^* = \frac{1}{2}mr^2$ for such a disk,

$$mk^{*2} = I^* = \frac{1}{2} mr^2,$$

and

$$k^* = \frac{\sqrt{2}}{2} r.$$

From the transfer of base point theorem,

$$I_A = I^* + mr^2 = \frac{3}{2} mr^2;$$

therefore,

$$mk_A^2 = \frac{3}{2} mr^2, \qquad k_A = \frac{\sqrt{6}}{2} r.$$

Example 4.5-2

Suppose you have a disk of total mass m and radius r, but you do not know the mass distribution. Someone tells you that the radius of gyration about a point on the rim has been determined by suspending the body as a pendulum and measuring the oscillation frequency, and that this $k = 2.2r$. Should you believe this report?

Solution: No. If all the mass were concentrated at one point on the rim, and the moment of inertia measured for the diametrically opposite point, I would be $md^2 = 4mr^2$; thus k cannot be bigger than $2r$. In general, the radius of gyration at any point cannot be bigger than the distance from the point to the farthest point on the body. (Prove this.)

Example 4.5-3

Write the equations of motion for a rigid body with a fixed point in plane motion, the plane of motion being vertical. No forces act except gravity and the reaction at the smooth pin support. In particular, show how the period of small oscillations about equilibrium may be used to find the radius of gyration about the support (Fig. 4.5-2a).

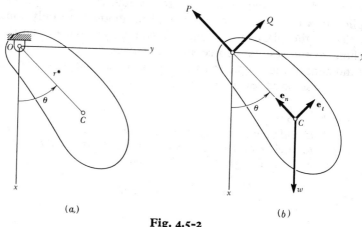

(a)   (b)

Fig. 4.5-2

Solution: The fixed x,y-coordinates, and the angle θ from the x-axis to the line OC, are shown in Fig. 4.5-2a; clearly, $\theta = 0$ is the equilibrium position of the body. When a body moves about a fixed point in a vertical plane, it is called a *compound pendulum*. In Fig. 4.5-2b, a free-body diagram of the pendulum is given, showing the weight force and the pin reaction force. Note that the latter is given in components along and perpendicular to OC, rather than in the fixed x- and y-directions. This way is chosen, because it is easier to work with normal and tangential coordinate representations than with x,y-coordinates. We have

$$F_n = P - w \cos \theta = ma_n^* = \frac{w}{g} r^* \dot{\theta}^2,$$

$$F_t = Q - w \sin \theta = ma_t^* = \frac{w}{g} r^* \ddot{\theta},$$

$$M_O = -wr^* \sin \theta = \dot{H}_O = I_O \ddot{\theta} = \frac{w}{g} k_O^2 \ddot{\theta}.$$

The last equation results from the fact that the fixed point O is also a point on the rigid body. Rewriting the last equation, we find

$$\ddot{\theta} + \frac{gr^*}{k_O^2} \sin \theta = 0.$$

The small oscillation assumption allows us to replace $\sin \theta$ by θ so that the equation becomes

$$\ddot{\theta} + \frac{gr^*}{k_O^2} \theta = 0.$$

We recognize this as a simple harmonic motion equation. As for a simple pendulum, if we pull the pendulum away from equilibrium a small angle θ_0 and release it from rest, the pendulum will oscillate with the angular displacement from equilibrium being given at any time t by

$$\theta = \theta_0 \cos \omega_n t,$$

where

$$\omega_n^2 = \frac{gr^*}{k_O^2}$$

is the square of the natural circular frequency of the pendulum, and

$$T_n = \frac{2\pi}{\omega_n} = \frac{2\pi k_O}{\sqrt{gr^*}}$$

is its period. By measuring the period of small oscillations, we may determine k_O:

$$k_O = \frac{T_n \sqrt{gr^*}}{2\pi}.$$

We may also determine the *equivalent length*, l, of the compound pendulum; this is the length of the cord on which a bob of mass m must be suspended in order that both pendula have the same frequency. The frequency of such a simple pendulum is given by

$$\omega^2 = \frac{g}{l};$$

thus

$$l = \frac{k_O^2}{r^*}.$$

Returning to the equations of motion, we may find the tangential bearing reaction easily. Substituting from the moment equation into the tangential equation of motion,

$$Q = w \sin \theta + \frac{w}{g} r^* \left(-\frac{gr^*}{k_O^2} \sin \theta \right)$$

$$= w \left(1 - \frac{r^{*2}}{k_O^2} \right) \sin \theta.$$

With the conditions that $\dot\theta = 0$ when $\theta = \theta_0$, the (exact) moment equation can be integrated to obtain

$$\frac{\dot\theta^2}{2} + \frac{gr}{k_O^2}(\cos\theta_0 - \cos\theta) = 0.$$

Then

$$P = w\cos\theta + \frac{w}{g}r^*\left[\frac{2gr^*}{k_O^2}(\cos\theta - \cos\theta_0)\right],$$

$$= w\left(1 + \frac{2r^{*2}}{k_O^2}\right)\cos\theta - \frac{2wr^{*2}}{k_O^2}\cos\theta_0.$$

The student may wish to set up the force equations of motion in x- and y-coordinates and compare them with those obtained here.

Example 4.5-4

A uniform rigid disk of radius r and mass m rolls without slipping on a horizontal line. A constant force of magnitude P is applied to the rim of the

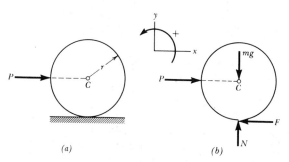

Fig. 4.5-3

disk in the direction of motion at distance r above the line (*Fig.* 4.5-3a). Find the angular acceleration of the disk at any time t in terms of m, r, g, and P. What P will cause the disk to begin to slip, if the coefficient of limiting friction is μ?   What is α then?

Solution: A free-body diagram of the disk at any time t is shown in Fig. 4.5-3b. Taking x, y-axes in the directions shown, the equations of motion are, from 4.5-10a and 4.5-13

$$F_x = P - F = m\ddot{x}^*,$$

$$F_y = N - mg = m\ddot{y}^*,$$

$$M^* = -rF = I^*\alpha = \frac{1}{2}mr^2\alpha.$$

These constitute three equations in the five unknowns F, N, $\ddot{x}^*$, $\ddot{y}^*$, and α. Two additional kinematical conditions are needed:

$$\ddot{y}^* = 0$$

$$\ddot{x}^* = -r\alpha,$$

the last expressing the rolling-without-slipping condition (Eq. 4.4-4). For the first part of the problem we need the first, third, and fifth of these equations. Eliminating F and $\ddot{x}^*$ between them, we find

$$(P - F) - (-F) = m(-r\alpha) - \left(\frac{1}{2}mr\alpha\right), \qquad P = -\frac{3}{2}mr\alpha,$$

and

$$\alpha = -\frac{2P}{3mr}.$$

We see that the sign is proper since the disk rotates in a clockwise sense.

For the second part, we need all equations. From the second and fourth, $N = mg$. From the result for α, we may compute the friction force if the disk does not slip:

$$F = -\frac{1}{2}mr\alpha = +\frac{P}{3}.$$

(The sign shows that we have chosen the direction of F correctly.) The disk will not slip if P is small enough; it begins to slip when

$$\frac{F}{N} = \frac{P}{3mg} = \mu, \qquad P = 3\mu mg.$$

The corresponding α is

$$\alpha = -\frac{6\mu mg}{3mr} = -\frac{2\mu g}{r}.$$

If the disk rolls and slips, we can solve for the unknowns by replacing the fifth fundamental equation $\ddot{x}^* = -r\alpha$ by the limiting friction equation $F = \mu N$.

4.6 Impulse-Momentum Principles for Systems

Suppose that we know the external forces acting on a system in general motion as functions of time or position, and suppose we know some initial configuration of the system—that is, we know the position and velocity of the system at some instant of time. How can we describe the subsequent motion of the system? How do we solve the equations of motion, especially those governing the motion of the system as a whole?

The methods of solution for systems parallel exactly those for a particle. Both impulse-momentum and work-energy principles can be found to give the necessary first integrals—finding relations involving velocities from those involving accelerations.

If the forces, and hence the accelerations, are functions of time, we may integrate the principle of motion of the mass center directly:

$$\hat{\mathbf{F}} = \int_{t_0}^{t_1} \mathbf{F}\, dt = m[\mathbf{v}^*(t_1) - \mathbf{v}^*(t_0)] = \Delta(m\mathbf{v}^*). \qquad \textbf{4.6-1}$$

The integral is the resultant *linear impulse* due to the resultant external force $\mathbf{F}$ over the time interval $t_0 \le t \le t_1$; $m\mathbf{v}^*$ is the linear momentum of the system, equal to $\sum m_i \dot{\mathbf{r}}_i$ or $\int \dot{\mathbf{r}}_i\, dm$. We have the formal

Principle of Linear Impulse and Momentum:

The change in the linear momentum of any system during any interval of time is equal to the linear impulse of the resultant external force during that same time interval:

$$\hat{\mathbf{F}} = \int_{t_0}^{t_1} \mathbf{F}\, dt = \Delta(m\mathbf{v}^*). \qquad \textbf{4.6-2}$$

Similarly, the angular-momentum principle may be integrated to obtain the

Principle of Angular Impulse and Momentum:

The change in the angular momentum of a system (with respect to a fixed point or with respect to the mass center) during any time interval is equal to the angular impulse of the external forces about the same point during the same time interval:

$$\hat{\mathbf{M}}_O = \int_{t_0}^{t_1} \mathbf{M}_O\, dt = \Delta \mathbf{H}_O \qquad \text{or} \qquad \hat{\mathbf{M}}^* = \int_{t_0}^{t_1} \mathbf{M}^*\, dt = \Delta \mathbf{H}^*.$$

$$\textbf{4.6-3}$$

In particular, for *plane motion*, Eq. 4.6-3 reduces to a scalar equation in the scalar functions $\hat{M}$ and H. For a *rigid body in plane motion*,

$$\int_{t_0}^{t_1} M^*\, dt = I^*[\omega(t_1) - \omega(t_0)] = I^* \Delta\omega = \Delta(I^*\omega). \qquad \textbf{4.6-4}$$

When the resultant external force or moment vanishes, the *conservation-of-momentum* principles hold.

Principle of Conservation of Linear Momentum:

If the resultant external force on a system vanishes at each instant during any time interval, the linear momentum of the system remains constant during that interval.

Proof: If $\mathbf{F} = \mathbf{0}$ during $t_0 \leq t \leq t_1$, then $\int_{t_0}^{t} \mathbf{F}\, dt = \mathbf{0}$ for all t in the interval. But $\int_{t_0}^{t} \mathbf{F}\, dt = \Delta(m\mathbf{v}^*)$ always; therefore $m\mathbf{v}^*(t) = m\mathbf{v}^*(t_0)$, a constant, for all t in the interval $t_0 \leq t \leq t_1$.

A similar proof holds for the

Principle of Conservation of Angular Momentum:

If the resultant external moment about a fixed point or about the mass center vanishes at each instant during any time interval, then the angular momentum of the system remains constant during that interval.

The student will notice that the impulse-momentum principles have been stated in full three-dimensional form; there is no advantage to restriction to plane motion. In application, however, we shall study only plane motion until the general $\mathbf{H}$ vector has been discussed. Also, note that any couples applied to a body contribute to the angular impulse but not to the linear impulse.

Example 4.6-1

A man weighing 150 lb stands on one end of a 50-lb, 20-ft uniform plank; the other end of the plank touches the shore of a frozen lake. Considering the ice to be perfectly smooth, calculate the distance the man will be from shore if he walks to the other end of the plank.

Solution: The system that we consider here is the man and plank together. The external forces that act are the two weights and the normal reaction from the ice. A free-body diagram of the system in general position (Fig. 4.6-1) shows the features we consider essential in the problem: the three forces, the location of the man and of the mass center of the uniform plank. For no vertical acceleration of the system, and the man remaining in contact with the plank, $N = 200$ lb. The important fact, however, is that the assumption of perfectly smooth ice gives no resultant force on the system in the x-direction, and hence at least the x-component of linear momentum is conserved. We can use this condition, noting that the man and plank start from rest, to write

$$m\dot{x}^* = \frac{50}{g}\dot{x}_p + \frac{150}{g}\dot{x}_m = 0.$$

This equation involves two unknowns, the speed of the man and the speed of the plank. What other condition do we have? We want to find the value of x_m when the man has walked 20 ft to the left *with respect to the plank;* that is, we have a relative displacement condition, based on the general relative position equation

$$x_m = x_p + x_{m/p}.$$

Initially, $x_m = 20$ ft, $x_p = 10$ ft, $x_{m/p} = 10$ ft; finally, $x_{m/p} = -10$ ft. We

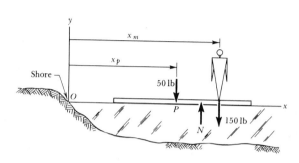

Fig. 4.6-1

obtain by integration of the momentum equation that the position of the mass center of the system does not change:

$$\frac{200}{g}\,\Delta x^* = \frac{50}{g}\,\Delta x_p + \frac{150}{g}\,\Delta x_m = 0$$

or

$$\frac{50}{g}\,(x'_p - 10) + \frac{150}{g}\,(x'_m - 20) = 0,$$

where x'_m, x'_p are final positions. But

$$x'_p = x'_m - x'_{m/p} = x'_m - (-10) = x'_m + 10$$

so that

$$\frac{200}{g}\,x'_m - \frac{3000}{g} = 0$$

or

$$x'_m = 15 \text{ ft.}$$

Notice that this does not say anything about the time taken to do this or how it is done; once we have assumed that the only external forces acting on the system as a whole are the weights and the normal force of reaction, the given result follows.

Example 4.6-2

A sandbag weighing 100 lb is suspended from a 4-ft rope. A bullet weighing 1.5 ounces traveling at 1500 ft/sec strikes the sandbag horizontally

and is embedded in it. How fast does the sandbag move after impact
(*Fig.* 4.6-2a)?

Solution: Regarding the sandbag as a particle, the external forces on
the system as a whole look something like Fig. 4.6-2b during impact.
The unknown force T, the cord tension, changes during impact, to give the
system its appropriate acceleration toward the fixed point O. The fundamental assumption here is that the impact and capture of the particle takes
place over such a short time that the configuration of the system does not

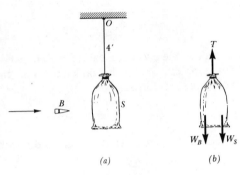

(a)   (b)

Fig. 4.6-2

change. Since no external forces act horizontally, linear momentum is
conserved in that direction, and (since bullet and sandbag stick together)

$$\frac{1.5(1500)}{(16)(32.2)} = \frac{[100+(1.5/16)]}{32.2}\, v_0$$

so that the horizontal speed after impact is

$$v_0 = \frac{(1.5)(1500)}{(16)[100+(1.5/16)]} \simeq \frac{45}{32} \text{ ft/sec.}$$

The cord begins to swing with an angular velocity

$$\omega_0 = \frac{v_0}{r} = \frac{45}{128} \text{ rad/sec.}$$

Conservation of angular momentum about O during impact can also be
used. Since during impact all the forces have lines of action that, to the
first degree of approximation, pass through O, there is no moment about O,
so that H_O is conserved. Multiplying the basic equation above by 4,
we obtain the angular momentum before and after impact. For complex
pendulums, the angular-momentum principle is used rather than the
linear-momentum principle.

Example 4.6-3

Consider the disk of Example 4.5-4 once again. How long, T, does it take for the mass center to reach speed v_1 from rest?

Solution: The free-body diagram 4.5-3b still serves as a picture of the system at any instant. One solution to our problem is to solve for the accelerations at any instant, as in Example 4.5-4, then integrate $\ddot{x}^* = -r\alpha = 2P/3m$. We obtain

$$\ddot{x}^* - \dot{x}_0^* = v_1 - 0 = v_1 = \int_0^T \ddot{x}^* \, dt = 2PT/3m,$$

or

$$T = \frac{3mv_1}{2P}.$$

But this does require a complete solution valid for each instant of time and, in a more complex problem, might be difficult. The linear impulse-momentum principle in its full form is

$$\int_0^T \{(P-F)\mathbf{i} + (N-mg)\mathbf{j}\} \, dt = m(\mathbf{v}_T^* - \mathbf{v}_0^*).$$

The kinematic condition $\dot{y}^* \equiv 0$ reduces the momentum change to

$$m(v_1 - 0)\mathbf{i} = mv_1\mathbf{i}.$$

In this form, we see that the y-component of impulse must vanish; this does *not* say that $N = mg$, but only that $\int_0^T N \, dt = \int_0^T mg \, dt = mgT$. The x-component equation is

$$\int_0^T (P-F) \, dt = PT - \int_0^T F \, dt = mv_1.$$

Notice that we do not write the frictional impulse as FT; this would require knowing that F is constant in magnitude, as P is, beforehand. Though this problem is simple, we wish to show the procedures for a general problem.

The linear impulse-momentum equation in the x-direction contains two unknowns: T and the impulse of F. An additional equation results from the angular impulse-momentum principle:

$$\int_0^T M^* \, dt = \int_0^T (-rF) \, dt = -r \int_0^T F \, dt;$$

$$\Delta H^* = \Delta(I^*\omega) = \frac{1}{2} mr^2(\omega_1 - 0),$$

where ω_1 is the final angular velocity and is a new unknown. Therefore,

$$\int_0^T M^* \, dt = \Delta H^*$$

becomes

$$-r \int_0^T F \, dt = \frac{1}{2} mr^2\omega_1.$$

The rolling-without-slipping kinematical condition is now introduced: $v_1 = -r\omega_1$. Eliminating ω_1 and the impulse of F, we find

$$PT - \int_0^T F\, dt - \left(- \int_0^T F\, dt\right) = mv_1 - \frac{1}{2} m(-v_1),$$

or

$$PT = \frac{3}{2} mv_1; \qquad T = \frac{3mv_1}{2P}.$$

As we have stated, we have used the impulse-momentum principles in a much more formal way than we probably would in actually solving such a simple problem. We have done this so that the procedure will be clear for more complex problems. Notice that the difficulty in using the principles arises from the fact that *all* external forces, including unknown constraint forces, have impulse.

As a final word on this section, let us list the conditions under which the impulse-momentum principles are most likely to be used and the advantages and difficulties that arise in their use. The student should look for their applicability in analyses where the forces are given explicitly as functions of time or where a specific time interval is referred to or where the answer to the question "how long a time interval?" is wanted. Also, if the force components vanish in all or only some directions or if there is a point about which moments vanish, conservation-of-momentum principles are indicated. The basic advantage of the impulse-momentum principles is the same as that of the fundamental system equations: the internal forces do not enter the computations. Further, since the impulse integral is with respect to time, paths of points do not need to be known. The difficulties are two-fold. First, the principles are vector principles in general, and the difficulty of representing the vectors in an appropriate coordinate system must be handled. This, of course, must be done whatever way we treat the problem—if we treat it fully. The second difficulty arises from the fact that *all* external forces, known and unknown, appear in the impulse integral.

The next section deals with the work-energy principle that to some extent reverses these advantages and disadvantages. It is a scalar principle, not a vector one; often unknown external reactions can be eliminated from consideration; but internal forces generally do not drop out of the computations, and some information about paths actually traveled must be known.

4·7 The Work-Energy Principle for Particle Systems and Plane Rigid Bodies

In Section 2.6 the work-energy principle

$$\Delta W = \Delta T \qquad \qquad \textbf{4·7-1}$$

for a particle was derived.   This equation expresses the principle for a system of particles also if ΔW, the work done on the system, and T, the kinetic energy of the system, are properly defined.   Consider the system of N particles of Section 4.3; for each of the particles,

$$\Delta W_i = \Delta T_i, \qquad i = 1, 2, 3, \ldots N$$

where $T_i = \tfrac{1}{2}m\mathbf{v}_i \cdot \mathbf{v}_i$ and ΔW_i is the work done by all forces, *external and internal*, on the i-th particle.   Defining the total work done on the system by

$$\Delta W = \sum_{i=1}^{N} \Delta W_i$$

and the kinetic energy of the system by

$$T = \sum_{i=1}^{N} T_i = \frac{1}{2} \sum_{i=1}^{N} m_i \mathbf{v}_i \cdot \mathbf{v}_i, \qquad\qquad \textbf{4.7-2}$$

addition of the N scalar work-energy equations results in

$$\Delta W = \sum_{i=1}^{N} \Delta W_i = \sum_{i=1}^{N} \Delta T_i = \Delta \left(\sum_{i=1}^{N} T_i \right) = \Delta T.$$

Thus 4.7-1 expresses the work-energy principle for particle systems:

The work done by all forces, external and internal, on a system of particles during any motion of the system is equal to the change in value of the kinetic energy of the system.

The most important feature of this is the fact that the internal forces in general will do work on the system.   We shall examine the conditions on the system that eliminate the work done by the internal forces a little later.

The work-energy principle for systems can be reformulated in the same way as that for a particle (Section 2.8).   Introducing the concepts of conservative and nonconservative forces, the potential energy function, V, assigned to account for the work done by the conservative force fields, and the mechanical energy, $E = T + V$, of the system, we obtain the alternative form of the work-energy principle:

The work done by all nonconservative forces, external and internal, on a system of particles during any motion of the system is equal to the change in value of the mechanical energy of the system:

$$\Delta W^* = \Delta E. \qquad\qquad \textbf{4.7-3}$$

Our only problem is the definition of potential energy for pairs of internal forces; this will be discussed briefly in a later section. Finally, we have the principle of *conservation of mechanical energy*:

If all forces that do work on a system of particles are conservative, the mechanical energy remains constant:

$$E = E_0 \quad \text{or} \quad \Delta E = 0. \qquad \textbf{4.7-4}$$

Consider now the expression for the work done. We can use the line-integral-over-particle-path definition of the work. If C_i is the path of the i-th particle, then the external forces do work

$$\Delta W_E = \sum_{i=1}^{N} \int_{C_i} \mathbf{F}_i \cdot d\mathbf{r}_i. \qquad \textbf{4.7-5}$$

The internal forces $\mathbf{f}_{ij}$ on the i-th particle due to the j-th particle do work

$$\int_{C_i} \sum_{j=1}^{N} (\mathbf{f}_{ij} \cdot d\mathbf{r}_i) = \int_{C_i} \left(\sum_{j=1}^{N} \mathbf{f}_{ij} \right) \cdot d\mathbf{r}_i;$$

the total work done by the internal forces is

$$\Delta W_I = \sum_{i=1}^{N} \int_{C_i} \left(\sum_{j=1}^{N} \mathbf{f}_{ij} \right) \cdot d\mathbf{r}_i. \qquad \textbf{4.7-6}$$

Of course, $\Delta W = \Delta W_E + \Delta W_I$. The work ΔW_E needs no further comment, since it is simply the sum of work integrals of the particle motion sort. The internal work ΔW_I, however, is clearly quite complex. Not only is there the explicit dependence on the paths of integration, C_i, involved in the formal integrals but also there is, in each integral, an implicit dependence on the paths of every other particle, since $\mathbf{f}_{ij}$ changes as the j-th particle moves as well as with the motion of the i-th particle. We look therefore for another way of evaluating ΔW_I, or rather for special systems for which ΔW_I can be evaluated easily. The simplest case and the only one we consider in this section is the rigid body, for which the internal work vanishes whatever the motion.

Compute the work* done by the pair of internal forces $\mathbf{f}_{ij}$ and $\mathbf{f}_{ji}$ during time dt as the particles displace $d\mathbf{r}_i$ and $d\mathbf{r}_j$:

$$\mathbf{f}_{ij} \cdot d\mathbf{r}_i + \mathbf{f}_{ji} \cdot d\mathbf{r}_j = \mathbf{f}_{ij} \cdot (d\mathbf{r}_i - d\mathbf{r}_j) = \mathbf{f}_{ij} \cdot d\mathbf{r}_{ij}, \qquad \textbf{4.7-7}$$

where $d\mathbf{r}_{ij}$ is the relative displacement vector. This result shows that *the internal forces do work only during the relative motion of parts of the*

---

* More properly, we should use $\mathbf{v}_i$ and $\mathbf{v}_j$ and compute the power.

system, so that internal forces do no work on any system in pure translational motion.   If the work $\mathbf{f}_{ij} \cdot d\mathbf{r}_{ij}$ vanishes for all i and j, then the total internal work will vanish during time dt, and so vanishes over any extended motion.   Moreover, if ΔW_I is to vanish for all possible motions, it must vanish for motions of the i-th and j-th masses only, all others fixed.   Therefore, a necessary and sufficient condition that the internal work is zero for *all* motions is

$$\mathbf{f}_{ij} \cdot d\mathbf{r}_{ij} = 0, \quad \text{all } i, j. \qquad \textbf{4.7-8}$$

The line of action of $\mathbf{f}_{ij}$ is along the line joining m_i and m_j; therefore,

$$\mathbf{f}_{ij} = A\mathbf{r}_{ij}, \qquad \textbf{4.7-9}$$

where A is a scalar function of proportionality.   For non-zero $\mathbf{f}_{ij}$ and non-zero relative motion $d\mathbf{r}_{ij}$, then, the elementary internal work term vanishes if, and only if,

$$\mathbf{r}_{ij} \cdot d\mathbf{r}_{ij} = d\left(\frac{1}{2}\mathbf{r}_{ij} \cdot \mathbf{r}_{ij}\right) = 0. \qquad \textbf{4.7-10}$$

But $\mathbf{r}_{ij} \cdot \mathbf{r}_{ij}$ is the square of the magnitude of the relative position vector; therefore, *the internal work vanishes for all motions* if, and only if, the magnitude of $\mathbf{r}_{ij}$ is constant for all i and j; i.e., *if, and only if, the system is rigid.*

The three work-energy principles 4.7-1, 3, and 4 are valid for *rigid* systems of particles, with the work done by all forces replaced by *the work done by the external forces only.*

Turning now to the continuous body, we restrict ourselves to a single rigid lamina moving in its plane.   The principles for rigid particle systems apply to such a body.   In particular, the work done by the internal forces vanishes by the same argument that holds for the rigid system of particles.   The only additional hypothesis that we need is the one made in Section 4.3 about the nature of the internal forces in a continuous body, namely that they remain finite in magnitude and obey Newton's third law.   Generally, the work done by the external forces must be defined as time integrals of power now, rather than line integrals along paths of specific particles.   Certain forces can be considered as applied at the same point of the body always— the weight force at the mass center, for instance.   For these, the line integral definition of work may be used.   Other forces are not always applied at the same point of the body, so that we cannot identify a $\mathbf{v} \, dt$ expression always with the $d\mathbf{r}$ of the same material point.   This does not cause difficulty in most of our problems.   The examples will show how to handle the situation that arises.   We also need the concept of work as the time integral of power to prove some useful results about the work due to constraint forces such as friction at a rolling contact.

For the continuous body, we must also be concerned with the work done by couples applied to the body. The determination of the proper expression comes from an argument very similar to that leading to 4.7-7 for the work done by internal forces. We restrict the argument to rigid bodies in plane motion for the present.

Consider a rigid body in plane motion subjected to a couple with plane the same as the plane of motion and moment M about any point of the plane. Represent the couple in any way by two opposite forces in the plane of motion applied at any two points of the body such that the moment of the couple is preserved.

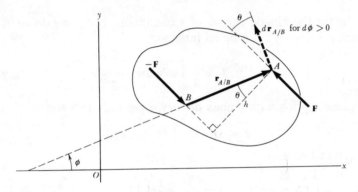

Fig. 4.7-1

Figure 4.7-1 shows a typical representation of a couple; the moment, M, of the couple is given in terms of the quantities shown by $M\mathbf{k} = \mathbf{r}_{A/B} \times \mathbf{F}$. The work done by the forces of the couple during time dt is

$$\mathbf{F} \cdot d\mathbf{r}_A + (-\mathbf{F}) \cdot d\mathbf{r}_B = \mathbf{F} \cdot (d\mathbf{r}_A - d\mathbf{r}_B) = \mathbf{F} \cdot d\mathbf{r}_{A/B};$$

the couple does work during relative motion of the points. For a rigid body, we know the form of $d\mathbf{r}_{A/B}$ from the relative motion equations. If $d\phi$ is the (positive) angular displacement during dt, $d\mathbf{r}_{A/B}$ has magnitude $|\mathbf{r}_{A/B}| \, d\phi$ and direction 90° counterclockwise from $\mathbf{r}_{A/B}$ as shown. Introducing the angle θ between $\mathbf{F}$ and $d\mathbf{r}_{A/B}$, we have

$$\mathbf{F} \cdot d\mathbf{r}_{A/B} = (F)(|\mathbf{r}_{A/B}| \, d\phi)(\cos \theta)$$
$$= (F)(|\mathbf{r}_{A/B}|\cos \theta)(d\phi)$$
$$= Fh \, d\phi,$$

where h is the moment arm of the couple. Therefore, since Fh is the magnitude of the couple moment, the work done by the couple on a rigid body during time dt is $M\,d\phi$. This shows that the result is independent of the particular representation of the couple in terms of forces. Also, although this has been derived for a couple with positive moment and for a positive angular displacement, the result is true whatever the signs of M and $d\phi$ are; the student should verify this by considering the other possible combinations. The total work done by a couple with scalar moment M during an angular displacement of a rigid lamina is therefore

$$\Delta W = \int_{\phi_1}^{\phi_2} M\,d\phi. \qquad \textbf{4.7-11}$$

As for the kinetic energy of a continuous body, we define it by replacing the sum 4.7-2 by an integral,

$$T = \frac{1}{2}\int \mathbf{v}\cdot\mathbf{v}\,dm. \qquad \textbf{4.7-12}$$

For plane motion with a mass density σ per unit area and

$$\mathbf{v} = \dot{x}\mathbf{i} + \dot{y}\mathbf{j} = \dot{r}\mathbf{e}_r + r\dot{\phi}\mathbf{e}_\phi,$$

Eq. 4.7-12 becomes

$$T = \frac{1}{2}\int\int \sigma(x, y)[\dot{x}^2 + \dot{y}^2]\,dx\,dy = \frac{1}{2}\int\int \sigma(r, \phi)(\dot{r}^2 + r^2\dot{\phi}^2)r\,dr\,d\phi.$$

$$\textbf{4.7-13}$$

For a rigid lamina, there is a further simplification of the form of T that we shall develop shortly.

The fundamental principle for a single plane rigid body is then the power-equals-rate-of-change-of-kinetic-energy relation, generalized from that of Section 2.6 for a particle, where the power is that of the external forces only. Integrating the principle and transforming the resulting work-energy relation as we have done that for the particle system, we may show that the three work-energy principles of this section hold for a single plane rigid body as well. Again, the work done by external forces is the total work done on a rigid body. The next important extension of the work-energy principle is to systems of rigid bodies and particles moving in a plane. This is presented in the next section, together with a discussion of the work done by various common external and internal constraints and connections.

Finally, we shall find some new forms of the kinetic energy function T useful in application as well as in development of theoretical conclusions. We start with the definition 4.7-2 of the kinetic energy of a particle system and transform it using the relative motion equations to obtain a general change-of-base-point formula for T. The $\mathbf{r}_i$ and $\mathbf{v}_i$ of the typical particle are measured in an inertial frame based on the fixed origin, O. As in 4.2, choose another point, P, with position $\mathbf{R}(t)$ relative to O, and let $\mathbf{p}_i$ be the position of m_i relative to P. Then $\mathbf{r}_i = \mathbf{R} + \mathbf{p}_i$, $\mathbf{v}_i = \dot{\mathbf{R}} + \dot{\mathbf{p}}_i$, and 4.7-2 becomes

$$T = \frac{1}{2} \sum_{i=1}^{N} m_i \mathbf{v}_i \cdot \mathbf{v}_i = \frac{1}{2} \sum_{i=1}^{N} m_i (\dot{\mathbf{R}} + \dot{\mathbf{p}}_i) \cdot (\dot{\mathbf{R}} + \dot{\mathbf{p}}_i)$$

$$= \frac{1}{2} \sum_{i=1}^{N} m_i (\dot{\mathbf{R}} \cdot \dot{\mathbf{R}}) + \sum_{i=1}^{N} m_i (\dot{\mathbf{R}} \cdot \dot{\mathbf{p}}_i) + \frac{1}{2} \sum_{i=1}^{N} m_i \dot{\mathbf{p}}_i \cdot \dot{\mathbf{p}}_i$$

$$= \frac{1}{2} (\dot{\mathbf{R}} \cdot \dot{\mathbf{R}}) \sum_{i=1}^{N} m_i + \dot{\mathbf{R}} \cdot \sum_{i=1}^{N} m_i \dot{\mathbf{p}}_i + \frac{1}{2} \sum_{i=1}^{N} m_i \dot{\mathbf{p}}_i \cdot \dot{\mathbf{p}}_i,$$

or

$$T = \frac{1}{2} m (\dot{\mathbf{R}} \cdot \dot{\mathbf{R}}) + m \dot{\mathbf{R}} \cdot \dot{\mathbf{p}}^* + \frac{1}{2} \sum_{i=1}^{N} m_i \dot{\mathbf{p}}_i \cdot \dot{\mathbf{p}}_i. \qquad \textbf{4.7-14}$$

This is the fundamental transfer theorem for the kinetic energy. The last term is the kinetic energy of the system in an inertial system based on P, the first term is the kinetic energy of a particle moving with P and having mass equal to that of the system, and the middle term is the usual sort of coupling term between the motion of P and the motion of the distributed particles we have seen before. Identifying P with the mass center C, so that $\dot{\mathbf{R}} = \dot{\mathbf{r}}^* = \mathbf{v}^*$ and $\dot{\mathbf{p}}^* = 0$, we have

$$T = \frac{1}{2} m (\mathbf{v}^* \cdot \mathbf{v}^*) + \frac{1}{2} \sum_{i=1}^{N} m_i \dot{\mathbf{p}}_i \cdot \dot{\mathbf{p}}_i, \qquad \textbf{4.7-15}$$

where $\dot{\mathbf{p}}_i$ is the velocity of m_i relative to the mass center. The same formulas hold for general continuous systems, with integrals replacing sums, and can be derived from 4.7-12 by the same procedure.

The answer to one basic question arises naturally from the formula 4.7-14. We have been talking about "the" kinetic energy of the system as though it were an absolute quantity. In Section 4.3, we have seen that the equations of motion of the system are exactly the same if a point P moving at constant velocity $\dot{\mathbf{R}}$ is chosen as origin instead of O. The integrals of the equations of motion in such a new system must lead to $\Delta W = \Delta T$, where the work done and kinetic energy are measured in the new coordinates. The T for such a system would be the last term in Eq. 4.7-14. The student should be able to show, with a little effort perhaps, that the difference in the work done measured in the two different coordinate systems—$\int \mathbf{F} \cdot d\mathbf{r}$ as opposed to $\int \mathbf{F} \cdot d\mathbf{p}$—just equals the remaining terms in 4.7-14 if $\dot{\mathbf{R}}$ is constant. The term "the" kinetic energy of the system is only a convenience; it means the kinetic energy of the system relative to an inertial frame of reference.

For a rigid lamina, 4.7-14 and 4.7-15 give useful forms for the kinetic energy. Take P to be a point in or moving with the rigid lamina; then the relative velocity vector $\dot{\mathbf{p}}$ from P to any other point in the lamina has the form 4.4-3, and

$$\dot{\mathbf{p}} \cdot \dot{\mathbf{p}} = p^2 \omega^2$$

where ω is the angular velocity of the lamina and p is the distance from P to the second point. The last term in 4.7-14 (with sum replaced by integral) is

$$\int \dot{\mathbf{p}} \cdot \dot{\mathbf{p}} \, dm = \int p^2 \omega^2 \, dm = \omega^2 \int p^2 \, dm = I_P \omega^2;$$

therefore, the kinetic energy of a rigid body in plane motion is

$$T = \frac{1}{2} m\dot{\mathbf{R}} \cdot \dot{\mathbf{R}} + m\dot{\mathbf{R}} \cdot \dot{\mathbf{p}}^* + \frac{1}{2} I_P \omega^2, \qquad \textbf{4.7-16}$$

where P is a point moving with the body. Choosing P to be the mass center, we find the most common form for T:

$$T = \frac{1}{2} m\mathbf{v}^* \cdot \mathbf{v}^* + \frac{1}{2} I^* \omega^2$$

$$= \frac{1}{2} m v^{*2} + \frac{1}{2} I^* \omega^2, \qquad \textbf{4.7-17}$$

where v^* is the speed of the mass center. An alternative form of 4.7-17, which is often useful, is obtained by introducing the instantaneous center of rotation, Q, of the lamina. Let d^* be the distance from Q to the mass center C; then $v^* = d^* |\omega|$, $v^{*2} = d^{*2} \omega^2$, and

$$T = \frac{1}{2} (I^* + md^{*2}) \omega^2.$$

But, by the transfer of base-point theorem 4.5-6, $I^* + md^{*2} = I_Q$, the moment of inertia with respect to the instantaneous center. Therefore,

$$T = \frac{1}{2} I_Q \omega^2. \qquad \textbf{4.7-18}$$

If the lamina is in pure translation, $\omega = 0$ and I_Q approaches infinity, so that direct application of 4.7-18 does not make sense; however, 4.7-17 (or, for that matter, 4.7-15 for any translating system) reduces to

$$T = \frac{1}{2} mv^{*2} = \frac{1}{2} mv^2 \qquad\qquad \textbf{4.7-19}$$

for a body in *pure translation*, for which every point has the same velocity **v** and speed v. If the instantaneous center Q is the same at all times (i.e., if the body is in *pure rotation*), then 4.7-18 holds with I_Q being the moment of inertia with respect to the fixed point.

Example **4.7-1**

A uniform rigid disk of mass m and radius r rolls without slipping on a horizontal line. What is its kinetic energy when its center has speed v_0 ?

Solution: Since the point of contact of disk and line is the instantaneous center, the angular velocity, ω_0, has magnitude v_0/r (see Eq. 4.4-4). The centroidal moment of inertia of a uniform disk is $I^* = \frac{1}{2}mr^2$. From 4.7-17

$$T = \frac{1}{2} mv_0^2 + \frac{1}{2} \left(\frac{1}{2} mr^2 \right) \omega_0^2$$

$$= \frac{1}{2} mv_0^2 + \frac{1}{4} mr^2 \frac{v_0^2}{r^2} = \frac{3}{4} mv_0^2.$$

The same result is obtained from 4.7-18:

$$I_Q = I^* + md^{*2} = \frac{1}{2} mr^2 + mr^2 = \frac{3}{2} mr^2,$$

$$T = \frac{1}{2} \left(\frac{3}{2} mr^2 \right) \omega_0^2 = \frac{3}{4} mr^2 \frac{v_0^2}{r^2} = \frac{3}{4} mv_0^2.$$

Example **4.7-2**

If the compound pendulum of Example 4.5-3, shown here again in Fig. 4.7-2a, has angular velocity $\dot{\theta} = \omega_0$ when $\theta = 0$, how far, θ_1, will it turn? What ω_0 will cause the pendulum to turn completely around its pivot?

Solution: Since a change in position is asked for, we try a work-energy approach. From the free-body diagram 4.7-2b, we see that the reactions due to the smooth pin at O are applied at a fixed point and hence are workless constraints. Only the weight force does work, and we know it to be conservative. The principle of conservation of mechanical energy can be applied. Since the body is in pure rotation about O, Eq. 4.7-18 may be used for the kinetic energy:

$$T = \frac{1}{2} I_0 \dot{\theta}^2 = \frac{1}{2} mk_0^2 \dot{\theta}^2.$$

Taking the lowest position of C as the datum level, the potential energy is

$$V = mgh = mgr^*(1 - \cos\theta),$$

and the mechanical energy is

$$E = T + V = \frac{1}{2}mk_O^2\dot{\theta}^2 + mgr^*(1 - \cos\theta).$$

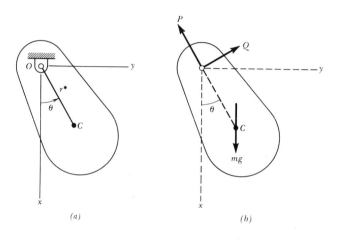

Fig. 4.7-2

Note that this has been found for a general position.   Since we are interested in a change in position from $\theta = 0$ to a position of rest, we have

$$\Delta E = 0 = E\big|_{\substack{\theta = \theta_1 \\ \dot{\theta} = 0}} - E\big|_{\substack{\theta = 0 \\ \dot{\theta} = \omega_0}}$$

$$= mgr^*(1 - \cos\theta_1) - \frac{1}{2}mk_O^2\omega_0^2,$$

so that

$$\cos\theta_1 = 1 - \frac{k_O^2\omega_0^2}{2gr^*}.$$

For there to be a solution for θ_1, $0 \leq \theta_1 \leq \pi$, of course $-1 \leq \cos\theta_1 \leq 1$ and

$$0 \leq \frac{k_O^2\omega_0^2}{2gr^*} \leq 2.$$

The minimum ω_0 for which the pendulum could first pivot around is then the ω_0 for $\theta_1 = \pi$:

$$\omega_0\big|_{\theta_1 = \pi} = \frac{2\sqrt{gr^*}}{k_O}.$$

Example **4·7-3**

Consider the rolling disk of Examples 4.5-4 and 4.6-3 again, shown here in Fig. 4.7-3a. How far (x_0) will the center travel while the center acquires a speed v_0 from rest?

Solution: The free-body diagram in general position is given in 4.7-3b. Since a change in position is to be found, we try to apply the work-energy

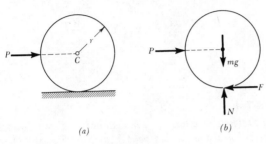

(a)   (b)

Fig. 4·7-3

principle. The change in kinetic energy for the conditions of the problem can be found from Example 4.7-1:

$$\Delta T = \frac{3}{4}\, mv_0^2 - 0 = \frac{3}{4}\, mv_0^2.$$

We can compute the work done by the weight force in general as a line integral over the path of the mass center; here the weight clearly does zero work, since the mass center moves horizontally only. The contact forces in general require the power definition to be used; they are not always applied to the same particle or material point of the body. Here the rolling-without-slipping condition shows that the forces F and N do zero work, since the point at which they are applied at any instant of time is the instantaneous center of zero velocity for the disk. Therefore, the power of the forces vanishes at each instant,

$$(F\mathbf{i} + N\mathbf{j}) \cdot \mathbf{v} = 0$$

and the work done in any motion (as long as the disk does not slip) is zero:

$$\int_{t_1}^{t_2} (F\mathbf{i} + N\mathbf{j}) \cdot \mathbf{v}\, dt = 0.$$

The force $\mathbf{P} = P\mathbf{i}$ is also of this type; its power can be found by using the relative motion equations. Call A the point of application of $\mathbf{P}$ at a typical instant; then

$$\mathbf{v}_A = \mathbf{v}_C + \mathbf{v}_{A/C} = \dot{x}^*\mathbf{i} - r\omega\mathbf{j},$$

and the power of P is

$$P\mathbf{i} \cdot \mathbf{v}_A = P\dot{x}^*.$$

The work done by P is then

$$\int_0^T P\dot{x}^*\, dt = \int_0^{x_0} P\, dx^* = Px_0.$$

This is not a surprising result, and leads one to wonder why the power is introduced at all. The next example may serve to clarify the matter.

The total work done on the body is then Px_0; the work-energy principle is

$$\Delta W = Px_0 = \frac{3}{4} mv_0^2 = \Delta T$$

from which

$$x_0 = \frac{3mv_0^2}{4P}.$$

Example **4.7-4**

Solve the previous example for the distance x_1 that C travels when P is applied at a height h above the horizontal surface (*Fig.* 4.7-4).

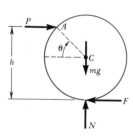

Solution: Fig. 4.7-4 serves as a free-body diagram at a typical instant when P is in contact with point A on the rim. The angle θ from the horizontal to the radius from C to the point of application of P is a constant, with

$$\sin\theta = \frac{h-r}{r};$$

since $0 \leqq h \leqq 2r$, $-(\pi/2) \leqq \theta \leqq (\pi/2)$.

Fig. 4.7-4

The arguments of the previous example still give $\Delta T = \frac{3}{4}mv_0^2$ and ΔW equal to the work of P alone. A hasty conclusion that the work done is still P times the horizontal displacement of C leads to the false result $x_1 = x_0$.

Now

$$\mathbf{v}_A = \mathbf{v}_C + \mathbf{v}_{A/C} = \dot{x}^*\mathbf{i} - r\omega \sin\theta\mathbf{i} - r\omega \cos\theta\mathbf{j}$$
$$= (\dot{x}^* - r\omega \sin\theta)\mathbf{i} - r\omega \cos\theta\mathbf{j}$$
$$= \dot{x}^*(1 + \sin\theta)\mathbf{i} + \dot{x}^* \cos\theta\mathbf{j},$$

the last line coming from the kinematical rolling-without-slipping condition $\dot{x}^* = -r\omega$. Thus the power is

$$P\dot{x}^*(1 + \sin\theta)$$

and the work done is

$$\Delta W = \int_0^T P\,\dot{x}^*(1 + \sin\theta)\, dt = P(1 + \sin\theta)\int_0^{x_1} dx^*$$
$$= Px_1(1 + \sin\theta).$$

Therefore, from

$$\Delta W = \Delta T,$$

we find

$$x_1 = \frac{3mv_0^2}{4P(1+\sin\theta)}.$$

Example 4.7-5

Solve the last problem if $\mathbf{P} = P\mathbf{i}$ *is always applied to a definite point* A *of the rim.*

Solution: Now $\mathbf{P}$ moves around with A, remaining constant in magnitude and direction but not line of action. The formula for $\mathbf{v}_A$ developed in the last example still holds, but now we let θ change. Since θ is measured positive clockwise, $\dot\theta = -\omega = \dot x^*/r$, and the power of P is

$$P\dot x^*(1+\sin\theta) = rP\dot\theta(1+\sin\theta)$$

$$= rP\frac{d}{dt}(\theta - \cos\theta);$$

therefore,

$$\Delta W = \int_0^T rP\frac{d}{dt}(\theta - \cos\theta)\,dt = rP\int_{\theta_0}^{\theta_1} d(\theta - \cos\theta),$$

where θ_0 and θ_1 are the initial and final values of the angle of rotation. The distance x_1 traveled by the mass center will be $x_1 = r(\theta_1 - \theta_0)$ for rolling without slipping.

$$\Delta W = rP[\theta_1 - \theta_0 - \cos\theta_1 + \cos\theta_0]$$

$$= rP[(\theta_1 - \theta_0) - \cos(\theta_0 + \theta_1 - \theta_0) + \cos\theta_0]$$

$$= Px_1 - rP[\cos\theta_0\cos(\theta_1 - \theta_0) - \sin\theta_0\sin(\theta_1 - \theta_0)] + rP\cos\theta_0.$$

Therefore, depending just where (θ_0) around the circle we begin,

$$\Delta W = Px_1 + rP\cos\theta_0\left[1 - \cos\left(\frac{x_1}{r}\right)\right] - rP\sin\theta_0\sin\left(\frac{x_1}{r}\right).$$

Setting this equal to ΔT gives a transcendental equation for x_1.

4.8 Work and Energy for General Plane Systems; Real and Ideal Constraints

Most mechanical systems of engineering interest cannot be adequately represented by a particle system or single rigid-body model. Even when deformations of systems can be ignored or adequately represented by ideal springs, the system may have to be considered as consisting of a number of rigid bodies and particles joined by pins, springs, cables, and other constraining connections. The analysis of such a system can be based on the analyses of each part of the system, and must be, if we are interested in a detailed study of forces and motion. Often, however, the details are not of interest, and we want to say something about the system as a whole.

The impulse-momentum principles of Section 4.6 do apply to whole systems, and have the advantage that the internal forces have no resultant impulse. The work-energy principle often eliminates some of the external forces from consideration—the reactions at a rolling-without-slipping contact, for instance, as we have seen in the examples of the last section. However, internal forces may do work, and the extension of the work-energy principle to systems of plane rigid bodies must account for the work done at the internal connections between bodies. Before extending the principle, therefore, we shall discuss some of the common constraints on motion of systems and evaluate the work done by the forces of constraint, both external and internal to the system.

Constraints on motion can be divided into two classes, real and ideal. *Ideal constraints* are those for which the forces of constraint either do zero work (*workless constraints*) or are conservative. *Real constraints* are all others, in particular those in which a dissipative frictional force or couple is present. We shall discuss a number of ideal constraints, with some occasional comments on the corresponding real constraints.

If a rigid body slides on a smooth, fixed surface that it cannot penetrate, the only force of constraint on the body when it is isolated is a normal reaction force. The only displacements of the body that do not violate the no-penetration condition are those that have a component tangent to the sliding surface and a normal component that separates the bodies. Since the force is normal to the surface, it does no work during any tangential displacement; if there is a normal displacement that breaks the contact, the normal force must become zero itself. In either case, the reaction force at a smooth sliding contact does no work during any displacement of the rigid body that does not violate the constraint.

Now, suppose that the surface on which the body slides is not fixed, but is a moving rigid body itself; in general, it will have a component of displacement along the common normal to the two bodies. If we isolate as our system just one of these bodies, then the normal reaction force will, in general, do work; for both bodies must have at least that common normal displacement that will prevent mutual penetration. However, if we include *both* bodies in the system to be considered, the *pair* of normal reactions (now internal to the system) do no work. They do no work on either body during any tangential displacements of the bodies; they do no work during any separation of the two, for then they become zero; and they do no work during an actual sliding motion, for the normal displacements of the points of contact must be the same, whereas the forces of reaction are negatives of one another. That is, work is done on each body separately; but, by the third law, the forces are equal in magnitude but opposite in direction, and hence the two work quantities are negatives of one another. Thus zero work is done on the system as a whole by the pair of reactive forces at a smooth sliding contact in any displacement not violating the constraint.

Similar arguments hold for a body joined to a fixed surface by a smooth pin or a smooth ball-and-socket joint or for two moving bodies so connected. For the fixed connection, there is only a force of reaction and no frictional couple at the joint; therefore, in any motion not violating the constraint (i.e., any motion leaving the point fixed), there is no displacement of the point, and hence no work is done. For both bodies moving, the pair of reaction forces do no work on a system in which both bodies are included; again the third law tells us that the forces are negatives of one another while the displacements of the points of application are the same.

Such workless constraints are, of course, idealizations themselves of real contacts, useful in simplifying the analysis of real systems just as the idealization of the rigid body is useful. In real systems, some sort of friction is always present at contacts between bodies. If the frictional effects can be ignored within the degree of accuracy required, then the mathematical model we make usually employs ideal constraints. If frictional effects are important, then the constraints can no longer be considered as workless. They must be considered as real constraints, *dissipative* for the most part; that is, the frictional forces tend to oppose the relative motions between bodies and hence do negative work on the system. Hence the change in mechanical energy is negative, or mechanical energy is dissipated—usually being transformed into thermal energy.

Whether the frictional force is one of dry (or Coulomb) friction or one due to viscous effects, the important thing to remember is that the frictional force is always opposed to the direction of relative motion at the contact. For instance, consider two bars hinged or pinned together, with friction in the hinge; here the frictional forces distributed over the pin surface give rise to a resultant frictional couple. If the first bar rotates counterclockwise relative to the second, then the friction couple on the first bar is clockwise—even though the absolute angular velocity of that first bar is clockwise. The work done by the frictional couple on the system of two bars is negative; it is the product of the couple moment and the relative angular displacement, which are opposite in sense.

One important exception to the usual rule of energy dissipation by friction arises, as we have mentioned, when the constraint between two bodies is that of rolling without slipping. If a body rolls without slipping on a fixed surface, then the reaction force does no work; if two bodies roll without slipping on one another, then the pair of reaction forces do no work on a system containing both bodies.

Let us see why this should be so in a very rough manner first. Consider a rigid body rolling on a fixed surface (Fig. 4.8-1a) and

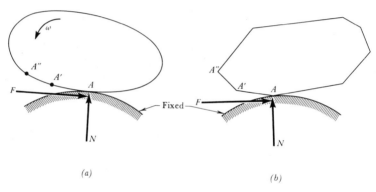

Fig. 4.8-1

isolate the body, representing the reaction force by its normal and frictional components in the usual way. Let us take the rather Archimedean view given by replacing the body by a polygon of a great number of sides (Fig. 4.8-1b). How would we describe the rolling motion of the polygonal body?

Suppose the corner, A, is in contact. The polygon tips around A until the flat side, AA', comes into contact. Then we tip the polygon around A' until $A'A''$ lies flat, and so on. If the tipping is done without slipping, then the corners are successively fixed points of the motion and the reaction forces do no work. We thus describe rolling with slipping as a tipping about a corner followed by a slipping along a flat side (in which the friction force does negative work). Rolling without slipping occurs simply as the tipping about corners, with no slipping of the flat sides. Ignoring work done during impact of a flat side, we expect no work to be done in a rolling-without-slipping motion of a polygon, and, by a limiting argument involving the passage to an "infinite number of infinitesimal sides," we expect it to be generally true.

To make such a geometrical proof precise for a general pair of curved surfaces is relatively complicated. However, we have developed the necessary analytic machinery by defining work as the integral of power. In particular, the power of the contact forces is $\mathbf{F} \cdot \mathbf{v}$, where $\mathbf{F}$ is the force at the contact, and $\mathbf{v}$ is the velocity of the contact point. For rolling without slipping on a fixed surface, $\mathbf{v} = \mathbf{0}$ since the contact point is the instantaneous center. The power is always zero, so that the work done is zero. For rolling without slipping on a moving surface, the total internal force does no work, since the two power expressions are negatives of one another.

Another workless constraint is that due to a light, inextensible cord connecting bodies. If the cord is slack, there is no force in the cord, and no work is done. If the cord is taut, the pair of tension forces equal in magnitude on any segment of the cord do no work since the displacements of each end of the segment in the direction of the cord (and hence along the line of the forces) must be the same, by inextensibility. Thus the forces exerted by the cord on the bodies at either end of the cord segment also do zero work. The cord can then be considered as part of a system containing both bodies, with no contribution to the work on the system.

The ideal linear spring, discussed in Section 2.7, provides an example of a conservative ideal constraint. In Section 2.7, we stated without proof that work is done by the external forces applied to the spring only during a change in length of the spring. We can now prove this statement, at least if the spring moves in a plane. Recall that forces are transmitted only along the spring and not perpendicularly to it. If the spring does not change length, it can be treated as a rigid body, and we have seen (Section 4.4) that any motion of a rigid body in the plane can be considered as a pure translation, equal to the displacement of one of its points, followed by a pure rotation about that point. During a translation of the spring, both ends displace the same amount; the end forces are equal in magnitude but opposite in direction, and so one does work in the translation that is the negative of the work of the other. If the translational motion brings one end of the spring to its final position, then the rest of the rigid-body motion is a rotation about that end. The force at that end does no work, since the point does not move; the force at the other does zero work, since the displacement of the point of application is perpendicular to the line of the spring, and hence of the force. Thus the forces on a spring do work during change of length only, and, as we have seen in 2.7, this work by the external forces is

$$\Delta W_E = \frac{1}{2} k(e_2^2 - e_1^2),\qquad\qquad \textbf{4.8-1}$$

where e_1 and e_2 are the initial and final extensions.

Let us apply the work-energy principle to the light spring, considered as a system of particles—but neglecting the mass. Then the change in kinetic energy is zero, although the work done by the external forces is not. In order to apply the work-energy principle consistently for such ideal systems, we must conclude that there are internal forces that do work during the deformation of the spring, and that this internal work is the negative of the external work. This is reasonable. If we isolate a segment from the interior of the spring, the internal forces exerted by the rest of the spring on the segment in the complete spring become external forces on the segment. Since each segment of the spring experiences extension when the whole spring does, these forces do work on the segment. The extension of the segment is only a portion of the total, and so the work done on the partial spring is not the negative of the work done on the rest by the reversed forces exerted by the segment. Thus, putting all these pieces together, net work is done by the internal forces.

Since the total work done by the internal forces depends only on the initial and final elongations and not on how they are produced, we can say the internal forces are conservative. The potential energy $V = \frac{1}{2}ke^2$ of elastic strain can thus be assigned to account for the work of the internal forces; then the work done by the external forces equals the change in internal strain energy:

$$\Delta W_E = \Delta V.$$

Now we have a basis for including ideal springs in systems. In Section 2.7, a potential energy was assigned to account for the work done on a particle by the spring force acting on the particle. We may now do the same for a spring attached to any body, if the spring force is considered as an external force. We now change our interpretation slightly. The work done by the spring force on the body is the negative of this change in potential, or the negative of the work done (4.8-1) on the spring by the force due to the body (or forces due to the bodies at both ends of the spring). Including the spring with the bodies in a common system, these work terms cancel one another. But now the internal forces in the system—the internal spring

forces—do work on the system; they may be accounted for by assigning to the system the potential energy of elastic strain of the spring:

$$V = \frac{1}{2}ke^2. \qquad \textbf{4.8-2}$$

A second kind of ideal spring is also useful as a model of a physical
situation.   This is the ideal light *torsional* spring, an abstraction of the
spiral spring found in watch mainsprings.   The torsional spring, as it
extends and contracts, provides a resultant *restoring couple* on a body
similar to the restoring force due to the linear spring.   The over-all

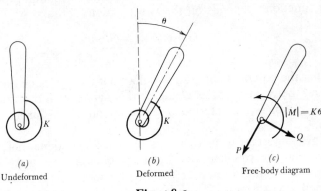

| *(a)* | *(b)* | *(c)* |
| Undeformed | Deformed | Free-body diagram |

Fig. 4.8-2

deformation of the torsional spring is measured by an angular displacement from an undeformed state (Fig. 4.8-2); the linear torsional
spring provides a couple proportional to the angular displacement and
opposed in sense to the displacement:

$$M = -K\theta, \qquad \textbf{4.8-3}$$

the spring constant K having dimension (force-length)/radian.   The
work done by such a couple is

$$\int_{\theta_1}^{\theta_2} M\,d\theta = -\frac{1}{2}K(\theta_2^2 - \theta_1^2);$$

the spring may be included in a system by adding its strain energy to
the potential energy:

$$V = \frac{1}{2}K\theta^2. \qquad \textbf{4.8-4}$$

Still another conservative constraint force is the mutual gravitational attraction of two bodies.   This is not of importance in most

engineering problems, particularly those dealing with ordinary devices near the surface of the earth, where only the earth's attraction need be considered. In celestial mechanics, this is important. For completeness, we give the potential energy for the pair of internal gravitational forces acting on two particles of mass m_1 and m_2. The two forces are (Section 2.2)

$$\mathbf{f}_{12} = -\mathbf{f}_{21} = +\frac{Gm_1m_2(\mathbf{r}_2 - \mathbf{r}_1)}{|\mathbf{r}_2 - \mathbf{r}_1|^3} = \frac{Gm_1m_2\mathbf{p}}{p^3},$$

where $\mathbf{p}$ is the relative position vector from $\mathbf{r}_1$ to $\mathbf{r}_2$ and $p = |\mathbf{r}_2 - \mathbf{r}_1| = [(\mathbf{r}_2 - \mathbf{r}_1) \cdot (\mathbf{r}_2 - \mathbf{r}_1)]^{1/2}$ is its magnitude. The corresponding potential energy function* depends on the two positions through $\mathbf{p}$:

$$V = -\frac{Gm_1m_2}{p} = -\frac{Gm_1m_2}{|\mathbf{r}_2 - \mathbf{r}_1|}. \qquad \textbf{4.8-5}$$

Note that the potential energy 4.8-5 does not change value unless the distance p between particles changes; this agrees with our finding of the last section—that internal forces only do work during relative motion.

More important to us than this mutual gravitational potential is the fact that we can consider the attraction on one body due to another to be concentrated at the mass center. (We shall not be concerned with systems of such large extent that differences between center of mass and center of gravity need to be considered.) In particular, the earth's gravitational attraction on a body acts at its mass center. We shall show in the examples that, for a sphere with radially symmetrical mass density, the attraction due to the sphere at any exterior point is the same as the attraction due to an equivalent particle at the center of the sphere. Assuming the earth can be so treated, then the attraction of the earth on a body small in extent compared to the earth can be expressed by approximately parallel forces at each point of the small body directed toward the center of the earth. The resultant of parallel forces is easily found, and, by

---

* The interpretation of the force as the negative gradient of potential energy must be carefully handled here. The force $\mathbf{f}_{12}$ is the force on m_1 at a position $\mathbf{r}_1$ with the position $\mathbf{r}_2$ of m_2 held fixed; $\mathbf{f}_{12}$ should then be the negative gradient of V with the partial derivatives taken with respect to the coordinates of m_1. Similarly, $\mathbf{f}_{21}$ is computed by holding $\mathbf{r}_1$ constant and taking the gradient with respect to the coordinates of $\mathbf{r}_2$. That such a procedure gives the right answer we will not prove.

comparing the resultant for different configurations of the body relative to the earth, we find (see *Statics*) that the resultant always passes through the mass center of the body.

We can now prove the extended form of the work-energy principle for systems in plane motion. (Again, a power principle is the basic one.) Of course, we have that the work done by all forces, external and internal, equals the change in kinetic energy of a system. What we want is not this general systems principle, but a generalization of the single rigid-body form of the principle. Consider only systems consisting of rigid bodies and particles moving in a plane, with all constraints, internal and external, of the ideal type (so that springs, inextensible cords, etc., can be included in the system). The external constraining forces having been accounted for, the only other forces are the so-called *applied* external loads. For such a system, the work-energy principle can be stated in the form:

The work done by the applied loads equals the change in mechanical energy of the system

$$\Delta W = \Delta E = \Delta(T + V).$$ **4.8-6**

Here the potential energy of conservative ideal constraints is included in the mechanical energy of the system, and the kinetic energy is the sum of the kinetic energies of the parts of the system. The restriction to ideal constraints means that we do not have to show all internal forces on the free-body diagram, but only identify those that have a potential energy.

If all the applied loads are conservative, we obtain a conservation-of-energy principle. However, as the examples of the force on the rolling disk in the last section showed, there may be some difficulty in establishing the conservative nature of the loads.

Finally, the remarks about the extension of the energy principle to thermomechanical and electromechanical systems made in Section 2.8 should be repeated here. We are concerned only with the purely mechanical work-energy principles as consequences of the mechanical laws of motion and for forces of the type discussed in 2.2.

Example 4.8-1

Suppose the compound pendulum of Example 4.7-2 has a torsional spring of constant K, which is undeformed when the angle $\theta = 0$, attached to it on the line OC, the other end of the spring being fixed at the pin. If the angular velocity $\dot{\theta} = \omega_0$ when $\theta = 0$, how far, θ_2, will the pendulum swing?

Solution: Fig. 4.8-3 shows a free-body diagram of the system, pendulum and spring, in general position. The only applied force is the weight force, which is conservative with potential energy $V = mgr^*(1 - \cos \theta)$. The external constraint forces at the pin, P and Q, are workless; such constraints can be denoted on the free-body diagram by some special symbol if desired, such as the circle placed around them here. (This is *not* a standard notation.) The only internal forces that do work are the spring forces, and we

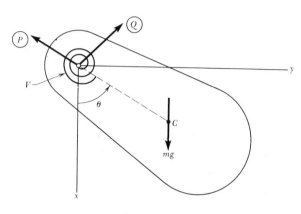

Fig. 4.8-3

have noted this by placing the symbol V (for potential energy) by the spring. Whatever systematic approach is used, it is wise to indicate all external forces and all working internal forces on the free-body diagram. Since the forces that do work are conservative, the system is said to be conservative. Its mechanical energy is

$$E = T + V = \frac{1}{2} I_0 \dot{\theta}^2 + mgr^*(1 - \cos \theta) + \frac{1}{2} K\theta^2$$

$$= \frac{1}{2} mk_O^2 \dot{\theta}^2 + mgr^*(1 - \cos \theta) + \frac{1}{2} K\theta^2.$$

Applying the conservation principle, with initial state $\theta = 0$, $\dot{\theta} = \omega_0$ and final state $\theta = \theta_2$, $\dot{\theta} = 0$, we find

$$\Delta E = 0 = \left[mgr^*(1 - \cos \theta_2) + \frac{1}{2} K\theta_2^2 \right] - \left[\frac{1}{2} mk_O^2 \omega^2 \right].$$

Therefore, θ_2 is determined by the transcendental equation

$$\frac{1}{2} K\theta_2^2 + mgr^*(1 - \cos \theta_2) = \frac{1}{2} mk_O^2 \omega_0^2.$$

An approximate answer for θ_2 may be obtained assuming θ_2 to be sufficiently small; then $1 - \cos \theta_2 \cong \theta_2^2/2$, and

$$\theta_2^2 \cong \frac{mk_O^2 \omega_0^2}{mgr^* + K} = \frac{k_O^2 \omega_0^2}{gr^* + (K/m)}.$$

A similar approximation in Example 4.7-2 ($\cos \theta_1 \cong 1 - \theta_1^2/2$) would lead to

$$\theta_1^2 \cong \frac{k_O^2 \omega_0^2}{gr^*}.$$

Example 4.8-2

The crank-connecting rod-piston system of Example 4.4-10 is reproduced here, with a free-body diagram in the general position given in Fig. 4.8-4. The pins at O, A, and B, and the cylinder walls are smooth; bars OA and AB can be taken as uniform rigid bars of weights 64.4 and 16.1 lb respectively; and the piston C may be treated as a 5-lb particle. A constant counterclockwise torque, M, is applied to OA through a shaft at O. The system starts from rest with OA horizontal to the right. What torque M is needed to give OA an angular velocity of 5 rad/sec when OA is vertically upward?

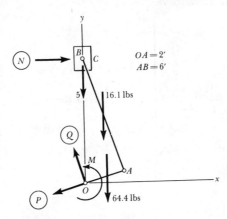

$OA = 2'$
$AB = 6'$

Fig. 4.8-4

Solution: The external constraints, P, Q, and N, are workless, since O is fixed and the cylinder is smooth. The internal force pairs at A and B do zero work because the pins are smooth. The weight forces do work, as does the couple, M. Because of uniformity, the mass centers of the bars are halfway along the bar. The mass center of OA is raised one foot during the motion; therefore, the 64.4-lb force does work -64.4 ft-lb. The mass center of B is initially at y-height $\frac{1}{2}\sqrt{6^2-2^2}=2\sqrt{2}$ ft and finally at height $2+\frac{1}{2}(6)=5$ ft; therefore, the 16.1-lb force does $-16.1(5-2\sqrt{2})$ ft-lb of work. The piston C is initially at height $\sqrt{6^2-2^2}=4\sqrt{2}$ ft, finally at $2+6=8$ ft; its weight does $-5(8-4\sqrt{2})$ ft-lb work on the system. The couple does $M\pi/2$ ft-lb. The total work is

$$W = -64.4-16.1(5-2\sqrt{2})-40+20\sqrt{2}+\frac{\pi M}{2} \text{ ft-lb}$$

$$= 1.57M-111.1 \text{ ft-lb}.$$

The initial kinetic energy is zero, since the system is at rest.   The final kinetic energy is the sum of the final kinetic energies of the parts.   For bar OA in pure rotation,

$$T_{OA} = \frac{1}{2} I_O \omega_{OA}^2 = \frac{1}{2} \left(\frac{1}{3} ml^2 \right) \omega^2$$

$$= \left(\frac{1}{6} \right) \left(\frac{64.4}{32.2} \right) (2)^2 (5)^2 = 33.3 \ \text{ft-lb.}$$

When $OA-AB-C$ lie along the y-axis, the piston must be at one of its extreme positions and hence be momentarily at rest.   Therefore, its kinetic energy is zero.   Moreover, B is then the instantaneous center for AB, and the speed of A is $6|\omega_{AB}|$.   But the speed of A is also $2|\omega_{OA}|$; therefore, $|\omega_{AB}| = \frac{1}{3}|\omega_{OA}|$ in the final position.   Using the instantaneous center formulation for T, we have

$$T_{AB} = \frac{1}{2} I_B \omega_{AB}^2 = \frac{1}{2} \left(\frac{1}{3} ml^2 \right) \omega_{AB}^2$$

$$= \left(\frac{1}{6} \right) \left(\frac{16.1}{32.2} \right) (6)^2 \left(\frac{1}{9} \right) (25) = 8.33 \ \text{ft-lb.}$$

The change in kinetic energy is the sum of the final kinetic energies of OA and AB:

$$\Delta T = T_{OA} + T_{AB} = 41.7 \ \text{ft-lb.}$$

Then, from $\Delta W = \Delta T$,

$$1.57M - 111.1 = 41.7,$$

$$M = 97.3 \ \text{lb-ft.}$$

We could also have introduced the potential energies of the weight forces and set the work done by the couple alone equal to the change in mechanical energy of the system.

Example 4.8-3

Prove that the gravitational attraction due to a uniform sphere or a sphere with mass density depending only on the distance from the center of the sphere is the same as that due to a single particle of mass equal to the total mass of the sphere placed at the sphere's center.

Solution: Suppose a sphere of radius a, center O, and mass density ρ attracts a particle of mass m_1 located at a distance $h > a$ from O (Fig. 4.8-5) according to Newton's law of gravitation.   Choose a coordinate system with origin O and z-axis passing through the particle as pictured.   Consider a volume element dV of the sphere, located at the point (x, y, z); its mass is $dm = \rho \, dV = \rho \, dx \, dy \, dz$.   Its attraction on m_1 is

$$d\mathbf{F} = -\frac{Gm_1 \, dm}{R^2} \mathbf{e}_R = -\frac{Gm_1 \rho \mathbf{R} \, dV}{R^3}$$

where **R** is the vector from dV to the particle, and R is its magnitude:

$$\mathbf{R} = h\mathbf{k} - \mathbf{r} = h\mathbf{k} - (x\mathbf{i} + y\mathbf{j} + z\mathbf{k})$$

$$R = [x^2 + y^2 + (h-z)^2]^{\frac{1}{2}}.$$

Then the total force exerted by the sphere on m_1 is

$$\mathbf{F} = -Gm_1 \iiint \rho \mathbf{R} \frac{dV}{R^3},$$

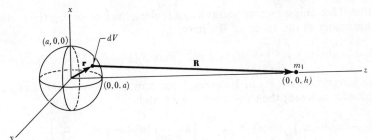

Fig. 4.8-5

the integration being carried out over the sphere. As one might expect, the evaluation of the integral is simpler if we change to spherical polar coordinates (r, θ, ϕ) related to (x, y, z) by the formulas

$$x = r \sin \theta \cos \phi, \qquad y = r \sin \theta \sin \phi, \qquad z = r \cos \theta.$$

The element of volume $dV = dx\, dy\, dz = r^2 \sin \theta\, dr\, d\theta\, d\phi$, and the ranges of integration on the new variables are $0 \leqq \phi \leqq 2\pi$, $0 \leqq \theta \leqq \pi$, $0 \leqq r \leqq a$. We will now make the assumption that the density, ρ, is a function of r only, $\rho = \rho(r)$, with the constant mass density a special case of this; the total mass m_2 of the sphere is then

$$m_2 = \int_0^a \int_0^\pi \int_0^{2\pi} \rho r^2 \sin \theta\, dr\, d\theta\, d\phi$$

$$= 2\pi \int_0^a \int_0^\pi r^2 \rho(r) \sin \theta\, dr\, d\theta$$

$$= 2\pi \left[(-\cos \theta) \Big|_0^\pi \right] \left(\int_0^a r^2 \rho(r)\, dr \right)$$

$$= 4\pi \int_0^a r^2 \rho(r)\, dr.$$

The attraction force **F** can now be written as

$$\mathbf{F} = -Gm_1 \int_0^a \int_0^\pi \int_0^{2\pi} [x^2+y^2+(h-z)^2]^{-3/2}[-x\mathbf{i}-y\mathbf{j}$$
$$+(h-z)\mathbf{k}]\rho(r)r^2 \sin\theta \, dr \, d\theta \, d\phi$$
$$= Gm_1 \int_0^a \int_0^\pi \int_0^{2\pi} r^2\rho(r) \sin\theta [r^2+h^2-2hr\cos\theta]^{-3/2}[r\sin\theta\cos\phi\mathbf{i}$$
$$+r\sin\theta\sin\phi\mathbf{j}-(h-r\cos\theta)\mathbf{k}] \, dr \, d\theta \, d\phi.$$

Performing the integration on ϕ first, we find that $F_x = F_y = 0$:

$$\int_0^{2\pi} \cos\phi \, d\phi = \int_0^{2\pi} \sin\phi \, d\phi = 0,$$

so that **F** has only a z-component; i.e., it is along the line joining the particle to the center of the sphere. We have

$$\mathbf{F} = -2\pi Gm_1\mathbf{k} \int_0^a \int_0^\pi r^2\rho(r) \sin\theta(h-r\cos\theta)[h^2+r^2-2hr\cos\theta]^{-3/2} \, dr \, d\theta.$$

The integration on θ can be carried out now. Let $s=-2hr\cos\theta$, and think of r as fixed; then $ds=2hr\sin\theta \, d\theta$, and

$$\mathbf{F} = -2\pi Gm_1\mathbf{k} \int_0^a r^2\rho(r) \, dr \left[\int_{-2hr}^{2hr} \left(h+\frac{s}{2h}\right)(h^2+r^2+s)^{-3/2} \frac{ds}{2hr}\right]$$
$$= -\frac{\pi Gm_1}{h} \mathbf{k} \int_0^a r\rho(r) \, dr \left[\int_{-2hr}^{2hr} \left\{h(h^2+r^2+s)^{-3/2}+\frac{s}{2h}(h^2+r^2+s)^{-3/2}\right\} ds\right]$$
$$= -\frac{\pi Gm_1}{h} \mathbf{k} \int_0^a r\rho(r) \, dr \left[-2h(h^2+r^2+s)^{-1/2}+\frac{2}{h}(h^2+r^2+s)^{1/2}\right.$$
$$\left. -\frac{s}{h}(h^2+r^2+s)^{-1/2}\right]_{-2hr}^{2hr}$$
$$= -\frac{\pi Gm_1}{h^2} \mathbf{k} \int_0^a r\rho(r) \, dr \left[\frac{2hr+2r^2}{h+r}-\frac{-2hr+2r^2}{h-r}\right]$$
$$= -\frac{4\pi Gm_1}{h^2} \mathbf{k} \int_0^a r^2\rho(r) \, dr$$
$$= -\frac{Gm_1m_2}{h^2} \mathbf{k}.$$

This is the desired result, the total force on m_1 being that due to a particle of mass m_2 placed at O. The student should note that, provided it is radially symmetric, the density distribution need not be uniform. In fact, the result is correct for a hollow sphere; the lower limit of the r-integration is then the inner radius of the sphere instead of being zero. He who feels ambitious may compute the gravitational field due to this hollow sphere at an arbitrary point inside the cavity and show that it is zero. The computation of the potential due to the sphere is easier than that for the force, and the student may wish to try that.

Exercises

4.2-1: A particle moves at constant speed V in a straight line. A second particle moves at constant speed v along an intersecting straight line that makes an angle θ with the first. Initially, the second particle is at position $\mathbf{p}_0$ with respect to the first, which in turn is distance L from the point of intersection. The first particle moves toward the point of intersection.

At a later time t, the relative position vector $\mathbf{p}_1$ is found to be in the same direction as $\mathbf{p}_0$. Show that the two particles will collide at the point of intersection; find the speed v of the second particle in terms of V, L, θ, and $p_0 = |\mathbf{p}_0|$.

Ans.: $v/V = \cos \theta \pm [(p_0/L)^2 - \sin^2 \theta]^{1/2}$.

4.2-2: The relative acceleration of particle B with respect to particle A is proportional to the position of B relative to A and always directed toward A. Show that the relative position vector has the form $\mathbf{p} = \mathbf{C}_1 \sin kt + \mathbf{C}_2 \cos kt$, where $\mathbf{C}_1$ and $\mathbf{C}_2$ are constant vectors, and k is a constant scalar.

4.2-3: Two particles remain at constant distance from one another as they move (a) in a plane, (b) in space. What can you say, at least qualitatively, about the forms of the relative velocity and acceleration vectors?

4.2-4: Two beads slide on a circular wire of radius r, one at constant speed v, the other at constant speed V. They start at diametrically opposite points. How far along the wire does the particle with speed v travel before the two collide if the two travel in (a) opposite senses, (b) the same sense around the wire?

Ans.: (a) $\pi rv/(V+v)$; (b) $\pi rv/(|V-v|)$.

4.3-1: Find the position, velocity, and acceleration of the mass centers of the following systems of particles:

Particle		Mass	Position	Velocity	Acceleration
(a)	1	0.5 slug	$2\mathbf{i} - 3\mathbf{j}$ ft	$-4\mathbf{k}$ ft/sec	$-3\mathbf{j} + 5\mathbf{k}$ ft/sec^2
	2	0.3 slug	$-2\mathbf{i} + 4\mathbf{j}$ ft	$-\mathbf{i} + 3\mathbf{j}$ ft/sec	$4\mathbf{i} - 3\mathbf{j}$ ft/sec^2
	3	0.4 slug	$-\mathbf{i} - 2\mathbf{j} - \mathbf{k}$ ft	$4\mathbf{i} - 3\mathbf{j}$ ft/sec	$\mathbf{i} + \mathbf{j} + \mathbf{k}$ ft/sec^2
(b)	1	m	$a\mathbf{i} + b\mathbf{j}$	$3a\mathbf{i} - 2b\mathbf{j}$	$2a\mathbf{i} + b\mathbf{j}$
	2	$(3/2)m$	$-a\mathbf{i} - b\mathbf{j}$	$-2a\mathbf{i} + 3b\mathbf{j}$	$-b\mathbf{i} - 2a\mathbf{j}$
	3	m	$(a/4)\mathbf{i} + (b/2)\mathbf{j}$	$b\mathbf{i} + b\mathbf{j}$	$(b - 2a)\mathbf{i} + b\mathbf{j}$
(c)	1	6 gm	$2\mathbf{i} + 2\mathbf{j} + 2\mathbf{k}$ cm	$-\mathbf{i} - \mathbf{j}$ cm/sec	$2\mathbf{k}$ cm/sec^2
	2	3 gm	$-4\mathbf{i} - 4\mathbf{k} - 4\mathbf{j}$ cm	$4\mathbf{i} + 3\mathbf{j}$ cm/sec	$-4\mathbf{k}$ cm/sec^2
(d)	1	$2m$	$6\mathbf{e}_r - 2\mathbf{e}_\phi$	$\mathbf{e}_r$	$5\mathbf{e}_r$
	2	$3m$	$4\mathbf{e}_r - 5\mathbf{e}_\phi$	$\mathbf{e}_\phi$	$3\mathbf{e}_r + 2\mathbf{e}_\phi$
	3	$4m$	$-2\mathbf{e}_r - 4\mathbf{e}_\phi$	$-\mathbf{e}_r$	$-4\mathbf{e}_\phi$
	4	$5m$	$\mathbf{e}_r + \mathbf{e}_\phi$	$-\mathbf{e}_\phi$	$-\mathbf{e}_r - \mathbf{e}_\phi$

272   *Dynamics of Particle Systems and Plane Rigid Bodies*

Ans.:

(a) $\mathbf{a}^* = 1.33\mathbf{i} - 1.67\mathbf{j} + 2.42\mathbf{k}$ ft/sec^2.

(b) $\mathbf{r}^* = -\dfrac{a}{14}\,\mathbf{i}$; $\mathbf{v}^* = b\left(\dfrac{2}{7}\mathbf{i} + \mathbf{j}\right)$;

$\mathbf{a}^* = -\dfrac{1}{7}\,b\mathbf{i} + \dfrac{1}{7}\,(4b - 6a)\mathbf{j}$.

(c) $\mathbf{r}^* = \mathbf{a}^* = \mathbf{0}$; $\mathbf{v}^* = (2\mathbf{i} + \mathbf{j})/3$ cm/sec.

(d) $\mathbf{r}^* = 1.5\mathbf{e}_r$; $\mathbf{v}^* = -(\mathbf{e}_r + \mathbf{e}_\phi)/7$; $\mathbf{a}^* = \mathbf{e}_r - \dfrac{15}{14}\,\mathbf{e}_\phi$.

4.3-2: Find the resultant external force acting on each of the systems of Exercise 4.3-1.
Ans.: (a) $1.6\mathbf{i} - 2\mathbf{j} + 2.9\mathbf{k}$ lb; (d) $14m\mathbf{e}_r - 15m\mathbf{e}_\phi$.

4.3-3: Find the angular momentum vector, with respect to the origin, for each of the systems of Exercise 4.3-1.
Ans.:

(a) $\mathbf{H}_O = 4.8\mathbf{i} + 2.4\mathbf{j} + 3.8\mathbf{k}$ lb-ft-sec.
(b) $\mathbf{H}_O = -mb(12.25a + 0.5b)\mathbf{k}$.
(c) $\mathbf{H}_O = 48\mathbf{i} - 60\mathbf{j} + 12\mathbf{k}$ dyne-cm-sec.
(d) $\mathbf{H}_O = -5m\mathbf{k}$.

4.3-4: Particles of mass m_1 and m_2 connected by a light spring are released from rest. The unstretched length of the spring is λ and a force k is required to produce unit extension of the spring. Write the equation of motion expressing $\mathbf{F}$ and $\mathbf{a}$ in terms of $\mathbf{r}_1$, $\mathbf{r}_2$, λ, and k for each particle. Show that $d^2(m_1\mathbf{r}_1 + m_2\mathbf{r}_2)/dt^2 = \mathbf{0}$. Ignore all forces except those exerted by the spring. Obtain the result directly from the principle of motion of the mass center. Compare with Example 4.3-3.

4.3-5: The same problem as 4.3-4 except that now, instead of a spring, consider the gravitational attraction between the bodies.

4.4-1: A rigid bar of length l slides with its ends constrained to move in

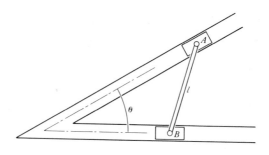

slots that make an angle θ with one another. (a) Prove that when the bar is perpendicular to one slot the velocity of the point in contact with the other

slot must vanish. (b) Show that, if the bar makes equal angles with the slots, the speeds of the two ends are the same, and find that speed in terms of l, θ, and the angular velocity, ω, of the bar.
Ans.: $v_A = v_B = (l\omega/2) \sec (\theta/2)$.

4.4-2: For the bar of Exercise 4.4-1 show that, in the case when one end is perpendicular to a groove, the other end has an acceleration directed toward the point of intersection of the grooves and of magnitude $l\omega^2 \csc \theta$.

4.4-3: For the bar of Exercise 4.4-1 find the accelerations of the two ends for the case when the bar makes equal angles with the slots. Express your answer in terms of l, θ, ω, and α where α is the angular acceleration of the bar.
Ans.: $|\mathbf{a}_B| = (l/2)|\omega^2 \csc (\theta/2) - \alpha \sec (\theta/2)|$.

4.4-4: Work Exercise 4.4-1 by the instantaneous center of zero velocity method.

4.4-5: A disk of radius R rolls on a horizontal surface with a (counterclockwise) angular velocity ω and angular acceleration α. Locate the point in the disk that has zero acceleration.
Ans.: Distance of point from center is $r = \left(\dfrac{R\alpha}{\omega^2}\right)\left[1 + \dfrac{\alpha^2}{\omega^4}\right]^{-1/4}$

4.4-6: A 1-ft diameter gear is held between parallel racks that are made to move in the same direction at speeds of 5 and 7 in/sec. If the disk does not slip, what will be its angular velocity and the velocity of its center?
Ans.: $\mathbf{v} = 6$ ips to right.

4.4-7: In the following figures, various combinations of information about velocities, angular velocities, and instantaneous centers of zero velocity are given for a rigid body moving in the plane. Some are possible (P); others impossible (I). Classify them and state why each belongs in its particular group.
Ans.: P, I, P, P, I, I, I, P, I, P, P, P.

4.4-8: Consider the familiar crank and connecting rod. (a) For a given constant angular velocity, ω, of the crank, what is the velocity of the piston? Express the answer in terms of r, l, ω, and θ. (b) Sketch the ratio v_C/v_B as a function of θ for the case $l^2/r^2 = 5$ indicating, approximately, the maximum value of this ratio.
Ans.: $(v_C/v_B)_{\max} = 1.10$.

4.4-9: The diagram shows a four-bar linkage. (*AD* essentially constitutes a fourth bar.) If *AB* is rotating clockwise at the rate of 100 rpm at the instant pictured, what is the angular velocity of bar *CD*?
Ans.: 55.5 rpm *CW*.

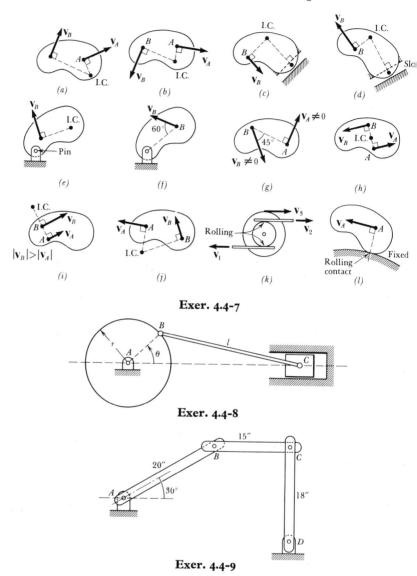

Exer. 4.4-7

Exer. 4.4-8

Exer. 4.4-9

4.4-10: Bar AB has a constant angular velocity of 10 rad/sec counterclockwise. What are the velocity and acceleration of point C? (Note: Point A is *not* vertically above point D.)

Ans.: $v_C = -173\mathbf{i} + 100\mathbf{j}$ ips;
$\mathbf{a}_C = -1475\mathbf{i} - 455\mathbf{j}$ ips².

4.4-11: Cylindrical specimens used in fatigue tests of metals must be polished longitudinally rather than circumferentially. One way of doing this without creating any flat spots is to mount the specimen in a lathe and place the polishing belt in contact with the specimen at an angle θ with the axis of the lathe. If the lathe runs at 800 rpm and the specimen diameter is 0.5 in, what is the correct angle θ for a belt speed of 4.2 in/sec?

Ans.: $\theta = 30°$.

Exer. 4.4-10

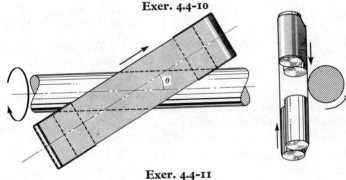

Exer. 4.4-11

4.4-12: The rod AC is rotating clockwise at a constant rate of 10 rad/sec. What is the velocity of point D when BD makes an angle of $45°$ and AC makes an angle of $60°$ with the horizontal?

Ans.: $\mathbf{v}_D = 350(\mathbf{i} - \mathbf{j})$ ips.

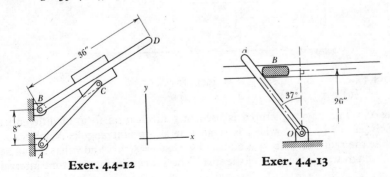

Exer. 4.4-12   **Exer. 4.4-13**

4.4-13: The rod OA has a clockwise angular velocity of 3 rad/sec. Find the speed of the block B, which slides in the horizontal guide.
Ans.: $v_B = 93.8$ ips.

4.4-14: The disk shown is rolling downhill. Its center has a speed of 8 in/sec and an acceleration whose magnitude is 5 in/sec and is directed downhill. What are the velocity and acceleration of the piston?
Ans.: $\mathbf{v} = 16.3$ ips$\leftarrow$;
$\qquad \mathbf{a} = 3.78$ ips$^2\leftarrow$.

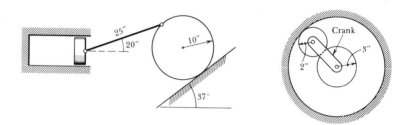

4.4-15: The outer track shown is stationary. The crank turns at 10 rad/sec *CCW*. Find the angular velocity of the inner disk.
Ans.: $\omega = 33.3$ rad/sec *CCW*.

4.4-16: The sketch shows the driving wheels of a steam locomotive that is traveling at a constant speed of 51 mph to the right. Find the velocity and acceleration of the piston when (a) $\theta = 90°$ and when (b) $\theta = 0°$. In each case locate the instantaneous center of zero velocity for the 6-ft bar.

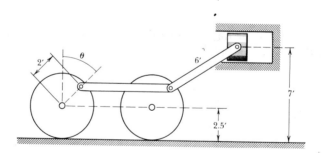

Ans.: (a) $v = 6.8$ fps, $\qquad a = 4960$ fps^2.
$\qquad$ (b) $v = 135$ fps, $\qquad a = 9100$ fps^2.

4.4-17: The device pictured is used in a mechanical form of differential analyzer. The large wheel is rotated at a constant angular velocity, ω, while the radial distance λ is adjusted so that $\lambda = \lambda(t)$. Show that the angle θ through which the shaft of the small wheel turns during any time interval

$(0, t^*)$ is given by $\theta = (\omega/r) \int_0^{t^*} \lambda(t) \, dt$, provided the small wheel does not slip.

4.4-18: The "differential" of an automobile is pictured schematically in the figure. Show that if the shaft A is rotated at the rate ω_A and the shaft B at the rate ω_B, the shaft C must rotate at the rate $\omega_C = (R/2r)(\omega_A + \omega_B)$.

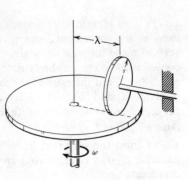

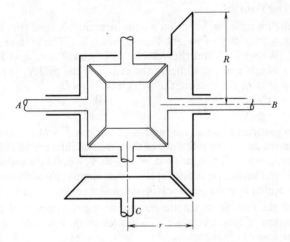

4.5-1: A uniform disk of mass m and radius r rolls without slipping down an incline of slope angle θ. Find the forces acting on the disk at any instant, the angular acceleration of the disk, and the acceleration of the mass center.

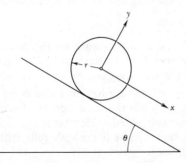

Ans.: Contact force =

$$-\frac{1}{3} mg \sin \theta \mathbf{i} + mg \cos \theta \mathbf{j};$$

$$\ddot{x}^* = \frac{2g}{3} \sin \theta, \qquad \alpha = \frac{2g}{3r} \sin \theta \ \ CW.$$

4.5-2: The rigid disk of Exercise 4.5-1 rolls and slips on the incline. Write all the equations necessary to determine the motion and solve for F, N, $\ddot{x}^*$, and α. The coefficient of kinetic friction is denoted μ. For what value of μ will the disk be on the borderline between rolling with and without slip?

Ans.: $\ddot{x} = g(\sin \theta - \mu \cos \theta)$; limiting $\mu = \frac{1}{3} \tan \theta$.

4.5-3: Two identical, uniform, equilateral triangular plates of sides b and mass m are suspended from pivots that permit them to oscillate in the vertical plane through the plate. In one case (a), the pivot is attached at a corner of the plate; in the other case (b), the pivot is attached at the center of a side. Find the ratio of the periods of free, small harmonic oscillations of plates (a) and (b). $I^* = mb^2/12$ for an equilateral triangular lamina and the c.g. is at one third the altitude from the base.
Ans.: $T_a/T_b = \sqrt{5}/2$.

4.6-1: Find the resultant linear impulse in T time units on the disk of Exercise 4.5-1. Express your answer in terms of m, g, r, θ, T and the unit coordinate vectors.
Ans.: $\hat{\mathbf{F}} = \frac{2}{3} mgT \sin\theta\mathbf{i}$.

4.6-2: A small weight, w, hangs on a light inextensible cord that is wrapped around a smooth pulley of weight W and radius r. The system is released from rest. We wish to find the velocity of w after T sec. (a) Find H_O of the pulley + weight system, O being the center of the pulley; (b) determine the velocity of w at $t = T$ using the principle $M_O = \dot{H}_O$.
Ans.: $H_O = \dfrac{r^2\omega}{g}\left(w + \dfrac{W}{2}\right);$ $\quad v = gT/\left(1 + \dfrac{W}{2w}\right).$

4.6-3: Two particles of masses m_1 and m_2, positions $\mathbf{r}_1$ and $\mathbf{r}_2$, and velocities $\mathbf{v}_1$ and $\mathbf{v}_2$ move under the influence of their mutual interaction only. If the initial velocities are such that, at $t = 0$, $m_1\mathbf{v}_1 + m_2\mathbf{v}_2 = \mathbf{0}$, (a) show that the mass center remains fixed in position; (b) show that angular momentum about the origin from which $\mathbf{r}_1$ and $\mathbf{r}_2$ are measured remains constant and is equal to $\mathbf{H}^*$.

4.7-1: Find the change in kinetic energy during the impact of the bullet-sandbag system of Example 4.6-2. What forces do work on the system to produce the loss of kinetic energy?
Ans.: $T_f \cong 10^{-3} T_i$.

4.7-2: If the rigid disk of Exercise 4.5-1 starts from rest, find its kinetic energy when the center has traveled a distance s along the axis. (Hint: Find $\mathbf{v}^*$ and ω after this distance by integrating the $\ddot{x}^*$ and α of Exercise 4.5-1 and use Eq. 4.7-17.)
Ans.: $T = mgs \sin\theta$.

4.7-3: Show that the contact forces F and N do no work on the disk of the previous problem by computing the work done by the weight force and showing that it is equal to the change in kinetic energy computed previously.

4.7-4: The uniform rigid disk of mass m and radius r has clockwise angular velocity ω_0 when the ideal spring of constant k is unstretched. How far to the right will the center move if the disk rolls without slipping?

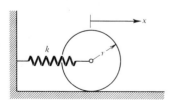

Ans.: $r\omega_0\sqrt{\dfrac{3m}{2k}}.$

4.7-5: Solve the previous problem under

the same initial conditions for the distance the center travels down the slope, if the whole system is tilted so that the disk rolls on an incline of angle θ.

Ans.: $\dfrac{mg}{k} \sin \theta + \sqrt{\dfrac{3mr^2\omega_0^2}{2k} + \dfrac{m^2g^2}{k^2} \sin^2 \theta}$.

4.8-1: Solve Exercise 4.7-4 by applying conservation of energy to the system spring and disk.

4.8-2: Solve Exercise 4.7-5 by applying conservation of energy to the system spring and disk.

4.8-3: A uniform bar of mass m and length l is pinned at one end and moves in a *horizontal* plane. A torsional spring of modulus K restrains its motion. Find the period of harmonic oscillation of the bar by writing the conservation equation of the system and differentiating it to find an equation of motion. The spring is undeformed in the position shown.

Ans.: $T_n = 2\pi l \sqrt{\dfrac{m}{3K}}$.

4.8-4: Suppose the bar of the previous problem moves in a vertical plane, with the position shown being the vertically downward equilibrium position. Find the equation of motion for the angular displacement of the bar. What approximation is needed to obtain the simple harmonic motion equation?

Ans.: $\ddot{\theta} + \dfrac{3g}{2l} \sin \theta + \dfrac{3K}{ml^2} \theta = 0$.

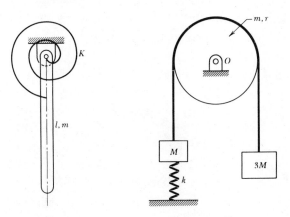

4.8-5: Two masses, M and $3M$, are attached by a light inextensible cord that passes over a pulley pinned smoothly at its center, O. The pulley may be treated as a uniform rigid disk of mass m and radius r. An ideal spring of constant k is fixed at one end and attached to M at the other.

The masses move in vertical lines. When the system is in equilibrium, the spring is extended an amount e_0. Suppose the system is released from rest with the spring extended an amount $e_1 > e_0$.

(a) Find the spring constant k in terms of m, M, r, g, and e_0.
Ans.: $k = 2Mg/e_0$.

(b) What will be the angular speed of the disk when the system passes through its equilibrium position?
Ans.: $[(e_1 - e_0)/r][4Mg/(8M + m)e_0]^{\frac{1}{2}}$.

(c) What will be the extension, e_2, in the spring when the system comes to rest again? Under what circumstances will it in fact be a compression?
Ans.: $e_2 = 2e_0 - e_1$.

CHAPTER V

Technical Applications in
Plane Motion

5.1 Introduction

The principles developed in the preceding chapter find many applications in technology. Indeed, that is the primary reason for developing the two-dimensional theory explicitly when, from a logical point of view, one could proceed directly to three-dimensional mechanical analysis in vectorial form and regard plane motion merely as a special case. To do this, however, would be to risk loss of that familiarity with the commoner dynamical effects which is so valuable in technology. We therefore consider here the way in which the equations of motion are used to analyze the dynamical behavior of typical systems in plane motion. In order to place these illustrations in a familiar context and to deal with automobiles, gears, beams, and other real objects, it is necessary to introduce assumptions that simplify the analysis and permit the establishment of useful results without unnecessary complexity. These assumptions can be justified only by investigation of the possible alternatives. The thoughtful student must ask himself: "When is it permissible to treat an automobile as a rigid body in translational motion?" "Can air resistance be neglected?" "Is the elastic deformation of the machine part unimportant?" "Is the coefficient of friction really constant?" All of these are questions that arise in practice. They can usually be answered to the engineer's satisfaction, and we shall indicate certain guides to judgment, but in a fundamental course of study it is hardly possible to cover more than the commoner situations that arise in the field, laboratory, and design office.

There is another kind of difficulty which arises after a decision has been made as to the physical assumptions that may be introduced into the mechanical analysis. This other difficulty is that of deciding on a mode of analysis well adapted to reveal the desired information. Shall we (a) work directly with the principle of the motion of the mass center and the principle of angular momentum, (b) use the work-energy principle, or (c) use the linear and angular impulse-momentum relations? To answer this question we isolate the mechanical system under investigation, draw its free-body diagram at a typical instant during the interval under consideration, and write the equations for the acceleration of the mass center and the rate of change of angular momentum. If the external forces, known and unknown, that appear in these equations are constants, the linear and angular accelerations will be constant and integration of the equations of motion will present no difficulty. (Kinematic relationships between the dependent variables will, however, be needed if the number of unknowns exceeds the number of equations of motion.) If the work done by the external forces is easily expressed as a function of position and if the internal forces that do work can be replaced by a potential energy of strain, use of the work-energy principle is indicated—particularly if ideal workless constraints are present. If the external forces are known as functions of time, or if abrupt changes in velocity occur, the impulse-momentum integral provides a solution of the equations of motion. It should not be thought that there is in each case a single correct method of analysis. Attempting an alternative approach is often instructive.

5.2 Elementary Analysis; Force and Acceleration at Particular Instants

There are many occasions when the dynamical analysis of a structure or machine only entails the determination of the forces necessary to produce prescribed motions or the accelerations that will accompany the application of specified forces. These analyses may fairly be termed elementary because the equations of motion reduce to ordinary algebraic equations relating the force and acceleration components. No integration is required for their solution. Only one step removed from these elementary cases are those in which the external forces exerted on the system under analysis are constant. Then the instant of time in which interest centers is any typical instant. The linear and angular accelerations found for that instant hold for all time and the determination of linear and angular velocities and displacements from these constant accelerations presents no difficulty.

For a rigid body in two-dimensional motion, the equations of motion, $\mathbf{F} = m\mathbf{a}$ and $\mathbf{M} = \dot{\mathbf{H}}$, referred to fixed axes take the scalar form (4.5-10, 13)

$$F_x = m\ddot{x}^*, \qquad F_y = m\ddot{y}^*, \qquad M^* = I^*\ddot{\phi}. \qquad \textbf{5.2-1}$$

Here ϕ is the angle made by any line in the body with the x-axis ($\dot{\phi} \equiv \omega$, $\ddot{\phi} \equiv \alpha$). The last of these equations may be replaced by $M_O = I_O\ddot{\phi}$ or $M_A = I_A\ddot{\phi}$, where, as discussed in 4.3, the subscript O denotes a fixed point and the subscript A a point whose acceleration passes through the mass center. If the external forces and their moments are all known, Eqs. 5.2-1 give the (constant) values of $\ddot{x}$, $\ddot{y}$, and $\ddot{\phi}$ from which the velocity, displacement, and rotation of the body may be written down at once. Usually, however, some of the forces acting are unknown. Then the equations of motion must be supplemented by kinematical relations. Often the system under analysis consists of several interconnected parts. Then it is usually advisable, at least for the beginner, to separate the system into its component parts. A set of Eqs. 5.2-1 can be written for each part; naturally the internal forces of the original system will appear explicitly in these equations, and in pairs. Care must then be exercised to avoid unconscious violation of the third law in writing the equations of motion. These points are best illustrated by specific examples.

Example 5.2-1

A 3500-lb automobile traveling at 50 mph is arrested by application of the brakes. If the coefficient of kinetic friction is 0.7, how far will the automobile travel before it is brought to a stop?

Solution: The free-body diagram for the automobile is shown in Fig. 5.2-1. Axes have been chosen in the direction of motion and in the vertical direction. The reactions at the front and rear wheels have been shown decomposed into normal and frictional components. Assuming that the four-wheel brakes are strong enough to "lock" the wheels, each frictional component will be seven tenths of the corresponding normal component and will tend to oppose the relative motion of wheel and road.

Its direction will, therefore, be to the rear, as shown. The first two of Eqs. 5.2-1 imply

$$-\mu N_1 - \mu N_2 = m\ddot{x}^*, \qquad N_1 + N_2 - mg = m\ddot{y}^* = 0. \qquad \textbf{5.2-2}$$

Here μN_1 and μN_2 have been entered as negative forces because they are shown in the free-body diagram directed toward the negative x-axis. The kinematic relation $\ddot{y}^* = 0$ follows from the assumption that the vehicle is in

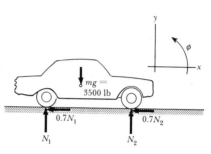

Fig. 5.2-1

horizontal translatory motion: we are neglecting the small vertical motions due to the spring suspension of the body.

Equations 5.2-2 include three unknown quantities, N_1, N_2 and $\ddot{x}^*$, so that we should have to write the third of Eqs. 5.2-1 in order to determine all of them. In the present case, however, we are only interested in the acceleration $\ddot{x}^*$ and so we may notice that N_1 and N_2 appear only in the combination $N_1 + N_2$.

$$N_1 + N_2 = mg,$$
$$-\mu(N_1 + N_2) = -\mu mg = m\ddot{x}^*,$$
$$\ddot{x}^* = -\mu g = -(0.7)(32.2) = -22.5 \ \text{ft/sec.}^2 \qquad \textbf{5.2-3}$$

The negative sign means that the acceleration vector is directed toward the negative x-axis. Since the velocity is directed toward the positive x-axis, the speed will decrease. The analysis is easily completed once the constant magnitude of the acceleration is known:

$$\dot{x}^* = -22.5t + v_0 = -22.5t + 73.3,$$
$$x^* = -11.25t^2 + 73.3t. \qquad \textbf{5.2-4}$$

The automobile comes to rest ($\dot{x}^* = 0$) when $t = 3.25$ sec. At that time $x^* = -(11.25)(3.25)^2 + (73.3)(3.25) = 119$ ft.

Example 5.2-2

Suppose the automobile of the preceding problem is accelerated, starting from rest. The wheelbase is 117 in and the mass center (c.m.) is located

20 *in from the ground and* 50 *in from the front axle. How long will it take the automobile to reach a speed of* 50 *mph?*

Solution: It is instructive (and good practice) to work the analysis in symbols. For this purpose, a suitable notation is indicated in Fig. 5.2-2, the free-body diagram. In drawing this diagram, it has been supposed that unlimited torque is available at the rear axle and that no torque at all is

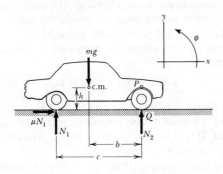

Fig. 5.2-2

supplied to the front wheels. Then the frictional force at the rear wheels (which is what produces the acceleration) is limited only by the coefficient of friction. The Eqs. 5.2-1 now take the form

$$N_1 + N_2 - mg = m\ddot{y}^*,$$

$$\mu N_1 = m\ddot{x}^*, \qquad \text{5.2-5}$$

$$N_2 b + \mu N_1 h - N_1(c-b) = I^* \ddot{\phi}.$$

As in the preceding example, $\ddot{y}^* = \ddot{\phi} = 0$ because the motion is one of horizontal translation. The three Eqs. 5.2-5 are now solved for N_1, N_2, and $\ddot{x}^*$. We find

$$\ddot{x}^* = \mu g \frac{b}{c - \mu h},$$

$$N_1 = mg \frac{b}{c - \mu h}, \qquad \text{5.2-6}$$

$$N_2 = mg \left(1 - \frac{b}{c - \mu h} \right).$$

In the present case, $b = 50$ in, $c = 117$ in, $h = 20$ in, $\mu = 0.7$, so that $\ddot{x}^* = g(35)/(117-14) = 0.34g = 11$ ft/sec², $N_1 = mg(50)/(117-14) = 0.485mg = 1700$ lb, $N_2 = 1800$ lb. Having found the constant acceleration $\ddot{x}^* = 11$ ft/sec², we see that the time required to reach a speed of 73.3 ft/sec from rest is $73.3/11 = 6.66$ sec. It may be noted that, if the automobile were stationary, the weight distribution on the rear and front axles would be 1500 and 2000 lb respectively. Forward acceleration increases the load on the rear axle. The reader may verify that in the previous example braking the vehicle will increase the pressure on the front axle markedly. We also note that the maximum acceleration possible with a two-wheel drive is only about half the deceleration possible with four-wheel brakes.

In analyses of this type, where the equation $M = \dot{H}$ is essential, moments must be taken about an axis through the mass center or through a point whose acceleration vector passes through the mass center. Instead of using the third of Eqs. 5.2-5, moments could have been taken about an axis through a point directly above the front axle at a height h (point P in Fig. 5.2-2). Then

$$\mu N_1 h - N_1 c + mgb = 0, \qquad 5.2\text{-}7$$

and we can solve for N_1 at once: $N_1 = mgb/(c - \mu h)$, just as in Eq. 5.2-6. On the other hand it would *not* be correct to take moments about an axis through, say, point Q and equate them to zero. The acceleration of this point does not pass through the mass center.

Before leaving this example, it is instructive to examine some of the engineering assumptions that were made in the analysis. Can the automobile be regarded as a rigid body in translation? Certainly the wheels are not in pure translational motion. If the automobile has a speed v and the wheels have a radius a, the angular velocity of the wheels will be v/a. According to Eq. 4.7-17, the kinetic energy of the four wheels will be

$$4 \left\{ \frac{1}{2} I^* \left(\frac{v}{a} \right)^2 + \frac{1}{2} m_w v^2 \right\} \qquad 5.2\text{-}8$$

where $I^* = m_w k^2$ is the moment of inertia of a wheel about an axis through the hub. The assumption that the rotation of the wheels could be neglected was equivalent to assuming that all the mass of each wheel, m_w, was concentrated at the hub, or, what is the same thing, that the radius of gyration of each wheel was zero. Now the total kinetic energy of the vehicle is

$$\frac{1}{2} mv^2 + 2m_w v^2 \left(\frac{k}{a} \right)^2, \qquad 5.2\text{-}9$$

and the ratio of rotational to translational kinetic energy is

$$4 \frac{m_w}{m} \left(\frac{k}{a} \right)^2. \qquad 5.2\text{-}10$$

In a conventional automobile, the total wheel weight is about 260 lb so that $4m_w/m \cong 0.074$. The ratio k/a can never exceed 1; for a uniform disk it would be $1/\sqrt{2}$. It follows that the rotational kinetic energy never exceeds 7% of the translational. We are therefore led to believe that neglecting the moment of inertia of the wheels is not a serious defect of the analysis. In a later example we shall learn how to take this inertia properly into account in a case in which it is not negligible.

It was assumed that the torque applied to the rear axle by the motor and transmission apparatus was unlimited. How much torque is actually required to develop the full 11 ft/sec² acceleration? If we continue to neglect the moment of inertia of the wheels, this torque is $\mu N_1 a$, which amounts to 1430 ft-lb for $a = 1.2$ ft. If a larger torque is supplied, the wheels will slip; if a smaller torque, the maximum acceleration, 11 ft/sec², will not be achieved. The work done by this torque during any time interval will be (Eq. 4.7-11) $M\Delta\theta$ where $\Delta\theta$ is the angle through which the wheel turns during the time interval. The rate at which work is being done is $M\omega = M(v/a)$. To maintain an acceleration of 11 ft/sec² at a speed of 50 mph = 73.3 ft/sec will require 1430 (73.3/1.2) = 87,500 ft-lb/sec. Since one horsepower is the same as 550 ft-lb/sec, this corresponds to 159 HP.

What of air resistance? The foregoing analysis shows that, at 50 mph, a torque corresponding to 158 HP will nearly cause the wheels to slip. Now if we add to Fig. 5.2-2 a horizontal force acting to the rear and through the mass center, the first and third of Eqs. 5.2-5 will be unchanged. The reactions N_1 and N_2 will be unaffected since they can be found from these two equations alone. The computed acceleration, $\ddot{x}^*$, given at slip by the second of Eqs. 5.2-5 will, however, be reduced. If, for example, the resistance has a magnitude of 125 lb, a not unreasonable value for a conventional automobile traveling at 50 mph, the reader may verify that the acceleration will be reduced to 9.8 ft/sec². Note that the horsepower required is unaltered.

Example 5.2-3

A 3000-kg mine cage falls freely. Its cable is wound around a pulley weighing 800 kg and having a radius of 1.5 m. Find the tension in the cable and the acceleration of the hoist.

Solution: It will be necessary to know the polar moment of inertia of the pulley. If we take it to be a uniform disk,

$$I^* = \frac{1}{2} m_p a^2.$$

Perhaps the most straightforward way to approach problems of this type is to separate the system into its component rigid-body parts, as shown in Fig. 5.2-3. The forces X, Y, T, $m_c g$, and $m_p g$ are constants during the motion. For the pulley, the Eqs. 5.2-1 take the form

$$X = 0, \qquad Y - m_p g - T = 0, \qquad -Ta = I^*\ddot{\phi}. \qquad \textbf{5.2-11}$$

The torque, Ta, is entered with a negative sign in the last of these equations since it is clockwise, whereas the positive direction of rotation chosen for ϕ

is counterclockwise. The only nontrivial equation of motion for the cage is the second of Eqs. 5.2-1:

$$T - m_c g = m_c \ddot{y}_c. \qquad \textbf{5.2-12}$$

The third of Eqs. 5.2-11 and Eq. 5.2-12 are two equations that involve three unknowns, T, ϕ, and $\ddot{y}_c$. Since the equations of motion can give no further assistance we must look to a kinematical relationship that will provide the necessary third equation. In this case, if we regard the cable as inextensible, the velocity of point P on the rim of the pulley must be the same as the velocity of the cage at all times:

$$a\dot{\phi} = \dot{y}_c. \qquad \textbf{5.2-13}$$

Note that if ϕ is positive (counterclockwise rotation of the pulley) $\dot{y}_c$ will be positive (upward motion of the cage). The student should form the

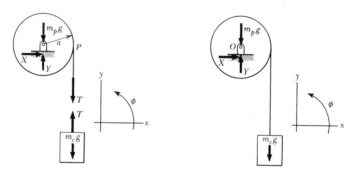

Fig. 5.2-3   **Fig. 5.2-4**

habit of checking the signs in his kinematical equations in this way. On differentiating 5.2-13 we have

$$a\ddot{\phi} = \ddot{y}_c, \qquad \textbf{5.2-14}$$

which is the wanted third equation. Now 5.2-11, 12 and 14 may be solved to yield

$$\ddot{y}_c = \frac{-g}{1 + \dfrac{I^*}{m_c a^2}} = \frac{-g}{1 + \dfrac{1}{2}\dfrac{m_p}{m_c}} = \frac{-9.81}{1 + \dfrac{800}{6000}} = -7.37 \text{ m/sec}^2, \qquad \textbf{5.2-15}$$

$$T = \frac{m_c g}{1 + \dfrac{m_c a^2}{I^*}} = \frac{m_c g}{1 + \dfrac{2m_c}{m_p}} = \frac{3000}{1 + \dfrac{6000}{800}} = 353 \text{ kg (force)}. \qquad \textbf{5.2-16}$$

It is instructive to consider the combined system of pulley and cage. For this system, whose free-body diagram is shown in Fig. 5.2-4, the first two of Eqs. 5.2-1 are not helpful; the first is trivial since it tells us only that

$X = 0$ and the second involves the unwanted, unknown reaction component
Y. If we write, instead of the third of 5.2-1, the equation $M_O = \dot{H}_O$, which
is equally valid since the center of the pulley is a fixed point, we shall have

$$-m_c g a = I_O \ddot{\phi} + m_c \ddot{y}_c a \qquad\qquad 5.2\text{-}17$$

where I_O is again $\frac{1}{2} m_p a^2$, the I^* of the previous treatment.   The left-hand
side of this equation is M_O.   The moment of the force $m_c g$ is entered as a
negative term because it is clockwise.   The first term on the right-hand side
is $\dot{H}_O$ for the pulley.   The second term on the right-hand side is $\dot{H}_O$ for
the mine cage.   This part of $\dot{H}_O$ is the proper rate of change of the moment
of momentum vector since the mine cage is treated as a particle.   We can
see that Eq. 5.2-17, in combination with the kinematic relation $a\ddot{\phi} = \ddot{y}_c$
leads to exactly the same result given by 5.2-15.   Indeed, if we multiply
Eq. 5.2-12 by a and add it to the third of Eqs. 5.2-11, thus eliminating T,
we get Eq. 5.2-17.

Example 5.2-4

A light tractor ascends a 10% *grade, the motor exerting a torque of* 2300
ft-lb on the rear axle.   The weight of the two 6-ft driving wheels is 900 *lb,
and their centroidal radius of gyration is 2.5 ft.   The remainder of the tractor*

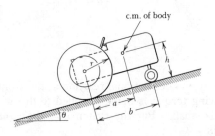

Fig. 5.2-5

(the body) weighs 2000 *lb, and its mass center is located 3.5 ft above the ground
and 4 ft from the rear axle (as shown in Fig. 5.2-5).   The wheelbase is 6 ft.
Find the acceleration of the tractor, the reactions under the wheels, and the
coefficient of friction needed to prevent slipping.*
    Solution: We use the symbolism indicated in Fig. 5.2-5.   In this
example, we can neglect the radius of gyration of the front wheels, which
are relatively light in comparison with the other parts of the vehicle, but we
cannot neglect the radius of gyration of the rear wheels, which are large and
which account for a considerable fraction of the mass of the vehicle.   This
means that we cannot treat the tractor as a single translating rigid body as
we did the automobile in Examples 5.2-1, 2.   We therefore begin by
separating the two systems: (a) rear wheels and axle, (b) remainder of

vehicle. Part (a) is undergoing a motion of rolling without slipping while part (b) is translating. The free-body diagrams of these systems are shown in Fig. 5.2-6. The weights of the rear wheels and of the remainder of the tractor are denoted $m_w g$ and $m_b g$ respectively. Note that the torque of known magnitude L exerted by the driving shaft on the axle is shown clockwise in Fig. 5.2-6a as is implied by the statement that the tractor is ascending the grade. The torque that the axle exerts on the drive shaft is an external force for the system shown in Fig. 5.2-6b. In view of the third law, it must be shown counterclockwise and of magnitude L. Similarly, the (unknown) force components V and H must be given opposite directions in (a) and (b). In (a) the arrows represent the force exerted by the body on the rear axle, and in (b) they represent the force exerted by the

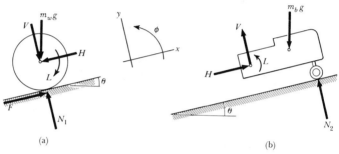

(a)   (b)

Fig. 5.2-6

rear axle on the body. The frictional reaction at the front wheel is negligible since no driving torque is being supplied to this wheel and since its rotational inertia is small. For the system (a), the equations of motion 5.2-1 take the form

$$F - m_w g \sin \theta - H = m_w \ddot{x}^*, \qquad \textbf{5.2-18a}$$

$$N_1 - m_w g \cos \theta - V = 0, \qquad \textbf{5.2-18b}$$

$$Fr - L = m_w k^2 \ddot{\phi}. \qquad \textbf{5.2-18c}$$

The right-hand side of the second of these equations vanishes because $\ddot{y}^* = 0$; the mass-center of the rear wheels does not move in the y-direction. The quantity $\ddot{x}^*$, which appears on the right-hand side of the first of these equations, is the acceleration of the mass-center of the rear wheels; i.e., the acceleration of the rear axle. Notice how the choice of axes along and perpendicular to the incline rather than horizontal and vertical simplifies Eqs. 5.2-18. Since the rear wheels roll without slipping we may express the angular acceleration, $\ddot{\phi}$, in terms of $\ddot{x}^*$:

$$\ddot{x}^* = -r\ddot{\phi}. \qquad \textbf{5.2-19}$$

The negative sign is necessary here because positive $\ddot{x}^*$ (meaning acceleration uphill) is accompanied by clockwise rotation of the wheels. We have used counterclockwise as the positive direction for moments in Eq. 5.2-18c; consequently ϕ and $\dot{\phi}$ are positive counterclockwise. This means that a positive acceleration will be accompanied by a negative angular velocity. In view of this kinematic relation, Eq. 5.2-18c may be written

$$Fr - L = -\left(\frac{m_w k^2}{r}\right)\ddot{x}^*. \qquad \textbf{5.2-20}$$

The unknown quantities F, H, N_1, and $\ddot{x}^*$ cannot be computed at once since there are four of them and we have only three equations. The equations of motion for system (b) are:

$$H - m_b g \sin \theta = m_b \ddot{x}^*,$$

$$N_2 + V - m_b g \cos \theta = 0, \qquad \textbf{5.2-21}$$

$$N_2(b - a) + L - Va + H(h - r) = 0.$$

The right-hand side of the last two of these equations vanishes because the body is moving with a translational motion in the direction of the x-axis. The quantity $\ddot{x}^*$ in the first of 5.2-21 denotes the acceleration of the mass center of the body. This is the same as the acceleration of the rear axle so that we are justified in using the same symbol that was used in Eqs. 5.2-18, 19, 20. There are now six equations in the six unknowns $\ddot{x}^*$, F, N_1, N_2, H, and V. Adding 5.2-18a and the first of 5.2-21 we have

$$F - mg \sin \theta = m\ddot{x}^* \qquad \textbf{5.2-22}$$

where $mg = (m_b + m_w)g$ is the weight of the entire tractor. Eliminating F between this equation and 5.2-20, we find

$$\ddot{x}^* = g\frac{\dfrac{L}{mgr} - \sin \theta}{1 + \dfrac{m_w}{m}\dfrac{k^2}{r^2}}. \qquad \textbf{5.2-23}$$

For a 10% grade, $\theta = \arctan 0.1 = 6°$, and

$$\ddot{x}^* = g\frac{\dfrac{2300}{(3)(2900)} - 0.1}{1 + \dfrac{900}{2900}\left(\dfrac{2.5}{3.0}\right)^2} = 0.135g = 4.35 \text{ ft/sec}^2. \qquad \textbf{5.2-24}$$

The remaining unknowns are easily found:

$$F = mg\left(\sin \theta + \frac{\ddot{x}^*}{g}\right) = 2900(0.1 + 0.135) = 682 \text{ lb},$$

$$H = m_b g\left(\sin \theta + \frac{\ddot{x}^*}{g}\right) = 470 \text{ lb},$$

$$N_2 = m_b g \frac{a}{b} \cos \theta - \frac{1}{b} [L + H(h-r)] = 1330 - \frac{2300 + (470)(\frac{1}{2})}{6} = 908 \text{ lb,}$$

$$N_1 = mg \cos \theta - N_2 = 2880 - 908 = 1972 \text{ lb.}$$

The necessary coefficient of friction is

$$\mu = \frac{F}{N_1} = \frac{680}{1972} = 0.35.$$

It may be seen from Eq. 5.2-23 that, if the torque provided by the motor is too small, $\ddot{x}^*$ will be negative and the tractor will not be able to ascend the grade. On the other hand, if L is too large, N_2 will be negative. Actually the tractor will tip over backward as soon as L is large enough to reduce N_2 to zero, a point that the designer must take into account. If we were to neglect the rotatory inertia of the wheels (i.e., take $k=0$) and use the analysis of Example 5.2-2, we should find the acceleration to be about 5.3 ft/sec² instead of the value given above.

Example 5.2-5

A uniform beam is supported at an angle θ to the horizontal by vertical cables at each end. One of the cables breaks. What is the tension in the other cable immediately after the break?

Solution: The analysis is of a type known as "initial motion" analysis. The time interval in which interest centers is a short one, and during it the free-body diagram of the beam is as shown in Fig. 5.2-7. It is important to realize that during this brief interval the bar does not have time to acquire velocity or to alter its initial inclination appreciably. The equations of motion 5.2-1 *at time zero* are

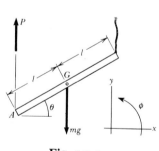

Fig. 5.2-7

$$0 = m\ddot{x}^*, \qquad P - mg = m\ddot{y}^*,$$
$$-Pl \cos \theta = I^* \ddot{\phi}. \qquad \textbf{5.2-25}$$

Were we interested in the long-term motion of the beam it would be necessary to consider P, ϕ, x^*, and y^*, as well as θ, as functions of time and to draw the free-body diagram and write the equations of motion for a typical instant during the long-term motion. Here, however, we are concerned only with $P(0)$, $\ddot{\phi}(0)$ and all the terms in Eqs. 5.2-25 are constants.

Equations 5.2-25 are three equations in four unknowns. To complete the solution we must find a kinematic relation between $\ddot{\phi}$, $\ddot{x}^*$, and $\ddot{y}^*$ at time zero. If we examine the constraints to which the bar is subject, we note that point A where the intact cable is attached swings around the upper point of support of the cable in an arc of fixed radius. Point A, at time zero, has no speed. Since $v^2/\rho = 0$, the initial acceleration of point A must be horizontal:

$$\mathbf{a}_A = a_A \mathbf{i}. \qquad\qquad \text{5.2-26}$$

We are interested in the acceleration of the mass center, G.

$$\mathbf{a}^* = \ddot{x}^*\mathbf{i} + \ddot{y}^*\mathbf{j} = \mathbf{a}_A + \mathbf{a}_{G/A}, \qquad\qquad \text{5.2-27}$$

$$\mathbf{a}_{G/A} = l\ddot{\phi}(\cos\theta\mathbf{j} - \sin\theta\mathbf{i}) + l\dot{\phi}^2(-\sin\theta\mathbf{j} - \cos\theta\mathbf{i}). \qquad \text{5.2-28}$$

At the time zero, however, $\dot{\phi} = 0$ so that

$$\ddot{x}^*\mathbf{i} + \ddot{y}^*\mathbf{j} = a_A\mathbf{i} + l\ddot{\phi}(\cos\theta\mathbf{j} - \sin\theta\mathbf{i}). \qquad\qquad \text{5.2-29}$$

This vector equation implies

$$\ddot{x}^* = a_A - l\ddot{\phi}\sin\theta, \qquad \ddot{y}^* = l\ddot{\phi}\cos\theta. \qquad\qquad \text{5.2-30}$$

The second of these, in conjunction with the last two of Eqs. 5.2-25, provides the wanted information.

$$P = mg + m\ddot{y}^* = mg + ml\ddot{\phi}\cos\theta = mg + ml\left(\frac{-Pl\cos\theta}{I^*}\right)\cos\theta,$$

$$P = \frac{mg}{1 + \dfrac{ml^2\cos^2\theta}{I^*}}. \qquad\qquad \text{5.2-31}$$

Since, for a uniform rod of length $2l$, $I^* = (1/3)ml^2$, we have

$$P(0) = \frac{mg}{1 + 3\cos^2\theta}. \qquad\qquad \text{5.2-32}$$

Before the right-hand cable broke, P had the value $(1/2)mg$. We see that after the break P may either increase or decrease, depending on the magnitude of θ. For an initially horizontal bar, $\theta = 0$, the tension decreases to half its original value immediately after the break. We may also notice that the initial value of $\ddot{x}^*$ is zero, as appears from the first of 5.2-25. The initial angular acceleration of the bar is, from 5.2-32 and 5.2-25

$$\ddot{\phi}(0) = \frac{-3g\cos\theta}{l(1 + 3\cos^2\theta)},$$

and the initial acceleration of the mass center is, from 5.2-30,

$$\ddot{y}^*(0) = \frac{-3g\cos^2\theta}{1 + 3\cos^2\theta}.$$

All of the foregoing analysis is true for the instant of release only and tells nothing about the subsequent motion of the beam. For future reference we also note that there is no abrupt change in velocity here.

Example 5.2-6

A crate is placed on the flatbed of a truck. As the truck acceleration is increased to a magnitude $\ddot{x}$ will the crate slip, tip, or remain in its original position on the truck?

Solution: Questions of this class resemble the previous one in that interest centers on the state of affairs at a particular moment, time zero, just before slipping or tipping occurs. Now, however, the actual state of affairs is unknown and has to be found by a process of reasoning. We

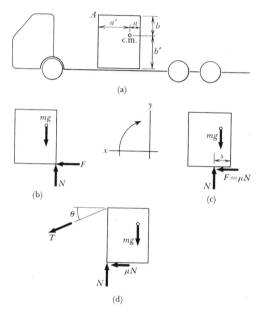

Fig. 5.2-8

begin by assuming that the crate will tip at a lower acceleration than that which would cause it to slip. Such tipping must occur by rotation about the rear edge of the crate. The free-body diagram of the crate *a moment before tipping takes place* is shown in Fig. 5.2-8b. The dimensions *a* and *b* of Fig. 5.2-8a locate the mass center of the crate. Since tipping has not yet taken place, the acceleration of the mass center is $\ddot{x}^*$, and there is no angular acceleration. Since tipping is about to occur, the reaction of the flatbed on the crate is concentrated at the rear edge. The equations of motion read

$$F = m\ddot{x}^*, \qquad N - mg = 0, \qquad Fb - Na = 0. \qquad \textbf{5.2-33}$$

We conclude that $N = mg =$ weight of crate, $F = mg(a/b)$, $\ddot{x}^* = g(a/b)$.

Tipping will occur when the acceleration of the truck has reached a value equal to the acceleration of gravity multiplied by the ratio a/b. But will tipping actually occur before slipping? Our assumption requires $F/N = a/b$. If the coefficient of limiting friction is greater than a/b, this ratio is permissible; otherwise slipping will occur first.

Suppose that $\mu < a/b$. The foregoing analysis, which has served its purpose of showing that slipping will occur at a lower acceleration than will tipping, must now be discarded. We consider instead the instant before onset of slip. The free-body diagram is shown in Fig. 5.2-8c; note that whereas F is now known (in terms of N), the location of the resultant pressure on the base is unknown. We denote this location by the symbol s, the distance s being measured from the rear edge of the crate to the location of the resultant pressure. The number of unknowns in (c) is three, the same as in (b), F being replaced as an unknown by s. The three equations of motion now read

$$\mu N = m\ddot{x}^*, \qquad N - mg = 0, \qquad \mu Nb + N(s-a) = 0. \qquad \textbf{5.2-34}$$

whence $N = mg$, as before, and $\ddot{x}^* = \mu g$. The third of Eqs. 5.2-34 tells us that $s = a - \mu b$ and locates the position of the resultant of the distributed force acting on the base. We note that we could have started with the assumption that sliding would occur first. The criterion for the acceptability of this assumption would have been a positive value for s; that is $a > (\mu b)$, which is the same criterion found previously.

Now suppose that not being satisfied with an acceleration μg or $(a/b)g$, whichever is smaller, the driver fastens the forward upper corner of the crate (point A in Fig. 5.2-8a) to the bed of the truck by means of a cable making an angle θ with the horizontal. The free-body diagram is as shown in Fig. 5.2-8d. There appears to be a fourth unknown, the tension, T, in the cable. But now the point A is not free. As a result the only initial motion possible is a rotation about A in which the rear of the crate starts to lift while, at the same time, sliding occurs at the front edge. This is the exceptional case in which tipping and sliding are made to occur simultaneously. The equations of motion are

$$N - T \sin \theta - mg = 0,$$

$$\mu N + T \cos \theta = m\ddot{x}^*, \qquad \textbf{5.2-35}$$

$$\mu Nb + Na' - a'T \sin \theta - b'T \cos \theta = 0.$$

Here a' and b' are the dimensions of the crate complementary to a and b, as shown in Fig. 5.2-8a. These equations solved yield

$$\ddot{x}^* = g\left[\frac{\mu(b' + b) \cos \theta + a'(\cos \theta + \mu \sin \theta)}{b' \cos \theta - \mu b \sin \theta}\right],$$

$$\qquad \textbf{5.2-36}$$

$$T = mg\,\frac{a' + \mu b}{b' \cos \theta - \mu b \sin \theta}, \qquad N = mg\,\frac{b' \cos \theta + a' \sin \theta}{b' \cos \theta - \mu b \sin \theta}.$$

The denominator in 5.2-36 has the interpretation common in friction-lock analyses. If $\tan \theta \geq b'/\mu b$, no forward acceleration—however great—will produce slipping or tipping.

5.3 Impact and Impulsive Motion

In the examples of the preceding section accelerations were constant, or else interest centered on the acceleration at a particular instant. In the former case, the equations of motion are easily integrated, and, in the latter case, they are only ordinary algebraic equations. The situation is quite different, however, when forces and accelerations vary during the time interval of interest. One systematic way of effecting the integration that is then necessary for the determination of velocities and positions is provided by the impulse-momentum principles (Eqs. 4.6-2, 3):

$$\hat{\mathbf{F}} = \int_{t_1}^{t_2} \mathbf{F} \, dt = m(\mathbf{v}_2^* - \mathbf{v}_1^*); \qquad \text{5.3-1}$$

$$\hat{\mathbf{M}}_O = \int_{t_1}^{t_2} \mathbf{M}_O \, dt = \mathbf{H}_2 - \mathbf{H}_1. \qquad \text{5.3-2}$$

For plane motion, the first of these is equivalent to two scalar equations, and the second to one. We recall also that, for a lamina in plane motion, $H_O = I_O \omega$. These relations are immediately effective when the forces are known functions of time. Suppose, for example, that a flywheel operating at speed ω_0 is subject to a "sawtooth" torque, which increases from zero to a peak value M in T seconds, then decreases abruptly to zero—remaining at that value for T seconds before repeating the cycle. What is the speed at the end of $3T$ seconds? We have

$$\hat{M}_O = \int_0^T \frac{Mt}{T} \, dt + \int_{2T}^{3T} \frac{M(t - 2T)}{T} \, dt = MT = I_O(\omega - \omega_0) \qquad \text{5.3-3}$$

$$\omega = \omega_0 + \frac{MT}{I_O}. \qquad \text{5.3-4}$$

The student should observe that the point O denoted by the subscript in Eq. 5.3-3 is the fixed axis of rotation of the flywheel and therefore a point for which Eq. 5.3-2 holds. He should also verify, by means of a free-body diagram, that none of the other forces acting on the flywheel has any moment about the shaft.

In the end, however, the result embodied in Eq. 5.3-4 may be obtained just as readily by direct integration of the equation of motion 4.5-11a in the form $M_O = I_O \ddot{\phi}$. A more effective exploitation of the ideas of impulse and momentum occurs when we recognize an axis for which the equation $\hat{M} = H_2 - H_1$ holds and about which the external forces have no moment, or a direction along which the external forces vanish. Angular momentum about such an axis or linear momentum in such a direction is constant. Consider, for instance, the following example.

Example 5.3-1

A disk is rotating freely about a vertical axis with an angular velocity ω_1 when a concentric second disk rotating with angular velocity ω_2 is placed on it. The centroidal moments of inertia of the two disks are denoted by I_1 and I_2. Suppose that a pin in the upper disk engages a slot in the lower one. What is the common angular velocity ω' of the disks after they engage?

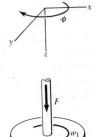

Solution: The free-body diagram of the two disks is shown in Fig. 5.3-1. Only vertical forces directed along the z-axis act on the disks before they engage. These forces are simply the weights of the disks and the counterbalancing upward bearing reactions. We are not interested in these z-directed forces and so treat the question as one of motion in the horizontal plane. When the disks are brought together, the upper will exert a force on the lower and the lower an opposite force on the upper. But if we take *both* disks as our mechanical system, these will be *internal* forces. The external forces on this combined system, therefore, have no moment about the z-axis. Referring to Eq. 5.3-2, it may be seen that this implies that H_O (which in this case is the same as H^*) must be constant. This is also the conclusion to be drawn from the principle of conservation of angular momentum stated in 4.6. Since the initial angular momentum of the system about O is $I_1\omega_1 + I_2\omega_2$ and the final is $(I_1 + I_2)\omega'$ we conclude at once that

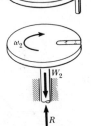

Fig. 5.3-1

$$\omega' = \frac{I_1\omega_1 + I_2\omega_2}{I_1 + I_2}. \qquad \textbf{5.3-5}$$

The student should be alert to notice points about which the external forces have no moment. They often permit straightforward application of the principle of conservation of angular momentum.

It is important to realize that there is an energy loss when the two disks are brought together. In view of Eq. 4.7-17

$$T_0 = \frac{1}{2} I_1 \omega_1^2 + \frac{1}{2} I_2 \omega_2^2,$$

$$T' = \frac{1}{2} (I_1 + I_2) \omega'^2.$$

$$T_0 - T' = \frac{1}{2} \left[I_1 \omega_1^2 + I_2 \omega_2^2 - (I_1 + I_2) \left(\frac{I_1 \omega_1 + I_2 \omega_2}{I_1 + I_2} \right)^2 \right]$$

$$= \frac{1}{2} \frac{(\omega_1 - \omega_2)^2}{(1/I_1) + (1/I_2)}. \qquad \textbf{5.3-6}$$

Since the right-hand side of 5.3-6 is non-negative it follows that energy is always lost, except in the trivial case $\omega_1 = \omega_2$. This energy loss may be considerable. If the disks are identical and one of them is initially at rest, half the energy in the system will be dissipated. We shall see that energy loss is characteristic of all cases in which instantaneous changes in velocity occur. Of course the energy has not disappeared; it has been converted into heat. We may, however, speak of it as lost from the point of view of classical mechanics. For the present, the point to be borne in mind is that momentum, not energy, is conserved in impact.

Example **5.3-2**

Suppose that the disks of the previous problem, instead of having a pin and slot, bear on each other at their rims with a coefficient of friction. How long will it take them to reach a common speed?

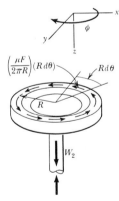

Fig. **5.3-2**

Solution: In the first place, we see that, if our system includes both disks, the friction force exerted by one on the other is again an internal force. Consequently angular momentum is still conserved, and ω' is again given by Eq. 5.3-5. The energy loss is again given by Eq. 5.3-6; now, however, it is due to friction rather than to impact. It is a remarkable fact that the *amount* of energy dissipated has nothing to do with the magnitude of the coefficient of friction in this case.

To find the time required to bring the disks to the common speed ω', we examine the free-body diagram of one of the disks. That of the lower one is shown in Fig. 5.3-2. The normal force on an element of rim of length $R\,d\theta$ is $(F/2\pi R)(R\,d\theta)$. The frictional force is μ times as great, and the moment of this frictional force is $-\mu R(F/2\pi R)(R\,d\theta)$. The negative sign is used

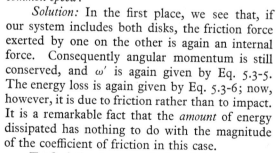

because Fig. 5.3-2 has been drawn for the case $\omega_2 > \omega_1$, and the frictional forces are then counterclockwise (viewed from above) whereas the positive direction of ω is clockwise. The total moment exerted by the upper disk on the lower is

$$M^* = -\int_0^{2\pi} \frac{\mu RF}{2\pi}\, d\theta = -\mu RF. \qquad \text{5.3-7}$$

The equation of motion for the lower disk is therefore

$$-\mu RF = I_2\ddot{\phi}_2, \qquad \text{5.3-8}$$

and, if we integrate both sides of this expression with respect to time, we obtain the angular impulse-momentum principle. Since μRF is a constant,

$$-\int_0^t \mu RF\, dt = -\mu RFt = I_2(\dot{\phi}_2 - \omega_2). \qquad \text{5.3-9}$$

If we take the upper limit in the above integral as the time at which the two disks reach their common final angular velocity, $\dot{\phi}_2$ will be ω', which is given by Eq. 5.3-5. Then

$$-\mu RFt = I_2(\omega' - \omega_2) = I_2\left[\frac{I_1\omega_1 + I_2\omega_2}{I_1 + I_2} - \omega_2\right] \qquad \text{5.3-10}$$

or

$$t = \frac{\omega_2 - \omega_1}{\mu RF(1/I_1 + 1/I_2)}, \qquad \text{5.3-11}$$

and this is the time required to bring the disks to a common speed. We see that if μ is small, t will be large. On the other hand, $t \to 0$ as $\mu \to \infty$, and the motion approaches that of a sudden impact.

Alternatively we might write the equation of motion of the upper disk, 1. This is the same as 5.3-9 except that the sign of the moment is reversed, since the forces exerted on disk 1 by disk 2 are opposite in direction to those exerted on disk 2 by disk 1.

$$\mu RF = I_1\ddot{\phi}_1, \qquad \text{5.3-12}$$

or, in the angular impulse-momentum form,

$$\mu RFt = I_1(\dot{\phi}_1 - \omega_1). \qquad \text{5.3-13}$$

By adding 5.3-9 and 5.3-13 we recover the principle of conservation of angular momentum in the form

$$0 = I_2(\dot{\phi}_2 - \omega_2) + I_1(\dot{\phi}_1 - \omega_1),$$

or

$$I_2\omega_2 + I_1\omega_1 = I_2\dot{\phi}_2(t) + I_1\dot{\phi}_1(t), \qquad \text{5.3-14}$$

so that when $\dot{\phi}_1(t)$ and $\dot{\phi}_2(t)$ have a common value, ω', it is again that given by Eq. 5.3-5.

Example **5·3-3**

Two gears rotating freely on parallel shafts are brought into contact. What is the angular velocity of the pair after engagement?

Solution: We denote the pitch radii of the two gears by r_1 and r_2, their (counterclockwise) angular velocities before engagement by ω_1 and ω_2, and their centroidal moments of inertia by I_1 and I_2. Let $F(t)$ be the force exerted by one gear on the other during the short interval of time, Δt, it takes them to mesh. If we take the first gear as our system, the free-body

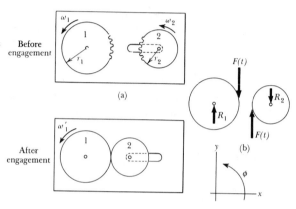

Fig. 5·3-3

diagram is as shown in Fig. **5·3-3**. The angular-momentum principle of Eq. 5·3-2 asserts that

$$-\int_0^{\Delta t} F(t)r_1\, dt = I_1(\omega_1' - \omega_1).\qquad\textbf{5·3-15}$$

The symbol ω_1' denotes the angular velocity of gear 1 after meshing. The negative sign on the left-hand side of 5·3-15 is needed because $F(t)$ is shown in the free-body diagram as producing a clockwise torque about a z-axis through the mass center of the left-hand gear. With gear 2 as our isolated mechanical system, the angular-momentum principle asserts

$$-\int_0^{\Delta t} F(t)r_2\, dt = I_2(\omega_2' - \omega_2).\qquad\textbf{5·3-16}$$

Since r_1 and r_2 are constants, they may be taken outside the integral sign, and then the ratio of Eqs. 5·3-15 and 5·3-16 yields a relationship free of the unknown impulse $\hat{F} = \int_0^{\Delta t} F\, dt$.

$$\frac{r_2}{r_1} = \frac{I_2(\omega_2' - \omega_2)}{I_1(\omega_1' - \omega_1)}.\qquad\textbf{5·3-17}$$

Finally we note that after engagement the contact points must have identical velocities.

$$\mathbf{v}_A = r_1\omega_1'\mathbf{j}, \qquad \mathbf{v}_B = -r_2\omega_2'\mathbf{j}; \qquad r_1\omega_1' = -r_2\omega_2'. \qquad \textbf{5.3-18}$$

Equations 5.3-17 and 5.3-18 serve to determine ω_1' and ω_2' when I_1, I_2, r_1, r_2, ω_1, ω_2 are given. For example,

$$r_2\omega_2' = -r_1\omega_1' = \frac{(I_2/r_2)\omega_2 - (I_1/r_1)\omega_1}{(I_1/r_1^2) + (I_2/r_2^2)}. \qquad \textbf{5.3-19}$$

It is a common error to assume that the angular momentum of the first disk about its mass center plus the corresponding quantity for the second disk about its mass center must be unchanged by impact. This is not true. If we wish to use a system consisting of both bodies, their angular momenta must be computed for an axis through the mass center of the combined system as it was in the two previous examples. Then the reactions $R_1(t)$ and $R_2(t)$ at the shafts must be counted as producing angular impulse. Such a choice of system is awkward.

Since this, like Example 5.3-1, is a case of impact (sudden change in velocity), it may be inferred that energy will be lost.

$$T_0 = \frac{1}{2}I_1\omega_1^2 + \frac{1}{2}I_2\omega_2^2,$$

$$T' = \frac{1}{2}I_1\omega_1'^2 + \frac{1}{2}I_2\omega_2'^2 = \frac{1}{2}\left(\frac{I_1}{r_1^2} + \frac{I_2}{r_2^2}\right)(r_2^2\omega_2'^2).$$

In view of Eq. 5.3-19,

$$T_0 - T' = \frac{1}{2}\frac{(I_1/r_1^2)(I_2/r_2^2)}{(I_1/r_1^2) + (I_2/r_2^2)}(\omega_1 r_1 + \omega_2 r_2)^2. \qquad \textbf{5.3-20}$$

Since the right-hand side of 5.3-20 can never be negative, we see that energy is always lost. If $\omega_1 r_1 = -\omega_2 r_2$, the loss is zero. This is the case in which the gears are synchronized before they engage.

The foregoing examples serve to illustrate the idea of conservation of angular momentum, and also some of the pitfalls associated with its use. The impulse-momentum relationships are especially useful in connection with the analysis of the effects of large forces applied for very brief time intervals. Such forces are called *impulsive* forces (or couples), and, when they occur, interest is usually focused on finding the state of motion immediately after the impact interval. It is permissible then to assume that all nonimpulsive forces will have negligible impulse during the impact. In order to expose the essential ideas involved in the treatment of impact effects, we treat the simplest case first.

Suppose that two solid spheres move without rotation along the same straight line with constant speeds v_1 and v_2 and that they strike one another. What will be their speeds v_1', v_2' after they separate? To answer this question, we take as our isolated system *both* bodies. Then the impulsive forces exerted by one body on the other are internal forces, which do not enter the impulse-momentum principle. It follows that the linear momentum of the system will be the same after impact as it was before impact:

$$m_1 v_1 + m_2 v_2 = m_1 v_1' + m_2 v_2'. \qquad \textbf{5.3-21}$$

This result can also be derived from the principle of the motion of the mass center (4.3-9). If we take the line of motion to be the x-axis, it follows from the definition of x^* that

$$(m_1 + m_2)x^* = m_1 x_1 + m_2 x_2. \qquad \textbf{5.3-22}$$

Differentiating, we have for any instant prior to the impact

$$(m_1 + m_2)v^* = m_1 v_1 + m_2 v_2.$$

But, since 5.3-22 is equally true after the impact, we have a corresponding expression

$$(m_1 + m_2)v^{*\prime} = m_1 v_1' + m_2 v_2'$$

after the impact. The velocity of the mass center is, however, unaffected by internal forces so that $v^* = v^{*\prime}$, whence the conservation-of-momentum equation, 5.3-21, follows at once. At this point, the equations of motion have been fully utilized and their consequences expressed in Eq. 5.3-21. Both the quantities v_1' and v_2' cannot be found by means of this single equation. The necessary second relation would be given by the principles of deformable-body continuum mechanics were it feasible to carry out an analysis along those lines for the two spheres during the contact interval. In practice we use an empirical relationship expressed by the statement that the (relative) velocity of separation is a definite fraction of the (relative) velocity of approach. In symbols,

$$v_2' - v_1' = e(v_1 - v_2). \qquad \textbf{5.3-23}$$

The number e is known as the *coefficient of restitution*. It cannot be negative else the overtaking sphere would pass through the overtaken one. We shall see, on examining its physical significance, that it cannot exceed unity in magnitude. For the present, we note that

Eqs. 5.3-21 and 5.3-23 suffice to determine the post-impact speeds. They are

$$v_1' = \frac{I}{m_1 + m_2}[(m_1 - m_2 e)v_1 + m_2(I + e)v_2],$$

$$v_2' = \frac{I}{m_1 + m_2}[m_1(I + e)v_1 + (m_2 - m_1 e)v_2]. \qquad \textbf{5.3-24}$$

A special case arises if one of the bodies, say m_2, is much more massive than the other one. If we allow m_2 in Eqs. 5.3-24 to increase without limit, we have

$$v_1' = v_2 + e(v_2 - v_1) \quad \text{and} \quad v_2' = v_2. \qquad \textbf{5.3-25}$$

If the large body is stationary, the small one rebounds with its speed reduced by a factor e.

The introduction of a coefficient of restitution enables us to evade an analysis that would entail the methods of the modern theories of elasticity, plasticity, and mechanical vibrations. Some insight into the physical meaning of the quantity can be gained, however, without recourse to these subjects by a consideration of the way in which the energy of the system varies during the impact. We divide the time of contact into a period of compression during which the mass centers of the two spheres are approaching one another and a period of restitution in which they are moving apart. The velocities of the mass centers must be identical at the division point, $t = \tilde{t}$, of the two intervals. This common speed $\tilde{v}$ may be computed directly from the conservation-of-momentum principle.

$$(m_1 + m_2)\tilde{v} = m_1 v_1 + m_2 v_2. \qquad \textbf{5.3-26}$$

$$\tilde{v} = \frac{I}{m_1 + m_2}(m_1 v_1 + m_2 v_2). \qquad \textbf{5.3-27}$$

The initial kinetic energy of the system, T, is $(m_1 v_1^2/2) + (m_2 v_2^2/2)$; whereas the kinetic energy, $\tilde{T}$, at $t = \tilde{t}$ is $(m_1 + m_2)\tilde{v}^2/2$. The loss in kinetic energy during the compression interval is

$$\Delta T_c = T - \tilde{T} = \frac{(v_1 - v_2)^2}{2\left(\dfrac{I}{m_1} + \dfrac{I}{m_2}\right)}. \qquad \textbf{5.3-28}$$

Since this expression cannot be negative, it follows that there is always a loss of kinetic energy during the compression interval. Part of this "lost" energy is stored in the form of strain energy while part has been converted to heat, sound, and vibration. If all of the "lost" kinetic energy is restored during the period of restitution, we say that the impact is *perfectly elastic*. If none of it is restored, we say that the impact is *completely inelastic*. The kinetic energy after the collision, T', is, however, given by Eqs. 5.3-24 in terms of the original speeds and the coefficient of restitution so that we may compute

$$T - T' = \left(\frac{1}{2} m_1 v_1^2 + \frac{1}{2} m_2 v_2^2\right) - \left(\frac{1}{2} m_1 v_1'^2 + \frac{1}{2} m_2 v_2'^2\right)$$

$$= \frac{1}{2}(1 - e^2)\frac{(v_1 - v_2)^2}{\dfrac{1}{m_1} + \dfrac{1}{m_2}}. \qquad \textbf{5.3-29}$$

This is the total loss in kinetic energy; i.e., the energy converted to heat and vibration. On subtracting this expression from Eq. 5.3-28, we have

$$\Delta T_R = T' - \tilde{T} = e^2 \Delta T_C \qquad \textbf{5.3-30}$$

so that e^2 is, from a physical point of view, the ratio of the energy returned to the system during the restitution interval to the energy lost during the compression interval. For this reason, e can never exceed unity. The value $e = 1$ corresponds to a perfectly elastic impact with no over-all change in kinetic energy. The value $e = 0$ corresponds to a perfectly inelastic impact; the two bodies adhere after the impact, and the energy loss is the largest possible. The numerical value of e that is appropriate in any specific case will depend upon the materials, speeds, and shapes of the colliding bodies and should be regarded as a quantity to be determined by experiment. Whatever the value assigned, momentum is conserved on impact.

The ideas of this section may be extended to cases in which the initial velocities of the spheres do not lie along the line connecting their centers. It must then be supposed that the initial velocity vectors and the line joining the centers of the spheres all lie in the same *xy*-plane; otherwise the motion cannot be described as two-dimensional. We also suppose that the spheres are smooth so that they are not set into rotation. Then the impulsive force exerted by one sphere on the other must be along the line passing through their centers and through the point of contact. The velocity components of the two spheres at right angles to this line are therefore not affected by the impact. Those along the line connecting the centers are determined by conservation of momentum and coefficient of restitution just as in Eqs. 5.3-21, 23. In the usual case, one of the bodies, say m_2, is initially at rest. The line joining the centers is taken as the *x*-axis. Then $\dot{y}_2 = 0$ after the collision because it is unaffected by the impact, and the path of m_2 after collision lies along the line joining the centers of the spheres at first contact. This theory has found extensive application in the interpretation of cloud-chamber photographs of the collision paths of alpha particles, protons, and electrons. A complete discussion of the range of validity of so-called "billiard-ball analysis" in physics would be beyond the scope of this book. So long, however, as we are not interested in the details of the motion near the "contact" (which are inaccessible to observation in any event), momentum and energy conservation considerations—together with the observed angles made by the diverging paths of the particles— determine the mass and energy ratios of the particles. Of course there must be no spin effects else an additional variable would enter the analysis.

Example 5.3-4

An airplane of mass m flying with speed v picks up a stationary glider of mass m/3. What are the speeds of airplane and glider immediately after the long tow tope becomes taut? Take e=0.5.

Solution: Using subscripts p and g to distinguish airplane and glider, we have

$$mv_p + \frac{m}{3} v_g = mv'_p + \frac{m}{3} v'_g,$$

$$e(v_p - v_g) = v'_g - v'_p.$$

Setting $v_p = v$, $v_g = 0$ and solving, we have

$$v'_p = \frac{3}{4} v \left(1 - \frac{1}{3} e \right), \qquad v'_g = \frac{3}{4} v(1 + e).$$

Note that the speed of the glider will be greater than the speed of the airplane so that the cable will become slack immediately after the glider is jerked into motion. The loss in energy divided by the original kinetic energy is

$$\frac{\Delta T}{T} = \frac{1 - e^2}{4}.$$

For $e = 0.5$, this ratio is $3/16$, and $v'_p = \frac{5}{8} v$, $v'_g = \frac{9}{8} v$.

Example 5.3-5

A cloud-chamber photograph shows the Y-shaped track of a collision. The path of the incident particle makes angles α and β with the paths after collision. Assuming the second particle to have been at rest initially and neglecting any energy loss, deduce the relative masses of the particles.

Solution: The tracks are shown in Fig. 5.3-4a, and a schematic view

of the event is shown in Fig. 5.3-4b.   We choose an x-axis along the line of
motion of the struck particle.   Then conservation of momentum in the
x-direction requires that

$$m_1 v_1 \cos \beta = m_1 v'_1 \cos (\alpha + \beta) + m_2 v'_2,$$

and, since there is no energy loss, $e = 1$ so
that

$$v_1 \cos \beta = v'_2 - v'_1 \cos (\alpha + \beta).$$

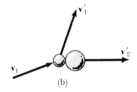

(a)

In the y-direction velocities are unchanged
by the collision:

$$v_1 \sin \beta = v'_1 \sin (\alpha + \beta).$$

We have already taken advantage of the fact
that the component of v'_2 in the y-direction is
zero in setting up axes.   The last two
equations are easily solved for v'_1 and v'_2 in
terms of v_1 and the observed angles α and β.

(b)

Fig. 5.3-4

$$v'_1 = v_1 \frac{\sin \beta}{\sin (\alpha + \beta)},$$

$$v'_2 = v_1 [\cos \beta + \sin \beta \cot (\alpha + \beta)].$$

When these expressions are substituted in
the momentum relation, v_1 cancels out, leaving

$$m_1 \cos \beta = m_1 \frac{\sin \beta}{\sin (\alpha + \beta)} \cos (\alpha + \beta) + m_2 \cos \beta + m_2 \sin \beta \cot (\alpha + \beta),$$

$$m_1 [\cos \beta \sin (\alpha + \beta) - \sin \beta \cos (\alpha + \beta)] =$$
$$m_2 [\cos \beta \sin (\alpha + \beta) + \sin \beta \cos (\alpha + \beta)],$$

$$\frac{m_1}{m_2} = \frac{\sin (\alpha + 2\beta)}{\sin \alpha}.$$

This is the desired result.   Expressions for the ratio of the energies of the
particles after impact may also be derived.

Example **5.3-6**

A ball bearing strikes a steel plate
at an angle α with the vertical.   If the
coefficient of restitution is e, what angle will
the rebound make with the vertical?

Solution: This is a case in which the
struck object is so massive, compared with
the striking object, that its change in
velocity is negligible.   We may use Eqs.

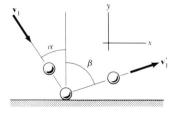

Fig. 5.3-5

5.3-25 provided we interpret the velocities therein as the vertical components of velocity in the present case.

$$v_1' \cos \beta = -e(-v_1 \cos \alpha),$$

and

$$v_1' \sin \beta = v_1 \sin \alpha,$$

since the horizontal component is unaffected by the impact. On taking the ratio of these expressions, we have

$$\tan \beta = \frac{1}{e} \tan \alpha.$$

The angle of reflection is greater than the angle of incidence.

Next we consider the case of a rigid lamina, unrestrained, which is struck a blow in its plane. We may think of the blow as the result of a force **F** applied at a point P for a short time interval, Δt. Since we are not interested in the details of what happens during this brief time interval but only want to know how the body will be moving after the blow, the force is completely specified by its point of application and its impulse $\hat{\mathbf{F}}$. To see this clearly, write the equations of motion for any instant during the impact:

$$\mathbf{F} = m\mathbf{a}^*, \qquad M^* = I^*\alpha. \qquad \textbf{5.3-31}$$

Now integrating both sides of these equations with respect to time over the interval $0 \leqq t \leqq \Delta t$, we recover the linear and angular impulse-momentum principles

$$\hat{\mathbf{F}} = m(\mathbf{v}^* - \mathbf{v}_0^*), \qquad \hat{M}^* = I^*(\omega - \omega_0). \qquad \textbf{5.3-32}$$

These are ordinary algebraic equations for the values of $\mathbf{v}^*$ and ω after the impulse. If the lamina is initially at rest, ω_0 and $\mathbf{v}_0^*$ are zero.

Suppose now that we choose x and y axes as shown in Fig. 5.3-6, with x in the direction of **F**. The moment arm of **F** about the mass center C is a. Eqs. 5.3-32 become

$$\hat{F} = mv_x^*, \qquad 0 = mv_y^*,$$

$$\hat{F}a = I^*\omega. \qquad \textbf{5.3-33}$$

We have supposed the lamina to be unrestrained and to start from rest. From Eqs. 5.3-33, it follows that after the blow

$$v_y^* = 0, \qquad v_x^* = \frac{\hat{F}}{m}, \qquad \omega = \frac{mv_x^*a}{I^*} = \frac{v_x^*a}{k^{*2}}. \qquad \textbf{5.3-34}$$

This means that the mass center starts to move in the same direction as the blow. If no other forces are applied to the body, v^* and ω will, of course, remain constant. The post-impact velocity of any other point, O, having coordinates x_0, y_0 is easily found:

$$\mathbf{v}_O = \mathbf{v}^* + \mathbf{v}_{O/C},$$

$$= (v_x^* - \omega y_0)\mathbf{i} + \omega x_0 \mathbf{j}. \qquad \textbf{5.3-35}$$

The point whose coordinates, measured from C, are $x_0 = 0$, $y_0 = k^{*2}/a$ will have zero velocity. It is the point about which the unrestrained body will begin to rotate. This point, which lies on PC on the opposite side of the mass center from P, is known as the *center of percussion*.

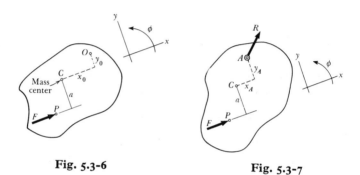

Fig. 5.3-6   **Fig. 5.3-7**

Now suppose that the lamina instead of being free to move is constrained to rotate about some point A whose coordinates, measured from C, are x_A, y_A. The free-body diagram during the impulse is shown in Fig. 5.3-7. Notice that an impulsive reaction $\mathbf{R}$ acts at the bearing. This must be taken into consideration even though non-impulsive forces such as the weight of the lamina may be ignored. The equations of motion during the impact are

$$F + R_x = ma_x^*, \qquad R_y = ma_y^*,$$

$$Fa + R_y x_A - R_x y_A = I^*\alpha. \qquad \textbf{5.3-36}$$

On integrating over the brief time of the blow, these become

$$\hat{F} + \hat{R}_x = mv_x^*, \qquad \hat{R}_y = mv_y^*,$$

$$\hat{F}a + \hat{R}_y x_A - \hat{R}_x y_A = I^*\omega. \qquad \textbf{5.3-37}$$

There appear to be five unknown quantities here—the two components of the impulse of the reaction at A and the three unknowns that were present when the body was unrestrained, v_x^*, v_y^*, and ω. Since the body must now rotate about A, the velocity of the mass center can be expressed in terms of ω:

$$v_x^* = \omega y_A \quad \text{and} \quad v_y^* = -\omega x_A. \qquad \textbf{5.3-38}$$

Now Eqs. 5.3-37, 38 are readily solved.

$$\omega = \frac{\hat{F}}{m}\frac{a+y_A}{(k^{*2}+x_A^2+y_A^2)},$$

$$\hat{R}_x = -\hat{F}\frac{k^{*2}+x_A^2-ay_A}{k^{*2}+x_A^2+y_A^2}, \qquad \textbf{5.3-39}$$

$$\hat{R}_y = -\hat{F}\frac{x_A(a+y_A)}{k^{*2}+x_A^2+y_A^2}.$$

These formulas are not of importance themselves, but the method by which the angular velocity and the reaction impulses were obtained is important. It is worthwhile to repeat the analysis taking moments about an axis through A instead of one through the mass center. We see from Eqs. 5.3-39 that if $x_A = 0$ (which means that the blow is at right angles to the line joining the point of support to the mass center) there will be no impulse in the y-direction exerted by (or on) the support. If, in addition, $ay_A = k^{*2}$, the x-component of the impulse exerted by the pin also vanishes. This means that, if the support is located at the center of percussion, there is no impulsive reaction at the bearing—a result which is consistent with the previous observation that the body, if free, would rotate about the center of percussion. Notice that the location of the center of percussion depends upon the direction of the force $\mathbf{F}$. It lies on the perpendicular to $\mathbf{F}$ through the mass center. If the force $\mathbf{F}$ were applied at A and the body were hinged at P, the quantities a and y_A in Eqs. 5.3-39 would be interchanged. It follows that, if A is the center of percussion for a force $\mathbf{F}$ applied at P, P will be the center of percussion for a force $\mathbf{F}$ applied at A.

The analysis of impulsive motion bears a superficial resemblance to the analysis of initial motion treated in Section 5.2. In both cases, interest centers on the state of affairs at a particular time, and the differential equations of motion reduce to ordinary algebraic ones. In one case, velocities are zero, but accelerations are not; in the other case, only velocities enter. It is natural to think that the sudden removal of a force that is holding a body in equilibrium could be treated as the sudden application of a negative force of the same magnitude to the same body at rest. This is true. But the sudden application of a finite force is not the same as an impulse. A finite force requires time to generate velocity, whereas an impulse produces the change in velocity instantaneously.

Example 5.3-7

Two equal bars of a linkage, AB and BC, are smoothly hinged at B and laid on a smooth surface at right angles to one another as shown in Fig. 5.3-8a. A sharp blow of impulse $\hat{\mathbf{F}}$ is struck at A in the direction BC. Discuss the subsequent motion.

Solution: We draw the free-body diagrams of the individual bars as shown in Fig. 5.3-8b. An impulsive force is exerted at B by BC on AB and, of course, the equal and opposite one is exerted by AB on BC. We designate the components of the impulse $\hat{Q}_x$ and $\hat{Q}_y$. The impulse $\hat{\mathbf{Q}}$ is

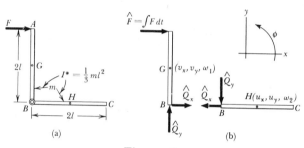

Fig. 5.3-8

not known. The vectors $\hat{\mathbf{F}}$ and $\hat{\mathbf{Q}}$, whose components appear in this free-body diagram, are impulses, not forces. The notation is simplified by designating the velocity of the mass center of AB after the impact $\mathbf{v} = v_x\mathbf{i} + v_y\mathbf{j}$ and that of BC by $\mathbf{u} = u_x\mathbf{i} + u_y\mathbf{j}$. We drop the usual primes because no confusion with velocities *before* impact can arise. The angular velocities of AB and BC after the impact we may denote by ω_1 and ω_2 respectively. With this notation, the equations of motion, integrated over the brief interval of the impact, yield the impulse-momentum relationships: for AB:

$$\hat{F} + \hat{Q}_x = mv_x, \qquad \hat{Q}_y = mv_y, \qquad \hat{Q}_x l - \hat{F}l = \frac{ml^2}{3}\omega_1,$$

for BC:

$$-\hat{Q}_x = mu_x, \qquad -\hat{Q}_y = mu_y, \qquad \hat{Q}_y l = \frac{ml^2}{3}\omega_2. \qquad \textbf{5.3-40}$$

These are six equations with eight unknowns: $\hat{Q}_x$, $\hat{Q}_y$, v_x, v_y, u_x, u_y, ω_1, and ω_2. The additional relations needed must be provided by kinematic considerations. The velocity of point B must be the same as computed from (v_x, v_y, ω_1) as it is when computed from (u_x, u_y, ω_2).

$$\mathbf{v}_B = \mathbf{v} + \mathbf{v}_{B/G} = v_x\mathbf{i} + v_y\mathbf{j} + \omega_1 l\mathbf{i},$$

$$\mathbf{v}_B = \mathbf{u} + \mathbf{v}_{B/H} = u_x\mathbf{i} + u_y\mathbf{j} - \omega_2 l\mathbf{j}. \qquad \textbf{5.3-41}$$

It follows that

$$v_x + \omega_1 l = u_x \quad \text{and} \quad v_y = u_y - \omega_2 l. \qquad \textbf{5.3-42}$$

These are the two additional relations needed. On solving 5.3-40, 42, we find

$$v_x = \frac{7}{5}\frac{\hat{F}}{m}, \quad v_y = 0, \quad \omega_1 = -\frac{9}{5}\frac{\hat{F}}{ml},$$

$$u_x = -\frac{2}{5}\frac{\hat{F}}{m}, \quad u_y = 0, \quad \omega_2 = 0, \qquad \textbf{5.3-43}$$

$$\hat{Q}_x = \frac{2}{5}\hat{F}, \quad \hat{Q}_y = 0.$$

After being struck, the bar BC will be moving to the left with a translatory motion at a speed $(2/5)(\hat{F}/m)$. The bar AB, on the other hand, moves to the right and starts with a clockwise rate of rotation. The analysis tells nothing about the long-term motion of the system. This, however, would not be difficult to work out since the bars, presumably, slide freely.

Example 5.3-8

A 12 ft by 16 ft homogeneous crate slides on its 12-ft base until, traveling at 20 ft/sec, it strikes a low cleat. What will be its angular velocity after the impact?

Solution: We perform the analysis symbolically first, letting a, h denote the width of the base and the height of the crate, respectively. Then the free-body diagram is as shown in Fig. 5.3-9. During the impact, the crate is rotating about the cleat, and we may write $M_O = \dot{H}_O$ where O denotes the corner of the crate in contact with the cleat. But only the impulsive force, $\mathbf{F}$, exerted by the cleat need be considered during impact; the impulse of the constant weight force may be neglected in comparison. Since $\mathbf{F}$ does not have any moment about O, $\hat{M}_O$ will be zero, and H_O will be a constant, the same at the end of the impact as it was at the beginning. At the beginning of the impact, the crate is sliding to the right with speed v so that its moment of momentum

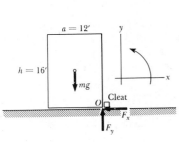

Fig. 5.3-9

about O is $-mvh/2$. At the end of the impact it is rotating about O so that $H_O = I_O\omega$. Since $I_O = m(a^2 + h^2)/3$, we have

$$-\frac{mvh}{2} = \frac{m(a^2 + h^2)}{3}\,\omega, \quad \text{or} \quad \omega = -\frac{3vh}{2(a^2 + h^2)};$$

$$\omega = \frac{-(3)(20)(16)}{(2)(400)} = -1.2 \text{ rad/sec.}$$

This answers the question posed: after striking the cleat, the box rotates about it with an angular velocity of 1.2 rad/sec clockwise. The impulse at the cleat is given by the other two (linear) impulse-momentum equations:

with

$$-\hat{F}_x = m(v_x^* - v), \qquad \hat{F}_y = mv_y^*$$

$$v_x^* = -\frac{h}{2}\,\omega \quad \text{and} \quad v_y^* = -\frac{a}{2}\,\omega.$$

The calculations of this example have been facilitated by the fact that the crate was initially in pure translation. This made it simple to compute the initial value of H_O. If, instead of a crate, we had to deal with a rolling disk of radius b and centroidal radius of gyration k^* that struck a step of height h, we should have had to refer to Eq. 4.3-18 or 4.3-22 in order to compute H_O, the initial angular momentum about the edge of the step. In that case, $H_O = mk^{*2}(-v/b) + mv(h - b)$ where v denotes the speed of the mass center and geometrical center of the disk.

This problem is typical of all those in which some point of a moving body is suddenly arrested. The motion after the impact is found by noting that the angular momentum about the arrested point is unaffected by the impact.

In this case, as in all cases in which a sudden change in velocity occurs (i.e., all cases involving impact or impulsive forces), a loss of energy is to be expected.

$$\frac{T'}{T} = \frac{I_O\omega^2}{mv^2} = \frac{3}{8[1 + (a^2/h^2)]}.$$

This is clearly less than unity, no matter what the ratio a/h.

Finally, we may ask whether the crate will tip over on its side. The answer depends on whether or not the crate, after impact, has enough residual kinetic energy to lift the mass center from a height $h/2$ to a height $(a^2 + h^2)^{1/2}/2$. The requirement is

$$\frac{1}{2}\,mg(\sqrt{a^2 + h^2} - h) = \frac{1}{2}\,mv^2\,\frac{3}{8[1 + (a^2/h^2)]},$$

$$v^2 = \frac{8}{3}\,gh[1 + (a^2/h^2)][\sqrt{1 + (a^2/h^2)} - 1].$$

For striking speeds greater than this, the crate will tip; if v is less than the value given by this expression, the crate will rock on its base.

5.4 Variable Mass

When a body gathers or ejects material as it moves, its motion is affected by the material added or removed. Simple illustrations of this situation are presented by a raindrop that acquires additional mass by condensation as it falls through a cloud, a snowball rolling downhill, or a rocket ejecting burned fuel in the form of hot gases. The study of such motions is sometimes referred to as variable mass analysis. This terminology is misleading unless we realize that no real change in the mass of any of the bodies under consideration is implied. We have actually to deal with a continuous sequence of inelastic collisions, and the subject is therefore a natural sequel to the analysis of impulsive motion. It is only in relativistic mechanics that we encounter a *bona fide* variable mass.

We treat the case of rectilinear translation. The body in which we are interested is acted upon by forces whose resultant, $\mathbf{F}(t)$, is in the line of motion. As the body moves, it acquires mass by accretion and loses mass by ejecting material. When we speak of the mass of the body at time t, we mean its mass m_0 at the initial instant $t = t_0$ plus all the mass, m', it has acquired and less all the mass, m'', that it has ejected since that time. If we denote the mass of the body by the symbol m we have

$$m(t) = m_0 + m'(t) - m''(t), \qquad \textbf{5·4-1}$$

$$\frac{dm}{dt} = \frac{dm'}{dt} - \frac{dm''}{dt}. \qquad \textbf{5·4-2}$$

The momentum of the body is conveniently denoted by the symbol p. It is the product of the mass of the body and its velocity.

$$p(t) = mv. \qquad \textbf{5·4-3}$$

$$\frac{dp}{dt} = m\frac{dv}{dt} + v\left(\frac{dm'}{dt} - \frac{dm''}{dt}\right). \qquad \textbf{5·4-4}$$

The acquisition and ejection of mass by the body moving under the action of the force $\mathbf{F}$ can be considered as the result of a sequence of collisions. Suppose the body overtakes at $t = t_1$ a particle of mass $\Delta m'_1$ moving with speed V'_1. After the collision the two bodies adhere. At the same instant, a mass $\Delta m''_1$ is ejected at speed V''_1. The total change in the momentum of the body in which we are interested, from $t = t_0$ until and including $t = t_1$, is

$$p(t_1) - p(t_0) = \int_{t_0}^{t_1} F\,dt + V'_1 \Delta m'_1 - V''_1 \Delta m''_1. \qquad \textbf{5·4-5}$$

The first term on the right-hand side of this equation is the impulse of the external force. The second and third terms represent the changes in momentum due to the acquisition and loss of mass. Suppose now that this process is repeated at times $t = t_2, t_3, \ldots t_s$. We shall have

$$p(t_2) - p(t_1) = \int_{t_1}^{t_2} F\, dt + V_2' \Delta m_2' - V_2'' \Delta m_2'',$$

$$p(t_3) - p(t_2) = \int_{t_2}^{t_3} F\, dt + V_3' \Delta m_3' - V_3'' \Delta m_3'',$$

$$\vdots \qquad \vdots \qquad\qquad \vdots \qquad \vdots \qquad \vdots$$

$$p(t_s) - p(t_{s-1}) = \int_{t_{s-1}}^{t_s} F\, dt + V_s' \Delta m_s' - V_s'' \Delta m_s''. \tag{5.4-6}$$

Notice that V_2' need not be the same as V_1' and $\Delta m_2'$ need not be the same as $\Delta m_1'$. The same is true of the quantities V'' and $\Delta m''$. If we add all the Eqs. 5.4-5, 6, all the terms on the left-hand side will cancel in pairs except for $-p(t_0)$ in Eq. 5.4-5 and $p(t_s)$ in the last of Eqs. 5.4-6. The sum of these equations is

$$p(t_s) - p(t_0) = \int_{t_0}^{t_s} F\, dt + \sum_{n=1}^{n=s} (V_n' \Delta m_n' - V_n'' \Delta m_n''). \tag{5.4-7}$$

At this point it is necessary to introduce the physical hypothesis that, if the instants $t_1, t_2, \ldots t_s$ increase in number so that the time interval between them decreases without limit and the mass increments $\Delta m'$ and $\Delta m''$ all approach zero, Eq. 5.4-7 will, in the limit, apply to a condition in which mass is continuously being added and ejected. For such a continuous process, the summation in Eq. 5.4-7 may be replaced by an integral:

$$p(t_s) - p(t_0) = \int_{t_0}^{t_s} F\, dt + \int V'\, dm' - \int V''\, dm'', \tag{5.4-8}$$

or

$$p(t_s) - p(t_0) = \int_{t_0}^{t_s} \left(F + V' \frac{dm'}{dt} - V'' \frac{dm''}{dt} \right) dt. \tag{5.4-9}$$

This is the equation of motion of a body adding and ejecting mass, in integral form. It is clearly very similar to the standard impulse-momentum relation. We can put it in the form of a differential equation by, in effect, reversing the process by which the impulse-momentum relation is obtained from the differential equation of motion. To do this we observe that 5.4-9 must be true for any time interval $t_0 < t < t_s$. If we set $t_0 = t$, $t_s = t + \Delta t$ and divide both sides of 5.4-9 by Δt, we have

$$\frac{p(t + \Delta t) - p(t)}{\Delta t} = \frac{1}{\Delta t} \int_t^{t + \Delta t} \left(F + V' \frac{dm'}{dt} - V'' \frac{dm''}{dt} \right) dt. \tag{5.4-10}$$

If we allow Δt to approach zero, the left-hand side of this expression will approach dp/dt as a limit. The integral on the right-hand side is equal to the value of the integrand in parentheses taken at some time in the interval

t, $t+\Delta t$ multiplied by the length of the interval, Δt. As $\Delta t \to 0$ we therefore have

$$\frac{dp}{dt} = F + V' \frac{dm'}{dt} - V'' \frac{dm''}{dt}.$$ 5.4-11

This expression may be seen to yield Eq. 5.4-9 on integration. It is the differential equation corresponding to the integral relationship 5.4-9. Finally, on substituting 5.4-4 in 5.4-11 we have

$$F = m \frac{dv}{dt} + (v - V') \frac{dm'}{dt} - (v - V'') \frac{dm''}{dt}.$$ 5.4-12

This is the basic equation of rectilinear variable mass motion. All of the quantities F, m, V', V'' and, of course, v may be functions of time. The terms F and $m(dv/dt)$ require no comment. The quantity dm'/dt is the rate at which mass is being added to the body of interest, and V' is the velocity of that mass just before it becomes adherent. The quantity dm''/dt is the rate at which mass is being ejected at a speed V''. Note that dm'/dt and dm''/dt are never negative quantities. They may be functions of time.

It may be seen from Eq. 5.4-12 that the acquisition of mass that is moving less rapidly than the main object has the same general effect as the presence of a fluid drag. Indeed, the methods of solving the equation of motion are similar in the two cases. Since variable mass analysis is a limiting case of a collision process, it cannot be expected that the work done by the force **F** will be equal to the change in kinetic energy, $mv^2/2$, of the body.

The reader will have noted that in the present treatment we began by considering as our system all the particles included in the mass m during some time interval. There is an alternative procedure, not described here, in which attention is directed to the material occupying a particular region of space, sometimes termed the "control volume." In this alternative procedure, allowance must, of course, be made for the momentum outflow from the control volume.

Example 5.4-1

A trailer full of sand is pulled by a constant force, F. Sand leaks out at the rate of c units of mass per second. Discuss the motion.

Solution: In this case, no mass is being added so that $dm'/dt = 0$. The mass ejected leaves with the same speed as the trailer so that $V'' = v$. The equation of motion, 5.4-12, reduces to

$$F = m \frac{dv}{dt}.$$

Since $m = m_0 - ct$ where m_0 is the initial mass of trailer and contents,

$$\frac{dv}{dt} = \frac{F}{m_0 - ct},$$

$$v = -\frac{F}{c} \log \left(1 - \frac{ct}{m_0} \right)$$

where the constant of integration has been evaluated on the supposition that $v = 0$ at $t = 0$. Writing $v = dx/dt$, we have

$$x = -\frac{F}{c} \int_0^t \log\left(1 - \frac{ct}{m_0}\right) dt = \frac{Fm_0}{c^2} \left\{\left(1 - \frac{ct}{m_0}\right)\left[\log\left(1 - \frac{ct}{m_0}\right) - 1\right]\right\}\bigg|_0^t$$

$$= \frac{Fm_0}{c^2}\left[\left(1 - \frac{ct}{m_0}\right)\log\left(1 - \frac{ct}{m_0}\right) + \frac{ct}{m_0}\right],$$

measuring x from the position of the truck at time zero. Notice that the work done by the force F at any time t is

$$\Delta W = \int_0^t Fv\, dt = -\frac{F^2}{c}\int_0^t \log\left(1 - \frac{ct}{m_0}\right) dt$$

$$= Fx = \frac{F^2 m_0}{c^2}\left[\left(1 - \frac{ct}{m_0}\right)\log\left(1 - \frac{ct}{m_0}\right) + \frac{ct}{m_0}\right].$$

On the other hand, the kinetic energy of the truck and contents at time t is

$$T = \frac{1}{2}(m_0 - ct)v^2 = \frac{F^2 m_0}{2c^2}\left(1 - \frac{ct}{m_0}\right)\left[\log\left(1 - \frac{ct}{m_0}\right)\right]^2.$$

The difference between the two expressions is the work done in accelerating sand that fell out of the truck prior to time t.

Example **5.4-2**

A spherical drop of liquid falling freely in a vapor acquires mass by condensation at a constant rate, c. Find the velocity after falling from rest in time t.

Solution: Here $dm''/dt = 0$; there is no loss of mass. We have $dm'/dt = c$ and $V' = 0$ since the mass is picked up from rest. The equation of motion is

$$mg = m\frac{dv}{dt} + cv.$$

This equation should be contrasted with the equation of motion in the previous example. In the present case,

$$m = m_0 + ct.$$

The homogeneous equation

$$\frac{dv}{dt} + \frac{cv}{m_0 + ct} = 0$$

has the solution

$$v = \frac{Ac}{m_0 + ct}.$$

The complete equation of motion therefore has the solution

$$v = \frac{Ac}{m_0 + ct} + \frac{g}{2c}(m_0 + ct).$$

When A is adjusted so as to satisfy the requirement that $v=0$ at $t=0$, we have

$$v = \tfrac{1}{2}gt\left(1 + \frac{1}{1 + \dfrac{ct}{m_0}}\right).$$

This can be integrated again to find the distance fallen as a function of time.

Example 5.4-3

A rocket whose total initial mass (fuel + shell) is m_0 ejects fuel at a constant rate cm_0 and at a velocity V relative to the case. Show that the lowest rate of fuel consumption that will permit the rocket to rise at once is $c=g/V$. Assuming this design condition is met, find the greatest speed and height reached by the rocket.

Solution: We have $dm'/dt=0$, $v-V''=V$, $dm''/dt=cm_0$, $F=-mg$ because the positive direction of the x-axis is now upward, in contrast to the previous example. The equation of motion is

$$-mg = m\frac{dv}{dt} - Vcm_0, \quad \text{with} \quad m = m_0(1-ct). \qquad \textbf{5.4-13}$$

$$\frac{dv}{dt} = \frac{Vc}{1-ct} - g. \qquad \textbf{5.4-14}$$

This is true for all t. Initially, at $t=0$,

$$\left.\frac{dv}{dt}\right|_{t=0} = Vc-g.$$

In order to have the rocket rise at once, we must have a positive value for dv/dt. This requires that

$$c = \frac{g}{V}$$

at least. This is quite an impressive rate of fuel consumption. If we think of $V=1500$ m/sec, $m_0=150{,}000$ kg, $g=9.8$ m/sec it amounts to approximately 980 kg/sec. We can, incidentally, see that the rocket will never rise at all unless its rate of fuel consumption exceeds a certain minimum value. Let m_1 be the mass of the shell or case. The rocket will be lightest when $m=m_1$, and all the fuel is burned. On setting $m=m_1$ in Eq. 5.4-13, we see that we must have

$$c > \frac{m_1}{m_0}\frac{g}{V}$$

in order to get upward motion at all.

Returning to Eq. 5.4-14 and assuming that the designer has arranged matters so that the rocket lifts at time zero ($c \geqq g/V$), we have, on integrating,

$$v = -gt + Vc \int_0^t \frac{dt}{1 - ct} = -gt - V \log (1 - ct),$$

$$x = -\frac{1}{2}gt^2 - V \int_0^t \log (1 - ct)\, dt \qquad \textbf{5.4-15}$$

$$= -\frac{1}{2}gt^2 + \frac{V}{c}(1 - ct)[\log (1 - ct) - 1] + \frac{V}{c}.$$

The speed v reaches its maximum value when the fuel is exhausted; that is, when $ct = 1 - (m_1/m_0)$. If we use this value of t in 5.4-15 we find

$$v_{\max} = -\frac{g}{c}\left(1 - \frac{m_1}{m_0}\right) - V \log \frac{m_1}{m_0}.$$

At this time the altitude, x, is

$$-\frac{1}{2}\frac{g}{c^2}\left(1 - \frac{m_1}{m_0}\right)^2 + \frac{V}{c}\left[\frac{m_1}{m_0} \log \frac{m_1}{m_0} + \left(1 - \frac{m_1}{m_0}\right)\right].$$

After reaching this height, the shell rises freely as a projectile with initial velocity $v_{\max}$. It therefore achieves an additional height $v_{\max}^2/2g$, making the final altitude

$$x_{\max} = \frac{V}{c}\left(1 - \frac{m_1}{m_0} - \log \frac{m_1}{m_0}\right) + \frac{V^2}{2g}\left(\log \frac{m_1}{m_0}\right)^2.$$

For $m_1/m_0 = 0.1$, $c = g/V$, and $V = 1500$ m/sec,

$$x_{\max} = 1.35(10)^6 \text{ m} \quad \text{and} \quad v_{\max} = 2100 \text{ m/sec.}$$

5.5 Conservative Systems

Those mechanical questions in which the external forces are known functions of position usually lend themselves to analysis by energy methods. This is particularly true when the external and internal forces are conservative or are of the types that do no mechanical work. Nonconservative forces can be treated by energy methods only if the path of the point of application is known so that the work done by these forces can be computed.

The work-energy principle asserts that, during any time interval, the sum of the changes in the kinetic and the potential energies of a mechanical system is equal to the work done on the system by those forces, external and internal, which have not been accounted for in the potential energy. In applying the principle, it is essential to begin by isolating a specific mechanical system. There is no guide to the best choice of system that will cover all possible cases. In general, it is well to select the system so that the internal forces either do no work (as in the case of single rigid bodies or rigid bodies joined by smooth pins and inextensible cables) or are conservative forces such as those exerted by springs (in which case the work done by them will be accounted for by the change in their potential energy). The system should also be selected so that those external forces that do work are known and are of as simple a type as possible.

⸳The work-energy principle deals directly with velocity and position. It has the advantage that accelerations need not be calculated in setting up the equation of motion. Those questions in which the wanted and given data are in the form of velocities and positions may be worked directly; the time interval mentioned in the statement of the principle is then taken as the interval between the given and wanted situations. However, if a relation between position and time is desired, it becomes necessary to integrate the expression for velocity. This expression must therefore be one that is valid for all time and not merely for a particular position. One end of the time interval chosen must be a "typical" instant.

Work and energy are scalar quantities. Unlike the vector equations of motion, the work-energy principle provides only one scalar equation. For systems having more than one degree of freedom, it cannot yield all the information needed for a complete determination of the motion. Furthermore, the fact that certain so-called forces of constraint such as the reactions at smooth surfaces or rolling contacts or fixed points do no work and therefore do not appear in the mathematical statement of the principle is not entirely an asset. It may happen that these forces are precisely the ones that the engineer must know in order to design the structure at hand. If energy methods are used, the determination of these forces of constraint requires that accelerations subsequently be found by differentiating the velocity expressions and then reactions determined by means of Newton's equations of motion.

Energy methods are sometimes useful for the determination of natural frequencies of mechanical systems. Consider a system with one degree of freedom, its position being specified by means of a single coordinate, $x(t)$. Suppose (a) that the kinetic and potential energies can be expressed in terms of this coordinate and its time derivative by expressions of the type

$$T = a^2\dot{x}^2, \qquad V = b^2x^2 \qquad\qquad \textbf{5·5-1}$$

where a and b are constants and (b) that the system is conservative.

Then the natural frequency of free vibration, ω_n, is simply the ratio b/a. This follows from the fact that for all time

$$T + V = \text{constant}, \quad \text{say} \quad a^2\dot{x}^2 + b^2x^2 = C. \qquad \textbf{5·5-2}$$

The equation of motion is obtained by taking the time derivative of both sides of this equation:

$$2a^2\ddot{x}\dot{x} + 2b^2x\dot{x} = 0,$$

$$\ddot{x} + \frac{b^2}{a^2}\, x = 0. \qquad \textbf{5·5-3}$$

This is the standard form we have encountered before (Eq. 3.3-2). Its solution is the simple harmonic motion $x = A \cos(\omega_n t - \alpha)$ with $\omega_n = b/a$ as asserted. The argument is not affected by the presence of a constant term in the expression for V; such a term would vanish on differentiation. As we shall see in Chapters VIII and IX, there are a great many mechanical systems whose energies are given, at least for small motions, by expressions of the type 5.5-1.*

There is another point of view from which the conclusion of the previous paragraph may be reached. If we assume that the motion will be simple harmonic, the kinetic energy of the oscillator will be a maximum when it swings through the position $x = 0$, and the potential energy will be a maximum at the extremity of the swing as the system comes to momentary rest. Since the total energy is constant, these maximum potential and kinetic energies must be equal. If we substitute $x = A \cos \omega_n t$ in the expressions 5.5-1, we have

$$T = A^2a^2\omega_n^2 \sin^2 \omega_n t, \qquad V = A^2b^2 \cos^2 \omega_n t.$$

$$T_{\max} = A^2a^2\omega_n^2, \qquad V_{\max} = A^2b^2.$$

$$T_{\max} = V_{\max} \quad \text{or} \quad a^2\omega_n^2 = b^2; \qquad \omega_n = \frac{b}{a}. \qquad \textbf{5·5-4}$$

---

* We may suppose $V = f(x)$ to be expanded in a power series about the point $x = 0$. Then $V = b_0 + b_1x + b_2x^2 + \dots$. The constant term is immaterial. We shall see (Chapter VIII) that, if $x = 0$ is a position of static equilibrium, $b_1 = 0$. So for small values of x we can always write $V = b_2x^2$ to a first approximation. Similarly T may depend on x through the coefficient a^2; i.e., $a^2 = g(x)$. We are, however, only interested in the motion near $x = 0$ so that, to the same order of approximation as before, it suffices to take $a^2 = g(0)$, a constant. Regarded as a function of $\dot{x}$, T is always proportional to $\dot{x}^2$.

Example 5.5-1

A 250-*lb overhead door is held in an open position by a catch. Design counterweights so that when the catch is released the door will move downward, gently reaching the closed position where a second catch will hold it. Significant dimensions are shown in Fig. 5.5-1.*

Solution: We take as our system the door, the two counterweights, the cable, and the pulleys. The external forces are the weights W and w and the forces P exerted by the supporting structure on the pulleys. These appear in Fig. 5.5-1, which may serve as a free-body diagram. When the catch is released, the door is to move downward 6 ft. During this motion the length of cable between pulley and door changes from 5 ft to 9.9 ft so

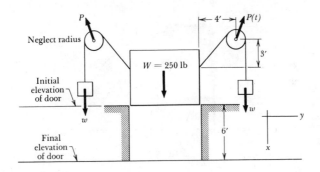

Fig. 5.5-1

that the counterweights move up a distance 4.9 ft. The work done by the external forces W and w is $6W - (2w)(4.9)$ ft-lb when W and w are in lb. Note that the work done by the forces w is negative because these forces are opposite in direction to the motion of the point to which they are applied. The forces P do no work since they are applied at stationary points. The kinetic energy of the system is zero initially and should be zero also when the door has moved down 6 ft if the closure is to be made "gently." Applying the work-energy principle to the time interval commencing with release of the upper catch and ending with closure of the door,

$$6W - 9.8w = 0,$$

$$w = 0.613W = (0.613)(250) = 153 \text{ lb}.$$

Note that gravitational potential need not be considered since we compute the actual work done by the gravity force. The utility of energy methods may be appreciated by visualizing the steps in the solution that would be required were Newton's equations of motion to be used directly.

Example 5.5-2

A 4-lb roller of 1 in radius moves on an elliptical track to which it is held by gravity and by a spring whose unstretched length is 7 in and whose modulus is 3 lb/in. The dimensions of the track are shown in Fig. 5.5-2. The roller is slightly displaced from its position on the vertical 5-in semi-minor axis of the ellipse; what will be its speed when it reaches the horizontal 9-in semi-major axis?

Solution: The system chosen consists of roller and spring; its free-body diagram is shown in Fig. 5.5-2. The initial instant of the time interval is

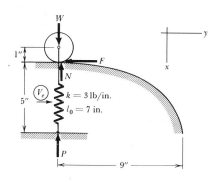

Fig. 5.5-2

that at which the roller is on the vertical axis, and the final instant is that at which it reaches the horizontal axis. Then

$$T_1 = 0; \qquad T_2 = \frac{1}{2}\left(\frac{4}{386}\right)v^2 + \frac{1}{2}\left[\frac{(4)(1)^2}{(2)(386)}\right]\left(\frac{v}{1}\right)^2 = \left(\frac{3}{4}\right)\left(\frac{4}{386}\right)v^2.$$

$$V_1 = \frac{1}{2}3(6-7)^2 \text{ in-lb}; \qquad V_2 = \frac{1}{2}3(10-7)^2 \text{ in-lb}.$$

Work done by external forces (gravity) $=(4)(6)=24$ in-lb. The potential energy of the spring is never negative. It is 1.5 in-lb initially, when the spring is compressed, and it is 13.5 in-lb in the terminal position where the spring is extended. By the work-energy principle

$$24 = (13.5 - 1.5) + (3/4)(4/386)v^2.$$

$$v^2 = (16)(386/4); \qquad v = 39.4 \text{ in/sec}.$$

Note that $m=4/386$, not $4/32.2$; since all dimensions used are in inches, g must be expressed in inches per sec². The (external) force exerted by the track on the roller does no work. The force exerted by the support on the lower end of the spring also does no work. The fact that the track is elliptical in shape does not enter the problem. This example should be compared with Example 3.2-4.

Example 5·5-3

A uniform roller of radius a and a rectangular block of equal mass are joined by a light member that is parallel to the incline down which the bodies roll and slide respectively. The coefficient of limiting friction for both bodies is μ. Find the acceleration of the bodies and the load carried by the link.

Solution: The system chosen consists of the roller, the block, and the connecting link; its free-body diagram is shown in Fig. 5.5-3a with the usual symbolism. A free-body diagram of the block alone (Fig. 5·5-3b) shows at once that $N_1 = W \cos \theta$, and therefore the frictional force acting on the block is $\mu W \cos \theta$. Note that we could not reach this conclusion immediately were the link not parallel to the incline. Returning now to Fig. 5.5-3a, we take the instant of release as the beginning of the time

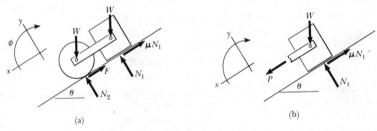

(a)   (b)

Fig. 5·5-3

interval and a time at which the assembly has moved a distance x down the plane as the end of the time interval. Then the equation of energy asserts

$$(2W \sin \theta)x - (\mu W \cos \theta)x = \frac{1}{2} \frac{W}{g} v^2 + \frac{3}{4} \frac{W}{g} v^2,$$

$$v^2 = \frac{4}{5} gx(2 \sin \theta - \mu \cos \theta). \qquad\qquad 5\cdot5\text{-}5$$

We note that $2 \sin \theta$ must exceed $\mu \cos \theta$ if v is to be real. Physically this means that if μ is larger than $2 \tan \theta$ the assembly will not move downhill under gravity. Since 5.5-5 is true for any x, it may be differentiated with respect to time.

$$2v\ddot{x} = \frac{4}{5} gv(2 \sin \theta - \mu \cos \theta),$$

$$\ddot{x} = \frac{2}{5} g(2 \sin \theta - \mu \cos \theta).$$

This answers the initial question. Turning now to Fig. 5.5-3b and writing $F_x = ma_x$, we have

$$P + W \sin \theta - \mu W \cos \theta = \frac{W}{g} \ddot{x} = \frac{2}{5} W(2 \sin \theta - \mu \cos \theta),$$

$$P = \frac{1}{5} W(3\mu \cos \theta - \sin \theta).$$

The force P will be tensile if μ exceeds $(1/3) \tan \theta$. Unless μ has at least this value, the roller will slip. The above analysis is therefore valid for $(1/3) \tan \theta \leqq \mu \leqq 2 \tan \theta$.

Example 5.5-4

In designing the governor of a turbogenerator, it is important to know how quickly it will have to shut off the steam supply in an emergency. Suppose that the operating speed of a 45,000-HP installation is 1750 rpm and that the 200,000-lb rotor with radius of gyration 1.6 ft can be run only as high as 2000 rpm without damage. When a short circuit occurs, a circuit breaker opens and there is no load on the unit. How quickly must the governor shut off the steam supply?

Solution: The system is the rotor, the initial time is that at which the circuit breaker opens, and the final time, t, is that at which the governor shuts off the steam supply. Now 45,000 HP is $(45,000)(550) = 24.8(10)^6$ ft-lb/sec, and, assuming the steam supply to the turbine remains constant until the governor closes, the work done by the pressure of the steam on the blades will be $24.8(10)^6 t$ ft-lb. During this time, the rotor speed is to increase from 1750 rpm to 2000 rpm.

$$(24.8)(10)^6 t = \frac{1}{2} \frac{200{,}000}{32.2} (1.6)^2 \left[\left(2000 \frac{2\pi}{60}\right)^2 - \left(1750 \frac{2\pi}{60}\right)^2 \right],$$

$$t = 3.25 \text{ sec.}$$

Example 5.5-5

Find the natural frequency of the mass-spring system shown in Fig. 3.3-1.
Solution: $T = \frac{1}{2} m \dot{x}^2$, $V = \frac{1}{2} k x^2$. Referring to Eq. 5.5-1, we see that $a^2 = m/2$, $b^2 = k/2$ and therefore $\omega_n = \sqrt{k/m}$.

Example 5.5-6

Find the natural frequency of small vibrations of the system shown in Fig. 5.5-4a.
Solution: The position shown in (a) is one of static equilibrium; therefore the spring must exert a moment mgr to counterbalance the weight. This means that the spring, in the position shown in (a), must be extended an amount mgr/ka beyond its unstretched length. The position of the system is conveniently specified by the angle θ through which the disk

turns, measured from the position shown in (a). A free-body diagram of the system is shown in Fig. 5.5-4b for a small rotation θ. The effect of this rotation is to increase the length of the spring by an amount $a\theta$. The total extension of the spring from its unstretched length is therefore

$$e = \frac{mgr}{ka} + a\theta. \qquad \text{5.5-6}$$

At the same time the mass m moves down a distance $r\theta$ so that the potential energy of the gravitational force decreases by an amount $mgr\theta$. We have

$$V = \frac{1}{2} ke^2 - mgr\theta = \frac{1}{2} k \left(\frac{mgr}{ka} + a\theta\right)^2 - mgr\theta$$

$$= \frac{1}{2} k \left(\frac{mgr}{ak}\right)^2 + \left(\frac{1}{2} ka^2\right) \theta^2. \qquad \text{5.5-7}$$

Except for the constant term, which has been shown to be immaterial, this

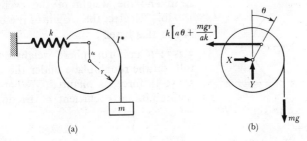

(a)   (b)

Fig. 5.5-4

expression is in the form of Eq. 5.5-1. Notice, however, that it is an approximation valid only for small motions. If θ is large, the extension of the spring is not quite correctly given by Eq. 5.5-6. Turning now to the kinetic energy, we see that for a rate of rotation $\dot{\theta}$ the mass has a speed $r\dot{\theta}$ so that

$$T = \frac{1}{2} I^* \dot{\theta}^2 + \frac{1}{2} m(r\dot{\theta})^2 = \frac{1}{2} (I^* + mr^2)\dot{\theta}^2. \qquad \text{5.5-8}$$

In view of Eqs. 5.5-1 and 5.5-4, we have at once

$$\omega_n = \sqrt{\frac{ka^2}{I^* + mr^2}}.$$

The student should differentiate the expression $T + V$ to get the equation of motion. The only further point which teaching experience shows to require comment is the presence of the constant term in the expression for V. This term does not affect the equation of motion and therefore cannot have any bearing on the natural frequency. It arises from the choice of datum for strain energy of the spring. We want to say that the strain energy of the spring is $\frac{1}{2}ke^2$ where e denotes the extension. But e is not zero when θ is zero because θ is measured from a position of static equilibrium. It is the latter consideration that is essential since otherwise V would contain a term proportional to θ.

Exercises

5.2-1: A flywheel that weighs 150 lb has a radius of gyration 0.8 in and an outside diameter of 24 in. If it is rotating about a fixed axis through its center at 220 rpm when a brake bar applies a radial force of 25 lb to the rim, how long will it take to come to rest? The coefficient of friction at the rim is 0.4.
Ans.: 45.7 sec.

5.2-2: A bicyclist exerts a torque of 100 ft-lb on the rear axle of his bicycle. Assuming that the rear wheel does not slip, what will be his acceleration on

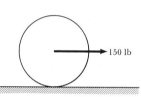

a level track? Take the wheel radius to be 14 in and the weight of the cyclist to be 150 lb. Neglect the weight of the bicycle.
Ans.: 18.4 ft/sec².

5.2-3: A uniform sphere weighs 80 lb. It rolls on the rough plane under the action of a 150-lb force, as pictured. What must be the minimum coefficient of friction if the sphere is not to slip? $I^* = \frac{2}{5}mr^2$.
Ans.: 0.54.

5.2-4: A railroad flat car carrying a uniform roll of material on its bed moves forward from rest with a constant acceleration. If the roller was initially placed a distance s_0 from the rear end of the car, how far will the car have moved forward by the time the roll falls off the rear end?

Assume that friction is sufficient to prevent slipping.
Ans.: $1.5s_0$.

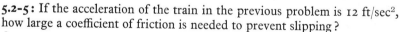

5.2-5: If the acceleration of the train in the previous problem is 12 ft/sec², how large a coefficient of friction is needed to prevent slipping?
Ans.: 0.124.

5.2-6: If the coefficient of friction for the roller on the flat car of Exercises 5.2-4 and 5.2-5 is $\mu = 0.1$ and if the train accelerates forward at the constant rate of 12 ft/sec², how far will the train have moved when the roller reaches the rear end of the flat car? Express your answer as a multiple of s_0, and compare with Exercise 5.2-4.
Ans.: $1.37s_0$.

5.2-7: A uniform 10-ft beam is held by two vertical cables. One of the cables breaks. Immediately after the break the tension in the intact cable is the same as it was before the break. How far from the end of the beam is the intact cable attached?

Ans.: 2.12 ft.

5.2-8: What is the angular acceleration of the bar shown immediately after the catch at the right-hand end is released? Denote the mass of the bar by the symbol m and the centroidal radius of gyration by the symbol k^*. Express your answer in terms of k^* and such of the dimensions as you may find it necessary to use.

Ans.: $gc/(k^{*2}+c^2)$.

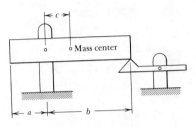

5.2-9: A girder 12 ft long weighs 1200 lb. It is being lifted upward with an acceleration of 10.7 ft/sec² by means of cables attached at symmetrical points 6 ft apart and extending vertically upward when the right-hand cable breaks. What is the load carried by the left-hand cable immediately after the break?

Ans.: 910 lb.

5.2-10: A uniform rod 10 ft long and weighing 161 lb is held so as to make a 45° angle with a horizontal surface against which its lower end rests. The coefficient of friction is 0.3. The rod is released from rest. Immediately after release, (a) does the lower end slide; and (b) what is the vertical component of the force exerted on the rod by the horizontal surface?

Ans.: 80 lb.

5.2-11: A hollow drum weighing 128 lb and rotating at 240 rpm is brought to rest by application of a constant force $P = 20$ lb to a light brake rod as shown in the accompanying figure, which is drawn to a scale of 1 in = 1 ft. Friction in the bearings provides a constant torque of 5 ft-lb, and the coefficient of friction at the brake contact is 0.5. Find the time required to bring the drum to rest and the number of revolutions through which it turns. Scale any needed dimensions from the figure.

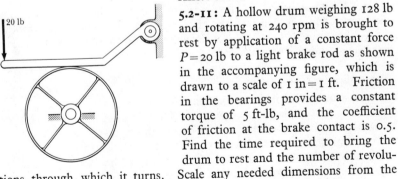

Ans.: 4.6 sec, 9 rev.

5.2-12: The homogeneous block shown weighs 48.3 lb. The coefficient of friction between the block and the plane is 0.20, and the block is sliding to the right. Determine the maximum value of the force P that can be

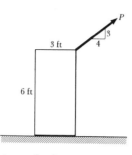

applied without causing the block to tip. When P has this value what is the magnitude of the acceleration of the block?

Ans.: 21.3 lb, 6.7 ft/sec².

5.2-13: A plunger of mass m can slide freely in a cylinder of cross-sectional area A, but no air can escape past it (at least for the purposes of this problem). If the plunger is released from a height h, and if the gas pressure in the cylinder follows the law $pV^\gamma = p_0 V_0^\gamma$, where p_0 denotes atmospheric pressure, initially the same above and below the piston, how far will the plunger fall before its acceleration is reduced to zero?

Ans.: $x/h = 1 - \left(1 + \dfrac{mg}{p_0 A}\right)^{-1/\gamma}$.

Exer. 5.2-13

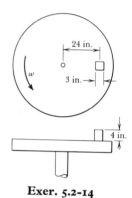

Exer. 5.2-14

5.2-14: The homogeneous block rests on the turntable as shown. The coefficient of friction between the block and the surface of the turntable is 0.7. If the angular velocity, ω, is slowly increased from zero will the block first tip or slide? At what angular velocity will this occur?

Ans.: Slips first, at 32 rpm.

5.2-15: A uniform sphere of mass m rolls on a rough plane under the action of its weight and a force through its mass center. This force varies with time in magnitude and in direction, but it always lies in the vertical xy-plane. Show that the motion of the center of the sphere is exactly the same as that of a particle of mass m sliding on a smooth horizontal plane under the action of the same force reduced in magnitude by a factor $5/7$.

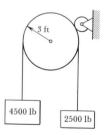

5.2-16: An elevator weighing 4500 lb is supported by a cable that draws it upward at a constant acceleration of 4 ft/sec². The cable is wound around a 3-ft radius drum. Also wound around the drum is another cable

supporting a 2500-lb counterweight. The drum weighs 7200 lb and has a radius of gyration of 2.5 ft. It is driven by an electric motor through an 8:1 gear ratio. The inertia of the motor may be neglected in comparison with that of the drum. (a) What torque must the motor exert? (b) If this acceleration is to be maintained for 5 sec, what horsepower will be required for the motor?
Ans.: 1300 ft-lb; 127 HP.

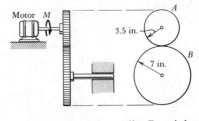

5.2-17: A motor drives a pair of gears, *A* and *B*, by applying a constant torque, *M*, to the shaft of gear *A*. If the motor is to accelerate *B* from rest to 955 rpm in one second, find the torque that the motor must deliver. Dimensions of the gears are shown. *A* weighs 16 lb, *B* weighs 32 lb; $k^* = 3$ in for *A*, and $k^* = 5$ in for *B*.
Ans.: 15 lb-ft.

5.3-1: The horizontal rod has a moment of inertia about the vertical axis of 0.10 lb-ft-sec^2, and each of the sliding balls with negligible dimensions weighs 3.16 lb. The assembly is rotating freely about *O-O* at an angular

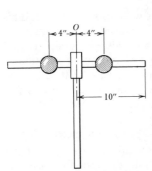

velocity of 25 rad/sec with the balls latched in the position shown. The latches are released. Determine the angular velocity of the rod when the balls are 10 in from *O-O*. Is there any change in the kinetic energy of the system of rod and balls during this time interval, assuming the rod to be smooth? If not, what is the radial velocity of the balls at the end of this time interval?
Ans.: 12.9 rad/sec; 13.4 ft/sec.

5.3-2: A sled carrying a boy is moving at 30 ft/sec when a second boy running at 10 ft/sec in the same direction as the sled is moving jumps on. If the boys weigh 96 lb each and the sled weighs 16 lb, what effect does the addition of the second boy have upon the speed of the sled?
Ans.: 22 ft/sec.

5.3-3: A 20 kg mass is released from rest on a smooth 20° incline. After it has acquired a velocity of 5 ft/sec down the plane, a constant force *P* directed up the plane and parallel to it is applied to the mass until it comes to rest. What is the magnitude of *P* if the block comes to rest 3 sec after *P* is applied?
Ans.: 77 newtons.

5.3-4: The figure shown represents the pendulum of an impact-testing machine. It weighs 140 lb, its centroidal moment of inertia is 15.2

in-lb-sec^2, and its mass center is 22.14 in from the point of support A. (a) Determine the distance, d, that the striking edge should be placed from the mass center of the pendulum in order to have zero horizontal component of bearing reaction at the instant of impact. (b) What is the average magnitude of the (horizontal) striking force if the angular velocity of the pendulum is reduced from 7 rad/sec to 1 rad/sec in 0.05 sec?
Ans.: 2 in; 960 lb.

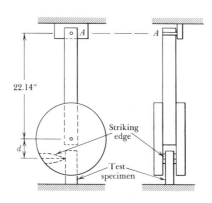

5.3-5: An ice skater who weighs 70 kg pirouettes with his knees bent and his arms outstretched at the rate of 10 rpm.   In this position he has a radius of gyration of 0.5 m.   What will be his rate of rotation after he straightens up and brings his arms to his sides, thus reducing his radius of gyration to 0.25 m?   Does his kinetic energy increase or decrease?   If his mass center rises 0.3 m during this change, how much work do his muscles do? Contrast this situation, so far as energy is concerned, with that of Exercise 5.3-1.
Ans.: 40 rpm; T increases; work of muscles $= 235$ newton-meters.

5.3-6: A 2000-lb pile driver falls 3 ft and inelastically strikes the head of a 1500-lb pile.   How far will it drive the pile into the ground if the soil resistance has a constant value of 5000 lb?
Ans.: 2.3 ft.

5.3-7: A jet engine on a test stand takes in 40 lb of air each second at 350 ft/sec, heats and compresses it, and discharges it at 1600 ft/sec.   What is the thrust exerted by the engine on the test stand?   If this engine were in an airplane flying at 350 ft/sec, what horsepower would it develop?
Ans.: 1550 lb; 990 HP.

5.3-8: A sphere is dropped from a height h above a floor.   Each time it rebounds, the coefficient of restitution is e.   Show (a) that the total time the sphere is in motion is $\sqrt{2h/g}(1+e)/(1-e)$, (b) that the total distance traversed before coming to rest is $h(1+e^2)/(1-e^2)$, (c) that the energy lost in the bounces is *mgh*.

5.3-9: Show that the energy of the struck particle in Example 5.3-5 is $4m_1m_2 \cos^2 \theta/(m_1+m_2)^2$ times the initial energy of the striking particle.

5.3-10: The cloud-chamber track of a collision shows the paths of the colliding particles to be at right angles after impact. On the assumption of no energy loss, show that the particles have equal mass. Do this by starting from the momentum and energy equations. Finally, check your result with that of Example 5.3-5. Assume one particle stationary initially.

5.3-11: A sphere of mass m_1 collides with a less massive stationary sphere, m_2. There is no energy loss. Show that the largest possible angle through which the direction of motion of the sphere can be turned is arcsin (m_2/m_1).

5.3-12: Two spheres moving along the same straight line collide. (a) Show that the ratio of the impulse on either sphere during the restitution period to the impulse during the compression period is e; (b) that for axes with origin at the mass center of the spheres the ratio of the kinetic energy after impact to the kinetic energy before impact is e^2.

5.3-13: A sphere $(I^* = \frac{2}{5}mr^2)$ of radius r and mass m rolling with speed v on a horizontal surface strikes an obstacle of height h. What is the largest value h can have if the sphere is able to roll over the obstacle? (See Example 5.3-8.)

Ans.: $(h/r) = \dfrac{7}{5}\left[\left(1+\dfrac{gr}{v^2}\right)-\dfrac{gr}{v^2}\left(1+\dfrac{2v^2}{gr}\right)^{1/2}\right].$

5.3-14: A plane lamina at rest on a smooth table is struck a blow of impulse $\hat{\mathbf{F}}$ at a point P. The velocity of P after the blow is $\mathbf{v}$. Show that the kinetic energy of the lamina after the blow is $\frac{1}{2}\hat{\mathbf{F}}\cdot\mathbf{v}$.

5.3-15: A plane lamina is at rest on a smooth table when the point P is suddenly forced to move with the velocity $\mathbf{v}$. Find the angular velocity of the lamina in terms of (x_0, y_0), the centroidal coordinates of P; (v_x, v_y), the components of $\mathbf{v}$; and k, the radius of gyration about P. Hint: the angular momentum about P remains zero.

Ans.: $\omega = (x_0 v_y - y_0 v_x)/(x_0^2 + y_0^2 - k^2).$

5.3-16: Show that the angular velocity of the lamina in the previous problem is such as to make the kinetic energy smaller than it would be with any other angular velocity.

5.3-17: Two identical uniform bars, AB and BC, of length l and mass m hinged at B lie in a straight line. A blow of impulse $\hat{F}$ is struck at C in a direction at right angles to that line. Find the angular velocities of AB and BC after the blow and the velocities of their mass centers.

Ans.: $\omega_{BC} = -3\omega_{AB} = (9/2)(\hat{F}/ml);\ v_{BC}^* = -5v_{AB}^* = (5/4)(\hat{F}/m).$

5.3-18: Two uniform bars—AB of length $2l$ and mass $2m$, and BC of length l and mass m—are hinged at B and laid in a straight line. They are struck a blow at right angles to their length and afterwards move with the same angular velocity (like a rigid body). How far from A were they struck?

Ans.: $6l/7$.

5.3-19: A door 7 ft high is brought to rest by striking a stop on the ground at the point farthest from the doorpost. The door is supported by two hinges each located 1.5 ft from the nearest horizontal edge of the door. Find the ratio of the impulsive force on the upper hinge to that on the lower hinge. **Ans.:** 9/5.

5.4-1: A uniform, flexible (but inextensible), fine string or chain of mass μ per unit length lies in a coil on a smooth table. A constant horizontal force F is applied to one end of the chain. Find the length of chain uncoiled in time t. What is the ratio of the kinetic energy of the chain to the work done by F? Account for the difference. **Ans.:** $t\sqrt{F/\mu}$; 0.5.

5.4-2: A tank car of mass m_1 holds water of mass m_2. The water is pumped out at the rate of c units of mass per unit of time. If the pumping is started when the car is at rest and if the stream of water is directed to the rear at a constant speed V relative to the ground, (a) ignoring friction what will be the speed of the tank car when the water is exhausted; (b) and what will be its speed if it encounters track resistance with coefficient of friction μ? **Ans.:** $(m_2 V/m_1) - (\mu g/2cm_1)(m_2^2 + 2m_1 m_2)$.

5.4-3: Suppose in the previous problem the water is discharged at constant speed, V, relative to the tank car. What is then the answer to (a)? Which assumption do you think more realistic?

5.4-4: A steam locomotive pulling a train of mass m exerts a constant tractive force F on the rails that just balances air resistance and friction at the speed of the train. A scoop of cross-sectional area A picks up water from a tank between the rails. If the train approaches the tank with a speed v_0, what will be its speed when it has picked up a volume Q of water? Neglect any changes in F and the resistances that may occur during this interval.

5.4-5: A uniform chain of fine inelastic links hangs from one end with its lower end just in contact with a platform scales. Show that, if the chain is let fall, the reading on the scales at any time while the chain is falling will be equal to three times the weight of chain at rest on the platform.

5.4-6: A single-stage rocket is to lift a one-kilogram shell to a height of 100 km. It ejects combustion products with relative speed 1000 m/sec. At what rate of mass flow must fuel be ejected if this rocket is to rise as soon as the motors are started? What will be the minimum mass of the entire shell and fuel at launch? Neglect the variation in g.

5.4-7: A drop of fluid falls in a vapor that has an upward speed V. It acquires mass by condensation at the constant rate c. If its velocity and mass at time zero are m_0 and v_0, what will they be at time t?

5.4-8: Work the previous problem on the assumption that the drop acquires mass at a rate proportional to its speed and its cross-sectional area. Do you think this the more realistic assumption?

5.4-9: A uniform chain of fine inelastic links and mass μ per unit length lies coiled on the ground. One end is lifted by a constant vertical force F. At what height will the lifted end first come to rest?

Ans.: $h = 3F/2\mu g$.

5.4-10: In the previous problem, at what height will the lifted end next come to rest?

Ans.: $(0.626F/\mu g)$.

5.5-1: An object of mass m is projected with velocity v_0 up a slope inclined to the horizontal by an angle θ. The object is connected to the slope by a spring of modulus k that is parallel to the slope and that is unstretched when the object starts. How far up the slope will the object rise (a) if there is no friction, and (b) if the coefficient of sliding friction is μ?

Ans.: $(mg/k) \sin \theta [\sqrt{1 + (kv_0^2)/(mg^2 \sin^2 \theta)} - 1]$; substitute $\sin \theta + \mu \cos \theta$ for $\sin \theta$ in previous answer.

5.5-2: A uniform disk of mass m and radius r is projected up a plane inclined at an angle θ to the horizontal. The initial speed of its center is v_0, and its initial angular velocity is v_0/r so that it rolls without slipping. In what distance will it come to rest? Compare your answer with that of the previous problem, taking $\mu = k = 0$.

Ans.: $3v_0^2/4g \sin \theta$.

5.5-3: Design a buffer spring that will stop a 3800-lb automobile traveling at 40 mph in a distance of 1 ft.

Ans.: $k = 407{,}000$ lb/ft.

5.5-4: What is the natural frequency of the system shown? The mass of the disk is m, its radius r, and its centroidal radius of gyration k^*. The spring has a modulus k.

Ans.: $\omega_n^2 = (k/m)\left(1 + \dfrac{k^{*2}}{r^2}\right)^{-1}$.

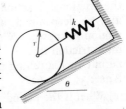

5.5-5: An object produces a deflection s when placed gently on a light elastic beam. What deformation will it produce if dropped from a height h, and what will be its peak velocity? Assume that the object remains in contact with the beam during its downward motion but that there is no energy loss when the object strikes the beam.

Ans.: $s[1 + \sqrt{1 + (2h/s)}]$.

5.5-6: Find the period of small oscillations of a compound pendulum; that is, a lamina that oscillates in its plane. The lamina is suspended at a point whose distance from the mass center is h. The radius of gyration of the lamina about its center of mass is k^*.

Ans.: $T_n = 2\pi \sqrt{(k^{*2} + h^2)/(hg)}$.

5.5-7: A compound pendulum (see previous problem) suspended from a point O has a period T_n. When suspended from a point O' on the line through O and the mass center, it is found to have the same period. Show that the distance OO' is $(k^{*2} + h^2)/h$.

5.5-8: Show that the period of oscillation of a compound pendulum is a minimum when the distance between the point of support and the mass center is k^*. The result is due to Schuler. Can you explain how knowledge of this fact was of help to him in the design of high-precision pendulum clocks?

5.5-9: Find the period of small vibrations of the device shown. The mass center of the rocker of mass m is at a distance h below the point of support when the upper bar is horizontal.

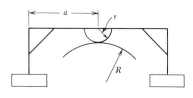

5.5-10: A uniform cylinder weighing 48.3 lb and of radius 2 ft ($I^* = \frac{1}{2}mr^2$) rolls without slipping on the horizontal surface. The center is constrained by two light ideal springs, each of constant $k = 15$ lb/in, and undeformed in the equilibrium position. The cylinder is displaced to the right so that its c.m. is 3 in to the right of equilibrium, then released from rest. (a) Show that the system is conservative, and write the equation of energy conservation in terms of the displacement x_C and velocity $\dot{x}_C$ of the mass center. (b) Differentiate the energy equation to find an equation of motion governing x_C. (c) Write the conservation equation in terms of the angle of rotation and angular velocity of the cylinder; differentiate to find an equation of angular motion. (d) Show how the frictional reaction at the contact may be determined, once the angular motion is known. What is the maximum friction force? What is the minimum coefficient of friction that will permit such a rolling motion?

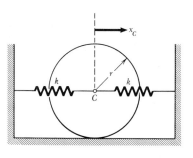

Ans.: 30 lb, 0.62.

(e) What is the period of free vibration of this system?
Ans.: 0.70 sec.

5.5-11: A door 2.5 ft wide, when left ajar, closes in 1 sec. Find the angle between the line of the hinges and the vertical.
Ans.: 7.3 degrees.

5.5-12: Three particles, two of mass m and one of mass M, move in vertical lines as shown. They are connected by inextensible cords that pass over light, smooth pulleys. The system is released from rest

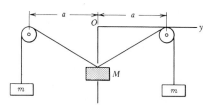

with M at the origin O. (a) How far down, s, will mass M fall? Are there any restrictions on M (to keep s finite)? (b) From the energy equation for the system (and the necessary kinematical relations), find the equation of motion governing the position function x_M of M.

Ans.:

(a) $\dfrac{s}{a} = \dfrac{M/m}{1 - (M/2m)^2}$.

(b) $(a^2 + x_M^2)[Ma^2 + (M + 2m)x_M^2]\ddot{x}_M + 2ma^2 x_M \dot{x}_M^2$
$$+ 2mg(a^2 + x_M^2)^{3/2}x_M - Mg(a^2 + x_M^2)^2 = 0.$$

5.5-13: A hemisphere of radius r is placed on a horizontal surface, flat face up. Find the period of free small vibration.

Ans.: $T_n = 2\pi\sqrt{1.73R/g}$.

5.5-14: When the electromagnet is energized by an alternating current with a frequency of $200/\pi$ cycles per second, the suspended mass m_2 vibrates through a double (vertical) amplitude of 0.001 ft in the steady state. Determine the peak value (F_0) of the alternating magnetic force

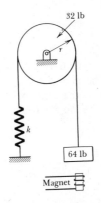

$F = F_0 \sin \omega t$ if the period of undamped free vibrations of the system is 0.01π sec. (The value of the magnetic force has been assumed independent of the distance between m_2 and the magnet for the small motions considered here.)

Ans.: 150 lb.

5.5-15: A barrel has the form of a right circular cylinder of radius r, mass m, and centroidal radius of gyration k^* about its axis of symmetry. The barrel contains a mass m' of a liquid. Starting from rest, it rolls down a plane inclined at an angle θ to the horizontal. What is the speed of the barrel after it has rolled a distance s down the incline?

Ans.: $v^2 = \dfrac{m' + m}{m' + (1 + k^{*2}/r^2)m} 2gs \sin \theta$.

5.5-16: The device shown is hinged at O. Its mass m is concentrated in a particle at the end of the arm of length l. Find the natural frequency of small oscillations (a) if the device swings in a horizontal plane and (b) if it swings in a vertical plane, gravity acting from A toward O. What do you think will happen if $2kb^2/mlg < 1$?

Ans.: $f_n = \dfrac{1}{2\pi} \sqrt{\dfrac{2kb^2}{ml^2} - \dfrac{g}{l}}$.

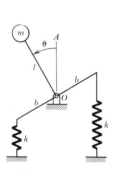

Exer. 5.5-16

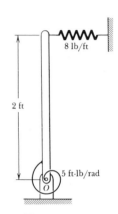

Exer. 5.5-17

5.5-17: An 18-lb, uniform rigid bar is pinned smoothly at end O, has a spiral spring attached to it there, and a straight spring at the other end, P. Neither spring is deformed in the equilibrium position shown. The bar moves in a horizontal plane. Find the frequency of small oscillations about equilibrium.

Ans.: 1.2 cps.

CHAPTER VI

Rigid-Body Dynamics in
Three Dimensions

6.1 Introduction to Rigid-Body Kinematics in Space

In Chapter IV, the dynamical principles for systems were derived. The only theoretical limitation that arose was in the work-energy principle for systems including rigid bodies of finite size and distributed mass. For this, as well as for specific representation of the angular momentum vector and of auxiliary kinematic equations in applications, we limited ourselves to systems in strictly plane motion. The reason for the limitation was kinematic: the relative motion equations are essential both for theory and application, and only for plane motion have we derived the form of the relative velocity vector for two points on a rigid body.

Three-dimensional applications require a mathematically reasonable representation of functions like **H** and T in terms of the kinematical variables on which they depend. In particular, we must be able to discuss the relative velocity and acceleration vectors for a rigid body with the same facility in three as in two dimensions. To do so, we must solve what may be called the fundamental space-kinematics problem: how may rotation of a body be described in three dimensions.

337

We know what form the relative velocity vector $\dot{\mathbf{p}}$ must have if the relative position vector $\mathbf{p}$ joins two points on the same rigid body. As we have seen in Chapter I, a nonconstant vector $\mathbf{p}$ of constant magnitude $|\mathbf{p}|$ must have derivative $\dot{\mathbf{p}}$ orthogonal to $\mathbf{p}$; in particular, $\dot{\mathbf{p}}$ has the direction of a unit vector perpendicular to $\mathbf{p}$ and has a magnitude equal to the product of $|\mathbf{p}|$ and the rate of change of some angle. For plane motion, $\dot{\mathbf{p}}$ as given by Eq. 4.4-1 is of this form. What we did not find was a vectorial form for $\dot{\mathbf{p}}$ independent of the choice of coordinates. This is easily done. Introduce an angular velocity vector $\boldsymbol{\omega}$ with magnitude equal to the absolute value of the scalar ω of Chapter IV and direction perpendicular to the plane of motion and agreeing by the right-hand rule with the sense of ω. (If x and y are rectangular coordinates in the plane of motion and $\omega > 0$ for rotations in the sense from positive x toward positive y, then $\boldsymbol{\omega} = \omega\mathbf{k}$.) With due regard for the sign conventions involved, Eq. 4.4-1 may be written

$$\dot{\mathbf{p}} = \boldsymbol{\omega} \times \mathbf{p}. \qquad \textbf{6.1-1}$$

Since this is a vectorial relation, it is valid for any coordinate representation of the vectors. Note that it shows the equivalence of a derivative operation and an algebraic operation—a mathematical simplification that permits us to compute the value of the derivative of $\mathbf{p}$ at any particular instant knowing $\boldsymbol{\omega}$ and $\mathbf{p}$ at that instant, but not necessarily knowing $\mathbf{p}$ as a function of time throughout some interval including that instant. In this chapter, we show that an angular velocity vector $\boldsymbol{\omega}$ can be introduced so that Eq. 6.1-1 is valid for any rigid body whether it is in plane motion or not.

Some of the difficulties that must be faced in finding a simple representation of the relative velocity vector are easily pointed out. The kinematics of a plane lamina is simplified because the relative motion of two points is "circular." For the rigid body in space, the relative motion is "spherical"; i.e., an observer at one point sees the other trace out a path on a sphere of radius $|\mathbf{p}|$. A glance at Section 1.11 suggests that the "proper" coordinates for the description of spherical motion are not simple. Also, rotations of a body about nonparallel axes in space are not easy to describe mathematically.

Once these difficulties have been overcome and the angular velocity vector has been introduced, we will be able not only to solve the relative motion problem for the rigid body but also to approach the nonrigid relative motion problem and the dynamical equations in a new way. By assigning an angular velocity to a rigid rotating coordinate frame, we can compute the derivative of the angular momentum vector easily. The proper statement of the dynamical equations in rotating coordinates enables us to solve truly three-dimensional problems. The concept of the rotating coordinate system is a difficult but unifying one; the student's mastery of this is essential to his comprehension of advanced dynamical theory.

Before discussing velocity and acceleration of a rigid body, we must first consider how position and displacement of a rigid body are prescribed. What we shall say in Section 6.2 is elementary for the most part. The student will know much of it, at least intuitively. We also introduce some standard terminology that will facilitate our later discussions.

6.2 General Displacement of a Rigid Body; Finite Rotations and Euler's Theorem

Position and its specification have been discussed for the particle, but we have not yet had need for a formal treatment of what may be termed "the position of a system"—properly called its *configuration*. A set of particular positions of every point in a system is a configuration of the system. Usually, owing to the presence of constraints on the system, we need not give the actual coordinates of every particle. For example, in the case of a straight rigid bar moving in a plane, it is sufficient to give the (x, y) coordinates of the mass center and the angle that the bar makes with the x-axis. From these three pieces of information the location of any point in the bar can be found. The scalar quantities employed to specify the configuration of a system—often cartesian components or angles—are known as *generalized coordinates*. We restrict the number of generalized coordinates to the minimum number necessary and sufficient to describe the configuration of the system. If there are n generalized coordinates and they can each change independently without violating any constraints placed on the system, we say that the system has n *degrees of freedom*. This is the common case. It may happen, however, that there are constraints on the system that prevent the independent change of all of the coordinates.* In this exceptional case, the number of degrees of freedom is the number of generalized coordinates diminished by the number of such constraint relations.

Before considering the general rigid body, let us discuss the rigid lamina once again. How many degrees of freedom has a lamina free to move in its plane? The answer is found easily by treating the

---

* Such constraints are known as nonholonomic constraints.

related question: how can the lamina be constrained from moving at all? Suppose the coordinates of one point, A, are fixed; then the lamina can only rotate about A. If a second point, B, is fixed, so is the line AB, and no rotation is possible. By rigidity, the position of any other point, C, is determined if those of A and B are. The four coordinates of A and B are not independent, however; the rigidity constraint for the length of AB reduces the number to three. Remove all constraints so that the lamina is free to move: clearly it has three degrees of freedom. Generalized coordinates may be taken as x_A, y_A, and ϕ_{AB}, the angle between the positive x-axis fixed in the plane and the line AB fixed in the body. We see that the lamina can be said to have two translational and one rotational degrees of freedom.

In three dimensions, the configuration of a rigid body is determined by three noncollinear points (A, B, C), any other point, D, being determined by the geometry of the body and the rigidity conditions once A, B, and C are in known positions. Consider the complete constraint of the body. Fix point A, say by a ball-and-socket joint. Then the rest of the body may only pivot about A. Now constrain point B, say by a sleeve bearing, so that B can only move along the line AB. Since the distance AB is constant, B cannot move at all; the whole line AB is fixed. The body may still rotate about AB. Fix a third point C not on AB, say by placing it on rollers constrained to move between parallel planes. Then the plane ABC is fixed, and the body cannot rotate about AB. Thus three points determine the configuration of a rigid body. The nine coordinates of (A, B, C) are not independent; the three rigidity conditions $(AB, BC, AC$ all constant) reduce the number to six. Remove all constraints; a rigid body free to move in three dimensions has six degrees of freedom.

Three of these degrees of freedom may be considered translational, the other three rotational. Just how the rotational degrees of freedom may be measured is not important to us now; one way, using the *Eulerian angles*, will be given later with the appropriate applications. The important fact is that there are six degrees of freedom and six equations of motion, $\mathbf{F} = m\mathbf{a}^*$ and $\mathbf{M}^* = \dot{\mathbf{H}}^*$. The equations of motion of a system (together with initial conditions) are sufficient to determine the motion of a rigid continuum, but are not sufficient for any deformable continuous medium. This is another reason why the study of rigid-body mechanics is important; in order to determine the motion of a rigid body, no further physical hypothesis about the properties of matter need be made.

A general change in the configuration of a rigid system can be considered to consist of a translation and a rotation, just as in the plane. We start with the simplest motion, *pure rotation about a fixed axis in space.* In this motion, every point in the body travels in a circle about a fixed line in space. There is no essential difference between this motion and pure rotation in strictly plane motion, as we shall see by comparison of the two.

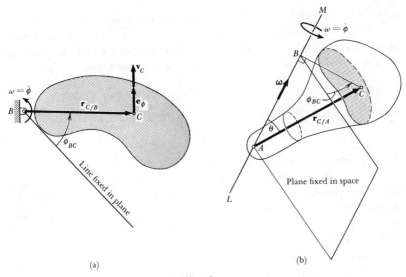

Fig. 6.2-1

Let the fixed axis in space, which may or may not intersect the body, be given as a directed line LM (Fig. 6.2-1); let C be any point in the body not on LM, and let B be the point on LM so situated that BC is the perpendicular dropped from C on LM. Let A be any other point on LM so that the directed line AB has the same sense as LM; A will be the fixed origin for measuring position in the three-dimensional body. Consider also the plane section of the body containing B and C and perpendicular to LM; this will be the rigid lamina used for comparing pure rotation in the plane to pure rotation about a space axis. The lamina is shown in Fig. 6.2-1a, the full body in Fig. 6.2-1b.

For the lamina, the configuration is fixed by the value of the single coordinate ϕ_{BC}, the angle between some line fixed in the plane of motion and the line BC fixed in the lamina. For the full body, there is a single degree of freedom; the configuration is determined again by a single angle ϕ_{BC}, now the angle between a plane fixed in space containing the axis of rotation and the plane ABC fixed in the body. The rate of change of angle, $\dot{\phi}_{BC} = \omega$, is a property of the whole body because of rigidity; a positive sense for measuring ϕ and ω may be determined from the positive sense of AB by the usual right-hand rule. An angular velocity vector

$$\boldsymbol{\omega} = \omega \mathbf{e}_{AB} \qquad\qquad \textbf{6.2-1}$$

may be introduced for the lamina and for the full body.

That the velocity of C is given by $\boldsymbol{\omega} \times \mathbf{r}_{C/A}$ is almost obvious now. Since B is a fixed point, we know that the velocity of C is given by $|\mathbf{r}_{C/B}| \omega \mathbf{e}_\phi \equiv \boldsymbol{\omega} \times \mathbf{r}_{C/B}$; from the relative motion equations,

$$\mathbf{v}_{C/A} = \mathbf{v}_{C/B} + \mathbf{v}_{B/A} = \mathbf{v}_{C/B},$$

since B is fixed. Then

$$\mathbf{v}_C = \mathbf{v}_{C/A} = \boldsymbol{\omega} \times \mathbf{r}_{C/B} = \boldsymbol{\omega} \times (\mathbf{r}_{C/A} - \mathbf{r}_{B/A}) = \boldsymbol{\omega} \times \mathbf{r}_{C/A},$$

since $\boldsymbol{\omega}$ and $\mathbf{r}_{B/A}$ have the same direction.

The same result is clear by direct considerations. The velocity of C is perpendicular to both $\mathbf{r}_{C/B}$ and AB and hence is perpendicular to the plane ABC. The speed of C equals $|\mathbf{r}_{C/B}| \omega = |\mathbf{r}_{C/A}| \omega \sin \theta$ where θ is the constant angle between the axis of rotation AB and the position vector $\mathbf{r}_{C/A}$. The speed of C is, therefore, equal to the magnitude of $\boldsymbol{\omega} \times \mathbf{r}_{C/A}$, and considerations of sense of rotation and direction of velocity show that, if A is fixed,

$$\mathbf{v}_C = \mathbf{v}_{C/A} = \boldsymbol{\omega} \times \mathbf{r}_{C/A}. \qquad\qquad \textbf{6.2-2}$$

We have seen that three points determine the configuration of a rigid body. Pure rotation about a fixed axis, a single degree of freedom motion, corresponds to having two points, A and B, fixed. For this case, an angular velocity vector has been defined. Let us now remove the constraint on B so that it is free to move; that is, consider the motions of a rigid body with a single fixed point, A. This motion is called *rotation about a fixed point*, a name that we shall justify.

Consider the following motion of such a rigid body. Pick any axis in space through the fixed point A and rotate the body about that axis through an angle ϕ_1. This *finite rotation* can be represented by a directed line segment by choosing a positive direction along the axis of rotation as before, and defining

$$\tilde{\phi}_1 = \phi_1 \mathbf{e}_1$$

to be the rotation through angle ϕ_1 about the axis having direction $\mathbf{e}_1$ according to the right-hand rule for rotations. Now rotate the body about some other axis through A, the rotation being given by $\tilde{\phi}_2$, and consider the final position of the body obtained by the successive rotations. Let us call this result the "sum" of the two rotations, and denote it in the usual way by $\tilde{\phi}_1 + \tilde{\phi}_2$, which we shall read as the result of applying rotation $\tilde{\phi}_1$ followed by rotation $\tilde{\phi}_2$ to the rigid body.

These finite rotation quantities, though representable by directed line segments, are not vector quantities. First, they do not compound by the parallelogram law of addition, if we define addition in the natural way that we have. If we construct the diagonal $\tilde{\phi}_3$ of the parallelogram of which $\tilde{\phi}_1$ and $\tilde{\phi}_2$ are sides, then the rotation $\tilde{\phi}_3$ applied to the body does not give the same result as $\tilde{\phi}_1 + \tilde{\phi}_2$, as defined above. This alone is not so bad; it might mean that we have a different type of mathematical beast to deal with, but that an appropriate simple algebra could be devised. Even this possibility is destroyed by the further result that addition as we have defined it is not commutative: $\tilde{\phi}_1 + \tilde{\phi}_2 \neq \tilde{\phi}_2 + \tilde{\phi}_1$. The result is immediately apparent from experience. Apply 90° rotations about orthogonal axes in space to a simple object like a book or a die with one corner held fixed; the final position obtained depends on the order in which the rotations are applied.

Finite rotations are not nice to work with. In advanced dynamical problems, we must deal with them; for instance, large rotations must be considered when problems involving gyroscopic inertial guidance systems are solved. In this first course in dynamics, we need not compute finite rotations. We need only the concept of the rotation about an axis in order to prove the following two theorems about the displacements of the general rigid body. The first of these, due to Euler, is fundamental to our understanding of the kinematics of a rigid body. It justifies the name of rotation for the motion of a rigid body with a fixed point.

Euler's kinematical theorem: Any position of a rigid body with a fixed point is obtainable from any other position of the body by a single rotation about some axis through the fixed point.

To prove Euler's theorem, we use the result that the configuration of a rigid body is fixed by any three points in it. Consider a rigid body with fixed point A (Fig. 6.2-2) and any two positions of the body. Let an arbitrary point be located at B in the initial position and move to C in the final position. We wish to show that the motion from B to C can be obtained by a pure rotation about some axis through A, the same rotation holding for the motion of the whole body by rigidity of the body. We may do this by choosing as the third point which determines the configuration the point that was at C originally and moves to D as B moves to C. This third point lies at the same distance from A as the second point does, and so moves on the same spherical surface.

Since B, C, and D are on the same sphere, the great-circle arcs BC and CD are equal by rigidity of the body. On the sphere with center A and radius $AB = AC = AD$, construct the great circles that bisect the arcs BC and CD orthogonally; these two circles intersect at two points, one of which we choose and call E. Draw the great-circle arcs BE, CE, and DE; by construction, these arcs are equal. The two spherical triangles BCE and CDE are then congruent. Therefore, the angle ϕ between the tangents to BE and CE at E is equal to the angle between the tangents to CE and DE at E. This proves the theorem, for a rotation of magnitude ϕ in the proper sense about AE will bring B to C and C to D and determine the final position of the body from the initial position.

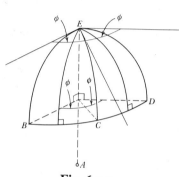

Fig. 6.2-2

We can now remove the fixed-point constraint and prove that any displacement of a rigid body in space can be obtained by a translation followed by a rotation. Consider any two positions of a rigid body in space. Pick any point in the body and move the whole body without rotating it (translation) so that the chosen point is in its final position. Any other position of the body leaving that point in its final position must be obtained, by Euler's theorem, by a single rotation about an axis through that point.

6.3 Small Rotations of a Rigid Body; Angular Velocity

Although large rotations do not combine vectorially, rotations that are small enough in magnitude do combine geometrically to the first order of approximation as though they were vectors. Consider again the fixed-axis rotation problem, Fig. 6.2-1b, for which we were able to define an angular velocity vector and to show that $\mathbf{v} = \boldsymbol{\omega} \times \mathbf{r}$ holds, with positions and velocities measured with respect to a point on the axis of rotation. In time interval Δt, the body undergoes an angular displacement $\Delta\boldsymbol{\phi} = \int_0^{\Delta t} \boldsymbol{\omega}\, dt$, or, approximately, $\Delta\boldsymbol{\phi} = \boldsymbol{\omega}\,\Delta t$ when Δt is small.   For small time intervals, then,

$$\Delta\mathbf{r} = \Delta\boldsymbol{\phi} \times \mathbf{r} \qquad\qquad \textbf{6.3-1}$$

is a close approximation to the true displacement during that time interval.   The approximation is valid to terms of order $(\Delta t)^2$ or $|\Delta\boldsymbol{\phi}|^2$.

Now consider the motion of a body with a fixed point.   By Euler's theorem, any displacement of the body may be obtained by a single rotation about an axis through the fixed point.   Let us consider small displacements only; that is, we consider successive displacements that are so small that the magnitude of the displacement vector is large compared to the square of the magnitude.   Consider an arbitrary point in the body at position $\mathbf{r}$ from the fixed point, and consider the final position of the point after two successive small displacements.   The first displacement can be considered as due to a rotation $\Delta\tilde{\phi}_1$ about some axis (note the change in notation from 6.3-1, since we do not know that such rotations can be combined vectorially as yet); to the degree of approximation given by Eq. 6.3-1, we know that the new position of the point will be

$$\mathbf{r}_1 = \mathbf{r} + \Delta\mathbf{r}_1, \qquad\qquad \textbf{6.3-2a}$$

where

$$\Delta\mathbf{r}_1 = \Delta\tilde{\phi}_1 \times \mathbf{r}, \qquad\qquad \textbf{6.3-2b}$$

the cross product being defined as though the quantity $\Delta\tilde{\phi}_1$ were a vector.   Now consider the effect of a second small displacement, representable by a rotation $\Delta\tilde{\phi}_2$; the final position will be

$$\mathbf{r}_2 = \mathbf{r}_1 + \Delta\tilde{\phi}_2 \times \mathbf{r}_1 = \mathbf{r} + (\Delta\tilde{\phi}_1 + \Delta\tilde{\phi}_2) \times \mathbf{r} + \Delta\tilde{\phi}_2 \times (\Delta\tilde{\phi}_1 \times \mathbf{r}). \qquad \textbf{6.3-3}$$

Here $\Delta\tilde{\phi}_1 + \Delta\tilde{\phi}_2$ is the *parallelogram resultant* of the two directed line segments, and not the finite rotation sum defined in the last section.

Let us find the final position resulting from the application of the rotations in the opposite order:

$$\mathbf{r}_3 = \mathbf{r} + \Delta\tilde{\phi}_2 \times \mathbf{r};$$

$$\mathbf{r}_4 = \mathbf{r}_3 + \Delta\tilde{\phi}_1 \times \mathbf{r}_3 = \mathbf{r} + (\Delta\tilde{\phi}_2 + \Delta\tilde{\phi}_1) \times \mathbf{r} + \Delta\tilde{\phi}_1 \times (\Delta\tilde{\phi}_2 \times \mathbf{r}). \qquad \textbf{6.3-4}$$

From the distributive property of the vector product, $\Delta\tilde{\phi}_2 + \Delta\tilde{\phi}_1$ is again the parallelogram resultant of the two line segments representing the rotations and so is the same in magnitude and direction as the

$\Delta\tilde{\phi}_1 + \Delta\tilde{\phi}_2$ in Eq. 6.3-3. Therefore, the two final positions differ only in the second-order terms:

$$\mathbf{r}_4 - \mathbf{r}_2 = \Delta\tilde{\phi}_1 \times (\Delta\tilde{\phi}_2 \times \mathbf{r}) - \Delta\tilde{\phi}_2 \times (\Delta\tilde{\phi}_1 \times \mathbf{r}).$$

To the degree of approximation we are using, however, these second-order terms may be neglected, involving as they do products of small rotation magnitudes. Then, to the first order of approximation, $\mathbf{r}_2 = \mathbf{r}_4$; there is no difference in the final positions, and the small rotations behave like vectors, combining by the parallelogram law of addition. This means that the rotation $\Delta\tilde{\phi}_3 = \Delta\tilde{\phi}_1 + \Delta\tilde{\phi}_2 = \Delta\tilde{\phi}_2 + \Delta\tilde{\phi}_1$ is the geometric resultant of combining the other two, to within the order of approximation given. We drop the special notation $\Delta\tilde{\phi}$ and use standard vector notation $\Delta\boldsymbol{\phi}$ for small rotations.

The displacement vector during a small rotation is given by 6.3-1; dividing by the time interval Δt and letting Δt approach zero, 6.3-1 becomes

$$\dot{\mathbf{r}} = \boldsymbol{\omega} \times \mathbf{r}, \qquad \text{6.3-5}$$

where

$$\boldsymbol{\omega} = \lim_{\Delta t \to 0} \Delta\boldsymbol{\phi}/\Delta t. \qquad \text{6.3-6}$$

The limiting position of the axis of rotation through the fixed point is called the *instantaneous axis of rotation*; $\boldsymbol{\omega}$ has the direction of the instantaneous axis.

The angular velocity vector $\boldsymbol{\omega}$ of a rigid body with a fixed point has been defined by considering the change in a vector $\mathbf{r}$ emanating from the fixed point. All lines in the body rotate about the instantaneous axis at rate $\boldsymbol{\omega}$, so that $\boldsymbol{\omega}$ is a property of the body as a whole. Let us show that the relative position $\mathbf{p}$ of any two points in the body located at $\mathbf{r}$ and $\mathbf{R}$ from the fixed point changes according to Eq. 6.3-5. The velocities of the two points are, by 6.3-5,

$$\dot{\mathbf{r}} = \boldsymbol{\omega} \times \mathbf{r}, \qquad \dot{\mathbf{R}} = \boldsymbol{\omega} \times \mathbf{R};$$

the relative velocity is

$$\dot{\mathbf{p}} = \dot{\mathbf{r}} - \dot{\mathbf{R}} = \boldsymbol{\omega} \times \mathbf{r} - \boldsymbol{\omega} \times \mathbf{R} = \boldsymbol{\omega} \times (\mathbf{r} - \mathbf{R}),$$

or

$$\dot{\mathbf{p}} = \boldsymbol{\omega} \times \mathbf{p}. \qquad \text{6.3-7}$$

The fixed-point restriction can now be removed. Split the motion of a rigid body into its translational and rotational parts. The small displacement $\Delta\mathbf{r}_B$ of any point B may be considered as the sum of the translational displacement $\Delta\mathbf{r}_A$ of another point A and the rotational displacement due to a small rotation $\Delta\boldsymbol{\phi}$ about an axis through A:

$$\Delta\mathbf{r}_B = \Delta\mathbf{r}_A + \Delta\boldsymbol{\phi} \times \mathbf{r}_{B/A}.$$

Dividing by Δt and passing to the limit, we obtain the general *relative velocity equation* for two points on the same rigid body:

$$\mathbf{v}_B = \dot{\mathbf{r}}_B = \dot{\mathbf{r}}_A + \boldsymbol{\omega} \times \mathbf{r}_{B/A} = \mathbf{v}_A + \boldsymbol{\omega} \times \mathbf{r}_{B/A}, \qquad \textbf{6.3-8}$$

where $\boldsymbol{\omega}$ is the angular velocity of the body. That $\boldsymbol{\omega}$ is a property of the body independent of the choice of the base point A for general rigid-body motion can be proved by the same type of argument that led to 6.3-7. A third point, C, in the body will have velocity

$$\mathbf{v}_C = \mathbf{v}_A + \boldsymbol{\omega} \times \mathbf{r}_{C/A}.$$

The relative velocity of C with respect to B is, by definition,

$$\mathbf{v}_{C/B} = \mathbf{v}_C - \mathbf{v}_B;$$

therefore,

$$\mathbf{v}_{C/B} = \mathbf{v}_C - \mathbf{v}_B = (\mathbf{v}_A + \boldsymbol{\omega} \times \mathbf{r}_{C/A}) - (\mathbf{v}_A + \boldsymbol{\omega} \times \mathbf{r}_{B/A})$$

$$= \boldsymbol{\omega} \times (\mathbf{r}_{C/A} - \mathbf{r}_{B/A}) = \boldsymbol{\omega} \times \mathbf{r}_{C/B},$$

and

$$\mathbf{v}_C = \mathbf{v}_B + \boldsymbol{\omega} \times \mathbf{r}_{C/B}.$$

This is of the same form as Eq. 6.3-8; therefore, the angular velocity does not depend on the choice of the base point for the translational part of the motion.

For general motion, there is no single axis such that, if the points on it were considered to move with the rigid body, the body would be in pure rotation about the axis. The instantaneous axis of rotation only exists for the body with a fixed point. The truth of this assertion is not obvious; but we shall not prove it here. We can find a line parallel to the direction of the angular velocity vector such that the translational velocity of every point on that line is the same and parallel to $\boldsymbol{\omega}$. In plane motion, we could consider a lamina to be moving instantaneously in pure translation or in pure rotation about its instantaneous center of zero velocity. In space, we may consider any instantaneous motion, i.e., rate of change of position or configuration, of a rigid body to be a translation plus a rotation about the direction of the translation* if we choose a proper base point for the

---

* Such a motion is called a *screw displacement*, the corresponding resultant force system mentioned a few lines later being termed a *wrench*. Further discussion of these may be found in many texts; e.g., Synge and Griffith, *Principles of Mechanics*, 3rd ed. (New York: McGraw-Hill Book Co., 1959), p. 255.

translation, but we cannot in general eliminate either translation or rotation. The situation is exactly analogous to that occurring in the study of the resultants of force systems. Coplanar (and some other) force systems may be reduced to a single force or a single couple. The general force system is reducible to at most a force and a couple, and the direction of the couple may be made parallel to the resultant force.

The angular velocity, like any vector, may be represented by the vector sum of components in some coordinate representation:

$$\boldsymbol{\omega} = \omega_x\mathbf{i} + \omega_y\mathbf{j} + \omega_z\mathbf{k}.$$

Like any other vector, $\boldsymbol{\omega}$ may change both in magnitude and direction with time. The first derivative $\dot{\boldsymbol{\omega}}$ is the *angular acceleration vector*. The integral of $\boldsymbol{\omega}$ with respect to time is also a vector and has dimensions of angular displacement. Finding the proper relation between this integral and the true finite rotations is an interesting but difficult question that we shall not pursue.*

Differentiating the relative velocity equation (6.3-8), we obtain the relative acceleration equation for a rigid body:

$$\mathbf{a}_B = \mathbf{a}_A + \dot{\boldsymbol{\omega}} \times \mathbf{r}_{B/A} + \boldsymbol{\omega} \times \dot{\mathbf{r}}_{B/A}.$$

But $\dot{\mathbf{r}}_{B/A}$ is the relative velocity; therefore

$$\mathbf{a}_B = \mathbf{a}_A + \dot{\boldsymbol{\omega}} \times \mathbf{r}_{B/A} + \boldsymbol{\omega} \times (\boldsymbol{\omega} \times \mathbf{r}_{B/A}). \qquad \textbf{6.3-9}$$

The first of the two relative acceleration terms corresponds to the relative tangential acceleration in plane motion; the second, to the relative normal acceleration.

Example 6.3-1

A rigid body with a fixed point O is rotating at a rate of 50 rpm about an axis with direction OP, where P has coordinates (5, 4, −3) *inches measured from O. Find the velocity of point Q, with coordinates* (−3, −2, +6) *inches at this instant.*

Solution: The rate of rotation is $\omega = (50)(2\pi/60) = 5\pi/3$ rad/sec; the unit vector in the positive sense of *OP* is

$$\mathbf{e} = \frac{\mathbf{r}_{P/O}}{|\mathbf{r}_{P/O}|} = \frac{5\mathbf{i} + 4\mathbf{j} - 3\mathbf{k}}{[5^2 + 4^2 + (-3)^2]^{1/2}} = \frac{\sqrt{2}}{2}\mathbf{i} + \frac{2\sqrt{2}}{5}\mathbf{j} - \frac{3\sqrt{2}}{10}\mathbf{k}.$$

---

* The interested student may examine, among other work, a paper in the *Journal of Applied Mechanics*, 25, No. 2 (1958), p. 210.

The angular velocity vector is

$$\boldsymbol{\omega} = \omega\mathbf{e} = \frac{5\pi\sqrt{2}}{6}\mathbf{i} + \frac{2\pi\sqrt{2}}{3}\mathbf{j} - \frac{\pi\sqrt{2}}{2}\mathbf{k} \quad \text{rad/sec.}$$

Since O is fixed, $\mathbf{v}_O = 0$; the relative velocity equation 6.3-8 gives

$$\mathbf{v}_Q = \boldsymbol{\omega} \times \mathbf{r}_{Q/O} = \begin{vmatrix} \mathbf{i} & \mathbf{j} & \mathbf{k} \\ \dfrac{5\pi\sqrt{2}}{6} & \dfrac{2\pi\sqrt{2}}{3} & \dfrac{-\pi\sqrt{2}}{2} \\ -3 & -2 & 6 \end{vmatrix}$$

$$= 3\pi\sqrt{2}\mathbf{i} - \frac{7\pi\sqrt{2}}{2}\mathbf{j} + \frac{\pi\sqrt{2}}{3}\mathbf{k} \quad \text{in/sec.}$$

Example 6.3-2

(a) *If the angular velocity of the previous example is constant for all time, what is the acceleration of Q?*

(b) *If the angular acceleration is $\dot{\boldsymbol{\omega}} = 2\pi^2\mathbf{i} - 5\pi^2\mathbf{j} + 3\pi^2\mathbf{k}$ rad/sec^2, what is the acceleration of Q when $\boldsymbol{\omega}$ has the value of the last example?*

(c) *If O is not fixed but has acceleration $(\pi^2/18)(505\mathbf{i} + 460\mathbf{j} + 537\mathbf{k})$ in/sec^2, what is the acceleration of Q if $\dot{\boldsymbol{\omega}}$ is as in part (b)?*

Solution:

(a) $\mathbf{a}_Q = \mathbf{a}_O + \dot{\boldsymbol{\omega}} \times \mathbf{r}_{Q/O} + \boldsymbol{\omega} \times (\boldsymbol{\omega} \times \mathbf{r}_{Q/O})$; since $\mathbf{a}_O = \dot{\boldsymbol{\omega}} = 0$,

$$\mathbf{a}_Q = \mathbf{a}_{Q/O} = \boldsymbol{\omega} \times (\boldsymbol{\omega} \times \mathbf{r}_{Q/O}) = \boldsymbol{\omega} \times \mathbf{v}_{Q/O} = \begin{vmatrix} \mathbf{i} & \mathbf{j} & \mathbf{k} \\ \dfrac{5\pi\sqrt{2}}{6} & \dfrac{2\pi\sqrt{2}}{3} & \dfrac{-\pi\sqrt{2}}{2} \\ 3\pi\sqrt{2} & \dfrac{-7\pi\sqrt{2}}{2} & \dfrac{\pi\sqrt{2}}{3} \end{vmatrix}$$

$$= \left(\frac{\pi\sqrt{2}}{6}\right)^2 \begin{vmatrix} \mathbf{i} & \mathbf{j} & \mathbf{k} \\ 5 & 4 & -3 \\ 18 & -21 & 2 \end{vmatrix} = \frac{\pi^2}{18}[-55\mathbf{i} - 64\mathbf{j} - 177\mathbf{k}] \quad \text{in/sec}^2.$$

(b) $\mathbf{a}_Q = \mathbf{a}_{Q/O} = \dot{\boldsymbol{\omega}} \times \mathbf{r}_{Q/O} + \boldsymbol{\omega} \times (\boldsymbol{\omega} \times \mathbf{r}_{Q/O})$

$$= \begin{vmatrix} \mathbf{i} & \mathbf{j} & \mathbf{k} \\ 2\pi^2 & -5\pi^2 & 3\pi^2 \\ -3 & -2 & 6 \end{vmatrix} + \boldsymbol{\omega} \times (\boldsymbol{\omega} \times \mathbf{r}_{Q/O})$$

$$= -24\pi^2\mathbf{i} - 21\pi^2\mathbf{j} - 19\pi^2\mathbf{k} + \boldsymbol{\omega} \times (\boldsymbol{\omega} \times \mathbf{r}_{Q/O})$$

$$= -\frac{\pi^2}{18}[487\mathbf{i} + 442\mathbf{j} + 519\mathbf{k}] \quad \text{in/sec}^2.$$

(c) $\mathbf{a}_Q = \mathbf{a}_O + \mathbf{a}_{Q/O}$

$$= (\pi^2/18)[(505-487)\mathbf{i} + (460-442)\mathbf{j} + (537-519)\mathbf{k}]$$

$$= \pi^2[\mathbf{i} + \mathbf{j} + \mathbf{k}] \quad \text{in/sec}^2.$$

Example 6.3-3

Could the rigid body of the previous two examples be given an angular acceleration $\dot{\boldsymbol{\omega}} = \dot{\omega}_x\mathbf{i} + \dot{\omega}_y\mathbf{j} + \dot{\omega}_z\mathbf{k}$ so that point Q would have the same acceleration that it has when $\dot{\boldsymbol{\omega}} = \mathbf{0}$, as in part (a) of the previous problem?

Solution: The answer is yes. If Q is to have the same acceleration as in part (a) of Example 6.3-2, all we need do is to make $\dot{\boldsymbol{\omega}} \times \mathbf{r}_{Q/O}$ vanish. Any angular acceleration vector parallel to $\mathbf{r}_{Q/O}$ will cause that term to vanish; i.e.,

$$\dot{\boldsymbol{\omega}} = \pm |\dot{\boldsymbol{\omega}}| \frac{\mathbf{r}_{Q/O}}{|\mathbf{r}_{Q/O}|} = \pm |\dot{\boldsymbol{\omega}}| \left[-\frac{3}{7}\mathbf{i} - \frac{2}{7}\mathbf{j} + \frac{6}{7}\mathbf{k} \right] \quad \text{rad/sec}^2.$$

This result is different from plane motion, where any non-zero angular acceleration will of course produce a non-zero relative tangential acceleration term, since the vector $\dot{\boldsymbol{\omega}} = \alpha\mathbf{k}$ is perpendicular to all position vectors in the plane.

6.4 Rotating Coordinates; General Relative Motion Equations

The relative motion of two points was discussed in Section 4.2 under the restriction that all coordinate systems used for representation of vectors have fixed directions relative to one another. This restriction can be removed now that we have introduced the angular velocity vector of a rigid body.

Before treating relative motion of two points that are not rigidly connected, we re-examine the relative motion equations for a rigid body in cartesian coordinate representations. Eliminate the translational term in the relative motion equations by taking a rigid body with fixed point O, and choose a fixed cartesian coordinate system with origin O. In order to eliminate the rather inconvenient primed coordinates (x', y', z') of 4.2, we shall call the fixed axes (X, Y, Z) and the fixed unit vectors $(\mathbf{I}, \mathbf{J}, \mathbf{K})$. Let a typical point in the body have position $\mathbf{r}$ and velocity $\dot{\mathbf{r}}$ relative to O; $\mathbf{r}$ and $\dot{\mathbf{r}}$ are given by:

$$\mathbf{r} = X\mathbf{I} + Y\mathbf{J} + Z\mathbf{K}, \qquad \dot{\mathbf{r}} = \frac{d\mathbf{r}}{dt} = \dot{X}\mathbf{I} + \dot{Y}\mathbf{J} + \dot{Z}\mathbf{K}. \qquad \textbf{6.4-1}$$

From Eq. 6.3-6 for a rigid body with a fixed point, we also know that $\dot{\mathbf{r}}$ is given by $\boldsymbol{\omega} \times \mathbf{r}$. Suppose that $\boldsymbol{\omega}$ has representation

$$\boldsymbol{\omega} = \Omega_X\mathbf{I} + \Omega_Y\mathbf{J} + \Omega_Z\mathbf{K} \qquad \textbf{6.4-2}$$

in the fixed coordinates; then, combining this with the first of 6.4-1,

$$\boldsymbol{\omega} \times \mathbf{r} = [\Omega_Y Z - \Omega_Z Y]\mathbf{I} + [\Omega_Z X - \Omega_X Z]\mathbf{J} + [\Omega_X Y - \Omega_Y X]\mathbf{K}. \quad \textbf{6.4-3}$$

Setting 6.4-3 equal to the second of 6.4-1, we obtain the scalar differential equations equivalent to $\dot{\mathbf{r}} = \boldsymbol{\omega} \times \mathbf{r}$ referred to fixed coordinates (compare with Exercises 6.3-6 and 6.3-7):

$$v_X = \dot{X} = \Omega_Y Z - \Omega_Z Y,$$

$$v_Y = \dot{Y} = \Omega_Z X - \Omega_X Z, \qquad\qquad \textbf{6.4-4}$$

$$v_Z = \dot{Z} = \Omega_X Y - \Omega_Y X.$$

Suppose we introduce a second coordinate system (x, y, z) at O with unit vectors $(\mathbf{i}, \mathbf{j}, \mathbf{k})$, not fixed in direction relative to $(\mathbf{I}, \mathbf{J}, \mathbf{K})$. Let $\mathbf{r}$ and $\boldsymbol{\omega}$ have representation

$$\mathbf{r} = x\mathbf{i} + y\mathbf{j} + z\mathbf{k},$$

$$\boldsymbol{\omega} = \omega_x \mathbf{i} + \omega_y \mathbf{j} + \omega_z \mathbf{k}, \qquad\qquad \textbf{6.4-5}$$

in these coordinates. The velocity $\mathbf{v} = d\mathbf{r}/dt$ is given (Eq. 4.2-15) by

$$\mathbf{v} = \frac{d\mathbf{r}}{dt} = \frac{\delta\mathbf{r}}{\delta t} + x\frac{d\mathbf{i}}{dt} + y\frac{d\mathbf{j}}{dt} + z\frac{d\mathbf{k}}{dt}, \qquad \textbf{6.4-6}$$

where $\delta\mathbf{r}/\delta t$ is the *frame derivative* in the (x, y, z) coordinates:

$$\frac{\delta\mathbf{r}}{\delta t} = \dot{x}\mathbf{i} + \dot{y}\mathbf{j} + \dot{z}\mathbf{k}. \qquad\qquad \textbf{6.4-7}$$

But $\mathbf{v} = \boldsymbol{\omega} \times \mathbf{r}$ is a vector relation valid in any coordinate system, and the vector product of $\boldsymbol{\omega}$ into $\mathbf{r}$ from 6.4-5 has the form of 6.4-3:

$$\boldsymbol{\omega} \times \mathbf{r} = (\omega_y z - \omega_z y)\mathbf{i} + (\omega_z x - \omega_x z)\mathbf{j} + (\omega_x y - \omega_y x)\mathbf{k}. \quad \textbf{6.4-8}$$

To derive scalar equivalents such as 6.4-4 in the moving coordinates by equating 6.4-6 and 6.4-8, we must find the derivatives of the unit vectors $\mathbf{i}$, $\mathbf{j}$, and $\mathbf{k}$ relative to the fixed axes. But this, in principle, we know how to do: the derivative of a vector $\mathbf{A}$ of constant magnitude is $\boldsymbol{\omega}' \times \mathbf{A}$, where $\boldsymbol{\omega}'$ is an appropriate angular velocity vector. The dimensionless unit vector $\mathbf{i}$ may also be thought of as a dimensional position vector by multiplying it by a scalar unit length; it is then the position vector of a point always one unit of length from O and so rigidly attached to O. This point may not be in the original rigid body we started with, or even moving with it; but we see now that, if we choose an (x, y, z) coordinate system fixed in the rigid body and rotating with it, every point in the body always has the same position vector referred to that coordinate system. For instance, consider a circular cylinder of length $2l$ and radius r (Fig. 6.4-1) pivoted at the center of one end; if the (x, y, z) axes shown are fixed in the body and rotate with it, the point A, shown always has position vector $2l\mathbf{i} + r\mathbf{j}$. Such axes are called *body-fixed axes*; a set like (X, Y, Z) are *space-fixed axes*.

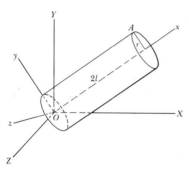

Fig. 6.4-1

For space axes, $\mathbf{I}$, $\mathbf{J}$, and $\mathbf{K}$ are constant vectors and the coordinates (X, Y, Z) of a point change with time. For axes fixed in a rigid body, the coordinates (x, y, z) of the point are always the same, but the unit vectors $(\mathbf{i}, \mathbf{j}, \mathbf{k})$ change with time. For body axes, we have

$$\dot{x} = \dot{y} = \dot{z} = 0 \quad \text{and hence} \quad \frac{\delta \mathbf{r}}{\delta t} = 0;$$

6.4-9

while, since $(\mathbf{i}, \mathbf{j}, \mathbf{k})$ rotate with the angular velocity $\boldsymbol{\omega}$ of the body,

$$\frac{d\mathbf{i}}{dt} = \boldsymbol{\omega} \times \mathbf{i}, \qquad \frac{d\mathbf{j}}{dt} = \boldsymbol{\omega} \times \mathbf{j}, \qquad \frac{d\mathbf{k}}{dt} = \boldsymbol{\omega} \times \mathbf{k}. \qquad \textbf{6.4-10}$$

Substituting these results in Eq. 6.4-6, we have

$$\mathbf{v} = \frac{d\mathbf{r}}{dt} = x(\boldsymbol{\omega} \times \mathbf{i}) + y(\boldsymbol{\omega} \times \mathbf{j}) + z(\boldsymbol{\omega} \times \mathbf{k})$$

$$= \boldsymbol{\omega} \times (x\mathbf{i} + y\mathbf{j} + z\mathbf{k}) = \boldsymbol{\omega} \times \mathbf{r}, \qquad \textbf{6.4-11}$$

a not unexpected result. This states, in a sense, that the velocity components (v_x, v_y, v_z) obtained by projecting the absolute velocity vector on each of the body axes are naturally given by the components of $\boldsymbol{\omega} \times \mathbf{r}$ referred to those axes. The scalar equations referred to body axes are of the same form as the equations 6.4-4:

$$v_x = \omega_y z - \omega_z y,$$

$$v_y = \omega_z x - \omega_x z, \qquad \textbf{6.4-12}$$

$$v_z = \omega_x y - \omega_y x.$$

Here (x, y, z) and $(\omega_x, \omega_y, \omega_z)$ are the scalar components of $\mathbf{r}$ and $\boldsymbol{\omega}$ obtained by projection on the body axes. Since $\mathbf{r}$ is referred to body axes, the numbers (x, y, z) are constants, and the scalar components (v_x, v_y, v_z) are not the derivatives of the scalars (x, y, z) respectively.

The acceleration components referred to body axes are found from $\mathbf{a} = \dot{\boldsymbol{\omega}} \times \mathbf{r} + \boldsymbol{\omega} \times (\boldsymbol{\omega} \times \mathbf{r})$ by using the body-axes representations of $\mathbf{r}$, $\boldsymbol{\omega}$, and $\dot{\boldsymbol{\omega}}$. The last term is computed from 6.4-5 and 6.4-8. We find, when we compute $\dot{\boldsymbol{\omega}}$ with respect to the body axes, that (compare with 6.4-6 and 6.4-11)

$$\frac{d\boldsymbol{\omega}}{dt} = \frac{\delta\boldsymbol{\omega}}{\delta t} + \omega_x \frac{d\mathbf{i}}{dt} + \omega_y \frac{d\mathbf{j}}{dt} + \omega_z \frac{d\mathbf{k}}{dt} = \frac{\delta\boldsymbol{\omega}}{\delta t} + \boldsymbol{\omega} \times \boldsymbol{\omega},$$

or

$$\frac{d\boldsymbol{\omega}}{dt} = \frac{\delta\boldsymbol{\omega}}{\delta t} = \dot{\omega}_x\mathbf{i} + \dot{\omega}_y\mathbf{j} + \dot{\omega}_z\mathbf{k}. \qquad \textbf{6.4-13}$$

This is a most important result. Let us examine its significance. First, compute the time rate of change of the angular velocity vector in the ordinary "absolute" way; i.e., give $\boldsymbol{\omega}(t)$ a representation in some set of space-fixed axes and compute its derivative $d\boldsymbol{\omega}/dt$ relative to these axes by computing the derivatives of the scalar components of $\boldsymbol{\omega}$. The resulting angular acceleration is a vector quantity $\dot{\boldsymbol{\omega}}$ giving the magnitude and direction of the instantaneous rate of change in the vectorial rate of rotation of the body. The scalar component of $\dot{\boldsymbol{\omega}}$ in any given direction may now be found in the usual way by orthogonal projection. Suppose we project $\dot{\boldsymbol{\omega}}$ on a direction instantaneously coinciding with a body-fixed direction, say the x-axis, thus obtaining the scalar $\dot{\boldsymbol{\omega}} \cdot \mathbf{i}$. Given $\mathbf{i}$ in terms of $(\mathbf{I}, \mathbf{J}, \mathbf{K})$, we can carry out the computation of $\dot{\boldsymbol{\omega}} \cdot \mathbf{i}$. But now suppose that our original computation of the absolute angular acceleration is not possible directly because we are not given $\boldsymbol{\omega}(t)$ relative to space axes. Suppose instead that the body-fixed axes representation of $\boldsymbol{\omega}$ is given, as it is so naturally given in many problems. How can we compute $\dot{\boldsymbol{\omega}}$ or $\dot{\boldsymbol{\omega}} \cdot \mathbf{i}$? The result embodied in Eq. 6.4-13 tells us that, in fact, $\dot{\boldsymbol{\omega}} = \delta\boldsymbol{\omega}/\delta t$ and that $\dot{\boldsymbol{\omega}} \cdot \mathbf{i} = \dot{\omega}_x$. The scalar component of the absolute angular acceleration in the x-direction—and indeed in any body-fixed direction—may be computed by the ordinary differentiation of the scalar component of $\boldsymbol{\omega}$ in that direction, just as though that body-fixed direction were space-fixed as well.

The student may verify that the mathematical form of $\dot{\boldsymbol{\omega}} \times \mathbf{r} + \boldsymbol{\omega} \times (\boldsymbol{\omega} \times \mathbf{r})$ is exactly the same in both sets of coordinates. Of course, the difference between them lies in the interpretation of the symbols and is the same as that between 6.4-4 and 6.4-12. In one case, (X, Y, Z) change, with $(a_X, a_Y, a_Z) = (\ddot{X}, \ddot{Y}, \ddot{Z})$, while in the other

(x, y, z) are constants and (a_x, a_y, a_z) are not the second derivatives of the point coordinates (x, y, z).

The fixed-point restriction may be removed now. For the general rigid body, let P be any point in the body and O be the origin of space axes. The velocity of any other point, Q, in the body with respect to the space axes at O is (Eq. 6.3-8)

$$\mathbf{v}_Q = \mathbf{v}_P + \boldsymbol{\omega} \times \mathbf{r}_{Q/P}.$$

The space axes may be used to compute $\mathbf{v}_P$; body axes based at P, to compute $\boldsymbol{\omega} \times \mathbf{r}_{Q/P}$. To write scalar versions of the full equation, we must of course know how to express all terms in the same coordinates. The point is that intermediate steps in the computation may be performed more easily in some cases if rotating body axes are used.

With the aid of the foregoing ideas, a fundamental result relating the frame derivatives of any vector function $\mathbf{A}(t)$ described in two coordinate systems that are in relative rotation may be obtained. Consider any vector function $\mathbf{A}(t)$ given in two different coordinate systems (X, Y, Z) and (x, y, z):

$$\mathbf{A} = A_X\mathbf{I} + A_Y\mathbf{J} + A_Z\mathbf{K} = A_x\mathbf{i} + A_y\mathbf{j} + A_z\mathbf{k}. \qquad \textbf{6.4-14}$$

The derivative $\dot{\mathbf{A}}$ of $\mathbf{A}$ we suppose to be given by the frame derivative in (X, Y, Z):

$$\dot{\mathbf{A}} = \frac{d\mathbf{A}}{dt} = \dot{A}_X\mathbf{I} + \dot{A}_Y\mathbf{J} + \dot{A}_Z\mathbf{K}. \qquad \textbf{6.4-15}$$

Differentiating the second representation, we have as in 4.2-15 or 6.4-6,

$$\dot{\mathbf{A}} = \frac{\delta\mathbf{A}}{\delta t} + A_x\dot{\mathbf{i}} + A_y\dot{\mathbf{j}} + A_z\dot{\mathbf{k}}. \qquad \textbf{6.4-16}$$

The changing unit vectors $(\mathbf{i}, \mathbf{j}, \mathbf{k})$ or the axes (x, y, z) may themselves be treated as a rigid body—as an abstraction of three perpendicular wires moving around in space. A rotating rigid body has an angular velocity $\boldsymbol{\omega}$. We introduce the angular velocity of one coordinate system with respect to another—of (x, y, z) relative to (X, Y, Z). Then the derivatives of the unit vectors $(\mathbf{i}, \mathbf{j}, \mathbf{k})$ in the fixed system are given by Eqs. 6.4-10, where $\boldsymbol{\omega}$ is now the *angular velocity of the coordinate axes*. The last three terms in 6.4-16 are then equal to $\boldsymbol{\omega} \times \mathbf{A}$; the proof is the same as that for 6.4-11.

We have shown the following fundamental result:

The frame derivatives of a vector in two coordinate systems are equal save for a term proportionate to the vector and to the rate of rotation of one system with respect to the other:

$$\left(\frac{d\mathbf{A}}{dt}\right)_{XYZ} \equiv \frac{d\mathbf{A}}{dt} = \frac{\delta\mathbf{A}}{\delta t} + \boldsymbol{\omega} \times \mathbf{A} \equiv \left(\frac{d\mathbf{A}}{dt}\right)_{xyz} + \boldsymbol{\omega} \times \mathbf{A} \qquad \textbf{6.4-17}$$

where $\boldsymbol{\omega}$ is the angular velocity of (xyz) relative to (XYZ). Equation 6.4-17 is all-important in later analysis. Notice that it makes no difference which system is considered as fixed and which as rotating from a purely kinematical point of view:

$$\frac{\delta\mathbf{A}}{\delta t} = \frac{d\mathbf{A}}{dt} - \boldsymbol{\omega} \times \mathbf{A} = \frac{d\mathbf{A}}{dt} + (-\boldsymbol{\omega}) \times \mathbf{A},$$

$-\boldsymbol{\omega}$ being the angular velocity of (XYZ) relative to (xyz). Only through the newtonian laws of motion are the special inertial frames of reference singled out as the appropriate "fixed" coordinates for dynamical applications.

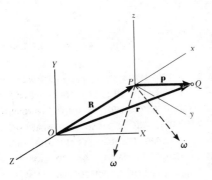

Fig. 6.4-2

We return now to the problem of the relative motion of any two points in space considered in Section 4.2. Suppose two moving points, P and Q, have positions $\mathbf{R}$ and $\mathbf{r}$ respectively with respect to a fixed point O, with the relative position vector of Q with respect to P denoted by $\mathbf{p}$ (Fig. 6.4-2). The relative motion equations are, of course, $\mathbf{r} = \mathbf{R} + \mathbf{p}$, $\dot{\mathbf{r}} = \dot{\mathbf{R}} + \dot{\mathbf{p}}$, $\ddot{\mathbf{r}} = \ddot{\mathbf{R}} + \ddot{\mathbf{p}}$. A fixed (X, Y, Z) coordinate system is based on O; a moving (x, y, z) system with angular velocity $\boldsymbol{\omega}$ and angular acceleration $\dot{\boldsymbol{\omega}}$ is based on P. We suppose $\mathbf{R}$, $\dot{\mathbf{R}}$, $\ddot{\mathbf{R}}$ to be computed in one of the systems, usually the fixed.

The relative position vector **p** is represented in the moving co-ordinates; let us compute its derivatives.   Apply 6.4-17 to **p**:

$$\dot{\mathbf{p}} = \frac{d\mathbf{p}}{dt} = \frac{\delta\mathbf{p}}{\delta t} + \boldsymbol{\omega} \times \mathbf{p}. \qquad\qquad \textbf{6.4-18}$$

Carrying out the computation on the right side totally in the moving coordinates, we have a representation of $\dot{\mathbf{p}}$ in moving coordinates. Computing its derivative, we find the relative acceleration:

$$\frac{d^2\mathbf{p}}{dt^2} = \frac{d\dot{\mathbf{p}}}{dt} = \frac{\delta\dot{\mathbf{p}}}{\delta t} + \boldsymbol{\omega} \times \dot{\mathbf{p}}$$

$$= \frac{\delta^2\mathbf{p}}{\delta t^2} + \frac{\delta}{\delta t}(\boldsymbol{\omega} \times \mathbf{p}) + \boldsymbol{\omega} \times \left(\frac{\delta\mathbf{p}}{\delta t} + \boldsymbol{\omega} \times \mathbf{p}\right)$$

$$= \frac{\delta^2\mathbf{p}}{\delta t^2} + \frac{\delta\boldsymbol{\omega}}{\delta t} \times \mathbf{p} + 2\boldsymbol{\omega} \times \frac{\delta\mathbf{p}}{\delta t} + \boldsymbol{\omega} \times (\boldsymbol{\omega} \times \mathbf{p}).$$

Here $\delta^2\mathbf{p}/\delta t^2$ is the second frame derivative of Section 4.2; by 6.4-13, $\delta\boldsymbol{\omega}/\delta t = d\boldsymbol{\omega}/dt = \dot{\boldsymbol{\omega}}$, the angular acceleration vector of the rotating coordinate system.   We write

$$\frac{d^2\mathbf{p}}{dt^2} = \frac{\delta^2\mathbf{p}}{\delta t^2} + 2\boldsymbol{\omega} \times \frac{\delta\mathbf{p}}{\delta t} + \dot{\boldsymbol{\omega}} \times \mathbf{p} + \boldsymbol{\omega} \times (\boldsymbol{\omega} \times \mathbf{p}). \qquad \textbf{6.4-19}$$

The relative motion terms of 6.4-18, 19 are of two types: the terms that would be present if the two points were rigidly connected *and the coordinate system were rotating with the angular velocity of the rigid body*, and the terms that express the nonrigidity of the system. The italicized phrase is important.   As we shall see in the treatment of the precessing symmetric gyro, we do not have to choose co-ordinates fixed in the rigid body and rotating with it; sometimes it is convenient to choose coordinates rotating with one angular velocity $\boldsymbol{\omega}'$, while the body itself has a different $\boldsymbol{\omega}$.   Referred to such co-ordinates, even the rigid-body relative velocity equation has a frame-derivative term appearing in it.

There is an alternative interpretation of the relations.   Suppose that an observer moves with P and measures the motion of Q with respect to the (x, y, z) axes.   If the observer believes his axes are fixed, the velocity and acceleration he computes are just the velocity and acceleration relative to the frame: $\delta\mathbf{p}/\delta t$ and $\delta^2\mathbf{p}/\delta t^2$.   At the same time, an observer at O, from measurement of the motion of P and Q, finds the relative velocity and acceleration to be $d\mathbf{p}/dt$ and $d^2\mathbf{p}/dt^2$. To correlate the two sets of measurements, correction terms must be added. These terms are of two types: rigid-body terms $\boldsymbol{\omega} \times \mathbf{p}$ and $\dot{\boldsymbol{\omega}} \times \mathbf{p} + \boldsymbol{\omega} \times (\boldsymbol{\omega} \times \mathbf{p})$, accounting for the relative rotation of the two coordinate frames, and an additional term in the relative acceleration that occurs only if the coordinate systems do rotate with respect to one another and if Q is not rigidly attached to the xyz-frame. This additional term is the *Coriolis acceleration*

$$2\boldsymbol{\omega} \times \frac{\delta \mathbf{p}}{\delta t}.$$

The full relative motion equations are

$$\mathbf{r} = \mathbf{R} + \mathbf{p},$$

$$\frac{d\mathbf{r}}{dt} = \frac{d\mathbf{R}}{dt} + \frac{\delta \mathbf{p}}{\delta t} + \boldsymbol{\omega} \times \mathbf{p}, \qquad\qquad \textbf{6.4-20}$$

$$\frac{d^2\mathbf{r}}{dt^2} = \frac{d^2\mathbf{R}}{dt^2} + \frac{\delta^2 \mathbf{p}}{\delta t^2} + \dot{\boldsymbol{\omega}} \times \mathbf{p} + \boldsymbol{\omega} \times (\boldsymbol{\omega} \times \mathbf{p}) + 2\boldsymbol{\omega} \times \frac{\delta \mathbf{p}}{\delta t}.$$

Only by careful and repeated application will the student gain a feeling for the significance of Eqs. 6.4-20. We shall give a number of examples of their use, starting with plane-motion problems and building to full three-dimensional applications. The most important step in these applications is choosing the auxiliary rotating frame and assigning the proper angular velocity to that frame. Doing so in the easiest or most elegant way requires experience—which may be gained only by working problems.

Before looking at the examples, however, let us consider the equation of motion for a particle of mass m subject to resultant force $\mathbf{F}$. Referring to Fig. 6.4-2, suppose Q is the position of the particle and $OXYZ$ is an inertial frame. Then

$$\mathbf{F} = m\ddot{\mathbf{r}} = m\left(\ddot{\mathbf{R}} + \frac{\delta^2 \mathbf{p}}{\delta t^2} + \dot{\boldsymbol{\omega}} \times \mathbf{p} + \boldsymbol{\omega} \times (\boldsymbol{\omega} \times \mathbf{p}) + 2\boldsymbol{\omega} \times \frac{\delta \mathbf{p}}{\delta t}\right) \quad \textbf{6.4-21}$$

is the equation of motion. We may now amplify the statement made in Chapter IV about the validity of Newton's laws in coordinate systems that translate and rotate with respect to an inertial frame. In that chapter, we showed that $\mathbf{F} = m\mathbf{a}$ when $\mathbf{a}$ was measured in a frame based on P only if P was not accelerating with respect to O; i.e., only if $\ddot{\mathbf{R}} = \mathbf{0}$. It was further stated that such a frame had to be translating with respect to the original frame. We now see why; the acceleration measured in a frame based on P is $\delta^2\mathbf{p}/\delta t^2$, and

$$\mathbf{F} = m\frac{\delta^2 \mathbf{p}}{\delta t^2} \qquad\qquad \textbf{6.4-22}$$

always only if $\ddot{\mathbf{R}} = \mathbf{0}$ *and* $\boldsymbol{\omega} = \dot{\boldsymbol{\omega}} = \mathbf{0}$. In general, the law of motion in a rotating coordinate system is not 6.4-22, but

$$\mathbf{F} - m\ddot{\mathbf{R}} - 2m\boldsymbol{\omega} \times \frac{\delta \mathbf{p}}{\delta t} - m\dot{\boldsymbol{\omega}} \times \mathbf{p} - m\boldsymbol{\omega} \times (\boldsymbol{\omega} \times \mathbf{p}) = m \frac{\delta^2 \mathbf{p}}{\delta t^2}. \quad \textbf{6.4-23}$$

A procedure often used is based on this equation. One might say that $\mathbf{F} = m\mathbf{a}$ holds in any coordinate system provided the term "force" is redefined to include the so-called "reversed effective forces" or "inertia forces." In particular, $-m\boldsymbol{\omega} \times (\boldsymbol{\omega} \times \mathbf{p})$ is called "centrifugal force" and $-2m\boldsymbol{\omega} \times \delta \mathbf{p}/\delta t$, the "Coriolis force." By transferring the right-hand side of 6.4-23 to the left, and treating the resulting expression as another inertia force, we find the mathe-

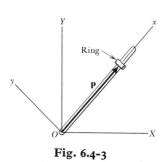

Fig. 6.4-3

matical form of *d'Alembert's principle* for a particle: a particle is in equilibrium in any coordinate system if the resultant force is considered to be the sum of the active ($\mathbf{F}$) and inertia forces. This principle and its counterpart for systems is often useful, particularly for extending the moment of momentum equations. We shall not employ it in our applications; the student should work with the direct equations as stated in Chapter IV and in the next sections of this chapter. Some familiarity with d'Alembert's principle and its use is, however, necessary for the understanding of much of engineering literature.

The student should attempt to rework the first three examples of Section 4.2 in appropriate rotating coordinates after reading the examples of this section.

Example 6.4-1

A rigid 10-ft rod rotates in a plane about one end at a constant counter-clockwise angular velocity of 4 rad/sec. A ring slides out along the rod at a constant speed of 3 ft/sec relative to the rod. Find the velocity and acceleration of the ring as it leaves the free end of the rod (Fig. 6.4-3).

Solution: Take x, y-axes fixed in the rod and rotating with it with respect to some axes X, Y fixed in the plane. The Z- and z-axes are the same. We have:

$$\boldsymbol{\omega} = 4\mathbf{k} = 4\,\mathbf{K} \text{ rad/sec}, \qquad \dot{\boldsymbol{\omega}} = \mathbf{0}, \qquad \mathbf{R} = \dot{\mathbf{R}} = \ddot{\mathbf{R}} = \mathbf{0},$$

$$\mathbf{r} = \mathbf{p} = x\mathbf{i} \text{ ft}; \qquad \delta \mathbf{p}/\delta t = \dot{x}\mathbf{i} = 3\mathbf{i} \text{ ft/sec}; \qquad \delta^2 \mathbf{p}/\delta t^2 = \mathbf{0} \text{ ft/sec}^2.$$

We are interested in the particular instant when $x = 10$ ft.   Then

$$\mathbf{r} = \mathbf{p} = 10\mathbf{i} \text{ ft,}$$

$$\dot{\mathbf{r}} = \frac{\delta \mathbf{p}}{\delta t} + \boldsymbol{\omega} \times \mathbf{p} = 3\mathbf{i} + (4\mathbf{k} \times 10\mathbf{i}) = 3\mathbf{i} + 40\mathbf{j} \text{ ft/sec,}$$

$$\ddot{\mathbf{r}} = \boldsymbol{\omega} \times (\boldsymbol{\omega} \times \mathbf{p}) + 2\boldsymbol{\omega} \times \frac{\delta \mathbf{p}}{\delta t} = (4\mathbf{k} \times 40\mathbf{j}) + (8\mathbf{k} \times 3\mathbf{i}) = -160\mathbf{i} + 24\mathbf{j} \text{ ft/sec}^2.$$

Example 6.4-2

A disk rotates about its center at constant angular velocity ω.   A block slides in a radial groove, its distance from the center of the disk being given by $a + b \cos \Omega t$.   Find its velocity and acceleration at any time t (Fig. 6.4-4).

Solution: Take x, y-axes fixed in the disk and rotating with it, with x along the groove.   We find

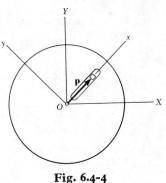

$$\mathbf{R} = \dot{\mathbf{R}} = \ddot{\mathbf{R}} = 0;$$

$$\boldsymbol{\omega} = \omega\mathbf{k}, \qquad \dot{\boldsymbol{\omega}} = 0;$$

$$\mathbf{p} = (a + b \cos \Omega t)\mathbf{i},$$

$$\frac{\delta \mathbf{p}}{\delta t} = -b\Omega \sin \Omega t\mathbf{i},$$

$$\frac{\delta^2 \mathbf{p}}{\delta t^2} = -b\Omega^2 \cos \Omega t\mathbf{i}.$$

Fig. 6.4-4

Then

$$\mathbf{r} = \mathbf{R} + \mathbf{p} = \mathbf{p} = (a + b \cos \Omega t)\mathbf{i};$$

$$\dot{\mathbf{r}} = \dot{\mathbf{R}} + \dot{\mathbf{p}} = \frac{\delta \mathbf{p}}{\delta t} + \boldsymbol{\omega} \times \mathbf{p}$$

$$= -b\Omega \sin \Omega t\mathbf{i} + \omega(a + b \cos \Omega t)\mathbf{j};$$

$$\ddot{\mathbf{r}} = \ddot{\mathbf{R}} + \ddot{\mathbf{p}} = \frac{\delta^2 \mathbf{p}}{\delta t^2} + \boldsymbol{\omega} \times (\boldsymbol{\omega} \times \mathbf{p}) + 2\boldsymbol{\omega} \times \frac{\delta \mathbf{p}}{\delta t}$$

$$= -b\Omega^2 \cos \Omega t\mathbf{i} - \omega^2(a + b \cos \Omega t)\mathbf{i} - 2b\Omega\omega \sin \Omega t\mathbf{j}$$

$$= -[a\omega^2 + b(\omega^2 + \Omega^2) \cos \Omega t]\mathbf{i} - 2b\omega\Omega \sin \Omega t\mathbf{j}.$$

Example 6.4-3

A disk of radius R rotating at constant speed has a rod welded rigidly to it as shown, Fig. 6.4-5.   A ring slides on the rod in the direction AB at constant speed v_0 relative to the rod. Find the magnitude of its acceleration as it passes point A.

Solution: Choose axes with origin at A, fixed in the disk and rotating with it (Fig. 6.4-5b), such that x is tangent to the disk and y is along the radius OA. The general position vectors $\mathbf{R}$, $\mathbf{r}$, and $\mathbf{p}$ are shown. We have at any time that

$$\boldsymbol{\omega} = \omega\mathbf{k}, \qquad \dot{\boldsymbol{\omega}} = \mathbf{0};$$

$$\mathbf{R} = R\mathbf{j}, \qquad \dot{\mathbf{R}} = R\dot{\mathbf{j}} = R(\boldsymbol{\omega}\times\mathbf{j}) = \boldsymbol{\omega}\times\mathbf{R} = -R\omega\mathbf{i},$$

$$\ddot{\mathbf{R}} = \dot{\boldsymbol{\omega}}\times\mathbf{R}+\boldsymbol{\omega}\times(\boldsymbol{\omega}\times\mathbf{R}) = -R\omega^2\mathbf{j};$$

$$\frac{\delta\mathbf{p}}{\delta t} = v_0(\sin\psi\mathbf{i}-\cos\psi\mathbf{j});$$

$$\frac{\delta^2\mathbf{p}}{\delta t^2} = \mathbf{0};$$

and, at the instant we are considering, $\mathbf{p}=\mathbf{0}$. Therefore,

$$\mathbf{r} = \mathbf{R} = R\mathbf{j};$$

$$\dot{\mathbf{r}} = \dot{\mathbf{R}}+\frac{\delta\mathbf{p}}{\delta t}+\boldsymbol{\omega}\times\mathbf{p} = -R\omega\mathbf{i}+v_0(\sin\psi\mathbf{i}-\cos\psi\mathbf{j})$$

$$\ddot{\mathbf{r}} = \ddot{\mathbf{R}}+\frac{\delta^2\mathbf{p}}{\delta t^2}+\dot{\boldsymbol{\omega}}\times\mathbf{p}+\boldsymbol{\omega}\times(\boldsymbol{\omega}\times\mathbf{p})+2\boldsymbol{\omega}\times\frac{\delta\mathbf{p}}{\delta t}$$

$$= -R\omega^2\mathbf{j}+\mathbf{0}+\mathbf{0}+\mathbf{0}+2\omega v_0(\sin\psi\mathbf{j}+\cos\psi\mathbf{i}).$$

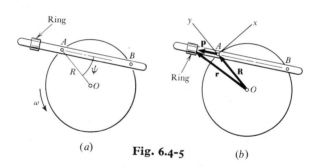

(a)   **Fig. 6.4-5**   (b)

The magnitude of the acceleration is

$$|\ddot{\mathbf{r}}| = [(2\omega v_0\cos\psi)^2+(2\omega v_0\sin\psi-R\omega^2)^2]^{1/2}$$
$$= \omega[4v_0^2-4Rv_0\omega\sin\psi+R^2\omega^2]^{1/2}.$$

The student should rework this problem, using different sets of rotating axes, to see just how the choice of axes affects the expression and computation of the different terms.   In particular, solve the problem for the following sets of axes:

    1. Origin A, x-axis along AB, y-axis perpendicular to AB;

    2. Origin O, axes parallel to those used in our solution;

    3. Origin O, axes parallel to those of Set 1.

The acceleration magnitude should be the same whatever axes are used, of course; the vectors will be different in form.

Example 6.4-4

Let us do one more formal disk-bar-ring problem; then indicate the real problem underlying the formal one.   Suppose that a disk of radius a rotates with constant clockwise angular velocity ω.   A rod AB in the shape of a circular quadrant, also of radius a, is attached rigidly to the disk in the plane of the disk as shown (Fig. 6.4-6).   A ring slides in along the rod at constant speed v_0 relative to the rod. Find its velocity and acceleration at any point C along the rod.

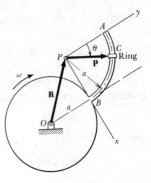

Fig. 6.4-6

Solution: Choose as origin of the rotating coordinate system the point P at the center of the circular arc AB, and regard P as moving with the rigid system consisting of the disk and the rod.   Take the x, y-axes as shown, x being the tangent PB to the disk and y being parallel to the radius OB. Then, using the angle θ with the y-axis to locate the ring, we have

$$\boldsymbol{\omega} = -\omega\mathbf{k}, \qquad \dot{\boldsymbol{\omega}} = 0;$$

$$\mathbf{R} = -a\mathbf{i} + a\mathbf{j},$$

$$\dot{\mathbf{R}} = \boldsymbol{\omega} \times \mathbf{R} = -a\omega(\mathbf{i} + \mathbf{j}),$$

$$\ddot{\mathbf{R}} = \dot{\boldsymbol{\omega}} \times \mathbf{R} + \boldsymbol{\omega} \times (\boldsymbol{\omega} \times \mathbf{R}) = a\omega^2(\mathbf{i} - \mathbf{j});$$

$$\mathbf{p} = a(\sin\theta\,\mathbf{i} + \cos\theta\,\mathbf{j}).$$

Now

$$\frac{\delta\mathbf{p}}{\delta t} = a\dot\theta(\cos\theta\,\mathbf{i} - \sin\theta\,\mathbf{j});$$

but $\delta\mathbf{p}/\delta t$ must have the constant magnitude v_0, so that $a\dot\theta = v_0$, $\dot\theta = v_0/a$, a constant.   Hence

$$\frac{\delta\mathbf{p}}{\delta t} = v_0(\cos\theta\,\mathbf{i} - \sin\theta\,\mathbf{j}),$$

$$\frac{\delta^2\mathbf{p}}{\delta t^2} = v_0\dot\theta(-\sin\theta\,\mathbf{i} - \cos\theta\,\mathbf{j}) = \frac{v_0^2}{a}(-\sin\theta\,\mathbf{i} - \cos\theta\,\mathbf{j}).$$

Therefore:

$$\mathbf{r} = \mathbf{R}+\mathbf{p} = a(\sin\theta-1)\mathbf{i}+a(1+\cos\theta)\mathbf{j};$$

$$\dot{\mathbf{r}} = \dot{\mathbf{R}}+\frac{\delta\mathbf{p}}{\delta t}+\boldsymbol{\omega}\times\mathbf{p} = -a\omega(\mathbf{i}+\mathbf{j})+v_0(\cos\theta\mathbf{i}-\sin\theta\mathbf{j})+a\omega(\sin\theta\mathbf{j}-\cos\theta\mathbf{i})$$

$$= [v_0\cos\theta-a\omega(1+\cos\theta)]\mathbf{i}-[v_0\sin\theta+a\omega(1-\sin\theta)]\mathbf{j};$$

$$\ddot{\mathbf{r}} = \ddot{\mathbf{R}}+\frac{\delta^2\mathbf{p}}{\delta t^2}+\dot{\boldsymbol{\omega}}\times\mathbf{p}+\boldsymbol{\omega}\times(\boldsymbol{\omega}\times\mathbf{p})+2\boldsymbol{\omega}\times\frac{\delta\mathbf{p}}{\delta t}$$

$$= a\omega^2(\mathbf{i}-\mathbf{j})-\frac{v_0^2}{a}(\sin\theta\mathbf{i}+\cos\theta\mathbf{j})+\mathbf{0}$$

$$+a\omega^2(-\sin\theta\mathbf{i}-\cos\theta\mathbf{j})+2v_0\omega(\cos\theta\mathbf{j}+\sin\theta\mathbf{i})$$

$$= \left[a\omega^2(1-\sin\theta)+2v_0\omega\sin\theta-\frac{v_0^2}{a}\sin\theta\right]\mathbf{i}$$

$$-\left[a\omega^2(1+\cos\theta)-2v_0\omega\cos\theta+\frac{v_0^2}{a}\cos\theta\right]\mathbf{j}.$$

This problem is suggested by turbine and pump machinery problems. Instead of a ring sliding on a rod, think of water moving along a curved turbine blade; change the direction of motion of the ring, and think of an impeller pump with water coming from a center pipe and being pushed out curved nozzles. The important step is the choice of origin for the auxiliary coordinates. For a general curved-blade shape, it is helpful to use relative normal and tangential coordinates and to choose the center of curvature at any point as an origin to study motion as the particle moves past that point on the curved vane.

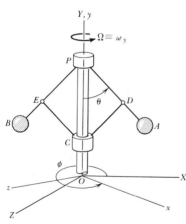

Fig. 6.4-7

Example 6.4-5

So far, we have looked at plane-motion problems with the angular velocity vector having but one component and that in a fixed direction in space. Consider now the governor device shown in Fig. 6.4-7. It consists of four rigid bars, BP, AP, EC, and DC, the two equal masses, A and B, and the collar, C, which is free to slide on the vertical shaft, OP. Let OP=h, PA=l. As the device rotates about OP, A and B move outward, the angle θ changing. Suppose $\omega_y=\Omega$ is constant, as is $\dot\theta=\omega$. Find the velocity and acceleration of A.

Solution: Choose (x, y, z) axes as shown, rotating with the shaft OP. The rod AP always is in the xy-plane. The $\boldsymbol{\omega}$ of the axes is then $\boldsymbol{\omega} = \Omega\mathbf{J} = \Omega\mathbf{j}$, with $\dot{\boldsymbol{\omega}} = \mathbf{0}$. Also, $\mathbf{R} = \dot{\mathbf{R}} = \ddot{\mathbf{R}} = \mathbf{0}$. Then

$$\mathbf{r} = \mathbf{p} = h\mathbf{j} + l(\sin\theta\mathbf{i} - \cos\theta\mathbf{j})$$

$$= l\sin\theta\mathbf{i} + (h - l\cos\theta)\mathbf{j},$$

$$\frac{\delta\mathbf{p}}{\delta t} = l\dot{\theta}\cos\theta\mathbf{i} + l\dot{\theta}\sin\theta\mathbf{j} = l\omega(\cos\theta\mathbf{i} + \sin\theta\mathbf{j}),$$

$$\frac{\delta^2\mathbf{p}}{\delta t^2} = l\omega^2(-\sin\theta\mathbf{i} + \cos\theta\mathbf{j}),$$

and

$$\mathbf{v} = l\omega(\cos\theta\mathbf{i} + \sin\theta\mathbf{j}) - l\Omega\sin\theta\mathbf{k},$$

$$\mathbf{a} = l\omega^2(-\sin\theta\mathbf{i} + \cos\theta\mathbf{j}) - l\Omega^2\sin\theta\mathbf{i} - 2l\omega\Omega\cos\theta\mathbf{k}$$

$$= -l(\omega^2 + \Omega^2)\sin\theta\mathbf{i} + l\omega^2\cos\theta\mathbf{j} - 2l\omega\Omega\cos\theta\mathbf{k}.$$

Since, quite obviously, the height h has nothing to do with the result, parallel axes with origin at P would serve as well. The only change is that the $h\mathbf{j}$-term is removed from $\mathbf{p}$, with $\mathbf{R}$ now equal to $h\mathbf{j}$.

Let us solve the problem using different axes. PA is a rigid body; we know that the relative motion terms become simpler in form if we choose coordinates fixed in a rigid body and rotating with it. With P as origin, take (x', y', z') axes as indicated in Fig. 6.4-8: x' along PA, z' parallel to the z-axis of Fig. 6.4-7, and y' such that the axes are right-handed axes. Now $\mathbf{R} = \overline{OP} = h\mathbf{J}$, $\dot{\mathbf{R}} = \ddot{\mathbf{R}} = \mathbf{0}$; the relative position

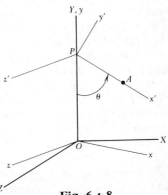

Fig. 6.4-8

vector $\mathbf{p}$ is always $\mathbf{p} = l\mathbf{i}'$, so that $\delta\mathbf{p}/\delta t = \delta^2\mathbf{p}/\delta t^2 = \mathbf{0}$ where the frame derivatives are now computed in the (x', y', z') frame. The relative motion terms are the rigid body terms $\boldsymbol{\omega}' \times \mathbf{p}$, $\dot{\boldsymbol{\omega}}' \times \mathbf{p} + \boldsymbol{\omega}' \times (\boldsymbol{\omega}' \times \mathbf{p})$, where $\boldsymbol{\omega}'$ is the angular velocity of both the axes and the rigid body PA. We have

$$\boldsymbol{\omega}' = \Omega\mathbf{j} + \dot{\theta}\mathbf{k} = \Omega(-\cos\theta\mathbf{i}' + \sin\theta\mathbf{j}') + \omega\mathbf{k}'.$$

Therefore,

$$\mathbf{v} = \boldsymbol{\omega}' \times \mathbf{p} = l\omega\mathbf{j}' - l\Omega\sin\theta\mathbf{k}'.$$

Since

$$\dot{\boldsymbol{\omega}}' = \Omega(\dot{\theta}\sin\theta\mathbf{i}' + \dot{\theta}\cos\theta\mathbf{j}')$$

$$= \Omega\omega(\sin\theta\mathbf{i}' + \cos\theta\mathbf{j}'),$$

$$\mathbf{a} = -l\Omega\omega\cos\theta\mathbf{k}' - l\Omega\omega\cos\theta\mathbf{k}' - l\Omega^2\sin\theta\cos\theta\mathbf{j}'$$

$$- l\Omega^2\sin^2\theta\mathbf{i}' - l\omega^2\mathbf{i}',$$

or

$$\mathbf{a} = -l(\omega^2 + \Omega^2\sin^2\theta)\mathbf{i}' - l\Omega^2\sin\theta\cos\theta\mathbf{j}'$$

$$- 2l\Omega\omega\cos\theta\mathbf{k}'.$$

The student may verify that the two solution forms are the same by using the transformation relations

$$\mathbf{i} = \sin\theta\mathbf{i}' + \cos\theta\mathbf{j}',$$

$$\mathbf{j} = \mathbf{J} = -\cos\theta\mathbf{i}' + \sin\theta\mathbf{j}',$$

$$\mathbf{k} = \mathbf{k}'.$$

Some comments on these two solutions are in order. We see that the two computations involve about the same amount of work, with the second one perhaps a bit harder. The difficulty with the first is in the computation of $\delta\mathbf{p}/\delta t$, $\delta^2\mathbf{p}/\delta t^2$, and remembering to include the Coriolis term. The difficulty with the second is all in the computation of the proper $\boldsymbol{\omega}$ and $\dot{\boldsymbol{\omega}}$. The interpretation of the results is interesting. The motion of A is a combination of two circular motions. If θ were constant, A would move in a horizontal circle of radius $l\sin\theta$ with Ω as the angular velocity of the radius of the circle. On top of this is superposed a vertical circular motion about P of radius l. The answer for $\mathbf{v}$ in the first part hides the nature of the vertical motion somewhat, while that in the second part clearly expresses the combination of the two motions. The acceleration of the first solution has the inward acceleration $-(l\sin\theta)\Omega^2\mathbf{i}$ of the horizontal motion explicitly; the second solution, the inward $-l\omega^2\mathbf{i}'$ of the vertical motion. The interaction between the two motions is expressed by the Coriolis term of the first and the $\dot{\boldsymbol{\omega}}\times\mathbf{p}$ term of the second solution. This points up the fact that speaking of "the" Coriolis acceleration or "the" centripetal acceleration $\boldsymbol{\omega}\times(\boldsymbol{\omega}\times\mathbf{p})$ means nothing until the coordinate systems used have been specified.

The student may wish to examine the solution in fixed coordinates (X, Y, Z), where $\Omega = \dot{\phi}$ and ϕ is the angle shown in Fig. 6.4-7 from the positive X- to the positive x-axis in the sense of rotation of Ω.

Example 6.4-6

An automobile travels in an easterly direction at constant speed v_0 along a road at latitude θ. What difference does the rotation of the earth make on its *acceleration?   Consider the earth as a sphere of radius R with its center fixed in space (Fig. 6.4-9).*

Solution: Suppose axes (x, y, z) are fixed in the earth and rotate with it, the car passing over point P in the xy-plane at the instant under consideration.   We have

$$\mathbf{p} = R(\cos\theta\mathbf{i} + \sin\theta\mathbf{k}),$$

$$\frac{\delta\mathbf{p}}{\delta t} = v_0\mathbf{j},$$

$$\frac{\delta^2\mathbf{p}}{\delta t^2} = -\frac{v_0^2}{R\cos\theta}\mathbf{i},$$

the last being the acceleration of a point moving in a circle of radius $R\cos\theta$ at constant speed v_0.   If the earth were not rotating, this would be the acceleration of the car.   With the angular velocity of the earth taken to be

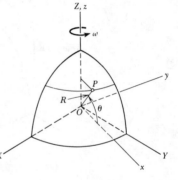

Fig. 6.4-9

$$\boldsymbol{\omega} = \frac{2\pi}{24}\mathbf{k} = \frac{\pi}{12}\mathbf{k}\,\text{rad/hr}, \quad\text{and}\quad \dot{\boldsymbol{\omega}} = 0,$$

we find

$$\mathbf{v} = \frac{\delta\mathbf{p}}{\delta t} + \boldsymbol{\omega}\times\mathbf{p} = v_0\mathbf{j} + \frac{\pi}{12}R\cos\theta\mathbf{j},$$

$$\mathbf{a} = \frac{\delta^2\mathbf{p}}{\delta t^2} + \boldsymbol{\omega}\times(\boldsymbol{\omega}\times\mathbf{p}) + 2\boldsymbol{\omega}\times\frac{\delta\mathbf{p}}{\delta t}$$

$$= -\frac{v_0^2}{R\cos\theta}\mathbf{i} - \left(\frac{\pi}{12}\right)^2 R\cos\theta\mathbf{i} - \frac{\pi}{6}v_0\mathbf{i}.$$

Here, if R is measured in miles, the units of v_0 and $\mathbf{v}$ are mi/hr and of $\mathbf{a}$, mi/hr².

Let us estimate the magnitude of the three acceleration terms at a latitude $\theta = 45°$.   The radius of the earth is a little less than 4000 mi; take v_0 as 60 mi/hr.   Then

$$\frac{v_0^2}{R\cos\theta} \simeq \frac{9\sqrt{2}}{10} \simeq 1.27 \text{ mi/hr}^2,$$

$$\left(\frac{\pi}{12}\right)^2 R\cos\theta \simeq 193 \text{ mi/hr}^2,$$

$$\frac{\pi}{6}v_0 \simeq 31.4 \text{ mi/hr}^2.$$

The relative magnitudes of these terms are evident; yet we find the forces acting on an automobile without considering any of them.   To answer the question posed in the problem, it is quite clear that the effect of the curvature of the earth can be neglected compared to the centripetal acceleration due to the earth's rotation or even compared to the Coriolis term (unless we are very close to the North or South Pole). The sum of all the terms is approximately 225 mi/hr^2 or 0.09 ft/sec^2 in magnitude, directed in toward the earth's axis. Such an acceleration is negligible for most purposes, and certainly can be neglected in finding the forces acting on an automobile accelerating from rest to 60 mph in about a minute. Fuller discussion of the effects of the earth's rotation may be found in Section 7.2.

Example **6.4-7**

Describe the effects of the earth's rotation on winds blowing parallel to the surface or on water flowing in a channel; in particular, consider the Coriolis effect.

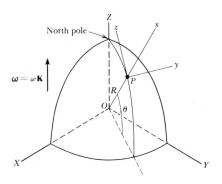

Fig. 6.4-10

Solution: Suppose the fluid is passing over a point P on the earth's surface at speed v_0 at the instant under consideration and consider one particle of the fluid. Choose coordinates with origin at P fixed to the earth and rotating with it, as shown in Fig. 6.4-10; x is radially outward, y is tangent to the surface in an easterly direction, and z is northerly. With P at latitude θ, the angular velocity of the earth is given by

$$\boldsymbol{\omega} = \omega\mathbf{K} = \omega(\sin\theta\mathbf{i} + \cos\theta\mathbf{k}),$$

with $\omega = \pi/12$ rad/hr. In the general relative motion equations, we have

$$\mathbf{R} = R\mathbf{i}, \qquad \dot{\mathbf{R}} = \boldsymbol{\omega}\times\mathbf{R},$$

$$\ddot{\mathbf{R}} = \dot{\boldsymbol{\omega}}\times\mathbf{R} + \boldsymbol{\omega}\times(\boldsymbol{\omega}\times\mathbf{R}) = \boldsymbol{\omega}\times(\boldsymbol{\omega}\times\mathbf{R}).$$

We take $\mathbf{p} = \mathbf{0}$; then the total acceleration is simply

$$\mathbf{a} = \boldsymbol{\omega}\times(\boldsymbol{\omega}\times\mathbf{R}) + 2\boldsymbol{\omega}\times\frac{\delta\mathbf{p}}{\delta t} + \frac{\delta^2\mathbf{p}}{\delta t^2}.$$

If the direction of flow is at an angle ϕ north of east, then

$$\frac{\delta \mathbf{p}}{\delta t} = v_0(\cos \phi \mathbf{j} + \sin \phi \mathbf{k}).$$

We shall ignore $\delta^2 \mathbf{p}/\delta t^2$, since we want the effects of rotation only.
Now

$$\boldsymbol{\omega} \times (\boldsymbol{\omega} \times \mathbf{R}) = R\omega^2(-\cos \theta \mathbf{i} + \sin \theta \mathbf{k});$$

$$2\boldsymbol{\omega} \times \frac{\delta \mathbf{p}}{\delta t} = 2v_0\omega(-\cos \theta \cos \phi \mathbf{i} - \sin \theta \sin \phi \mathbf{j} + \sin \theta \cos \phi \mathbf{k}).$$

Let us interpret these results. The centripetal acceleration $\boldsymbol{\omega} \times (\boldsymbol{\omega} \times \mathbf{R})$, directed toward the earth's axis, would of course be present if the particle of fluid were at rest relative to the earth. This, then, cannot be said to represent an effect of the rotation on the flow process. The Coriolis term involves both v_0 and ω. The x-component is an acceleration toward or away from the earth's surface, depending on the flow direction ϕ; this produces a radial velocity component that will be of the updraft or down-draft type. It is the other two terms, the acceleration parallel to the surface and perpendicular to $\delta \mathbf{p}/\delta t$, that are of main interest. Rewrite them as

$$2v_0\omega \sin \theta[-\sin \phi \mathbf{j} + \cos \phi \mathbf{k}],$$

and consider the effect of latitude. Measure latitudes in the Northern Hemisphere by values of θ in the range $0° \leqq \theta \leqq 90°$; in the Southern Hemisphere, by $0° \geqq \theta \geqq -90°$. Then $\sin \theta$ changes sign as we pass from the Northern to Southern Hemisphere, with this part of the Coriolis acceleration vanishing at the equator. In particular, since $-\sin \phi \mathbf{j} + \cos \phi \mathbf{k}$ is the unit vector parallel to the surface $90°$ counterclockwise from the direction of $\delta \mathbf{p}/\delta t$, we see that the surface Coriolis terms are counterclockwise $90°$ from $\delta \mathbf{p}/\delta t$ in the Northern Hemisphere, clockwise in the Southern. Air flowing south in the Northern Hemisphere is accelerated to the east, and so forth; this Coriolis effect must be taken into account in explaining the difference in the sense of rotation of cyclones in the two hemispheres. Water flowing in a river channel or draining from a basin is subject to the same acceleration; however, other effects of greater magnitude generally obscure the rotational Coriolis effect.

6.5 The Angular Momentum of a Rigid Body; Moments and Products of Inertia

We now turn to the dynamical principles for a rigid body, using the kinematical results to transform and simplify the expressions for moment of momentum and kinetic energy of a rigid body. We start with the angular momentum vector with respect to any point P moving with a rigid body. Then, if $\mathbf{p}$ is the position vector of a typical point in the body with respect to P, we know that $\dot{\mathbf{p}} = \boldsymbol{\omega} \times \mathbf{p}$, where $\boldsymbol{\omega}$ is the angular velocity of the body. Therefore, for a rigid body,

$$\mathbf{H}_P = \int \mathbf{p} \times \dot{\mathbf{p}} \, dm = \int \mathbf{p} \times (\boldsymbol{\omega} \times \mathbf{p}) \, dm. \qquad \textbf{6.5-1}$$

Since $\boldsymbol{\omega}$ is a property of the body as a whole, it does not depend on the coordinates of any point and is a constant insofar as the indicated integration is concerned. We look for a way to remove $\boldsymbol{\omega}$ from the integrand. This may be done partially by using the identity for the vector triple product, Eq. 1.3-22:

Hence
$$\mathbf{A} \times (\mathbf{B} \times \mathbf{C}) = (\mathbf{A} \cdot \mathbf{C})\mathbf{B} - (\mathbf{A} \cdot \mathbf{B})\mathbf{C}. \qquad \textbf{6.5-2}$$

$$\mathbf{H}_P = \int \{(\mathbf{p} \cdot \mathbf{p})\boldsymbol{\omega} - (\mathbf{p} \cdot \boldsymbol{\omega})\mathbf{p}\} \, dm. \qquad \textbf{6.5-3}$$

The $\boldsymbol{\omega}$ vector may be removed from the first term, but not from the second. Introduce a rectangular cartesian system (x, y, z) with P as origin, so that

Then
$$\boldsymbol{\omega} = \omega_x \mathbf{i} + \omega_y \mathbf{j} + \omega_z \mathbf{k}, \qquad \mathbf{p} = x\mathbf{i} + y\mathbf{j} + z\mathbf{k}.$$

$$(\mathbf{p} \cdot \mathbf{p})\boldsymbol{\omega} = (x^2 + y^2 + z^2)[\omega_x \mathbf{i} + \omega_y \mathbf{j} + \omega_z \mathbf{k}],$$

$$(\mathbf{p} \cdot \boldsymbol{\omega})\mathbf{p} = (x\omega_x + y\omega_y + z\omega_z)[x\mathbf{i} + y\mathbf{j} + z\mathbf{k}],$$

$$(\mathbf{p} \cdot \mathbf{p})\boldsymbol{\omega} - (\mathbf{p} \cdot \boldsymbol{\omega})\mathbf{p} = [(y^2 + z^2)\omega_x - xy\omega_y - xz\omega_z]\mathbf{i}$$
$$+ [-xy\omega_x + (x^2 + z^2)\omega_y - yz\omega_z]\mathbf{j}$$
$$+ [-xz\omega_x - yz\omega_y + (x^2 + y^2)\omega_z]\mathbf{k},$$

and the integrations may be performed to yield

$$\mathbf{H}_P = [I_{xx}^P \omega_x - I_{xy}^P \omega_y - I_{xz}^P \omega_z]\mathbf{i}$$
$$+ [-I_{yx}^P \omega_x + I_{yy}^P \omega_y - I_{yz}^P \omega_z]\mathbf{j} \qquad \textbf{6.5-4}$$
$$+ [-I_{zx}^P \omega_x - I_{zy}^P \omega_y + I_{zz}^P \omega_z]\mathbf{k}.$$

Here

$$I_{xx}^P = \int (y^2 + z^2) \, dm, \qquad I_{yy}^P = \int (x^2 + z^2) \, dm,$$

$$I_{zz}^P = \int (x^2 + y^2) \, dm, \qquad \textbf{6.5-5a}$$

are called the *moments of inertia* of the rigid body with respect to the (x, y, z) axes at point P, while

$$I_{xy}^P = I_{yx}^P = \int xy \, dm, \qquad I_{xz}^P = I_{zx}^P = \int xz \, dm,$$

$$I_{yz}^P = I_{zy}^P = \int yz \, dm, \qquad\qquad \textbf{6.5-5b}$$

are called the *products of inertia*. Properties of these inertia integrals will be discussed later.

The form 6.5-4 for $\mathbf{H}_P$ is a generalization of that for a lamina in plane motion. If the lamina moves in the $z = 0$ coordinate plane, then $\omega_x = \omega_y = 0$, while $I_{xz} = I_{yz} = 0$; it rotates about a z-axis perpendicular to the plane of motion, while all the mass lies in the $z = 0$ plane. I_{zz}^P is then the polar moment I_P of Chapter IV, and $\mathbf{H}_P = I_{zz}^P \omega_z \mathbf{k}$.

The derivation given for $\mathbf{H}_P$ is straightforward enough; difficulties arise when we compute its derivative for use in the moment-of-momentum principle. If the directions $(\mathbf{i}, \mathbf{j}, \mathbf{k})$ are fixed with respect to an inertial reference frame, then, as the body rotates, its mass distribution changes with respect to the axes at P and the moments and products of inertia are functions of time. Just how they change with time depends on the solution of the problem; they become unknowns for which we must solve. The inertia integrals are difficult enough to compute in any case; we prefer to perform the calculation only once. But then we must choose the (x, y, z) axes so that the mass distribution with respect to these axes is always the same, whatever the configuration of the body may be with respect to "absolute" coordinates. The axes must usually be body axes; for bodies with special symmetries, other axes can sometimes be used. We see that rotating coordinates are necessary not only for kinematical computations but also for the simplest approach to the dynamical principles.

Referred to body axes at P, we have two important results:

1. The inertia integrals have constant values when referred to body axes;

2. The time rate of change of the moment-of-momentum vector referred to body axes is

$$\frac{d\mathbf{H}_P}{dt} = \frac{\delta\mathbf{H}_P}{\delta t} + \boldsymbol{\omega} \times \mathbf{H}_P, \qquad\qquad \textbf{6.5-6}$$

where $\boldsymbol{\omega}$ is the angular velocity both of body and of axes. In computing $\delta\mathbf{H}_P/\delta t$, remember that not only $\mathbf{i}, \mathbf{j}, \mathbf{k}$ are considered as fixed but also the inertia integrals. That is, if

then
$$\mathbf{H}_P = H_x^P \mathbf{i} + H_y^P \mathbf{j} + H_z^P \mathbf{k},$$ **6.5-7**

$$\frac{\delta \mathbf{H}_P}{dt} = \dot{H}_x^P \mathbf{i} + \dot{H}_y^P \mathbf{j} + \dot{H}_z^P \mathbf{k},$$ **6.5-8**

where a typical component and its derivative are

$$H_y^P = -I_{yx}^P \omega_x + I_{yy}^P \omega_y - I_{yz}^P \omega_z,$$
$$\dot{H}_y^P = -I_{yx}^P \dot{\omega}_x + I_{yy}^P \dot{\omega}_y - I_{yz}^P \dot{\omega}_z.$$ **6.5-9**

The general expression (6.5-4) for $\mathbf{H}_P$ is rather complex and difficult to remember. Examination of the properties of the inertia integrals will help us see just what that form means. A general discussion of the properties of the integrals is given in Appendix II; here we shall state those properties needed for solution of problems.

We have been considering $\mathbf{H}_P$ referred to some arbitrarily chosen axes (x, y, z) at P, which we then fix in the body. Consider any other set of body axes at P, say (x', y', z'); we compute the inertia integrals $(I'_{xx}, I'_{yy}, \ldots I'_{zz})$ with respect to these axes and write $\mathbf{H}_P$ as

$$\mathbf{H}_P = H_x' \mathbf{i}' + H_y' \mathbf{j}' + H_z' \mathbf{k}',$$ **6.5-10**

where $(\mathbf{i}', \mathbf{j}', \mathbf{k}')$ are the unit vectors for the new axes, and the components of $\mathbf{H}_P$ are given by formulas such as

$$H_y' = -I'_{yx} \omega_x' + I'_{yy} \omega_y' - I'_{yz} \omega_y'.$$

Here $\boldsymbol{\omega} = \omega_x' \mathbf{i}' + \omega_y' \mathbf{j}' + \omega_z' \mathbf{k}'$ is the angular velocity vector referred to the new coordinates.

Now 6.5-7 and 6.5-10 are two representations of the same vector; if we know the direction cosines of $(\mathbf{i}', \mathbf{j}', \mathbf{k}')$ with respect to $(\mathbf{i}, \mathbf{j}, \mathbf{k})$, we may express the new components in terms of the old, just as we did in Section 4.2. If we also use the transformation relations under such a rotation of coordinates for the $\boldsymbol{\omega}$ vector, and compare terms, we obtain relations for expressing the inertia integrals with respect to one set of axes in terms of the inertia integrals with respect to the other. These general rotation of coordinates relations are derived in the Appendix, and show that, if we know the inertia integrals with respect to one set of axes at a point, we can compute them with respect to all axes at the point. The relations are generalizations of the vector component relations under rotations of axes, provided we regard the inertia integrals as an array of nine quantities, rather than the six independent ones, and provided we include the minus sign that appears in 6.5-4 with the products of inertia. The symmetric array

$$\tilde{I}_P = \begin{pmatrix} I_{xx} & -I_{xy} & -I_{xz} \\ -I_{yx} & I_{yy} & -I_{yz} \\ -I_{zx} & -I_{zy} & I_{zz} \end{pmatrix} \qquad \textbf{6.5-11}$$

is called the *inertia tensor* (or inertia matrix) at P, referred to the (x, y, z) axes; the tensor concept is a generalization of the vector concept of importance in deformable body mechanics and other fields of engineering and physics.

Just what the rotation relations are is of no concern to us now. The important results that arise from them are the one just referred to —the components of the inertia tensor referred to any axes at a point are obtainable from those based on any other set—and the concepts of the *principal axes and moments of inertia*. At any point P, there exists at least one set of axes, the principal axes of inertia, such that the products of inertia vanish when computed in this special coordinate system. The moments of inertia with respect to these axes are the *principal moments of inertia*; referred to principal axes, the moment-of-momentum vector takes on the simpler form

$$\mathbf{H}_P = I_{xx}\omega_x\mathbf{i} + I_{yy}\omega_y\mathbf{j} + I_{zz}\omega_z\mathbf{k}. \qquad \textbf{6.5-12}$$

Sometimes the principal moments of inertia are denoted by the letters A, B, and C instead of I_{xx}, I_{yy}, and I_{zz}.

The rotation relations at a point are not the only important transformation relations for the inertia integrals. We also have the *parallel-axes transfer theorems*. These are also derived in Appendix II. As for the polar moment-of-inertia transfer theorem of Chapter IV, we find that the mass center is a preferred point. The results are:

1. The moment of inertia, I, of a body about any axis is equal to the moment of inertia I^* about a parallel axis through the mass center added to the product of the mass m of the body times the square of the distance d between the axes:

$$I = I^* + md^2.$$

2. The product of inertia, P, of a body with respect to two orthogonal planes is equal to the product of inertia P^* with respect to parallel planes through the mass center added to the product of the mass m of the body and the directed distances d_1, d_2 *from* the planes at the mass center *to* the original planes.

In terms of a base point P located at position $\mathbf{p} = x\mathbf{i} + y\mathbf{j} + z\mathbf{k}$ from the mass center, these take the form

$$I_{xx}^P = I_{xx}^* + m(y^2 + z^2), \text{ etc.;} \qquad \textbf{6.5-13a}$$

$$I_{xy}^P = I_{xy}^* + mxy, \text{ etc.} \qquad \textbf{6.5-13b}$$

In Appendix II, the inertia matrix $\check{I}^*$ relative to principal axes at the mass center is tabulated for some simple uniform bodies. By use of the rotation and transfer of axes relations, any other inertia integral can be computed from this information. Determination of principal axes for symmetric mass distributions, radii of gyration, and other important topics are also discussed.

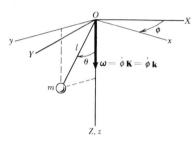

Fig. 6.5-1

Finally, we note that d'Alembert's principle may be extended to the moment equation by introducing "reversed effective" or "inertia" couples on the body, in the same way that inertia forces are introduced for $\mathbf{F} = m\mathbf{a}^*$.

Example **6.5-1** : *Conical pendulum*

A particle of mass m swings on the end of a string of length l as a conical pendulum (Fig. 6.5-1); that is, the angle θ between the string and the vertical remains constant. Find $\mathbf{H}_O$ and $\dot{\mathbf{H}}_O$ in (a) fixed coordinates OXYZ; (b) moving coordinates Oxyz, the string remaining in the yz-plane.

Solution: The position vector is

$$\mathbf{r} = l\cos\theta\mathbf{k} + l\sin\theta\mathbf{j}$$

$$= l\cos\theta\mathbf{K} + l\sin\theta(-\sin\phi\mathbf{I} + \cos\phi\mathbf{J})$$

in the two coordinate systems. In fixed coordinates, then,

$$\mathbf{r} = -l\sin\theta\sin\phi\mathbf{I} + l\sin\theta\cos\phi\mathbf{J} + l\cos\theta\mathbf{K},$$

$$\mathbf{v} = -l\dot{\phi}\sin\theta\cos\phi\mathbf{I} - l\dot{\phi}\sin\theta\sin\phi\mathbf{J},$$

$$\mathbf{a} = -l\ddot{\phi}\sin\theta(\cos\phi\mathbf{I} + \sin\phi\mathbf{J})$$

$$- l\dot{\phi}^2\sin\theta(-\sin\phi\mathbf{I} + \cos\phi\mathbf{J}).$$

Therefore,

$$\mathbf{H}_O = \mathbf{r} \times m\mathbf{v} = +ml^2\dot{\phi}\sin\theta\cos\theta\sin\phi\mathbf{I} - ml^2\dot{\phi}\sin\theta\cos\theta\cos\phi\mathbf{J}$$
$$+ ml^2\dot{\phi}\sin^2\theta\mathbf{K},$$

$\dot{\mathbf{H}}_O$ being found from $\mathbf{r} \times m\mathbf{a}$.

In moving coordinates, $\omega = \dot\phi\mathbf{k}$, $\dot\omega = \ddot\phi\mathbf{k}$,

$$\mathbf{r} = l\sin\theta\mathbf{j} + l\cos\theta\mathbf{k}, \qquad \frac{\delta\mathbf{r}}{\delta t} = \frac{\delta^2\mathbf{r}}{\delta t^2} = 0;$$

therefore,

$$\mathbf{v} = \omega\times\mathbf{r} = -l\dot\phi\sin\theta\mathbf{i},$$

$$\mathbf{a} = \dot\omega\times\mathbf{r} + \omega\times(\omega\times\mathbf{r}) = -l\ddot\phi\sin\theta\mathbf{i} - l\dot\phi^2\sin\theta\mathbf{j}.$$

Referred to moving coordinates,

$$\mathbf{H}_O = \mathbf{r}\times m\mathbf{v} = -ml^2\dot\phi\sin\theta\cos\theta\mathbf{j} + ml^2\dot\phi\sin^2\theta\mathbf{k}.$$

To compute $\dot{\mathbf{H}}_O$, we may proceed directly with $\mathbf{r}\times m\mathbf{a}$, or use the total derivative formula:

$$\dot{\mathbf{H}}_O = \frac{\delta\mathbf{H}_O}{\delta t} + \omega\times\mathbf{H}_O = -ml^2\ddot\phi\sin\theta\cos\theta\mathbf{j} + ml^2\ddot\phi\sin^2\theta\mathbf{k}$$
$$+ ml^2\dot\phi^2\sin\theta\cos\theta\mathbf{i}.$$

Example 6.5-2: Conical bar pendulum

A uniform rigid bar of mass m and length l moves as a conical pendulum. Find $\mathbf{H}_O$ and $\dot{\mathbf{H}}_O$ for the bar (Fig. 6.5-2).

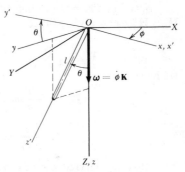

Fig. 6.5-2

Solution: The bar is shown in the same position as the simple pendulum of the previous example and the same coordinates are used. We have also shown a set of principal axes of inertia of the bar at O: $x'\equiv x$ and y' perpendicular to the bar, z' along it. These axes are fixed in the bar and rotate with it with angular velocity

$$\omega = \dot\phi\mathbf{K} = -\dot\phi\sin\theta\mathbf{j}' + \dot\phi\cos\theta\mathbf{k}'.$$

The principal moments are $I'_{xx} = I'_{yy} = \tfrac{1}{3}ml^2$, $I'_{zz} = 0$; therefore, by 6.5-12,

$$\mathbf{H}_O = \frac{1}{3}ml^2\omega'_x\mathbf{i}' + \frac{1}{3}ml^2\omega'_y\mathbf{j}'$$

$$= -\frac{1}{3}ml^2\dot\phi\sin\theta\mathbf{j}'.$$

Differentiating, we obtain

$$\frac{d\mathbf{H}_O}{dt} = \frac{\delta\mathbf{H}_O}{\delta t} + \omega\times\mathbf{H}_O$$

$$= -\frac{1}{3}ml^2\ddot\phi\sin\theta\mathbf{j}' + \frac{1}{3}ml^2\dot\phi^2\sin\theta\cos\theta\mathbf{i}'.$$

These results may be compared to those of the first example by substituting

$$\mathbf{i}' = \mathbf{i}, \qquad \mathbf{j}' = \cos\theta\mathbf{j} - \sin\theta\mathbf{k}, \qquad \mathbf{k}' = \sin\theta\mathbf{j} + \cos\theta\mathbf{k}$$

at the appropriate places. In particular, $\mathbf{H}_O$ becomes

$$\mathbf{H}_O = -\frac{1}{3}ml^2\dot{\phi}\sin\theta\cos\theta\mathbf{j} + \frac{1}{3}ml^2\dot{\phi}\sin^2\theta\mathbf{k}.$$

In these coordinates, $\boldsymbol{\omega} = \dot{\phi}\mathbf{k} = \omega_z\mathbf{k}$; comparing this expression for $\mathbf{H}_O$ with the general expression 6.5-4, we find

$$I_{zz} = \frac{1}{3}ml^2\sin^2\theta, \qquad I_{yz} = \frac{1}{3}ml^2\sin\theta\cos\theta.$$

The student may wish to verify these results by direct integration.

Example **6.5-3**

Compute $\mathbf{H}^*$ *in the previous example.*

Solution: From the change of base point theorem (Eq. 4.3-22), we have $\mathbf{H}_O = \mathbf{H}^* + \mathbf{r}^* \times m\mathbf{v}^*$. Since

$$\mathbf{r}^* = \frac{l}{2}\mathbf{k}', \qquad \mathbf{v}^* = \boldsymbol{\omega} \times \mathbf{r}^* = -\frac{l}{2}\dot{\phi}\sin\theta\mathbf{i}',$$

we have

$$\mathbf{H}^* = -\frac{1}{3}ml^2\dot{\phi}\sin\theta\mathbf{j}' + \frac{1}{4}ml^2\dot{\phi}\sin\theta\mathbf{j}'$$

$$= -\frac{1}{12}ml^2\dot{\phi}\sin\theta\mathbf{j}'.$$

This may be derived directly by noting that axes at the center of mass parallel to x' and y' are principal axes there;

$$I_{xx}^{*\prime} = I_{yy}^{*\prime} = \frac{1}{12}ml^2,$$

so that

$$\mathbf{H}^* = \frac{1}{12}ml^2\omega_y'\mathbf{j}'.$$

Example **6.5-4**: *Spherical pendulum*

If the angle θ *of the first two examples is not constant, then the pendulum is called spherical instead of conical. Find* $\mathbf{H}_O$ *and* $\dot{\mathbf{H}}_O$ *of the bar of Example 6.5-2 in these circumstances.*

Solution: The axes chosen remain the same. If there is a $\dot{\theta}$, then for θ increasing there is an angular velocity $-\dot{\theta}\mathbf{i}'$ by the right-hand rule for positive rotations. The (x', y', z') axes then rotate with the angular velocity of the body,

$$\boldsymbol{\omega} = -\dot{\theta}\mathbf{i}' - \dot{\phi}\sin\theta\mathbf{j}' + \dot{\phi}\cos\theta\mathbf{k}',$$

and

$$\mathbf{H}_O = -\frac{1}{3}\, ml^2\dot\theta\mathbf{i}' - \frac{1}{3}\, ml^2\dot\phi\, \sin\,\theta\mathbf{j}',$$

$$\dot{\mathbf{H}}_O = \frac{\delta\mathbf{H}_O}{\delta t} + \boldsymbol\omega\times\mathbf{H}_O$$

$$= -\frac{1}{3}\, ml^2\ddot\theta\mathbf{i}' - \frac{1}{3}\, ml^2[\ddot\phi\, \sin\,\theta + \dot\phi\dot\theta\, \cos\,\theta]\mathbf{j}' + \boldsymbol\omega\times\mathbf{H}_O$$

$$= \frac{1}{3}\, ml^2(\dot\phi^2\, \sin\,\theta\, \cos\,\theta - \ddot\theta)\mathbf{i}'$$

$$\qquad - \frac{1}{3}\, ml^2(\ddot\phi\, \sin\,\theta + 2\dot\phi\dot\theta\, \cos\,\theta)\mathbf{j}'.$$

It is instructive to solve this problem in axes that do not rotate with the body. Consider the (x, y, z) axes, which have angular velocity $\boldsymbol\omega' = \dot\phi\mathbf{k}$. Referred to such axes, the moments and products of inertia are not all constants if θ is not constant. The angular velocity of the *body* is

$$\boldsymbol\omega = \omega_x\mathbf{i} + \omega_z\mathbf{k} = -\dot\theta\mathbf{i} + \dot\phi\mathbf{k};$$

to write $\mathbf{H}_O$ in $(\mathbf{i}, \mathbf{j}, \mathbf{k})$ coordinates, one needs (by Eq. 6.5-4), $I_{xx} = \frac{1}{3}ml^2$; $I_{xz} = I_{xy} = 0$ (since the mass is in the $x = 0$ plane); and I_{zz} and I_{yz}, which were found in the second example:

$$I_{zz} = \frac{1}{3}\, ml^2\, \sin^2\,\theta, \qquad I_{yz} = \frac{1}{3}\, ml^2\, \sin\,\theta\, \cos\,\theta.$$

Therefore,

$$\mathbf{H}_O = I_{xx}\omega_x\mathbf{i} - I_{yz}\omega_z\mathbf{j} + I_{zz}\omega_z\mathbf{k}$$

$$= -\frac{1}{3}\, ml^2\dot\theta\mathbf{i} - \frac{1}{3}\, ml^2\dot\phi\, \sin\,\theta\, \cos\,\theta\mathbf{j} + \frac{1}{3}\, ml^2\dot\phi\, \sin^2\,\theta\mathbf{k}.$$

Now $\dot{\mathbf{H}}_O = \delta\mathbf{H}_O/\delta t + \boldsymbol\omega'\times\mathbf{H}_O$, where $\boldsymbol\omega'$ is the angular velocity of the axes:

$$\frac{\delta\mathbf{H}_O}{\delta t} = -\frac{1}{3}\, ml^2\ddot\theta\mathbf{i} - \frac{1}{3}\, ml^2[\ddot\phi\, \sin\,\theta\, \cos\,\theta + \dot\phi\dot\theta(\cos^2\,\theta - \sin^2\,\theta)]\mathbf{j}$$

$$\qquad\qquad + \frac{1}{3}\, ml^2[\ddot\phi\, \sin^2\,\theta + 2\dot\phi\dot\theta\, \sin\,\theta\, \cos\,\theta]\mathbf{k};$$

$$\boldsymbol\omega'\times\mathbf{H}_O = \dot\phi\mathbf{k}\times\mathbf{H}_O = \frac{1}{3}\, ml^2\dot\phi\, \sin\,\theta\, \cos\,\theta\mathbf{i} - \frac{1}{3}\, ml^2\dot\phi\dot\theta\mathbf{j}.$$

The student may add these and verify that the results for $\mathbf{H}_O$ and $\dot{\mathbf{H}}_O$ agree with those first computed.

Example **6.5-5**

Write the moment equations for Examples 6.5-1, 2, *and* 4.

Solution: Free-body diagrams are shown in Fig. 6.5-3 for the particle and bar problems. For the string-pendulum bob problem, the forces acting are the weight and the string tension. For the bar, there are the weight force and the support reaction, which consists in general of a force **P** and a couple **C**.

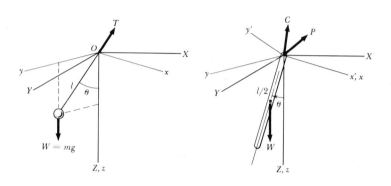

Fig. 6.5-3

Since O is a fixed point, $\dot{\mathbf{H}}_O = \mathbf{M}_O$. For the particle,

$$\mathbf{M}_O = l(\sin\theta\mathbf{j} + \cos\theta\mathbf{k}) \times mg\mathbf{k};$$

therefore,

$$\mathbf{M}_O = mgl\sin\theta\mathbf{i} = \dot{\mathbf{H}}_O,$$

and

$$mgl\sin\theta = ml^2\dot{\phi}^2\sin\theta\cos\theta,$$

$$0 = -ml^2\ddot{\phi}\sin\theta\cos\theta,$$

$$0 = ml^2\ddot{\phi}\sin^2\theta.$$

These equations tell us that, except for the trivial cases $\theta = 0$ or π (pendulum vertical), the pendulum can only proceed in conical motion if $\ddot{\phi} = 0$ and if the constant rate of rotation $\dot{\phi}$ is related to the angle θ by

$$\dot{\phi}^2\cos\theta = \frac{g}{l}.$$

The motion of the pendulum bob is then circular in a horizontal plane at level $l\cos\theta$ below the support. The radius of the circle is $l\sin\theta$; the motion is at constant speed $l\dot{\phi}$.

For the bar,

$$\mathbf{M}_O = \frac{l}{2}\,\mathbf{k}' \times mg\mathbf{k}$$

$$= \frac{l}{2}\,\mathbf{k}' \times mg(-\sin\theta\mathbf{j}' + \cos\theta\mathbf{k}')$$

$$= mg\,\frac{l}{2}\sin\theta\mathbf{i}'.$$

The spherical bar pendulum (Example 6.5-4), of which the conical pendulum is a special case (Example 6.5-2), is governed by the moment equations

$$mg\,\frac{l}{2}\sin\theta = \frac{1}{3}\,ml^2(\dot\phi^2\sin\theta\cos\theta - \ddot\theta),$$

$$0 = -\frac{1}{3}\,ml^2(\ddot\phi\sin\theta + 2\dot\phi\dot\theta\cos\theta).$$

These assume a smooth support with no reactive couple **C**. The trivial solutions $\theta = 0$, π correspond to the vertical bar. The conical-pendulum solution is given by $\theta = \text{const}$, $\dot\theta = \ddot\theta = 0$; again we find $\ddot\phi = 0$, $\dot\phi = \text{const}$, with the relation between $\dot\phi$ and θ being

$$\dot\phi^2\cos\theta = \frac{3}{2}\frac{g}{l}.$$

If θ is not constant, the problem is more difficult. The y'-moment equation may be integrated once:

$$\ddot\phi\sin\theta + 2\dot\phi\dot\theta\cos\theta = 0;$$

$$\frac{\ddot\phi}{\dot\phi} = -\frac{2\dot\theta\cos\theta}{\sin\theta};$$

$$\log\dot\phi = -2\log\sin\theta + \text{const};$$

$$\dot\phi\sin^2\theta = C, \text{ a constant.}$$

Notice that the sign of C determines the sense of rotation $\dot\phi$; we may take C and $\dot\phi$ positive. Substituting for $\dot\phi$ in the x'-moment equation, we obtain a second-order differential equation for $\theta(t)$:

$$\ddot\theta + \frac{3g}{2l}\sin\theta - \frac{C^2\cos\theta}{\sin^3\theta} = 0.$$

We shall not attempt to solve this equation now, but shall return to it in the next section in Example 6.6-2.

Example 6.5-6

A uniform rigid body is supported smoothly at its mass center and is set spinning with initial angular velocity $\boldsymbol{\omega}_0$. If no forces except gravity and the *support reaction act on the body, discuss the motion of the body; in particular, describe the cases in which the angular velocity $\boldsymbol{\omega}$ remains constant.*

   Solution: A free-body diagram of the body is shown in Fig. 6.5-4; the (x, y, z) axes are the principal axes of inertia at C fixed in the body and rotating with it. Since the mass center is fixed, $\mathbf{a}^* = \mathbf{0}$; the principle of motion of the mass center determines the reaction force $\mathbf{P}$ at the support:

$$\mathbf{W} + \mathbf{P} = m\mathbf{a}^* = \mathbf{0}, \qquad \mathbf{P} = -\mathbf{W}.$$

Since there is no resultant moment about the mass center, conservation of angular momentum holds:

$$\dot{\mathbf{H}}^* = \mathbf{M}^* = \mathbf{0}, \qquad \mathbf{H}^* = \mathbf{H}^*(0), \text{ a constant.}$$

The angular momentum vector, being constant, has constant magnitude and constant direction in space. This does not mean that the components of $\mathbf{H}^*$, referred to principal axes of inertia, are constants, since these axes rotate with the body and hence change direction in space. In particular, by Eq. 6.5-12,

$$\mathbf{H}^* = I_{xx}\omega_x\mathbf{i} + I_{yy}\omega_y\mathbf{j} + I_{zz}\omega_z\mathbf{k},$$

where (I_{xx}, I_{yy}, I_{zz}) are the principal moments of inertia at the mass center. All we know so far is that

$$|\mathbf{H}^*| = [I_{xx}^2\omega_x^2 + I_{yy}^2\omega_y^2 + I_{zz}^2\omega_z^2]^{1/2}$$

is constant, and so is the direction of $\mathbf{H}^*$.

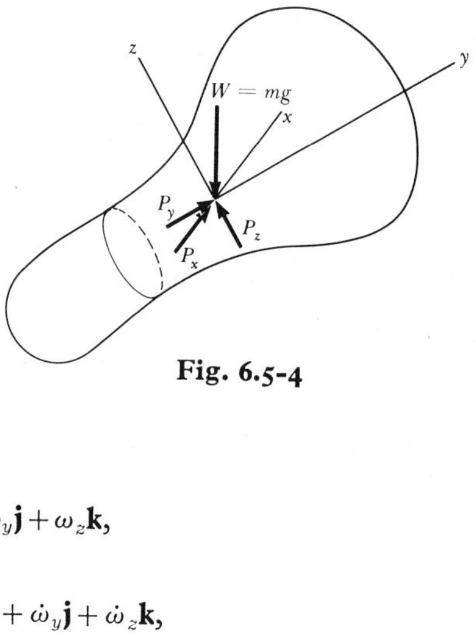

Fig. 6.5-4

   When is $\boldsymbol{\omega}$ also constant? Since

$$\boldsymbol{\omega} = \omega_x\mathbf{i} + \omega_y\mathbf{j} + \omega_z\mathbf{k},$$

and

$$\dot{\boldsymbol{\omega}} = \frac{\delta\boldsymbol{\omega}}{\delta t} = \dot{\omega}_x\mathbf{i} + \dot{\omega}_y\mathbf{j} + \dot{\omega}_z\mathbf{k},$$

$\boldsymbol{\omega}$ will be constant if and only if $\dot{\omega}_x = \dot{\omega}_y = \dot{\omega}_z = 0$, even when referred to rotating axes. Since $\mathbf{H}^*$ is constant, $\dot{\mathbf{H}}^* = \mathbf{0}$; therefore,

$$\frac{\delta\mathbf{H}^*}{\delta t} + \boldsymbol{\omega} \times \mathbf{H}^* = \mathbf{0},$$

or

$$I_{xx}\dot{\omega}_x\mathbf{i} + I_{yy}\dot{\omega}_y\mathbf{j} + I_{zz}\dot{\omega}_z\mathbf{k} + \boldsymbol{\omega} \times \mathbf{H}^* = \mathbf{0}.$$

For $\boldsymbol{\omega} = \text{constant}$, each component of $\delta\mathbf{H}/\delta t$ vanishes; therefore, $\boldsymbol{\omega} \times \mathbf{H}^* = \mathbf{0}$, and, except for the trivial case $\boldsymbol{\omega} = \mathbf{0}$, which also makes $\mathbf{H}^* = \mathbf{0}$, the body cannot spin with constant angular velocity unless $\boldsymbol{\omega}$ and $\mathbf{H}^*$ are parallel.

But if ω and H^* are to be parallel, their components must be proportional, or $H^* = k\omega$ where k is a scalar. There are the following cases:

1. The body is set spinning about one of its centroidal principal axes; i.e., one of the components of ω is not zero, whereas the other two are zero: $\omega_x \neq 0$, $\omega_y = \omega_z = 0$. Then $\omega = \omega_x \mathbf{i}$, $H^* = I_{xx}\omega_x \mathbf{i}$, and the i-direction is fixed in space as well as in the body, with the j- and k-directions rotating at constant angular velocity about $\mathbf{i}$:

$$\frac{d\mathbf{i}}{dt} = \omega \times \mathbf{i} = \mathbf{0}, \qquad \frac{d\mathbf{j}}{dt} = \omega \times \mathbf{j} = \omega_x \mathbf{k}, \qquad \frac{d\mathbf{k}}{dt} = \omega \times \mathbf{k} = -\omega_x \mathbf{j}.$$

2. The body is a circular cylinder set spinning about any axis in the plane of symmetry perpendicular to the axis of the cylinder:

$$\omega = \omega_x \mathbf{i} + \omega_y \mathbf{j}, \qquad I_{xx} = I_{yy}, \qquad H^* = I_{xx}(\omega_x \mathbf{i} + \omega_y \mathbf{j}).$$

This is the same as Case 1, really, since any diameter of the circular cross-section is a principal axis of inertia. The circular disk is a special case.

3. The body is a sphere, $I_{xx} = I_{yy} = I_{zz}$; any diameter is a principal axis of inertia.

The important fact is that ω will not be constant in general even if H^* is, when a body is set spinning about an arbitrary axis. Only for rotationally symmetric bodies like the circular cylinder and the sphere can we expect both the angular velocity vector and the angular momentum vector to behave in a simple manner.

Example 6.5-7

Referred to axes Oxyz, parallel to the principal axes of inertia at the mass center C of a rigid body, the body has mass center located at $\mathbf{r}^* = 5\mathbf{i} + 12\mathbf{j}$ *in. The body weighs 644 lb and has principal centroidal moments of inertia*

$$I_{xx}^* = 200 \text{ lb-in-sec}^2, \qquad I_{yy}^* = 400 \text{ lb-in-sec}^2, \qquad I_{zz}^* = 500 \text{ lb-in-sec}^2.$$

Find the inertia tensor components referred first to the axes at O and then to parallel axes at A, where $\mathbf{r}_{A/O} = -3\mathbf{i} + 4\mathbf{k}$.

Solution: Here we apply the parallel axis theorems. Since

$$\mathbf{r}_{C/O} = \mathbf{r}^* = 5\mathbf{i} + 12\mathbf{j}, \qquad \mathbf{r}_{O/C} = -5\mathbf{i} - 12\mathbf{j} \text{ in.}$$

The mass of the body is

$$m = (644)/(32.2)(12) = 5/3 \text{ lb-sec}^2/\text{in.}$$

Therefore,

$$I_{xx}^O = I_{xx}^* + m(y_{O/C}^2 + z_{O/C}^2) = 200 + (5/3)(144) = 460 \text{ lb-in-sec}^2;$$

$$I_{yy}^O = I_{yy}^* + m(x_{O/C}^2 + z_{O/C}^2) = 400 + (5/3)(25) = 1325/3 \text{ lb-in-sec}^2;$$

$$I_{zz}^O = I_{zz}^* + m(x_{O/C}^2 + y_{O/C}^2) = 500 + (5/3)(169) = 2345/3 \text{ lb-in-sec}^2;$$

$$I_{xy}^O = I_{xy}^* + mx_{O/C}\,y_{O/C} = 0 + (5/3)(-5)(-12) = 100 \text{ lb-in-sec}^2;$$

$$I_{xz}^O = I_{xz}^* + mx_{O/C}z_{O/C} = 0;$$

$$I_{yz}^O = I_{yz}^* + my_{O/C}z_{O/C} = 0.$$

The inertia tensor appears as

$$\tilde{I}_O = \begin{pmatrix} 460 & -100 & 0 \\ -100 & \dfrac{1325}{3} & 0 \\ 0 & 0 & \dfrac{2345}{3} \end{pmatrix} \text{ lb-in-sec}^2.$$

Remember that the negatives of the products of inertia are used in writing the off-diagonal terms of the inertia tensor.

For point A, $\mathbf{r}_{A/C} = \mathbf{r}_{A/O} + \mathbf{r}_{O/C} = -8\mathbf{i} - 12\mathbf{j} + 4\mathbf{k}$ in.   Then

$$I_{xx}^A = 200 + (5/3)(144 + 16) = 1400/3 \text{ lb-in-sec}^2;$$

$$I_{yy}^A = 400 + (5/3)(64 + 16) = 1600/3 \text{ lb-in-sec}^2;$$

$$I_{zz}^A = 500 + (5/3)(64 + 144) = 2540/3 \text{ lb-in-sec}^2;$$

$$I_{xy}^A = 0 + (5/3)(-8)(-12) = 120 \text{ lb-in-sec}^2;$$

$$I_{xz}^A = 0 + (5/3)(-8)(4) = -160/3 \text{ lb-in-sec}^2;$$

$$I_{yz}^A = 0 + (5/3)(-12)(4) = -80 \text{ lb-in-sec}^2;$$

and

$$\tilde{I}_A = \begin{pmatrix} \dfrac{1400}{3} & -120 & \dfrac{160}{3} \\ -120 & \dfrac{1600}{3} & 80 \\ \dfrac{160}{3} & 80 & \dfrac{2540}{3} \end{pmatrix} \text{ lb-in-sec}^2.$$

The student should note, besides the method of computation, that principal directions at one point are not principal directions at other points, in general; also, that moments of inertia are always positive while products of inertia may be positive or negative.

6.6 The Kinetic Energy of a Rigid Body; the Work-Energy Principle

Using the relative-motion relations for a rigid body, we may also express the kinetic energy of the body in simple form. In Chapter IV, we derived the basic representation theorem for the kinetic energy using the relative velocity equation $\mathbf{v} = \dot{\mathbf{r}} = \dot{\mathbf{R}} + \dot{\mathbf{p}}$:

$$T = \frac{1}{2} \int \mathbf{v} \cdot \mathbf{v} \, dm = \frac{1}{2} m\dot{\mathbf{R}} \cdot \dot{\mathbf{R}} + m\dot{\mathbf{R}} \cdot \dot{\mathbf{p}}^* + \frac{1}{2} \int \dot{\mathbf{p}} \cdot \dot{\mathbf{p}} \, dm. \qquad \textbf{6.6-1}$$

Now suppose P is a point moving with a rigid body having angular velocity $\boldsymbol{\omega}$. Then $\dot{\mathbf{p}} = \boldsymbol{\omega} \times \mathbf{p}$, $\dot{\mathbf{p}}^* = \boldsymbol{\omega} \times \mathbf{p}^*$, and the integrand of the last term in 6.6-1 becomes

$$\dot{\mathbf{p}} \cdot \dot{\mathbf{p}} = [\boldsymbol{\omega} \times \mathbf{p}] \cdot [\boldsymbol{\omega} \times \mathbf{p}].$$

Again we wish to factor $\boldsymbol{\omega}$ from the expression, since it is not involved in the integration. Using the basic identity for the scalar triple product (Eq. 1.3-13)

$$(\mathbf{A} \times \mathbf{B}) \cdot \mathbf{C} = \mathbf{A} \cdot (\mathbf{B} \times \mathbf{C}), \qquad \textbf{6.6-2}$$

we find that

$$[\boldsymbol{\omega} \times \mathbf{p}] \cdot [\boldsymbol{\omega} \times \mathbf{p}] = \boldsymbol{\omega} \cdot [\mathbf{p} \times (\boldsymbol{\omega} \times \mathbf{p})]. \qquad \textbf{6.6-3}$$

Therefore,

$$\int \dot{\mathbf{p}} \cdot \dot{\mathbf{p}} \, dm = \boldsymbol{\omega} \cdot \left\{ \int [\mathbf{p} \times (\boldsymbol{\omega} \times \mathbf{p})] \, dm \right\} = \boldsymbol{\omega} \cdot \mathbf{H}_P, \qquad \textbf{6.6-4}$$

and 6.6-1 becomes for a rigid body

$$T = \frac{1}{2} m\mathbf{v}_P \cdot \mathbf{v}_P + m\mathbf{v}_P \cdot (\boldsymbol{\omega} \times \mathbf{p}^*) + \frac{1}{2} \boldsymbol{\omega} \cdot \mathbf{H}_P. \qquad \textbf{6.6-5}$$

Identifying P with the mass center C, $\mathbf{v}_P = \dot{\mathbf{R}} = \mathbf{v}^*$, $\mathbf{p}^* = \mathbf{0}$, and

$$T = \frac{1}{2} m\mathbf{v}^* \cdot \mathbf{v}^* + \frac{1}{2} \boldsymbol{\omega} \cdot \mathbf{H}^*. \qquad \textbf{6.6-6}$$

For plane motion, T reduces to Eq. 4.7-17: $\boldsymbol{\omega} = \omega_z \mathbf{k}$, $\mathbf{H}^* = I^* \omega_z \mathbf{k}$, $\boldsymbol{\omega} \cdot \mathbf{H}^* = I^* \omega_z^2$.

Another form of the kinetic energy is appropriate for a rigid body with a fixed point P. With $\mathbf{v}_P = \mathbf{0}$, Eq. 6.6-5 becomes

$$T = \frac{1}{2} \boldsymbol{\omega} \cdot \mathbf{H}_P. \qquad \textbf{6.6-7}$$

The work done by the forces on a rigid body is defined as the time integral of the power of the forces. Internal forces do no work; the proof of Section 4.7 still holds for the rigid particle system, and carries over to the continuous body by the hypothesis about the nature of internal forces made in Chapter IV. An alternative, purely vectorial, proof can be given now, based on the power concept and the relative-velocity relation for the rigid body. Let $\mathbf{r}$ and $\mathbf{R}$ be the positions of two particles in a rigid system with angular velocity $\boldsymbol{\omega}$, and $\mathbf{p} = \mathbf{r} - \mathbf{R}$ the relative position vector. Let $\mathbf{f}$ be the internal force on the particle at $\mathbf{r}$ due to the particle at $\mathbf{R}$; $\mathbf{f}$ has the direction of $\mathbf{p}$. Then the power of $\mathbf{f}$ and the paired internal force $-\mathbf{f}$ on the particle at $\mathbf{R}$ is

$$\mathbf{f} \cdot \dot{\mathbf{r}} + (-\mathbf{f}) \cdot \dot{\mathbf{R}} = \mathbf{f} \cdot (\dot{\mathbf{r}} - \dot{\mathbf{R}}) = \mathbf{f} \cdot \dot{\mathbf{p}} = \mathbf{f} \cdot (\boldsymbol{\omega} \times \mathbf{p}) = \boldsymbol{\omega} \cdot (\mathbf{p} \times \mathbf{f}),$$

by Eq. 1.3-13. Since $\mathbf{p}$ and $\mathbf{f}$ are parallel, the power of the internal forces vanishes. A similar derivation allows us to find the work done by a couple $\mathbf{C}$ on a rigid body. Represent the couple in any appropriate way by a force $\mathbf{F}$ at a point P and a force $-\mathbf{F}$ at a point Q, with $\mathbf{r}_{P/Q} = \mathbf{p}$; then $\mathbf{C} = \mathbf{p} \times \mathbf{F}$. The power of the pair of forces is

$$\mathbf{F} \cdot \mathbf{v}_P + (-\mathbf{F}) \cdot \mathbf{v}_Q = \mathbf{F} \cdot (\mathbf{v}_P - \mathbf{v}_Q) = \mathbf{F} \cdot (\boldsymbol{\omega} \times \mathbf{p}) = \boldsymbol{\omega} \cdot (\mathbf{p} \times \mathbf{F}) = \boldsymbol{\omega} \cdot \mathbf{C};$$

the power of the couple does not depend on the particular representation we choose. The work done by the couple is

$$\Delta W = \int \boldsymbol{\omega} \cdot \mathbf{C} \, dt.$$

For a rigid body we can now prove in its general form the fundamental principle:

The power of the external force system acting on a rigid body equals the time rate of change of the kinetic energy of the body.

Consider a rigid body acted on by external forces $\mathbf{F}_i$, $i = 1, 2, 3, \ldots N$, at points with velocities $\mathbf{v}_i$ at any instant; also, suppose external couples $\mathbf{C}_j$, $j = 1, 2, 3, \ldots M$ are applied. The rigid body has angular velocity $\boldsymbol{\omega}$ and angular acceleration $\dot{\boldsymbol{\omega}}$. The power of the external force system is

$$P = \sum_{i=1}^{N} (\mathbf{F}_i \cdot \mathbf{v}_i) + \sum_{j=1}^{M} (\mathbf{C}_j \cdot \boldsymbol{\omega}). \qquad \textbf{6.6-8}$$

The $\boldsymbol{\omega}$ can be factored from the last sum. The $\mathbf{v}_i$, by the relative velocity equation, may be written

$$\mathbf{v}_i = \mathbf{v}^* + \dot{\mathbf{p}}_i = \mathbf{v}^* + \boldsymbol{\omega} \times \mathbf{p}_i$$

where $\mathbf{p}_i$ is the position of the i-th point relative to the mass center. Equation 6.6-8 becomes

$$P = \sum_{i=1}^{N} (\mathbf{F}_i \cdot \mathbf{v}^*) + \sum_{i=1}^{N} \mathbf{F}_i \cdot (\boldsymbol{\omega} \times \mathbf{p}_i) + \left(\sum_{j=1}^{M} \mathbf{C}_j \right) \cdot \boldsymbol{\omega}$$

$$= \left(\sum_{i=1}^{N} \mathbf{F}_i \right) \cdot \mathbf{v}^* + \boldsymbol{\omega} \cdot \left[\sum_{i=1}^{N} (\mathbf{p}_i \times \mathbf{F}_i) + \sum_{j=1}^{M} \mathbf{C}_j \right]. \qquad \textbf{6.6-9}$$

But $\sum \mathbf{F}_i$ is the resultant external force on the body, and so equals $m\mathbf{a}^*$;

similarly, $\sum (\mathbf{p}_i \times \mathbf{F}_i) + \sum \mathbf{C}_j$ is the resultant external moment $\mathbf{M}^*$ about the mass center, and equals $\dot{\mathbf{H}}^*$. Therefore,

$$P = m\mathbf{a}^* \cdot \mathbf{v}^* + \boldsymbol{\omega} \cdot \dot{\mathbf{H}}^*. \qquad \text{6.6-10}$$

The derivative of the kinetic energy (Eq. 6.6-6) is

$$\frac{dT}{dt} = \frac{1}{2} m(\mathbf{a}^* \cdot \mathbf{v}^* + \mathbf{v}^* \cdot \mathbf{a}^*) + \frac{1}{2} (\dot{\boldsymbol{\omega}} \cdot \mathbf{H}^* + \boldsymbol{\omega} \cdot \dot{\mathbf{H}}^*)$$

$$= m\mathbf{a}^* \cdot \mathbf{v}^* + \frac{1}{2} \boldsymbol{\omega} \cdot \dot{\mathbf{H}}^* + \frac{1}{2} \dot{\boldsymbol{\omega}} \cdot \mathbf{H}^*. \qquad \text{6.6-11}$$

In order to prove the equality of 6.6-10 and 6.6-11, we must show that the last two terms of 6.6-11 are equal. In fact, $\boldsymbol{\omega} \cdot \dot{\mathbf{H}}_Q = \dot{\boldsymbol{\omega}} \cdot \mathbf{H}_Q$ where Q is *any* point moving with the rigid body. From Eq. 6.5-6,

$$\boldsymbol{\omega} \cdot \dot{\mathbf{H}}_Q = \boldsymbol{\omega} \cdot \frac{\delta \mathbf{H}_Q}{\delta t} + \boldsymbol{\omega} \cdot (\boldsymbol{\omega} \times \mathbf{H}_Q) = \boldsymbol{\omega} \cdot \frac{\delta \mathbf{H}_Q}{\delta t}.$$

The last step follows from the scalar triple product identity, Eq. 1.3-13 or 6.6-2. We now compute $\delta \mathbf{H}_Q / \delta t$, with $\mathbf{H}_Q$ given by Eq. 6.5-1:

$$\frac{\delta \mathbf{H}_Q}{\delta t} = \frac{\delta}{\delta t} \left[\int \mathbf{p} \times (\boldsymbol{\omega} \times \mathbf{p}) \, dm \right] = \int \frac{\delta}{\delta t} [\mathbf{p} \times (\boldsymbol{\omega} \times \mathbf{p})] \, dm = \int \mathbf{p} \times \left(\frac{\delta \boldsymbol{\omega}}{\delta t} \times \mathbf{p} \right) dm.$$

Here $\mathbf{p}$ is the relative position vector from Q to a general point in the mass element dm. Since the differentiation operation is the frame derivative relative to body-fixed axes, $\delta \mathbf{p} / \delta t = \mathbf{0}$. The interchange of the integration and differentiation operations is justified by the fact that the body-fixed frame derivative is used. Relative to body axes, the configuration remains unchanged and, therefore, the limits of integration are not functions of the time variable indicated in the derivative operation. Since $\delta \boldsymbol{\omega} / \delta t = \dot{\boldsymbol{\omega}}$ (Eq. 6.4-13),

$$\boldsymbol{\omega} \cdot \dot{\mathbf{H}}_Q = \boldsymbol{\omega} \cdot \left[\int \mathbf{p} \times (\dot{\boldsymbol{\omega}} \times \mathbf{p}) \, dm \right] = \int \boldsymbol{\omega} \cdot [\mathbf{p} \times (\dot{\boldsymbol{\omega}} \times \mathbf{p})] \, dm.$$

The last step follows from the fact that $\boldsymbol{\omega}$ is a property of the whole body, independent of the coordinates of any particular point, and therefore independent of the indicated integration. We now make use of the fundamental scalar triple product identity (Eq. 1.3-13 or 6.6-2) twice and the commutativity $(\mathbf{A} \cdot \mathbf{B} = \mathbf{B} \cdot \mathbf{A})$ of the scalar product once to transform the integrand:

$$\boldsymbol{\omega} \cdot \dot{\mathbf{H}}_Q = \int [(\boldsymbol{\omega} \times \mathbf{p}) \cdot (\dot{\boldsymbol{\omega}} \times \mathbf{p})] \, dm = \int [(\dot{\boldsymbol{\omega}} \times \mathbf{p}) \cdot (\boldsymbol{\omega} \times \mathbf{p})] \, dm$$

$$= \int \dot{\boldsymbol{\omega}} \cdot [\mathbf{p} \times (\boldsymbol{\omega} \times \mathbf{p})] \, dm = \dot{\boldsymbol{\omega}} \cdot \left[\int \mathbf{p} \times (\boldsymbol{\omega} \times \mathbf{p}) \, dm \right],$$

or*

$$\boldsymbol{\omega} \cdot \dot{\mathbf{H}}_Q = \dot{\boldsymbol{\omega}} \cdot \mathbf{H}_Q. \qquad \text{6.6-12}$$

Identifying Q with the mass center, we see that the last two terms of 6.6-11 are equal, and therefore the power of the external forces (6.6-10) equals the time rate of change of the kinetic energy:

$$P = \frac{dT}{dt}. \qquad \text{6.6-13}$$

The other forms of the work-energy principle for a single rigid body and for systems containing a rigid body then may be obtained by integration from the power principle.

Example **6.6-1**

Compute the kinetic energies of the systems of Examples 6.5-1, 2, *and* 4.
Solution: The particle of 6.5-1 has kinetic energy

$$T = \frac{1}{2} m \mathbf{v} \cdot \mathbf{v} = \frac{1}{2} m l^2 \dot{\phi}^2 \sin^2 \theta,$$

since $\mathbf{v} = -l\dot{\phi} \sin \theta \mathbf{i}$ in the rotating coordinates or $\mathbf{v} = -l\dot{\phi} \sin \theta \cos \phi \mathbf{I} - l\dot{\phi} \sin \theta \sin \phi \mathbf{J}$ in the fixed coordinates.

For the conical bar pendulum, O is a fixed point, and 6.6-7 may be used:

$$T = \frac{1}{2} \boldsymbol{\omega} \cdot \mathbf{H}_O = \frac{1}{2} [-\dot{\phi} \sin \theta \mathbf{j}' + \dot{\phi} \cos \theta \mathbf{k}'] \cdot \left[-\frac{1}{3} m l^2 \dot{\phi} \sin \theta \mathbf{j}' \right]$$

$$= \frac{1}{6} m l^2 \dot{\phi}^2 \sin^2 \theta.$$

From the results of Example 6.5-3, we may also find T from 6.6-6:

$$T = \frac{1}{2} m \mathbf{v}^* \cdot \mathbf{v}^* + \frac{1}{2} \boldsymbol{\omega} \cdot \mathbf{H}^*$$

$$= \frac{1}{2} m \left(\frac{l^2}{4} \dot{\phi}^2 \sin^2 \theta \right) + \frac{1}{2} \left(\frac{m l^2}{12} \dot{\phi}^2 \sin^2 \theta \right)$$

$$= \frac{1}{6} m l^2 \dot{\phi}^2 \sin^2 \theta.$$

---

* The student may prove this fundamental identity in an alternate way by giving $\mathbf{H}_Q$ a particular body-axes representation, say with respect to principal axes of inertia at Q. He may also show that the interchange of the absolute time derivative, and the integral over the mass distribution is justified by showing the identity of

$$\int \frac{d}{dt} [\mathbf{p} \times (\boldsymbol{\omega} \times \mathbf{p})] \, dm \quad \text{with} \quad \delta \mathbf{H}_Q / \delta t + \boldsymbol{\omega} \times \mathbf{H}_Q.$$

For the bar as spherical pendulum, again O is a fixed point:

$$T = \frac{1}{2}\,\boldsymbol{\omega}\cdot\mathbf{H}_O$$

$$= \frac{1}{2}\,[-\dot\theta\mathbf{i}' - \dot\phi\sin\theta\mathbf{j}' + \dot\phi\cos\theta\mathbf{k}']\cdot\left[-\frac{1}{3}\,ml^2\dot\theta\mathbf{i}' - \frac{1}{3}\,ml^2\dot\phi\sin\theta\mathbf{j}'\right]$$

$$= \frac{1}{6}\,ml^2\dot\theta^2 + \frac{1}{6}\,ml^2\dot\phi^2\sin^2\theta.$$

All of these results illustrate an important fact. Notice that T is a function of the angle θ, which may change, as well as of ϕ and $\dot\theta$. Too often one thinks of the kinetic energy as dependent on linear and angular velocity quantities only; this shows that the kinetic energy may also be a function of the generalized coordinates that specify configuration.

Example 6.6-2

Write the energy equations for each of the systems discussed in the previous example, assuming the supports at O for the bars are frictionless.

Solution: In all cases, the support reactions then do no work; only the conservative gravitational force does work. Taking the horizontal level at O as the zero datum level for potential energy, the potential in each case will be

$$-\mathbf{W}\cdot\mathbf{r}^* = -Wz^*,$$

since z is measured positively downward. For the particle, $z^* = z = l\cos\theta$; for the bar, $z^* = (l/2)\cos\theta$. In each case, conservation of energy applies:

$$E = T + V = E_0, \quad \text{a constant.}$$

Particle:

$$\frac{1}{2}\,ml^2\dot\phi^2\sin^2\theta - mgl\cos\theta = E_0.$$

Bar as a conical pendulum:

$$\frac{1}{6}\,ml^2\dot\phi^2\sin^2\theta - \frac{mgl}{2}\cos\theta = E_0.$$

Bar as a spherical pendulum:

$$\frac{1}{6}\,ml^2\dot\theta^2 + \frac{1}{6}\,ml^2\dot\phi^2\sin^2\theta - \frac{mgl}{2}\cos\theta = E_0.$$

Compare Example 6.5-5 with this example. The first two of these energy equations tell us that ϕ must be constant since θ is a constant, but not what the constant is, as the moment equations of 6.5-5 did. Of course, if we are given initial conditions, E_0 may be evaluated—but that amounts to knowing the proper ϕ from the beginning. The spherical-pendulum equation is interesting. It again contains less information than the full moment equations do; in particular, we do not know from energy considerations that $\dot\phi \sin^2 \theta$ is constant. The first integral of the last equation of Example 6.5-5 is just the energy integral with the additional information included. Take that equation and multiply by $2\dot\theta$ as an integrating factor:

$$2\dot\theta\ddot\theta + \frac{3g}{l}(\sin\theta\dot\theta) - 2C^2 \frac{\cos\theta\dot\theta}{\sin^3\theta} = 0$$

or

$$\frac{d}{dt}\left[\dot\theta^2 - \frac{3g}{l}\cos\theta + \frac{C^2}{\sin^2\theta}\right] = 0;$$

therefore,*

$$\dot\theta^2 + \frac{C^2}{\sin^2\theta} - \frac{3g}{l}\cos\theta = \text{constant}.$$

Substituting $C = \dot\phi \sin^2\theta$ and multiplying by $\frac{1}{6}ml^2$, we find the energy equation we have given.

6.7 Special Forms of the Dynamical Equations; Euler's Equations

Let us write the forms of the dynamical equations of a rigid body for some special motions, partly as a reference for the applications to come and partly as a summary review of the concepts of this chapter.

(a) *Fixed-axis rotation:* A body in rotation about a fixed axis has a single rotational degree of freedom. For the representation of **H**, we choose coordinates fixed in the body and rotating with it. Take the origin O at any point of the fixed axis, which we take as the z-axis; x and y are chosen in some convenient way. We have

$$\boldsymbol{\omega} = \omega_z\mathbf{k}, \qquad \dot{\boldsymbol{\omega}} = \dot\omega_z\mathbf{k} \qquad\qquad \textbf{6.7-1}$$

$$\mathbf{H}_O = -I^O_{xz}\omega_z\mathbf{i} - I^O_{yz}\omega_z\mathbf{j} + I^O_{zz}\omega_z\mathbf{k}, \qquad\qquad \textbf{6.7-2}$$

$$\dot{\mathbf{H}}_O = \frac{\delta\mathbf{H}_O}{\delta t} + \boldsymbol{\omega} \times \mathbf{H}_O$$

$$= [-I^O_{xz}\dot\omega_z + I^O_{yz}\omega_z^2]\mathbf{i} + [-I^O_{yz}\dot\omega_z - I^O_{xz}\omega_z^2]\mathbf{j} + I^O_{zz}\dot\omega_z\mathbf{k}. \qquad \textbf{6.7-3}$$

The scalar moment equations can then be written by setting the components of $\dot{\mathbf{H}}_O$ equal to the corresponding components of $\mathbf{M}_O$ computed from the forces. This requires that we find $\mathbf{M}_O$ relative to the

---

* The equation may be integrated once more to obtain $\theta(t)$, but this integration would involve elliptic functions and integrals. For a discussion of the spherical-pendulum problem, see Synge and Griffith, *Principles of Mechanics*, 3rd ed. (McGraw-Hill Book Co., 1959), pp. 335 ff.

body axes, so that we usually show the forces on the free-body diagram in components in the direction of the body axes rather than in directions of the space axes. The equations are

$$M_x^O = (\dot{\mathbf{H}}_O)_x = -I_{xz}^O \dot{\omega}_z + I_{yz}^O \omega_z^2$$
$$M_y^O = -I_{yz}^O \dot{\omega}_z - I_{xz}^O \omega_z^2, \qquad \qquad \textbf{6.7-4}$$
$$M_z^O = I_{zz}^O \dot{\omega}_z.$$

The student should not attempt to memorize these. They are presented for reference; the applications will show how they are to be used. One important difference between this and pure rotation in the plane can be seen immediately; even for constant angular velocity ($\dot{\omega}_z = 0$), the x and y moment equations are important here.

The motion of the mass center is determined by the force equations $\mathbf{F} = m\mathbf{a}^*$. With $\mathbf{r}^* = x^*\mathbf{i} + y^*\mathbf{j} + z^*\mathbf{k}$, the relative acceleration relations give

$$\mathbf{a}^* = \dot{\boldsymbol{\omega}} \times \mathbf{r}^* + \boldsymbol{\omega} \times (\boldsymbol{\omega} \times \mathbf{r}^*) = -(x^*\omega_z^2 + y^*\dot{\omega}_z)\mathbf{i} - (y^*\omega_z^2 - x^*\dot{\omega}_z)\mathbf{j},$$

or an acceleration $l^*\omega_z^2$ toward the axis and $l^*\dot{\omega}_z$ perpendicular to the axis in the proper sense, where l^* is the distance from C to the axis. Remember that x^*, y^*, z^* are constants referred to body axes. The scalar force equations are

$$F_x = ma_x^* = -m(x^*\omega_z^2 + y^*\dot{\omega}_z),$$
$$F_y = ma_y^* = m(x^*\dot{\omega}_z - y^*\omega_z^2), \qquad \qquad \textbf{6.7-5}$$
$$F_z = ma_z^* = 0.$$

A two-degree-of-freedom motion results from combining this with a translation in some fixed direction; if the translation is in the z-direction, only the last equation changes, to $F_z = m\ddot{z}^*$. Note that the rotating body axes for fixed-axis rotation, or rotation plus translation in the direction of the rotation axis, are much like cylindrical polar coordinates.

(b) *Fixed-point rotation:* Choose principal axes of inertia of the body at the fixed point O, rotating with the body. (We shall see another choice of axes for symmetrical bodies with a fixed point in the applications.) There are three rotational degrees of freedom. We have:

$$\boldsymbol{\omega} = \omega_x\mathbf{i} + \omega_y\mathbf{j} + \omega_z\mathbf{k},$$
$$\dot{\boldsymbol{\omega}} = \frac{\delta\boldsymbol{\omega}}{\delta t} = \dot{\omega}_x\mathbf{i} + \dot{\omega}_y\mathbf{j} + \dot{\omega}_z\mathbf{k}, \qquad \qquad \textbf{6.7-6}$$

$$\mathbf{H}_O = I^O_{xx}\omega_x\mathbf{i} + I^O_{yy}\omega_y\mathbf{j} + I^O_{zz}\omega_z\mathbf{k}, \qquad \textbf{6.7-7}$$

$$\dot{\mathbf{H}}_O = \frac{\delta\mathbf{H}_O}{\delta t} + \boldsymbol{\omega} \times \mathbf{H}_O$$

$$= [I^O_{xx}\dot{\omega}_x + (I^O_{zz} - I^O_{yy})\omega_y\omega_z]\mathbf{i} + [I^O_{yy}\dot{\omega}_y + (I^O_{xx} - I^O_{zz})\omega_x\omega_z]\mathbf{j}$$

$$+ [I^O_{zz}\dot{\omega}_z + (I^O_{yy} - I^O_{xx})\omega_x\omega_y]\mathbf{k}. \qquad \textbf{6.7-8}$$

Here $(I^O_{xx}, I^O_{yy}, I^O_{zz})$ are the principal moments of inertia at O. The scalar equivalents of $\mathbf{M}_O = \dot{\mathbf{H}}_O$ referred to principal axes of inertia are called *Euler's equations of motion*:

$$M^O_x = (\dot{\mathbf{H}}_O)_x = I^O_{xx}\dot{\omega}_x + (I^O_{zz} - I^O_{yy})\omega_y\omega_z,$$

$$M^O_y = I^O_{yy}\dot{\omega}_y + (I^O_{xx} - I^O_{zz})\omega_x\omega_z, \qquad \textbf{6.7-9}$$

$$M^O_z = I^O_{zz}\dot{\omega}_z + (I^O_{yy} - I^O_{xx})\omega_x\omega_y.$$

The moments are, of course, computed in the rotating coordinate frame. The motion of the mass center, located at

$$\mathbf{r}^* = x^*\mathbf{i} + y^*\mathbf{j} + z^*\mathbf{k},$$

with (x^*, y^*, z^*) constants, is governed by

$$\mathbf{F} = m\mathbf{a}^* = m[\dot{\boldsymbol{\omega}} \times \mathbf{r}^*_{_.} + \boldsymbol{\omega} \times (\boldsymbol{\omega} \times \mathbf{r}^*)]. \qquad \textbf{6.7-10}$$

(c) *General plane motion:* All points of the body move parallel to a fixed plane. There are two translational degrees of freedom, and one rotational. Take the xy-plane to be the plane of motion of the mass center, and the z-axis perpendicular to that plane; the axes themselves are body axes with origin at C. Then $\boldsymbol{\omega} = \omega_z\mathbf{k}$, and the angular momentum and the moment equations are given by 6.7-2 and 6.7-4. The difference between fixed-axis rotation and general plane motion is expressed by force equations; now $\mathbf{a}^* = a^*_x\mathbf{i} + a^*_y\mathbf{j}$, and we have

$$F_x = ma^*_x, \qquad F_y = ma^*_y, \qquad F_z = 0 \qquad \textbf{6.7-11}$$

instead of 6.7-5.

(d) *Motion in space:* When all six degrees of freedom are involved, we may use equations of Euler's type (6.7-9) for $\mathbf{M}^* = \dot{\mathbf{H}}^*$ by taking principal inertia axes at C as our body axes; the moments of inertia that appear are then the principal moments at C: $I^*_{xx}, I^*_{yy}, I^*_{zz}$. The principle of motion of the mass center is

$$F_x = ma^*_x, \qquad F_y = ma^*_y, \qquad F_z = ma^*_z. \qquad \textbf{6.7-12}$$

Of course, for all of these (and for other motions) different equation forms may be more suitable for particular problems. The force equations often are not best written in rotating body coordinates; fixed space or intrinsic path coordinates may be better. There is always a problem of relating motion described in moving axes to the motion relative to fixed axes. No substitute for thoughtful formulation of each problem exists. The cases presented here, however, may serve as guides to the establishment of appropriate equations.

6.8 Equilibrium of a Rigid Body

In statics, the necessity of the equilibrium equations for systems $F = 0$, $M = 0$ in terms of the external forces is shown. That is, if a system is in equilibrium, then the resultant external force system must be equipollent to the zero or null system. The converse is not always true: two particles may be subjected to no external force, but each in general has an acceleration corresponding to the internal force acting on it. For the rigid body, however, the equations of equilibrium are sufficient as well as necessary. We shall prove that a rigid body subject to a vanishing resultant force system must be in equilibrium.

First, what do we mean by equilibrium of a system? For a particle, motion at constant velocity relative to an inertial system proceeds under zero force and so is an equilibrium state. As we have seen in Section 2.2, we can find a second inertial frame in which the particle is at rest. For a system, equilibrium may be defined as a state of motion in which each particle of the system is in equilibrium. By this definition, the mass center of the system can at most translate at a constant velocity. We can find an inertial frame in which the mass center is at rest. Every other particle (or point in a continuous body) has a constant velocity relative to the mass center, so that steady rotational motions are ruled out as equilibrium motions. Indeed, for continuous bodies in general, further translational motion relative to the mass center is so special a case—and an impossible one for a rigid body—that we rule out such additional motions also. Thus a system is in equilibrium if it is at rest in some inertial frame. The appropriate statement of the sufficiency theorem is:

If the resultant external force and moment on a rigid body (which is in equilibrium momentarily) vanish, the body remains in equilibrium.

Suppose a rigid body momentarily at rest in an inertial frame is subjected to a vanishing resultant external system ($F = 0$, $M = 0$), and suppose it does not remain in equilibrium. Let us constrain the body so that it is in equilibrium (Fig. 6.8-1); we have seen how we may do this in Section 6.2.

Fix one point, A, by a smooth ball-and-socket joint; this produces a constraint reaction force A on the body. A second point, B, can be fixed by placing it in a smooth sleeve bearing with axis along the line AB, so that a constraint force B normal to AB is produced. Finally, the whole configuration is fixed by placing a third point, C, not on AB on a smooth roller between parallel planes; the reaction force **C** is normal to the plane *ABC*. Choosing axes at *A* with the *x*-axis along *AB*, the *y*-axis in the plane *ABC*, and the *z*-axis normal to *ABC*, the constraint forces have representation $\mathbf{A} = A_x\mathbf{i} + A_y\mathbf{j} + A_z\mathbf{k}$, $\mathbf{B} = B_y\mathbf{j} + B_z\mathbf{k}$, $\mathbf{C} = C_z\mathbf{k}$.

Since the body can no longer move, it must be in equilibrium under the action of the original force system $\mathbf{F} = \mathbf{0}$, $\mathbf{M} = \mathbf{0}$ plus the constraint reactions **A**, **B**, and **C**. The equilibrium equations now apply; in particular,

$$\mathbf{R} = \mathbf{F} + \mathbf{A} + \mathbf{B} + \mathbf{C} = \mathbf{A} + \mathbf{B} + \mathbf{C} = \mathbf{0},$$

$$\mathbf{M}_A = \mathbf{M} + \mathbf{r}_B \times \mathbf{B} + \mathbf{r}_C \times \mathbf{C} = \mathbf{r}_B \times \mathbf{B} + \mathbf{r}_C \times \mathbf{C} = \mathbf{0}. \qquad \textbf{6.8-1}$$

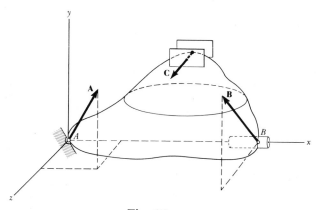

Fig. 6.8-1

This says that the additional constraint reactions constitute a force system equipollent to zero also. But now we may determine these reactions individually. We have

$$\begin{aligned}
\mathbf{0} &= \mathbf{r}_B \times \mathbf{B} + \mathbf{r}_C \times \mathbf{C} \\
&= x_B\mathbf{i} \times (B_y\mathbf{j} + B_z\mathbf{k}) + (x_C\mathbf{i} + y_C\mathbf{j}) \times C_z\mathbf{k} \\
&= y_C C_z\mathbf{i} - (x_B B_z + x_C C_z)\mathbf{j} + x_B B_y\mathbf{k}.
\end{aligned}$$

But $x_B \neq 0$, $y_C \neq 0$; therefore,

$$C_z = 0, \qquad B_z = 0, \qquad B_y = 0.$$

The resultant force equation then reduces to $\mathbf{A} = A_x\mathbf{i} + A_y\mathbf{j} + A_z\mathbf{k} = \mathbf{0}$, or $A_x = A_y = A_z = 0$.

What we have shown is this: by supposing the body not in equilibrium we have found that the forces necessary to put the body in equilibrium not only sum to a zero system but are individually zero. Therefore, we do not need to add any forces, and the body must remain in equilibrium under the original force system. This proves that the vanishing of the resultant external force system is sufficient for continuing rigid-body equilibrium.

Exercises

6.3-1: A rigid body with fixed point O rotates with constant angular velocity $\boldsymbol{\omega} = 3\mathbf{i} - 4\mathbf{j} + 12\mathbf{k}$ rad/sec. What is the velocity of P if P is located at position $\mathbf{r} = 2\mathbf{i} + \mathbf{j} + \mathbf{k}$ ft from O? Sketch the vectors involved.
Ans.: $\mathbf{v}_P = -16\mathbf{i} + 21\mathbf{j} + 11\mathbf{k}$ ft/sec.

6.3-2: A rigid body with fixed point O rotates with constant angular speed 13 rad/sec about an axis having direction of the line OQ, where Q has position $4\mathbf{i} - \frac{16}{3}\mathbf{j} + 16\mathbf{k}$ ft relative to O; the sense of rotation agrees with this direction according to the right-hand rule. What is the velocity of the point P having position $2\mathbf{i} + \mathbf{j} + \mathbf{k}$ ft?
Ans.: Same as Exercise 6.3-1.

6.3-3: A rigid body with fixed point O rotates with constant angular velocity of magnitude 200 rpm and of direction agreeing with OQ, where $\mathbf{r}_Q = \mathbf{i} - \mathbf{j} - \mathbf{k}$ in.
   (a) Find the velocity of P, if $\mathbf{r}_P = 2\mathbf{i} + \mathbf{j} + \mathbf{k}$ in.
   (b) Find the velocity of S, if $\mathbf{r}_S = \mathbf{i} - \mathbf{j} + 2\mathbf{k}$ in.
   (c) Find the velocity of S with respect to P, both directly from the definition of $\mathbf{v}_{S/P}$ and from the fact that S and P are on the same rigid body.
      Ans.: (a) $\mathbf{v}_P = -36.3\mathbf{j} + 36.3\mathbf{k}$ in/sec; (c) $\mathbf{v}_{S/P} = -36.3\mathbf{i} - 36.3\mathbf{k}$ in/sec.

6.3-4: The rigid body of Exercise 6.3-1 is rotating with the same angular velocity as given there, but point O is no longer fixed; at the instant considered, $\mathbf{v}_O = 12\mathbf{i} - 9\mathbf{j} + \mathbf{k}$ ft/sec. What is the velocity of P?
Ans.: $\mathbf{v}_P = -4\mathbf{i} + 12\mathbf{j} + 12\mathbf{k}$ ft/sec.

6.3-5: The body of Exercise 6.3-3 rotates with the same angular velocity as given there, but point O is no longer fixed; at the instant considered, $\mathbf{v}_O = 18.3\mathbf{i} - 3.7\mathbf{j} + 20\mathbf{k}$ in/sec.
   (a) What is $\mathbf{v}_P$?
   (b) What is $\mathbf{v}_S$?
   (c) Is $\mathbf{v}_{S/P}$ the same or different? If the same, why?; if different, find it.
Ans.: $\mathbf{v}_S = -18\mathbf{i} - 40\mathbf{j} + 20\mathbf{k}$ in/sec.

6.3-6: A rigid body with a fixed point O has constant angular velocity $\boldsymbol{\omega} = \omega_x\mathbf{i} + \omega_y\mathbf{j} + \omega_z\mathbf{k}$, the components being measured relative to axes at O fixed in space. Consider the motion of a point P in the body at position $\mathbf{r} = x(t)\mathbf{i} + y(t)\mathbf{j} + z(t)\mathbf{k}$.
   (a) Find $\mathbf{v}_P$ directly.
   (b) Find $\mathbf{v}_P$, using the angular velocity concept.
   (c) Equate these two and write the three scalar differential equations for x, y, and z.
Ans.: (c) $\dot{x} = \omega_y z(t) - \omega_z y(t)$, etc.

6.3-7: If, in Exercise 6.3-6, ω is not constant, but $\omega_x = \omega_x(t)$, etc., is the form of the final equations any different?

6.3-8: In Exercise 6.3-2, what will $v_{P/Q}$ be?

6.3-9: A rigid body with fixed point O has, at a given instant, angular velocity $\omega = 3\mathbf{i} - 4\mathbf{j} + 12\mathbf{k}$ rad/sec and angular acceleration $\dot{\omega} = -\mathbf{i} + 2\mathbf{j} + 5\mathbf{k}$ rad/sec² referred to ($\mathbf{i}$, $\mathbf{j}$, $\mathbf{k}$) directions fixed in space. What is the acceleration of a point P in the body having position $\mathbf{r} = 2\mathbf{i} + \mathbf{j} + \mathbf{k}$ ft?
Ans.: $\ddot{\mathbf{r}} = -299\mathbf{i} - 214\mathbf{j} - 6\mathbf{k}$ ft/sec².

6.4-1: Suppose that, in Exercises 6.3-1 to 6.3-5 and 6.3-9, the directions referred to are fixed in the body and rotate with it; do any answers change? Why?

6.4-2: Suppose a rigid disk of radius r is rotating in its plane about an axis perpendicular to its plane with angular velocity ω and angular acceleration $\dot{\omega}$ as shown. Find the velocity and acceleration of point P on the rim (a) relative to (X, Y, Z) axes fixed in space, (b) relative to (x, y, z) axes fixed in the body and rotating with it at the instant when the angle between X and x is θ. Show that the answers are, in fact, the same.

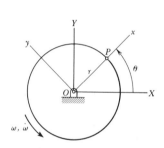

Ans.: $a = -r(\dot{\omega}\sin\theta + \omega^2\cos\theta)\mathbf{I}$
$+ r(\dot{\omega}\cos\theta - \omega^2\sin\theta)\mathbf{J}$
$= -r\omega^2\mathbf{i} + r\dot{\omega}\mathbf{j}$.

6.4-3: Suppose the disk of Exercise 6.4-2 is set spinning about a diameter, with angular velocity and acceleration at some instant being ω and $\dot{\omega}$ as pictured. Take axes as shown, with (x, y, z) being body axes and (X, Y, Z) being space axes. Find the velocity and acceleration of a point, P, on the rim, where OP makes the constant angle ϕ with Ox. Express your answers both in body and space coordinates. At the given instant, the plane of the disk (Oxz) makes angle θ with the fixed reference plane (OXZ).

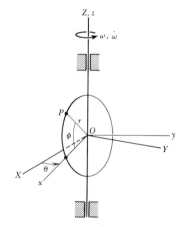

Ans.: $a = -r\omega^2\cos\phi\,\mathbf{i} + r\dot{\omega}\cos\phi\,\mathbf{j}$
$= -r\cos\phi(\dot{\omega}\sin\theta + \omega^2\cos\theta)\mathbf{I}$
$+ r\cos\phi(\dot{\omega}\cos\theta - \omega^2\sin\theta)\mathbf{J}$.

6.4-4: A rigid disk rotates with constant angular velocity 4 rad/sec counter-clockwise. A pin P moves in a radial slot in the disk. When the pin is 5 in from the center O, it is traveling at 3 in/sec outward relative to the slot and has an acceleration of 16 in/sec² inward relative to the slot. Find the velocity and acceleration of the pin.

Ans.: $v = 3i + 20j$ in/sec; $a = -96i + 24j$ in/sec².

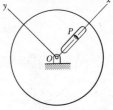

6.4-5: A pin P moves in a slot in a disk that rotates at a constant rate of 4 rad/sec counterclockwise. The perpendicular distance from the center to the slot is 3 in. When the pin is 5 in from the center of the disk, its velocity relative to the slot is 3 in/sec directed away from the midpoint of the slot, while

Exer. 6.4-4

its acceleration relative to the slot is 16 in/sec² toward the midpoint of the slot. Find the velocity and acceleration of P.

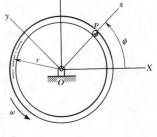

Ans.: $v = 16i + 9j$ in/sec,

$a = -24i + 80j$ in/sec².

Exer. 6.4-5

6.4-6: A circular disk rotates about a centroidal axis at constant rate ω. A circular groove of mean radius r is cut in the disk, and a small ball, P, rolls in the groove at speed v_0 relative to the disk in a sense opposed to the sense of rotation of the disk. Take axes OXY fixed in space and axes Oxy fixed in the disk. Consider an instant when the ball crosses the x-axis and that axis makes an angle ϕ with the X-axis, as pictured.

(a) Relative to OXY, what is the Coriolis acceleration of P?

(b) Relative to Oxy, what is the Coriolis acceleration of P?

(c) Find the total acceleration of P in both of the coordinate systems.

Which computation is simpler? Why do you think so?

Ans.:

(b) $2v_0\omega i$ (c) $a = -\dfrac{(v_0 - r\omega)^2}{r}i$

$= -\dfrac{(v_0 - r\omega)^2}{r}(\cos\phi I + \sin\phi J)$.

6.4-7: An insect is placed on a circular turntable of radius r that turns at constant rate ω. It is attracted by a light that is placed just off the rim of the turntable, and tries to run toward it always. If the insect travels at constant speed v_0 relative to the turntable, find its velocity and acceleration when it is at a distance a from the center of the table and when the radius line to the insect makes an angle θ with the diameter from the light source.

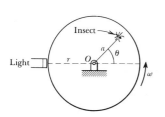

Ans.:

$$|\dot{\mathbf{r}}|^2 = v_0^2 + a^2\omega^2 + \frac{2av_0r\omega \sin\theta}{(a^2 + r^2 + 2ar\cos\theta)^{1/2}},$$

$$|\ddot{\mathbf{r}}|^2 = \omega^2 \left[4v_0^2 + a^2\omega^2 + \frac{4av_0r\omega \sin\theta}{(a^2 + r^2 + 2ar\cos\theta)^{1/2}} \right].$$

6.4-8: A disk of radius r rotates with constant angular velocity ω as shown. A rod of length l is welded rigidly to the disk in its plane, making an angle θ with a radius of the disk. A ring, P, slides outward along the rod at constant speed v_0 relative to the rod. What is the velocity and acceleration of the ring as it flies off the end of the rod?

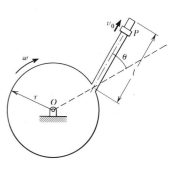

Ans.: $|\mathbf{v}|^2 = v_0^2 - 2v_0r\omega \sin\theta$
$$+ (l^2 + r^2 + 2lr\cos\theta)\omega^2,$$
$$|\mathbf{a}|^2 = \omega^2[4v_0^2 - 4v_0r\omega \sin\theta$$
$$+ (l^2 + r^2 + 2lr\cos\theta)\omega^2].$$

6.4-9: A governor like that of example 6.4-5 consists of two heavy balls, A, A', on the end of 8 in rods hinged to a vertical shaft at P and a collar, C, that slides on the vertical shaft, its motion being related to that of the rest of the system by rods BC, $B'C$. The device rotates at a constant rate $\omega = 100$ rpm about the vertical, causing the side arms PA, PA' to move out from the vertical at rate $\dot{\theta} = 2.0$ rad/sec. Find the velocity of one of the balls when $\theta = 30°$.

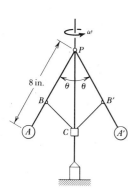

Ans.: The speed of each ball is 44.6 in/sec.

6.4-10: A rigid circular disk of radius r is mounted on a shaft and supporting frame so that its center is fixed in space. The disk can rotate about the horizontal shaft and about a vertical diameter. Let (X, Y, Z)

axes be fixed in space; (x, y, z) axes, fixed in the supporting frame and rotating with it; and (x', y', z') axes, fixed in the disk and rotating with it. Let θ be the angle between the fixed vertical plane (OXZ) and the plane of the disk (Oxz or $Ox'z'$); let ϕ be the angle between Oyz and $Oy'z'$. Find the velocity and acceleration of point P on the rim in all three coordinate systems, for the configuration shown, with the indicated angular motion quantities.

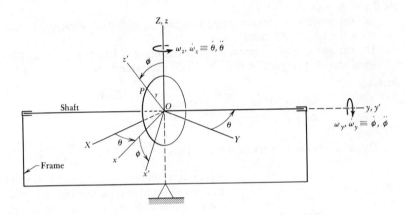

6.4-11: A particle P slides down a rigid wire in the shape of a circular helix. The equation of the helix is given parametrically by $x = a \cos \theta$, $y = a \sin \theta$, $z = a\theta$, where (x, y, z) are axes fixed to the helix. Relative to the helix, the particle has a constant speed v_0. Suppose that the wire is

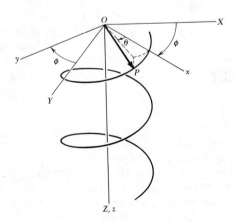

set into oscillation about its axis so that the angle ϕ between the x-axis and another axis, X, fixed in space is given by $\phi = \phi_0 \sin pt$, and that the particle starts from $\theta=0$ at $t=0$. Find the maximum and minimum speeds of P.

Ans.: $|\mathbf{v}|^2_{\max} = v_0^2 + \sqrt{2}v_0ap\phi_0 + a^2p^2\phi_0^2;$

$$|\mathbf{v}|^2_{\min} = \frac{v_0^2}{2}, \text{ provided } \frac{\sqrt{2}v_0}{2ap\phi_0} \leqq 1;$$

$$= v_0^2 - \sqrt{2}v_0ap\phi_0 + a^2p^2\phi_0^2, \quad \frac{\sqrt{2}v_0}{2ap\phi_0} \geqq 1.$$

6.4-12: For the particle on the helix of the previous problem, compute the acceleration $\mathbf{a}$ at $t=\pi/2p$ sec if:

(a) the angle ϕ is always zero; i.e., the (x, y, z) axes always coincide with the (X, Y, Z) axes;

(b) the angle ϕ is as given in problem 6.4-11; i.e., the (x, y, z) axes oscillate with respect to the (X, Y, Z) axes about the $z=Z$ axis.

Ans.:

(a) $\mathbf{a} = -\dfrac{v_0^2}{2a}\left(\cos\dfrac{\sqrt{2}v_0\pi}{4ap}\mathbf{i} + \sin\dfrac{\sqrt{2}v_0\pi}{4ap}\mathbf{j}\right),$

(b) $\mathbf{a} = $ answer to part (a) $+ p^2\phi_0a\left(\sin\dfrac{\sqrt{2}v_0\pi}{4ap}\mathbf{i} - \cos\dfrac{\sqrt{2}v_0\pi}{4ap}\mathbf{j}\right).$

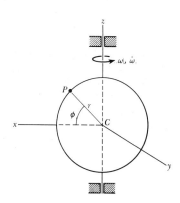

6.5-1: A uniform rigid disk like that of Exercise 6.4-3 of mass m and radius r spins with angular velocity ω and angular acceleration $\dot{\omega}$ about a fixed diameter. Take (x, y, z) axes fixed in the disk and rotating with it as shown. Find $\mathbf{H}^*$ and $\dot{\mathbf{H}}^*$ for the disk.

Ans.: $\mathbf{H}^* = \frac{1}{4}mr^2\omega\mathbf{k}; \qquad \dot{\mathbf{H}}^* = \frac{1}{4}mr^2\dot{\omega}\mathbf{k}.$

6.5-2: For the disk of Exercise 6.5-1, what is $\mathbf{H}_P$, where P is a point on the rim located at a fixed angle ϕ from the x-axis? (See Eq. 4.3-22; also Exercise 6.4-3.)

Ans.: $\mathbf{H}_P = \frac{1}{4}mr^2\omega(1 + 4\cos^2\phi)\mathbf{k}$
$\qquad\qquad - mr^2\omega\sin\phi\cos\phi\mathbf{i}.$

6.5-3: A rigid arm rotates about a vertical axis through its center O at rate Ω; its moment of inertia about the axis is I_O. Two small balls, A and B, each of mass m, slide on the arm, moving out from O symmetrically at constant rate v_0 relative to the arm. When the balls are each at distance r from O, find $\mathbf{H}_O$ and $\dot{\mathbf{H}}_O$ for the system.

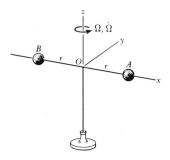

Ans.: $\mathbf{H}_O = (I_O + 2mr^2)\Omega\mathbf{k};$

$\dot{\mathbf{H}}_O = [(I_O + 2mr^2)\dot{\Omega} + 4mrv_0\Omega]\mathbf{k}.$

6.5-4: The three gears are driven from the shaft of A, which rotates at rate ω as shown. The gear ratios are proportional to the given radii. Each gear may be treated as a uniform disk of mass proportional to its area, the mass of gear B being m. Find $\mathbf{H}$ of the system about point A; point B; point C.

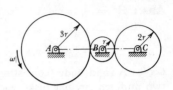

Ans.: All three equal $51mr^2\omega\mathbf{k}$.

6.5-5: A light, thin vertical shaft AB is mounted in bearings and caused to rotate at rate Ω_1. A uniform disk of mass m_1, radius r_1 is rigidly attached to the shaft at the center, O, of the disk, and rotates with the shaft. A second disk of mass m_2 and radius r_2 is supported at a height h_2 above the first, but is not rigidly attached to the shaft. The second disk rotates freely at rate Ω_2 about the shaft. What is $\mathbf{H}_O$ of the system?

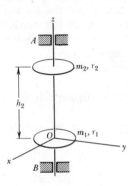

Ans.: $\mathbf{H}_O = \frac{1}{2}(m_1 r_1^2 \Omega_1 + m_2 r_2^2 \Omega_2)\mathbf{k}$.

6.5-6: Two identical gears, A and B—which may be treated as uniform disks each of mass m and radius r—have their centers connected by a link as shown. Gear A is fixed. If the link is driven at constant counterclockwise angular velocity Ω, find:

(a) the velocity of the center P of gear B and its angular velocity ω;
(b) the angular momentum of the system with respect to O, regarding the link to be of negligible mass;
(c) the angular momentum of the system with respect to O, regarding the link as a thin, uniform rigid bar of mass M;
(d) $\dot{\mathbf{H}}_O$ of parts (b) and (c).

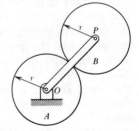

Ans.:

(b) $\mathbf{H}_O = 5mr^2\Omega\mathbf{k}$,
(c) $\mathbf{H}_O = (5m + \frac{4}{3}M)r^2\Omega\mathbf{k}$,
(d) $\dot{\mathbf{H}}_O = \mathbf{0}$.

6.5-7: Suppose that the rigid circular disk of Exercise 6.4-10 is uniform and of mass m, and that the shaft on which it is mounted is of negligible mass. Find $\mathbf{H}^*$ for the disk referred to the frame axes (x, y, z) and to the body axes (x', y', z').

Ans.: $\mathbf{H}^* = \frac{1}{2}mr^2\dot{\phi}\mathbf{j} + \frac{1}{4}mr^2\dot{\theta}\mathbf{k} = -\frac{1}{4}mr^2\dot{\theta}\sin\phi\,\mathbf{i}' + \frac{1}{2}mr^2\dot{\phi}\mathbf{j}' + \frac{1}{4}mr^2\dot{\theta}\cos\phi\mathbf{k}'$.

6.5-8: Find $\dot{\mathbf{H}}^*$ for the disk of the previous problem in both coordinate systems.

Ans.: $\dot{\mathbf{H}}^* = -\frac{1}{2}mr^2\dot{\phi}\dot{\theta}\mathbf{i} + \frac{1}{2}mr^2\ddot{\phi}\mathbf{j} + \frac{1}{4}mr^2\ddot{\theta}\mathbf{k}$

$= -\frac{1}{4}mr^2(\ddot{\theta}\sin\phi + 2\dot{\phi}\dot{\theta}\cos\phi)\mathbf{i}' + \frac{1}{2}mr^2\ddot{\phi}\mathbf{j}'$

$+ \frac{1}{4}mr^2(\ddot{\theta}\cos\phi - 2\dot{\phi}\dot{\theta}\sin\phi)\mathbf{k}'.$

6.5-9: A rigid body (consisting of a light, horizontal shaft of length l and two uniform circular disks, each of mass m and radius r, rigidly keyed to

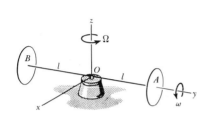

the shaft) is so mounted at the center, O, of the shaft that it can rotate about the vertical z-axis and about the axis of the shaft (y-axis). Suppose that Ω and ω are the *constant* rates of rotation about the vertical and horizontal directions as shown. Take (x, y, z) axes as shown, rotating about the vertical but not with the body.

(a) Find the angular velocity $\mathbf{\Omega}$ of the axes and the angular velocity $\boldsymbol{\omega}$ of the rigid body.

(b) What is $\mathbf{H}_A$ for the disk with center A? What is $\mathbf{H}_O$ for that disk?

(c) What is $\mathbf{H}_O$ of the whole rigid body?

(d) What is $\dot{\mathbf{H}}_O$?

Ans.:

(b) $\mathbf{H}_A = \frac{1}{2}mr^2\omega\mathbf{j} + \frac{1}{4}mr^2\Omega\mathbf{k}$,

(c) $\mathbf{H}_O = mr^2\omega\mathbf{j} + \frac{1}{2}m(r^2 + 4l^2)\Omega\mathbf{k}$,

(d) $\dot{\mathbf{H}}_O = -mr^2\omega\Omega\mathbf{i}$.

6.5-10: Suppose that the two disks of the previous problem are not rigidly keyed to the shaft, but can rotate freely about it. The system as a whole still has the angular velocity Ω about the vertical as before, and the disk with center A has the angular velocity ω about the shaft in the sense shown. Now, however, disk B rotates about the shaft at rate ω in the opposite sense. Find $\mathbf{H}_O$ and $\dot{\mathbf{H}}_O$ for this system.

Ans.: $\mathbf{H}_O = \frac{1}{2}m(r^2 + 4l^2)\Omega\mathbf{k}$.

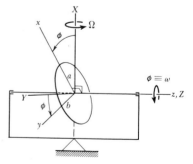

6.5-11: A uniform elliptical disk of mass m and semi-axes a and b is mounted rigidly on a light horizontal shaft, which in turn is mounted in bearings on a light frame that rotates about the vertical at constant rate Ω.

Exer. 6.5-11

The disk rotates about the shaft at constant rate $\dot{\phi} \equiv \omega$ where ϕ is the angle between the vertical and the major axis of the ellipse. Take (X, Y, Z) axes fixed in the frame and (x, y, z) axes fixed in the disk as shown.

(a) What is the $\boldsymbol{\Omega}$ of the (X, Y, Z) axes; the $\boldsymbol{\omega}$ of the body (x, y, z) axes?

(b) What is $\mathbf{H}^*$ of the body in each axis system?

(c) What is $\dot{\mathbf{H}}^*$ of the body in each axis system?

Ans.:

(a) $\quad \boldsymbol{\omega} = \Omega \cos \phi \mathbf{i} - \Omega \sin \phi \mathbf{j} + \omega \mathbf{k},$

(b) $\mathbf{H}^* = \dfrac{mb^2}{4} \Omega \cos \phi \mathbf{i} - \dfrac{ma^2}{4} \Omega \sin \phi \mathbf{j} + \dfrac{m}{4}(a^2 + b^2)\omega \mathbf{k}$

$\quad = \dfrac{m\Omega}{4}(b^2 \cos^2 \phi + a^2 \sin^2 \phi)\mathbf{I} - \dfrac{m\Omega(a^2 - b^2) \sin \phi \cos \phi}{4} \mathbf{J}$

$\qquad + \dfrac{m(a^2 + b^2)}{4} \omega \mathbf{K},$

(c) $\dot{\mathbf{H}}^* = \dfrac{-mb^2}{2} \Omega\omega \sin \phi \mathbf{i} - \dfrac{ma^2}{2} \Omega\omega \cos \phi \mathbf{j}$

$\qquad - \dfrac{m(a^2 - b^2)}{4} \Omega^2 \sin \phi \cos \phi \mathbf{k}.$

6.5-12: For the arm and balls of Exercise 6.5-3, suppose that the arm has angular velocity Ω_1 when the balls are at distance r_1 from O; what will be the angular velocity Ω_2 when the balls are at distance r_2?

Ans.: $\Omega_2/\Omega_1 = (I_O + 2mr_1^2)/(I_O + 2mr_2^2).$

6.5-13: In the previous exercise, suppose the arm is forced to rotate at constant angular velocity Ω_1; what external torque M_z must be applied for this to be true at any $r > r_1$?

Ans.: $M_z = 4mrv_0\Omega_1.$

6.5-14: Suppose you throw a coin in the air, giving its mass center an initial velocity $\mathbf{v}_0^*$ and the coin an initial angular velocity $\boldsymbol{\omega}_0$. Neglect air resistance and treat the coin as a uniform disk of mass m and radius r. Describe in general terms its subsequent motion. In particular, what will be the path of the mass center? How does $\mathbf{H}^*$ change? Does $\boldsymbol{\omega}$ remain constant? For what initial conditions will $\boldsymbol{\omega}$ remain constant?

6.5-15: Do the previous problem for a general rigid body with principal moments of inertia at the mass center being given as A, B, and C.

6.5-16: Do Exercise 6.5-14 for a rigid body consisting of two particles, each of mass m, joined by a light rigid rod of length $2l$.

6.5-17: Suppose the two particles of the previous problem are joined by a light spring of constant k and undeformed length $2l_0$. The system is thrown in the air with the spring initially deformed, initial mass center velocity $\mathbf{v}_0^*$, and initial angular velocity $\boldsymbol{\omega}_0$ for axes one of which is always along the line joining the masses and with origin at the mass center of the system. Describe the motion in general terms; in what ways is it the same and in what ways does it differ from the motion of the rigid body of the previous problem?

6.6-1: Find the kinetic energy of the disk of Exercise 6.5-1.
Ans.: $T = \frac{1}{8}mr^2\omega^2$.

6.6-2: Find the kinetic energy of the disk of Exercise 6.5-7.
Ans.: $T = \frac{1}{4}mr^2\dot{\phi}^2 + \frac{1}{8}mr^2\dot{\theta}^2$.

6.6-3: Find the kinetic energy of the system of Exercise 6.5-9; of Exercise 6.5-10.
Ans.: Both have $T = \frac{1}{2}mr^2\omega^2 + \frac{1}{4}m(r^2 + 4l^2)\Omega^2$.

6.6-4: Find the kinetic energy of the elliptical disk of Exercise 6.5-11.
Ans.: $T = \frac{1}{8}m(b^2\cos^2\phi + a^2\sin^2\phi)\Omega^2 + \frac{1}{8}m(a^2 + b^2)\omega^2$.

6.6-5: A rigid body is mounted in a ball-and-socket joint at point O. At the instant shown, it is rotating with angular velocity $\omega = 2\mathbf{i} - 3\mathbf{j} + 4\mathbf{k}$ rad/sec with the axes of reference being principal axes of inertia at O, fixed in the body and rotating with it. The principal moments of inertia are

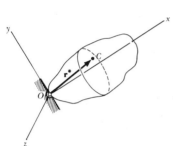

$$I_{xx}^O = 300 \text{ lb-ft-sec}^2;$$
$$I_{yy}^O = 500 \text{ lb-ft-sec}^2;$$
$$I_{zz}^O = 600 \text{ lb-ft-sec}^2.$$

Find the kinetic energy T.
Ans.: $T = 7650$ ft-lb.

6.6-6: In the previous exercise, suppose O is not fixed, but has velocity $\mathbf{v}_O = -5\mathbf{i} + 2\mathbf{j} - \mathbf{k}$ ft/sec. The mass of the body is 10 slugs; the position of the mass center relative to O is $\mathbf{r}^* = 4\mathbf{i} + \mathbf{j}$ ft. Find T.
Ans.: $T = 8180$ ft-lb.

6.6-7: The same as the previous exercise if $\mathbf{r}^* = 4\mathbf{i} + \mathbf{j} - 2\mathbf{k}$ ft.
Ans.: $T = 8158$ ft-lb.

6.6-8: Find the kinetic energy of the arm and masses of Exercise 6.5-3 under the conditions of Exercise 6.5-13 when the masses are at general distance $r > r_1$.

6.6-9: What is the change in kinetic energy of the arm and masses of Exercise 6.5-3 during the motion described in Exercise 6.5-12? Since there is no change in the gravitational potential energy of the system, to what agency do you attribute the change in kinetic energy?

6.6-10: Is the type of system described in Exercises 6.5-14, 15, 16, air resistance being neglected, conservative? If not, why not? If so, what is the mechanical energy E in general position?

6.6-11: Is the two-mass and spring system of Exercise 6.5-17 conservative? If not, why not? If so, what is E in general position? (Take the spring length to be $2l$ in general position if needed.)

CHAPTER VII

Three-Dimensional Applications
of the Principles of Dynamics

7.1 Introduction

In three-dimensional motion as in two-dimensional motion, the equations $\mathbf{F}^* = m\mathbf{a}^*$ and $\mathbf{M}_O = \dot{\mathbf{H}}_O$ govern the motion of mechanical systems. The interpretation of these equations is, however, greatly complicated by the fact that all six of the components of the inertia tensor affect the angular momentum. Furthermore, if space-fixed axes were employed in the equations of motion, these inertia tensor components would have to be regarded as functions of the position of the system, and therefore as unknown functions of time. This intolerable complication can be avoided, in the case of a rigid body, by the use of body-fixed, moving axes in place of space-fixed axes. Referred to such axes, the components of the inertia tensor—moments and products of inertia—are simply constants. The use of moving axes is, therefore, the theme of the discussion of three-dimensional motion. We begin with a study of the effects of the earth's rotation on the motion of a particle. The results here serve mainly to justify the normal hypothesis that earth-fixed axes may be regarded as forming an inertial frame of reference. Next we consider the general problem of the constraining reactions associated with fixed-axis rotation. The effects of systematic changes in the direction of the angular momentum vector, first encountered in connection with the dynamically unbalanced rotor, are then discussed. A complication arises in connection with these gyroscopic effects owing to the fact that body-fixed axes are no longer the ones of greatest physical interest nor the ones most easily observed. The way in which the two demands, simplicity of analysis and ease of interpretation, are reconciled in each case repays careful study. Here also we encounter some of the most striking predictive achievements of newtonian mechanics.

7.2 Effects of the Earth's Rotation on Particle Motion near the Surface

In previous chapters, axes fixed in the surface of the earth have been regarded as forming an inertial frame of reference, although, as explained in 2.2, this is only an approximation. We are now in a position to estimate the accuracy of the approximation by analyzing some of the dynamical effects of the earth's motion. The two most prominent features of this motion are a rotation about a polar axis in a period of twenty-four hours and revolution about the sun with a period of one year. The former is by far the more important for our present purposes. In the absence of rotation, revolution around the sun would entail only a translational motion of axes fixed in the earth. While this translation is not quite uniform since the center of the earth does not move in a straight line with constant speed, still it is associated with an acceleration that is small compared with the acceleration due to rotation. It is therefore usually neglected.

Consider first the case of a particle of mass m suspended from a string—the surveyor's plumb bob. In elementary statics, we think of the bob as subject to two forces, a gravitational attraction directed toward the center of the earth and a pull from the string equal in magnitude and opposite in direction. But the bob is moving with the earth in a circle whose radius depends upon the latitude. It therefore has an acceleration, and the forces exerted on it cannot exactly cancel one another. It is the small difference in direction between these two forces, known as the *deviation of the plumb bob*, that we now investigate. Let (X, Y, Z) be nonrotating axes with origin O at the center of the earth, Z directed toward the North Pole, X and Y in the plane of the equator. Let (x, y, z) be a set of rectangular axes that are fixed in the rotating earth. Their origin is also at the center of the earth; z coincides with Z; x and y lie in the plane of the equator with x intersecting the circle of longitude that passes through P, the location of the particle. These coordinates are pictured in Fig. 7.2-1a. The forces that act on the particle are shown in Fig. 7.2-1b. This free-body diagram is a section of Fig. 7.2-1a containing the zx-plane. The force $\mathbf{T}$, which appears in that figure, is exerted on the bob by the string. The magnitude of this force is mg. The direction of $\mathbf{T}$ is, by definition, the *local vertical* and the angle, λ, that $\mathbf{T}$ makes with the equatorial plane is the *astronomical latitude** of the point P. The other force exerted on the bob is the gravitational attraction of the earth. It is directed toward the center of the earth, making an angle λ', known as the *geocentric*

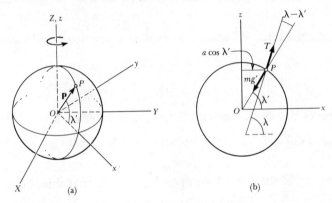

Fig. 7.2-1

latitude, with the equatorial plane. This force is written mg'. If axes fixed in the earth were truly inertial axes, we could say at once that $g' = g$ and $\lambda' = \lambda$. As a matter of fact, as we shall see, these pairs of quantities are very nearly equal; the object of the present investigation is to estimate the difference between them. To do this we write the equation of motion of the particle at P, Eq. 6.4-23.

$$\mathbf{F} - m\ddot{\mathbf{R}} - 2m\boldsymbol{\omega} \times \frac{\delta\mathbf{p}}{\delta t} - m\dot{\boldsymbol{\omega}} \times \mathbf{p} - m\boldsymbol{\omega} \times (\boldsymbol{\omega} \times \mathbf{p}) = m\frac{\delta^2\mathbf{p}}{\delta t^2}.$$

6.4-23 $\equiv$ 7.2-1

In the present circumstances, the fixed coordinate system (X, Y, Z) and the moving coordinate system (x, y, z) have the same origin so

---

* Also known as the *geographic* latitude. It is the quantity that is ordinarily understood when the word latitude is used without qualification.

that $\mathbf{R} = \mathbf{0}$ for all time and therefore $\ddot{\mathbf{R}}$ vanishes. The derivatives $\delta\mathbf{p}/\delta t$ and $\delta^2\mathbf{p}/\delta t^2$ represent the velocity and acceleration of the bob in the rotating coordinate system (x, y, z). These are zero because the particle has no velocity or acceleration in a coordinate system fixed in the earth. The vector $\boldsymbol{\omega}$ is the angular velocity of the rotating coordinate frame (x, y, z); $\boldsymbol{\omega} = \omega\mathbf{k}$ since the earth is rotating about its polar axis. The magnitude of $\boldsymbol{\omega}$ is small. It is $7.292(10)^{-5}$ rad/sec. Since $\boldsymbol{\omega}$ is constant, $\dot{\boldsymbol{\omega}}$ vanishes, and the term $m\dot{\boldsymbol{\omega}} \times \mathbf{p}$ makes no contribution to Eq. 7.2-1. The vector $\mathbf{p}$ is the position vector of the bob:

$$\mathbf{p} = a(\cos \lambda'\mathbf{i} + \sin \lambda'\mathbf{k}), \qquad \text{7.2-2}$$

$$\boldsymbol{\omega} \times (\boldsymbol{\omega} \times \mathbf{p}) = \omega\mathbf{k} \times [\omega\mathbf{k} \times a(\cos \lambda'\mathbf{i} + \sin \lambda'\mathbf{k})] = -a\omega^2 \cos \lambda'\mathbf{i}.$$

$$\text{7.2-3}$$

The external force $\mathbf{F}$ consists, as explained previously, of two forces,

$$\mathbf{T} = mg(\cos \lambda\mathbf{i} + \sin \lambda\mathbf{k})$$

and

$$-mg'(\cos \lambda'\mathbf{i} + \sin \lambda'\mathbf{k}). \qquad \text{7.2-4}$$

In view of these observations, Eq. 7.2-1 reduces to

$$mg(\cos \lambda\mathbf{i} + \sin \lambda\mathbf{k}) - mg'(\cos \lambda'\mathbf{i} + \sin \lambda'\mathbf{k}) + ma\omega^2 \cos \lambda'\mathbf{i} = \mathbf{0}.$$

$$\text{7.2-5}$$

On separating the $\mathbf{i}$ and $\mathbf{k}$ components, we see that this is equivalent to the two scalar equations

$$g \cos \lambda - g' \cos \lambda' + a\omega^2 \cos \lambda' = 0,$$

$$g \sin \lambda - g' \sin \lambda' = 0. \qquad \text{7.2-6}$$

Since g and λ may be measured directly and $a \cos \lambda'$ is known in terms of λ when the shape of the earth has been found by geodetic surveying, these equations may be regarded as determining the quantities λ' and g'. Up to this point nothing has been assumed as to the shape of the earth. If we take the earth to be made of concentric spherical layers of uniform density, the law of gravitational attraction tells us that the force mg' will be directed toward the center of the sphere and that $g' = m_E G/a^2$ where m_E denotes the mass of the earth, G is the universal constant of gravitation, and a, now the same for every point on the earth's surface, is the radius of the earth. With this value for g', the second of Eqs. 7.2-6 becomes

$$g = g' \frac{\sin \lambda'}{\sin \lambda} = \frac{m_E G}{a^2} \frac{\sin \lambda'}{\sin \lambda} \qquad \text{7.2-7}$$

and the first becomes

$$g \left(\cos \lambda - \frac{\sin \lambda}{\sin \lambda'} \cos \lambda' \right) = -a\omega^2 \cos \lambda',$$

$$\sin (\lambda - \lambda') = \frac{a\omega^2}{g} \sin \lambda' \cos \lambda'. \qquad \textbf{7.2-8}$$

The dimensionless quantity $a\omega^2/g$ is a small number. It follows that $\lambda - \lambda'$, the difference between the astronomical and the geocentric latitude of a place, is a small angle. Knowing $a = 6368$ km, $\omega = 7.292(10)^{-5}$ rad/sec, and $g = 9.81$ m/sec, we compute $(a\omega^2/g) = 3.452(10)^{-3}$. The angle $\lambda - \lambda'$, the deviation of the plumb line, is given approximately by the expression

$$\lambda - \lambda' = 3.452(10)^{-3} \sin \lambda' \cos \lambda', \qquad \textbf{7.2-9}$$

derived from 7.2-8.

The angle $\lambda - \lambda'$ is shown in Fig. 7.2-1b. It is a maximum at a latitude of $45°$ where its magnitude is only about 0.12 seconds of arc. Equation 7.2-7 now enables us to predict the variation of g with latitude. If we write

$$\sin \lambda' = \sin [\lambda - (\lambda - \lambda')] = \sin \lambda \cos (\lambda - \lambda') - \cos \lambda \sin (\lambda - \lambda')$$

$$\cong \sin \lambda - \frac{a\omega^2}{g} \sin \lambda' \cos \lambda' \cos \lambda,$$

then, since $\lambda' \cong \lambda$, $\sin \lambda' \cong \sin \lambda - (a\omega^2/g) \sin \lambda \cos^2 \lambda$. From 7.2-7 we have

$$g = \frac{m_E G}{a^2} \left(1 - \frac{a\omega^2}{g} \cos^2 \lambda \right). \qquad \textbf{7.2-10}$$

This expression is an approximation to the variation of g with latitude, subject to the assumption of a spherical earth. The quantity $m_E G/a^2$ is the value of g at the poles. If we replace $\cos^2 \lambda$ by $1 - \sin^2 \lambda$, this formula can be put in the form

$$g = g_0(1 + \beta \sin^2 \lambda)$$

where g_0 is the value of g at the equator, 978.049 cm/sec^2, and $\beta = (g/a\omega^2 - 1)^{-1} = 0.0035$. The best measurements, taking into account the spheroidal shape of the earth,[*] give $\beta = 0.0053$ so that the earth's

---

[*] See H. Jeffreys, *The Earth*, 4th ed. (Cambridge University Press, 1959), p. 139. A term $\gamma \sin^2 2\lambda$, due to the spheroidal shape of the earth, is also given, but γ is much smaller than β.

rotation may be seen to account for most of the systematic variation in g.

We next find the equations of motion of a particle, taking into account the rotation of the earth. We suppose the particle to be subject to a force **P** and to the earth's gravitational field. For convenience in interpreting results of the analysis, let (x, y, z) be axes with origin at the surface of the earth at a location whose geocentric latitude is λ' and whose astronomical latitude is λ. These axes rotate with the earth; x and y lie in the horizontal plane, x pointing south and y east; whereas z is in the vertical direction, as shown in Fig. 7.2-2. The angular velocity of these axes is

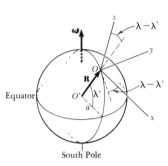

Fig. 7.2-2

$$\boldsymbol{\omega} = -\omega \cos \lambda \mathbf{i} + \omega \sin \lambda \mathbf{k}. \qquad \textbf{7.2-11}$$

The vector **R** from the fixed origin O' to the moving origin O is

$$\mathbf{R} = a \sin (\lambda - \lambda')\mathbf{i} + a \cos (\lambda - \lambda')\mathbf{k}. \qquad \textbf{7.2-12}$$

The derivatives of **R** are obtained by the operation indicated in Eq. 6.4-17.

$$\dot{\mathbf{R}} = \frac{\delta \mathbf{R}}{\delta t} + \boldsymbol{\omega} \times \mathbf{R} = \boldsymbol{\omega} \times \mathbf{R} = \omega a \cos \lambda' \mathbf{j}, \qquad \textbf{7.2-13}$$

$$\ddot{\mathbf{R}} = \boldsymbol{\omega} \times (\boldsymbol{\omega} \times \mathbf{R}) = -a\omega^2 \cos \lambda'(\sin \lambda \mathbf{i} + \cos \lambda \mathbf{k}). \qquad \textbf{7.2-14}$$

The frame derivatives, $\delta \mathbf{R}/\delta t$ and $\delta^2 \mathbf{R}/\delta t^2$, vanish because a, λ, and λ' are constants. The gravitational force on the particle when it is at the origin is

$$-mg' \sin (\lambda - \lambda')\mathbf{i} - mg' \cos (\lambda - \lambda')\mathbf{k}. \qquad \textbf{7.2-15}$$

As the particle moves, the direction and magnitude of the gravitational force change. To avoid the complication that such a variation would entail, we restrict the analysis to cases in which the motion takes place within a moderate distance from the origin, O. Then the gravitational attraction may be treated as constant in magnitude and in direction, relative to earth-fixed axes. Furthermore, the terms $\mathbf{F} - m\ddot{\mathbf{R}}$ in Eq. 7.2-1 can be combined to yield a simple result:

$$\mathbf{F} - m\ddot{\mathbf{R}} = \mathbf{P} - m\{[g' \sin(\lambda - \lambda') - a\omega^2 \sin \lambda \cos \lambda']\mathbf{i}$$
$$+ [g' \cos(\lambda - \lambda') - a\omega^2 \cos \lambda \cos \lambda']\mathbf{k}\}$$
$$= \mathbf{P} - m\{[(g' - a\omega^2)\cos \lambda' \sin \lambda - g' \cos \lambda \sin \lambda']\mathbf{i}$$
$$+ [(g' - a\omega^2)\cos \lambda' \cos \lambda + g' \sin \lambda \sin \lambda']\mathbf{k}\}.$$

From the first of Eqs. 7.2-6, $(g' - a\omega^2)\cos \lambda' = g \cos \lambda$ and from the second, $g' \sin \lambda' = g \sin \lambda$. On making these substitutions, we have

$$\mathbf{F} - m\ddot{\mathbf{R}} = \mathbf{P} - mg\mathbf{k}. \qquad \text{7.2-16}$$

The result expresses the important fact that the gravitational attraction together with the centripetal acceleration due to the rotation of the earth are equivalent to a force of magnitude mg directed along the vertical. Equation 7.2-1 now reduces to

$$\mathbf{P} - mg\mathbf{k} - 2m\boldsymbol{\omega} \times \frac{\delta \mathbf{p}}{\delta t} - m\boldsymbol{\omega} \times (\boldsymbol{\omega} \times \mathbf{p}) = m\frac{\delta^2 \mathbf{p}}{\delta t^2}. \qquad \text{7.2-17}$$

This equation is still too complex to admit elementary solutions that permit a ready estimate of the effects of the earth's rotation. It may, however, be simplified further by a second approximation. The term $\boldsymbol{\omega} \times (\boldsymbol{\omega} \times \mathbf{p})$ is proportional in magnitude to the product of ω^2 and the coordinates of the moving particle. Now $\omega^2 = 53(10)^{-10}$ sec^{-2}, and we have already assumed that the range is small enough to permit the gravitational force to be treated as constant. We therefore assume that this term may be neglected, and we write

$$\mathbf{P} - mg\mathbf{k} - 2m\boldsymbol{\omega} \times \frac{\delta \mathbf{p}}{\delta t} = m\frac{\delta^2 \mathbf{p}}{\delta t^2} \qquad \text{7.2-18}$$

with

$$\frac{\delta \mathbf{p}}{\delta t} = \dot{x}\mathbf{i} + \dot{y}\mathbf{j} + \dot{z}\mathbf{k} \quad \text{and} \quad \frac{\delta^2 \mathbf{p}}{\delta t^2} = \ddot{x}\mathbf{i} + \ddot{y}\mathbf{j} + \ddot{z}\mathbf{k}.$$

This is equivalent to the three scalar equations

$$P_x + 2m\omega\dot{y} \sin \lambda = m\ddot{x},$$
$$P_y - 2m\omega(\dot{x} \sin \lambda + \dot{z} \cos \lambda) = m\ddot{y}, \qquad \text{7.2-19}$$
$$P_z - mg + 2m\omega\dot{y} \cos \lambda = m\ddot{z}.$$

These are the equations of motion of a particle, taking into account the most important effects of the earth's rotation. They differ from the equations that we should get if we considered the (x, y, z) axes fixed in the earth to be an inertial frame of reference. The difference may be seen to consist in the presence of the terms proportional to ω. These terms are the Coriolis component of acceleration for the particle, multiplied by a factor m. They are sometimes termed the components of a fictitious "Coriolis force."

The solution of the Eqs. 7.2-18 or 7.2-19 depends upon the way in which **P** varies with time or position. For a particle whose motion is due only to the earth's gravitational field **P = 0**. In this case, the first and third of Eqs. 7.2-19 may be integrated at once:

$$\dot{x} = \dot{x}_0 + 2\omega(y - y_0) \sin \lambda, \qquad \dot{z} = \dot{z}_0 - gt + 2\omega(y - y_0) \cos \lambda.$$

7.2-20

The constants of integration have been evaluated by using the initial conditions $y = y_0$, $\dot{x} = \dot{x}_0$, $\dot{z} = \dot{z}_0$ at $t = 0$. If these expressions for $\dot{x}$ and $\dot{z}$ are substituted in the second of Eqs. 7.2-19 and the terms proportional to ω^2 are again dropped,

$$\ddot{y} = -2\omega(\dot{x}_0 \sin \lambda + \dot{z}_0 \cos \lambda - gt \cos \lambda),$$

$$\dot{y} = \dot{y}_0 + \omega g t^2 \cos \lambda - 2\omega t(\dot{x}_0 \sin \lambda + \dot{z}_0 \cos \lambda),$$

$$y = y_0 + \dot{y}_0 t + \frac{1}{3} \omega g t^3 \cos \lambda - \omega t^2(\dot{x}_0 \sin \lambda + \dot{z}_0 \cos \lambda). \qquad \textbf{7.2-21}$$

The initial conditions $y = y_0$, $\dot{y} = \dot{y}_0$ at $t = 0$ have been employed in evaluating the constants of integration in 7.2-21. Now that y has been found, $\dot{x}$ and $\dot{z}$ are known functions of time. When 7.2-21 is substituted in 7.2-20 and the terms proportional to ω^2 again dropped, integration yields

$$x = x_0 + \dot{x}_0 t + \dot{y}_0 \omega t^2 \sin \lambda,$$

$$z = z_0 + \dot{z}_0 t - \frac{1}{2} g t^2 + \dot{y}_0 \omega t^2 \cos \lambda. \qquad \textbf{7.2-22}$$

Here the initial conditions $x = x_0$, $z = z_0$ at $t = 0$ have been used. Equations 7.2-21, 22 describe the motion of an unresisted particle. In the next two examples, this analysis is applied to the unresisted motion of a projectile. The effects of the earth's rotation are shown to be small, though not imperceptible, during the time of flight. Then we discuss a celebrated case of constrained motion in which the effects of the earth's rotation are cumulative.

Example 7.2-1

A particle is dropped from a height h. How far will its path deviate from the vertical?

Solution: The initial position of the particle relative to (x, y, z) axes with origin at the surface of the earth is (o, o, h); its initial speed relative to these axes is zero. Referring to Eqs. 7.2-21, 22 we see that all the initial-condition quantities vanish except z_0, which is h. It follows that, to the accuracy of these equations,

$$x = o, \qquad y = \frac{1}{3}\omega g t^3 \cos \lambda, \qquad z = h - \frac{1}{2}g t^2.$$

The coordinates x and z are exactly as given by the elementary theory, which takes axes fixed in the earth as forming an inertial frame of reference. There is a motion in the y-direction; i.e., to the east. When $z = o$, the particle strikes the earth. Then $t^2 = 2h/g$ and the amount of the eastward deviation, which is in this case the principal effect of the earth's rotation, is

$$\frac{2}{3}\omega h\sqrt{\frac{2h}{g}}\cos\lambda.$$

For a 1000-ft fall in latitude $45°$, this amounts to 3.26 in.

Example 7.2-2

Investigate the deviation of a projectile from the plane determined by the vertical and the initial velocity.

Solution: As before, air resistance is to be neglected. Taking origin at the point on the earth where the projectile is fired, we have $x_0 = y_0 = z_0 = o$. Then Eqs. 7.2-21, 22 read

$$x = \dot{x}_0 t + \dot{y}_0\omega t^2 \sin \lambda,$$

$$y = \dot{y}_0 t + \frac{1}{3}\omega g t^3 \cos \lambda - \omega t^2(\dot{x}_0 \sin \lambda + \dot{z}_0 \cos \lambda),$$

$$z = \dot{z}_0 t - \frac{1}{2}g t^2 + \dot{y}_0\omega t^2 \cos \lambda.$$

It can be seen from the third of these equations that $\dot{z}$ will vanish when

$$t = t_1 = \frac{\dot{z}_0}{g - 2\dot{y}_0\omega \cos \lambda}$$

and that the corresponding value of z will be

$$z_1 = \frac{\dot{z}_0^2}{2g - 4\omega\dot{y}_0 \cos \lambda}.$$

This is the maximum altitude of the projectile. Since λ—which is positive in the northern latitudes and negative in the southern—never exceeds $\pi/2$, it follows that the peak altitude of the projectile will be slightly increased by an eastward initial velocity component (which makes $\dot{y}_0$ positive) and decreased by a westward initial velocity component. This is a reflection of the energy that the particle has, initially, owing to the rotation of the earth.

To investigate the deviation from the vertical plane through the initial velocity vector, we suppose the projectile to have been fired at an angle ϕ measured from the south to the east, and at an angle θ to the horizontal. Let (x', y') be axes in the horizontal plane with x' in the vertical plane through the initial velocity vector $\mathbf{v}_0$. Then

$$x' = x \cos \phi + y \sin \phi, \qquad y' = -x \sin \phi + y \cos \phi,$$
$$\dot{x}_0 = v_0 \cos \theta \cos \phi, \qquad \dot{y}_0 = v_0 \cos \theta \sin \phi,$$

$$x' = (v_0 t \cos \theta) + (\omega t \cos \lambda \sin \phi) \left(\frac{1}{3} g t^2 - \dot{z}_0 t \right),$$

$$y' = -(v_0 t \cos \theta)(\omega t \sin \lambda) + (\omega t \cos \lambda \cos \phi) \left(\frac{1}{3} g t^2 - \dot{z}_0 t \right).$$

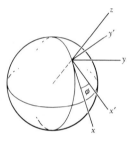

Fig. 7.2-3

The deviation of the projectile from the $x'z$-plane is given by the y'-coordinate. Under the usual conditions of long-range firing, the first term on the right-hand side of the equation for y' is much larger than the second. As a result, y' is negative in the Northern Hemisphere where $\lambda > 0$ and positive in the Southern where $\lambda < 0$. This is summarized in what is known as Ferel's Rule: the deviation is to the right in the Northern Hemisphere, to the left in the Southern. The effect is not inconsiderable. For a projectile released at a speed of 2600 ft/sec at an angle of 30° to the horizontal in a southeast direction in latitude 45°N, we have for the time of flight, t_2,

$$t_2 = 2t_1 = \frac{(2)(1300)}{(32.2) - (2)(1595)(7.292)(10)^{-5}(0.707)} = 81.3 \text{ sec,}$$

$$y'(t_2) = -(2250)(81.3)^2 (7.292)(10)^{-5}(0.707)$$

$$+ (7.292)(10)^{-5}(0.707)(0.707) \left[\frac{(32.2)(81.3)^2}{3} - (1300)(81.3) \right]$$

$$= -765 - 1 = -766 \text{ ft.}$$

The range is $v_0 t \cos \theta = (2250)(81.3) = 183{,}000$ ft.

Example 7.2-3

   Describe the effects of the earth's rotation on the motion of an ideal pendulum (Foucault pendulum).

Solution: The bob of the pendulum in question is supposed free to take any position making a small angle with the vertical through the point of support and is not restricted to motion in a plane. A free-body diagram for the pendulum bob is shown in Fig. 7.2-4. The tension in the cord is denoted **T**. If (x, y, z) are the coordinates of the moving particle and l the length of the pendulum, the cosine of the angle between the force **T** and the x-axis is x/l, and the corresponding direction cosines for the y- and z-axes are y/l and $(l-z)/l$.

$$\mathbf{P} = \mathbf{T} = -(T/l)[x\mathbf{i} + y\mathbf{j} + (l-z)\mathbf{k}].$$

The equations of motion (7.2-19) become

$$m\ddot{x} - 2m\omega\dot{y}\sin\lambda = -T\frac{x}{l}$$

$$m\ddot{y} + 2m\omega(\dot{x}\sin\lambda + \dot{z}\cos\lambda) = -T\frac{y}{l} \qquad \textbf{7.2-23}$$

$$m\ddot{z} - 2m\omega\dot{y}\cos\lambda = T\frac{l-z}{l} - mg.$$

In addition to these, we must satisfy the constraint condition

$$x^2 + y^2 + (l-z)^2 = l^2. \qquad \textbf{7.2-24}$$

Since (x, y, z) must satisfy this condition at all times, we may differentiate with respect to time. The constraint equation is then seen to imply that

$$x\dot{x} + y\dot{y} - (l-z)\dot{z} = 0. \qquad \textbf{7.2-25}$$

The first step in the solution of the equations of motion is the elimination of T, a quantity of no special interest. To do this, multiply the first of 7.2-23 by $\dot{x}$, the second by $\dot{y}$, and the third by $\dot{z}$, and add. In view of 7.2-25, this yields the expression

$$\ddot{x}\dot{x} + \ddot{y}\dot{y} + \ddot{z}\dot{z} = -g\dot{z}$$

or

$$\frac{1}{2}\frac{d}{dt}(\dot{x}^2 + \dot{y}^2 + \dot{z}^2) = -g\frac{dz}{dt}.$$

We infer that

$$\dot{x}^2 + \dot{y}^2 + \dot{z}^2 = C - 2gz. \qquad \textbf{7.2-26}$$

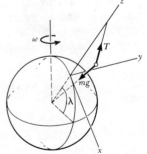

Fig. 7.2-4

This is seen to be a form of the principle of conservation of energy. We can simplify it by two approximations. In the first place, since the bob moves primarily in the horizontal, or xy, plane the velocity component $\dot{z}$ may be neglected, compared to $\dot{x}$ and $\dot{y}$.

In the second place, if we solve the constraint equation 7.2-24 for z, we have

$$l-z = l\left(1-\frac{x^2+y^2}{l^2}\right)^{1/2} \cong l\left(1-\frac{x^2+y^2}{2l^2}\right),$$

$$z = \frac{x^2+y^2}{2l}. \hspace{4cm} \textbf{7.2-27}$$

The approximation is justified by the fact that the pendulum swings through only a small angle with the vertical so that x and y are small compared with l. It is the same approximation that is made in the elementary two-dimensional analysis when $\sin \theta$ is replaced by θ. With these simplifications the energy integral becomes

$$\dot{x}^2+\dot{y}^2 = C-\frac{g}{l}(x^2+y^2). \hspace{3cm} \textbf{7.2-28}$$

A second way to eliminate T from the equations of motion is to multiply the first of 7.2-23 by $-y$ and the second by x and add. Then

$$-y\ddot{x}+2\omega y\dot{y}\sin\lambda+x\ddot{y}+2\omega x\dot{x}\sin\lambda+2\omega x\dot{z}\cos\lambda = 0. \hspace{1cm} \textbf{7.2-29}$$

Again this equation may be simplified by dropping the $\dot{z}$ term. Equation 7.2-29 may then be written

$$\frac{d}{dt}(x\dot{y}-y\dot{x})+\omega\sin\lambda\frac{d}{dt}(x^2+y^2) = 0,$$

$$x\dot{y}-y\dot{x} = D-(x^2+y^2)\omega\sin\lambda. \hspace{2cm} \textbf{7.2-30}$$

This equation may be seen to be closely related to the angular momentum integral.

It remains to express the constants C and D in terms of the initial conditions and to interpret the motion given by Eqs. 7.2-28, 30. The simplest way to do this is to introduce polar coordinates r, ϕ in the usual way: $x=r\cos\phi$, $y=r\sin\phi$. Then Eqs. 7.2-28 and 7.2-30 become

$$\dot{r}^2+r^2\dot{\phi}^2 = C-\frac{gr^2}{l}$$

and

$$r^2\dot{\phi} = D-r^2\omega\sin\lambda \hspace{3cm} \textbf{7.2-31}$$

respectively. Here ϕ is the same angle shown in Fig. 7.2-3, and r is the amplitude of the pendulum displacement. If we take for $t=0$ an instant when the pendulum is swinging through the origin, we shall have $D=0$. The second of Eqs. 7.2-31 is then

$$\dot{\phi} = -\omega\sin\lambda, \text{ which implies that } \phi = -\omega t\sin\lambda. \hspace{1cm} \textbf{7.2-32}$$

This is the most important conclusion of the analysis. It tells us that the pendulum will move in a vertical plane that rotates at a uniform rate about the vertical. The rotation is from east to south (clockwise to an observer looking downward) in the Northern Hemisphere. The rate of rotation depends upon the latitude; at the poles, it is the same as the rate of rotation of the earth. In view of Eq. 7.2-32, $\dot\phi^2$ will be proportional to ω^2 and will therefore be small compared to g/l. If we neglect this term, the first of Eqs. 7.2-31 may be written $\dot r^2 + r^2(g/l) = C$, and, on differentiating this, we recover the equation of simple harmonic motion: $\ddot r + (g/l)r = 0$. So far as its excursion from the vertical is concerned, the pendulum behaves like a simple pendulum of length l.

The design of a successful Foucault pendulum requires considerable ingenuity. Not only must the suspension permit a universal motion, but the initial conditions of the theory must be realized with precision. If a spherical pendulum is set swinging in an elliptical path, the axis of the ellipse will tend to rotate, and this effect will be much more evident than that due to the rotation of the earth.

7.3 Fixed-Axis Rotation

The rigid body rotating about a fixed axis is so common in technology that it deserves explicit treatment. It is encountered in turbines, pumps, and all other rotating machinery. We have dealt with such rotors in the two-dimensional analysis of Chapters IV and V. There the mass distribution was symmetrical about the xy-plane and the axis of rotation was the z-axis. Now we wish to consider the general case in which the mass distribution is not necessarily symmetrical.

The system consists of a rigid body mounted on a shaft that is held in bearings at two points, A and B, a distance l apart. The external forces acting on the body are its weight, the bearing reactions $\mathbf{A}$ and $\mathbf{B}$, and a torque, M_z, exerted on the shaft. The free-body diagram is shown in Fig. 7.3-1 for a typical position of the body. We choose (x, y, z) axes fixed in the body with z along the axis of rotation. The origin may be taken anywhere along the shaft; to fix ideas we take it at a point O between A and B. The distance from this origin to A is denoted a, and its distance from B we call b. Of course $a + b = l$. Note that the x, y-axes rotate with an angular velocity $\boldsymbol{\omega}$, which is the angular velocity of the rotor. The equations of motion for a rigid body rotating about a fixed axis, developed in Section 6.7, are applicable:

$$\boldsymbol{\omega} = \omega_z\mathbf{k}, \qquad \dot{\boldsymbol{\omega}} = \dot\omega_z\mathbf{k}. \qquad \textbf{6.7-1} \equiv \textbf{7.3-1}$$

The mass center is located at G, whose coordinates, referred to the rotating axes, are constants (x^*, y^*, z^*).   The position vector of the mass center G is

$$\mathbf{r}^* = x^*\mathbf{i} + y^*\mathbf{j} + z^*\mathbf{k}.$$

Then

$$\mathbf{v}^* = \frac{\delta\mathbf{r}^*}{\delta t} + \boldsymbol{\omega} \times \mathbf{r}^* = \boldsymbol{\omega} \times \mathbf{r}^* \qquad 7.3\text{-}2$$

so that

$$\mathbf{a}^* = \dot{\boldsymbol{\omega}} \times \mathbf{r}^* + \boldsymbol{\omega} \times (\boldsymbol{\omega} \times \mathbf{r}^*)$$
$$= -(\omega_z^2 x^* + \dot{\omega}_z y^*)\mathbf{i} - (\dot{\omega}_z^2 y^* - \dot{\omega}_z x^*)\mathbf{j}. \qquad 7.3\text{-}3$$

The rate of change of the angular momentum for a body rotating about a fixed axis is (Section 6.7)

$$\dot{\mathbf{H}}_O = (\omega_z^2 I_{yz} - \dot{\omega}_z I_{xz})\mathbf{i} - (\omega_z^2 I_{xz} + \dot{\omega}_z I_{yz})\mathbf{j} + \dot{\omega}_z I_{zz}\mathbf{k}.$$
$$6.7\text{-}3 \equiv 7.3\text{-}4$$

To form the equations of motion, we must write down expressions for the external forces and their moment about the origin.   As a rule,

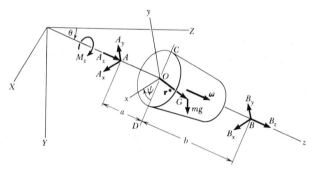

Fig. 7.3-1

the rotor is mounted either horizontally or vertically.   Since, however, we wish for the time being to consider a general situation, we take the axis of rotation to be inclined to the horizontal by an angle θ as shown in Fig. 7.3-1.   For reference purposes, a set of fixed axes (X, Y, Z) are also shown on this figure. Z is horizontal, and Y is vertical; z lies in the ZY-plane.   The position of any particle in the rotor is given, relative to the moving axes, by its (x, y, z) coordinates, and the (x, y, z) axes in turn are located in space by the angles θ (constant) and ψ (time-variable).   The latter angle is measured as a positive rotation about the z-axis from the vertical plane to the moving x-axis.

A unit vector in the fixed Y-direction will have a component $\sin \theta$ in the z-direction and $\cos \theta$ along the dotted line CD, which lies in the vertical plane. This latter component will have projections on the x- and y-axes proportional to $\cos \psi$ and $-\sin \psi$ respectively. It follows that the unit downward vertical vector

$$\mathbf{J} = (\cos \theta \cos \psi)\mathbf{i} - (\cos \theta \sin \psi)\mathbf{j} + (\sin \theta)\mathbf{k}. \qquad \textbf{7.3-5}$$

The weight force is $m g \mathbf{J}$. Its moment about the origin is $\mathbf{r}^* \times m g \mathbf{J}$. In vector form the equations of motion of the rotor are

$$\mathbf{F} = m\mathbf{a}^* \quad \text{or} \quad \mathbf{A} + \mathbf{B} + m g \mathbf{J} = m\mathbf{a}^*, \qquad \textbf{7.3-6}$$

$$\mathbf{M}_O = \dot{\mathbf{H}}_O \quad \text{or} \quad \mathbf{r}^* \times m g \mathbf{J} - a\mathbf{k} \times \mathbf{A} + b\mathbf{k} \times \mathbf{B} + M_z \mathbf{k} = \dot{\mathbf{H}}_O. \qquad \textbf{7.3-7}$$

Since $\mathbf{J}$, $\mathbf{a}^*$, $\mathbf{r}^*$, and $\dot{\mathbf{H}}_O$ have all been expressed in terms of their $(\mathbf{i}, \mathbf{j}, \mathbf{k})$ components, we can easily write the scalar form of these equations:

$$A_x + B_x + mg \cos \theta \cos \psi = -m(\omega_z^2 x^* + \dot{\omega}_z y^*),$$

$$A_y + B_y - mg \cos \theta \sin \psi = -m(\omega_z^2 y^* - \dot{\omega}_z x^*), \qquad \textbf{7.3-8}$$

$$A_z + B_z + mg \sin \theta = 0,$$

and

$$A_y a - B_y b + mgy^* \sin \theta + mgz^* \cos \theta \sin \psi = \omega_z^2 I_{yz} - \dot{\omega}_z I_{xz},$$

$$-A_x a + B_x b - mgx^* \sin \theta + mgz^* \cos \theta \cos \psi = -\omega_z^2 I_{xz} - \dot{\omega}_z I_{yz}. \qquad \textbf{7.3-9}$$

$$M_z - mgx^* \cos \theta \sin \psi - mgy^* \cos \theta \cos \psi = \dot{\omega}_z I_{zz}.$$

These equations of motion now require interpretation. The third of Eqs. 7.3-8 expresses the fact that the resultant force in the z-direction must be zero, there being no acceleration in this direction. Unless the axis of rotation is horizontal ($\theta = 0$), one of the bearings must be fitted with a collar so that it may serve as a thrust bearing and carry the z-component of the weight of the rotor. The third of Eqs. 7.3-9 may be regarded as an expression for the determination of M_z if ψ and ω_z are known. These last two quantities are not independent of course; $\dot{\psi} = \omega_z$ as may be seen by reference to Fig. 7.3-1. Conversely, if M_z is known, this equation may be regarded as a differential equation for the determination of ψ. The remaining four equations serve to determine the reaction components A_x, A_y and B_x, B_y.

Next consider what happens if no external torque, M_z, is supplied to the shaft. Write $\ddot{\psi}$ for $\dot{\omega}_z$ in the third of Eqs. 7.3-9. Then this equation has solutions in which ψ has a constant value given by

$$\tan \psi = -\frac{y^*}{x^*}. \qquad \textbf{7.3-10}$$

Since ψ is a constant, ω_z and $\dot{\omega}_z$ are zero. The rotor simply rests in static equilibrium with its mass center either directly above or directly below the shaft. If the x-axis is chosen so that the mass center lies in the xz-plane, $y^* = 0$. With this choice of x-axis, the third of Eqs. 7.3-9 reads

$$I_{zz}\ddot{\psi} + (mgx^* \cos \theta) \sin \psi = 0. \qquad \textbf{7.3-11}$$

If the initial conditions are $\psi = \dot{\psi} = 0$, this equation has the static equilibrium solution $\psi = 0$ or π, which is given by Eq. 7.3-10. For any other initial conditions, the rotor behaves like a compound pendulum whose period is the same as that of a simple pendulum of length $I_{zz}/(mx^* \cos \theta)$. For small oscillations about the position of stable equilibrium, $\sin \psi \cong \psi$, and Eq. 7.3-11 reduces to the equation of simple harmonic motion. The natural circular frequency and the period are, as we recall from Section 3.3,

$$\omega_n = \sqrt{\frac{mgx^* \cos \theta}{I_{zz}}} \frac{\text{rad}}{\text{sec}} \quad \text{and} \quad T_n = \frac{2\pi}{\omega_n} = 2\pi \sqrt{\frac{I_{zz}}{mgx^* \cos \theta}} \text{ sec.}$$

$$\textbf{7.3-12}$$

A door whose hinges are not in a vertical line is a pendulum of this sort. An aspect of the conclusion that is of some technological importance is the possibility it raises of designing a mechanical system with a very long period. By inclining the axis of rotation only slightly off the vertical, θ will be made close to $\pi/2$ radians, and $\cos \theta$ will be extremely small. The period will then be made large without any need for a bulky or massive apparatus. This principle is employed in a number of seismic detection devices, which must be designed to have a low natural frequency.

The Eqs. 7.3-8, 9 find their principal application in connection with the balancing of rotors. It is easy to see that if the mass center, G, does not lie on the axis of rotation, its path will be a circle about that axis. This means that the mass center will have a centripetal acceleration, and that a force must be exerted on the rotor by the bearings at A and B. This force is in addition to the dead weight of the rotor. It can be removed by mounting the rotor so that its mass center lies on the axis of rotation. Then $x^* = y^* = 0$, and the third of Eqs. 7.3-9 reduces to the familiar $M_z = \dot{\omega}_z I_{zz}$. In the absence of any torque

M_z, ω_z must be constant. This means that, if the rotor is turned gently to any position on the shaft and left at rest, it will remain placidly in the position to which it has been turned. The rotor is said to be *statically balanced*. If the rotor is statically balanced and is at rest, the bearing reactions, easily computed from the first two of both sets of Eqs. 7.3-8, 9, are:

$$A_x = mg\,\frac{z^*-b}{l}\cos\theta\cos\psi, \qquad A_y = -mg\,\frac{z^*-b}{l}\cos\theta\sin\psi,$$

$$B_x = mg\,\frac{z^*+a}{l}\cos\theta\cos\psi, \qquad B_y = mg\,\frac{z^*+a}{l}\cos\theta\sin\psi.$$

7.3-13

These components are referred to axes that move with the rotor. It is instructive to find the components along the axes (X, Y, Z) fixed in space. Making use of Eqs. 7.3-5 and 7.3-13,

$$A_Y = \mathbf{A}\cdot\mathbf{J} = mg\,\frac{z^*-b}{l}\cos^2\theta + A_z\sin\theta,$$

$$B_Y = \mathbf{B}\cdot\mathbf{J} = -mg\,\frac{z^*+a}{l}\cos^2\theta + B_z\sin\theta. \qquad 7.3\text{-}14$$

Similarly, referring to Fig. 7.3-1, we see that

$$\mathbf{I} = (-\sin\psi\cos\theta)\mathbf{i} + (-\cos\psi\cos\theta)\mathbf{j}$$

so that

$$A_X = \mathbf{A}\cdot\mathbf{I} = 0, \qquad B_X = \mathbf{B}\cdot\mathbf{I} = 0.$$

The bearing reactions always lie in the vertical plane through the rotor (the YZ-plane). They are independent of the position of the rotor (ψ does not appear in 7.3-14). The sum of the vertical components is simply the weight of the rotor. To see this, note that

$$A_Y + B_Y = -mg\cos^2\theta + (A_z + B_z)\sin\theta.$$

But according to the third of Eqs. 7.3-8, $A_z + B_z$ is the same as $-mg\sin\theta$ so that $A_Y + B_Y = -mg$.

It might be thought that a statically balanced design would represent the optimum situation so far as bearing reactions are concerned, making them constant in magnitude and direction and just large enough to support the dead weight of the rotor. This, however, is not the case. To appreciate what is needed to produce this ideal situation, consider a rotor, not necessarily statically balanced, spinning at a constant operating speed, ω_z. Then $\dot{\omega}_z = 0$. The bearing reactions, again computed from the first two of each of Eqs. 7.3-8 and 9, are

$$A_x = \left(mg\, \frac{z^* - b}{l} \cos \theta \cos \psi \right) - \frac{x^*}{l} \left(mb\omega_z^2 + mg \sin \theta \right) + \left(\frac{\omega_z^2}{l} I_{xz} \right),$$

$$A_y = \left(-mg\, \frac{z^* - b}{l} \cos \theta \sin \psi \right) - \frac{y^*}{l} \left(mb\omega_z^2 + mg \sin \theta \right) + \left(\frac{\omega_z^2}{l} I_{yz} \right),$$

$$B_x = \left(-mg\, \frac{z^* + a}{l} \cos \theta \cos \psi \right) - \frac{x^*}{l} \left(ma\omega_z^2 - mg \sin \theta \right) - \left(\frac{\omega_z^2}{l} I_{xz} \right),$$

$$B_y = \left(mg\, \frac{z^* + a}{l} \cos \theta \sin \psi \right) - \frac{y^*}{l} \left(ma\omega_z^2 - mg \sin \theta \right) - \left(\frac{\omega_z^2}{l} I_{yz} \right).$$

$$\text{7.3-15}$$

It may be seen that each bearing reaction component is the sum of three terms. The first parentheses contain the static reaction given by Eqs. 7.3-13; this term is inevitable and would be present even if the rotor were not spinning. The second parentheses terms have x^* or y^* as multiplying factors; they do not enter if the rotor is statically balanced. The first term in these parentheses represents the effect due to the centripetal acceleration of the mass center. Being proportional to the square of the angular velocity, it can present a serious design consideration in high-speed machinery. The second term in this second parentheses, $\pm mg \sin \theta$, enters only if the unbalanced rotor is turning about an axis inclined to the horizontal. In that case, the weight force exerts a varying torque about the bearing support points A and B. The term in the third parentheses, surprisingly, is present even for a statically balanced rotor. Like the centripetal acceleration terms, these terms are proportional to the square of the rotational speed. The contributions of these terms to A_x and B_x are equal in magnitude and opposite in direction, forming a couple. This is also true of the contributions to A_y and B_y. The resultant couple of magnitude

$$\omega_z^2 \sqrt{I_{xz}^2 + I_{yz}^2} \qquad\qquad \text{7.3-16}$$

is sometimes known as the "rocking couple" since it tends to make the rotor rock on its shaft. Both the second and third parentheses terms represent forces that follow the moving axes and change in direction as the rotor turns on its shaft. They alternately relieve and reinforce the static reactions.

From the point of view of the designer, bearing reactions must be held to a minimum. Excessive forces, particularly those that vary periodically in magnitude or direction, greatly reduce the fatigue life of high-speed bearings. It may be seen from Eqs. 7.3-15 that, in order to keep the bearing reactions at a minimum, the rotor must (a) be statically balanced with its mass center on the axis of rotation and (b) have a mass distribution such that the products of inertia I_{xz} and I_{yz} are each zero. The desired mass distribution may be achieved by adding (or removing) material in each of any two planes perpendicular to the axis of rotation. When this has been done, the axis of rotation is a principal axis of inertia passing through the mass center. The rotor is then said to be *dynamically balanced* as well as statically balanced.

Example 7.3-1

A 50-lb disk of 10-in radius is mounted on an 18-in shaft at a point 12 in. from one end. The horizontal shaft is perpendicular to the plane of the disk but intersects it at a point 0.01 in. from the mass center. What are the bearing reactions when the shaft is made to rotate steadily at 2400 rpm?

Solution: The rotor and its free-body diagram are shown in Fig. 7.3-2. Note that the origin has been chosen in the plane of the disk. This is a

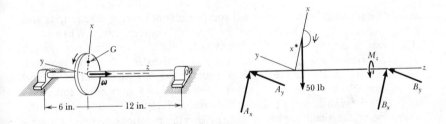

Fig. 7.3-2

major convenience; since no mass particle on the disk has an appreciable z-component, I_{xz} and I_{yz}, which are the integrals of $xz\,dm$ and $yz\,dm$, both vanish. Actually, I_{xz} and I_{yz} will be zero whenever there is symmetry of mass distribution about the xy-plane because then for every mass element with coordinates (x, z) there is another with coordinates $(x, -z)$, and similarly for (y, z). The x-axis has been chosen to pass through the mass center. This is a minor convenience. The free-body diagram shows a typical position of the rotor when the x-axis makes an angle ψ with the vertical.

$$\boldsymbol{\omega} = \omega_z \mathbf{k}, \qquad \mathbf{H}_O = I_{zz}\omega_z \mathbf{k},$$

$$\dot{\mathbf{H}}_O = I_{zz}\dot{\omega}_z \mathbf{k} = 0, \qquad \mathbf{a}^* = -x^*\omega_z^2 \mathbf{i}.$$

The equations of motion, $\mathbf{F} = m\mathbf{a}^*$ and $\mathbf{M}_O = \dot{\mathbf{H}}_O$ take the form

$$mg \cos \psi + A_x + B_x = -mx^*\omega_z^2,$$

$$-mg \sin \psi + A_y + B_y = 0,$$

$$6A_y - 12B_y = 0,\qquad\qquad \textbf{7.3-17}$$

$$-6A_x + 12B_x = 0,$$

$$M_z - mgx^* \sin \psi = 0.$$

Although these equations are a special case of Eqs. 7.3-8, 9, the student should form the habit of deriving them as is done here and not attempt to memorize Eqs. 7.3-8, 9.

The first four of these equations determine the bearing reactions:

$$A_x = -\frac{2}{3}(mx^*\omega_z^2 + mg \cos \psi) = -\frac{2}{3}\left[\frac{50}{386}0.01\left(\frac{2400}{60}2\pi\right)^2 + 50 \cos \psi\right]$$

$$= -54 - 33 \cos \psi \text{ lb,}$$

$$B_x = \frac{1}{2}A_x = -27 - 17 \cos \psi \text{ lb,}$$

$$A_y = \frac{2}{3}mg \sin \psi = 33 \sin \psi, \qquad B_y = \frac{1}{2}A_y = 17 \sin \psi \text{ lb.}$$

It may be seen that the "dynamic" components of bearing reaction, 54 and 27 lb respectively, are larger than the "static" components. When $\psi = 0$, the x-axis is directed vertically downwards, and the bearing reactions are upward forces of magnitude 87 lb at A and 44 lb at B. When $\psi = 90°$, the x-axis is horizontal; the bearing reactions consist of upward forces A_y and B_y of magnitudes 33 lb and 17 lb respectively, and horizontal forces A_x and B_x of magnitudes 54 and 27 lb respectively. When $\psi = 180°$, the x-axis points vertically upward, and the bearing reactions consist of downward forces of magnitude 21 lb and 10 lb at A and B respectively. These are forces exerted on the rotor shaft by the bearings. Forces equal to them in magnitude and direction must be exerted by the foundation on each bearing. In the present case, the apparatus must be bolted to the foundation else it will lift off at every revolution. The last equation of motion tells us that, on account of the static unbalance, the torque required to produce a uniform rate of rotation will have a variable component of magnitude 0.5 lb and frequency 40 cps.

Example **7.3-2**

A 966-lb flywheel rotates in a horizontal plane. Its mass center is 0.25 ft from the vertical axis of rotation. Find the bearing reactions for the position shown when the angular velocity is 180 rpm (clockwise when looking down) and is increasing in magnitude at the rate of 100 rad/sec².

Solution: The free-body diagram is shown in Fig. 7.3-3. The thrust is carried entirely at the lower bearing.

$$\boldsymbol{\omega} = -\frac{180}{60}2\pi\mathbf{k} = -18.8\mathbf{k}\ \text{rad/sec},$$

$$\dot{\boldsymbol{\omega}} = -100\mathbf{k}\ \text{rad/sec}^2,$$

$$\mathbf{a}^* = -0.25(-18.8)^2\mathbf{i} - (0.25)(100)\mathbf{j}$$

$$= -89\mathbf{i} - 25\mathbf{j}\ \text{ft/sec}^2.$$

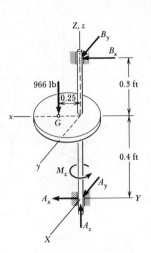

As in the preceding example, $I_{xz} = I_{yz} = 0$, so that

$$\mathbf{H}_O = I_{zz}\omega_z\mathbf{k}, \qquad \dot{\mathbf{H}}_O = I_{zz}\dot{\omega}_z\mathbf{k}.$$

The equations of motion are:

$$A_x + B_x = -(30)(89),$$
$$A_y + B_y = -(30)(25),$$
$$A_z - 966 = 0,$$
$$0.4A_y - 0.3B_y = 0,$$
$$-0.4A_x + 0.3B_x + (0.25)(966) = 0,$$
$$M_z = -100I_{zz}.$$

Fig. 7.3-3

These equations yield:

$$A_x = -A_Y = -800\ \text{lb}, \qquad B_x = -B_Y = -1870\ \text{lb},$$
$$A_y = A_X = -322\ \text{lb}, \qquad B_y = B_X = -428\ \text{lb},$$
$$A_z = A_Z = 966\ \text{lb}.$$

Example 7.3-3

A horizontal shaft carries a light 1-ft radius pulley and two bodies whose planes of symmetry are at right angles to the shaft, as shown. The weights of the bodies and significant dimensions and forces applied to the pulley are given in Fig. 7.3-4 as is the total moment of inertia of the system about the shaft: $I_{zz} = 6$ lb-ft-sec^2. What are the bearing reactions when the shaft is in the position shown and has an angular velocity of 3 rad/sec?

Solution: The figure may also serve as a free-body diagram. We choose the origin at a convenient point, say at O in the plane of symmetry of body C. Then, for body C, $I_{xz} = I_{yz} = 0$. For body D, these products of inertia will not be zero. They would be zero, however, for (x', y', z) through the symmetry plane, D. We may write for body D

$$I_{xz} = I_{x'z} + (x^*z^*)_D m_D = 0 + (0)(12)\left(\frac{300}{386}\right) = 0,$$

$$I_{yz} = I_{y'z} + (y^*z^*)_D m_D = 0 + (-4)(12)\left(\frac{300}{386}\right) = -37.3\ \text{lb-in-sec}^2.$$

The computation here is the transfer-of-axes theorem Eq. 6.5-13b for products of inertia. There is no need for confusion as to sign since it may

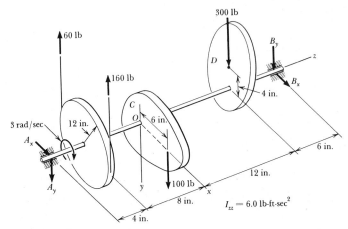

Fig. 7.3-4

be seen that, for axes (x, y, z), most of the material of body D has a negative y- and a positive z-coordinate. Of course, $I_{zz} = (6)(12) = 72$ lb-in-sec^2.

$$\boldsymbol{\omega} = \omega_z \mathbf{k}, \qquad \dot{\boldsymbol{\omega}} = \dot{\omega}_z \mathbf{k}, \qquad \mathbf{H}_O = \omega_z[72\mathbf{k} - (-37.3)\mathbf{j}],$$

$$\dot{\mathbf{H}}_O = \dot{\omega}_z(72\mathbf{k} + 37.3\mathbf{j}) + \omega_z^2(37.3)(-\mathbf{i})$$

$$= -(9)(37.3)\mathbf{i} + 37.3\dot{\omega}_z\mathbf{j} + 72\dot{\omega}_z\mathbf{k},$$

$$m\mathbf{a}^* = m_C(\mathbf{a}^*)_C + m_D(\mathbf{a}^*)_D = \left(\frac{100}{386}\right)(6)(-3^2\mathbf{i} + \dot{\omega}_z\mathbf{j})$$

$$+ \left(\frac{300}{386}\right)(4)(3^2\mathbf{j} + \dot{\omega}_z\mathbf{i}),$$

$$\mathbf{a}^* = (3\dot{\omega}_z - 13.5)\mathbf{i} + \left(\frac{3}{2}\dot{\omega}_z + 27\right)\mathbf{j}.$$

The equations of motion are

$$A_x + B_x = \frac{400}{386}(3\dot{\omega}_z - 13.5),$$

$$A_y + B_y - 60 - 160 + 300 + 100 = \frac{400}{386}\left(\frac{3}{2}\dot{\omega}_z + 27\right),$$

$$12A_y - 18B_y - (220)(8) - (300)(12) = -335,$$ **7.3-18**

$$-12A_x + 18B_x = 37.3\dot{\omega}_z,$$

$$-(160)(12) + (60)(12) + (100)(6) = 72\dot{\omega}_z.$$

The last equation of motion at once gives $\dot{\omega}_z = -8.33$ rad/sec^2 whereupon the other four may be solved. We find that in the position shown

$$A_x = -13.7 \text{ lb}, \qquad B_x = -26.3 \text{ lb},$$
$$A_y = 68.5 \text{ lb}, \qquad B_y = -233 \text{ lb}.$$

Note that this solution is not valid for a general position because the weight force is not always parallel to the y-axis. In other words, unlike Example 7.3-1, the free-body diagram in this case has not been drawn for a typical position. In reading these three examples, the student should be conscious that no blind application of memorized equations such as 7.3-8, 9 has any place in mechanics. In each instance, a free-body diagram of the isolated system should be drawn, suitable axes chosen, and expressions for the acceleration of the mass center and for the angular momentum written down. In the present example, the pitfalls for the beginner lie in the incorrect assumption that $\dot{\omega}_z$ vanishes, in the computation of $\mathbf{a}^*$, and in the computation of the products of inertia. In connection with the last named point, it is suggested that the example be re-worked using axes parallel to those shown in Fig. 7.3-4 but with origin at bearing A. Then the products of inertia are

$$I_{xz} = \left(\frac{100}{386}\right)(6)(12) \quad \text{and} \quad I_{yz} = \left(\frac{300}{386}\right)(-4)(24).$$

The final answer is, of course, unchanged.

Example 7.3-4

A 10-lb bicycle wheel of 16-in radius is slightly misaligned on its shaft, the angle, α, between the shaft and the geometrical axis of the wheel being

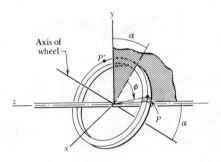

Fig. 7.3-5

0.02 radians. If the cyclist travels at 20 mph what is the rocking couple exerted on the bearings?

    Solution: We idealize the bicycle wheel as a hoop of radius r. Taking axes as shown in Fig. 7.3-5, we note that the hoop is always symmetrical about the yz-plane. To every mass element P, there will correspond a mass element P' with the same z-coordinate but with an x-coordinate of opposite sign. Consequently, $I_{xz} = \int xz\, dm = 0$. On the other hand, I_{yz} is not zero. The y- and z-coordinates of P and P' are the same. These elements reinforce rather than annul one another in the computation of I_{yz}. To compute I_{yz}, we locate P by an angle ϕ measured from the intersection of the yz-plane with the hoop. The mass of the element at P will be

$$dm = \frac{m}{2\pi r}(r\, d\phi)$$

and the y- and z-coordinates of P are $r \cos \phi \cos \alpha$ and $-r \cos \phi \sin \alpha$ respectively.

$$I_{yz} = \int_0^{2\pi} (r \cos \phi \cos \alpha)(-r \cos \phi \sin \alpha) \frac{m}{2\pi r}(r\, d\phi)$$

$$= \frac{-mr^2}{4\pi} \sin 2\alpha \int_0^{2\pi} \cos^2 \phi\, d\phi = -\frac{mr^2}{4} \sin 2\alpha.$$

The sign of I_{yz} is simply a result of the way the positive directions of the y- and z-axes were chosen. It may be seen by inspection of Fig. 7.3-5 that the upper half of the disk will have negative z- and positive y-coordinates; whereas the lower half has positive z- and negative y-coordinates. If, however, the positive direction of z had been chosen to the right instead of to the left (necessitating a change in the positive direction of the x-axis to keep the axes right-handed), I_{yz} would have been positive. The rocking couple on the shaft is given at once by Eq. 7.3-16:

$$\omega_z^2 \sqrt{I_{xz}^2 + I_{yz}^2} = \frac{1}{4} mr^2 \omega_z^2 \sin 2\alpha. \qquad \textbf{7.3-19}$$

In the present case,

$$\frac{1}{4} mr^2 \omega_z^2 \sin 2\alpha = \frac{1}{4} \frac{10}{386} (16)^2 \left(\frac{(20)(88)}{(5)(16)}\right)^2 (0.04) = 32.1 \text{ in-lb.}$$

This is not a large torque. If, however, we were concerned with a gyroscope rotor, most of whose mass is in the rim, the weight might be 1 lb, the radius 2 in, and the angular velocity 2000 rad/sec. Then

$$\frac{1}{4} mr^2 \omega_z^2 \sin 2\alpha = \frac{1}{4} \frac{1}{386} (2)^2 (4)(10)^6 (0.04) = 415 \text{ in-lb,}$$

and clearly this one-degree misalignment would be intolerable. The misalignment of bicycle wheels, small though it is, can often be detected by inverting the bicycle so that it rests on its saddle and handle bars. When a misaligned wheel is spun the bicycle will rock sideways.

Example 7.3-5

A rod of mass m and length l is hinged at one end to a thin, vertical shaft that rotates at a constant rate ω. Find the angles ϕ between shaft and rod at which the rod can remain stationary with respect to the shaft.

Solution: We idealize the question by assuming that the vertical shaft is so slender that the point of support, A, lies on the axis of rotation. The support at A is supposed to be a "universal" joint, which can exert force components (but no torque) in any direction. Choose rotating axes as shown in the free-body diagram, Fig. 7.3-6, with the rod in the yz-plane. We have, since the weight force is the only external force with non-vanishing moment about A,

$$\mathbf{M}_A = \left(\frac{l}{2}\sin\mathbf{j}\phi - \frac{l}{2}\cos\phi\mathbf{k}\right) \times (-mg\mathbf{k}) = -\frac{1}{2}mgl\sin\phi\mathbf{i}.$$

In the situation whose possibility we are considering, ϕ is a constant, $\mathbf{\omega} = \omega\mathbf{k}$, and $\dot{\mathbf{\omega}} = \mathbf{0}$ so that

$$\mathbf{H}_A = \omega(I_{zz}\mathbf{k} - I_{xz}\mathbf{i} - I_{yz}\mathbf{j}),$$

$$\dot{\mathbf{H}}_A = \omega I_{zz}\frac{d\mathbf{k}}{dt} - \omega I_{xz}\frac{d\mathbf{i}}{dt} - \omega I_{yz}\frac{d\mathbf{j}}{dt} = \omega I_{zz}\mathbf{\omega} \times \mathbf{k} - \omega I_{xz}\mathbf{\omega} \times \mathbf{i} - \omega I_{yz}\mathbf{\omega} \times \mathbf{j}$$

$$= -\omega^2 I_{xz}\mathbf{j} + \omega^2 I_{yz}\mathbf{i}.$$

In the present case, $I_{xz} = 0$ because the x-coordinate of any point is zero.

$$I_{yz} = \int_0^l yz\left(\frac{m}{l}\,ds\right)$$

where $dm = (m/l)\,ds$, s being length measured along the rod. But

$$y = s\sin\phi \quad \text{and} \quad z = -s\cos\phi,$$

so that

$$I_{yz} = -\frac{m}{l}\sin\phi\cos\phi\int_0^l s^2\,ds = -\frac{1}{3}ml^2\sin\phi\cos\phi,$$

$$\dot{\mathbf{H}}_A = -\frac{1}{3}ml^2\omega^2\sin\phi\cos\phi\mathbf{i}.$$

Equating the expressions for $\mathbf{M}_A$ and $\dot{\mathbf{H}}_A$, we have

$$-\frac{1}{3}ml^2\omega^2\sin\phi\cos\phi = -\frac{1}{2}mgl\sin\phi.$$

This equation has the solutions $\phi = 0$, $\phi = 180°$, $\phi = \arccos(3g/2l\omega^2)$.

The last solution, which is the only value of ϕ that could not have been foreseen, is possible only if ω^2 exceeds $3g/2l$. Otherwise, the argument of the inverse cosine will exceed one. This last solution always lies between zero and ninety degrees.

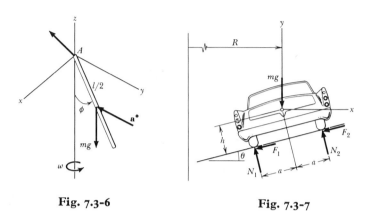

Fig. 7.3-6   **Fig. 7.3-7**

Example 7.3-6

An automobile of mass m traveling at constant speed v rounds a curve of radius R "banked" at an angle θ.   Will it tip or slide sideways?

Solution: This question is one usually treated by elementary methods although it is not, strictly speaking, a case of plane motion.   The approximations underlying the conventional analysis are interesting.   We begin by drawing the free-body diagram as shown in Fig. 7.3-7.   This figure embodies several assumptions: (1) F_1, N_1 represent the normal and frictional components of the sum of the forces exerted on front and rear left-side tires; similarly, F_2, N_2 are the sum for the front and rear right-side tires.   This implies that the front and rear wheels are pointed in the same direction.★   (2) No force is shown in the z-direction (perpendicular to the plane of the figure).   This implies that the forward frictional force exerted by the road is balanced by air resistance; in other words, that the speed is constant.   If we (3) neglect the inertia of the wheels and other rotating parts and (4) consider the body and frame to be a single rigid body, $\mathbf{H}^* = I_{yy}(v/R)\mathbf{j}$, a constant.   This implies that $\mathbf{M}^* = \mathbf{0}$ or, what is the same thing, that $M_z = 0$.   In addition $F_y = 0$ since there is no upward motion of the mass center, and $F_x = -mv^2/R$ since the mass center is moving in a circle of radius R with constant speed v.   These three equations effectively reduce the analysis to one in plane motion.   We have

$$\Sigma F_x = -(N_1 + N_2)\sin\theta - (F_1 + F_2)\cos\theta = -\frac{mv^2}{R},$$

$$\Sigma F_y = (N_1 + N_2)\cos\theta - (F_1 + F_2)\sin\theta - mg = 0.$$

★ An implication that is a gross simplification of the facts.

We may note from these equations that $F_1 + F_2 = 0$ if

$$\tan \theta = \frac{v^2}{Rg},$$

and, since F_1 and F_2 must be in the same direction, they must each vanish for this value of θ. The roadway is said to be properly banked for the speed v if θ has the value given above. If the automobile is about to slip (outward), F_1 and F_2 will be directed to the left, as assumed in writing the equations of motion above, and $F_1 + F_2 = \mu(N_1 + N_2)$, μ being the limiting value of the coefficient of friction. If this substitution is made in the equations of motion, the second of them reduces to

$$N_1 + N_2 = \frac{mg}{\cos \theta - \mu \sin \theta}$$

and, when this value is substituted in the first, we find the speed at slip to be

$$v_S^2 = Rg \frac{\sin \theta + \mu \cos \theta}{\cos \theta - \mu \sin \theta}.$$

Taking moments about the mass center, we have the third equation of motion

$$-(N_1 - N_2)a - (F_1 + F_2)h = 0$$

so that

$$N_2 - N_1 = \frac{h}{a} \frac{mg\mu}{\cos \theta - \mu \sin \theta}.$$

This expression, together with the previous one for $N_1 + N_2$, yields

$$N_1 = \frac{1}{2} \frac{mg}{\cos \theta - \mu \sin \theta}\left(1 - \frac{h\mu}{a}\right), \qquad N_2 = \frac{1}{2} \frac{mg}{\cos \theta - \mu \sin \theta}\left(1 + \frac{h\mu}{a}\right).$$

We see that most of the weight is carried on the outside tire. If $\mu > a/h$, N_1 will be negative; this implies that the vehicle will tip over before the speed v_S is reached.

To examine the tipping case, set $F_1 = N_1 = 0$: then the three equations of motion become

$$N_2 \sin \theta + F_2 \cos \theta = \frac{mv^2}{R},$$

$$N_2 \cos \theta - F_2 \sin \theta - mg = 0,$$

$$N_2 a - F_2 h = 0.$$

These equations are easily solved for N_2, F_2, and v. We see at once from the third of them that $F_2/N_2 = a/h$ so that tipping cannot occur before slipping unless μ exceeds a/h; this conclusion was reached previously. Further,

$$v_T^2 = Rg \frac{\sin \theta + (a/h) \cos \theta}{\cos \theta - (a/h) \sin \theta}.$$

7.4 Application of d'Alembert's Principle

Questions of the type discussed in the preceding section are sometimes approached by the use of what are known as "inertia forces" and "inertia torques." The use of these quantities is an extension of d'Alembert's principle (Sections 6.4, 6.5). The development of this principle, it will be recalled, starts with Newton's equations of motion for a particle. The product of the mass of this particle and its acceleration is a vector called the "effective force on the particle"; in view of the second law of motion this vector is equal to the resultant of all the forces acting on the particle. If the mechanical system consists of a number of particles, the forces acting on any of the particles may be divided into two classes: (A) those exerted by fields or bodies outside the system and (B) those exerted by other particles of the system. The latter are called internal forces. The vector sum of the internal and external forces for the entire system is equal to the sum of the effective forces. D'Alembert's principle consists in the assertion that the assemblage of internal forces, by themselves, have zero resultant (force and moment). It follows that the sum of the external forces will be equal to the sum of the "effective" forces.

D'Alembert's principle is of interest from historical, philosophical, and practical points of view. Stated in 1743, it introduced, for the first time, a general method of approach to the analysis of the dynamical behavior of systems more complicated than a single particle. It made possible the use of the principle of virtual work in dynamics; for a rigid body the virtual work of the effective forces in the actual motion was taken equal to the virtual work of the external forces. But it was soon superseded in this respect by a far more elegant treatment of the equations of motion originated by Lagrange. From a philosophical point of view, d'Alembert's principle offers an alternative treatment of the internal forces in the body of finite size in newtonian mechanics. Instead of asserting that the internal forces in a distributed mass conform to Newton's third law of motion, as was done in Chapter IV, one may assume that d'Alembert's principle applies to such systems. This may be done whether or not the body in question is rigid. Rigid bodies are of special interest in mechanics simply because they have exactly as many degrees of freedom as there are equations of motion. As a result their motion may be discussed without additional physical assumptions such as those required in fluid mechanics and in the deformation theory of elastic solids.

In its role as a practical device for the analysis of the motion of mechanical systems, the principle is usually stated in terms of the *reversed* effective forces, sometimes called the "inertia" forces, associated with the particles of the system. The sum of these and the external forces forms a force system that is in static equilibrium. The principle, used in this way, appears to reduce dynamic problems to static ones. Actually, the appearance is partly illusion because, in writing down the "inertia forces," the same derivatives appear that are required for the acceleration vectors.

Nevertheless, the idea of retreating to the notions of static equilibrium and working in the friendly shelter of fixed axes with no irritating products of inertia to compute is an appealing one.   Let us examine it.

If the principle is to be an effective aid in the analysis of the motion of rigid bodies, it is most desirable that the infinite number of inertia forces acting on the separate particles of the body be replaced by a single resultant "inertia force."   There is no question about the magnitude and direction of this vector.   Its magnitude would be equal to the product of the total mass of the body into the magnitude of the acceleration of the mass center; its direction, opposite to that of the acceleration of the mass center.   Then the three linear momentum equations of motion, $\mathbf{F} = m\mathbf{a}^*$, are the same as the equations of equilibrium, $\mathbf{F} - m\mathbf{a}^* = \mathbf{0}$.   But if the location of the point of application of the resultant "inertia force" is the mass center, the moments of the external force system and the inertia force system will not, in general, add to zero.   The angular momentum equations of motion are

$$\sum_i \mathbf{r}_i \times \mathbf{F}_i = \dot{\mathbf{H}}_O. \qquad\qquad 7.4\text{-}1$$

But

$$\mathbf{H}_O = \mathbf{r}^* \times m\mathbf{v}^* + \mathbf{H}^*$$

so that

$$\dot{\mathbf{H}}_O = \frac{d}{dt}(\mathbf{r}^* \times m\mathbf{v}^* + \mathbf{H}^*) = \mathbf{r}^* \times m\mathbf{a}^* + \dot{\mathbf{H}}^*. \qquad\qquad 7.4\text{-}2$$

Substitute this expression in 7.4-1 and transpose the $\mathbf{a}^*$ term:

$$\sum_i \mathbf{r}_i \times \mathbf{F}_i + \mathbf{r}^* \times (-m\mathbf{a}^*) = \dot{\mathbf{H}}^*. \qquad\qquad 7.4\text{-}3$$

The quantity on the left-hand side of this equation is the moment of the external forces and the moment of the "inertia force" applied at the mass center.   Only if $\dot{\mathbf{H}}^* = \mathbf{0}$ does this system have zero resultant moment and correspond to a force system in static equilibrium.   But if $\dot{\mathbf{H}}^* = \mathbf{0}$, $\mathbf{H}^*$ must be constant in magnitude and direction.   This happens in two-dimensional motion at a constant rate of rotation.   In general, it occurs in the case of a rigid body rotating at a constant rate about a fixed axis that is a principal axis of inertia for the body, since in that case Eq. 6.5-4 has only one non-zero term, and it is a constant.   These are rather special cases.   The useful range of the principle may be extended, it is true, to cases in which the magnitude (but not the direction) of the angular velocity vector varies. This may be accomplished by the introduction of still another fictitious quantity, the so-called "inertia torque," a torque of magnitude $I\dot{\omega} = \dot{H}^*$ exerted about the axis of rotation and opposite in sense to the angular acceleration $\dot{\omega}$.   Needless to say, the appearance of this fresh device presents the student with fresh opportunities to make errors in sign.

We conclude by solving Examples 1, 2, 3, and 5 of the preceding section using the concept of inertia forces.

Example 7.4-1

This situation is pictured in Fig. 7.3-2 and described in the first paragraph of Example 7.3-1. Since the axis of rotation is fixed and parallel to a principal axis of the disk, we may use the concept of a resultant inertia force. Since the angular speed is constant, no "inertia torque" need be introduced. The free-body diagram is shown in Fig. 7.4-1 below. The resultant inertia force of magnitude $ma^* = mx^*\omega_z^2$ is shown dotted. Its direction is taken opposite to that of the acceleration vector. If we

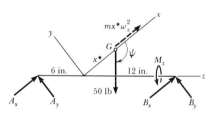

Fig. 7.4-1

now equate to zero the sum of the components of the forces in the coordinate directions and the moments about the coordinate axes, we have

$$A_x + B_x + mg \cos \psi + mx^*\omega_z^2 = 0,$$
$$A_y + B_y - mg \sin \psi = 0,$$
$$6A_y - 12B_y = 0,$$
$$-6A_x + 12B_x = 0,$$
$$M_z - mgx^* \sin \psi = 0,$$

and these are exactly the same as Eqs. 7.3-17. Notice that there is no restriction here on the choice of axes as there was, to some extent, in the treatment of Example 7.3-1.

Example 7.4-2

The situation under investigation is pictured in Fig. 7.3-3 and described in the first paragraph of Example 7.3-2. Here again the axis of rotation is fixed in direction and parallel to a principal axis of the disk. We may, therefore, usefully employ the concept of a resultant inertia force. Since, however, the angular acceleration is not zero, it is necessary to introduce a fictitious "inertia torque." The free-body diagram is shown in Fig. 7.4-2 below. The inertia forces and the inertia torque are shown dotted. Notice that the c.m. of the system has an acceleration component $r\omega^2 = (1/4)(18.8)^2$ directed toward the axis of rotation; therefore, we show an "inertia force" component directed away from the axis of rotation and of magnitude $30(1/4)(18.8)^2$. Since the angular acceleration is clockwise

when viewed from the positive end of the Z-axis, there is an acceleration
component of the mass center directed along the negative X-axis; we therefore show an inertia force component
$mr\dot{\omega}_z$ directed along the positive X-axis.
Since the angular acceleration is clock-
wise when viewed from the positive
end of the Z-axis, we show a
counterclockwise inertia torque $I_{zz}\dot{\omega}_z$
acting about that axis. Now, using
the fixed (X, Y, Z) axes, the equations
that express the fact that this system
of real and fictitious forces is a null
system are

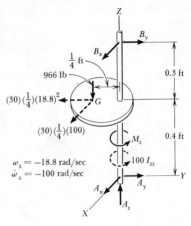

Fig. 7.4-2

$$A_X + B_X + 750 = 0,$$

$$A_Y + B_Y - 267 = 0, \qquad A_Z - 966 = 0$$

$$-0.7B_Y + \frac{966}{4} + (2660)(0.4) = 0,$$

$$0.7B_X + (750)(0.4) = 0,$$

$$M_Z + 100I_{zz} + \frac{750}{4} = 0;$$

whence

$$B_X = -428 \text{ lb}, \qquad B_Y = 1870 \text{ lb},$$
$$A_X = -322 \text{ lb}, \qquad A_Y = 800 \text{ lb}, \qquad A_Z = 966 \text{ lb},$$

in agreement with the results given for Example 7.3-2.

Example 7.4-3

The situation under analysis is described in Example 7.3-3 and
pictured in Fig. 7.3-4. Since the axis of rotation is fixed in direction and is
always parallel to a principal axis of inertia of the two parts of the system,
we may use the concept of a resultant inertia force and torque. The direction of the latter is unknown, however, in this case. We assume it to be
positive. Then the directions that the inertia torque and the $mr\dot{\omega}_z$ components of the inertia force must take are determined. The free-body
diagram is shown below. Since this is a null force system,

$$A_X + B_X + \frac{100}{386} 54 - \frac{300}{386} 4\dot{\omega}_z = 0,$$

$$A_Y + B_Y + 300 + 100 - 60 - 160 - \frac{300}{386} 36 - \frac{100}{386} 6\dot{\omega}_z = 0,$$

$$12A_Y - 18B_Y - (220)(8) - (300)(12) + \frac{300}{386}(36)(12) = 0,$$

$$-12A_X + 18B_X - \frac{300}{386}(4\dot{\omega}_z)(12) = 0,$$

$$-(160)(12) + (60)(12) + (100)(6) - 72\dot{\omega}_z = 0.$$

These are exactly the same as Eqs. 7.3-18, as may be seen by direct comparison. The student should note the pitfalls that arise in the proper choice of signs when this method is used.

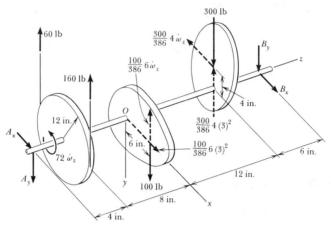

Fig. 7.4-3

Example **7.4-4**

We now treat again the rod of Example 7.3-5, which is suspended from a fixed point by means of a universal joint and made to rotate about a vertical axis at a constant rate. Now, however, the axis of rotation, though fixed, is not a principal axis of inertia. As a result, we cannot simply assume that a resultant inertia force acts at the mass center. We must subdivide the bar into particles if we wish to use d'Alembert's principle. Each particle will have a mass $dm = (m/l)\,ds$ and an acceleration of magnitude $\omega^2(s\sin\phi)$ directed toward the z-axis. As in Example 7.3-5, s denotes length measured along the rod from its point of support. The "inertia forces" associated with the particles are shown dotted in Fig. 7.4-4. They are directed away from the z-axis in the yz-plane. The moment of a typical one of these forces about the x-axis is

$$\left[\omega^2(s\sin\phi)\frac{m}{l}\,ds\right][s\cos\phi]$$

and the balance of moments about the x-axis requires

$$\int_0^l \left\{\left[\omega^2(s\sin\phi)\frac{m}{l}\,ds\right][s\cos\phi]\right\} - (mg)\left(\frac{l}{2}\sin\phi\right) = 0,$$

or

$$\frac{m\omega^2}{l}\sin\phi\cos\phi\int_0^l s^2\,ds - \frac{1}{2}mgl\sin\phi = 0,$$

$$\frac{1}{3}m\omega^2 l^2\sin\phi\cos\phi - \frac{1}{2}mgl\sin\phi = 0.$$

This is the same as the solution given for Example 7.3-5. The reader should observe that the last integration is the same as the one that arose in the conventional solution (7.3-5). He should also observe that the resultant inertia force does not act through the mass center, a sufficient warning in itself of the dangers of extending the notion of "inertia forces."

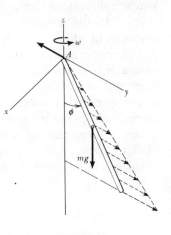

Fig. 7.4-4

7.5 Gyroscopic Effects

The equations $\mathbf{M}_O = \dot{\mathbf{H}}_O$ imply that the moment of momentum of a mechanical system about a point O will change if, and only if, there is an externally applied torque about O. The point O mentioned must, as we have seen, be one whose acceleration vector always passes through the mass center. Usually this condition is met by taking as O either the mass center itself or a point that has no acceleration. The change in $\mathbf{H}_O$ may be a change in magnitude, in direction, or both. The mechanical system need not be a rigid body. The sun and its planets or a finely divided powder falling in a vacuum provide examples of systems free of externally applied torque about the mass center. For the most part, however, the system of technological interest is one that can be treated as a rigid body. The equations $\mathbf{M}_O = \dot{\mathbf{H}}_O$ then take the form derived in Section 6.7 and known as Euler's dynamical equations:

$$M_x = I_{xx}\dot{\omega}_x + (I_{zz} - I_{yy})\omega_y\omega_z,$$
$$M_y = I_{yy}\dot{\omega}_y + (I_{xx} - I_{zz})\omega_z\omega_x, \qquad \textbf{6.7-9} \equiv \textbf{7.5-1}$$
$$M_z = I_{zz}\dot{\omega}_z + (I_{yy} - I_{xx})\omega_x\omega_y.$$

The subscripts (x, y, z) refer to rectangular axes fixed in the body, with origin at O. They are principal axes of the inertia tensor so that $I_{xy} = I_{yz} = I_{zx} = 0$.

If there is no externally applied moment, these equations may be solved for the unknown angular velocity components. In that case $\mathbf{H}_O$ is constant. The line through O in the direction of $\mathbf{H}_O$ is then known as the *invariable line*, and the plane through O at right angles to $\mathbf{H}_O$ is known as the *invariable plane*. In any general case, however, the solution of Euler's dynamical equations presents great difficulty, mainly owing to the fact that the moment components (M_x, M_y, M_z), being referred to axes moving with the body, are known only after the motion has been determined. Equations 7.5-1 do, however, suggest two simplifications that apply in almost all cases of technical importance. In the remainder of this section, we limit the discussion to instances in which two of the principal moments of inertia, say I_{xx} and I_{yy}, are equal and in which there is no applied torque about the third or z-axis. Any solid of revolution made of a uniform material will meet this condition. The axis of symmetry is then the z-axis. It is not essential, however, that the object be radially symmetric; a three-blade propeller will also meet these conditions provided the z-axis is taken through the hub at right angles to the plane of the blades. When $I_{xx} = I_{yy}$, the last of Eqs. 7.5-1 reduces to $M_z = I_{zz}\dot{\omega}_z$. If there is no moment about the z-axis, ω_z is constant. The z-axis is

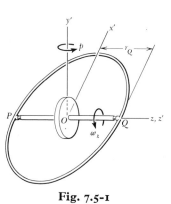

Fig. 7.5-1

then known as the *spin reference axis*, or, in the case of a solid of revolution, the *axis of figure*. In practice, friction always exerts some retarding torque about the z-axis, but its effect is often slight and gradual. Where necessary, as in the gyro-compass or rate-of-turn indicator, friction is offset by the torque provided by a spin motor.

The principal gyroscopic effect can be illustrated most simply by considering the forces required to make the spin axis of a rotating flywheel revolve in a horizontal plane at a constant rate, p rad/sec. The flywheel is shown in Fig. 7.5-1. It is attached to a shaft held in bearings at P and Q, the bearings being part of a light gimbal ring. In order to describe the motion, we shall want to use axes (x', y', z'), which are attached to the gimbal. The axis z' is chosen to lie along the shaft, whereas the axis y' is perpendicular to the plane of the gimbal ring. Then z' is the same as z, the spin axis fixed in the flywheel, and y' is fixed in space, being always directed vertically upward. The third axis, x', completes the right-handed orthogonal triad. Like z', it lies in the horizontal plane of the gimbal ring. The origin, O, is located at the mass center of the flywheel. We use the symbols $(\mathbf{i}', \mathbf{j}', \mathbf{k}')$ to denote unit vectors in the (x', y', z') directions respectively; $\mathbf{k}' = \mathbf{k}$.

The first step in the analysis is the determination of the angular velocity vector for the flywheel. Since this is a critical step, it is worthwhile to make it carefully, even though the final result is, in this instance, elementary. We note that the velocity of point Q distant r_Q from O is given by $\boldsymbol{\omega} \times r_Q \mathbf{k}'$ since Q is a point on the flywheel. But Q is also a point on the gimbal, which is simply rotating about the vertical, and its velocity is therefore $p r_Q \mathbf{i}'$. We therefore have

$$\mathbf{v}_Q = \boldsymbol{\omega} \times r_Q \mathbf{k}' = p r_Q \mathbf{i}'; \qquad \text{7.5-2}$$

$$(\omega_{x'} \mathbf{i}' + \omega_{y'} \mathbf{j}' + \omega_{z'} \mathbf{k}') \times r_Q \mathbf{k}' = p r_Q \mathbf{i}',$$

$$-\omega_{x'} r_Q \mathbf{j}' + \omega_{y'} r_Q \mathbf{i}' = p r_Q \mathbf{i}'. \qquad \text{7.5-3}$$

It follows that $\omega_{x'} = 0$ and $\omega_{y'} = p$. Therefore

$$\boldsymbol{\omega} = p \mathbf{j}' + \omega_{z'} \mathbf{k}'. \qquad \text{7.5-4}$$

Since z' is the same as z, $\omega_{z'}$ is the same as ω_z, and we do not need to make any distinction between them. Some texts give ω_z a distinctive symbol, usually n or s. The quantity p, the rate at which the spin axis is revolving, is known as the *precession rate*. It should be borne in mind that, although Eq. 7.5-4 gives the angular velocity of the flywheel, the angular velocity of the (x', y', z') axes (or of the gimbal in which they are embedded) is simply

$$\boldsymbol{\omega}' = p \mathbf{j}'. \qquad \text{7.5-5}$$

The second step in the analysis consists in writing down the angular momentum of the flywheel, $\mathbf{H}_O$. In the present case, point O is the mass center of the flywheel. In writing $\mathbf{H}_O$, we take advantage of the fact that (x', y', z') are also principal axes of the inertia tensor. This follows from the fact that, if (x, y) are principal axes having the same moment of inertia, the moment of inertia about *any* axis in the xy-plane will have this common value. In the case of a solid of revolution such as that pictured in Fig. 7.5-1, the conclusion that $I_{x'x'} = I_{xx} = I_{yy} = I_{y'y'}$ is obvious from symmetry. Since (x', y', z') are principal axes, it follows at once from Eq. 7.5-4 that

$$\mathbf{H}_O = I_{y'y'} p \mathbf{j}' + I_{zz} \omega_z \mathbf{k}'. \qquad \text{7.5-6}$$

In order to simplify the notation, it is customary to write

$$I_{xx} = A, \qquad I_{yy} = B, \qquad I_{zz} = C.$$

In the present case, $A = B$. Equation 7.5-6 is therefore written

$$\mathbf{H}_O = A p \mathbf{j}' + C \omega_z \mathbf{k}'. \qquad \text{7.5-7}$$

Of course A and C are constants, properties of the flywheel. If, for example, the flywheel is a uniform disk, $I_{zz} = C = (mr^2/2)$ and $I_{yy} =$

$I_{xx} = A = (m/12)(3r^2 + h^2)$, r and h being the radius and thickness of the disk, respectively.

Finally we differentiate the expression for the angular momentum with respect to time and equate the resulting expression to the moment applied to the flywheel. In Eq. 7.5-7, A and C are constants, the applied moment is such that p is maintained constant, $\mathbf{j}'$ is a constant because the y'-axis is fixed in space, and the spin rate, ω_z, will be constant if there is no moment about the spin axis. But $\mathbf{k}'$ changes in direction:

$$\frac{d\mathbf{k}'}{dt} = \boldsymbol{\omega}' \times \mathbf{k}' = (p\mathbf{j}') \times \mathbf{k}' = p\mathbf{i}' \qquad 7.5\text{-}8$$

so that

$$\mathbf{M}_O = \dot{\mathbf{H}}_O = (C\omega_z p)\mathbf{i}'. \qquad 7.5\text{-}9$$

We conclude from the analysis that in order for the flywheel spin axis to revolve at a uniform rate, p, a torque of magnitude $(C\omega_z p)$ must be applied to the flywheel about the axis x' fixed in the gimbal at right angles to the spin axis. This torque is known as a gyroscopic moment and the rotating body itself is known as a *gyroscope*.*

Another way of establishing the need for a gyroscopic moment is pictured in Fig. 7.5-2. The first two parts of the figure show a plan

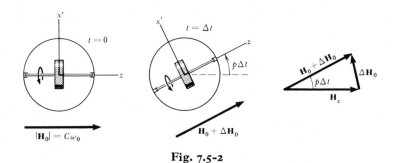

Fig. 7.5-2

view of the gyroscope at two successive instants. It may be seen that the z-component of the angular momentum is rotated through an angle $p \Delta t$ in time Δt. The change in $\mathbf{H}_O$, $\Delta \mathbf{H}_O$, is directed along the x'-axis, and its magnitude is, in the limit, $(C\omega_z p) \, dt$.

---

* The word *gyroscope* was coined by J. B. L. Foucault to indicate that the device could be used to show the rotation of the earth. Kelvin used the word *gyrostat* to refer to a concealed rotating object. In present-day usage, either expression is employed to refer to a rapidly spinning body.

The forces needed to produce the moment $\mathbf{M}_O$ of Eq. 7.5-9 must be exerted on the flywheel by the gimbal at P and Q. These forces

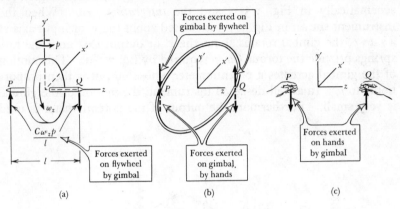

Fig. 7.5-3

are pictured in Fig. 7.5-3a. Equal and opposite forces exerted on the gimbal by the flywheel are shown in Fig. 7.5-3b; these are balanced by the forces exerted on the gimbal ring by the hands (or by whatever else constrains the gimbal to precess about the vertical axis). Finally, in 7.5-3c, the forces exerted by the gimbal ring on the hands are shown. To a person holding the gimbal ring, the gyroscope would appear to "want to move" so as to make the positive end of the spin axis (z) coincide with the positive end of the precession axis (y'). In the absence of the constraint represented by the gyroscopic torque, the positive end of the spin axis will tend to align itself with the positive end of the precession axis. This is exemplified by the behavior of the "free" gyroscope held in a Cardan or two-gimbal suspension (Fig. 7.5-4). When the vertical ring is rotated

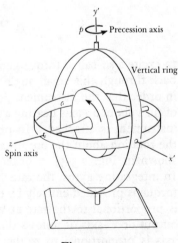

Fig. 7.5-4

in a positive direction as indicated in the figure, the z-axis rises to line up with the y'-axis.

The foregoing analysis provides the theoretical basis for the design of the so-called single-degree-of-freedom gyroscope. These instruments are of two basic kinds: the *rate gyro*, which is pictured schematically in Fig. 7.5-5, and the *integrating gyro*. When the instrument shown in Fig. 7.5-5 is rotated about the y' or input axis at a rate p, the gimbal rotates about the x' or output axis until the rate springs provide the torque $C\omega_z p$ required by Eq. 7.5-9. This motion of the gimbal actuates a potentiometer whose output is then proportional to p. In a well-designed instrument, the motion of the gimbal is very small. Furthermore the output of the potentiometer is used

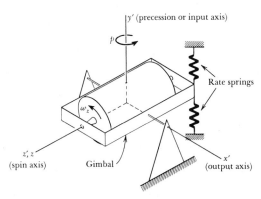

y' (precession or input axis)

p

Rate springs

ω_z

z', z
(spin axis)   Gimbal x'
(output axis)

Fig. 7.5-5

to excite a so-called torque generator motor, which rotates the gimbal back through this small angle to its null position. This is desirable in order that the instrument produce a signal proportional to the rate of turn about an axis bearing a fixed relation to the object to which the instrument is attached. In practice, it is usually necessary to damp the rotation about the output axis by means of a viscous damper (not shown in Fig. 7.5-5) in order to prevent an undesirable overshoot. In integrating gyros, the rate springs are omitted, and the gyroscopic torque is provided entirely by the viscous damper. Since this torque is proportional to the rate at which the gimbal is rotating about the output or x'-axis, it follows that the rate of rotation about the output axis is proportional to p, the rate of rotation about the input axis. The angle through which the gimbal rotates is therefore proportional to the integral of $p\,dt$. This instrument therefore measures the total angle through which the precession axis has been rotated.

The analysis of the general case of constrained precessional motion follows the same lines as the special case just treated, except that the geometry is somewhat more complex. We consider now a flywheel held in a Cardan suspension, as shown in Fig. 7.5-6, and suppose that the outer gimbal ring rotates about a fixed vertical axis, OZ, at a constant rate, p, while the plane of the inner gimbal makes a constant angle θ with the vertical, and we ask what constraint must be imposed upon the flywheel to make this motion possible. The analysis reduces to the previous special case when $\theta = 90°$. We again use axes (x', y', z') fixed in the inner gimbal; z' coincides with z, the axis of figure. The plane of $y'z'$ is vertical; it contains OZ. The axis x' passes through the bearings R, S; it is horizontal. As before, we begin by finding an expression for the angular velocity of the flywheel. The point

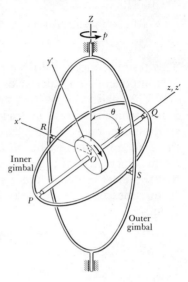

Fig. 7.5-6

Q distant r_Q from O now moves in a horizontal circle of radius $r_Q \sin \theta$.

Since Q is a point on the flywheel, we have

$$\mathbf{v}_Q = \boldsymbol{\omega} \times r_Q \mathbf{k}' = p r_Q \sin \theta \mathbf{i}', \qquad \text{7.5-10}$$

$$(\omega_x \mathbf{i}' + \omega_{y'} \mathbf{j}' + \omega_z \mathbf{k}') \times r_Q \mathbf{k}' = p r_Q \sin \theta \mathbf{i}',$$

$$(-\omega_x \mathbf{j}' + \omega_{y'} \mathbf{i}') r_Q = p r_Q \sin \theta \mathbf{i}'. \qquad \text{7.5-11}$$

It follows that $\omega_{x'} = 0$ and $\omega_{y'} = p \sin \theta$.

$$\boldsymbol{\omega} = p \sin \theta \mathbf{j}' + \omega_z \mathbf{k}'. \qquad \text{7.5-12}$$

The development follows Eqs. 7.5-2, 3, 4 very closely. Since (x', y', z') are principal axes for the flywheel, the equation corresponding to 7.5-7 is

$$\mathbf{H}_O = A p \sin \theta \mathbf{j}' + C \omega_z \mathbf{k}'. \qquad \text{7.5-13}$$

When this expression is differentiated to find $\mathbf{M}_O$, it must now be remembered that $\mathbf{j}'$ as well as $\mathbf{k}'$ is changing direction. Since the inner gimbal is rotating at the rate

$$\boldsymbol{\omega}' = p\mathbf{K} = p \sin \theta \mathbf{j}' + p \cos \theta \mathbf{k}', \qquad \text{7.5-14}$$

we have

$$\mathbf{M}_O = \dot{\mathbf{H}}_O = \frac{\delta \mathbf{H}_O}{\delta t} + \boldsymbol{\omega}' \times \mathbf{H}_O = \boldsymbol{\omega}' \times \mathbf{H}_O,$$

$$\mathbf{M}_O = (p \sin \theta \mathbf{j}' + p \cos \theta \mathbf{k}') \times (Ap \sin \theta \mathbf{j}' + C\omega_z \mathbf{k}'), \qquad \textbf{7.5-15}$$

$$\mathbf{M}_O = (C\omega_z p - Ap^2 \cos \theta) \sin \theta \mathbf{i}'. \qquad \textbf{7.5-16}$$

This result reduces to Eq. 7.5-9 when $\theta = \pi/2$. We note that $\mathbf{M}_O$ has no component along the z-axis so that ω_z is a constant.

The analysis shows that provided a moment is exerted about the x-axis, which is at right angles to the spin axis, a gyroscope can precess at a uniform rate. Such a moment can be supplied by unbalancing the gyroscope; that is, by putting the mass center at a point on the z-axis other than the geometrical center of the gimbals, O. Say that the mass center of the gyroscope is at the point whose position vector, measured from O, is $h\mathbf{k}'$. Then gravity exerts a moment about O.

$$\mathbf{M}_O = h\mathbf{k}' \times mg(-\mathbf{K}) = mgh\mathbf{k}' \times (-\sin \theta \mathbf{j}' - \cos \theta \mathbf{k}'), \qquad \textbf{7.5-17}$$

$$\mathbf{M}_O = mgh \sin \theta \mathbf{i}'. \qquad \textbf{7.5-18}$$

If the bearings at R and S are smooth, no other torques are exerted on the flywheel about the x-axis. Equating 7.5-16 and 7.5-18, we have

$$mgh \sin \theta = C\omega_z p \sin \theta - Ap^2 \sin \theta \cos \theta. \qquad \textbf{7.5-19}$$

If we discard the trivial cases $\theta = 0$, π, this equation reduces to a quadratic in p:

$$(A \cos \theta)p^2 - (C\omega_z)p + mgh = 0,$$

$$p = \frac{C\omega_z}{2A \cos \theta} \left[1 \pm \sqrt{1 - \frac{4Amgh \cos \theta}{C^2 \omega_z^2}} \right]. \qquad \textbf{7.5-20}$$

We may think of the angle θ as lying in the range $0°$–$90°$ and h as either positive or negative; this covers all possible cases. If h is negative, the gyroscope is supported at a point above its mass center and is said to be a *pendulous gyroscope*. We see from Eq. 7.5-20 that, for a pendulous gyroscope, p is always real and that, of its two possible values, one will be negative and one positive. The negative value of p is known as a *retrograde* precession. When h is positive, the precession rate, p, has real values if

$$\omega_z^2 > \frac{4Amgh}{C^2}, \qquad \textbf{7.5-21}$$

as may be seen by inspection of Eq. 7.5-20. It is for this reason that, in general, the gyroscope must be spinning rapidly in order to obtain a simple precessional motion. As ω_z increases, the two roots of Eq. 7.5-20 approach the limiting values

$$p_1 = \frac{C\omega_z}{A \cos \theta} \quad \text{and} \quad p_2 = \frac{mgh}{C\omega_z}. \qquad \text{7.5-22}$$

These are known as the *rapid* and *slow* rates of precession respectively. The slow rate of precession is the one most easily observed in practice. The motion of a child's toy top provides a good illustration of this precession rate. Finally, to avoid the possibility of misunderstanding, it should be said that, while a simple precessional motion *can* take place, it *will* take place only if the initial conditions are appropriate. The gyroscope must be set into motion with one of the rotational speeds p given by Eq. 7.5-19 and with $\dot\theta = 0$. On the other hand, if the gyroscope, with mass center between O and Q in Fig. 7.5-6, is released from rest, the bearing Q will dip downward initially, and the precessional motion of Q will be complicated by an alternate increase and decrease in θ which is known as *nutation*. This motion is discussed in Section 7.6.

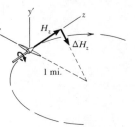

Fig. 7.5-7

Example 7.5-1

A turboprop airplane has four propellers, which rotate at 1020 rpm clockwise as viewed from the rear. They weigh 1031 lb each, and have a radius of gyration of 4.5 ft. What gyroscopic moment must the atmosphere, pushing on the control surfaces, provide, if the nose of the plane is not to dip or rise when the plane makes a one-mile radius turn to the right at 220 mph?

Solution: Isolate one of the propellers; z lies in the direction of the plane's velocity, y' is vertical upward, x' is horizontal and directed outward as shown in Fig. 7.5-7. The angular velocity of the propeller is $\boldsymbol{\omega}$, that of the (x', y', z') axes is $\boldsymbol{\omega}'$. Then

$$\boldsymbol{\omega} = p\mathbf{j}' + \omega_z\mathbf{k}, \qquad \boldsymbol{\omega}' = p\mathbf{j}',$$
$$\mathbf{H}^* = Ap\mathbf{j}' + C\omega_z\mathbf{k},$$
$$\mathbf{M}^* = \dot{\mathbf{H}}^* = C\omega_z(\boldsymbol{\omega}' \times \mathbf{k}),$$
$$\mathbf{M}^* = C\omega_z(p\mathbf{j}' \times \mathbf{k}) = C\omega_z p\mathbf{i}'.$$

This is, of course, the same as Eq. 7.5-9. In the present case,

$$C = \frac{(1031)(4.5)^2}{32.2} = 650 \text{ lb-ft-sec}^2, \qquad \omega_z = \frac{1020}{60} 2\pi = 107 \text{ rad/sec},$$

$$p = \frac{-220}{(1)(3600)} = -0.061 \text{ rad/sec}.$$

The negative sign of the numerical value of p is required by the fact that the rotation about the y'-axis is clockwise as viewed from above, and the right-hand rule tells us that this is a negative rotation rate.   We have

$$\mathbf{M}^* = (650)(107)(-0.061)\mathbf{i}' = -4250\mathbf{i}' \text{ ft-lb.}$$

We note that the negative value of the x-component of $\mathbf{M}^*$ corresponds to the negative direction of $\Delta \mathbf{H}_z$ as shown in Fig. 7.5-7.   Since there are four propellers and since couples about parallel axes can be added algebraically, the solution tells us that a negative moment of $(4)(4250) = 17{,}000$ ft-lb must be applied about the x-axis in order to make the propellers move in a horizontal right turn of one-mile radius.

The forces acting on the propeller to produce this torque are shown schematically in Fig. 7.5-8a.   The propeller will exert equal and opposite forces on the airframe, as shown schematically in Fig. 7.5-8b.   Unless

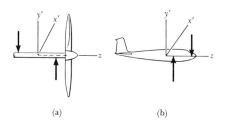

(a)   (b)

Fig. 7.5-8

measures are taken to prevent it, the nose of the plane will fall as a result of these forces exerted on the airframe.   The pilot wishing to maintain level flight must adjust the control surfaces so that aerodynamic forces exerted on the airframe counteract this gyroscopic moment.

Example 7.5-2

A simple gyroscopic grinder is made by causing two disks each of radius a and weight mg to revolve about a central shaft at a distance b as shown in Fig. 7.5-9.   Find the pressure exerted by each grinding wheel on the base.

Solution: Choose axes (x', y', z) as shown.   Isolate the right-hand grinding wheel and shaft.   Find $\boldsymbol{\omega}$, the angular velocity of the wheel, $\boldsymbol{\omega}'$, the angular velocity of the (x', y', z) axes, $\mathbf{H}_O$ and $\mathbf{M}_O$:

$$\mathbf{v}_P = \mathbf{0} = \boldsymbol{\omega} \times \mathbf{r}_P = (\omega_{x'}\mathbf{i}' + \omega_{y'}\mathbf{j}' + \omega_z\mathbf{k}) \times (-a\mathbf{j}' + b\mathbf{k}),$$

$$\mathbf{0} = (\omega_{y'}b + \omega_z a)\mathbf{i}' - \omega_{x'}b\mathbf{j}' - \omega_{x'}a\mathbf{k}.$$

Therefore,

$$\omega_{x'} = 0, \qquad \omega_y \cdot b + \omega_z a = 0,$$

$$\mathbf{v}^* = pb\mathbf{i}' = \boldsymbol{\omega} \times b\mathbf{k} = \omega_{y'} b\mathbf{i}'.$$

Therefore,

$$\omega_{y'} = p \quad \text{and} \quad \omega_z = -pb/a$$

$$\boldsymbol{\omega} = p\left(\mathbf{j}' - \frac{b}{a}\mathbf{k}\right),$$

$$\mathbf{H}_O = pA\mathbf{j}' - pC\frac{b}{a}\mathbf{k},$$

$$\dot{\mathbf{H}}_O = -pC\frac{b}{a}(\boldsymbol{\omega}' \times \mathbf{k}) = -pC\frac{b}{a}(p\mathbf{j}' \times \mathbf{k}),$$

$$\mathbf{M}_O = -p^2 C\frac{b}{a}\mathbf{i}'.$$

Since the mass center of the disk has no upward acceleration, the net upward force on the grinder and shaft must vanish, and the forces on the grinder (in the vertical plane) must be as shown in Fig. 7.5-10 so as to

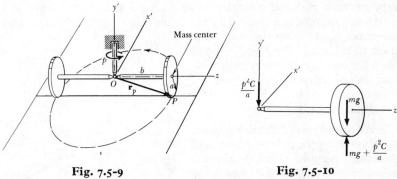

Fig. 7.5-9   Fig. 7.5-10

produce the required negative moment about the x'-axis. We see that the force exerted by the grinder on its base will be augmented over its weight mg by an amount $p^2 C/a$. The crushing action is greatly enhanced.

Example 7·5-3

A solid of revolution is attached by a hinge at a point on its axis of figure to an axis that is made to rotate in a horizontal plane at p rad/sec. If the angle θ between the vertical and the axis of figure is constant, what values may it have?

Solution: Since the body is *not* spinning about its axis of figure, its angular velocity is the same as that of the (x', y', z') triad, which rotates about the vertical; x' is the axis to which the body is hinged at O.

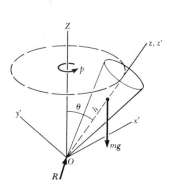

Fig. 7.5-11

$$\boldsymbol{\omega} = \boldsymbol{\omega}' = p\mathbf{K} = p(\cos\theta\mathbf{k}' + \sin\theta\mathbf{j}'),$$

$$\mathbf{H}_O = Cp\cos\theta\mathbf{k}' + Ap\sin\theta\mathbf{j}',$$

$$\dot{\mathbf{H}}_O = Cp\cos\theta(\boldsymbol{\omega}'\times\mathbf{k}') + Ap\sin\theta(\boldsymbol{\omega}'\times\mathbf{j}')$$

$$= (C - A)p^2\sin\theta\cos\theta\mathbf{i}'.$$

The only moment about O is due to the force mg:

$$\mathbf{M}_O = h\mathbf{k}'\times mg(-\mathbf{K}) = mgh\sin\theta\mathbf{i}'.$$

Equating $\mathbf{M}_O$ and $\dot{\mathbf{H}}_O$, we have

$$mgh\sin\theta = (C - A)p^2\sin\theta\cos\theta,$$

and θ may have the values 0 or π or

$$\theta = \arccos\frac{mgh}{p^2(C - A)}.$$

If the body is a thin rod held at one end, $C = 0$, $A = ml^2/3$, and $h = l/2$. Then $\cos\theta = -3g/2lp^2$. This result should be compared with the one given for Example 7.3-5 in which the problem was treated from the point of view of fixed-axis rotation (note that the angle ϕ in Example 7.3-5 is the supplement of θ in this example). For a cigar-shaped body, $A > C$, and therefore h must be negative if θ is to lie in the range 0, $90°$; this means that the mass center must lie below the point of support. For a body shaped like a flattened sphere, the point of support may be below the mass center.

Example 7.5-4

A hoop rolls in a circle on the ground, the forces acting on it being gravity and the contact reaction. Find the time required for the hoop to roll around the circle.

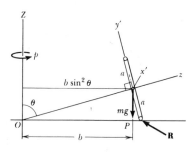

Fig. 7.5-12

Solution: The point of this example lies in the fact that the motion postulated can occur only if there is a special relation between the angle θ, the speed of rolling, and the radius of the track, b. We seek this relationship. With axes as shown in Fig. 7.5-12, we have

$$\mathbf{v}^* = pb\sin^2\theta\mathbf{i}',$$

$$\mathbf{v}_P = \mathbf{0} = \mathbf{v}^* + \boldsymbol{\omega}\times(-a\mathbf{j}'),$$

$$\mathbf{0} = pb\sin^2\theta\mathbf{i}' - a\omega_{x'}\mathbf{k}' + a\omega_z\mathbf{i}'$$

so that

$$\omega_{x'} = 0, \qquad \omega_z = -p\frac{b}{a}\sin^2\theta.$$

To find $\omega_{y'}$, we note that we can think of the hoop as the base of a cone with vertex at O. Then

$$\mathbf{v}_O = \mathbf{0} = \mathbf{v}^* + \boldsymbol{\omega} \times (-b \sin \theta \mathbf{k}),$$

$$\mathbf{0} = pb \sin^2 \theta \mathbf{i}' - \omega_{y'} b \sin \theta \mathbf{i}',$$

so that

$$\boldsymbol{\omega} = p \sin \theta \left(\mathbf{j}' - \frac{b}{a} \sin \theta \mathbf{k} \right),$$

$$\mathbf{H}^* = p \sin \theta \left(A \mathbf{j}' - C \frac{b}{a} \sin \theta \mathbf{k} \right),$$

$$\dot{\mathbf{H}}^* = p \sin \theta \boldsymbol{\omega}' \times \left(A \mathbf{j}' - C \frac{b}{a} \sin \theta \mathbf{k} \right)$$

$$= p \sin \theta (p \sin \theta \mathbf{j}' + p \cos \theta \mathbf{k}) \times \left(A \mathbf{j}' - C \frac{b}{a} \sin \theta \mathbf{k} \right)$$

$$= p^2 \sin \theta \left(-C \frac{b}{a} \sin^2 \theta - A \cos \theta \right) \mathbf{i}',$$

$$\mathbf{M}^* = -a \mathbf{j}' \times \mathbf{R}$$

where $\mathbf{R}$ is the ground reaction at P.

$$a \mathbf{j}' \times \mathbf{R} = p^2 \sin \theta \left(A \cos \theta + C \frac{b}{a} \sin^2 \theta \right) \mathbf{i}'.$$

We conclude from this equation that $R_{x'} = 0$ and that

$$R_z = \frac{p^2}{a} \sin \theta \left(A \cos \theta + C \frac{b}{a} \sin^2 \theta \right).$$

But the equation $\mathbf{F} = m\mathbf{a}^*$ must also be satisfied.

$$\mathbf{F} = -mg(\sin \theta \mathbf{j}' + \cos \theta \mathbf{k}) + \mathbf{R} = mp^2 b \sin^2 \theta (\cos \theta \mathbf{j}' - \sin \theta \mathbf{k}),$$

$$R_{y'} = mg \sin \theta + mp^2 b \sin^2 \theta \cos \theta,$$

$$R_z = mg \cos \theta - mp^2 b \sin^3 \theta.$$

On equating the two expressions for R_z, we have

$$p^2 \left(mb \sin^2 \theta + C \frac{b}{a^2} \sin^2 \theta + \frac{A}{a} \cos \theta \right) = mg \cot \theta.$$

This is the desired relationship. In the present case, we regard this equation as determining p. For a hoop, $C = ma^2$ and $A = ma^2/2$ so that p is easily expressed in terms of a, b, and θ. The time required to roll round the circle is $2\pi/p$.

Example 7·5-5

A gyroscope is mounted in a gimbal that lies in a horizontal plane but is free to rotate about a vertical axis (Fig. 7.5-13). Show that, if the gyroscope *is released from rest with the axis of figure at an angle ψ_0 to the west of north, this axis will oscillate about the northerly direction. Find the period of oscillation.*

Solution: This instrument is known as the *Foucault gyrocompass.* It may be realized by mounting the gyroscope of Fig. 7.5-6 so that the angle θ is fixed at ninety degrees. The gyroscope is shown schematically in Fig. 7.5-13b. Take (x', y') fixed in the gimbal with y' upward. We have for the angular velocity of the earth:

$$\boldsymbol{\omega}_e = \omega_e \mathbf{K}$$

where ω_e is the rotation rate of the earth denoted simply as ω in Section 7.5-2, which was concerned primarily with effects of the earth's rotation. The numerical value of ω_e is $7.292(10)^{-5}$ rad/sec. $\mathbf{K}$ is a unit vector in the direction OZ; that is, along the polar axis of the earth. It may be

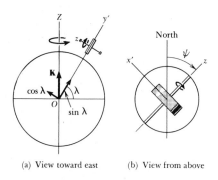

(a) View toward east   (b) View from above

Fig. 7.5-13

expressed as the sum of two components, $\sin \lambda$ in the direction y' and $\cos \lambda$ in the northerly direction in the plane $x'z$. This second component may be further decomposed into components along the x'- and z-axes. Then

$$\boldsymbol{\omega}_e = \omega_e \cos \lambda \sin \psi \mathbf{i}' + \omega_e \sin \lambda \mathbf{j}' + \omega_e \cos \lambda \cos \psi \mathbf{k}.$$

The angular velocity of the (x', y', z) axes is the same as the angular velocity of the earth except that these axes can rotate about y' as the angle ψ changes.

$$\boldsymbol{\omega}' = \omega_e \cos \lambda \sin \psi \mathbf{i}' + (\omega_e \sin \lambda - \dot{\psi})\mathbf{j}' + \omega_e \cos \lambda \cos \psi \mathbf{k}.$$

The term $\dot{\psi}$ is entered as a negative quantity because ψ is shown in Fig. 7.5-13b as being measured from the north to the z-axis. Since the y'-axis extends out of the plane of the drawing, toward the reader, a positive $\dot{\psi}$ implies a negative rotation about y'. The angular velocity of the gyroscope itself is the same as the angular velocity of the gimbal except for the gyroscope spin, denoted s.

$$\boldsymbol{\omega} = \omega_e \cos \lambda \sin \psi \mathbf{i}' + (\omega_e \sin \lambda - \dot{\psi}) \mathbf{j}' + (\omega_e \cos \lambda \cos \psi + s)\mathbf{k}.$$

In practice, s is a large quantity compared with ω_e, which, as we have seen, is very small. We write this term simply as ω_z and note that ω_z is constant since there is no moment about the z-axis.

$$\mathbf{H}^* = A\omega_e \cos \lambda \sin \psi \mathbf{i}' + A(\omega_e \sin \lambda - \dot{\psi})\mathbf{j}' + C\omega_z \mathbf{k},$$
$$\mathbf{M}^* = \dot{\mathbf{H}}^* = A\omega_e \dot{\psi} \cos \lambda \cos \psi \mathbf{i}' - A\ddot{\psi}\mathbf{j}' + \boldsymbol{\omega}' \times \mathbf{H}^*.$$

We are really only interested in $M_{y'}$, the moment about the vertical, exerted on the gyroscope by the inner gimbal.

$$M_{y'} = -A\ddot{\psi} - C\omega_z \omega_e \cos \lambda \sin \psi + A\omega_e^2 \cos^2 \lambda \sin \psi \cos \psi.$$

The last term is negligible compared with the second. Now taking the inner gimbal as our isolated system and denoting its moment of inertia about the vertical axis by I_g, we have

$$A\ddot{\psi} + C\omega_z \omega_e \cos \lambda \sin \psi = -I_g \ddot{\psi}.$$

The left-hand side of this expression is the y'-component of the moment exerted *by* the gyroscope *on* the inner gimbal. Since the gimbal is free to rotate about the y'-axis, no other torque is exerted on it. The negative sign on the right-hand side is again due to the fact that a positive value of ψ implies a negative rate of rotation about the y'-axis. From this expression we find that

$$\ddot{\psi} + \frac{C\omega_z \omega_e \cos \lambda}{A + I_g} \sin \psi = 0.$$

This is the equation of free vibration of a pendulum. For small angles ψ, the period of the motion is

$$T_n = 2\pi \sqrt{\frac{A + I_g}{C\omega_z \omega_e \cos \lambda}}.$$

If damping is provided, the oscillation will decay until $\psi = 0$, and the gyroscope axis of figure points north.

As a practical device, the Foucault gyrocompass is unsuitable for use in a moving vehicle. It would be difficult to maintain the gimbal in a horizontal position. In addition, the period given by the above formula tends to be too short. A short period is undesirable because it implies that the instrument will be sensitive to motions of the vehicle. These objections are overcome in the design of the *marine gyrocompass* (Sperry or Anschütz gyrocompass), which is, however, a true two-gimbal gyroscope.*

---

* For a discussion of the theory of the marine gyrocompass reference may be made to R. N. Arnold and L. Maunder, *Gyrodynamics* (New York: Academic Press, Inc., 1961), p. 230.

Its design is based upon the observation that a balanced gyroscope in a Cardan suspension will maintain its axis of figure fixed in space. If we think of this axis as pointed at a star rising in the east, it will follow the star. The axis will rise (from the point of view of an observer on the earth) until the star is on the meridian and then fall as the star sets in the west. By unbalancing the gyroscope and making it slightly pendulous, this rise and fall of the axis is made to produce a torque, which drives the axis back to the meridian.

7.6 Intrinsic Equations of the Gyroscope

In Section 7.5, it was shown that a solid of revolution spinning about its axis of symmetry could move with a simple precessional motion, provided a torque was applied about an axis at right angles to the axis of symmetry. Several instances of constrained precessional motion were investigated in detail. Finally it was noted that this simple motion would actually take place only for appropriate initial conditions and that for more general initial conditions a complex behavior might be anticipated. The essential features of this complex motion are exposed readily by what are known as the intrinsic equations of the gyroscope. These equations are a form of the equations $\mathbf{M}_O = \dot{\mathbf{H}}_O$. To derive them, we first imagine the fixed point or mass center of the gyroscope to be the center of a fixed sphere of unit radius. Let P denote the point at which the positive end of the axis of figure (the z-axis) intersects the sphere. The point P is known as the *pole* of the gyroscope, and it is in the motion of the pole that our interest centers. Next choose x, y-axes that, together with z, form a right-handed orthogonal triad, x being chosen so that the great-circle arc connecting its intersection on the unit sphere to P is tangent to the path of the pole. These axes are pictured in Fig. 7.6-1. They move with the gyroscope in a way that depends upon the path of the pole. The great-circle arc connecting the points where these axes intersect the sphere at time t are drawn full in the figure; dotted lines show these arcs at $t + \Delta t$. If we denote the speed of the pole by v, we have

$$\mathbf{v}_P = v\mathbf{i} = \boldsymbol{\omega} \times \mathbf{k} = -\omega_x\mathbf{j} + \omega_y\mathbf{i}, \qquad \text{7.6-1}$$

$\boldsymbol{\omega}$ being the angular velocity of the gyroscope. In view of this equation, $\omega_x = 0$, and $\omega_y = v$ so that

$$\boldsymbol{\omega} = v\mathbf{j} + \omega_z\mathbf{k}, \qquad \text{7.6-2}$$

$$\mathbf{H}_O = Av\mathbf{j} + C\omega_z\mathbf{k}, \qquad \text{7.6-3}$$

$$\mathbf{M}_O = \dot{\mathbf{H}}_O = A\frac{dv}{dt}\mathbf{j} + C\frac{d\omega_z}{dt}\mathbf{k} + \boldsymbol{\omega}' \times \mathbf{H}_O. \qquad \text{7.6-4}$$

Here $\boldsymbol{\omega}'$ is the angular velocity of the (x, y, z) axes. If we denote by ψ the angle that the tangent to the path at P makes with a fixed great-circle arc, the (x, y, z) axes will have a rotation rate $\dot{\psi}$ about the z-axis as well, of course, as a rotation rate v about the y-axis. In Fig. 7.6-1 the change in ψ, $\Delta\psi$, is shown. It follows that

$$\boldsymbol{\omega}' = v\mathbf{j} + \dot\psi\mathbf{k}. \qquad\qquad 7.6\text{-}5$$

Then

$$\mathbf{M}_O = A\dot v\mathbf{j} + C\dot\omega_z\mathbf{k} + (Cv\omega_z - Av\dot\psi)\mathbf{i}. \qquad\qquad 7.6\text{-}6$$

In scalar form this equation may be written

$$M_x - Cv\omega_z = -Av\frac{d\psi}{dt},$$

$$M_y \qquad\qquad = A\frac{dv}{dt}, \qquad\qquad 7.6\text{-}7$$

$$M_z \qquad\qquad = C\frac{d\omega_z}{dt}.$$

We can replace the forces that produce M_x and M_y by a force $\mathbf{F}$ tangent to

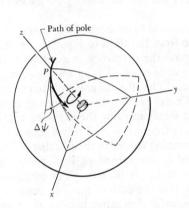

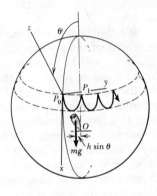

Fig. 7.6-1   Fig. 7.6-2

the sphere at P. Then, since the sphere is of unit radius, $M_x = -F_y$, and $M_y = F_x$ (numerically). We can also introduce the arc-length, s, measured along the path of the pole from some convenient starting point. Then we may think of s instead of t as the independent variable and write $\dot\psi = (d\psi/ds)(ds/dt) = v(d\psi/ds)$; also $\dot v = v(dv/ds)$. With these modifications, Eqs. 7.6-7 become

$$F_y + Cv\omega_z = Av^2\frac{d\psi}{ds},$$

$$F_x \qquad\qquad = Av\frac{dv}{ds}, \qquad\qquad 7.6\text{-}8$$

$$M_z \qquad\qquad = C\dot\omega_z.$$

Either form Eqs. 7.6-7 or 7.6-8 are known as the *intrinsic equations of the gyroscope* because the dependent variables ψ, v, ω_z are related to the path of the pole, P, and not to arbitrary reference axes. In this respect, they are analogous to the intrinsic equations of motion of a particle (Eq. 2.2-15). In fact, if a particle were moving on the surface of the sphere along the path of the pole P, its acceleration would have a component dv/dt along the x-axis and a component $v\, d\psi/dt$ in the direction of the y-axis. The equations of motion of this particle on the surface of the sphere would therefore be

$$ F_y = mv\,\frac{d\psi}{dt} = mv^2\,\frac{d\psi}{ds}, \qquad F_x = m\,\frac{dv}{dt} = mv\,\frac{dv}{ds}. \qquad \textbf{7.6-9} $$

It follows from the correspondence of Eqs. 7.6-8 and 7.6-9 that the motion of the gyroscope pole is the same as that of a particle of mass (numerically) equal to A moving on the surface of the unit sphere under the influence of the forces which, applied at P, produce the moments M_x, M_y *together with a fictitious force* $Cv\omega_z$ *directed to the left of the path as viewed from outside the unit sphere.*

We may now use the intrinsic equations to investigate the character of the motion of the gyroscope. We see from the third of Eqs. 7.6-7 that, if $M_z = 0$, ω_z will be a constant. Suppose the gyroscope is a top spinning about its axis of figure and that the pole is released from rest at an angle with the vertical, as shown in Fig. 7.6-2. The effect of gravity is to produce an initial downward motion of P. We can see this by transferring to the point P_0 a force proportional to $mg \sin \theta$ and applying the italicized rule of the previous paragraph. As v increases from zero—and it will increase as may be seen either by appeal to the foregoing rule or to the fact that $\mathbf{M}_O$ has a positive y-component to be inserted in the second of Eqs. 7.6-7—the deviating force $Cv\omega_z$ causes the pole to deviate to the left. The magnitude of this force increases as v increases so that the path of the pole eventually turns upward. On its upward motion, dv/dt is negative because the x-axis now points upward, whereas the force at P is still downward and therefore negative. The circumstances of the initial release are repeated at P_1 so that the motion thereafter repeats itself. The path resembles a cycloid. The alternate increase and decrease in θ is the nutation to which reference was made in Section 7.5. We see that the motion consists in this nutation superposed on the regular precession. If the pole, instead of being released from rest, were released with a velocity having an upward component, the cusps of the cycloid (points like P_0 and P_1) would become loops, and, if the initial velocity were downward, the cusps would be rounded off, as the student may verify.

Example **7.6-1**

Find the possible precession rates of a spinning top.

Solution: In general, in the application of the intrinsic equations, the evaluation of the term $d\psi/dt$ in Eqs. 7.6-7 (or $d\psi/ds$ in 7.6-8) presents difficulty. If, however, the pole is moving in a circle of radius $\sin\theta$ with constant speed v, we see that it must have an acceleration $v^2/\sin\theta$ directed toward the center of the circle, and the component of this acceleration in the plane tangent to the reference sphere must be $(v^2/\sin\theta)\cos\theta$, as shown in Fig. 7.6-3. Since $dv/dt=0$, it follows that this component must be the entire acceleration of P in the tangential plane; that is,

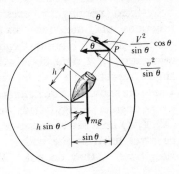

$$v\,\frac{d\psi}{dt} = v^2\cot\theta.$$

Since $M_x = mgh\sin\theta$, the first of Eqs. 7.6-7 becomes

Fig. 7.6-3

$$mgh\sin\theta - Cv\omega_z = -Av^2\cot\theta.$$

If the precession rate be denoted p as in 7.5, $v = p\sin\theta$ so that

$$mgh\sin\theta - Cp\omega_z\sin\theta = -Ap^2\sin\theta\cos\theta.$$

This is exactly the same as Eq. 7.5-19. It follows that, when we solve the quadratic for p, we recover the same two rates of precession given by Eq. 7.5-20.

7.7 Description of Spatial Position: Euler's Angular Coordinates

The angular velocity, which is a vector quantity, plays such a natural role in mechanical analysis that we sometimes overlook the fact that knowledge of the angular velocity as a function of time does not immediately reveal the spatial orientation of the rigid body. If the direction of the angular velocity vector is constant, as it is in plane motion or in fixed-axis rotation, the time integral of the magnitude of the angular velocity is equal to the number of radians through which the body has rotated about the fixed-axis direction. In general, however, the components of the angular velocity are not the time derivatives of any simple physical quantity. Usually this awkwardness is unimportant because we are not really interested in a complete description of spatial position. In studying the gyroscope, for example, the angle through which the flywheel has turned about its axis of figure is of no special interest, and we prefer to describe the motion by means of gimbal-fixed axes whose rotation rates are easy to visualize and measure. Occasionally, however, it is of importance to specify the complete spatial orientation of a rigid body—for example, in evaluating the automatic control of aircraft. This can be done in a variety of ways. One might use the nine direction cosines of a set of body-fixed rectangular axes. These would not be independent functions of time since six orthogonality relations would interconnect them. The most common method of specifying the spatial orientation of a rigid body is by means of three coordinates that are angles representing the rotation of the body about particular axes. These are known as *Euler's angular coordinates* or simply as *Euler's angles*.

Consider a rigid body one point of which, O, is fixed. Let (X, Y, Z) be a set of rectangular axes fixed in space, and let (x, y, z) be a set fixed in the body. Initially these axes coincide, but at a later time, t, they do not. Their positions at time t are shown in Fig. 7.7-1. Note in this figure that the intersection of the xy-plane with the XY-plane is the line ON, known as the *line of nodes*. We wish to show that the position of the body (i.e., of the axes (x, y, z) fixed in the body) at time t can be reached from its position at time zero by three successive rotations. These are: (1) a positive rotation about the z-axis of amount ϕ to bring the x-axis to the line of nodes. This is shown in Fig. 7.7-2a. The new position of the (x, y, z) axes we call x_1, y_1, z_1. A point whose coordinates are (X, Y, Z) will have coordinates

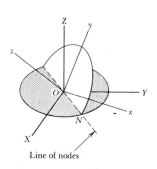

Fig. 7.7-1

$$x_1 = X \cos \phi + Y \sin \phi, \qquad y_1 = -X \sin \phi + Y \cos \phi,$$

$$z_1 = Z; \qquad\qquad \textbf{7.7-1}$$

(2) a positive rotation about the line of nodes or x_1-axis of amount θ to bring the z-axis to its final position. This is shown in Fig. 7.7-2b. If we denote the new positions (x_2, y_2, z_2), a point whose coordinates are (x_1, y_1, z_1) has coordinates

$$x_2 = x_1,$$

$$y_2 = y_1 \cos \theta + z_1 \sin \theta, \qquad \textbf{7.7-2}$$

$$z_2 = -y_1 \sin \theta + z_1 \cos \theta;$$

(3) a positive rotation about the final z-axis (z_2) of amount ψ to bring the x- and y-axes to their final positions, as shown in Figs. 7.7-1 and

7.7-2c. A point whose coordinates are (x_2, y_2, z_2), has, finally, coordinates

$$x = x_2 \cos \psi + y_2 \sin \psi,$$

$$y = -x_2 \sin \psi + y_2 \cos \psi, \qquad\qquad \textbf{7·7-3}$$

$$z = z_2.$$

The axes (x, y, z) have been carried to their final position. Substituting from 7.7-1 into 7.7-2 and from 7.7-2 into 7.7-3, we may find

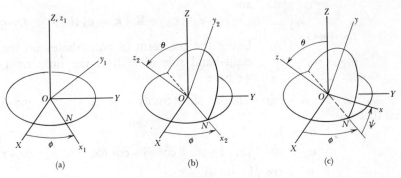

Fig. 7·7-2

the relation between the (X, Y, Z) and (x, y, z) coordinates of a point in terms of the three Eulerian angles, ϕ, θ, ψ:

$$\begin{aligned} x = \;& X(\cos \phi \cos \psi - \sin \phi \cos \theta \sin \psi) \\ & + Y(\sin \phi \cos \psi + \cos \phi \cos \theta \sin \psi) + Z(\sin \theta \sin \psi), \end{aligned}$$

$$\begin{aligned} y = \;& X(-\cos \phi \sin \psi - \sin \phi \cos \theta \cos \psi) \\ & + Y(-\sin \phi \sin \psi + \cos \phi \cos \theta \cos \psi) + Z(\sin \theta \cos \psi), \end{aligned} \qquad \textbf{7·7-4}$$

$$z = X(\sin \phi \sin \theta) + Y(-\cos \phi \sin \theta) + Z(\cos \theta).$$

The terms in parentheses are the direction cosines of the corresponding axes; that is, the cosine of the angle between final z-axis and original Y-axis is $-\cos \phi \sin \theta$.

We are now in a position to find the relation between the angular velocity components $(\omega_x, \omega_y, \omega_z)$ and the derivatives of the Eulerian angles. We consider an infinitesimal rotation of the body in which (ϕ, θ, ψ) change to $(\phi + \Delta\phi, \theta + \Delta\theta, \psi + \Delta\psi)$. Let $\mathbf{e}_\phi$ denote a unit vector along the axis about which the rotation $\Delta\phi$ is measured, i.e., along the Z-axis; $\mathbf{e}_\theta$ a unit vector along the instantaneous axis about which the rotation $\Delta\theta$ is measured, i.e., along the x_2-axis or line of nodes; and $\mathbf{e}_\psi$ a unit vector along the instantaneous axis about which the rotation $\Delta\psi$ is measured. These unit vectors are shown in Fig. 7.7-3. They are not orthogonal because the angle between $\mathbf{e}_\phi$ and $\mathbf{e}_\psi$ is θ rather than $\pi/2$. If $(\mathbf{i}, \mathbf{j}, \mathbf{k})$ are unit vectors along (x, y, z) and $(\mathbf{I}, \mathbf{J}, \mathbf{K})$ are unit vectors along (X, Y, Z), we have

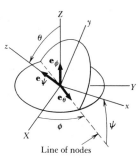

Fig. 7.7-3

$$\mathbf{e}_\psi = \mathbf{k}, \qquad \mathbf{e}_\phi = \mathbf{K},$$

and

$$\mathbf{e}_\phi \times \mathbf{e}_\psi = \mathbf{K} \times \mathbf{k} = \mathbf{e}_\theta \sin\theta. \qquad \textbf{7.7-5}$$

Using the last term in parentheses on the right-hand side of each of the Eqs. 7.7-4, we have

$$\mathbf{K} = \sin\theta \sin\psi\,\mathbf{i} + \sin\theta \cos\psi\,\mathbf{j} + \cos\theta\,\mathbf{k} \qquad \textbf{7.7-6}$$

so that

$$\mathbf{e}_\psi = \mathbf{k},$$
$$\mathbf{e}_\phi = \sin\theta \sin\psi\,\mathbf{i} + \sin\theta \cos\psi\,\mathbf{j} + \cos\theta\,\mathbf{k}, \qquad \textbf{7.7-7}$$
$$\mathbf{e}_\theta = \cos\psi\,\mathbf{i} - \sin\psi\,\mathbf{j}.$$

The rotation through angles $(\Delta\phi, \Delta\theta, \Delta\psi)$ being an infinitesimal rotation, we may write

$$\boldsymbol{\omega} = \dot{\phi}\mathbf{e}_\phi + \dot{\theta}\mathbf{e}_\theta + \dot{\psi}\mathbf{e}_\psi. \qquad \textbf{7.7-8}$$

On substituting Eqs. 7.7-7 in 7.7-8, we have

$$\boldsymbol{\omega} = (\dot{\phi} \sin\theta \sin\psi + \dot{\theta} \cos\psi)\mathbf{i} + (\dot{\phi} \sin\theta \cos\psi - \dot{\theta} \sin\psi)\mathbf{j}$$
$$+ (\dot{\phi} \cos\theta + \dot{\psi})\mathbf{k}. \qquad \textbf{7.7-9}$$

Since $\boldsymbol{\omega}$ can also be written $\omega_x\mathbf{i} + \omega_y\mathbf{j} + \omega_z\mathbf{k}$, it may be seen at once that

$$\omega_x = \dot{\phi} \sin\theta \sin\psi + \dot{\theta} \cos\psi,$$
$$\omega_y = \dot{\phi} \sin\theta \cos\psi - \dot{\theta} \sin\psi, \qquad \textbf{7.7-10}$$
$$\omega_z = \dot{\phi} \cos\theta + \dot{\psi}.$$

These relations make it relatively straightforward to write the equations of motion in terms of (ϕ, θ, ψ) and their derivatives; e.g., we may substitute 7.7-10 in Euler's dynamical equations 6.7-9. Alternatively, if we solve 7.7-10 for $(\dot{\phi}, \dot{\theta}, \dot{\psi})$, we find

$$\dot{\phi} = (\omega_x \sin\psi + \omega_y \cos\psi)\,\mathrm{cosec}\,\theta,$$
$$\dot{\theta} = \omega_x \cos\psi - \omega_y \sin\psi, \qquad \textbf{7.7-11}$$
$$\dot{\psi} = \omega_z - (\omega_x \sin\psi + \omega_y \cos\psi)\cot\theta.$$

If ω_x, ω_y, and ω_z are known as functions of time these expressions are of assistance in determining the rotation angles $(\phi,\ \theta,\ \psi)$.*

The angles θ and ψ, which appear in Section 7.3 (fixed axis rotation) and Section 7.5 (gyroscopic effects), are the same Eulerian angles discussed in this section.

Example 7.7-1

Write Euler's equations of motion for an unbalanced gyroscope.

Solution: The angles $(\phi,\ \theta,\ \psi)$ are shown in Fig. 7.7-4, which should be compared with Fig. 7.5-6. Note that p in the latter figure corresponds to ϕ. The moment of the weight force is $h\mathbf{k}\times(-mg\mathbf{K})$, and, in view of Eq. 7.7-6, this is

$$mgh(\sin\theta\cos\psi\mathbf{i}-\sin\theta\sin\psi\mathbf{j}).$$

Euler's dynamical equations are given as Eqs. 6.7-9 or 7.5-1. In view of Eqs. 7.7-10, these may be written

$$mgh\sin\theta\sin\psi = A\frac{d}{dt}(\dot\phi\sin\theta\sin\psi+\dot\theta\cos\psi)$$

$$+(C-A)(\dot\phi\sin\theta\cos\psi-\dot\theta\sin\psi)(\dot\phi\cos\theta+\dot\psi),$$

$$-mgh\sin\theta\sin\psi = A\frac{d}{dt}(\dot\phi\sin\theta\cos\psi-\dot\theta\sin\psi)$$

$$-(C-A)(\dot\phi\sin\theta\sin\psi+\dot\theta\cos\psi)(\dot\phi\cos\theta+\dot\psi),$$

$$M_z = C\frac{d}{dt}(\dot\phi\cos\theta+\dot\psi).$$

In these equations, M_z represents a moment about the axis of figure provided either by a motor or by friction. If neither of these influences is

---

* The Eulerian angles just described are not the only ones that may be used to describe the orientation of a rigid body. In describing the dynamic performance of aircraft, it is not uncommon to find roll, pitch, and yaw angles employed instead of Eulerian angles. Even among writers of texts on dynamics, there is a regrettable lack of uniformity in terminology. Many authors interchange the symbols ϕ and ψ. Others take the second rotation about the y_2-axis of Fig. 7.7-2b rather than about the x_2-axis. Occasionally, a left-handed convention is used. The notation of this text is in agreement with that of H. Goldstein, *Classical Mechanics* (Reading, Mass.: Addison-Wesley Publishing Company, Inc., 1950) and conforms with the practice of continental European and American authors generally. English writers make the previously mentioned change in the second rotation.

present, the term $\dot\phi \cos\theta + \dot\psi$ will be a constant.   It is this term that we have previously denoted simply ω_z.   If a motor is present, it will operate to keep $\dot\psi$ constant since the motor is mounted on the z-axis, and it senses only variations in $\dot\psi$. The solution of the first two equations is difficult even when $M_z = 0$.   As a rule, it is simpler to proceed from the energy and angular momentum integrals directly.

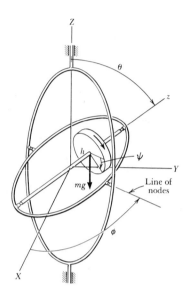

Fig. 7.7-4

Exercises

7.2-1: An object is projected vertically upwards with velocity v_0 at a place whose latitude is λ.   Find the distance from the point of projection at which the object will strike the ground.   Neglect air resistance.

Ans.: $4\omega v_0^3 \cos\lambda/3g^2$ to the west.   The result is due to Laplace.

7.2-2: In a place whose latitude is λ, an object is released from rest relative to, and at a height above, the surface of the earth.   Find the path of the particle relative to earth-fixed axes with origin at the point of release, z positive upward and y positive to the east. Assume that h is small compared with the radius of the earth, R, and that terms in the equations of motion proportional to ω^2 may be neglected.
Ans.: $y^2 = -z^3[(8/9g)\omega^2 \cos^2\lambda]$.

7.2-3: At what angle to the vertical should a projectile be fired if it is to fall to earth at the point of projection?
Ans.: $(2\omega v_0 \cos\lambda)/3g$.

7.2-4: Suppose that the earth, regarded as a homogeneous sphere, were to rotate so rapidly that objects at the equator had no weight.   What would then be the angle between the plumb line and the polar axis in a place of latitude λ?
Ans.: Zero.

7.2-5: The acceleration due to gravity at the North Pole is g_P; at the equator it is g_E.   What is it at latitude λ?
Ans.: $g_P \sin^2\lambda + g_E \cos^2\lambda$.

7.2-6: A projectile is fired westward in southern latitude $50°$ with muzzle velocity 2500 ft/sec and elevation angle $37°$.   Neglecting air resistance what is the deviation due to the rotation of the earth?
Ans.: 952 ft to the south.

7.2-7: From a position at north latitude 37°, we wish to hit a target 10 mi away in a northeastern direction using a gun whose muzzle velocity is 2500 ft/sec. In what direction should the gun be pointed to compensate for the rotation of the earth?
Ans.: 0.06 degrees to the north of northeast.

7.2-8: An object is projected with velocity V_o on the surface of a smooth, horizontal plane. Show that, owing to the rotation of the earth, it will start moving along an arc of radius $V_o/(2\omega \sin \lambda)$, where ω is the angular velocity of the earth, and λ is the latitude of the place of release.

7.2-9: A train of mass $2(10)^6$ kg moves at 30 m/sec in latitude 30°. Find the difference between the pressures on the rails when the train travels due east and when it travels due west.
Ans.: $4mv\omega \cos \lambda \cong 15{,}200$ newtons $= 3420$ lb.

7.2-10: Water flows south in a channel of width a with speed v. Show that, in a place of latitude λ, the water level on the west bank is higher than that on the east bank by $(2av\omega \sin \lambda)/g$. What does this difference in elevation amount to for the Mississippi River at St. Paul–Minneapolis; $a = 500$ ft, $v = 1$ ft/sec, $\lambda = 45°$?
Ans.: $1.6(10)^{-3}$ ft.

7.3-1: The rotor of a small electric motor weighs 2.3 lb. Normal operating speed is 2400 rpm. What dimensional tolerance must be maintained (i.e., how far from the axis of rotation may the mass center be allowed to stray) if the magnitude of the force on each of the two bearings is to be held to the dead weight of the rotor plus or minus 25 lb?
Ans.: 0.13 in.

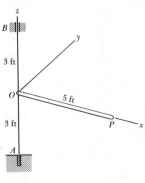

7.3-2: The 5-ft, 64.4-lb, uniform rigid rod OP is attached at O to the light vertical shaft AB, which is mounted in a smooth sleeve bearing at B and a smooth thrust bearing at A. The system rotates at the constant angular velocity $\omega_z = 2$ rad/sec in a positive sense about AB. Find the bearing reactions at A and B and the torque M_z necessary to sustain the motion. Use the body axes shown; write the moment equation with respect to O. Check your results by solving again, using the moment equation based on A or B.
Ans.: $M_z = A_y = B_y = 0$; $A_x = +16.8$ lb; $B_x = -36.8$ lb; $A_z = 64.4$ lb.

7.3-3: Suppose that the system of Exercise 7.3-2 has angular acceleration $\dot{\omega}_z = 5$ rad/sec^2 in a negative sense about AB at the instant when $\omega_z = 2$ rad/sec; find the bearing reactions and necessary torque.
Ans.: $M_z = -83.3$ lb-ft; $A_x = 16.8$ lb; $B_x = -36.8$ lb; $A_y = -12.5$ lb; $B_y = -12.5$ lb; $A_z = 64.4$ lb.

7.3-4: A symmetrical flywheel weighing 483 lb rotates in a horizontal plane about the vertical axis PQ to which it is rigidly keyed at point D. The center of mass C of the flywheel is 2 in from D; the radius of gyration of the wheel about an axis perpendicular to its plane at the mass center is 4 in. If $\omega_y = -3$ rad/sec, $\dot{\omega}_y = 10$ rad/sec^2, find the bearing reactions and the external applied torque M_y. Take xyz-axes as shown, with x parallel to CD.

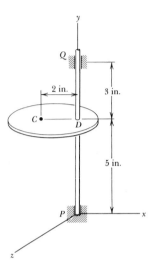

Ans.: $M_y = 250$ lb-in.

$$\mathbf{P} = -112\mathbf{i} + 483\mathbf{j} + 9.38\mathbf{k} \text{ lb.}$$

$$\mathbf{Q} = 135\mathbf{i} + 15.6\mathbf{k} \text{ lb.}$$

7.3-5: Suppose the shaft and flywheel of Exercise 7.3-4 are turned so that the shaft is horizontal. If the operating speed is to be 200 rpm, find the torque M_y and the bearing reaction at P when the c.m. of the flywheel is (a) directly over the shaft; (b) directly under the shaft; (c) horizontally to the right looking from Q to P.

Ans.: (a) $M_y = 0$, $\mathbf{P} = 230\mathbf{i}$ lb; (b) $\mathbf{P} = 592\mathbf{i}$ lb, $M_y = 0$; (c) $M_y = 966$ lb-in, $\mathbf{P} = 411\mathbf{i} + 181\mathbf{k}$ lb.

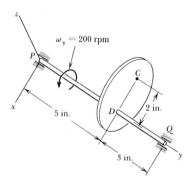

$\omega_y = 200$ rpm

7.3-6: Two symmetrical bodies are mounted on a light vertical shaft that is supported by a thrust bearing at A and a sleeve bearing at B. Planes of symmetry of the two bodies through their mass centers, C and F, are shown with D and E being the points of intersection of the shaft and the perpendicular planes of symmetry. F and C are in the same vertical plane, but on opposite sides of the shaft. Find the bearing reactions at A and B if the system is rotating at a constant rate of 2.5 rad/sec.

Ans.: $\mathbf{A} = -10.6\mathbf{j} + 750\mathbf{k}$ lb, $\mathbf{B} = 4.13\mathbf{j}$ lb.

7.3-7: Suppose body *CD* in the previous problem is loosened from the shaft at *D*, turned through a quarter turn so that the line *DC* points in the positive *x*-direction, and then is tightly fastened to the shaft again. The system is again set to rotating at a constant rate of 2.5 rad/sec; now what are the bearing reactions?

Ans.: A $= 73.2\mathbf{i} + 61.6\mathbf{j} + 750\mathbf{k}$ lb.

   B $= -111\mathbf{i} - 107\mathbf{j}$ lb.

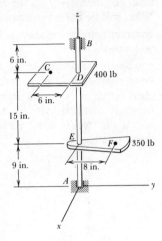

Exer. 7.3-6

7.3-8: Solve Exercise 7.3-6 if the shaft is mounted horizontally and if *C* is directly above, *F* directly below, the shaft. What torque must be applied about the shaft at this instant to sustain the motion?

Ans.: $M_z = 0$; **A** $= -349\mathbf{j}$ lb; **B** $= -408\mathbf{j}$ lb.

7.3-9: Solve Exercise 7.3-8 when *DC* is horizontal to the left, *EF* horizontal to the right when viewed from *B* toward *A*.

Ans.: $M_z = 33.3$ lb-ft; **B** $= -425\mathbf{i} + 17.5\mathbf{j}$ lb; **A** $= -325\mathbf{i} - 23.9\mathbf{j}$ lb.

7.3-10: Solve Exercise 7.3-7 if the shaft is mounted horizontally with *DC* horizontal to the left when viewed from *B* toward *A* (*EF* is then vertically down). What torque must be applied about the shaft at this instant?

Ans.: $M_z = -200$ lb-ft; **A** $= -7.76\mathbf{i} - 357\mathbf{j}$ lb; **B** $= -31.1\mathbf{i} - 439\mathbf{j}$ lb.

7.3-11: A light rod of length *l* carries masses *m* at each end. It is rotated at a uniform angular velocity, ω, about an axis that intersects the rod at its midpoint and makes an angle θ with it. Find the magnitude of the rocking couple (a) using body-fixed axes with *z* along the axis of rotation and (b) using body-fixed axes that are principal axes with origin at the mass center of the rod.

Ans.: $\frac{1}{4}ml^2\omega^2 \sin 2\theta$.

7.3-12: A thin rectangular plate of mass *m* and sides of length *a* and *b* is rotated with uniform angular velocity ω about an axis passing through a diagonal of the plate. What is the magnitude of the rocking couple? (It is advisable to use body-fixed principal axes with origin at the mass center of the plate.)

Ans.: $\dfrac{mab\omega^2}{12} \dfrac{(a^2 - b^2)}{(a^2 + b^2)}$.

7.3-13: A flywheel, whose mass *m* may be considered to be concentrated in its rim, has a radius *a*. It is mounted on a horizontal shaft midway between bearings distant *l* apart, and it rotates at constant speed ω. If the plane of the flywheel makes an angle θ with the vertical, what is the peak load carried by either bearing?

7.3-14: A rotor in the form of a uniform circular cylinder of mass m, radius r, and length l is statically balanced on a horizontal axis. This axis, however, deviates from the axis of symmetry of the cylinder by an angle, θ. What will be the magnitude of the rocking couple when the rotor is spun at constant angular velocity, ω? Show that, if $l = r\sqrt{3}/2$, the rocking couple will vanish.

7.3-15: A motorcycle stunt driver at the fair rides at constant speed on the vertical inner wall of a circular cylinder. The radius of the path of the mass center of cycle and driver is 50 ft. The limiting coefficient of friction f between tire and cylinder wall is 0.2. What is the minimum speed at which the cyclist must travel? Would this speed be reduced if f were made smaller?

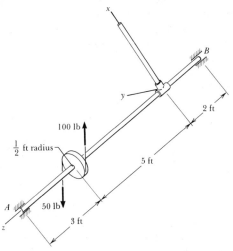

Exer. 7.3-16

7.3-16: A horizontal shaft in bearings at A and B, as shown, carries a disk and a rod that extends at right angles to the shaft. The weights of the shaft and disk may be neglected in comparison with the 96.6-lb weight of the rod. The moment of inertia of the assembly about an axis along the shaft is 30 lb-ft-sec². The center of gravity of the rod is 3 ft from the axis of the shaft. Vertical forces are applied to the disk as shown.

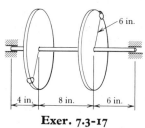

Exer. 7.3-17

Find the magnitudes of the bearing reactions at A and B at an instant when the rod extends horizontally to the left as viewed from A, and its angular velocity is 2.24 rad/sec.

Ans.: $A = 38$ lb, $B = 44.5$ lb.

7.3-17: Two equal disks are mounted on a horizontal shaft as shown. They rotate at 120 rpm. Find the dynamic bearing reactions due to the addition of two 10-lb weights at points on the rim of the disks 180 degrees apart. **Ans.:** 11 lb.

7.3-18: The shaft AB is inclined at 30° to the horizontal. It carries a pulley of radius 1/2 m, mass 30 kg, and radius of gyration 0.3 m to which is attached a horizontal cord carrying a 100-kg mass as shown. The shaft also carries a 70-kg eccentric disk whose mass center is displaced 1/4 m from the shaft. The centroidal radius of gyration of the eccentric disk is 0.5 m. The 100-kg weight is released from rest with the mass center of the eccentric disk vertically above the shaft AB. Find (1) the angular velocity of the

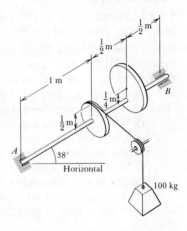

shaft when the weight has fallen 10 m, (2) the initial angular acceleration of the shaft, (3) the tension in the cord and the bearing reactions at A and B when the rate of rotation of the shaft is 20 rpm and the mass center of the eccentric disk is directly below the shaft AB.

7.3-19: The vertical shaft shown has two crank offsets weighing 5 lb each. As a designer, you wish to remove the horizontal forces acting on the bearings when the shaft rotates at 150 rpm by drilling a hole near the rim of each of the flywheels, A and B, at a distance of 12 in from the shaft axis. The dead weight of the assembly is carried on a thrust bearing not shown. (a) What weight of metal must be removed from each flywheel? (b) Sketch the proper location of the holes. (c) Will this shaft be in dynamic balance at all speeds or only at 150 rpm? **Ans.:** 0.416 lb; right-hand edge of A, left-hand edge of B; in balance at all speeds.

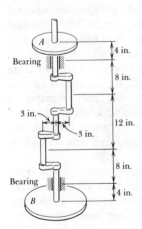

7.3-20: An automobile racetrack is banked at 30° on a curve of 200-ft radius. The width between the wheels of a racing car is 5 ft, and the mass center is 3 ft off the ground. The coefficient of limiting friction is 80 per cent. Will tipping or sliding occur at the critical velocity, and what is this critical speed? **Ans.:** Sliding; 87 mph.

7.5-1: The four-bladed propeller of a single-engine airplane weighs 322 lb and has a radius of gyration of 3 ft. It rotates at a speed of 1500 rpm.

When the airplane reaches the bottom of a vertical loop of 1200-ft radius at a speed of 420 mph what is the magnitude of the gyroscopic moment acting on the propeller bearing?

Ans.: 7280 ft-lb.

7.5-2: Explain why a bicyclist on a horizontal plane will lean toward the inside as he goes round a curve.

7.5-3: The rotor of a ship's turbine weighs 5000 lb and has a radius of gyration of 1 ft. It is mounted between bearings on a shaft parallel to the keel of the ship with its mass center 3.5 ft from the after bearing, A, and 2.5 ft from the forward bearing, B. Operating speed is 3500 rpm clockwise when viewed from the stern.

(a) When the ship, traveling at 20 knots, makes a turn to port of 1000-ft radius, what are the horizontal and vertical components of the bearing reactions at A and B? (1 knot = 1.69 ft/sec).

(b) What are the forces exerted on the hull if the ship, steaming on a straight course, descends a wave trough in such a way as to make the forward end of the rotor shaft dip at the rate of 0.3 rad/sec? Will the ship tend to turn to port (left) or starboard (right)?

Ans.:

(a) Forces exerted by forward bearing on rotor are 2600 lb up, 103 lb port. Forces exerted by rear bearing on rotor are 2400 lb up, 74 lb port.

(b) Forces exerted by forward bearing on rotor are 2920 lb up, 2830 lb starboard. Forces exerted by rear bearing on rotor are 2080 lb up, 2830 lb port.

Ship tends to turn to port (left).

7.5-4: An automobile has an engine flywheel that is mounted on a horizontal

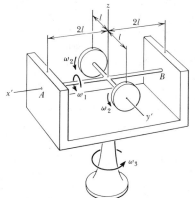

Exer. 7.5-5

shaft parallel to the longitudinal axis of the car. The flywheel weighs 322 lb, has a radius of gyration of 0.75 ft, and rotates at 800 rad/sec counterclockwise when viewed from the rear of the auto. The car traveling at 60 mi/hr makes a right turn around a curve of radius 700 ft. The distance between the centers of front and rear wheels is 11 ft.

Does the pressure of the front wheels on the road increase or decrease because of the gyroscopic effect, and by how many pounds?

Ans.: Decreases by 51.4 lb.

7.5-5: Two thin uniform disks each of mass m and radius r are mounted as shown in the figure. The x', y', z' axes are attached to the cross-bar frame on which the disks are mounted. Find the following at the instant depicted:

(a) Given $\omega_2 = \omega_0 \mathbf{j}'$, $\omega_1 = \omega_3 = \mathbf{0}$, find $\mathbf{H}_O$ for the system of two disks.

(b) Given $\omega_2 = \omega_0 \mathbf{j}'$, $\omega_1 = 0.01\omega_0 \mathbf{i}'$, $\omega_3 = \dot{\omega}_0 = 0$, find $\mathbf{H}_O$ and the forces exerted by the cross-bar frame on the bearings at A and B.

(c) If the system is in the state described in (a) and is then disturbed by having a positive ω_3 applied to it, what effect, if any, would you expect there to be on ω_1?

Ans.: (b) $A_{y'} = -B_{y'} = 0.01mr^2\omega_0^2/4l$; (c) $\dot{\omega}_1 = 2\omega_3\omega_0/(1 + 4l^2/r^2)$.

7.5-6: A uniform sphere of mass m, radius r, and centroidal moment of inertia about any diameter $I^* = 2mr^2/5$ is held in a smooth universal joint at one point, O, of its surface and set spinning at a uniform rate Ω, as shown, about the horizontal diameter OP. The sphere is started in its motion in such a way that it precesses steadily about the vertical through O.

(a) Find the magnitude and sense of the precession rate, p.

(b) What is the period of a complete precession?

(c) Find the total bearing reaction at O in appropriate coordinates.

Ans.:

(a) $p = 5g/(2r\Omega)$;

(b) $(4\pi/5)(r\Omega/g)$;

(c) vertical component $= mg$; horizontal component $= mg(25/4)(g/r\Omega^2)$.

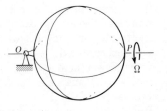

7.5-7: A gyroscopic stabilizer is to be installed in an automobile. Its function is to maintain equal pressures on the left and right tires when the car rounds an unbanked curve. Should the axis of the gyroscope be vertical, in the direction of motion, or at right angles thereto? What should be the sense of the rotation? For an automobile weighing 3500 lb (including gyro), moving at 44 ft/sec, and having both its mass center and that of the gyro at a distance $h = 18$ in above the ground, the largest practical gyroscope has $C = 20$ slug-ft^2. How fast would this gyroscope have to spin to accomplish the desired effect?

Ans.: 3425 rpm.

Would the effectiveness of the stabilizing action be independent of direction of turn, the radius of the curve, the length of the rear axle, and the distance between gyroscope bearings?

Ans.: Yes.

7.5-8: In another design, the vertical axis is stationary while the pan of 7.5-8 is made to rotate. Would you expect this grinder to be as effective as the one described in 7.5-10?

Ans.: No.

7.5-9: Find the fast and slow rates of precession of a boy's top in the form of a frustrum of a cone of base radius r and altitude a when the angle θ is small.

7.5-10: A gyroscopic grinder consists of a "muller" or grinder in the form of a disk of radius a and mass m, which is made to revolve about a vertical axis at a constant rate, p. Find the ratio of the force exerted by the muller on the pan to the value it would have if p were zero.

$$\text{Ans.: } 1 + \frac{ap^2}{2g}\left[\sin\theta - \left(\frac{a}{2l} + \frac{2l}{a}\right)\cos\theta\right].$$

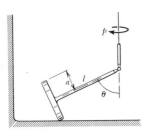

Exer. 7.5-10

7.5-11: An alternative design of grinding mill, the so-called Griffin or pendulum mill, is given in the figure shown below. Find the force exerted by the roller on the vertical edge of the pan in terms of p, m, l, a and θ.

Ans.: $mg \sin\theta$

$$\frac{(p^2a^2/gl)[(l/2a)\sin\theta + (a^2+4l^2)\cos\theta/4a^2] - 1}{\cos\theta - (a/l)\sin\theta}.$$

7.5-12: The front wheels of a truck are connected by an axle to which they are rigidly attached. When the left wheel passes over a hole in the road the axle acquires an angular velocity about a longitudinal axis. Does this tend to make the truck turn to the left or to the right? Work out the magnitude of the torque exerted by the axle on the truck frame for the case $C = 10$ slug-ft^2 for each wheel, speed of truck 40 mph, radius of wheels 2 ft, length of axle 5.5 ft, downward velocity of left wheel 5 ft/sec. Does your answer help to explain why front wheels of pleasure vehicles are individually suspended so that they will move in a vertical plane?

Ans.: Torque exerted on truck frame is of magnitude 530 ft-lb and tends to turn truck to left.

7.5-13: A U.S. fifty-cent piece has a diameter of about 3.0 cm and a mass of approximately 12.2 grams. It rolls in a circular path, its center describing a circle of 10 cm radius, while its plane makes a constant angle of 30° with the vertical. What must be the speed of the mass center?

7.5-14: A balanced gyroscope in a Cardan suspension is restricted to have its axis of figure always in the plane of the meridian. (This may be done by

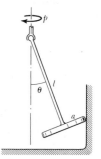

Exer. 7.5-11

clamping the outer gimbal in an east-west vertical plane.) Show that the angle θ between the direction of the North Pole of the earth and the axis of figure is governed by the equation $A\ddot{\theta} + C\omega_z\omega_e \sin\theta = 0$ where ω_e is the rate of rotation of the earth, terms proportional to ω_e^2 being neglected. It follows that there are two positions of equilibrium, $\theta = 0$ and $\theta = \pi$, that the latter is unstable, and that the period of small oscillation about the former is $2\pi(A/C\omega_e\omega_z)^{1/2}$. Neglect the inertia of the gimbal. (The result is due to Foucault.)

7.5-15: The gyroscope shown weighs 0.50 lb and has a centroidal radius of gyration of 1.50 in. The operating speed is 24,000 rpm, clockwise as viewed from A. The axis of rotation is connected to the case by two springs, each of constant $k = 40$ lb/in. If the gyro case is rotated about a vertical axis in a counterclockwise direction as viewed from above at a rate of 0.55 rad/sec, will point A move up or down, and how far?

Ans.: 0.025 in down.

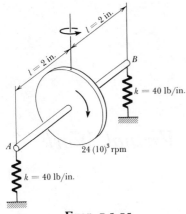

Exer. 7.5-15

7.6-1: Use the intrinsic equations of the gyroscope to explain why the spindle of a top will follow a curved wire guide.

7.6-2: Suppose that a spinning top is released with its axis of figure at an angle θ to the vertical and that its pole has an initial velocity that is horizontal. Use the intrinsic equations of the gyroscope to sketch the ensuing motion of the pole. Consider two cases: that in which the direction of the initial velocity corresponds to the direction of precession, and that in which it is opposite to the direction of precession.

7.7-1: Find the relation between the Eulerian angles (and their time derivatives) and the components of angular velocity along axes fixed in space.

Ans.: $\omega = (\dot{\theta} \cos \phi + \dot{\psi} \sin \theta \sin \phi)\mathbf{I} + (\dot{\theta} \sin \phi - \dot{\psi} \sin \theta \cos \phi)\mathbf{J}$
$$+ (\dot{\phi} + \dot{\psi} \cos \theta)\mathbf{K}.$$

7.7-2: Express the kinetic energy of a solid of revolution rotating about a fixed point in terms of the Eulerian angles and their time derivatives.

7.7-3: A rigid body moves under the action of zero external force and couple. The component of angular velocity along one of the principal axes is constant and has the value ω_1. Find the components of ω along the other two axes.

CHAPTER VIII

The Principle of Virtual Work

8.1 Work, Energy, and Equilibrium

We turn from dynamics at this point to look again at the problems of statics in the light of the general dynamical principles. The solution of problems in statics by direct application of the equilibrium equations can become tedious for complex frames and mechanisms. Also, we often wish to find only one or two unknown forces—for example, we may wish to check that a particular member in a truss is carrying a safe compressive load—and yet we may have to solve for almost all the internal forces in the structure before obtaining the information we desire.

An alternative approach to statics (and indeed to mechanics) can be based on the work and energy concepts. This approach is particularly well-adapted for the treatment of complex systems and for the solution of problems in which but a few unknown quantities are desired. Moreover, it is of great value in determining just which configurations of a system can be equilibrium configurations under a given set of loads.

Let us consider a system and any motion of the system during which it remains in equilibrium. Let us apply the work-energy principle $\Delta W = \Delta T$ to the system. Since each part of the system

466

moves with at most a constant velocity, the change in kinetic energy is zero. Thus, for a system in equilibrium, the work done by all forces on the system must vanish. This does not tell us very much. In all cases of interest to us, the system is in fact at rest in its equilibrium configuration. No point displaces, so no force does work.

At this point, a crucial step is made by imagining that the system displaces from equilibrium and by considering what would happen during such a displacement. In particular, suppose that some set of displacements, $\delta\mathbf{r}$, is assigned to each point of the system and the work, δW, that would be done by the forces acting on the structure during these displacements is computed. We shall show that, if the system is in equilibrium in its initial configuration under the action of the forces acting on the system, then δW must vanish for all possible sets of $\delta\mathbf{r}$, providing the magnitudes of the $\delta\mathbf{r}$ are sufficiently "small"; moreover, the converse is true: if δW vanishes for all $\delta\mathbf{r}$, then the system is in equilibrium. The displacement field $\delta\mathbf{r}$ is called a set of *virtual displacements*, and the work δW is the *virtual work*; the theorem embodying the result is the *principle of virtual work*. The adjective "virtual" here carries the connotation of "possible" or "permissible," as opposed to "actual."

The virtual displacements must in general satisfy constraint conditions. To satisfy these, we find that we must limit the virtual displacements in magnitude so that they are essentially differentials of position functions. This means that the constraint conditions connecting the virtual displacements of two points are like the relative velocity equations. Instead of assigning a set of virtual displacements, we can consider each point as given a velocity $\tilde{\mathbf{v}}$—a *virtual velocity*— and compute the *virtual power* $\tilde{P} = \mathbf{F} \cdot \tilde{\mathbf{v}}$ of the forces. A principle of virtual power that governs equilibrium can then be stated.

The price paid for using the principle of virtual work is the need for increased mathematical sophistication. The principle of virtual work is based upon the application of dynamical ideas to statical analysis. The equilibrium equations for systems subjected to concentrated forces are algebraic in nature. Because of the constraint conditions on the displacements, the principle of virtual work requires the use of the differential calculus. In particular, we must use the kinematics developed in previous chapters. We also note that we shall be concerned mainly, but not solely, with systems of rigid bodies having one degree of freedom over-all. The extension of the principle to systems with more degrees of freedom and, in particular, to deformable bodies is very important; the latter is one of the major methods for analysis and design of engineering structures.

8.2 Equilibrium of a Particle

The derivation of the virtual-work principle for a particle is quite simple. Consider a particle in equilibrium under a number of forces, $\mathbf{F}_1, \mathbf{F}_2, \ldots \mathbf{F}_n$ (Fig. 8.2-1), in some position $\mathbf{r}$ relative to a fixed point O; then the resultant force on the particle vanishes:

$$\mathbf{F} = \sum_{i=1}^{n} \mathbf{F}_i = 0. \qquad \text{8.2-1}$$

Imagine that the particle experiences a displacement, $\delta\mathbf{r}$, of any magnitude and in any direction; then the work done by the forces is

$$\delta W = \sum_{i=1}^{n} (\mathbf{F}_i \cdot \delta\mathbf{r}) = \left(\sum_{i=1}^{n} \mathbf{F}_i \right) \cdot \delta\mathbf{r} = \mathbf{F} \cdot \delta\mathbf{r} = 0. \qquad \text{8.2-2}$$

Zero virtual work δW is done by the forces $\mathbf{F}_i$ during the displacement $\delta\mathbf{r}$ if the particle is in equilibrium.

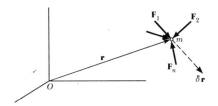

Fig. 8.2-1

The converse is also true. Suppose that a particle in position $\mathbf{r}$ is acted on by forces $\mathbf{F}_1, \mathbf{F}_2, \ldots \mathbf{F}_n$; further suppose that $\delta W = 0$ for all displacements $\delta\mathbf{r}$:

$$\delta W = \sum_{i=1}^{n} (\mathbf{F}_i \cdot \delta\mathbf{r}) = 0. \qquad \text{8.2-3}$$

We can then assert that the particle must be in equilibrium. We have

$$0 = \delta W = \left(\sum_{i=1}^{n} \mathbf{F}_i \right) \cdot \delta\mathbf{r} = \mathbf{F} \cdot \delta\mathbf{r}.$$

Now this can vanish if, and only if, $\mathbf{F} = 0$, $\delta\mathbf{r} = 0$, or $\mathbf{F}$ and $\delta\mathbf{r}$ are perpendicular. But, by hypothesis, $\delta W = 0$ for *any* choice of $\delta\mathbf{r}$; in particular, it must be true for a $\delta\mathbf{r}$ different from zero and not perpendicular to $\mathbf{F}$. Thus

$$\mathbf{F} = 0, \qquad \text{8.2-4}$$

the acceleration must vanish, and the particle must be in equilibrium. We have proved

The Principle of Virtual Work for a Particle:

A particle is in equilibrium under a set of forces if, and only if, the virtual work done by the forces on the particle is zero during any arbitrary virtual displacement of the particle.

Since $\delta W = \mathbf{F} \cdot \delta \mathbf{r}$ always for a particle, this seems to say nothing that $\mathbf{F} = \mathbf{0}$ does not say, and to say it in a more complex way. Even if one wanted to use the principle stated, how can one check that $\delta W = 0$ for all $\delta \mathbf{r}$? The answer leads us naturally to a discussion of constraint conditions.

We know that any vector $\mathbf{A}$ can be represented in terms of components in three independent directions, one such representation being $\mathbf{A} = A_x \mathbf{i} + A_y \mathbf{j} + A_z \mathbf{k}$. Moreover, once such a representation is given, the component of $\mathbf{A}$ in any direction $\mathbf{e}$ is known: $A_e = \mathbf{A} \cdot \mathbf{e}$. The displacement vector $\delta \mathbf{r}$ can be so represented: $\delta \mathbf{r} = \delta x \mathbf{i} + \delta y \mathbf{j} + \delta z \mathbf{k}$. By choosing the three special displacements $\delta \mathbf{r}_1 = \delta x \mathbf{i}$, $\delta \mathbf{r}_2 = \delta y \mathbf{j}$, $\delta \mathbf{r}_3 = \delta z \mathbf{k}$, for use in the virtual work principle, with known directions but arbitrary magnitudes ($\delta x, \delta y, \delta z$), we conclude that $F_x = 0$, $F_y = 0$, $F_z = 0$ are the equilibrium conditions. The vanishing of the force components in these independent directions ensures the vanishing of the force component in any direction; i.e., the resultant force $\mathbf{F}$ must be zero. With $\mathbf{F} = \mathbf{0}$, certainly $\mathbf{F} \cdot \delta \mathbf{r} = 0$ for all $\delta \mathbf{r}$. What we have shown is that it is sufficient to prove $\delta W = 0$ for arbitrary displacements in the coordinate directions in order to prove $\delta W = 0$ for all displacements.

The unconstrained particle in space has three degrees of freedom, and the three position coordinates are needed for a full discussion of its motion. Now suppose the particle is constrained in some way— a bead sliding on a wire, for instance; then we are not interested in equilibrium at a general position in space but only at positions satisfying the constraint conditions. It is still possible to vary all position coordinates. However, we may limit the displacements to those that satisfy the constraints and still use the virtual-work principle. This has the advantage, as does the full work-energy principle, of automatically eliminating workless constraint forces from consideration.

To ensure that the virtual displacements always satisfy the constraints, we require that they always be along, or tangent to, the surfaces or curves of constraint. This tangency condition is equivalent to the condition that the (virtual) velocity be tangent to the path.

Thus we limit ourselves to arbitrary small displacements, "small" meaning here that squares and products of magnitudes of displacements can be neglected compared to the magnitudes themselves. Indeed, the displacements are to be taken of such arbitrarily small magnitude that they may be considered as differentials of position functions, i.e., that they fit the pattern of small translations and rotations discussed in Section 6.3. We define an admissible virtual displacement of a constrained particle to be such a displacement $\delta \mathbf{r}$ of arbitrarily small magnitude that does not violate the constraint conditions. Thus the admissible displacements behave as if they were velocities. The set of all admissible displacements is called the kinematically admissible class of displacements.

We may now prove the virtual-work principle under these restrictions on the displacements:

A particle subject to constraints is in equilibrium if, and only if, the virtual work of all forces vanishes for all kinematically admissible virtual displacements.

The proof in one direction is simple. If the particle is in equilibrium, then the resultant force vanishes; if the resultant force vanishes, $\delta W = 0$ for any virtual displacement and in particular for all virtual displacements of the admissible class. The proof of the converse is more difficult. Suppose $\delta W = 0$ for all kinematically admissible displacements. We cannot now use the proof of sufficiency given previously, for we do not have completely arbitrary virtual displacements at our disposal. The proof is an indirect one. It parallels the sufficiency proof of Section 6.8 for the rigid-body equilibrium equations. Suppose the particle is not in equilibrium; then it must displace $d\mathbf{r} = \mathbf{v}\, dt$, and acquire a kinetic energy $dT > 0$. The work-energy principle for a particle requires that $dW = dT > 0$. But any actual displacement $d\mathbf{r}$ cannot violate the constraints and so must be an admissible displacement. By hypothesis, the work done in any such displacement must vanish; therefore, we have reached a contradiction and the particle must be in equilibrium.

A special case that is of importance arises when the constraints on the particle are workless; then we have only to consider the other external forces applied to the particle.

We have discussed these concepts in great detail for the particle although the principle of virtual work is of little use in particle applications. The excuse for the detail is that the same concepts carry over to systems, and that it is easier to fix these concepts in terms of the simple particle model than it is for systems—just as the dynamical concepts of Chapter II were first discussed for the particle.

Example **8.2-1**

Consider a particle weighing 5 lb suspended by two strings as shown in Fig. 8.2-2a; compute the string tensions.

Solution: The free-body diagram of the particle in equilibrium is given in Fig. 8.2-2b. Taking a coordinate system as shown,

$$\mathbf{T}_1 = T_1(-\cos 30°\mathbf{i} + \sin 30°\mathbf{j}),$$

$$\mathbf{T}_2 = T_2(\cos 15°\mathbf{i} + \sin 15°\mathbf{j}),$$

$$\mathbf{w} = -5\mathbf{j}.$$

Consider the virtual displacement $\delta\mathbf{r}_1 = \delta r(-\sin 15°\mathbf{i} + \cos 15°\mathbf{j})$. Then

$$\delta W = (\mathbf{T}_1 + \mathbf{T}_2 + \mathbf{w})\cdot\delta\mathbf{r}_1 = 0,$$

or

$$\delta W = [T_1(\sin 15° \cos 30° + \sin 30° \cos 15°) - 5 \cos 15°]\delta r = 0.$$

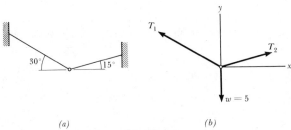

(a)   *(b)*

Fig. 8.2-2

Since δr is arbitrary, this can vanish for all δr only if

$$T_1(\sin 15° \cos 30° + \sin 30° \cos 15°) - 5 \cos 15° = 0,$$

or

$$T_1 \sin 45° = 5 \cos 15°.$$

Thus

$$T_1 = 5\sqrt{2} \cos 15° \cong 6.84 \text{ lb}.$$

Similarly, a displacement $\delta\mathbf{r}_2 = \delta r(\cos 60°\mathbf{i} + \sin 60°\mathbf{j})$ will lead directly to T_2.

The equations are, of course, exactly the equilibrium equations for the directions perpendicular to $\mathbf{T}_1$ and $\mathbf{T}_2$.

Example **8.2-2**

A particle is placed on the inside of a hemispherical bowl (coefficient of friction μ) so that the angle between the vertical and the radius to the particle is θ (Fig. 8.2-3). The particle is observed to stay there. What can be said about θ?

Solution: Fig. 8.2-3 shows a plane through the bowl, containing the center of the sphere, the lowest point, and the particle; the free-body diagram is also given. In this problem, the particle is to be constrained to move on the sphere. Moreover, as in all problems with friction, we must be very careful in considering the effect of possible motions—since the friction force should, properly, oppose the motion. In this case, we know that F must lie in the plane of w and N as shown. We take $\delta\mathbf{r}=R\,\delta\theta\mathbf{e}_\theta$,

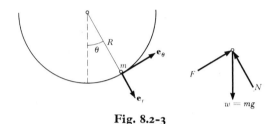

Fig. 8.2-3

a motion along the circle, even though F may not do negative work during this motion. Then

$$0 = \delta W = (\mathbf{w}+\mathbf{N}+\mathbf{F})\cdot\delta\mathbf{r}$$
$$= (-w \sin \theta\mathbf{e}_\theta+w \cos \theta\mathbf{e}_r - N\mathbf{e}_r + F\mathbf{e}_\theta)\cdot\delta\mathbf{r}$$
$$= R(F-w \sin \theta)\,\delta\theta.$$

By the principle of virtual work, this must vanish for arbitrary $\delta\theta$; thus

$$F-w \sin \theta = 0.$$

We can find N by destroying the constraint; i.e., letting $\delta\mathbf{r}=\delta r\mathbf{e}_r$; then

$$0 = \delta W = w \cos \theta\,\delta r - N\,\delta r$$
$$= (w \cos \theta - N)\,\delta r,$$

so that

$$w \cos \theta - N = 0.$$

For equilibrium,

$$\mu \geqq \frac{F}{N} = \tan \theta,$$

or θ must be less than the friction angle. Again, we could have written the equations directly.

Example **8.2-3**

A particle is constrained to move on the wavy smooth surface $z=5 \sin (x+y)$, where z is the vertically upward direction. Where can the particle be in equilibrium under its own weight and the forces of constraint?

Solution: Here the problem is really one of finding the admissible displacements $\delta \mathbf{r}$ from any position (x, y, z) on the surface. The particle has two degrees of freedom, which may be measured by the coordinates x and y. For small changes δx and δy in x and y, z must change by

$$\delta z = \frac{\partial z}{\partial x} \delta x + \frac{\partial z}{\partial y} \delta y = 5[\cos (x+y)](\delta x + \delta y)$$

if the displacement $\delta \mathbf{r} = \delta x \mathbf{i} + \delta y \mathbf{j} + \delta z \mathbf{k}$ is to be tangent to the surface. By the last principle proved, since the constraint is smooth, and thus workless, the virtual work of the applied weight force must vanish for all admissible displacements from equilibrium:

$$\delta W = -mg\mathbf{k} \cdot \delta \mathbf{r} = -mg \, \delta z = 0,$$

or

$$-5mg \cos (x+y)(\delta x + \delta y) = 0.$$

Clearly this is zero for arbitrary δx and δy only if

$$\cos (x+y) = 0$$

or

$$x+y = \frac{(2n+1)\pi}{2}, \qquad n = 0, \pm 1, \pm 2, \ldots.$$

A pair of values of x and y satisfying such a relation leads to $z = \pm 5$. The possible equilibrium positions are at the tops of ridges and along the bottoms of valleys of the sine-wave surface. (Draw a picture of the surface; that any position along these lines is a possible equilibrium position is clear by inspection.)

8.3 Equilibrium of Systems; The Rigid Body

Consider now a system of particles in equilibrium under external and internal forces. Then the principle of virtual work holds for each particle. By a virtual displacement of the system, we mean a virtual displacement of each part of the system. Thus, by addition of the work done on each part, the virtual work done on the system is zero for any virtual displacement if the system is in equilibrium. The converse is also true. Suppose the work done during any possible virtual displacement vanishes. Then, in particular, it vanishes if the displacement is chosen to be zero for all particles except one, and arbitrary for that one. This leads to the equilibrium equation for that particle. Since each particle of the system is in equilibrium, the system as a whole is in equilibrium.

The paragraph above contains several pitfalls for the unwary. It does not assert that the most general system is in equilibrium if only the resultant external force and resultant moment of external forces vanish.   In the virtual-work principle, as in any work-energy principle, the internal forces can, and usually do, do work.   This is one reason we are led to the study of the rigid system.   More important than the question of internal forces, which are included in the virtual-work principle, is the statement about the possibility of the virtual displacement.   In assuming that the displacements could be so chosen that each part could be moved independently, we have not permitted constraints.   For a rigid system, the choice of the motion of one point in the system limits the possible motion of any other. We must, therefore, modify the argument of the preceding paragraph in order to permit the inclusion of internal and external constraints. We also wish to extend our systems from those consisting of particles only to those containing rigid bodies.

The methods needed to treat constrained systems of particles have been developed already in our study of kinematics.   For the single particle, constraints limited the class of virtual displacements to the arbitrarily small displacements, essentially differentials of position vectors, that did not violate the constraints.   For a system, the constraints that we impose are again reflected in the construction of the kinematically admissible class of virtual displacements.   We may then prove the virtual-work principle for systems for all virtual displacements not violating the constraints.   The direct proof—from equilibrium of the system to the vanishing of the virtual work—is like that for the particle or like that of the first paragraph of this section. The only change to be made is the limitation to the admissible class of displacements, so that constraints will not be violated.[*]   Since each particle is in equilibrium, the virtual work of external and internal forces acting on it vanishes, and so the virtual work on the whole system must vanish.   The converse proof is one by contradiction, following that given for the particle.   Suppose the virtual work vanishes for all admissible displacements; we wish to assert that the system is in equilibrium.   Suppose it is not.   Then at least one particle acquires a velocity $\mathbf{v}$ and displaces $d\mathbf{r} = \mathbf{v}\,dt$; the system acquires a kinetic energy and positive work is done: $dW = dT > 0$. But this is a possible virtual work, contradicting our original hypothesis.   We have proved

---

[*] As a matter of fact, we often find it valuable to consider motions violating the constraints—especially external ones, as we did in Example 8.2-2. Internal constraints—connections of points rigidly or by a spring, cord, or pin—we do not usually violate; these allow us to evaluate the internal work, which would otherwise be difficult to compute.

The Principle of Virtual Work for a System of Particles:

A system of particles subject to constraints is in equilibrium if, and only if, the virtual work done on the system by the external and internal forces vanishes during any virtual displacement not violating the constraints.

For a rigid body, the class of admissible displacements is limited by the rigidity as an internal constraint. We have seen, in our study of kinematics (Section 6.2), that any motion of a rigid body can be compounded of a translation and a rotation. In particular, the small displacement of any point on a rigid body can be expressed analytically in terms of the small translational displacement of any other point on the body and the small rotation of the body as a whole (Section 6.3). Suppose point A at position $\mathbf{r}_A$ receives the small virtual displacement $\delta\mathbf{r}_A$, then the point B at position $\mathbf{r}_B = \mathbf{r}_A + \mathbf{r}_{B/A}$ must have displacement

$$\delta\mathbf{r}_B = \delta\mathbf{r}_A + \delta\boldsymbol{\theta} \times \mathbf{r}_{B/A}, \qquad \text{8.3-1}$$

where $\delta\boldsymbol{\theta}$ is the small *virtual rotation* of the body. In computing the virtual work done by forces on a rigid system during a virtual displacement given by such a translation and rotation, we know that the internal forces will do no work. Thus, we need consider only the external forces acting on a rigid body in proving the virtual-work principle.

Consider a constrained rigid body in equilibrium, and the work due to any external force $\mathbf{F}$ acting at point P of the rigid body: $\mathbf{F} \cdot \delta\mathbf{r}_P$. We have $\delta\mathbf{r}_P = \delta\mathbf{r}^* + \delta\boldsymbol{\theta} \times \mathbf{r}_{P/C}$ where C is the mass center. Then

$$\begin{aligned}
\mathbf{F} \cdot \delta\mathbf{r} &= \mathbf{F} \cdot \delta\mathbf{r}^* + \mathbf{F} \cdot (\delta\boldsymbol{\theta} \times \mathbf{r}_{P/C}) \\
&= \mathbf{F} \cdot \delta\mathbf{r}^* + \delta\boldsymbol{\theta} \cdot (\mathbf{r}_{P/C} \times \mathbf{F}) \\
&= \mathbf{F} \cdot \delta\mathbf{r}^* + \mathbf{M}^* \cdot \delta\boldsymbol{\theta},
\end{aligned} \qquad \text{8.3-2}$$

where $\mathbf{M}^*$ is the moment of $\mathbf{F}$ about the mass center C. Adding the work of all forces and couples, we have the total virtual work

$$\delta W = (\textstyle\sum \mathbf{F}) \cdot \delta\mathbf{r}^* + (\textstyle\sum \mathbf{M}^*) \cdot \delta\boldsymbol{\theta}. \qquad \text{8.3-3}$$

But the body is in equilibrium; the resultant external force and moment must vanish, and, hence, $\delta W = 0$ for all $\delta\mathbf{r}^*$, $\delta\boldsymbol{\theta}$.

Now suppose that δW of the external force system vanishes for all virtual displacements not violating the constraints. We wish to conclude that the rigid body is in equilibrium. The obvious thing to try is the argument of the first part in reverse order. That is, write δW in the form (8.3-3), and use the arbitrary nature of $\delta\mathbf{r}^*$ and

$\delta\boldsymbol{\theta}$ to conclude that the resultant force and moment must vanish. Only if the body is completely unconstrained can we do this. It cannot in general be done, because of constraint conditions that relate $\delta\mathbf{r}^*$ and $\delta\boldsymbol{\theta}$.

The proper argument is like that for the constrained particle. Assume the contrary of what we wish to prove: suppose the body is not in equilibrium. Then it must be accelerating, and acquire a kinetic energy $dT > 0$ in its initial small displacement $(d\mathbf{r}^*, d\boldsymbol{\theta})$. But, by the work-energy principle, the work done during this actual displacement $dW = dT > 0$; dW is certainly a possible "virtual work" since any actual displacements do not violate the constraints. Moreover, since the internal forces do no work, dW is the work done by the external forces only. But, by hypothesis, the virtual work of the external force system must vanish for all admissible virtual displacements. Thus, we have a contradiction, and the body must be in equilibrium.

We have proved

The Principle of Virtual Work for a Rigid Body:

A rigid body is in equilibrium if, and only if, the virtual work of the external forces vanishes for all arbitrarily small virtual displacements that do not violate the constraints.

Some further comments on the constraint conditions and the virtual displacements for a rigid body are in order. Note that we will be assured that the virtual work vanishes for all admissible displacements if it vanishes for arbitrary displacements corresponding to the (at most six) degrees of freedom of the rigid body. That is, if the configuration is described by generalized coordinates corresponding to the translational and rotational degrees of freedom of the body, then any virtual displacement may be compounded of the virtual changes in the independent generalized coordinates, and we need examine only what happens for arbitrary changes in these independent coordinates. As an example of the limitation of the displacement field permitted in a rigid body under constraints, let us consider a body with a fixed point. This external constraint reduces the number of degrees of freedom to the three rotational ones, which may be described (say) by the Eulerian angles of Section 7.7 as generalized coordinates. Then the virtual displacement of any point in the body depends on the virtual rotation of the body; for instance, the $\delta\mathbf{r}^*$ and $\delta\boldsymbol{\theta}$ of Eq. 8.3-2 or Eq. 8.3-3 must be related by $\delta\mathbf{r}^* = \delta\boldsymbol{\theta} \times \mathbf{r}^*$, where $\mathbf{r}^*$ is the position of the mass center relative to the fixed point. Therefore we need only assure ourselves that the virtual work vanishes for the three independent small rotations in order to know that it vanishes for all virtual displacements not violating the fixed-point constraint.

We obtain a modification of the virtual-work principle if the external constraints on the rigid body are workless; then we may restrict our considerations to the virtual work of the so-called "applied" external forces only, neglecting the constraint forces, in our statement of the principle. The principle for systems may also be extended to cover systems including rigid bodies as well as particles, provided the internal constraints are workless. We shall not state this separately here, since it is a special case of the principle for systems with conservative internal constraints discussed in the next section.

Constraint conditions for general systems must be treated with great care. For the systems we consider, any arbitrary virtual changes in the generalized coordinates represent a possible displacement of the system satisfying the constraints. Such constraints, which permit independent changes in all generalized coordinates equal in number to the degrees of freedom, are termed *holonomic*. Independent changes in each of the generalized coordinates needed to specify configuration will not satisfy the constraints in other cases, however; such constraints are *nonholonomic*. For further discussion of classes of constraints, reference may be made to more advanced texts on dynamics.*

Example **8.3-1**

A rigid uniform bar of length l and weight w rests on a smooth pivot at A and against a smooth wall at B; find the angle θ for equilibrium (Fig. 8.3-1).

Solution: The free-body diagram of the bar is shown also in Fig. 8.3-1. Coordinates are chosen with origin at the fixed point, A. Since the contacts are smooth, the forces at A and B will do no work in any motion that slides the bar on A and keeps end B along the wall. The position of C for any θ is given by

$$\mathbf{r}^* = \mathbf{r}_B + \mathbf{r}_{C/B}$$

$$= -a\mathbf{i} - a\tan\theta\mathbf{j} + \frac{l}{2}(\cos\theta\mathbf{i} + \sin\theta\mathbf{j})$$

$$= \left(\frac{l}{2}\cos\theta - a\right)\mathbf{i} + \left(\frac{l}{2}\sin\theta - a\tan\theta\right)\mathbf{j}.$$

---

* E.g., H. Goldstein, *Classical Mechanics* (Reading, Mass.: Addison-Wesley Publishing Company, Inc., 1950).

A small virtual rotation $\delta\boldsymbol{\theta} = \delta\theta\mathbf{k}$ will result in

$$\delta\mathbf{r}^* = \left[-\frac{l}{2}\sin\theta\mathbf{i} + \left(\frac{l}{2}\cos\theta - a\sec^2\theta\right)\mathbf{j} \right]\delta\theta.$$

The virtual work, due to the weight alone, is then

$$\delta W = -w\mathbf{j}\cdot\delta\mathbf{r}^* = w\left(a\sec^2\theta - \frac{l}{2}\cos\theta\right)\delta\theta,$$

which must vanish for all $\delta\theta$ if the bar is in equilibrium. Hence

$$a\sec^2\theta - \frac{l}{2}\cos\theta = 0,$$

$$\cos^3\theta = \frac{2a}{l}.$$

Thus the angle θ for equilibrium must satisfy $\theta = \arccos(2a/l)^{1/3}$. Note that there are two answers, one angle θ_1 in the first quadrant and another $\theta_2 = -\theta_1$ in the fourth.

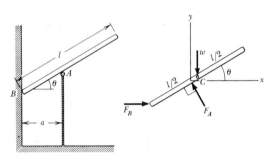

Fig. 8.3-1

Let us examine this solution carefully, so that the techniques are clear. First, let us recall how the problem would be solved by the ordinary methods of statics. We could write three equations of equilibrium for the three unknowns, F_A, F_B, and θ; eliminate F_A and F_B; and solve for θ. We could use the theorem concerning equilibrium of a rigid body acted on by three forces—F_A, F_B, and w—namely, that their lines of action must be concurrent (Fig. 8.3-2). Trigonometry and the properties of similar triangles then leads to the determination of θ.

The virtual-work principle is more sophisticated mathematically since it involves the calculus as well as geometry, trigonometry, and vector algebra; it is simpler to compute with, once it has been set up properly, since it eliminates immediately the unknowns that are not of concern.

What is the class of admissible displacements here? The constraints on the motion are these. First, the bar is constrained to move in a plane;

this reduces the degrees of freedom of the rigid body from six to three. This constraint can be expressed kinematically by saying that any point, say B, has only x and y position components and that any rotations can only be about an axis perpendicular to the plane. The constraint that B must move on the vertical line is expressed by the condition that $x_B = -a$ always; the bar now has only two degrees of freedom.   The final constraint is the requirement that the bar remain in contact with the fixed point A. This constraint condition can be expressed by the rest of the B-position equation: $y_B = -a \tan \theta$.   The bar has, thus, a single degree of freedom, measured by the position angle θ as generalized coordinate.

The constraint conditions can then be satisfied by any displacement that leaves B on the wall: $\delta \mathbf{r}_B = \delta y_B \mathbf{j}$ and keeps the bar on A: $y_B + \delta y_B = -a \tan (\theta + \delta \theta) \cong -a \tan \theta - a \sec^2 \theta \, \delta \theta$ for small displacements, or $\delta y_B = -a \sec^2 \theta \, \delta \theta$. We then can compute the virtual displacement of any other point on the bar during a virtual rotation $\delta \mathbf{\theta} = \delta \theta \mathbf{k}$ of the bar; in particular, the student may check that $\delta \mathbf{r}^*$ is given by

$$\delta \mathbf{r}^* = \delta \mathbf{r}_B + \delta \mathbf{\theta} \times \mathbf{r}_{C/B}.$$

The actual computation of $\delta \mathbf{r}^*$ was made by realizing that our definition of virtual displacements is based on the differential of position definition; that is, since $\mathbf{r}^*$ is a function of θ,

$$\delta \mathbf{r}^* = \frac{d \mathbf{r}^*}{d \theta} \, \delta \theta.$$

Fig. 8.3-2

Once the appropriate virtual displacement expressions have been decided upon and δW computed in terms of the virtual changes in the coordinates corresponding to the degrees of freedom, the next important step depends on the fact that δW vanishes for arbitrary choice of the magnitudes of the virtual displacements.   This enables us to set the coefficient of $\delta \theta$ equal to zero. We may note that the resulting equation is exactly the moment equilibrium equation about the point of intersection of forces F_A and F_B.   Since we have expressed the work done as the product of "something" and the dimensionless rotation $\delta \theta$, that "something" must be dimensionally a moment—and indeed it is, $w(a \sec^2 \theta - (l/2) \cos \theta)$. If the center of mass is to the right of the intersection point of F_A and F_B, then $a \sec^2 \theta - (l/2) \cos \theta$ is negative, and we have a negative or clockwise moment, as we should; the work done during a positive rotation $\delta \theta$ would then be negative.   Similarly, a positive moment leads to positive work done during the rotation.   We can see, then, that the $\delta W = 0$ condition leads exactly to the type of moment equilibrium equation expected.

The second answer must be interpreted. We do this in Example 8.3-3, after looking at an example for which there are clearly two equilibrium positions.

Example 8.3-2

The 10-lb rigid angle shown (Fig. 8.3-3) has two weights suspended from the ends of the arms, one of 5 lb, one of 3 lb; the c.g. of the angle is located as shown. Find θ for equilibrium.

Solution: The free-body diagram is shown in Fig. 8.3-4. A virtual displacement not violating the constraints is a rotation $\delta\boldsymbol{\theta} = \delta\theta\mathbf{k}$ about O; the pin reaction does no work. We have

$$\delta W = -10\mathbf{j}\cdot\delta\mathbf{r}^* - 3\mathbf{j}\cdot\delta\mathbf{r}_B - 5\mathbf{j}\cdot\delta\mathbf{r}_A$$

$$= -10\,\delta y^* - 3\,\delta y_B - 5\,\delta y_A.$$

With the cords inextensible, the y-positions of A and B differ by constants from those of A' and B'; therefore, $\delta y_A = \delta y_{A'}$, $\delta y_B = \delta y_{B'}$. Now

$$y_{A'} = 6\cos\theta, \qquad\qquad \delta y_{A'} = -6\sin\theta\,\delta\theta;$$

$$y_{B'} = 24\sin\theta, \qquad\qquad \delta y_{B'} = 24\cos\theta\,\delta\theta;$$

$$y^* = 6\sin\theta + 2\cos\theta, \qquad \delta y^* = (6\cos\theta - 2\sin\theta)\,\delta\theta.$$

Hence

$$\delta W = [-60\cos\theta + 20\sin\theta - 72\cos\theta + 30\sin\theta]\,\delta\theta = 0.$$

This must vanish for arbitrary $\delta\theta$; thus $50\sin\theta - 132\cos\theta = 0$ or $\tan\theta =$

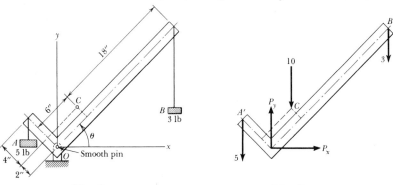

Fig. 8.3-3   **Fig. 8.3-4**

$132/50 = 2.64$. The solutions are then $\theta = 69°\ 15'$, $249°\ 15'$; these are the two equilibrium positions of the structure.

Example 8.3-3

We can, by removing constraints, find unknown reactions. Let us find the reaction at A in Example 8.3-1.

Solution: We know that θ for equilibrium must satisfy $\cos^3\theta = 2a/l$. With this value for θ, let us remove the restriction that the rod must remain in contact with A, but preserve the contact at B. We now take as a virtual displacement a translation $\delta y\mathbf{j}$ of the whole bar. Then the force at B still does no work, while

$$0 = \delta W = -w\mathbf{j}\cdot\delta y\mathbf{j}+(-F_A\sin\theta\mathbf{i}+F_A\cos\theta\mathbf{j})\cdot\delta y\mathbf{j}$$

$$= (F_A\cos\theta-w)\,\delta y.$$

This must vanish for arbitrary δy; hence $F_A\cos\theta-w=0$ and

$$F_A = w\sec\theta = w\left(\frac{l}{2a}\right)^{-\frac13}.$$

With this result for the magnitude of the reaction at A, we may write the vector $\mathbf{F}_A$ at equilibrium. Referring to Fig. 8.3-1 or 8.3-2 for the appropriate direction cosines of $\mathbf{F}_A$, we find

$$\mathbf{F}_A = F_A(-\sin\theta\mathbf{i}+\cos\theta\mathbf{j})$$

$$= w(-\tan\theta\mathbf{i}+\mathbf{j}),$$

where

$$\theta = \arccos(2a/l)^{\frac13}.$$

We are now ready to interpret the second answer found in Example 8.3-1. If θ is the negative angle having cosine equal to $(2a/l)^{\frac13}$, then its tangent is negative. The force at A has a positive x-component, as we see from the solution above for $\mathbf{F}_A$. For equilibrium, $\mathbf{F}_B$ must then be to the left. The second solution is a possible one only if the constraint at B is *bilateral*; i.e., if a force may be exerted in either sense. For instance, if B is constrained to move in a smooth slot, then a normal force can be exerted in either direction. We must reject this second solution otherwise. The student should make sure that the various possible solutions do have physical meaning for the problem under consideration.

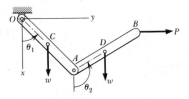

Fig. 8.3-5.

Example **8.3-4**

We have been looking at one-degree-of-freedom systems so far. Let us examine the more complicated case of two bars pinned smoothly together and constrained to move in a vertical plane (Fig. 8.3-5).
The two bars are identical, uniform rigid bars of weight w and length l; a horizontal force, P, is applied to the end of one, and the end of the other is pinned smoothly at O. Find the angles θ_1, θ_2 for equilibrium.
Solution: The forces at the smooth pins at O and A do no work; only those forces shown in Fig. 8.3-5 will do work during a virtual displacement. The virtual work will be

$$\delta W = w\mathbf{i}\cdot\delta\mathbf{r}_C+w\mathbf{i}\cdot\delta\mathbf{r}_D+P\mathbf{j}\cdot\delta\mathbf{r}_B.$$

Now

$$\mathbf{r}_C = \frac{l}{2}(\cos\theta_1\mathbf{i} + \sin\theta_1\mathbf{j});$$

$$\mathbf{r}_D = \mathbf{r}_A + \mathbf{r}_{D/A} = l(\cos\theta_1\mathbf{i} + \sin\theta_1\mathbf{j}) + \frac{l}{2}(\cos\theta_2\mathbf{i} + \sin\theta_2\mathbf{j});$$

$$\mathbf{r}_B = \mathbf{r}_A + \mathbf{r}_{B/A} = l(\cos\theta_1\mathbf{i} + \sin\theta_1\mathbf{j}) + l(\cos\theta_2\mathbf{i} + \sin\theta_2\mathbf{j}).$$

Here we can vary θ_1 and θ_2 independently; hence

$$\delta\mathbf{r}_C = \frac{l}{2}(-\sin\theta_1\mathbf{i} + \cos\theta_1\mathbf{j})\,\delta\theta_1;$$

$$\delta\mathbf{r}_D = \frac{l}{2}(-2\sin\theta_1\,\delta\theta_1 - \sin\theta_2\,\delta\theta_2)\mathbf{i} + \frac{l}{2}(2\cos\theta_1\,\delta\theta_1 + \cos\theta_2\,\delta\theta_2)\mathbf{j};$$

$$\delta\mathbf{r}_B = l(-\sin\theta_1\,\delta\theta_1 - \sin\theta_2\,\delta\theta_2)\mathbf{i} + l(\cos\theta_1\,\delta\theta_1 + \cos\theta_2\,\delta\theta_2)\mathbf{j}.$$

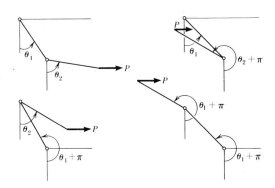

Fig. 8.3-6

Thus

$$\delta W = 0 = -\frac{wl}{2}\sin\theta_1\,\delta\theta_1 - wl\sin\theta_1\,\delta\theta_1 - \frac{wl}{2}\sin\theta_2\,\delta\theta_2$$

$$+ Pl\cos\theta_1\,\delta\theta_1 + Pl\cos\theta_2\,\delta\theta_2$$

$$= \left[Pl\cos\theta_1 - \frac{3wl}{2}\sin\theta_1\right]\delta\theta_1 + \left[Pl\cos\theta_2 - \frac{wl}{2}\sin\theta_2\right]\delta\theta_2.$$

Since θ_1 and θ_2 can be varied independently, this must vanish for $\delta\theta_1 \neq 0$, $\delta\theta_2 = 0$; thus

$$Pl\cos\theta_1 - \frac{3wl}{2}\sin\theta_1 = 0.$$

Similarly, δW must vanish for $\delta\theta_2 \neq 0$, which can occur only if

$$Pl \cos \theta_2 - \frac{wl}{2} \sin \theta_2 = 0$$

also. Therefore, the angles θ_1 and θ_2 for equilibrium are given by

$$\tan \theta_1 = \frac{2P}{3w}, \qquad \tan \theta_2 = \frac{2P}{w}.$$

The four possible equilibrium positions are shown in Fig. 8.3-6.

Example 8.3-5

Find the force F needed to hoist the weight for the two wheel-axle systems shown (Fig. 8.3-7). What advantage does system (b) have over system (a)?

Solution: In the simple wheel-axle system (a), as cord is unwound from the wheel, it is wrapped onto the axle. For a small revolution $\delta\theta$ of the

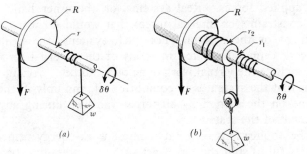

(a)   (b)

Fig. 8.3-7

system, we have (assuming the motion is slow and hence that equilibrium applies for determining the forces needed to just lift the weight)

$$\delta W = FR \, \delta\theta - wr \, \delta\theta = 0;$$

thus

$$FR - wr = 0,$$

or

$$\frac{F}{w} = \frac{r}{R}.$$

To gain a large mechanical advantage, either R must be large—giving a large, bulky wheel—or r must be small, with a weak shaft that may fail because of excessive bending.

For system (b), a rotation $\delta\theta$ still unwraps cord of length $R \, \delta\theta$ from the wheel. Now $r_2 \, \delta\theta$ is wrapped on the larger axle, $r_1 \, \delta\theta$ unwound from the smaller; the cord supporting the pulley and w thus shortens by $(r_2 - r_1)\, \delta\theta$, and w moves up half that distance:

$$\delta W = FR\, \delta\theta - \frac{w}{2}\, (r_2 - r_1)\, \delta\theta = 0.$$

Thus

$$FR - \frac{1}{2}\, w(r_2 - r_1) = 0,$$

or

$$\frac{F}{w} = \frac{r_2 - r_1}{2R}.$$

We can then obtain any mechanical advantage desired by making r_1 close to r_2, and eliminate the potential bending weakness of the shaft.

8.4 Real Systems; Potential Energy

The main advantage gained by the consideration of systems subjected to workless constraints is that we need consider only the external applied forces. Real systems, on the other hand, involve external constraints or internal forces that would do work during a displacement of the system. For such systems, the principle of virtual work cannot be stated in terms of the external forces only; we must include the virtual work done by all forces. Again, we have the result that the system is in equilibrium if, and only if, the virtual work done on the system by all forces vanishes during any virtual displacement of the system.

In the applications of the dynamical work-energy principle, we found it useful to split the forces acting on a system into two groups based on the methods necessary for the evaluation of the work integrals—conservative and nonconservative forces. The same division is useful here, since we can compute the work done by conservative forces easily from the potential energy function.

Consider some virtual displacement of the system, and split the virtual work into two parts: the work δW^* due to the nonconservative forces and the work $\delta \tilde{W}$ due to the conservative forces. Then

$$\delta W = \delta W^* + \delta \tilde{W} = 0,$$

$$\delta W^* = -\delta \tilde{W}.$$

Introduce the potential energy, V, corresponding to the conservative forces acting on the system. Since the work done by these forces is the negative of the change in potential energy, we have

$$\delta W^* = \delta V. \qquad \textbf{8.4-1}$$

Thus the principle of virtual work can be stated in the form:

A system is in equilibrium if, and only if, the virtual work done by the nonconservative forces is equal to the change in potential energy of the system during any kinematically admissible virtual displacement.

For a conservative system, we have:

A system subject to conservative forces is in equilibrium if, and only if, the virtual change in the potential energy vanishes for all kinematically admissible virtual displacements of the system:

$$\delta V = 0. \qquad\qquad \textbf{8.4-2}$$

For a real system for which all the applied forces and internal forces are conservative and which is subject to external constraints that are workless for a certain class of admissible displacements, we can prove a similar theorem to that for a completely conservative system:

A system subject to conservative applied and internal forces and to a set of workless constraints is in equilibrium if, and only if, the virtual change in potential energy vanishes for all kinematically admissible virtual displacements satisfying the constraints.

The difference between the latter statement and that expressed by Eq. 8.4-2 is, again, that of the simplification introduced by the automatic elimination of unknown forces of restraint from consideration. The proof proceeds along the same line as that for the single rigid body subject to workless constraints.

Let us consider the meaning of δV in this case more carefully. Suppose we are considering a conservative force, $\mathbf{F}$, and a corresponding scalar potential energy, V, given as functions of position in some region such that, at each point of the region,

$$\mathbf{F} = -\operatorname{grad} V \qquad\qquad \textbf{8.4-3a}$$

or, in cartesian component form,

$$F_x = -\frac{\partial V}{\partial x}, \qquad F_y = -\frac{\partial V}{\partial y}, \qquad F_z = -\frac{\partial V}{\partial z}. \qquad \textbf{8.4-3b}$$

By definition, for a virtual displacement $\delta \mathbf{r}$ of the point of application of $\mathbf{F}$, we have

$$\delta W = \mathbf{F} \cdot \delta \mathbf{r} = -\delta V; \qquad\qquad \textbf{8.4-4}$$

thus

$$\delta V = +(\operatorname{grad} V) \cdot \delta \mathbf{r} = \frac{\partial V}{\partial x}\delta x + \frac{\partial V}{\partial y}\delta y + \frac{\partial V}{\partial z}\delta z. \qquad \textbf{8.4-5}$$

We compute δV for a given virtual displacement in exactly the same way that we compute the differential of a function of several variables.

Example 8.4-1

Find the distance h that the spring of constant k is stretched when the weight w is in its equilibrium position (Fig. 8.4-1).

Solution: Let x be the distance of the weight below the fixed level and l_0 the unstretched length of the spring. The external force F does no

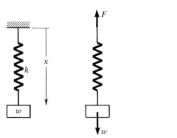

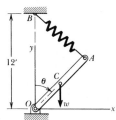

Fig. 8.4-1   **Fig. 8.4-2**

work if we do not move the support; the potential energy of the spring and mass is

$$V = -wx + \frac{1}{2} k(x-l_0)^2.$$

For an arbitrary change δx in x,

$$\delta V = \frac{dV}{dx} \delta x$$

$$= [-w + k(x-l_0)] \, \delta x.$$

Since the system is conservative, $\delta V = 0$ for arbitrary δx from the equilibrium position. Then the equilibrium distance, x_0, is given by

$$-w + k(x_0 - l_0) = 0,$$

or

$$x_0 = l_0 + \frac{w}{k},$$

with

$$h = x_0 - l_0 = \frac{w}{k}.$$

Example 8.4-2

The rigid bar OA is uniform of length 10 ft, weight 25 lb, and is pinned smoothly at O. The spring AB has constant $k=15$ lb/ft and unstretched length 4 ft. Find θ for equilibrium (Fig. 8.4-2).

Solution: For changes in θ only, the system is conservative, the pin force and reaction at B doing no work. The gravitational potential is

$$V_1 = wy^* = 125 \cos \theta \text{ ft-lb.}$$

The strain energy of the spring is

$$V_2 = \frac{1}{2} ke^2 = 7.5(l-4)^2 \text{ ft-lb.}$$

The length l of the spring for arbitrary θ is given by the law of cosines:

$$l^2 = 10^2 + 12^2 - 240 \cos \theta$$
$$= 244 - 240 \cos \theta,$$

or

$$l = 2\sqrt{61 - 60 \cos \theta}.$$

If δV is to vanish for arbitrary $\delta\theta$,

$$\frac{dV}{d\theta} = \frac{dV_1}{d\theta} + \frac{dV_2}{d\theta} = 0.$$

Since

$$\frac{dV_1}{d\theta} = -125 \sin \theta,$$

$$\frac{dV_2}{d\theta} = \frac{dV_2}{dl}\frac{dl}{d\theta} = 15(l-4)(2)\left(\frac{1}{2}\right)\frac{60 \sin \theta}{\sqrt{61 - 60 \cos \theta}} = 1800 \sin \theta \left[1 - \frac{4}{l}\right],$$

we have

$$\frac{dV}{d\theta} = -125 \sin \theta + 1800 \sin \theta \left[1 - \frac{4}{l}\right] = 0.$$

The roots of this equation are found by setting each factor of $dV/d\theta$ equal to zero in turn; i.e., from the two equations $\sin \theta = 0$, $-125 + 1800(1 - 4/l) = 0$. The first of these gives two possible equilibrium values for θ:

$$\theta_1 = 0°, \qquad \theta_2 = 180°.$$

The second equation may be solved for the third equilibrium position angle. We find

$$\frac{4}{l} = 1 - \frac{125}{1800} = \frac{67}{72},$$

$$l = 2\sqrt{61 - 60 \cos \theta_3} = \frac{288}{67},$$

$$61 - 60 \cos \theta_3 = \left(\frac{144}{67}\right)^2,$$

$$\cos \theta_3 = \frac{1}{60}[61 - 4.619] = 0.9397.$$

The third equilibrium position is given by $\theta_3 = 20°$, with a symmetric one on the other side of the vertical line OB.

Before considering further examples, examine the results of these first two. In both cases, the system has a single degree of freedom, and the potential energy is a function of that coordinate only, say $V(x)$. Since $\delta V = (dV/dx)\,\delta x$ for a virtual change in the generalized coordinate or degree of freedom x, the equilibrium positions are given by those values of x for which

$$\frac{dV}{dx} = 0. \qquad\qquad \textbf{8.4-6}$$

This condition is shown in the differential calculus to be the one by which "stationary" values of V are determined: relative maxima, relative minima, and "saddle" or horizontal inflection points. The principle of virtual work for conservative systems with a single degree of freedom can be stated in terms of this "stationary values of V" criterion:

A conservative system with a single degree of freedom is in equilibrium in a given configuration if, and only if, the potential energy possesses a stationary value for that configuration.

We can extend this same result to conservative systems that have the same number, n, of degrees of freedom as they have generalized coordinates $q_1, q_2, \ldots q_n$; the potential energy is a function of these coordinates:

$$V = V(q_1, q_2, \ldots q_n). \qquad\qquad \textbf{8.4-7}$$

For any admissible virtual change $\delta q_1, \delta q_2, \ldots \delta q_n$ in the coordinates,

$$\delta V = \frac{\partial V}{\partial q_1}\,\delta q_1 + \frac{\partial V}{\partial q_2}\,\delta q_2 + \ldots \frac{\partial V}{\partial q_n}\,\delta q_n. \qquad\qquad \textbf{8.4-8}$$

Since δV must vanish for arbitrary choice of the independent changes $\delta q_1, \ldots \delta q_n$ from equilibrium, we have

$$\frac{\partial V}{\partial q_1} = 0, \qquad \frac{\partial V}{\partial q_2} = 0, \ldots \frac{\partial V}{\partial q_n} = 0 \qquad\qquad \textbf{8.4-9}$$

for equilibrium. These conditions are, again, those for a stationary value of V.

Let us return to the single-degree-of-freedom case, with $V = V(q)$. Suppose that $q = q_0$ is a value of q corresponding to an equilibrium position, so that

$$\left.\frac{dV}{dq}\right|_{q=q_0} = 0. \qquad\qquad \textbf{8.4-10}$$

Suppose further that, for q close enough to q_0, we can expand in a Taylor's series about q_0, at least through the second-order term:

$$V(q) = V(q_0) + \left(\frac{dV}{dq}\right)\Big|_{q=q_0}(q-q_0) + \left(\frac{d^2V}{dq^2}\right)\Big|_{q=q_0}\frac{(q-q_0)^2}{2!} + \dots$$

Since $V'(q_0) = 0$, this becomes

$$V(q) = V(q_0) + V''(q_0)\frac{(q-q_0)^2}{2!} + \dots$$

Finally, we know that we can shift the position at which V vanishes arbitrarily—that the addition of a constant to V does not change the computation of the forces or of the work done in a change of position. We can, thus, choose $V(q_0) = 0$. Furthermore, we may introduce a new generalized coordinate $\tilde{q} = q - q_0$ measured from equilibrium; then

$$V(\tilde{q}) = V''(0)\frac{\tilde{q}^2}{2!} + \dots \qquad \text{8.4-11}$$

This is the form of the potential energy function used in Chapter IX in studying vibrations of an undamped system about its equilibrium position. We know that the kind of stationary value—maximum, minimum, or neither—that V has at equilibrium is determined usually by the sign of V'' at the equilibrium position. This topic will be discussed in the next section.

Let us examine a few more simple problems.

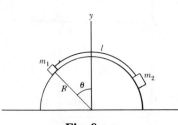

Fig. 8.4-3

Example 8.4-3

Two masses, m_1 and m_2, connected by a light inextensible cord of length l are placed on a smooth, circular arc as shown. Find θ for equilibrium.

Solution:

$$V = m_1 gR \cos\theta + m_2 gR \cos\left(\frac{l}{R} - \theta\right),$$

$$\frac{dV}{d\theta} = -m_1 gR \sin\theta + m_2 gR \sin\left(\frac{l}{R} - \theta\right).$$

This vanishes when

$$m_1 \sin\theta = m_2 \sin\left(\frac{l}{R} - \theta\right),$$

or when
$$[m_1 + m_2 \cos (l/R)] \sin \theta = m_2 \sin (l/R) \cos \theta.$$
Thus
$$\tan \theta = \frac{\sin (l/R)}{\dfrac{m_1}{m_2} + \cos (l/R)} \quad \text{for equilibrium.}$$

For $m_1 = m_2$, θ should be $(l/2R)$; check that the formula gives this result.

Example 8.4-4

The springs have unstretched lengths l_1 and l_2; the dimensions of the mass m are negligible. Find $y = y_0$ for equilibrium and the static deflections in each spring (*Fig.* 8.4-4).

Solution: Here,

$$V = mgy + \frac{1}{2} k_1 (h - l_1 - y)^2 + \frac{1}{2} k_2 (y - l_2)^2;$$

$$\frac{dV}{dy} = mg - k_1 (h - l_1 - y) + k_2 (y - l_2)$$

$$= mg - k_1 h + k_1 l_1 - k_2 l_2 + (k_1 + k_2) y.$$

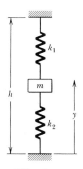   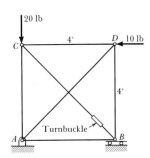

Fig. 8.4-4   **Fig. 8.4-5**

Setting this equal to zero, we find the equilibrium value of y:

$$y = y_0 = \frac{W}{k_1 + k_2} - \frac{k_1 (h - l_1) + k_2 l_2}{k_1 + k_2}.$$

The static deflections are then

$$\delta_1 = h - l_1 - y_0 = \frac{2k_1 (h - l_1) + k_2 (h + l_2 - l_1)}{k_1 + k_2} - \frac{W}{k_1 + k_2},$$

$$\delta_2 = y_0 - l_2 = -\frac{2k_2 l_2 + k_1 (h + l_2 - l_1)}{k_1 + k_2} + \frac{W}{k_1 + k_2}.$$

From these, one can compute whether the springs are in tension ($\delta > 0$) or compression ($\delta < 0$) when the system is in equilibrium.

Example 8.4-5

The square, pin-jointed truss ABCD is loaded as shown in Fig. 8.4-5. All pins are smooth, and bar weights are negligible. The force in BC can be adjusted by means of a turnbuckle. What should be the force in BC so that AD carries no load?

Solution: The truss is statically indeterminate; all bar forces could not be determined from the equations of statics. The requirement that *AD* carry no load reduces the truss to a just determinate condition. We could then solve for the load carried by *BC* from equilibrium at point *D*, then point *C*; *CD* carries a 10-lb compressive load and *BC*, a $10\sqrt{2}$ lb tensile load.

The application of the principle of virtual work to trusses is based on replacement of bars by equivalent forces in such a way that the remaining structure is a mechanism. Here, removing bars *BC* and *AD* results in the four-bar linkage mechanism of Fig. 8.4-6a. A virtual displacement of the mechanism consistent with the constraints is the rotation of the vertical bars shown in Fig. 8.4-6b.

During this displacement, the forces at *A* and *B* do no work, and the 20-lb load at *C* does no work since $\delta \mathbf{r}_C$ is horizontal:

$$\delta \mathbf{r}_C = \delta \theta \mathbf{k} \times \mathbf{r}_{C/A} = \delta \theta \mathbf{k} \times 4\mathbf{j} = -4\, \delta \theta \mathbf{i}.$$

The virtual work is

$$\delta W = T_{BC} \left[\frac{\sqrt{2}}{2} \mathbf{i} - \frac{\sqrt{2}}{2} \mathbf{j} \right] \cdot \delta \mathbf{r}_C$$

$$+ \left[T_{AD} \left(-\frac{\sqrt{2}}{2} \mathbf{i} - \frac{\sqrt{2}}{2} \mathbf{j} \right) - 10\mathbf{i} \right] \cdot \delta \mathbf{r}_D$$

$$= T_{BC} \left[\frac{\sqrt{2}}{2} \mathbf{i} - \frac{\sqrt{2}}{2} \mathbf{j} \right] \cdot (-4\, \delta \theta \mathbf{i})$$

$$+ \left[T_{AD} \left(-\frac{\sqrt{2}}{2} \mathbf{i} - \frac{\sqrt{2}}{2} \mathbf{j} \right) - 10\mathbf{i} \right] \cdot (\delta \theta \mathbf{k} \times \mathbf{r}_{D/B})$$

$$= [-2\sqrt{2}\, T_{BC} + 2\sqrt{2}\, T_{AD} + 40]\, \delta \theta = 0.$$

For $T_{AD} = 0$ and arbitrary $\delta \theta$, δW vanishes only if

$$-2\sqrt{2}\, T_{BC} + 40 = 0,$$

$$T_{BC} = 10\sqrt{2} \text{ lb.}$$

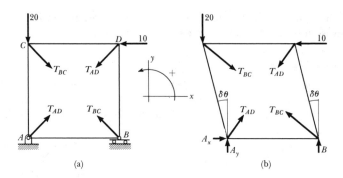

Fig. 8.4-6

Example 8.4-6

Find the force in member DG of the pin-jointed truss of Fig. 8.4-7.

Solution: The truss is statically determinate. The load carried by DG can be found in various ways, but the most efficient way is not obvious. A vertical section to the right of pins G and C cutting through bar DG involves four unknowns; the force in DG can be found from such a section without finding the reaction forces at A and C once GJ is found by working around from the load at I.

By removing DG, we reduce the truss to a "four-bar linkage" again: one "bar" is the rigid body $ABCEFG$, the second is $GHIJK$, and bars CD and DH are the third and fourth. A free-body diagram is shown in

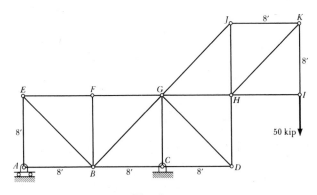

Fig. 8.4-7

Fig. 8.4-8a, and a kinematically admissible virtual displacement of the mechanism in 8.4-8b. The displacement keeps $ABCEFG$ fixed so that the constraints at A and C do no work. Bar CD rotates $\delta\theta$ about C, and

GHIJK rotates $\delta\theta$ about G; *DH* then translates vertically within the limits of the small displacement theory.   The only forces that do work are the 50-kip load at I and the force T in *DG* at D:

$$\delta W = 0 = -50\mathbf{j}\cdot\delta\mathbf{r}_I + T\left(-\frac{\sqrt{2}}{2}\mathbf{i} + \frac{\sqrt{2}}{2}\mathbf{j}\right)\cdot\delta\mathbf{r}_D.$$

The virtual displacement of D is given by

$$\delta\mathbf{r}_D = \delta\boldsymbol{\theta}_{CD}\times\mathbf{r}_{D/C} = \delta\theta\mathbf{k}\times 8\mathbf{i} = 8\,\delta\theta\mathbf{j}$$

since C is a fixed point; similarly, with G fixed,

$$\delta\mathbf{r}_I = \delta\boldsymbol{\theta}_{GI}\times\mathbf{r}_{I/G} = \delta\theta\mathbf{k}\times 16\mathbf{i} = 16\,\delta\theta\mathbf{j}.$$

Therefore,

$$\delta W = 0 = -800\,\delta\theta + 4\sqrt{2}T\,\delta\theta = (4\sqrt{2}T - 800)\,\delta\theta.$$

This must vanish for arbitrary $\delta\theta$; therefore,

$$4\sqrt{2}T - 800 = 0, \qquad T = 100\sqrt{2}\text{ kips,}$$

or *DG* carries a tensile load of $100\,\sqrt{2}$ kips.

One must check that the assumed displacement pattern is consistent with all constraints placed on the mechanism; here the student may show

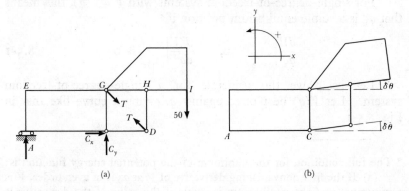

(a)   (b)

Fig. 8.4-8

that assigning different rotations $\delta\theta_1$, $\delta\theta_2$ to *CD* and *GHIJK* will lead to a violation of the rigidity of *DH*.   However, changing the constraint conditions on the admissible displacements is often useful, as in Examples 8.2-2 and 8.3-3.

8.5 Stability of Equilibrium

For conservative systems, we have seen that the principle of virtual work can be replaced by one of stationary potential energy.

If we examine what kind of stationary value occurs at the equilibrium position, we find that the result tells us whether or not the equilibrium position is stable.

If we look at the simple case of a bar pendulum pinned at one end, we know that there are two equilibrium positions—one with the mass center below the support, one with it above the support. These two configurations have obviously different properties. If we displace the bar slightly from its lower equilibrium position, the bar will oscillate about it and never get very far away from it. This is, qualitatively, what we mean by *stability* of equilibrium. Displacement of the bar away from its upper equilibrium position shows that position to be *unstable*. There is another case exemplified by the box resting on a table. If we slide it away from its equilibrium position, it will not move back; neither will it move farther away. This kind of stability is sometimes called *neutral*.

Our fundamental result is the following:

Principle of Minimum Potential Energy:

An equilibrium position of a conservative system is stable if, and only if, the potential energy is a minimum for that position.

For single-degree-of-freedom systems with $V = V(q)$, this means that q_0 is a stable equilibrium position if*

$$\frac{dV}{dq}\bigg|_{q=q_0} = 0, \qquad \frac{d^2V}{dq^2}\bigg|_{q=q_0} > 0. \qquad \textbf{8.5-1}$$

Let us prove the principle for a single-degree-of-freedom system. Let $V(q)$ be plotted against q, giving a curve like that in Fig. 8.5-1.

---

* The full condition for the minimum of the potential energy function is:

(a) If the first nonvanishing derivative of V at q_0 is of even order, V is a minimum and the equilibrium is stable if the value of the derivative is positive:

$$\frac{d^{2n}V}{dq^{2n}}\bigg|_{q=q_0} > 0;$$

if the value of the derivative is negative, V is a maximum and equilibrium is unstable. An example of a function where the extended minimum criterion must be used is $V = (q - q_0)^4$; V has a minimum at q_0, but $d^2V/dq^2 = 0$ there.

(b) If the first nonvanishing derivative of V at q_0 is of odd order, the equilibrium is unstable. (V has a horizontal inflection point like that at B in Fig. 8.5-1).

The stationary values of V are indicated on the figure. Consider a relative maximum point such as C. Suppose we release the system from rest at a value of q corresponding to C'; the energy of the system must then be the value of V at C'. Since C' is not an equilibrium position, the system must move away from there, acquiring a kinetic energy $T > 0$ in the process. But energy is conserved; thus V must decrease as T increases. The only way this can happen near a relative maximum is for q to move away from the equilibrium value; thus the system does not remain near its equilibrium configuration—exactly what we mean by instability of equilibrium.

A horizontal inflection point like B has a similar property. If we start the system from rest in a configuration corresponding to B', the same argument holds.

Starting from rest in a position corresponding to B'', the potential must again decrease, with the value of q changing toward the possible

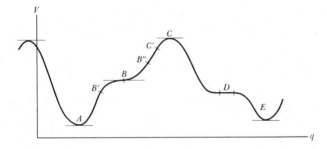

Fig. 8.5-1

equilibrium value associated with B. When that value of q is attained, however, the system has positive kinetic energy; the q-value continues to change, passing through the equilibrium value to values on the B' side of the curve. The system thus does not remain near the equilibrium configuration corresponding to B, again an unstable configuration.

If V is constant for some range of q, as along the line marked D, then the equilibrium configurations corresponding to values of q inside, but not at the end points, of D are called neutral or indifferent insofar as their stability is concerned. If a small enough change in q from such a position is prescribed and the system is brought to rest again, the system will still be in equilibrium without moving toward or away from the initial configuration. However, if the system is released from any such configuration with any initial velocity $\dot{q}$

whatsoever, q will change enough to move the system away from the equilibrium range D—an instability of a sort.

For sufficiently small initial motions near the relative minima A and E, however, we have stability. Consider any initial configuration of the system with value of $q = q_0$ near that corresponding to A and give the system a (small) initial kinetic energy T_0. The total mechanical energy of the system is then $E_0 = T_0 + V_0 = T_0 + V(q_0)$, which can be made positive for q_0 near enough to the minimizing value by redefining V so that $V = 0$ at A (Fig. 8.5-2). Then in the subsequent motion of the system, $T + V = E_0 > 0$; since $T \geqq 0$, $V \leqq E_0$. Let us suppose that the initial configuration and initial kinetic energy are so chosen that E_0 is less than the potential energy level corresponding to the neighboring equilibrium positions of Fig. 8.5-2. Then we have a lower bound on the potential energy also: $0 \leqq V \leqq E_0$. The value of q cannot, therefore, get very far away from that corresponding

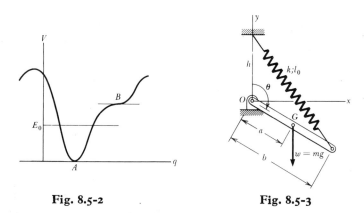

Fig. 8.5-2   **Fig. 8.5-3**

to the minimum at A. But this is exactly the meaning of stability as we have defined it. Thus any equilibrium configuration corresponding to a relative minimum potential energy is stable; no other "stationary value" configuration leads to stability.

We can also see that two stable equilibrium configurations must have at least one unstable one between them, usually a maximum. The horizontal inflection points are exceptional.

Example **8.5-1**

Discuss the stability of the equilibrium positions of the spring and bar of Example 8.4-2.

Solution: In that case,

$$V = 125 \cos \theta + 7.5(l-4)^2,$$

$$\frac{dV}{d\theta} = -125 \sin \theta + 1800 \sin \theta \left[1 - \frac{4}{l}\right],$$

where

$$l = 2\sqrt{61 - 60 \cos \theta}.$$

The roots of $V'(\theta) = 0$ are $\theta = 0°, 20°, 180°$. Now

$$\frac{d^2V}{d\theta^2} = -125 \cos \theta + 1800 \cos \theta [1 - (4/l)]$$

$$+ 1800 \sin \theta (4/l^2)(2)(1/2)(60 \sin \theta / \sqrt{61 - 60 \cos \theta})$$

$$= -125 \cos \theta + 1800 \cos \theta [1 - (4/l)] + (864{,}000 \sin^2 \theta)/l^3.$$

At $\theta = 0°$, $l = 2$, and $V''(0) = -125 - 1800 < 0$; $\theta = 0°$ is unstable.

At $\theta = 180°$, $l = 22$, and $V''(180°) = 125 - 1800(9/11) < 0$; $\theta = 180°$ is unstable.

At $\theta = 20°$, $l = 288/67$, and $V''(20°) = (864{,}000 \sin^2 20°)/l^3 > 0$.

This is a stable equilibrium position.

The instability of the $\theta = 0°$ position is not surprising; the interesting effect is that the introduction of the spring makes the $180°$ position unstable also.

Example 8.5-2

Discuss stability for the more general bar-and-spring problem of Fig. 8.5-3.

Solution: The spring length l for general angle θ is given by $l^2 = h^2 + b^2 - 2hb \cos \theta$ from which we find

$$\frac{dl}{d\theta} = (hb/l) \sin \theta.$$

The potential energy of the system, and its first two derivatives, are:

$$V = wa \cos \theta + \frac{1}{2} k(l - l_0)^2;$$

$$\frac{dV}{d\theta} = -wa \sin \theta + k(l - l_0) \frac{dl}{d\theta}$$

$$= \sin \theta \left[khb \left(1 - \frac{l_0}{l}\right) - wa\right];$$

$$\frac{d^2V}{d\theta^2} = \cos \theta \left[khb \left(1 - \frac{l_0}{l}\right) - wa\right] + \sin \theta \left[khb \left(\frac{l_0}{l^2}\right) \frac{dl}{d\theta}\right]$$

$$= \cos \theta \left[khb \left(1 - \frac{l_0}{l}\right) - wa\right] + \frac{kh^2b^2l_0}{l^3} \sin^2 \theta.$$

The equilibrium values of θ in the range $0° \leq \theta \leq 180°$ are always $\theta_1 = 0°$, $\theta_2 = 180°$ (from $\sin \theta = 0$) and any root θ_3 of

$$khb \left(1 - \frac{l_0}{l} \right) - wa = 0.$$

If the latter has a root (and it cannot have more than one in the given range), it necessarily makes $V''(\theta_3) > 0$ and hence corresponds to a stable configuration (unless, of course, $\theta_3 = \theta_1$ or θ_2, in which case we must examine higher derivatives of V at $0°$ or $180°$). For θ_1 and θ_2, we must examine the sign of $V''(\theta)$ more carefully.

For $\theta = 0°$, $l = |h - b|$; for $\theta = 180°$, $l = h + b$. Therefore, $\theta = \theta_1 = 0°$ is unstable if

$$1 - \frac{l_0}{|h-b|} \leq \frac{wa}{khb}$$

and $\theta = \theta_2 = 180°$ is unstable if

$$1 - \frac{l_0}{h+b} \geq \frac{wa}{khb}.$$

The student may check that these two conditions are the same as those needed to ensure the existence of the third equilibrium position—which is stable when it exists and is intermediate between two unstable positions.

This example shows that one can change the stability characteristics of a configuration without changing the fact that the configuration is, indeed, one of equilibrium. In particular, note that the $\theta = 180°$ position, always stable for the bar without the spring, becomes unstable if a spring with properly adjusted k, l_0, and h values is attached.

Example 8.5-3

An important use for the stability criterion occurs in problems in which one body is balanced statically on another. Suppose a uniform plank of length $2l$, thickness $2h$, and weight w is balanced on a fixed roller of radius a. When is the equilibrium stable (Fig. 8.5-4)?

Solution: Let us suppose the plank rolls without slipping on the disk; then, in a displaced position, we have the configuration shown in Fig. 8.5-5. The height of point C is given then by

$$y^* = (a+h) \cos \theta + a\theta \sin \theta$$

so that

$$V(\theta) = wy^* = w[(a+h) \cos \theta + a\theta \sin \theta],$$

$$V'(\theta) = w[-h \sin \theta + a\theta \cos \theta],$$

$$V''(\theta) = w[(a-h) \cos \theta - a\theta \sin \theta].$$

Equilibrium is given by the roots of $V'(\theta)=0$, or

$$\tan \theta = \frac{a}{h}\, \theta,$$

of which $\theta=0$ is obviously, and expectedly, a root. For stability, we must have

$$V''(0) = w(a-h) > 0$$

or

$$a > h.$$

Example 8.5-4

Do Example 8.5-3 for another circular roll of radius b balanced on the one of radius a.

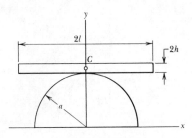

Fig. 8.5-4

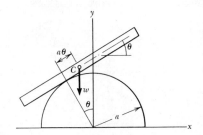

Fig. 8.5-5

Solution: The displaced position is shown in Fig. 8.5-6. Then

$$V(\theta) = wy^* = w(a+b) \cos \theta;$$

$$V'(\theta) = -w(a+b) \sin \theta;$$

$$V''(\theta) = -w(a+b) \cos \theta;$$

and $\theta=0°$ is an unstable equilibrium position. This result we expect.

Example 8.5-5

Now cut the disk of radius b in half, and balance the semicircle on the fixed disk. What happens if you displace it from equilibrium?

Solution: In Fig. 8.5-7, the displaced configuration is shown. The center of gravity of the uniform semicircle is at a distance

$$d = \frac{4b}{3\pi}$$

from the base; hence

$$V = w \left[(a+b) \cos \theta - \frac{4b}{3\pi} \cos (\phi + \theta) \right].$$

The rolling without slipping condition is $a\theta = b\phi$; thus

$$V = w(a+b) \left[\cos \theta - \frac{4b}{3\pi(a+b)} \cos \left(\frac{a+b}{b} \right) \theta \right].$$

Then

$$\frac{dV}{d\theta} = w(a+b) \left[-\sin \theta + \frac{4}{3\pi} \sin \left(\frac{a+b}{b} \right) \theta \right],$$

$$\frac{d^2V}{d\theta^2} = w(a+b) \left[-\cos \theta + \frac{4(a+b)}{3\pi b} \cos \left(\frac{a+b}{b} \right) \theta \right].$$

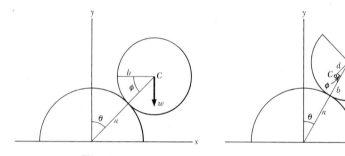

Fig. 8.5-6   **Fig. 8.5-7**

Thus $\theta = 0°$ is the equilibrium position as it should be, and it is stable if, and only if, $V''(0) > 0$, or

$$\frac{b}{a+b} < \frac{4}{3\pi}.$$

8.6 Summary

The principle of virtual work is, then, a powerful means for dealing with equilibrium problems, especially those for which the equilibrium configurations of a system are not known and must be found. The essential feature of the principle is the use of kinematic relations between parts of the system during small motions of the system away from a fixed, but arbitrary, configuration. We then compute the virtual work, δW, done in such a virtual displacement. If δW vanishes for all virtual displacements from the base configuration, then the base configuration is an equilibrium state for the system.

We have further seen that the introduction of the conservative-force concept and the associated potential energy lead to an equivalent formulation of the principle for systems; for conservative systems, we do not compute the virtual work directly but instead find the virtual change in potential energy.   We are also able to discuss the stability of equilibrium positions of conservative systems by use of the principle of minimum potential energy.

We remind the student that the proofs given here have been based implicitly on a limited class of constraints, mostly of the bilateral and holonomic types.   Unfamiliar constraint conditions should be examined with great care.   A simple example in which a unilateral constraint can lead to problems of interpretation is that of the particle resting on a rough horizontal table—certainly an equilibrium situation.   We know that the forces are as shown in Fig. 8.6-1a: no friction force, normal force equal to the weight in magnitude.   What are admissible displacements here?   The only constraint is that the block

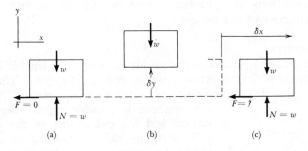

(a)   (b)   (c)

Fig. 8.6-1

cannot penetrate the table.   We may express this constraint by restricting the y-component of any virtual displacement by the condition $\delta y \geqq 0$ (Fig. 8.6-1b).   But then δy is not completely arbitrary; is it still proper to set the coefficient of δy in the virtual work expression equal to zero?   More important yet is the question of whether $(N - w)\,\delta y$ is still the proper virtual work expression. For, if we lift the block, there is no normal reaction, for there is no contact; the virtual work would be

$$\delta W = -w\mathbf{j} \cdot \delta y\mathbf{j} = -w\,\delta y < 0.$$

Similarly, for a virtual displacement $\delta x\mathbf{i}$ parallel to the table, should we set $\delta W = F\mathbf{i} \cdot \delta x\mathbf{i} = F\,\delta x$ equal to zero and conclude that $F = 0$, or should we use the fact that, in a real motion, F is governed by the sliding friction relation? In the latter case, $\mathbf{F}$ is μN in magnitude and opposed to $\delta x \mathbf{i}$ in direction; then

$$\delta W = -\mu N |\delta x| < 0.$$

(Similar questions may be properly raised in connection with Example 8.2-2.)

There are some other cases that are not as simple as this in which the same thing happens; the principle can be extended to state that $\delta W \leqq 0$ for all displacements is the condition for equilibrium. We have been concerned only with the cases for which $\delta W = 0$.

Finally, we note that methods based on the principle of virtual work are of basic importance in the study of equilibrium of deformable bodies—especially elastic and plastic structures. The student who pursues the study of mechanics will find it of great usefulness and importance. Expressing V as a function of the generalized coordinates is also a first step toward the alternative Lagrangian formulation of the equations of dynamics, based on the kinetic and potential energy functions for a system.

Exercises

8.2-1: A particle is placed on the outside of an inverted bowl of radius R, the coefficient of friction between particle and bowl being μ. The particle is observed to stay where it is placed. What can you say about the possible angles θ between the vertical and the radius line to the particle? Solve both by the principle of virtual work and by the equations of equilibrium; see Example 8.2-2.

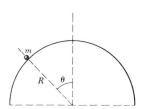

Ans.: $\theta \leqq \arctan \mu$.

8.3-1: Two small blocks, one weighing 75 lb, rest on smooth inclines of slope angles as shown. They are connected by a light inextensible cord that passes over a smooth pulley. Find the weight, W, for equilibrium (a) by the principle of virtual work, (b) by the equations of equilibrium; compare the two solutions.
Ans.: $W = 126$ lb.

8.3-2: Consider the general problem for the configuration of Exercise 8.3-1. That is, suppose two blocks of weights W_1 and W_2 rest on smooth inclines of slope angles

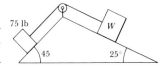

θ_1 and θ_2, the weights being connected by a light inextensible cord that passes over a smooth pulley. Find the ratio W_2/W_1 for equilibrium; check the solution to Exercise 8.3-1. See figure at top of following page.
Ans.: $W_2/W_1 = \sin \theta_1/\sin \theta_2$.

8.3-3: Three masses are connected by inextensible cords as shown, the cords passing over smooth pulleys. Find the sag, s, at equilibrium.

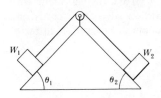

W_1 W_2

θ_1 θ_2

Exer. 8.3-2

8.3-4: A uniform rod, AB, of length L and weight W rests in a smooth-sided, right-angled trough: one side (OB) of the trough is tilted at $15°$ with the horizontal. Find the angle between the rod and the horizontal at equilibrium.
Ans.: $\phi = -60°$.

8.3-5: Consider the configuration of Exercise 8.3-4 again, for a general angle θ ($\theta < 90°$) between OB and the horizontal (instead of $15°$). Find ϕ for equilibrium.
Ans.: $\tan \phi = -\cot 2\theta$ or $\phi = 2\theta - (\pi/2)$.

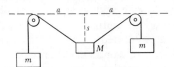

Exer. 8.3-3

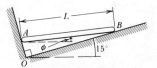

Exer. 8.3-4

8.3-6: Suppose the rod of Exercise 8.3-4 is replaced by a uniform block, $ABB'A'$, of weight w, length L, and height H; find ϕ for equilibrium.
Ans.: $\tan \phi = -\sqrt{3}/(1 + 2H/L)$.

8.3-7: Solve Exercise 8.3-6 under the conditions of Exercise 8.3-5.
Ans.: $\tan \phi = \dfrac{-\cos 2\theta}{\sin 2\theta + H/L}$.

8.3-8: An L-section is made by joining two uniform rods, OA and OB, at right angles at O; the system can swing freely in a vertical plane about the smooth pin at O. OA is 4 ft long and weighs 48.3 lb; OB is 3 ft long and weighs 32.2 lb. Find the angle or angles θ, $0° \le \theta < 360°$ between the horizontal and OA at equilibrium.
Ans.: $\theta = 63° \ 26'$, $243° \ 26'$.

8.3-9: What vertical force, F, would have to be applied at B in the previous problem to make $\theta = 30°$ an equilibrium position?
Ans.: 39.6 lb down.

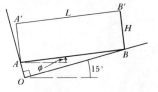

Exer. 8.3-6

8.3-10: If the masses of Exercise 8.3-3 are replaced by unequal masses, as shown here, the central mass will no longer move along the vertical centerline between the pulleys. The system now has two degrees of freedom.   We wish to find the angles α and β for equilibrium of the system.

(a) Suppose the central mass m_2 is given a virtual displacement with components $(\delta x_2, \delta y_2)$. From the condition that the cords are inextensible, express the virtual displacements of m_1 and m_3 in terms of the position and displacement of m_2.
Ans.:

$$\delta x_3 = \frac{a-y_2}{\sqrt{x_2^2+(a-y_2)^2}}\,\delta y_2 - \frac{x_2}{\sqrt{x_2^2+(a-y_2)^2}}\,\delta x_2$$

$$= \cos\beta\,\delta y_2 - \sin\beta\,\delta x_2.$$

(b) Using the principle of virtual work for the system and the results of part (a), find α and β for equilibrium.
Ans.: $\sin\alpha = (m_2^2 + m_1^2 - m_3^2)/2m_1m_2.$

8.3-11: The two uniform rods of Exercise 8.3-8, one 4 ft long and weighing 48.3 lb, the other 3 ft long and weighing 32.2 lb, are now mounted on a light horizontal shaft, PQ, as shown, the shaft being supported in smooth bearings at P and Q. Find the angle or angles θ for equilibrium between the horizontal to the right looking from P to Q and the 4-ft rod. Compare with Exercise 8.3-8. The angle between the rods is still 90°.

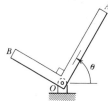

Exer. 8.3-8

8.3-12: Three flywheels are mounted eccentrically on a horizontal shaft supported in smooth bearings at A and B; the center of mass of each fly-wheel is shown, with its distance from the shaft and its weight. When O_1C_1 is horizontal to the right, looking from A to B, then O_2C_2 is vertically up and O_3C_3 is horizontal to the left, as pictured. Find the angle or angles θ for equilibrium between the pictured horizontal position of O_1C_1 and the equilibrium position or positions of O_1C_1.
Ans.: $\theta = 21°\ 48',\ 201°\ 48'.$

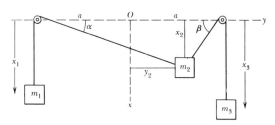

Exer. 8.3-10

8.3-13: In Roberval's balance, the arms AC and $A'C'$ always remain parallel. Show that, if $AB = BC = A'B' = B'C' = a$, the weights W_1 and W_2 (a) will be equal whenever the balance is in equilibrium; (b) will continue to be in equilibrium if they are moved to new positions on the horizontal support arms; (c) will continue to be in equilibrium if the horizontal support arms are displaced vertically. Neglect the weight of the support arms and parallelogram members.

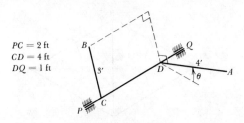

$PC = 2$ ft
$CD = 4$ ft
$DQ = 1$ ft

Exer. 8.3-11

8.3-14: Now suppose that the points B and B' of the balance described in the preceding problem are not exactly at the mid-points of the corresponding rods. Take $BC = B'C' = a$ and $AB = A'B' = b$. What will be the relationship between W_1 and W_2? Will we still have equilibrium regardless of the position of the weights on the weighing platform and regardless of the vertical position of the weighing platform? Suppose you put an unknown weight on the left-hand platform and balanced it with a 1-lb weight on the right-hand platform; then put the unknown on the right-hand platform and balanced it with a 1.5-lb weight. What would be the true weight of the unknown?
Ans.: 1.22 lb.

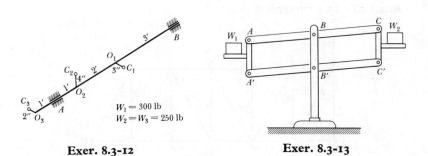

$W_1 = 300$ lb
$W_2 = W_3 = 250$ lb

Exer. 8.3-12   **Exer. 8.3-13**

8.3-15: Now, still considering the balance of Exercises 8.3-13, 14, take into account the weights of the movable parts of the balance. Suppose that $BC = B'C' = a$ and $AB = A'B' = b$ as before. Let $w =$ the weight of rod $AC =$ weight of rod $A'C'$, and let $W =$ the weight of each of the weighing platforms together with its attached vertical member. (a) What will be the relationship between W_1, W_2, w, W, a, b in equilibrium? (b) Will we still have equilibrium in all positions if this relation is satisfied? (c) If $a=b$, will $W_1 = W_2$?

Ans.: (a) $W_1 b - W_2 a = (a-b)(W + \frac{1}{2}w)$.

8.4-1: The pin-jointed rhomboidal truss *ABCD* is in equilibrium under the

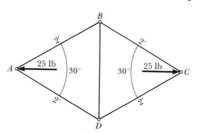

Exer. 8.4-1

loads shown; find the load carried by the strut *BD*. (Hint: Remove bar *BD* and replace it by two forces of magnitude *P*, one at *B* and one at *D*; use the principle of virtual work to find *P*.)

Ans.: $P = 25 \tan 15° = 6.7$ lb comp.

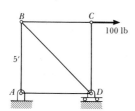

8.4-2: The square, pin-jointed truss *ABCD* is loaded as shown. Find the load carried by member *BD*.

Ans.: 141 lb comp.

8.4-3: Find the external constraints at pin *A* in the previous problem by relaxing the constraints and using the principle of virtual work.

8.4-4: Find the loads in members *BI* and *EJ*.

Ans.: $BI = 13.3$ kip tension.

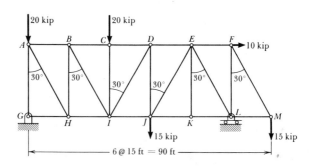

8.4-5: Three wheels constituting a friction drive mechanism are used to lift the weight *W*. If there is no slip, what torque *M* is needed to lift the weight *W* slowly?

Ans.: $M = aW$.

8.4-6: The four-bar mechanism consists of two 4-ft bars, *DF* and *EF*, and two 8-ft bars, *AE* and *BD*, pinned together at their centers, *C*. End *B* is pinned to the foundation: and *A* is constrained to move in a smooth slot. All pins are smooth, and the weights of the members may be neglected. For a 25-lb load at pin *F* as shown, what force *P* at roller *A* will hold the mechanism in equilibrium with the angle $\theta = 60°$?

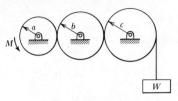

Exer. 8.4-5

Ans.: $P = 21.6$ lb.

8.4-7: Find *P* in Exercise 8.4-6 when the equilibrium value of θ is a general value θ_0, $0 < \theta_0 < 90°$.

Ans.: $P = 37.5 \cot \theta_0$.

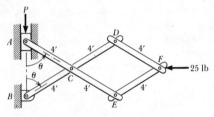

Exer. 8.4-6

8.4-8: Suppose the mechanism of Exercise 8.4-6 is complicated by the addition of two more 8-ft bars as pictured; what is the relation between *P* and θ_0 (where θ_0 is the value of θ at equilibrium as in 8.4-7)?

Ans.: $P = 62.5 \cot \theta_0$ lb.

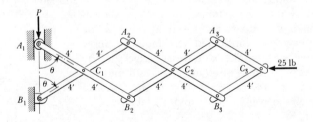

8.4-9: A hoisting drum-pulley-weight combination on a horizontal shaft has the dimensions pictured. Find the equilibrium values of the angle θ between the vertical and the line *OC* from the centroid of the drum to the mass center, *C*. The shaft is light; the bearings, *A*, *B*, and the pulley are smooth; the cord is inextensible and wraps and unwraps from the drum without slipping.

Ans.: $\theta = 62° \; 44'$, $117° \; 16'$.

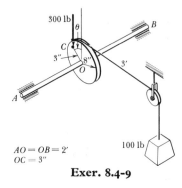

$AO = OB = 2'$
$OC = 3''$

Exer. 8.4-9

300 lb

100 lb

8.4-10: The designer of this platform scale wishes to arrange matters so that the balance weight, w, is independent of the position x of the load W on the weighing platform, EG. (Why is this desirable?) The scale consists of two beams, AD and FH, which are horizontal in the equilibrium position, two bars, CE and DF, which are vertical, and the platform scale EG itself. All pins and pivots are smooth. The weights of the members can be neglected (they are usually balanced by a separate counterweight).

(a) What should be the relationship between the dimensions $BC \equiv b$, $CD \equiv c$, $FG \equiv h$, $GH \equiv d$ so that the desired result may be achieved?
Ans.: $d/(d+h) = b/(b+c)$.

(b) With this design, what is the relationship between w, W, b, and $AB \equiv a$?
Ans.: $w/W = b/a$.

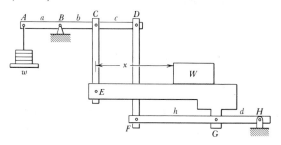

8.4-11: A homogeneous square block of weight W and side 3.5 ft is supported at A and B on the same level as shown. The points of support are 1.5 ft apart, and the contacts may be considered as smooth. Show that there are (within a mirror image in the vertical) two positions of equilibrium, and find the corresponding angles θ between the vertical direction of the weight force and the diagonal of the square.
Ans.: $\theta = 0°$, $34° 25'$.

8.4-12: Do Exercise 8.4-11 for a general square of side b and weight W and a general separation a between A and B.
Ans.: $\theta = 0°$, $\arccos(b\sqrt{2}/4a)$.

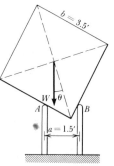

8.4-13: A crane boom and counterweight, W, are shown supporting a 2500-lb weight. The weight of the boom may be neglected. The counterweight is connected to the boom by a light inextensible cable that passes over a smooth pulley of negligible radius. The pin support of the boom is smooth. Find the relationship between W and θ for which the crane is in equilibrium.

Ans.: $\theta = \arccos\left[(41/40) - (W/750)^2\right]$.

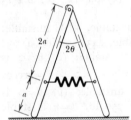

Exer. 8.4-13   **Exer. 8.4-14**

8.4-14: The uniform bar AB is of length 12 in and weight 20 lb. The weight $W = 6.7$ lb is attached to the bar by means of a light inextensible cord passing over the smooth pulley of negligible radius. Find the value of $\cos\theta$ at equilibrium.

Ans.: 2/3.

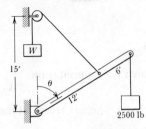

8.4-15: Each leg of the A-frame shown is of weight W. The stiffness of the connecting spring is k and its unstretched length is negligibly small. The joint and the base contacts are smooth. Find the angles θ for which the system may be in static equilibrium.

Ans.: $\theta = \arccos(3W/16ka)$ or $\theta = 0$.

8.4-16: Suppose the two-bar system of Example 8.3-4—each bar being of weight W and length L—is subjected to a vertically upward force of magnitude P; find the equilibrium angles θ_1 and θ_2.

Ans.: If $P = \dfrac{W}{2}$: $\theta_1 = 0, \pi$; θ_2 arbitrary;

If $P = \dfrac{3W}{2}$: $\theta_2 = 0, \pi$; θ_1 arbitrary;

If P neither: $\theta_1 = 0, \pi$, $\theta_2 = 0, \pi$.

8.4-17: Suppose the load P on the two-bar system of Example 8.3-4 and the previous problem is always directed along AB; what are the equilibrium configurations?

Ans.: $\theta_2 = 0, \pi$.

8.4-18: Suppose a third bar identical to the other two is added to the system of Example 8.3-4; find the equilibrium angles θ_1, θ_2, θ_3 under the horizontal load P. $OA = AB = BC = L$; all weights $= W$.

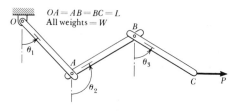

$OA = AB = BC = L$
All weights $= W$

Exer. 8.4-18

8.4-19: Find the force F if the system shown is in equilibrium.
Ans.: 223 lb.

8.4-20: The arrangement shown is known as a Wichert truss.   Find the
reaction at B due to a load P as shown.
Ans.: $B = 2P/(6-a/b)$.

8.5-1: Investigate the stability of the equilibrium position or positions for
the systems of Exercises:

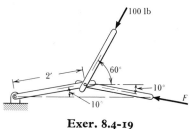

Exer. 8.4-19

(a) 8.3-4   (b) 8.3-6   (c) 8.3-8
(d) 8.4-9   (e) 8.4-12   (f) 8.4-13
(g) 8.4-14.

Ans.: (a) unstable; (b) unstable;
(c) 63° unstable, 243° stable; (d) 63°
unstable, 117° stable; (e) $\theta = 0$ is
stable if $a > b/2\sqrt{2}$, $\theta = \arccos$
$(b/2a\sqrt{2})$ is unstable; (f) $\theta = 0$ is
stable if $W > 750$ lb, $\theta = \pi$ is stable
if $W < 6750$ lb.   The intermediate position is unstable; (g) stable.

8.5-2: Investigate the stability of equilibrium for the bar of Example 8.3-1.
Ans.: Unstable.

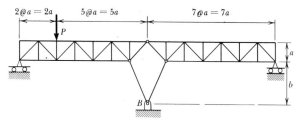

Exer. 8.4-20

8.5-3: A half cylinder of radius R rests on a rough inclined plane.   What is
the maximum value of the inclination angle, θ, for which the equilibrium is
stable?   (Note: the c.g. of a homogeneous half cylinder is distant $4R/3\pi$
from the base).
Ans.: $\theta = \arcsin (4/3\pi)$.

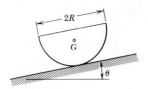

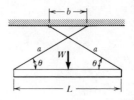

Exer. 8·5-3   **Exer. 8.5-4**

8.5-4: The platform shown is supported by a set of crossed wires each of length a. It carries a weight W at its midpoint. What is the maximum allowable value of b if the platform is to be in stable equilibrium? Express your answer in terms of L and the angle θ.

8.5-5: Find the angle or angles θ and the weight W for which this crane will be in equilibrium. Will the equilibrium be stable? Neglect the radius of the pulley.

8.5-6: The center span of a cantilever bridge is being hoisted slowly into position, as shown in the accompanying figure. Will the equilibrium be stable in the position shown?

8.5-7: Suppose charged particles attract each other according to the law $F = k(r - r_0)$, where r_0 and k are constants, and r is the distance between particles. (If $r < r_0$, F will be negative and the force will be repulsive.) Say we have three particles spaced at equal distances $\frac{2}{3}r_0$ along a line. They will be in equilibrium.

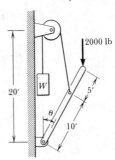

Exer. 8·5-5

Will the equilibrium be stable (a) for displacements in which the particles remain in the original straight line, (b) for displacements in which they move at right angles to the original straight line? (Hint: Since we are only concerned with relative motions, let one particle be considered fixed.)

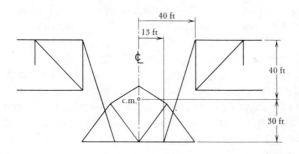

Exer. 8.5-6

CHAPTER **IX**

Elements of the Theory of
Mechanical Vibrations

9.1 Introduction

When the motion of a machine part or structural element continually repeats itself, the motion is said to be periodic, and the time required for a complete cycle of the motion is called the period. The simple harmonic motion of a linear harmonic oscillator discussed in Section 3.3 is an example of periodic motion. As was shown in Section 3.4, the motion that results from the application of periodic forces to a mechanical system may be much larger than that which forces of the same magnitude would produce if applied slowly. This enhanced response is sometimes desirable, but as a rule it is not; the high repetitive stresses produce premature fatigue failure, large accelerations damage delicate apparatus, and excessive displacements result in rough and noisy operation. Since these dynamic effects are more apt to manifest themselves at high than at low speeds, the advent of high-speed machinery has tended to bring the subject of periodic motion, under the name of mechanical vibration, into prominence in engineering. Excessive vibration is probably responsible for more mechanical and structural failures than is any other single cause.

We begin with the mechanical system having a single degree of freedom. All of the essential features of the linear harmonic oscillator including resonance and a "natural" frequency of vibration reappear, modified now by damping. The effects of a disturbing force are next considered. This may take the form of a periodic excitation or of a transient load; both cases have important technological application. Turning next to the case of systems having two and three degrees of freedom we find that these exhibit an equal number of natural frequencies at which resonance may occur. Each of these frequencies is found to be associated with a particular mode of vibration, and the various modes, in general orthogonal to one another, are shown to be associated with certain "principal" coordinates. The principal coordinates, in effect, reduce the two-degree-of-freedom system to two single-degree-of-freedom systems. This is in part our excuse for detailed study of the single-degree-of-freedom special case. Finally the motions of systems having a finite number of degrees of freedom are shown to be analogous to the properties of lumped-parameter electrical circuits. The analogy has been of help primarily in suggesting the application of circuit-theoretical principles to the design of complex mechanical systems.

The treatment of this chapter is limited in that it deals primarily with linear mechanical systems. It is also limited in another way. Using the methods of newtonian mechanics, equations of motion must be supplemented by equations of constraint. These depend upon the individual circumstances of the case at hand. It is therefore difficult to derive general theorems that will hold for *any* mechanical system having, say, *n* degrees of freedom. Powerful results of this nature can be reached through an extension of Newton's equations of motion due to Lagrange, but they are beyond the scope of the present chapter.

9.2   Free Vibrations of a Simple Mechanical System

Consider a mechanical system having a single degree of freedom. This means that the position of every point in the system at any time is completely specified by a single coordinate. Simple examples of such systems are provided by the pendulum, by a mass attached to a light spring the other end of which is held fixed, or by a disk rolling without slip down an incline. It must not be supposed, however, that the single-degree-of-freedom system is necessarily simple in appearance or construction. An internal combustion engine, with all its complexities, is a single-degree-of-freedom system. Once the angular position of the crankshaft has been specified, the location of every valve and piston is determined.   A circus carrousel, with its wooden horses rising and falling as well as rotating, is a single-degree-of-freedom system, and so is a lathe when the feed is engaged to cut automatically.   The elements of the typical single-degree-of-freedom system are shown in Fig. 9.2-1a.   The configuration in this case is specified by the coordinate x; $P(t)$ is called the *exciting* or *disturbing force*; a *restoring force* is provided by the spring of modulus k, and the *damping* present is represented by a dashpot.   We shall suppose that the damping force is proportional to the velocity, $\dot{x}$.   This type of damping is known as viscous or Stokes damping.   The damping force is c units of force per unit of speed.   When k and c are constants, the equation of motion is a linear differential equation, and for this reason

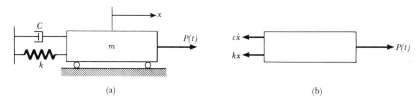

(a)   (b)

Fig. 9.2-1

the system is said to be a linear system.   It is, perhaps, unnecessary to add that in practice many technological systems depart from linearity and that the popularity of the linear system (at least in textbooks) is due primarily to the simplicity of its mathematical analysis.   If, however, the damping is small and the motions and stresses are not excessively large, the assumption of a linear restoring force and viscous damping is realistic.

The equation of motion of the typical system is found by considering the forces that act on the mass when it has a positive displacement and velocity.   These forces are shown in the free-body diagram, Fig. 9.2-1b.   Notice that the restoring force, kx, and the damping force, $c\dot{x}$, are drawn to the left since this is the direction in which they act when the displacement and velocity are in the positive direction, which is to the right.   The equation of motion, $\mathbf{F} = m\mathbf{a}$, is

$$P(t) - kx - c\dot{x} = m\ddot{x},$$ 9.2-1

or

$$m\ddot{x} + c\dot{x} + kx = P(t).$$ 9.2-2

This is the typical form for the equation of motion of a vibrating single-degree-of-freedom system. It is a linear equation when k and c are, as we suppose here, independent of x and $\dot{x}$. Of course, the dependent variable will not always be a displacement; often it is a rotation angle, and the coefficients m, c, and k may well be different quantities for other systems. What is important is that the terms on the left-hand side of Eq. 9.2-2 must be positive in sign if they are to represent an inertia, a damping force, and a restoring force. A negative restoring or damping force would tend to produce an unstable rather than a periodic motion.

Having isolated a system, drawn its free-body diagram, written the equations of motion, the next step is a mathematical one: we seek a solution of the equations of motion that can be adjusted to satisfy the initial conditions $x = x_0$ and $\dot{x} = v_0$ at $t = 0$. Now the complete solution of a linear differential equation is the sum of two parts, a so-called homogeneous part, which corresponds to $P = 0$, and a so-called particular solution. These correspond physically to the *free vibration* (i.e., the motion that would occur if the system were started with definite initial conditions and there were no exciting force) and the *forced* or *steady-state* vibration (i.e., the motion that remains after damping has caused the influence of the initial conditions to decay). To obtain the free vibration, divide Eq. 9.2-2 by m to get

$$\ddot{x} + \left(\frac{c}{m}\right)\dot{x} + \left(\frac{k}{m}\right)x = \frac{P}{m}. \qquad \textbf{9.2-3}$$

Introduce the symbols

$$\omega_n = (k/m)^{1/2} \quad \text{and} \quad \zeta = c/2(mk)^{1/2}. \qquad \textbf{9.2-4}$$

Then Eq. 9.2-3 takes the form

$$\ddot{x} + 2\zeta\omega_n\dot{x} + \omega_n^2 x = \frac{P}{m}. \qquad \textbf{9.2-5}$$

The quantity ω_n we have encountered in Section 3.3; it is the natural frequency of the undamped system. The dimensionless quantity ζ is a measure of the damping present; it is known as the fraction of critical damping. Since we are for the moment interested in the free vibration, we set $P = 0$ and take advantage of the fact that any linear differential equation with constant coefficients will have a solution of the form $x = e^{st}$. On substituting this form in Eq. 9.2-5, we find that the equation will be satisfied for all t provided

$$s = -\zeta\omega_n \pm \omega_n\sqrt{\zeta^2 - 1}. \qquad \textbf{9.2-6}$$

The solution assumes two different forms depending on whether ζ

is larger or smaller than unity.   If $\zeta > 1$ so that the values given by the above expression are real numbers

$$x = e^{-\zeta\omega_n t}(C_1' e^{\omega_n t\sqrt{2\zeta-1}} + C_2' e^{-\omega_n t\sqrt{\zeta^2-1}}.) \qquad \textbf{9.2-7}$$

In order to avoid lengthy exponents in printed material, it is a common practice to introduce the notation exp (x) in place of e^x.   With this notation, Eq. 9.2-7 would be written

$$x = e^{-\zeta\omega_n t}[C_1' \exp (\omega_n t\sqrt{\zeta^2-1}) + C_2' \exp (-\omega_n t\sqrt{\zeta^2-1})].$$

This can be put into a slightly more convenient form by introducing the hyperbolic sine and cosine:

$$2 \sinh \theta = e^\theta - e^{-\theta} \quad \text{and} \quad 2 \cosh \theta = e^\theta + e^{-\theta}. \qquad \textbf{9.2-8}$$

Then

$$e^\theta = 2(\cosh \theta + \sinh \theta)$$

and
$$\qquad\qquad\qquad\qquad\qquad\qquad\qquad\qquad\qquad\qquad \textbf{9.2-9}$$

$$e^{-\theta} = 2(\cosh \theta - \sinh \theta);$$

and, setting $\theta = \omega_n t\sqrt{\zeta^2-1}$, we have

$$x = e^{-\zeta\omega_n t}[2(C_1' + C_2') \cosh (\omega_n t\sqrt{\zeta^2-1})$$

$$+ 2(C_1' - C_2') \sinh (\omega_n t\sqrt{\zeta^2-1})]. \qquad \textbf{9.2-10}$$

Since C_1' and C_2' are arbitrary constants, we may replace them by constants C_1, C_2 where $C_1 = 2(C_1' + C_2')$ and $C_2 = 2(C_1' - C_2')$.   Then the free motion takes the form

$$x = e^{-\zeta\omega_n t}[C_1 \cosh (\omega_n t\sqrt{\zeta^2-1}) + C_2 \sinh (\omega_n t\sqrt{\zeta^2-1})].$$
$$\textbf{9.2-11}$$

In order to satisfy the initial conditions, we must have $C_1 = x_0$ and $C_2 = (v_0 + \zeta\omega_n x_0)/(\omega_n\sqrt{\zeta^2-1})$ so that, finally,

$$x = e^{-\zeta\omega_n t}\left[x_0 \cosh (\omega_n t\sqrt{\zeta^2-1}) + \frac{v_0 + \zeta\omega_n x_0}{\omega_n\sqrt{\zeta^2-1}} \sinh (\omega_n t\sqrt{\zeta^2-1})\right].$$
$$\textbf{9.2-12}$$

The foregoing expression has been developed from Eq. 9.2-6 on the assumption that $\zeta > 1$.   If $\zeta < 1$, as is usually the case, we appear to encounter the hyperbolic sine or cosine of an imaginary number.

But the hyperbolic cosine of an imaginary number is simply the ordinary cosine of that number:

$$e^{i\theta} = \cos\theta + i\sin\theta \quad \text{and}^\star \quad e^{-i\theta} = \cos\theta - i\sin\theta \qquad \textbf{9.2-13}$$

so that

$$2\cosh i\theta = e^{i\theta} + e^{-i\theta} = (\cos\theta + i\sin\theta) + (\cos\theta - i\sin\theta),$$

$$\cosh i\theta = \cos\theta,$$

and

$$2\sinh i\theta = e^{i\theta} - e^{-i\theta} = (\cos\theta + i\sin\theta) - (\cos\theta - i\sin\theta),$$

$$\sinh i\theta = i\sin\theta.$$

When these two results are used, Eq. 9.2-12 becomes

$$x = e^{-\zeta\omega_n t}\left[x_0\cos(\omega_n t\sqrt{1-\zeta^2}) + \frac{v_0 + \zeta\omega_n x_0}{\omega_n\sqrt{1-\zeta^2}}\sin(\omega_n t\sqrt{1-\zeta^2})\right],$$

$$\textbf{9.2-14}$$

which is the appropriate form of solution of the equation of motion when the fraction of critical damping is less than unity.

Since x_0 and v_0 are arbitrary so far as the differential equation 9.2-5 is concerned, we see that this solution form may be written

$$x = e^{-\zeta\omega_n t}[C_1\cos(\omega_n t\sqrt{1-\zeta^2}) + C_2\sin(\omega_n t\sqrt{1-\zeta^2})], \quad \textbf{9.2-15}$$

which corresponds with 9.2-11. An equivalent form, which is sometimes encountered, is obtained by setting $C_1 = A\cos\phi$ and $C_2 = A\sin\phi$; then

$$x = Ae^{-\zeta\omega_n t}\cos(\omega_n t\sqrt{1-\zeta^2} - \phi). \qquad \textbf{9.2-16}$$

Here A and ϕ are the constants of integration corresponding to C_1 and C_2.

It is interesting to note that, if $\zeta = 1$, the two solution forms 9.2-12 and 9.2-14 coalesce. In that case we have, from 9.2-14,

$$x = e^{-\omega_n t}\left[x_0 + (v_0 + \omega_n x_0)\lim_{\zeta\to 1}\frac{\sin(\omega_n t\sqrt{1-\zeta^2})}{\omega_n\sqrt{1-\zeta^2}}\right].$$

$\star$ Here $i = \sqrt{-1}$. Electrical engineers frequently use j to avoid confusion with the symbol for current. The first of 9.2-13 is Euler's formula.

But applying de L'Hospital's rule

$$\lim_{\zeta \to 1}\left[\frac{\sin(\omega_n t\sqrt{1-\zeta^2})}{\omega_n\sqrt{1-\zeta^2}}\right] = \lim_{\zeta \to 1}\left[\frac{\omega_n t\left(\dfrac{-\zeta}{\sqrt{1-\zeta^2}}\right)}{-\omega_n\dfrac{\zeta}{\sqrt{1-\zeta^2}}}\cos(\omega_n t\sqrt{1-\zeta^2})\right]$$

$$= t, \qquad\qquad \textbf{9.2-17}$$

so that

$$x = x_0 e^{-\omega_n t} + (v_0 + \omega_n x_0)t e^{-\omega_n t}. \qquad\qquad \textbf{9.2-18}$$

Equation 9.2-12 approaches the same limit when $\zeta \to 1$, it being only necessary to replace the circular by the hyperbolic sine in the calculation leading to Eq. 9.2-17. The student may verify by direct substitution that the result is indeed a solution of the equation of motion 9.2-5 (with $P = 0$) for the case $\zeta = 1$.

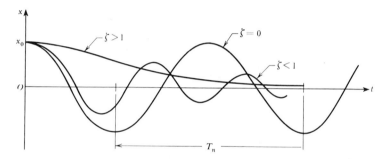

Fig. 9.2-2

The two mathematical forms, 9.2-12 and 9.2-14, correspond to two fundamental ways in which the system may behave when released from rest in a nonequilibrium position. If ζ exceeds unity, Eq. 9.2-12 with $v_0 = 0$ applies; the system returns slowly to its equilibrium position ($x = 0$) and does not overshoot, as we see from the fact that x never becomes negative. If ζ is less than unity, the displacement oscillates about the equilibrium position with oscillations whose amplitudes gradually decrease owing to the eventual dominance of the factor $\exp(-\zeta\omega_n t)$. These motions are depicted in Fig. 9.2-2. Owing to the change from oscillatory to nonoscillatory behavior, which occurs at $\zeta = 1$, the value of c corresponding to $\zeta = 1$ is known as the *critical damping value*:

$$c_{cr} = 2\sqrt{mk} = 2m\omega_n = 2k/\omega_n. \qquad\qquad \textbf{9.2-19}$$

Since $\zeta = c/c_{cr}$, it does justify its name and represent the fraction of critical damping present.

Equation 9.2-15 reduces to Eq. 3.3-3 when $\zeta = 0$. This is as it should be; in the absence of damping the single-degree-of-freedom system behaves exactly as a linear harmonic oscillator of period $2\pi/\omega_n$. The damped oscillatory motion described by Eq. 9.2-14 is not, strictly speaking, simple harmonic motion. It does not repeat itself. But if the amount of damping present is small, as it often is in engineering practice, it is common to speak of damped harmonic motion.

Example **9.2-1**

In order to measure the fraction of critical damping present in a structure, it is set into free vibration and a decay curve is recorded. If the record has

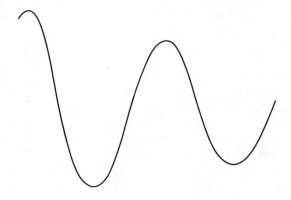

Fig. 9.2-3

the appearance shown in Fig. 9.2-3, *what is the fraction of critical damping present?*

Solution: A decay curve is a record of displacement vs. time. It may be seen at once from the appearance of the curve that the damping present is less than critical. The motion is therefore represented by an equation of the type of Eq. 9.2-16,

$$x = Ae^{-\zeta\omega_n t} \cos\,(\omega_n \sqrt{1 - \zeta^2} t - \phi).$$

If we measure the amplitude of the decay curve, x_1, at some time t_1 and again at a later time $t_2 = t_1 + (2\pi)/(\omega_n \sqrt{1 - \zeta^2})$, we shall have

$$x_1 = A \exp\,\{-\zeta\omega_n t_1\} \cos\,(\omega_n t_1 \sqrt{1 - \zeta^2} - \phi),$$

$$x_2 = A \exp\,\{-\zeta\omega_n [t_1 + (2\pi)/(\omega_n \sqrt{1 - \zeta^2})]\} \cos\,(\omega_n t_1 \sqrt{1 - \zeta^2} - \phi + 2\pi).$$

The two trigonometric terms have identical values because their arguments differ by 2π. Consequently, the ratio of the two amplitudes will be

$$\frac{x_1}{x_2} = \frac{\exp\{-\zeta\omega_n t_1\}}{\exp\{-\zeta\omega_n[t_1 + (2\pi)/(\omega_n\sqrt{1-\zeta^2})]\}} = e^{2\pi\zeta/\sqrt{1-\zeta^2}}.$$

The (natural) logarithm of this ratio is known as the *logarithmic decrement*. It is commonly denoted by the symbol Δ.

$$\Delta = \log\frac{x_1}{x_2} = \frac{2\pi\zeta}{\sqrt{1-\zeta^2}}.$$

Once the logarithmic decrement has been measured, the computation of the fraction of critical damping present is simple.

$$\zeta = \frac{\Delta}{\sqrt{4\pi^2 + \Delta^2}}.$$

As Δ is usually small compared with 2π, it is customary to write

$$\zeta \cong \frac{\Delta}{2\pi}.$$

But how do we go about selecting two abscissae on the decay curve differing by the interval $(2\pi)/(\omega_n\sqrt{1-\zeta^2})$? To answer this question we need to know a few facts about the behavior of curves represented by equations of the type of 9.2-16. In the first place, the decay curve will never exceed in magnitude the curve $x = A\exp(-\zeta\omega_n t)$. This follows from the fact that the trigonometric term cannot exceed unity. The decay curve has for envelope the two exponentials $x = \pm A\exp(-\zeta\omega_n t)$. It is tangent to these envelopes at points where $\cos(\omega_n\sqrt{1-\zeta^2}t - \phi) = \pm 1$; that is, where

$$\omega_n\sqrt{1-\zeta^2}t - \phi = 0, 2\pi, 4\pi, \ldots$$

or

$$t = \frac{\phi}{\omega_n\sqrt{1-\zeta^2}}, \qquad t = \frac{\phi}{\omega_n\sqrt{1-\zeta^2}} + \frac{2\pi}{\omega_n\sqrt{1-\zeta^2}},$$

$$t = \frac{\phi}{\omega_n\sqrt{1-\zeta^2}} + \frac{4\pi}{\omega_n\sqrt{1-\zeta^2}}, \ldots,$$

the decay curve is tangent to its upper envelope, $x = A\exp(-\zeta\omega_n t)$. These points of tangency are distributed at intervals of $(2\pi)/(\omega_n\sqrt{1-\zeta^2})$ sec. They would serve as suitable points for the determination of the logarithmic decrement if they could be located with accuracy. Their positions are slightly to the right of the peaks in the decay curve, as shown in Fig. 9.2-4.

The fact that the tangents to the envelopes have a period

$$(2\pi)/(\omega_n\sqrt{1-\zeta^2}) \text{ sec}$$

suggests that other points, more easily located, may have the same property. The zeros (points where $x=0$) certainly have the desired periodicity, but their amplitudes, being zero, are clearly of no value in determining the logarithmic decrement. The peaks of the decay curve occur when $\dot{x}=0$; that is, when

$$-\zeta\omega_n \cos(\omega_n\sqrt{1-\zeta^2}t-\phi) - \omega_n\sqrt{1-\zeta^2}\sin(\omega_n\sqrt{1-\zeta^2}t-\phi) = 0,$$

$$\tan(\omega_n\sqrt{1-\zeta^2}t-\phi) = \frac{-\zeta}{\sqrt{1-\zeta^2}},$$

$$\omega_n\sqrt{1-\zeta^2}t-\phi = -\arctan\frac{\zeta}{\sqrt{1-\zeta^2}}+2k\pi = -\arcsin\zeta+2k\pi,$$

$$t = \frac{\phi-\arcsin\zeta}{\omega_n\sqrt{1-\zeta^2}}+\frac{2k\pi}{\omega_n\sqrt{1-\zeta^2}},$$

where k takes on the values $0, 1, 2, 3, \ldots$ successively. We see that the first term on the right-hand side of this expression is a constant and that therefore

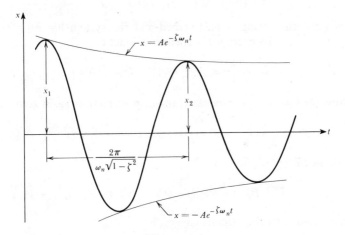

Fig. 9.2-4

the peaks of the decay curve occur at values of t separated by the interval

$$(2\pi)/(\omega_n\sqrt{1-\zeta^2}).$$

The logarithmic decrement may be determined by taking for x_1 and x_2 the amplitudes of any two successive peaks of the decay curve, as illustrated in Fig. 9.2-4. In the figure, $x_1=1.0$ in and $x_2=0.75$ in so that

$$\Delta = \log\frac{1.0}{0.75} = \log 1.33 = 0.287,$$

$$\zeta = \frac{0.287}{2\pi} = 0.0458.$$

The decay curve of a damped vibration is not a periodic motion since it does not repeat itself in all respects. As we have seen, however, it does have a kind of periodicity; its peaks and zeros occur at uniformly spaced time intervals of $(2\pi)/(\omega_n\sqrt{1-\zeta^2})$ sec. These intervals are sometimes spoken of as the damped natural period.

The fraction of critical damping present in structures is apt to be small unless viscous damping has been deliberately introduced in the form, say, of shock absorbers. For this reason, x_1 and x_2 are apt to be very nearly the same. It is then more accurate to measure the second ordinate, x_{n+1}, after n cycles. The student should have no difficulty showing that under these circumstances $\Delta = (1/n)\log(x_1/x_{n+1})$.

The logarithmic decrement also provides a simple measure of the rate at which the damping forces are converting mechanical energy into heat. Consider a "cycle" in which, initially, $x_1 = 0$. This implies

$$\cos(\omega_n\sqrt{1-\zeta^2}t_1 - \phi) = 0$$

and therefore

$$\sin(\omega_n\sqrt{1-\zeta^2}t_1 - \phi) = \pm 1.$$

At this time, the spring is unstretched and the system has no potential energy of strain. Its energy, E_1, is entirely kinetic:

$$E_1 = \frac{1}{2}m\dot{x}^2 = \frac{1}{2}m\omega_n^2(1-\zeta^2)e^{-2\zeta\omega_n t_1}.$$

At a time $(2\pi)/(\omega_n\sqrt{1-\zeta^2})$ sec later, the displacement is again zero, and

$$E_2 = \frac{1}{2}m\omega_n^2(1-\zeta^2)\exp[-2\zeta\omega_n t_1 - (4\pi\zeta)/\sqrt{1-\zeta^2}].$$

The loss in energy is

$$E_1 - E_2 = \frac{1}{2}m\omega_n^2(1-\zeta^2)e^{-2\zeta\omega_n t_1}(1-e^{-2\Delta}),$$

and this, divided by the original energy, is

$$\frac{E_1 - E_2}{E_1} = 1 - e^{-2\Delta}.$$

We see that, in each damped cycle, a definite fraction of the energy originally present is dissipated in heat. This fraction has been expressed above in terms of the logarithmic decrement. For small values of Δ, we may expand the exponential on the right-hand side of the preceding expression and retain only the first two terms. Then

$$\frac{E_1 - E_2}{E_1} = 2\Delta = 4\pi\zeta$$

so that the logarithmic decrement gives a very convenient measure of the energy loss per cycle.

The logarithmic decrement is obtained from a relatively simple measurement. The absolute values of ordinates and abscissae of the decay curve need not be known; in other words, the measuring apparatus need not be calibrated. So convenient is this quantity that engineers sometimes overlook the assumptions on which its use is based, namely that the actual system can be approximated by one with a single degree of freedom and viscous damping.

9.3 Effect of a Disturbing Force

In the preceding section, the homogeneous solution of the equation of motion (9.2-5), $\ddot{x} + 2\zeta\omega_n\dot{x} + \omega_n^2 x = P/m$, was found to represent a motion which, if any damping were present, tended to die away with time. If there is a disturbing force, $P(t)$, the particular solution needed to complete the analysis is of the form

$$x = e^{-\zeta\omega_n t}[f(t)\cos(\omega_n t\sqrt{1-\zeta^2}) + g(t)\sin(\omega_n t\sqrt{1-\zeta^2})]$$

$$\textbf{9.3-1}$$

where f and g denote functions of time that are to be determined so that 9.3-1 will satisfy 9.2-5. On comparison with the homogeneous solution 9.2-15, to which 9.3-1 would reduce if f and g were constants, it is apparent that, of the terms that arise when 9.3-1 is substituted in 9.2-5, only those that contain derivatives of f and g will give the left-hand side of 9.2-5 a non-zero value. Of these terms, the ones that appear in $\dot{x}$ are made to vanish by the condition

$$\dot{f}\cos(\omega_n t\sqrt{1-\zeta^2}) + \dot{g}\sin(\omega_n t\sqrt{1-\zeta^2}) = 0. \qquad \textbf{9.3-2}$$

In view of this restriction, no derivatives of f and g appear in $\dot{x}$, and therefore only first derivatives of f and g appear in $\ddot{x}$. These terms are made equal to the right-hand side of 9.2-5 by the condition

$$-\dot{f}\sin(\omega_n t\sqrt{1-\zeta^2}) + \dot{g}\cos(\omega_n t\sqrt{1-\zeta^2}) = \frac{P(t)e^{\zeta\omega_n t}}{m\omega_n\sqrt{1-\zeta^2}}. \qquad \textbf{9.3-3}$$

These two conditions are satisfied if

$$\dot{f} = \frac{-P(t)e^{\zeta\omega_n t}}{m\omega_n\sqrt{1-\zeta^2}}\sin(\omega_n t\sqrt{1-\zeta^2})$$

and $$\textbf{9.3-4}$$

$$\dot{g} = \frac{P(t)e^{\zeta\omega_n t}}{m\omega_n\sqrt{1-\zeta^2}}\cos(\omega_n t\sqrt{1-\zeta^2}).$$

It follows that

$$f(t) = \int_0^t \frac{-P(\tau)e^{\zeta\omega_n\tau}}{m\omega_n\sqrt{1-\zeta^2}} \sin(\omega_n\tau\sqrt{1-\zeta^2})\, d\tau$$

and

$$g(t) = \int_0^t \frac{P(\tau)e^{\zeta\omega_n\tau}}{m\omega_n\sqrt{1-\zeta^2}} \cos(\omega_n\tau\sqrt{1-\zeta^2})\, d\tau.$$

9.3-5

The symbol τ is a "dummy" variable, which disappears after the integration has been performed and the limits inserted. The lower limit is arbitrary, but there is a distinct convenience associated with the choice of zero. This choice makes the particular integral and its first time derivative vanish at $t = 0$. Substituting 9.3-5 in 9.3-1, we have

$$x = e^{-\zeta\omega_n t}\cos(\omega_n\sqrt{1-\zeta^2}t) \int_0^t \frac{-P(\tau)e^{\zeta\omega_n\tau}}{m\omega_n\sqrt{1-\zeta^2}} \sin(\omega_n\sqrt{1-\zeta^2}\tau)\, d\tau$$

$$+ e^{-\zeta\omega_n t}\sin(\omega_n\sqrt{1-\zeta^2}t) \int_0^t \frac{P(\tau)e^{\zeta\omega_n\tau}}{m\omega_n\sqrt{1-\zeta^2}} \cos(\omega_n\sqrt{1-\zeta^2}\tau)\, d\tau.$$

9.3-6

This can be written in a concise way. Since we took the precaution of using a special symbol, τ, to denote the variable of integration, we may take t inside the integral sign without fear of confusion; t is a constant so far as the integration is concerned. Then the two terms in 9.3-6 may be combined.

$$x = \int_0^t \frac{P(\tau)e^{-\zeta\omega_n(t-\tau)}}{m\omega_n\sqrt{1-\zeta^2}} \sin(\omega_n\sqrt{1-\zeta^2}[t-\tau])\, d\tau.$$

9.3-7

This is the particular integral of the equation of motion. It is of a form known as the *Duhamel integral* (sometimes as the *Faltung* or *convolution integral*). Since the equation of motion is linear, its complete solution is simply the sum of the homogeneous and particular solutions:

$$x = e^{-\zeta\omega_n t}\left[x_0\cos(\omega_n\sqrt{1-\zeta^2}t) + \frac{v_0+\zeta\omega_n x_0}{\omega_n\sqrt{1-\zeta^2}}\sin(\omega_n\sqrt{1-\zeta^2}t)\right]$$

$$+ \int_0^t \frac{P(\tau)e^{-\zeta\omega_n(t-\tau)}}{m\omega_n\sqrt{1-\zeta^2}} \sin(\omega_n\sqrt{1-\zeta^2}[t-\tau])\, d\tau.$$

9.3-8

Since the Duhamel integral is independent of the initial conditions, it represents the steady-state part of the motion. The first line of

9.3-8 represents the difference between the total motion and the steady-state motion. It is referred to as the *transient* motion.

Example **9.3-1**

An undamped, spring-supported mass at rest is subjected to a "rectangular" force pulse of magnitude F_0 and duration $T_0/2 = \pi/p$ sec. Find the maximum displacement.

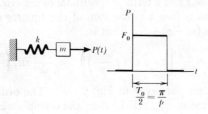

Fig. 9.3-1

Solution: Since the system is undamped and starts from rest, $\zeta = x_0 = v_0 = 0$; Eq. 9.3-8 then becomes

$$m\omega_n x = \int_0^t P(\tau) \sin \omega_n(t - \tau)\, d\tau.$$

Since $P(t) = F_0$ for $0 < t < \pi/p$ and $P(t) = 0$ for $t > \pi/p$, for $t < \pi/p$,

$$x = \frac{F_0}{m\omega_n} \int_0^t \sin \omega_n(t - \tau)\, d\tau$$

$$= \frac{F_0}{m\omega_n} \left[\sin \omega_n t \int_0^t \cos \omega_n \tau\, d\tau - \cos \omega_n t \int_0^t \sin \omega_n \tau\, d\tau \right]$$

$$= \frac{F_0}{m\omega_n^2} \left[\sin \omega_n t \left(\sin \omega_n \tau \Big|_0^t \right) + \cos \omega_n t \left(\cos \omega_n \tau \Big|_0^t \right) \right]$$

$$= \frac{F_0}{k} (1 - \cos \omega_n t) = 2\frac{F_0}{k} \sin^2 \left(\frac{\omega_n t}{2} \right). \qquad \textbf{9.3-9}$$

But if $t > \pi/p$, P will be non-zero only for the first part of the time interval. It follows that, for $t > \pi/p$,

$$x = \frac{F_0}{m\omega_n} \int_0^{\pi/p} \sin \omega_n(t - \tau)\, d\tau$$

$$= \frac{F_0}{m\omega_n^2} \left[\sin \omega_n t \left(\sin \omega_n \tau \Big|_0^{\pi/p} \right) + \cos \omega_n t \left(\cos \omega_n \tau \Big|_0^{\pi/p} \right) \right]$$

$$= \frac{F_0}{k} \left[\sin \omega_n t \left(\sin \frac{\omega_n \pi}{p} \right) + \cos \omega_n t \left(\cos \frac{\omega_n \pi}{p} - 1 \right) \right]. \qquad \textbf{9.3-10}$$

Note that the expressions for both displacement and velocity are continuous at $t = \pi/p$, since the values of x and $\dot{x}$ computed from 9.3-9 and 9.3-10 match at that time.   We are interested in the maximum value of x.   Clearly if $t = \pi/\omega_n$, the right-hand side of 9.3-9 attains its maximum value $2F_0/k$. But to reach this value, we must have $p/\omega_n < 1$—else $(1 - \cos \omega_n t)$ will reach the value 2 at an instant when Eq. 9.3-9 is no longer valid.   If $p/\omega_n > 1$, the peak value of x may occur after the force pulse has dropped to zero.   The displacement then will be given by 9.3-10 as the sum of a term proportional to $\sin \omega_n t$ and a term proportional to $\cos \omega_n t$.   The amplitude of this displacement is (see 3.3) the sum of the squares of the coefficients $\sin (\omega_n \pi/p)$ and $\cos (\omega_n \pi/p) - 1$.   That is,

$$x_{\max} = \frac{F_0}{k} \left[2 - 2 \cos \left(\frac{\omega_n \pi}{p} \right) \right]^{1/2} = \frac{2F_0}{k} \sin \left(\frac{\omega_n \pi}{2p} \right). \qquad \textbf{9.3-11}$$

These conclusions are portrayed in Fig. 9.3-2.   The ordinate is the actual maximum displacement, $x_{\max}$, divided by the displacement that a force F_0 would produce if applied slowly and maintained.   For a long-duration

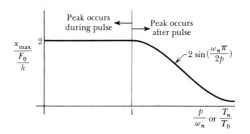

Fig. 9.3-2

pulse acting on a high natural-frequency system, the peak occurs during the pulse; for a short-duration pulse acting on a low natural-frequency system, it occurs after the pulse.

9.4 Effect of a Harmonic Disturbing Force

A type of exciting force that is encountered widely is the harmonic disturbance

$$P(t) = F_0 \cos pt \qquad \textbf{9.4-1}$$

of amplitude F_0 and (circular) frequency p.   It is met, for example, wherever there is imperfectly balanced rotating or reciprocating machinery.   In Section 3.4, we found that such a force could produce a large response if the exciting frequency were near the natural frequency of the mechanical system. It is of some interest to observe the influence of damping on the response. This could be done by substituting $P(\tau)$ in the Duhamel integral (Eq. 9.3-7) of the preceding section, but the integrations, while straightforward, are tedious. There is a simpler way to proceed in this special case. We may infer that, since the homogeneous solution dies out, the steady-state motion will consist of a simple harmonic displacement at the exciting frequency:

$$x = A \cos{(pt - \alpha)} \qquad\qquad \textbf{9.4-2}$$

where A is the amplitude of the response and α is the *phase angle* by which the response lags behind the excitation. When this trial solution and Eq. 9.4-1 are substituted in the equation of motion (9.2-5) it becomes a trigonometric equation each term of which, when expanded, is a multiple of the sine or cosine of the argument pt. Since this equation must be satisfied at all times, the sum of the coefficients of the sine terms must vanish, and the sum of the co-efficients of the cosine terms on the left-hand side must equal the coefficient of $\cos pt$ on the right-hand side. These two conditions are expressed by the equations

$$(\omega_n^2 - p^2)\cos\alpha + 2\zeta\omega_n p \sin\alpha = F_0/mA,$$

$$(\omega_n^2 - p^2)\sin\alpha - 2\zeta\omega_n p \cos\alpha = 0. \qquad\qquad \textbf{9.4-3}$$

If (a) the first of 9.4-3 is multiplied by $\cos\alpha$, the second by $\sin\alpha$, and they are added; and (b) the first of 9.4-3 is multiplied by $\sin\alpha$ and the second by $\cos\alpha$, and they are subtracted, these equations become

$$\sin\alpha = (mA/F_0)2\zeta\omega_n p,$$

$$\cos\alpha = (mA/F_0)(\omega_n^2 - p^2). \qquad\qquad \textbf{9.4-4}$$

The amplitude of the steady-state motion, A, is found by squaring and adding these expressions.

$$A = \frac{\dfrac{F_0}{m}}{[(\omega_n^2 - p^2)^2 + (2\zeta\omega_n p)^2]^{1/2}} = \frac{\dfrac{F_0}{k}}{\left[\left(1 - \dfrac{p^2}{\omega_n^2}\right)^2 + \left(2\zeta\dfrac{p}{\omega_n}\right)^2\right]^{1/2}}.$$

$$\textbf{9.4-5}$$

The angle α, which is the phase angle between force and displacement, is determined unambiguously by Equations 9.4-4. The complete solution of the motion of a single-degree-of-freedom system subject to a harmonic exciting force involves both a transient and a steady-state part. This solution takes the general form

$$x = e^{-\zeta \omega_n t}[C_1 \cos (\omega_n t \sqrt{1 - \zeta^2}) + C_2 \sin (\omega_n t \sqrt{1 - \zeta^2})]$$

$$+ \frac{\dfrac{F_0}{k}}{\left[\left(1 - \dfrac{p^2}{\omega_n^2}\right)^2 + \left(2\zeta \dfrac{p}{\omega_n}\right)^2\right]^{1/2}} \cos \left(pt - \arctan\left[\frac{2\zeta \dfrac{p}{\omega_n}}{1 - \dfrac{p^2}{\omega_n^2}}\right]\right) \qquad \textbf{9.4-6}$$

The arbitrary constants, C_1 and C_2, of the transient part must be adjusted in each case so that the entire solution satisfies initial conditions on x and $\dot{x}$ at $t = 0$. Note that the steady-state part does not satisfy $x = \dot{x} = 0$ at $t = 0$ as does the particular solution of Section 9.3.

In practice, it is rarely necessary to use the complete solution given above. To see why this is so, consider the motion of the mass shown

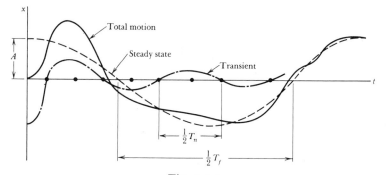

Fig. 9.4-1

in Fig. 9.2-1, which starts from rest in the equilibrium position $(x_0 = v_0 = 0)$ and is subject to an exciting force, $F_0 \cos pt$. The behavior of the mass is illustrated in Fig. 9.4-1. In this figure, the steady-state solution is shown in broken lines. It consists of a simple harmonic motion of period $T_f = 2\pi/p$ and amplitude $x_{\max} = A$. The actual motion is shown in heavy line. It starts, in this case, from $x = 0$ with horizontal slope. As time progresses, the transient part of the solution dies out owing to the factor $e^{-\zeta \omega_n t}$. The influence of the transient term is then seen only in the small oscillations of period $T_n = 2\pi/\omega_n$ superposed on the steady-state motion. After the first few natural periods have elapsed, the transient can be neglected for most practical purposes. This is the ordinary case in mechanical engineering design; some unbalanced machine is a source of exciting force, and the designer wishes to isolate it from its environment.

It is usually only when interest centers in the details of the motion immediately after the exciting force is applied that a kr owledge of the complete response given by Eq. 9.3-8 or Eq. 9.4-6 is essential.

Focusing attention on the steady-state response, we note that its amplitude, given by Eq. 9.4-5, depends upon F_0/k, p/ω_n and ζ. Now F_0/k is the displacement that would be produced by a slowly applied force of peak magnitude F_0 acting on a system of stiffness k. The ratio of x_{max} to F_0/k is known as the *dynamic amplification factor*. In Fig. 9.4-2, the dynamic amplification factor is plotted as a function of the frequency ratio p/ω_n for various amounts of damping.   The case $\zeta = 0$ has previously been developed in Section 3.4 (see Fig. 3.4-2). At very low exciting frequencies, the amplification factor is unity.

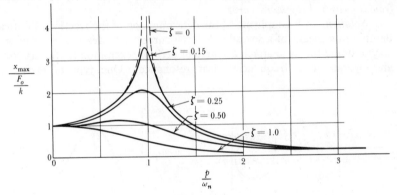

Fig. 9.4-2

This implies that the dynamic response is essentially the same as that which would occur if the force F_0 were applied very slowly.   Furthermore, small values of p/ω_n, as may be seen by taking the ratio of the two Eqs. 9.4-4, imply $\alpha \cong 0$, which means that the response is in phase with the exciting force.   At very high exciting frequencies, $p/\omega_n \gg 1$, the dynamic amplification factor tends to zero, and the phase lag between force and displacement tends to 180 degrees.   This means that what small dynamic response does occur at these high excitation frequencies will reach a maximum value to the right when the force is a maximum to the left, and vice versa.

When the frequency ratio $p/\omega_n = 1$, a condition prevails which by analogy with the undamped case is known as *resonance*.   Each of the curves of Fig. 9.4-2 is known as a *resonance curve* or *response curve*. The dynamic amplification factor at resonance is equal to $1/(2\zeta)$ and is limited in magnitude only by the damping that may be present in the system.   There is then a phase lag of ninety degrees between the exciting force and the response of the mass.   This means that the displacement is zero when the exciting force is a maximum in either direction.   Strictly speaking, the dynamic amplification factor is a maximum   when $p/\omega_n = \sqrt{1 - 2\zeta^2}$,   and   this   maximum   value   is $1/(2\zeta\sqrt{1 - \zeta^2})$ as may be verified by differentiating Eq. 9.4-5.   If the damping is small, this value essentially coincides with $1/(2\zeta)$, which occurs at resonance as defined previously.   If ζ exceeds $1/\sqrt{2} = 0.707$, the dynamic amplification factor never exceeds unity.

Example 9.4-1

Explain how the fraction of critical damping present may be estimated from a measured resonance curve.

Solution: In Example 9.2-1, the determination of the fraction of critical damping by means of a so-called "decay curve" was described.   Another way of doing this is to attach a source of periodic excitation to the structure and operate it at frequencies near resonance.   One type of exciter is

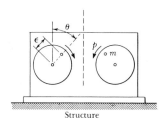

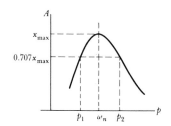

Fig. 9.4-3   Fig. 9.4-4

pictured in Fig. 9.4-3.   The two matched eccentrics of mass m on the rotating disks have accelerations ϵp^2 directed toward the centers of the disks. It follows that forces $m\epsilon p^2$ must be exerted on them and that they will exert on the attached structure forces whose horizontal components cancel and whose vertical components are $m\epsilon p^2 \cos \theta$.   Since $\theta = pt$, this is an harmonic force of the type given by 9.4-1.   In the test p is varied while $2m\epsilon p^2 (= F_0)$ is held constant.   A resonance curve such as that shown in Fig. 9.4-4 is obtained.   If the damping present is small, the peak in the curve will correspond to $p = \omega_n$ and will be of amplitude $1/(2\zeta)$ times the equivalent static deflection F_0/k.   We have

$$\frac{F_0^2}{k^2 x_{\max}^2} = 4\zeta^2.$$

Now draw the line corresponding to $0.707x_{\max}$; it will intersect the resonance curve at forcing frequencies p_1 and p_2. At each of these frequencies $A = x_{max}/\sqrt{2}$; that is,

$$\frac{F_0^2}{k^2 A^2} = 2\,\frac{F_0^2}{k^2 x_{max}^2} = 8\zeta^2 = \left(1 - \frac{p^2}{\omega_n^2}\right)^2 + \left(2\zeta\,\frac{p}{\omega_n}\right)^2.$$

We have made use of Eq. 9.4-5 in the last step. The values of p determined by this last expression are p_1 and p_2; we solve for them:

$$\left(\frac{p^2}{\omega_n^2}\right)^2 + 2(2\zeta^2 - 1)\left(\frac{p^2}{\omega_n^2}\right) + 1 - 8\zeta^2 = 0,$$

$$\frac{p_1^2}{\omega_n^2} = 1 - 2\zeta^2 - 2\zeta\sqrt{1 + \zeta^2} \cong 1 - 2\zeta,$$

$$\frac{p_2^2}{\omega_n^2} = 1 - 2\zeta^2 + 2\zeta\sqrt{1 + \zeta^2} \cong 1 + 2\zeta.$$

In the last step, the square of ζ is neglected in comparison with ζ itself. This again assumes that ζ is small compared with unity; if it is not, the resonance curve is a less effective device than the decay curve described in Example 9.2-1 for measurement of damping. From the last two expressions,

$$\frac{p_2}{\omega_n} - \frac{p_1}{\omega_n} = \sqrt{1 + 2\zeta} - \sqrt{1 - 2\zeta} \cong 2\zeta$$

to the same approximation. The quantity $(p_2/\omega_n) - (p_1/\omega_n)$ is known as the *band width at the half-power points*, and we say that the fraction of critical damping present is equal to half the band width.

Example 9.4-2

A 3000-lb machine includes a piston of weight 60 lb, speed 600 rpm, and total stroke (back and forth) 18 in. The motion of the piston may be considered to be harmonic. Design a vibration-isolating support for this machine that will (a) reduce the transmitted force to a maximum of 275 lb (over the dead weight) when the machine runs at the design speed and (b) keep the peak displacement of the machine to no more than 0.4 in when running at resonant speed.

Solution: On account of requirement (b) some damping will be needed in the mount (contrast Example 3.4-2). To determine the necessary value of ζ, we recall that at resonance $x_{max} = (F_0/k)/(2\zeta)$. In the present case, $F_0 = m\epsilon p^2$ where m denotes the mass of the piston and ϵ the length of its excursion. Note that the same expression would hold for an unbalanced rotor, ϵ being the distance of the mass center from the axis of rotation. If we denote the mass of the entire machine by m', we have

$$x_{max} = \frac{m\epsilon\,\dfrac{p^2}{k}}{2\zeta} = \frac{\dfrac{m}{m'}\,\epsilon\,\dfrac{p^2}{\omega_n^2}}{2\zeta}.$$

At resonance, $p = \omega_n$ so that

$$\zeta = \frac{\dfrac{m}{m'}\epsilon}{2x_{max}} = \frac{\left(\dfrac{60}{3000}\right)(9)}{(2)(0.4)} = 0.22.$$

The force transmitted to the foundation by the springs is

$$kx = \frac{F_0 \cos\,(pt - \alpha)}{\left[\left(1 - \dfrac{p^2}{\omega_n^2}\right)^2 + \left(2\zeta\,\dfrac{p}{\omega_n}\right)^2\right]^{1/2}},$$

and by the damping device or "shock absorber"

$$c\dot{x} = \frac{-\left(cp\,\dfrac{F_0}{k}\right)\sin\,(pt - \alpha)}{\left[\left(1 - \dfrac{p^2}{\omega_n^2}\right)^2 + \left(2\zeta\,\dfrac{p}{\omega_n}\right)^2\right]^{1/2}}.$$

Since these two forces are ninety degrees out of phase and may therefore be represented by rotating vectors (Section 3.3) ninety degrees apart, their vector sum in the rotating-vector plane, the total force transmitted to the foundation, will have an amplitude

$$F_T = \sqrt{(kx)^2{}_{max} + (c\dot{x})^2{}_{max}} = F_0 \sqrt{\frac{1 + \dfrac{c^2 p^2}{k^2}}{\left(1 - \dfrac{p^2}{\omega_n^2}\right)^2 + \left(2\zeta\,\dfrac{p}{\omega_n}\right)^2}}.$$

The ratio F_T/F_0 is known as the "transmissibility" of the foundation. In view of the fact that $c^2 = 4\zeta^2 m'k$, we may write

$$\frac{F_T}{F_0} = \sqrt{\frac{1 + \left(2\zeta\,\dfrac{p}{\omega_n}\right)^2}{\left(1 - \dfrac{p^2}{\omega_n^2}\right)^2 + \left(2\zeta\,\dfrac{p}{\omega_n}\right)^2}}.$$

In the present case,

$$F_0 = m\epsilon p^2 = \left(\frac{60}{32.2}\right)\left(\frac{9}{12}\right)\left(600\,\frac{2\pi}{60}\right)^2 = 5500 \text{ lb.}$$

Requirement (a) is that F_T be 275 lb so that, knowing ζ to be 0.22, we may solve the above transmissibility expression for p/ω_n:

$$\left(\frac{275}{5500}\right)^2\left[\left(1 - \frac{p^2}{\omega_n^2}\right)^2 + \left(0.44\,\frac{p}{\omega_n}\right)^2\right] = 1 + \left(0.44\,\frac{p}{\omega_n}\right)^2;$$

$$\frac{p}{\omega_n} = 9.1 \quad \text{so that} \quad \omega_n = \frac{62.8}{9.1} = 6.9 \text{ rad/sec.}$$

It is now a simple matter to compute the necessary spring stiffness and damping constant:

$$k = \frac{3000}{32.2}(6.9)^2 = 4440 \text{ lb/ft} = 370 \text{ lb/in.}$$

$$c = 2\zeta\sqrt{m'k} = 0.44\sqrt{\frac{(3000)(370)}{(32.2)(12)}} = 23.6 \text{ lb-sec/in.}$$

This completes the design from our present point of view. It is of some interest, however, to sketch the variation of the transmissibility with frequency ratio for different amounts of damping. This is done in Fig. 9.4-5. We note that if $p/\omega_n > \sqrt{2}$ the transmissibility is increased by the presence of damping. Since p/ω_n must be larger than $\sqrt{2}$ in order for the mounting to be effective at all, we may infer that damping does not lower the transmissibility of a vibration-isolating mount. It would, however, be a mistake to conclude that damping in a vibration-isolating mount is worthless. Although the operating speed of the engine is p, it may, at some time, be run at a speed close to ω_n. In the absence of damping, disastrous vibration amplitudes would then occur.

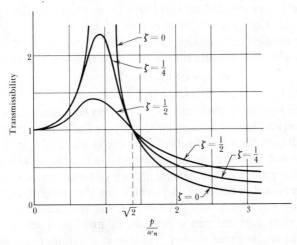

Fig. 9.4-5

9.5 Multiple-Degree-of-Freedom Mechanical Systems

Suppose now that the configuration of a mechanical system requires more than a single coordinate for its complete description. As in Section 6.2, if n independent coordinates are required, we say that the system has n degrees of freedom. We wish to consider the free and forced vibrations of such systems when they are conservative and when the restoring forces are linear functions of the coordinates. The former restriction is closely approximated in practice, but the latter is only accurate when the displacements, measured from a position of stable equilibrium, are small. For this reason the analysis to be outlined is sometimes known as small vibration theory.

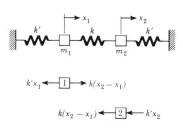

Fig. 9.5-1

We begin with a simple typical system: two masses m_1 and m_2, connected to each other by a spring of modulus k and to a fixed support by springs of modulus k' and free to move in a horizontal direction only. The masses are shown in Fig. 9.5-1. The most natural variables to use as coordinates are the displacements x_1, x_2 of the two masses from their equilibrium positions. The springs are taken to be undeformed in the equilibrium configuration. Then, if the bodies are given positive displacements, the forces exerted on them will be as shown in the free-body diagrams of Fig. 9.5-1. Notice that if $x_2 > x_1$, $(x_2 - x_1)$ will be a positive number, and so the force exerted on m_1 by the spring k will be to the right, as the figure indicates. The equations of motion are

$$m_1\ddot{x}_1 + (k + k')x_1 - kx_2 = 0,$$
$$m_2\ddot{x}_2 - kx_1 + (k + k')x_2 = 0. \qquad \text{9.5-1}$$

The equality of the coefficients of x_1 in the first equation and of x_2 in the second is an accident of our choice of example and is not generally true. The equality of the coefficients of x_2 in the first and of x_1 in the second equation is not, however, coincidental and is of fundamental importance in the development of the general theory of small vibrations.

We now ask whether it is possible for this system to execute a free vibration in which each part oscillates at the same frequency and in which each part reaches a position of maximum excursion from equilibrium at the same instant. If that is possible, the equations

$$x_1 = A_1 \cos(\omega_n t - \alpha), \qquad x_2 = A_2 \cos(\omega_n t - \alpha) \qquad \text{9.5-2}$$

must satisfy the equations of motion. On substituting them into 9.5-1 and canceling the common factor $\cos(\omega_n t - \alpha)$, we have two ordinary algebraic equations:

$$A_1[(k + k') - m_1\omega_n^2] - kA_2 = 0,$$
$$-kA_1 + A_2[(k + k') - m_2\omega_n^2] = 0. \qquad \text{9.5-3}$$

These equations have no solution other than the trivial one $A_1 = A_2 = 0$ unless the determinant of the coefficients of A_1 and A_2 vanishes. This determinant,

$$\begin{vmatrix} [(k+k') - m_1\omega_n^2] & -k \\ -k & [(k+k') - m_2\omega_n^2] \end{vmatrix},$$

is known as the *frequency determinant*. We note, in passing, that the equality of the cross-coefficients in Eq. 9.5-1 is reflected in the symmetry of the determinant about its main diagonal. This symmetry has important consequences, one of which is treated in Example 9.5-2. For the present, however, we return to the search for a nontrivial solution of Eqs. 9.5-3. On setting the frequency determinant equal to zero, we obtain the so-called *frequency equation*,

$$m_1 m_2 \omega_n^4 - (m_1 + m_2)(k+k')\omega_n^2 + k'(k'+2k) = 0. \qquad \textbf{9.5-4}$$

This equation is a quadratic in ω_n^2. It has two roots:

$$\omega_n^2 = \frac{1}{2}\left(\frac{1}{m_1} + \frac{1}{m_2}\right)(k+k') \pm \sqrt{\left[\frac{1}{2}\left(\frac{1}{m_1} + \frac{1}{m_2}\right)(k+k')\right]^2 - \frac{k'(k'+2k)}{m_1 m_2}},$$

$$\textbf{9.5-5}$$

which may be written in the alternative form

$$\omega_n^2 = \frac{1}{2}\left(\frac{1}{m_1} + \frac{1}{m_2}\right)(k+k') \pm \sqrt{\left[\frac{1}{2}\left(\frac{1}{m_1} - \frac{1}{m_2}\right)(k+k')\right]^2 + \frac{k^2}{m_1 m_2}}. \qquad \textbf{9.5-6}$$

We see from the second of these forms (9.5-6) that the quantity under the radical sign is always positive so that ω_n^2 is a real number. From the first form (9.5-5), we see that it is always a positive number, whatever the values of the masses and spring stiffnesses. There are, then, two possible frequencies at which a free vibration can take place, corresponding to the two roots of the frequency equation. These are *natural frequencies* of the system. It is customary to denote the smaller root by the symbol ω_1 and to call it the *fundamental, lowest,* or *gravest* frequency; the higher root, ω_2, is called the second natural frequency. We also note that, if k or k' is increased, both natural frequencies are increased, and, if m_1 or m_2 is increased, both natural frequencies are lowered. If the stiffness of the connecting spring, k, is allowed to increase without limit ω_2^2, which corresponds to the choice of the plus sign in 9.5-5, 6, will increase without limit, but ω_1^2, while increased, will approach the limit $2k'/(m_1 + m_2)$. This limit corresponds to the imposition of a constraint, which in this case may be visualized as a rigid rod (the limit of a stiff spring) connecting m_1 and m_2 and forcing the condition $x_1 = x_2$. It is, by the way, no coincidence that $2k'/(m_1 + m_2)$ is intermediate between the original values of ω_1^2 and ω_2^2 corresponding to a finite k.

The conclusions that we have here drawn from the analysis of a typical linear system with two degrees of freedom may be extended to conservative mechanical systems with n degrees of freedom executing small vibrations about a position of stable static equilibrium. To such systems and such motions, the discussion of this section is confined. The frequency determinant of such systems is symmetrical about its main diagonal. The frequency equation has n real, non-negative, finite, roots corresponding to n natural frequencies.* An increase in stiffness of any part of the system results in a system none of whose natural frequencies is lower than the corresponding ones of the original system. An increase in the inertia of any part of the system produces a new system whose natural frequencies are lower than or equal to the corresponding ones of the original system. Finally, the imposition of a constraint that reduces the number of degrees of freedom by one produces a system with $n-1$ natural frequencies that are intermediate between the frequencies of the original system. The proofs of the statements of this paragraph are, however, for the reasons mentioned in 9.1, beyond the scope of this text.**

Since there are two possible values for ω_n and, correspondingly, two possible values for A_1 and α, the solution 9.5-2 should be written

$$x_1 = A_1^{(1)} \cos(\omega_1 t - \alpha_1) + A_1^{(2)} \cos(\omega_2 t - \alpha_2),$$
$$x_2 = A_2^{(1)} \cos(\omega_1 t - \alpha_1) + A_2^{(2)} \cos(\omega_2 t - \alpha_2). \qquad \textbf{9.5-7}$$

The superscripts refer to the values of A_1 and A_2 associated with ω_1 and ω_2 respectively. But $A_1^{(1)}$ and $A_2^{(1)}$ are not independent.

When ω_n has either of the values given by 9.5-5, the determinant of the coefficients of A_1 and A_2 in 9.5-3 vanishes. The two Eqs. 9.5-3 are therefore linearly dependent, and A_2 can be written as a multiple of A_1 by means of either of them. To simplify the algebra suppose that $m_1 = m_2 =$, say, m. Then, from 9.5-6,

$$\omega_1^2 = \frac{k'}{m}, \qquad \omega_2^2 = \frac{2k+k'}{m}. \qquad \textbf{9.5-8}$$

Substituting first ω_1 and then ω_2 in the first of 9.5-3, we have

$$A_2^{(1)} = A_1^{(1)} \quad \text{and} \quad A_2^{(2)} = -A_1^{(2)}. \qquad \textbf{9.5-9}$$

---

* These roots need not all be distinct. A zero root corresponds to a uniform motion rather than a vibration.

** See, e.g., E. T. Whittaker, *A Treatise on the Analytical Dynamics of Particles and Rigid Bodies*, 4th ed. (New York: Dover Publications, 1944), p. 177ff.

Equations 9.5-7 become

$$x_1 = A_1^{(1)} \cos (\omega_1 t - \alpha_1) + A_1^{(2)} \cos (\omega_2 t - \alpha_2),$$
$$x_2 = A_1^{(1)} \cos (\omega_1 t - \alpha_1) - A_1^{(2)} \cos (\omega_2 t - \alpha_2). \qquad \textbf{9.5-10}$$

This is the complete solution of the equations of motion 9.5-1 for free vibration. The natural frequencies ω_1 and ω_2 are given by 9.5-8. The four constants of integration $A_1^{(1)}$, $A_1^{(2)}$, α_1, and α_2 are determined by the initial conditions $x_i(0)$, $\dot{x}_i(0)$, $i = 1, 2$, on the motion. For particular initial conditions, motion at either one of the natural frequencies alone is possible. Such a motion, in which each part of the system moves in a simple harmonic manner at the same frequency, is called a *natural mode of vibration*. In the first mode, for example,

$$x_1 = A_1^{(1)} \cos (\omega_1 t - \alpha_1),$$
$$x_2 = A_2^{(1)} \cos (\omega_1 t - \alpha_1). \qquad \textbf{9.5-11a}$$

Here, by 9.5-9, $A_2^{(1)} = A_1^{(1)}$ or, in alternative form,

$$A_2^{(1)} : A_1^{(1)} :: 1 : 1;$$

the numbers giving the ratios of the displacements of each part of the system when it is oscillating in a natural mode are said to determine the *mode shape*. For our example, the first mode shape is given by any two equal numbers or by the ratio $1:1$, and the first mode itself is

$$x_1 = x_2 = A_1^{(1)} \cos (\omega_1 t - \alpha_1). \qquad \textbf{9.5-11b}$$

In this mode, the equal masses m_1 and m_2 swing back and forth in synchronism with equal displacements. The center spring, of spring constant k, is not stretched. It is therefore not surprising that in this mode k does not enter the natural frequency. In the second mode,

$$x_1 = A_1^{(2)} \cos (\omega_2 t - \alpha_2) \quad \text{and} \quad x_2 = - A_1^{(2)} \cos (\omega_2 t - \alpha_2) \quad \textbf{9.5-12}$$

so that in this mode mass m_1 moves to the right while m_2 moves an equal distance to the left. The center spring is alternately compressed and stretched. The free motion consists, for general initial conditions, in the superposition of two simple harmonic oscillations corresponding to the two natural modes.

Consider now the coordinates $q_1(t)$, $q_2(t)$ defined by the expressions

$$q_1 = x_1 + x_2 \quad \text{and} \quad q_2 = x_1 - x_2, \qquad \textbf{9.5-13}$$

which are suggested by the first and second terms of Eqs. 9.5-10 respectively. These coordinates determine the position of the system just as well as do $x_1(t)$ and $x_2(t)$; in fact,

$$x_1 = \frac{1}{2}(q_1 + q_2) \quad \text{and} \quad x_2 = \frac{1}{2}(q_1 - q_2). \qquad \textbf{9.5-14}$$

If we substitute 9.5-14 in the equations of motion, 9.5-1, recalling that we are dealing with the special case $m_1 = m_2 = m$, we have

$$m\frac{1}{2}(\ddot{q}_1 + \ddot{q}_2) + (k + k')\frac{1}{2}(q_1 + q_2) - k\frac{1}{2}(q_1 - q_2) = 0,$$

$$m\frac{1}{2}(\ddot{q}_1 - \ddot{q}_2) + (k + k')\frac{1}{2}(q_1 - q_2) - k\frac{1}{2}(q_1 + q_2) = 0. \qquad \textbf{9.5-15}$$

On adding and subtracting these equations, they become

$$m\ddot{q}_1 + k'q_1 = 0, \qquad m\ddot{q}_2 + (2k + k')q_2 = 0. \qquad \textbf{9.5-16}$$

In this form, the equations of motion reduce to two separated or *uncoupled* equations of the simple harmonic form. Coordinates q_1 and q_2, which accomplish this separation, are known as *principal coordinates.*★

The two natural modes of vibration of the system expressed in terms of the principal coordinates are called *principal modes of oscillation*. In a principal mode of oscillation, only one principal coordinate changes with time, the rest vanishing identically. For our example, the first principal mode is given by the simple harmonic motion solution to the first of 9.5-16, whereas q_2 vanishes:

$$q_1 = C_1 \cos(\omega_1 t - \alpha_1), \qquad q_2 = 0. \qquad \textbf{9.5-17a}$$

Similarly, the second principal mode is

$$q_1 = 0, \qquad q_2 = C_2 \cos(\omega_2 t - \alpha_2), \qquad \textbf{9.5-17b}$$

whereas the general solution for arbitrary initial conditions is a superposition of these two:

$$q_1 = C_1 \cos(\omega_1 t - \alpha_1), \qquad q_2 = C_2 \cos(\omega_2 t - \alpha_2).$$
$$\textbf{9.5-17c}$$

Substitution of 9.5-17a in Eqs. 9.5-14 returns the first mode 9.5-11b in terms of x_1 and x_2, as the student may verify, with $A_1^{(1)} = \frac{1}{2}C_1$. Evaluation of the constants of integration C_1, C_2, α_1, and α_2 follows from the initial conditions.

★ The symbol q is reserved in the rest of this section for principal coordinates, whereas x is used for generalized coordinates which are not necessarily principal ones. In Sections 8.4, 8.5, q was used in the sense that x is used here. Also, note that the x's and q's do not in general have dimensions of length. They may be angular, as well as point position, coordinates; or, as in 9.5-18, 21 below, have more unusual dimensional properties.

In general, for a system having n degrees of freedom, the n principal coordinates are given by the expressions

$$q_r = \sum_{i=1}^{n} A_i^{(r)} m_i x_i \text{ for } r = 1, 2, \ldots n. \qquad \textbf{9.5-18}$$

In the present example, $n=2$, $m_1 = m_2 = m$, $A_1^{(1)} = A_2^{(1)}$, and $A_1^{(2)} = -A_2^{(2)}$ so that

$$q_1 = A_1^{(1)} m(x_1 + x_2), \qquad q_2 = A_1^{(2)} m(x_1 - x_2). \qquad \textbf{9.5-19}$$

These are the same as the expressions 9.5-13 previously obtained, except that the factor 1/2 is replaced by the factors $mA_1^{(1)}$ and $mA_1^{(2)}$. But a factor can be canceled without affecting the separation property of the principal coordinates, so that this difference is immaterial. It is, in fact, customary to give the factor a value such that the sum of the terms $m_i(A_i^{(r)})^2$ has a standard value, usually either unity or the total inertia. In other words, we make

$$\sum_{i=1}^{n} m_i(A_i^{(r)})^2 = 1 \text{ for } r = 1, 2, \ldots n. \qquad \textbf{9.5-20}$$

This is known as a *normalizing condition*. In the present example, the normalizing conditions require that

$$(A_1^{(1)})^2 m + (A_2^{(1)})^2 m = 1,$$

$$(A_1^{(2)})^2 m + (A_2^{(2)})^2 m = 1. \qquad \textbf{9.5-21}$$

Since $A_2^{(1)} = A_1^{(1)}$ and $A_1^{(2)} = -A_2^{(2)}$, these conditions yield the values $A_1^{(1)} = A_1^{(2)} = 1/\sqrt{2m}$. On inserting these values in 9.5-18, we get the so-called *normal coordinates* q_1^* and q_2^*:

$$q_1^* = (\sqrt{m/2})(x_1 + x_2), \qquad q_2^* = (\sqrt{m/2})(x_1 - x_2). \qquad \textbf{9.5-22}$$

These normal coordinates are simply a particular set of principal coordinates. When we substitute $x_1 = (q_1^* + q_2^*)/\sqrt{2m}$ and $x_2 = (q_1^* - q_2^*)/\sqrt{2m}$ into the equations of motion, the variables separate, exactly as before, and we get the equations

$$\ddot{q}_1^* + \omega_1^2 q_1^* = 0, \qquad \ddot{q}_2^* + \omega_2^2 q_2^* = 0. \qquad \textbf{9.5-23}$$

Of course, if we want to know the position of the system at any time we must solve these equations and use the initial conditions to determine the value of each of q_1^*, q_2^*, $\dot{q}_1^*$, and $\dot{q}_2^*$ at time zero.

The discussion thus far has been limited to free vibrations of a conservative linear system about a position of stable equilibrium.

If a disturbing force is present, it profoundly alters the motion, but with the aid of principal coordinates the analysis is easily effected. Suppose that a force $P_1(t)$ acts on the mass m_1 of Fig. 9.5-1. Then this force appears in the free-body diagram and in the equations of motion, which now read

$$m\ddot{x}_1 + (k + k')x_1 - kx_2 = P_1(t),$$

$$m\ddot{x}_2 - kx_1 + (k + k')x_2 = 0. \qquad \textbf{9.5-24}$$

When the principal coordinates q_1, q_2 defined by 9.5-13 are introduced, they affect only the left-hand side of 9.5-24. The equations of motion are again separable. If we make the substitution and then first add, then subtract the two equations, we get Eqs. 9.5-16 once more—now, however, modified by exciting-force terms on the right-hand side.

$$m\ddot{q}_1 + k'q_1 = P_1(t),$$

$$m\ddot{q} + (2k + k')q_2 = P_1(t). \qquad \textbf{9.5-25}$$

Each of these equations is of the form whose solution has been studied in detail in Sections 9.2-3, 4 in connection with the single-degree-of-freedom system. With the aid of Eq. 9.3-8, the complete solution may be written down at once. In fact, the justification for studying the single-degree-of-freedom system lies in the fact that with the aid of principal coordinates a multi-degree-of-freedom system is broken down into a set of systems each of this simple kind.

When $P_1(t)$ is of the form $F_0 \cos pt$, it is unncessary to carry out the separation into principal modes. The steady-state forced response, which is of primary interest, will then be of the form $x_1 = A_1 \cos pt$, $x_2 = A_2 \cos pt$, and when these expressions for x_1, x_2, and $P_1(t)$ are substituted in 9.5-24, we have, after canceling the common factor $\cos pt$,

$$[(k + k') - mp^2]A_1 - kA_2 = F_0,$$

$$-kA_1 + [(k + k') - mp^2]A_2 = 0. \qquad \textbf{9.5-26}$$

These equations are easily solved for A_1 and A_2:

$$A_1 = F_0 \frac{(k + k') - mp^2}{[mp^2 - k'][mp^2 - (2k + k')]},$$

$$A_2 = F_0 \frac{k}{[mp^2 - k'][mp^2 - (2k + k')]}. \qquad \textbf{9.5-27}$$

We notice that, if p^2 has either of the values ω_1^2 or ω_2^2 given by Eq. 9.5-8, the denominator in these expressions will vanish, implying that the amplitude of the excited motion increases without limit. There are two resonant frequencies corresponding to the cases in which the exciting frequency coincides with either of the two natural frequencies. It is also interesting to note that A_1 will vanish if

$$p^2 = \frac{k+k'}{m}.$$ **9.5-28**

At this frequency, $x_1 = 0$ even though the force is acting at m_1. All the energy of the disturbing force is being used to excite m_2. We say that m_2 is acting as a *dynamic vibration absorber*.

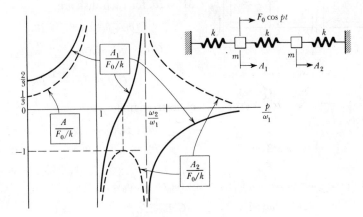

Fig. 9.5-2

The expressions 9.5-27 can be put in a form suitable for the construction of an amplification factor diagram.

$$\frac{A_1}{F_0/k} = \frac{(k/k')[(k+k')/k' - (p^2/\omega_1^2)]}{[1 - (p^2/\omega_1^2)][(\omega_2^2/\omega_1^2) - (p^2/\omega_1^2)]},$$

$$\frac{A_2}{F_0/k} = \frac{(k/k')^2}{[1 - (p^2/\omega_1^2)][(\omega_2^2/\omega_1^2) - (p^2/\omega_1^2)]}.$$ **9.5-29**

The quantities A_1 and A_2 are the amplitudes of the displacements of masses m_1 and m_2. In Fig. 9.5-2, they are plotted in dimensionless form for the case $k = k'$, $\omega_2^2/\omega_1^2 = 3$. We note that there is a phase change of 180 degrees in each displacement as p passes through a resonance frequency. The vibration absorbing frequency is the one at which $A_1 = 0$. In industrial practice, this diagram is often plotted so as to show the magnitudes of the amplitudes only, without regard to sign.

Example **9.5-1**

A shaft carries three equidistant sets of gears of polar moments of inertia I, I, $\frac{1}{2}I$ as shown in Fig. 9.5-3. The stiffness of a length l of the shaft is C in-lb per radian. Find the natural frequencies and the shapes of the principal modes of vibration.

Solution: We take as coordinates the rotation angles θ_1, θ_2, θ_3 of the three gears, measuring θ in a clockwise direction as viewed from the free end of the shaft. Then the free-body diagram of the displaced disks is as shown in Fig. 9.5-3. Remembering that clockwise, as viewed from the free end, is positive, the equations of motion, $M^* = I\ddot{\theta}$, for each disk are

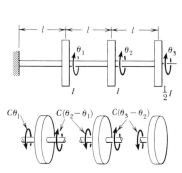

Fig. 9.5-3

$$C(\theta_2 - \theta_1) - C\theta_1 = I\ddot{\theta}_1,$$

$$C(\theta_3 - \theta_2) - C(\theta_2 - \theta_1) = I\ddot{\theta}_2,$$

$$-C(\theta_3 - \theta_2) = \frac{1}{2}I\ddot{\theta}_3.$$

or, rearranging,

$$I\ddot{\theta}_1 + 2C\theta_1 - C\theta_2 = 0,$$

$$I\ddot{\theta}_2 - C\theta_1 + 2C\theta_2 - C\theta_3 = 0,$$

$$\tfrac{1}{2}I\ddot{\theta}_3 - C\theta_2 + C\theta_3 = 0.$$

Let $\theta_1 = A_1 \cos(\omega_n t - \alpha)$, $\theta_2 = A_2 \cos(\omega_n t - \alpha)$, $\theta_3 = A_3 \cos(\omega_n t - \alpha)$. Then

$$(2C - I\omega_n^2)A_1 - CA_2 = 0,$$

$$-CA_1 + (2C - I\omega_n^2)A_2 - CA_3 = 0, \qquad \textbf{9.5-30}$$

$$-CA_2 + \left(C - \frac{1}{2}I\omega_n^2\right)A_3 = 0.$$

To simplify the notation, let $I\omega_n^2/C = \lambda$. The frequency equation is found by setting the determinant of the coefficients in the foregoing set of simultaneous equations equal to zero:

$$\begin{vmatrix} (2-\lambda) & -1 & 0 \\ -1 & (2-\lambda) & -1 \\ 0 & -1 & \left(1 - \dfrac{\lambda}{2}\right) \end{vmatrix} = 0,$$

$$(2-\lambda)(2-\lambda)\left(1 - \frac{\lambda}{2}\right) - (2-\lambda) - \left(1 - \frac{\lambda}{2}\right) = 0,$$

$$\lambda^3 - 6\lambda^2 + 9\lambda - 2 = 0.$$

The three roots of this equation are

$$\lambda_1 = 2 - \sqrt{3}, \qquad \lambda_2 = 2, \qquad \lambda_3 = 2 + \sqrt{3};$$

therefore,

$$\omega_1^2 = (2-\sqrt{3})\frac{C}{I}, \qquad \omega_2^2 = 2\frac{C}{I}, \qquad \omega_3^2 = (2+\sqrt{3})\frac{C}{I}.$$

These are the three natural frequencies. It is simplest now to express A_1 in terms of A_2 through the first of Eqs. 9.5-30 and A_3 in terms of A_2 through the third of Eqs. 9.5-30.

$$A_1^{(1)} = A_2^{(1)}\frac{C}{2C-I\omega_1^2} = \frac{I}{\sqrt{3}}A_2^{(1)},$$

$$A_3^{(1)} = A_2^{(1)}\frac{C}{C-\frac{I}{2}I\omega_1^2} = \frac{2}{\sqrt{3}}A_2^{(1)}.$$

In the second mode, $I\omega_2^2=2C$. Referring to either the first or third of Eqs. 9.5-30, we see that $A_2=0$ in this mode. The second of Eqs. 9.5-30 then makes $A_1^{(2)}=-A_3^{(2)}$. In this mode, the middle gear is motionless while the two outer ones oscillate through equal angles, 180 degrees out of phase. In the third mode,

$$A_1^{(3)} = \frac{-I}{\sqrt{3}}A_2^{(3)} \quad \text{and} \quad A_3^{(3)} = \frac{-2}{\sqrt{3}}A_2^{(3)}.$$

The solution of the equations of motion is

$$\theta_1 = \frac{I}{\sqrt{3}}A_2^{(1)}\cos(\omega_1 t-\alpha_1)+A_1^{(2)}\cos(\omega_2 t-\alpha_2)-\frac{I}{\sqrt{3}}A_2^{(3)}\cos(\omega_3 t-\alpha_3),$$

$$\theta_2 = \qquad A_2^{(1)}\cos(\omega_1 t-\alpha_1) \qquad\qquad + \qquad A_2^{(3)}\cos(\omega_3 t-\alpha_3),$$

$$\theta_3 = \frac{2}{\sqrt{3}}A_2^{(1)}\cos(\omega_1 t-\alpha_1)-A_1^{(2)}\cos(\omega_2 t-\alpha_2)-\frac{2}{\sqrt{3}}A_2^{(3)}\cos(\omega_3 t-\alpha_3).$$

The principal coordinates are

$$q_1 = A_1^{(1)}I\theta_1+A_2^{(1)}I\theta_2+A_3^{(1)}\frac{I}{2}I\theta_3$$

$$= A_2^{(1)}I\left(\frac{I}{\sqrt{3}}\theta_1+\theta_2+\frac{I}{\sqrt{3}}\theta_3\right),$$

$$q_2 = A_1^{(2)}I\theta_1+A_2^{(2)}I\theta_2+A_3^{(2)}\frac{I}{2}I\theta_3$$

$$= A_1^{(2)}I\left(\theta_1-\frac{I}{2}\theta_3\right),$$

$$q_3 = A_1^{(3)}I\theta_1+A_2^{(3)}I\theta_2+A_3^{(3)}\frac{I}{2}I\theta_3$$

$$= A_2^{(3)}I\left(-\frac{I}{\sqrt{3}}\theta_1+\theta_2-\frac{I}{\sqrt{3}}\theta_3\right).$$

The normalizing conditions are

$$(A_1^{(1)})^2 I + (A_2^{(1)})^2 I + (A_3^{(1)})^2 \frac{I}{2} I = \mathrm{I},$$

$$(A_2^{(1)})^2 \left(\frac{\mathrm{I}}{3} + \mathrm{I} + \frac{2}{3} \right) = \frac{\mathrm{I}}{I}, \qquad A_2^{(1)} = \frac{\mathrm{I}}{\sqrt{2I}};$$

and

$$(A_1^{(2)})^2 I + (A_2^{(2)})^2 I + (A_3^{(2)})^2 \frac{I}{2} I = \mathrm{I},$$

$$(A_1^{(2)})^2 \left(\mathrm{I} + 0 + \frac{\mathrm{I}}{2} \right) = \frac{\mathrm{I}}{I}, \qquad A_1^{(2)} = \sqrt{\frac{2}{3I}};$$

and

$$(A_1^{(3)})^2 I + (A_2^{(3)})^2 I + (A_3^{(3)})^2 \frac{I}{2} I = \mathrm{I},$$

$$(A_2^{(3)})^2 \left(\frac{\mathrm{I}}{3} + \mathrm{I} + \frac{2}{3} \right) = \frac{\mathrm{I}}{I}, \qquad A_2^{(3)} = \frac{\mathrm{I}}{\sqrt{2I}};$$

so that the normal coordinates are

$$q_1^* = \sqrt{\frac{I}{2}} \left(\frac{\mathrm{I}}{\sqrt{3}} \theta_1 + \theta_2 + \frac{\mathrm{I}}{\sqrt{3}} \theta_3 \right),$$

$$q_2^* = \sqrt{\frac{2I}{3}} \left(\theta_1 - \frac{\mathrm{I}}{2} \theta_3 \right),$$

$$q_3^* = \sqrt{\frac{I}{2}} \left(-\frac{\mathrm{I}}{\sqrt{3}} \theta_1 + \theta_2 - \frac{\mathrm{I}}{\sqrt{3}} \theta_3 \right).$$

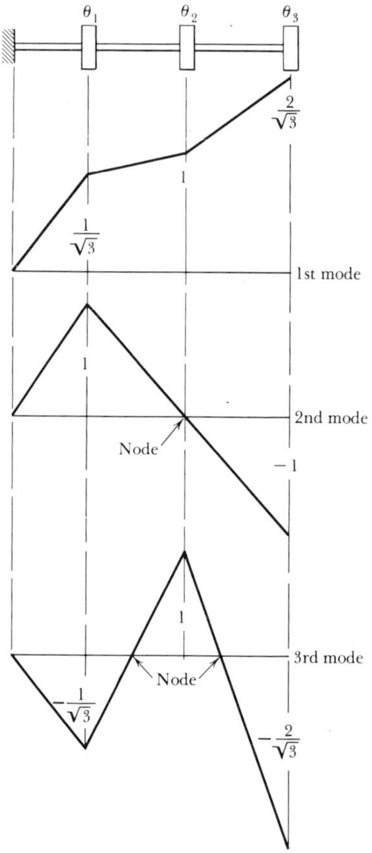

Fig. 9.5-4

The relative displacement amplitudes θ_1, θ_2, θ_3 corresponding to the three modes of free vibration are pictured in Fig. 9.5-4. We note that certain points have zero displacement: these points are called *nodes*. The *fundamental* or lowest-frequency mode has no interior nodes, the second has one (at the middle disk), and the third has two interior nodes. It is perhaps unnecessary to remark that in practice the left-hand end of the shaft is not usually held fixed. It is attached to a massive rotor and θ_1, θ_2, θ_3 are simply measured from the angular position of the left-hand end of the shaft. The analysis shows that the shaft ought not to be operated at certain critical speeds.

Example **9.5-2**

Show that, if the frequency determinant is symmetrical about the main diagonal, the coefficients of the principal modes satisfy the relation

$$\sum_{i=1}^{n} m_i A_i^{(p)} A_i^{(s)} = 0, \qquad p \neq s.$$

Solution: When ω_n is set equal to one of its possible values, say ω_p, the simultaneous equations that determine the principal mode coefficients are of the typical form

$$m_i \omega_p^2 A_i^{(p)} = k_{i1} A_1^{(p)} + k_{i2} A_2^{(p)} + \ldots + k_{in} A_n^{(p)} \qquad \textbf{9.5-31}$$

where i is any one of the integers $1, 2, 3, \ldots n$. When another natural frequency, say ω_s, is substituted for ω_n, they are

$$m_i \omega_s^2 A_i^{(s)} = k_{i1} A_1^{(s)} + k_{i2} A_2^{(s)} + \ldots + k_{in} A_n^{(s)} \qquad \textbf{9.5-32}$$

also for $i = 1, 2, \ldots n$. Since the frequency determinant is symmetric, $k_{ij} = k_{ji}$. Now multiply 9.5-31 by $A_i^{(s)}$ and 9.5-32 by $A_i^{(p)}$. Then we have

$$m_i \omega_p^2 A_i^{(p)} A_i^{(s)} = k_{i1} A_1^{(p)} A_i^{(s)} + k_{i2} A_2^{(p)} A_i^{(s)} + \ldots + k_{in} A_n^{(p)} A_i^{(s)},$$

$$m_i \omega_s^2 A_i^{(s)} A_i^{(p)} = k_{i1} A_1^{(s)} A_i^{(p)} + k_{i2} A_2^{(s)} A_i^{(p)} + \ldots + k_{in} A_n^{(s)} A_i^{(p)}.$$

We can write these equations more succinctly by the use of a summation symbol:

$$m_i \omega_p^2 A_i^{(p)} A_i^{(s)} = \sum_{j=1}^{n} k_{ij} A_j^{(p)} A_i^{(s)}, \qquad \textbf{9.5-33}$$

$$m_i \omega_s^2 A_i^{(s)} A_i^{(p)} = \sum_{j=1}^{n} k_{ij} A_j^{(s)} A_i^{(p)}. \qquad \textbf{9.5-34}$$

In these equations, i may have any of the values $1, 2, 3, \ldots n$ corresponding to the n equations of motion. Suppose we add all n equations of the type 9.5-33 and all n equations of the type 9.5-34. Then we have

$$\omega_p^2 \sum_{i=1}^{n} m_i A_i^{(p)} A_i^{(s)} = \sum_{i=1}^{n} \sum_{j=1}^{n} k_{ij} A_j^{(p)} A_i^{(s)}, \qquad \textbf{9.5-35}$$

$$\omega_s^2 \sum_{i=1}^{n} m_i A_i^{(p)} A_i^{(s)} = \sum_{i=1}^{n} \sum_{j=1}^{n} k_{ij} A_j^{(s)} A_i^{(p)}. \qquad \textbf{9.5-36}$$

The right-hand sides of 9.5-35 and 9.5-36 are identical. To show this, note that, since i and j are now simply indices that take on the values $1, 2, \ldots n$, we may interchange them in the double sum:

$$\sum_{i=1}^{n} \sum_{j=1}^{n} k_{ij} A_j^{(p)} A_i^{(s)} = \sum_{j=1}^{n} \sum_{i=1}^{n} k_{ji} A_i^{(p)} A_j^{(s)} = \sum_{j=1}^{n} \sum_{i=1}^{n} k_{ij} A_i^{(s)} A_j^{(p)}.$$

In the last step, we make use of the fact that $k_{ij} = k_{ji}$. Since the right-hand sides of 9.5-35, 36 are identical, we find when we subtract one from the other that

$$(\omega_p^2 - \omega_s^2) \sum_{i=1}^{n} m_i A_i^{(p)} A_i^{(s)} = 0,$$

and, since ω_p and ω_s are two different natural frequencies,[*] it follows at once that $(\omega_p^2 - \omega_s^2)$ is not zero and therefore that

$$\sum_{i=1}^{n} m_i A_i^{(p)} A_i^{(s)} = 0.$$

This type of relation is known as an *orthogonality relation*, and we say that *the principal modes of oscillation are orthogonal.* It should be borne in mind that the proof of orthogonality is based upon the symmetry of the frequency determinant and that this will hold, in general, only for a conservative mechanical system executing small vibrations about a position of stable static equilibrium. If gyroscopic effects or electromagnetic coupling are present, the frequency determinant may not be symmetrical.

The orthogonality of the principal modes is borne out by the preceding example. There $m_1 = I$, $m_2 = I$, $m_3 = I/2$. Comparing the first and second modes as shown in Fig. 9.5-4, we have

$$\left(\frac{I}{\sqrt{3}}\right)(I)I + (I)(0)I + \left(\frac{2}{\sqrt{3}}\right)(-I)\frac{I}{2}I = 0,$$

and, comparing the first and third modes, we have

$$\left(\frac{I}{\sqrt{3}}\right)\left(\frac{-I}{\sqrt{3}}\right)I + (I)(I)I + \left(\frac{2}{\sqrt{3}}\right)\left(\frac{-2}{\sqrt{3}}\right)\frac{I}{2}I = 0.$$

The student may make the comparison for modes two and three. The orthogonality property of the principal modes is more than a convenient check on the calculation of natural frequencies. It is of great value in numerical (approximate) methods of vibration analysis.

Example **9.5-3**

Design a dynamic vibration absorber for a machine operating at 1200 *rpm and subject to an oscillating force of amplitude* 600 *lb, due to imperfect balancing.*

Solution: The machine (m_1) on its spring foundation (k_1) is represented by the idealized model shown in Fig. 9.5-5. The problem is that of so selecting m_2 and k_2 that the amplitude of x_1 is zero. Since x_1, x_2 are measured from positions of static equilibrium, their weights will be balanced

---

[*] The frequency equation may have multiple roots, for which the mode shapes are ill-defined. However, it is still possible to construct corresponding orthogonal mode shapes, equal in number to the multiplicity of the root.

by the initial compressions in the springs. The free-body diagrams are as shown in Fig. 9.5-5. The equations of motion are

$$F_0 \cos pt + k_2(x_2 - x_1) + k_1 x_1 = m_1 \ddot{x}_1,$$

$$-k_2(x_2 - x_1) = m_2 \ddot{x}_2.$$

Set $x_2 = A_2 \cos pt$, $x_1 = A_1 \cos pt$ to find the steady-state motion. Then

$$[(k_2 - k_1) - m_1 p^2] A_1 - k_2 A_2 = F_0,$$

$$-k_2 A_1 + [k_2 - m_2 p^2] A_2 = 0.$$

We see at once from the second of these that $A_1 = 0$ if $k_2 = m_2 p^2$. This is the relation that governs the design. Since the large mass is to be stationary, the small one, m_2, must be "tuned" so that its natural frequency will be p. We have, with $p = 1200$ rpm $= 126$ rad/sec,

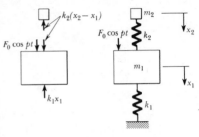

$$k_2 = (126)^2 m_2,$$

and this leaves some freedom in design. Clearly we want the added damper to be small; say we limit its weight to 32.2 lb. Then $m_2 = 1$ and $k_2 = 15,800$ lb/ft $= 1320$ lb/in. We also want the amplitude of the motion of the damper

Fig. 9.5-5

to be small, although to some extent these desires conflict. In the present case, with $A_1 = 0$,

$$|A_2| = \frac{F_0}{k_2} = \frac{600}{1320} = 0.45 \text{ in.}$$

9.6 The Analogies between Electrical and Mechanical Vibrations

Even when we ignore the complexities associated with nonlinear behavior, the amount of arithmetic drudgery entailed by the complete vibration analysis of a mechanical system of modest complexity is dismaying. Fortunately, high-speed analog and digital computers perform these mathematical operations rapidly, once the equations of motion have been written down. In recent years, too, much progress has been made in the efficient arrangement of the calculations through use of the notation of matrix algebra. There remains the problem of synthesis; that is, of selecting components so as to produce a desired over-all performance. The analogies between electrical and mechanical systems provide some insight into the handling of this problem. They enhance our understanding of the behavior of mechanical systems and so permit the extension to mechanics of some of the theorems of circuit analysis.

In its classical form, the analogy may be explained by reference to the simple system and circuit of Fig. 9.6-1. Newton's second law asserts that the resultant force acting on the mass m is equal to the product $m\ddot{x}$; Kirchhoff's second law asserts that the sum of the voltage drops iR, $L(di/dt)$, $C^{-1}\int^{t} i(\tau)\,d\tau$, around any closed loop of an electric circuit is equal to the applied electromotive force in the loop. In symbols,

$$m\ddot{x}+c\dot{x}+kx = P(t), \qquad L\frac{di}{dt}+Ri+C^{-1}\int^{t} i(\tau)\,d\tau = e(t). \qquad \textbf{9.6-1}$$

The notation is conventional: L, R, C denote inductance, resistance, and capacitance respectively; $i(t)$ and $e(t)$ denote current and voltage respec-

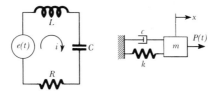

Fig. 9.6-1

tively. If we introduce the velocity $v=\dot{x}$, the first of these equations may be written

$$m\dot{v}+cv+k\int^{t} v(\tau)\,d\tau = P(t). \qquad \textbf{9.6-2}$$

This change of dependent variable brings the equation of motion into exactly the same mathematical form as the circuit equation. Alternatively, we can bring the second of Eqs. 9.6-1 into correspondence with the first by introducing the charge $q(t)$. Since $i=\dot{q}$, the second of 9.6-1 then becomes

$$L\ddot{q}+R\dot{q}+C^{-1}q = e(t), \qquad \textbf{9.6-3}$$

which is of the same mathematical form as the first of 9.6-1. The mathematical equivalence of these forms implies that there is an analogy between the electrical and mechanical systems in which self-inductance of the circuit corresponds to the inertia of the vibrator, resistance of the circuit corresponds to damping, and the reciprocal of capacitance corresponds to stiffness. The analogy is, in fact, complete. The velocity of the mass corresponds to current, i, so that momentum, mv, corresponds to Li. Even if there is no impressed electromotive force, a current, once established, will flow until all this "momentum" has been expended in overcoming resistance and charging the condenser. Correspondingly, if we give the mass, m, an initial velocity, it will move until brought to rest by extension of the spring and damper. Then it moves back as the spring contracts.   Similarly, after the current in the electrical circuit has momentarily ceased flowing, the condenser discharges, and a current flows in the opposite sense.   The potential energy of the spring is $\frac{1}{2}kx^2$; that of the condenser is $\frac{1}{2}C^{-1}q^2$.   The kinetic energy of the mass is $\frac{1}{2}mv^2$; the magnetic energy of the inductance is $\frac{1}{2}Li^2$.   The frequency of free vibration of a damped mechanical system has been found to be $\omega_n\sqrt{1-\zeta^2}$.   With $\omega_n = \sqrt{k/m}$ and $\zeta = c/2\sqrt{mk}$, we replace m by L, k by C^{-1}, c by R to get the natural frequency of the electrical circuit as $[(LC)^{-1}-(R^2/4L^2)]^{1/2}$.   What the electrical engineer calls the "Q" of the circuit corresponds to $1/(2\zeta)$, the amplitude of the resonance curve at $p=\omega_n$, and so on.   Of course, if the analogy were to be employed in a sort of experiment in which an actual electrical system were fabricated, it would be necessary to put the dependent and independent variables of Eq. 9.6-1 in dimensionless form and then to choose the electrical components so as to have the numerical values of the coefficients in the two equations match.   This usually involves making the forcing frequency in the electrical "model" higher than that of the mechanical system so that the values of L, C, and R will be in the range of

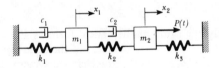

Fig. 9.6-2

components readily available commercially.   The main function of the analogy, however, is not the construction of actual electrical models.

Consider now the mechanical system shown in Fig. 9.6-2.   It has two degrees of freedom; hence its electrical analog must have two loops. We therefore begin the construction of an analogous electrical circuit by drawing a two-loop network as shown in Fig. 9.6-3a.   The equation $F_1=m_1\ddot{x}_1$ is to be "modeled" by the loop *ABEF*.   The inductance L_1 corresponding to the mass m_1 must be placed in the outer arm of this loop, as shown in Fig. 9.6-3b, because $\ddot{x}_1$ is an absolute acceleration and does not depend on the relative motions of m_1 and m_2.   Similarly, R_1 and C_1—since they correspond to c_1 and k_1, which are associated with forces that depend on x_1 (and not on x_2)—must be placed in this outer arm.   For like reasons, the inductance L_2, condenser C_3, and voltage generator $e(t)$ must be placed in the outer arm of the loop *BCDE*.   On the other hand, the force associated with the damper c_2 depends upon the velocity difference $\dot{x}_2-\dot{x}_1$, and the force exerted by the spring k_2 depends upon the displacement difference x_2-x_1; we therefore place the corresponding elements R_2 and C_2 in the common branch *BE*.   The complete circuit is shown in Fig. 9.6-3b.   The method may be extended to mechanical systems having any finite number of

degrees of freedom.   The analogous electrical circuit then provides a certain
insight into the behavior of the mechanical system.   Take, for example,
the case in which $P(t)$ is a periodic force so that $e(t)$ is an alternating
voltage.   If the impedance* of the circuit $ABEF$ is made low at the frequency of this voltage, relatively little current will flow in the loop $BCDE$.
In the equivalent mechanical circuit, the mass m_1 is acting as a dynamic
vibration absorber.   We see, however, that it cannot be completely
effective as such so long as c_1 and c_2 are different from zero because these
correspond to R_1 and R_2, which prevent the electrical impedance of the
loop $ABEF$ from vanishing.

Instead of making the comparison on the basis of Kirchhoff's second
law, it is possible to make it on the basis of the first.   Just as the forces
acting on a mass element, less the quantity $m\ddot{x}$, must add to zero so must
the currents at any junction in an electrical circuit.   This correspondence
is illustrated for the single-degree-of-freedom system by Fig. 9.6-4.   The
generator supplies a current, $i(t)$, to a junction, J, whence it flows to ground
through a resistance, inductance, and capacitance placed in parallel.
According to Kirchhoff's first law,

$$i(t) = C\frac{de}{dt} + \frac{1}{R}e + \frac{1}{L}\int^t e(\tau)\,d\tau. \qquad \textbf{9.6-4}$$

This is in precisely the same mathematical form as Eq. 9.6-2, which is a

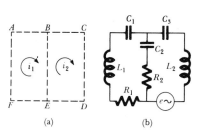

(a)   (b)

Fig. 9.6-3

form of the equation of motion of the
mechanical system.   In the electrical
circuit, current (i) corresponds to
force (P).   For this reason, this
analogy is sometimes known as the
force-current or "mobility" analogy.
This analogy has certain advantages
over the force-voltage analogy,
which become apparent when we
construct the circuit corresponding to
the mechanical system of Fig. 9.6-2.
Since there are two degrees of
freedom, the electrical diagram is
begun by drawing two junction points labeled *1* and *2* in Fig. 9.6-5.
Current flows into junction *2* from a current generator and to ground
through a capacitance C_2 and inductance L_3, which correspond to the
mass m_2 and spring k_3 respectively.   Current also flows out of junction *1*
through a capacitor C_1, resistance R_1, and inductance L_1, which correspond
to the mass m_1, damper c_1, and spring k_1 respectively.   The two junc-

---

* The impedance of a section of an electric circuit is the voltage drop
required to cause unit current to flow in that section.   For alternating-
current circuits, impedance plays the same role as resistance in a direct-
current circuit.

tions are connected by a resistance and inductance in parallel. These correspond to the damper and spring connecting m_1 and m_2. It may be seen that the circuit diagram of Fig. 9.6-5 is topologically similar to the idealized mechanical system diagram of Fig. 9.6-2. Because the two

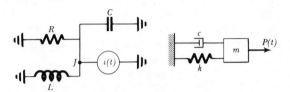

Fig. 9.6-4

figures to some extent resemble each other in appearance, it is easier to avoid errors in constructing the force-current analog than in constructing the force-voltage analog in which each mass corresponds to a loop of the electric circuit.

The analogies that have been described serve equally well when the mechanical system is nonlinear, provided corresponding nonlinear electric circuit elements can be employed. This is sometimes the case; for example, an iron-core coil that becomes saturated can be used to simulate a hardening spring in the force-current analogy. More often, however, when nonlinear equations of motion are encountered the engineer turns to a so-called "active network" or "electronic analog computer." These are devices for the solution of ordinary differential equations (differential analyzers).. All the variables are represented by voltages, and the computer carries out the integration, differentiation, multiplication, and addition of these quantities as well as generating the nonlinear, variable parameter

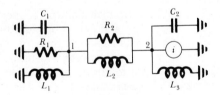

Fig. 9.6-5

relations required. The basic element and characteristic feature of such computers is the high-gain direct-coupled amplifier stabilized by negative feedback. A complete description of these commercial devices for solving differential equations is, however, outside the scope of our present interests.

Exercises

9.2-1: The left-hand figure shown represents a landing gear assembly: tire, springs, and shock absorber. It may be idealized to the mechanical system pictured on the right. The displacement x is measured from the position of static equilibrium; i.e., the upper spring is stretched a length mg/k_1 when $x = 0$. The spring k_2 is unstretched when x and x_2 are both zero.

(a) Write the equation of motion of the mass, assuming the lower end of the spring to be undergoing a displacement $x_2 = f(t)$.

(b) What is the undamped natural frequency?

(c) To design the shock absorber properly, one must know the critical damping of the system. Find an expression for the fraction of critical damping present in terms of m, k_1, k_2, and c.

Ans.: (a) $m\ddot{x} + c\dot{x} + (k_1 + k_2)x = k_2 f(t)$,   (c) $\zeta = [c^2/4m(k_1 + k_2)]^{1/2}$.

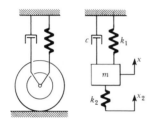

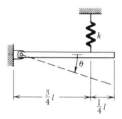

Exer. 9.2-1   Exer. 9.2-2

9.2-2: The uniform bar shown has a mass m and length l. The system moves in a horizontal plane. In the position shown the bar is in equilibrium with the spring unstretched. Show that, if the bar is displaced through a small angle θ_0 and then released, the equation of motion will correspond to simple harmonic motion. Derive an expression for the period, T_n.

Ans.: $T_n = (8\pi/3)(m/3k)^{1/2}$.

9.2-3: An inextensible cable passes over a pulley of diameter 1 ft and

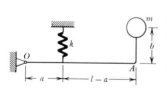

centroidal moment of inertia 4.0 lb-ft-sec². It is attached at one end to a 300-lb weight that hangs freely. At the other end, a 200-lb weight is attached. A spring, $k = 30$ lb/ft, is fastened to the 200-lb weight and extends vertically downward to a fixed point. What is the natural frequency of the system?

9.2-4: Derive the equation governing small free vibrations of the system shown, using the angle between the horizontal and the bar OA as co-ordinate. Neglect the inertia of the L-shaped bar, and assume that in static equilibrium OA is horizontal.

Ans.: $m(l^2 + b^2)\ddot{\theta} + (ka^2 - mgb)\theta = 0$.

9.2-5: The coefficient of friction between the disk and the horizontal surface is sufficient to prevent slipping. Find an expression for the natural period of vibration of the system. What value of c will produce critical damping? **Ans.:** $T_n = 2\pi(3m/2k)^{1/2}$; $c_{cr} = (6km)^{1/2}$.

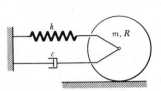

9.2-6: A structural element weighing 20 lb is set into free translational vibration. The amplitude is observed to decay from 0.40 to 0.10 in. in 20 cycles. If the stiffness of the member is 40 lb/in, (a) what is the logarithmic decrement? (b) What is the percentage of critical damping present? (c) What is the damping constant, c, in lb-sec/in? Assume viscous damping.

Ans.: Log. dec. $= 0.0693$, $\zeta = 0.0110$, $c = 0.0317$ lb-sec/in.

9.2-7: An accelerometer with a natural frequency of 20 cps is used to measure the motion of a structure that vibrates at 10 cps. If we turn the accelerometer upside down, the record deflects one inch. This means that an acceleration of $(2)(32.2)$ ft/sec² corresponds to a deflection of 1.0 in. When vibrating at 10 cps on the structure, the record amplitude is 0.20 in. The damping in this instrument is 20% of critical damping. What is the actual amplitude of the acceleration of the structure? **Ans.:** 10.0ft/sec².

9.2-8: The record shown is part of the decay curve of the free vibration of a structural element. Estimate the fraction of critical damping present.

9.2-9: One way of measuring the viscosity of a fluid (due to Coulomb) is to suspend a square plate of side A and mass m from a spring in such a way that the plane of the plate is vertical and then to allow the plate to oscillate freely up and down first in air and then immersed in the fluid. Coulomb assumed that the damping in air was negligible, and that the viscous resistance to motion when immersed was $-2A^2\mu\dot{x}$. Derive his formula for μ as a function of the observed period in air, T_1, and the observed period, T_2, when vibrating in the fluid.

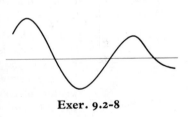

Exer. 9.2-8

Ans.: $\mu = (2\pi m/A^2)(T_1^{-2} - T_2^{-2})^{1/2}$.

9.3-1: A mass m hangs from a spring of stiffness k. Find the motion resulting from the application of a downward force $F_0 + a \sin pt$ to the mass initially at rest. Assume $p^2 \neq k/m$.

Ans.: $x = \dfrac{F_0}{k}(1 - \cos \omega_n t) + \dfrac{a/m}{\omega_n^2 - p^2}\left(\sin pt - \dfrac{p}{\omega_n}\sin \omega_n t\right).$

9.3-2: A railway carriage of mass m is pulled by an engine through a coupling of stiffness k. If the acceleration of the engine, $\ddot{x}_2$, is described by

the curve shown and the carriage starts from rest, find an expression for the relative displacement $x(= x_1 - x_2)$ at any time t that is greater than t_1.
Ans.: $x = (a/\omega_n^3 t_1)[\sin \omega_n t - \sin \omega_n(t - t_1)] - (a/\omega_n^2)$.

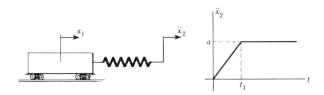

9.3-3: A damped single-degree-of-freedom system, initially at rest, is subjected to a suddenly applied force, F_0. Find the resulting motion.

9.3-4: An undamped single-degree-of-freedom system in a container, as shown, is subjected to a drop test that, in effect, makes $\ddot{x}_2$ a half sine wave pulse: $\ddot{x}_2 = -p\sqrt{2gh} \sin pt$, $0 \leq t \leq \pi/p$. Show that the maximum value of $x_1 - x_2$, during this time interval, is given by

$$\frac{\sqrt{2gh}}{\omega_n \left(\dfrac{\omega_n}{p} - 1\right)} \sin \left(\frac{2n\pi}{\dfrac{\omega_n}{p} + 1}\right)$$

where n is a positive integer chosen so as to make the sine term as large as possible while the argument remains less than π. (The result is due to Mindlin.)

Exer. 9.3-4

9.4-1: The machine shown rests on a fixed smooth pivot at O, its moment of inertia about O being I_O. The machine is excited by a force $F_0 \cos pt$. Find (a) the steady-state amplitude of the angle through which the base rotates and (b) the phase angle between the exciting force and the displacement.
Ans.: (b) $\tan \alpha = cl^2 p/(4l^2 k - p^2 I_O)$.

9.4-2: Suppose that the bar of Exercise 9.2-2 has a natural period of 0.2● sec, that $k = 100$ lb/ft, and that $l = 8$ ft. If a sinusoidal exciting force with a period of 0.15 sec and an amplitude of 10 lb acts on the right-hand end of the bar, what will be the maximum angle θ through which the bar will be displaced in the steady-state motion?
Ans.: $1/35$ radian.

9.4-3: The piston of a single-cylinder gas engine has a stroke (total horizontal motion) of 4 in. It weighs 5 lb. The engine as a whole weighs 40 lb. Normal operating speed for the engine is 720 rpm. Design a vibration-isolating mount for this machine that will meet the following specifications: (1) At normal operating speed the peak horizontal force transmitted to the support shall be 50 lb. (2) If the machine is operated at resonant speed the amplitude of the displacement shall be 0.5 in. Select the proper k and c for a horizontal mount to meet this specification.

9.4-4: The indicating pointer of a large meter weighs 0.10 lb and has a centroidal radius of gyration of 2.0 in. It is pivoted at its center of gravity. In the absence of any exciting signal, it is held at the zero position (from which it can rotate in either direction) by a spiral spring that exerts a restoring torque of 36 in-lb per radian rotation. (a) At what frequency of exciting signal will resonance occur? (b) If this instrument were calibrated by means of a constant (e.g., D.C.) signal and were then used to measure a voltage or current having a frequency of 10 cps would the reading of the meter be too high or too low, and what would be the per cent error?

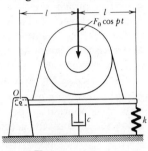

Exer. 9.4-1

Ans.: 29.6 cps; too high by 12.5%.

9.4-5: A reciprocating engine is subject to a fluctuating exciting force of constant amplitude and constant frequency, which frequency is the same as the running speed of the engine. Engine and base weigh 580 lb and are supported on a vibration-isolating mount that has a stiffness of 350 lb/in and damping equal to 25% of critical. (a) Over what speed range is the amplitude of the fluctuating force transmitted to the foundation actually larger than the excitation? (b) Over what speed range is the transmitted force amplitude less than 20% of the exciting force amplitude?

Ans.: 0–207 rpm; speeds greater than 469 rpm.

9.4-6: The amplitude of motion of a structural element subjected to a

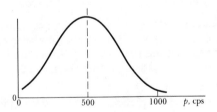

harmonic exciting force of constant peak magnitude is recorded as shown. Estimate the fraction of critical damping present.

9.4-7: A machine weighing 193 lb is supported on springs of total stiffness 200 lb/in. The motion is damped by a shock absorber with a viscous damping coefficient of 6.0 lb-sec/in. If a harmonic disturbing force with a peak magnitude of 100 lb acts on the machine at a frequency equal to the undamped natural frequency of the structure (a) what amplitude will

the motion of the machine have, and (b) how much energy will have to be dissipated each second?
Ans.: (a) 0.83 in.

9.4-8: A punch press operating at sixty strokes a minute and weighing 2000 lb is subjected to a downward force of 100 lb for 0.1 sec of each stroke. If the machine is supported on springs with a total stiffness of 2000 lb/in and a viscous damping of 100 lb per in/sec:

(a) sketch the periodic steady-state motion of the machine;
(b) what is the maximum force exerted on the floor?

9.4-9: A machine gun weighing 200 lb fires bullets weighing 0.1 lb at the rate of 6000 rounds per minute. The travel time down the barrel is 0.003 sec at constant acceleration. The fore-and-aft natural frequency of the gun is 50 cps and $c/c_{cr} = 0.2$. What is the steady-state periodic motion of the gun, what is its mean position, and what is its position and velocity at the time each bullet leaves the muzzle?

9.4-10: Calculate the steady-state amplitude of the mass m shown. What is the phase angle of the displacement with respect to the angular displacement of the yoke? $x' = R \cos pt$.

Ans.:
$$x_{max} = \frac{cR}{(c^2 + m^2 p^2)^{1/2}}, \qquad \phi = \arctan\left(\frac{c}{m\omega} - \frac{\pi}{2}\right).$$

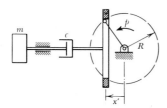

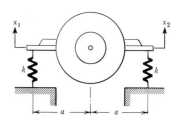

Exer. 9.4-10   Exer. 9.5-1

9.5-1: A generator of mass m and centroidal moment of inertia I is supported on identical springs, as shown. Taking the displacements x_1 and x_2 as coordinates (a) find the natural frequencies of small vibrations; (b) describe the motions in the normal modes; (c) find the normal coordinates.
Ans.: $\omega_1^2 = 2k/m$, $\quad \omega_2^2 = 2ka^2/I$.

9.5-2: One of the natural frequencies of the system shown is $\sqrt{2}$. Calculate the normal coordinate corresponding to this mode, and sketch the displacements of the three masses.
Ans.: $q^* = (\sqrt{3}/6)(x_1 + 4x_2 - 3x_3)$.

9.5-3: How many degrees of freedom does the system pictured possess? Is it possible to have a free vibration in which the mass m is stationary?

Exer. 9.5-2

What are its natural frequencies? Is it possible to have a free vibration in which the mass m is stationary?

9.5-4: Compute the steady-state amplitude of the force on the connection at O for the system shown.

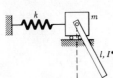

Exer. 9.5-3

9.5-5: Write the equations of motion for the pendulum, taking account of the elasticity of the cord. The length of the pendulum when at rest is a. Use θ and z as coordinates.

Ans.: $m\ddot{z} - m(a+z)\dot{\theta}^2 + kz + mg(1 - \cos\theta) = 0$;
$(a+z)^2\ddot{\theta} + 2\dot{\theta}(a+z)\dot{z} + g(a+z)\sin\theta = 0$.

9.5-6: A steel angle iron is fixed at one end and carries a 50-kg mass at the other. Unit force at the upper end in the x-direction produces an x-displacement of the mass of 1 cm and a y-displacement of $\frac{1}{2}$ cm; unit force in the y-direction produces an x-displacement of 0.8 cm and a y-displacement of 1.2 cm. Find the natural frequencies. When the mass is vibrating at its lower natural frequency, what angle does its direction of motion make with the x-axis? What angle at the higher frequency?

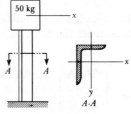

Exer. 9.5-4

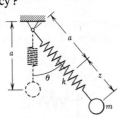

Exer. 9.5-5

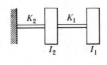

Exer. 9.5-6

9.5-7: Find the natural frequencies and mode shapes for the coupled pendulums shown.
Ans.: $\omega_1^2 = g/l$, $A_1^{(1)} = A_2^{(1)}$; $\omega_2^2 = (g/l) + (2ka^2/ml^2)$, $A_1^{(2)} = -A_2^{(2)}$.
9.5-8: Find the motion of the pendulums in the previous problem for the initial conditions $\theta_1 = A$, $\dot{\theta}_1 = 0$, $\theta_2 = \dot{\theta}_2 = 0$.
Ans.: $\theta_1 = \frac{1}{2}A \cos\omega_1 t + \frac{1}{2}A \cos\omega_2 t$; $\theta_2 = \frac{1}{2}A \cos\omega_1 t - \frac{1}{2}A \cos\omega_2 t$.
9.5-9: Find the natural frequencies and normal coordinates for the torsional system shown: $K_1 = K_2 = 6$ ft-lb/rad; $I_1 = 2$, $I_2 = 3$ slug-ft^2.
Ans.: $\omega_1^2 = 1$, $\omega_2^2 = 6$.

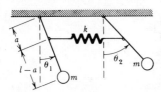

Exer. 9.5-7

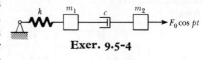

Exer. 9.5-9

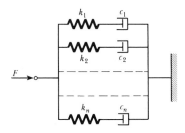

9.6-1: The so-called Maxwell model of a solid, which is sometimes used to describe the behavior of polymers, is shown in the accompanying figure. Construct the force-voltage electrical analog of this system. Does it resemble a filter?

Ans.:

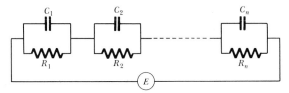

9.6-2: The so-called Voigt model of a solid is shown in the accompanying figure. Construct the force-voltage electrical analog of the system.

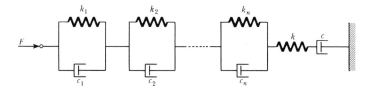

9.6-3: A mechanical model that has been used to represent the dynamical behavior of rubber is the four-element one shown. Construct the force-current electrical analog.

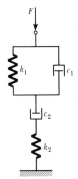

9.6-4: Construct the force-voltage and current-voltage analog circuits for the mechanical system of Exercise 9.4-1.

9.6-5: Construct the force-voltage and the current-voltage analog circuits for the mechanical system of Exercise 9.5-8.

> Time numbers motion, yet (without a crime
> 'Gainst old truth) motion numbered out his time
> And like an Engin mov'd with wheel and waight,
> His principles being ceast, he ended strait.
>
> JOHN MILTON

Vector Algebra

AI.1 Scalar and Vector Quantities

When we speak of a volume of seven cubic inches, the word "volume" denotes the kind of quantity we have in mind, the words "cubic inches" denote the unit, and the word "seven" denotes the *measure*—or number of units in the quantity under discussion. Many entities of importance in technology and science—mass, energy, time duration—may be characterized in this way. Such quantities are said to be *scalar quantities*. Attention tends to focus on the measure number, since it is the element that makes its appearance in mathematical equations, and it is said that a scalar quantity is determined by a single number. Indeed, the ordinary real number provides the typical example of a scalar quantity.

In contrast to scalar quantities, there is another large group, each of which requires a direction as well as a magnitude for its complete specification. Force, velocity, and angular momentum are all examples of this second class, which are known as *vector quantities*. A vector is determined by two points, say O and P, in an appropriate space (for our purposes, the ordinary Euclidean space of three dimensions). The *direction* of the vector is from its initial point, O, to its terminus, P, and the *magnitude* of the vector is the positive number that denotes the distance between these two points. The typical vector quantity is the directed line segment.

In print it is customary to distinguish vector from scalar quantities by the use of boldface type for vectors, as in this text. In handwritten material, a bar is often used over or under the symbol for a vector quantity. This convention offers the convenience of allowing the magnitude of the vector (which is a scalar quantity) to be represented by the same symbol as the vector quantity, but using ordinary type, or, in handwritten material, omitting the bar. Sometimes, when it is desired to emphasize the fact that the quantity under discussion is the magnitude of a vector, absolute value signs are used with the boldface symbol. For example, $|\mathbf{F}| = F$.

AI.2 Vector Addition

Two vectors, $\mathbf{A}$ and $\mathbf{B}$, are said to be equal if they have the same magnitude and the same direction. We indicate this by borrowing the equality sign from algebra and writing $\mathbf{A} = \mathbf{B}$. A vector, $\mathbf{B}$, is added to a vector, $\mathbf{A}$, by placing the initial point of $\mathbf{B}$ at the terminus of $\mathbf{A}$ and taking as the *sum* or *resultant* of $\mathbf{A}$ and $\mathbf{B}$ the vector from the initial point of $\mathbf{A}$ to the terminus of $\mathbf{B}$. This operation, pictured in Fig. AI.2-1, is known as the triangle law of addition. Calling the sum-vector $\mathbf{C}$, we borrow the plus sign from algebra and write $\mathbf{A} + \mathbf{B} = \mathbf{C}$. The vectors $\mathbf{A}$ and $\mathbf{B}$ are

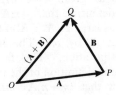

Fig. AI.2-1

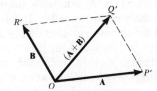

Fig. AI.2-2

said to be *components* of $\mathbf{C}$. Instead of using the triangle law we might equally well add $\mathbf{A}$ and $\mathbf{B}$ by making their initial points coincide and then completing the parallelogram of which $\mathbf{A}$ and $\mathbf{B}$ are the sides, as shown in Fig. AI.2-2. The vector $(\mathbf{A} + \mathbf{B})$ is then the diagonal of the parallelogram, with initial point at the common initial point of $\mathbf{A}$ and $\mathbf{B}$. The "triangle" and "parallelogram" laws of addition are completely equivalent, as appears from the fact that triangles OPQ and $O'P'Q'$ are congruent with parallel sides. Furthermore, since the vector $\overline{R'Q'} = \mathbf{A}$, it follows that $\mathbf{B} + \mathbf{A} = \mathbf{A} + \mathbf{B}$. If we add to the vector $(\mathbf{A} + \mathbf{B})$ a third vector, $\mathbf{D}$, as shown in Fig. AI.2-3, it is clear that $\overline{OR}$, which is the vector $(\mathbf{A} + \mathbf{B}) + \mathbf{D}$, is the same as the vector $\overline{OP}$ added to the vector $\overline{PR}$. Since $\overline{PR}$ is the vector $(\mathbf{B} + \mathbf{D})$, it follows that

$$(\mathbf{A} + \mathbf{B}) + \mathbf{D} = \mathbf{A} + (\mathbf{B} + \mathbf{D}). \qquad \text{AI.2-1}$$

The argument is readily extended to any number of terms. We conclude that the sum of any number of vectors is independent of the grouping of the terms.

The negative of a vector is defined as a vector having the same magnitude as the original one, but reversed in direction. We borrow the minus sign from algebra to indicate this. Then subtraction of **B** from **A** consists in adding −**B** to **A**. In order to make the operations of vector addition and subtraction always possible, we define the *null vector*, or vector of zero magnitude. It is denoted by the symbol **o** or, where no confusion will result, simply by o. Finally, it should be noted, the borrowing of the symbols =, +, and − from algebra is justified by the fact, just proven, that vectorial addition and subtraction obeys the same fundamental laws as the addition and subtraction of ordinary real numbers.

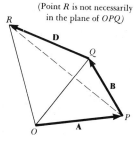

(Point *R* is not necessarily in the plane of *OPQ*)

Fig. AI.2-3

AI.3 Unit Vectors

The product of a number, *m*, and a vector **A** is defined as a vector having the same direction as **A** but with magnitude *m* times as great. We write this product-vector as *m***A**. It follows from the definition that −*m***A** is the vector opposite in direction to **A** and *m* times as large as **A**. Also $(1/m)\mathbf{A}$ may be regarded as the result of dividing **A** by *m*. The laws of ordinary algebra hold for this scalar multiplication. The fact that $n(m\mathbf{A}) = m(n\mathbf{A})$ follows at once from the preceding definition of the product of a number and a vector, as does the fact that $(m+n)\mathbf{A} = m\mathbf{A} + n\mathbf{A}$. That

$$m(\mathbf{A} + \mathbf{B}) = m\mathbf{A} + m\mathbf{B} \qquad \textbf{AI.3-1}$$

is easily proved. Let $\overline{OP}$ be **A** and $\overline{PQ}$ represent **B**, as shown in Fig. AI.3-1. Then $\overline{OR}$ will represent $m\mathbf{A}$ and $\overline{OQ}$ will represent $(\mathbf{A}+\mathbf{B})$. If $\overline{OQ}$ is extended to a point *S* such that $\overline{RS}$ is parallel to $\overline{PQ}$, it follows from the similarity of triangles *OPQ* and *ORS* that

$$|\overline{RS}|/|\overline{PQ}| = |\overline{OR}|/|\overline{OP}|. \qquad \textbf{AI.3-2}$$

But $|\overline{OR}|/|\overline{OP}| = m$, so that $\overline{RS}$ is both parallel to **B** and *m* times as large. Therefore $\overline{RS}$ represents the vector $m\mathbf{B}$. Similarly,

$$|\overline{OS}|/|\overline{OQ}| = |\overline{OR}|/|\overline{OP}| = m \qquad \textbf{AI.3-3}$$

Fig. AI.3-1

so that $\overline{OS}$ represents the vector $m(\mathbf{A}+\mathbf{B})$.

Equation AI.3-1 follows at once from the triangle law of addition.

There is no operation corresponding to division by a vector. As we have seen, however, division of a vector by a scalar changes the magnitude of the vector without altering its direction. In particular, division of a vector by its own magnitude produces a vector of unit magnitude having the same direction as the original one. If the original vector is denoted **A**, the vector **A**/A has unit magnitude and the direction of **A**. Such *unit vectors* play an important role in the applications of vector algebra. In this text, they have been denoted by the symbol **e**, with a subscript to denote the direction. For example,

$$\mathbf{A} = A\mathbf{e}_A \quad \text{or} \quad \mathbf{e}_A = (1/A)\mathbf{A} \quad \text{or} \quad m\mathbf{A} = (mA)\mathbf{e}_A. \qquad \textbf{AI.3-4}$$

The most important unit vectors for purposes of computation are a set directed along the (x, y, z) axes of a right-handed cartesian coordinate system, as shown in Fig. AI.3-2. These unit vectors are usually denoted by the special symbols **i**, **j**, and **k**. (A right-handed system of axes is one such that the fingertips of the right hand pass from the positive end of the x-axis to the positive end of the y-axis while the thumb points towards the positive end of the z-axis. For reasons that will appear later, right-handed axes should always be employed in conjunction with vector algebra.) If a vector **A**, represented by the line segment $\overline{OP}$ in Fig. AI.3-2, has projections (A_x, A_y, A_z) on the (x, y, z) axes respectively, we may write

$$\mathbf{A} = A_x\mathbf{i} + A_y\mathbf{j} + A_z\mathbf{k}. \qquad \textbf{AI.3-5}$$

The scalar components (A_x, A_y, A_z) are three numbers, a set of measure numbers of the vector. The magnitude of **A** is easily expressed in terms of these numbers:

$$A = (A_x^2 + A_y^2 + A_z^2)^{1/2}, \qquad \textbf{AI.3-6}$$

Fig. AI.3-2

and the angle that the vector **A** makes with, say, the x-axis is arccos (A_x/A). The vector equation $\mathbf{A} + \mathbf{B} = \mathbf{C}$ is equivalent to the three ordinary or scalar equations

$$A_x + B_x = C_x, \qquad A_y + B_y = C_y, \qquad A_z + B_z = C_z. \qquad \textbf{AI.3-7}$$

AI.4 The Scalar Product

Quite often in mechanics we wish to find the component of a vector in some particular direction. This task is greatly simplified by the introduction of an operation known as the scalar product of two vectors. The scalar, or "dot," product of two vectors is an ordinary number equal to the product of the magnitudes of the two vectors multiplied by the cosine of the angle between them. We write it **A** · **B**. It is important to note that in finding "the angle between them," the two vectors should be placed with their initial points coincident. The angle in question is then the interior one included by the directions of the vectors.

Since the scalar product is simply a positive or negative number, it may appear as the coefficient of a vector; $C(A \cdot B)$ is a vector in the direction of C with magnitude equal to the magnitude of C multiplied by the number $A \cdot B$. If two vectors are at right angles to each other, their scalar product is zero because the cosine of the angle between them vanishes. If they are parallel, their scalar product is simply the product of their magnitudes. In particular, $A \cdot A = A^2$. For this reason, one occasionally sees A^2 written in place of $A \cdot A$ or $(A+B)^2$ written in place of $(A+B) \cdot (A+B)$. As special cases, it may be noted that $i \cdot i = j \cdot j = k \cdot k = 1$ and that $i \cdot j = j \cdot k = k \cdot i = 0$. With the aid of the scalar product notation, the scalar component of a vector A in a direction specified by a unit vector e is $A \cdot e$. The vector component itself is simply $(A \cdot e)e$.

The scalar product operation obviously conforms to the commutative law of algebra: $A \cdot B = B \cdot A$. We also note that $A \cdot mB = m(A \cdot B)$. That the distributive law of algebra is also followed is easily proven. In this case we want to show that

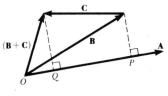

Fig. AI.4-1

$$A \cdot (B+C) = A \cdot B + A \cdot C. \quad \textbf{AI.4-1}$$

These vectors are pictured in Fig. AI.4-1. Since $A \cdot B = AB \cos \theta$ it follows that $A \cdot B$ is represented by the distance OP. The directed distance OQ represents $A \cdot (B+C)$, and PQ represents $A \cdot C$. But $\overline{OQ} = \overline{OP} - \overline{QP} = \overline{OP} + \overline{PQ}$, or $A \cdot (B+C) = A \cdot B + A \cdot C$. The proof is easily extended from three to any number of vectors. It follows from this result that, if we express A and B in cartesian components,

$$A \cdot B = (A_x i + A_y j + A_z k) \cdot (B_x i + B_y j + B_z k),$$
$$A \cdot B = A_x B_x + A_y B_y + A_z B_z. \quad \textbf{AI.4-2}$$

AI.5 The Vector Product

Two quantities that are of major interest in mechanics are the moment of a vector about a point and the velocity of a particle in a rotating body. The determination of these and many other quantities is facilitated by the introduction of an operation known as the *vector product*. The vector, or "cross," product of two vectors, A and B, denoted by the symbol $A \times B$, is itself a vector, whose magnitude is the product of the individual magnitudes of A and B multiplied by the sine of the angle between them. As in the case of the scalar product, the "angle between them" is determined by translating the vectors until their initial points coincide, as shown in Fig. AI.5-1. Then the angle in question, θ, is that traversed by the fingers of the right hand as they move from the positive direction of the first-named vector, **A**, to the positive direction of the second-named vector, **B**. We write

$$|\mathbf{A} \times \mathbf{B}| = AB \sin \theta. \qquad \text{AI.5-1}$$

The direction of the vector product is at right angles to the plane of **A** and **B**. Its sense is determined by the right-hand rule: when the fingertips of the right hand pass from the terminus of the first-named vector, **A**, to the terminus of the second-named vector, **B**, the thumb of the right hand points along the positive direction of **A** × **B**, as shown in Fig. AI.5-1. The adoption of this convention is the reason underlying the requirement that right-handed axes be used when cartesian components are employed.

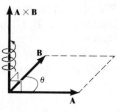

Fig. AI.5-1

The order of the vectors in the vector product obviously cannot be inverted unless allowance is made for the fact that, by interchanging the order of the symbols, the "first-named" becomes the "second-named" vector and vice-versa. Such an interchange reverses the sense of the vector product. In symbols,

$$\mathbf{A} \times \mathbf{B} = -\mathbf{B} \times \mathbf{A}. \qquad \text{AI.5-2}$$

AI.6 Triple Products

With the aid of the vector product, the moment of a force, **F**, about a point, O, is given succinctly by the expression $\mathbf{M}_O = \mathbf{r} \times \mathbf{F}$, where **r** denotes the displacement vector from O to any point on the line of action of **F**. The moment of this force about an axis through O in the direction of the unit vector **e** is the (scalar) component of $\mathbf{M}_O$ in the direction **e**. In symbols,

$$M_e^O = (\mathbf{r} \times \mathbf{F}) \cdot \mathbf{e}. \qquad \text{AI.6-1}$$

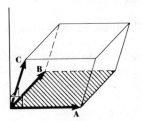

Fig. AI.6-1

An expression of this type is known as a *scalar triple product*. In order for the expression to be meaningful we must take the vector product first, and then form the scalar product. No ambiguity is therefore created by dropping the parentheses.

The scalar triple product $(\mathbf{A} \times \mathbf{B}) \cdot \mathbf{C}$ has a simple geometrical interpretation. **A** × **B** is a vector whose magnitude is equal to the area of the shaded face of the parallelopiped shown in Fig. AI.6-1. When the scalar product with **C** is taken, this area is multiplied by the projection of **C** on the normal to the shaded face. It follows that $(\mathbf{A} \times \mathbf{B}) \cdot \mathbf{C}$ represents the volume of the parallelopiped. This volume will be positive if the vectors

A, B, C taken in that order, form a right-handed system; otherwise it will be negative. Of course, the volume of the parallelopiped could equally well be taken as the area of the front face, $\mathbf{C} \times \mathbf{A}$, multiplied by the projection of **B** on the normal to the front face, i.e., $(\mathbf{C} \times \mathbf{A}) \cdot \mathbf{B}$. In fact,

$$(\mathbf{A} \times \mathbf{B}) \cdot \mathbf{C} = \mathbf{A} \cdot (\mathbf{B} \times \mathbf{C}) = (\mathbf{B} \times \mathbf{C}) \cdot \mathbf{A} = \mathbf{B} \cdot (\mathbf{C} \times \mathbf{A})$$

$$= (\mathbf{C} \times \mathbf{A}) \cdot \mathbf{B} = \mathbf{C} \cdot (\mathbf{A} \times \mathbf{B}). \qquad \textbf{AI.6-2}$$

We conclude that the scalar triple product depends only on the ordering of the terms (**A, B, C**) and that the positioning of the dot and cross symbols is immaterial.

We are now in a position to prove that the operation of taking the vector product is distributive over the operation of vector addition. That is,

$$\mathbf{A} \times (\mathbf{B} + \mathbf{C}) = \mathbf{A} \times \mathbf{B} + \mathbf{A} \times \mathbf{C}. \qquad \textbf{AI.6-3}$$

This is the only one of the rules of vector algebra whose proof is not obvious. To establish it, we let **V** denote the vector that is the difference between the left- and right-hand sides of Eq. AI.6-3 and show that the magnitude of **V** must be zero.

$$\mathbf{V} = \mathbf{A} \times (\mathbf{B} + \mathbf{C}) - \mathbf{A} \times \mathbf{B} - \mathbf{A} \times \mathbf{C},$$

$$\mathbf{V} \cdot \mathbf{V} = \mathbf{V} \cdot [\mathbf{A} \times (\mathbf{B} + \mathbf{C})] - \mathbf{V} \cdot (\mathbf{A} \times \mathbf{B}) - \mathbf{V} \cdot (\mathbf{A} \times \mathbf{C}).$$

The legitimacy of the last step follows from Eq. AI.4-1. Now $\mathbf{V} \cdot \mathbf{V} = V^2$, and, in view of Eq. AI.6-2, we may interchange the dot and cross symbols in the scalar triple products:

$$V^2 = (\mathbf{V} \times \mathbf{A}) \cdot (\mathbf{B} + \mathbf{C}) - (\mathbf{V} \times \mathbf{A}) \cdot \mathbf{B} - (\mathbf{V} \times \mathbf{A}) \cdot \mathbf{C},$$

$$V^2 = (\mathbf{V} \times \mathbf{A}) \cdot (\mathbf{B} + \mathbf{C}) - (\mathbf{V} \times \mathbf{A}) \cdot (\mathbf{B} + \mathbf{C}) = 0.$$

The last step again follows from Eq. AI.4-1. The theorem embodied in Eq. AI.6-3 follows immediately.

Now that the familiar algebraic rules have been established for vector addition and for the vector products, the remaining cartesian forms may be written out.

$$\mathbf{A} \times \mathbf{B} = (A_x \mathbf{i} + A_y \mathbf{j} + A_z \mathbf{k}) \times (B_x \mathbf{i} + B_y \mathbf{j} + B_z \mathbf{k})$$

$$= A_x B_x (\mathbf{i} \times \mathbf{i}) + A_x B_y (\mathbf{i} \times \mathbf{j}) + A_x B_z (\mathbf{i} \times \mathbf{k})$$

$$+ A_y B_x (\mathbf{j} \times \mathbf{i}) + A_y B_y (\mathbf{j} \times \mathbf{j}) + A_y B_z (\mathbf{j} \times \mathbf{k})$$

$$+ A_z B_x (\mathbf{k} \times \mathbf{i}) + A_z B_y (\mathbf{k} \times \mathbf{j}) + A_z B_z (\mathbf{k} \times \mathbf{k}).$$

But the vector product of parallel vectors is always zero ($\sin \theta = 0$) so that terms such as $\mathbf{i} \times \mathbf{i}$, $\mathbf{j} \times \mathbf{j}$, and $\mathbf{k} \times \mathbf{k}$ vanish. Furthermore, as may be seen by inspection of Fig. AI.3-2, $\mathbf{i} \times \mathbf{j} = \mathbf{k}$, $\mathbf{i} \times \mathbf{k} = -\mathbf{j}$, and $\mathbf{j} \times \mathbf{k} = \mathbf{i}$ so that

$$\mathbf{A} \times \mathbf{B} = (A_y B_z - A_z B_y)\mathbf{i} + (A_z B_x - A_x B_z)\mathbf{j} + (A_x B_y - A_y B_x)\mathbf{k}.$$
AI.6-4a

This is often represented in the easily remembered form

$$\mathbf{A} \times \mathbf{B} = \begin{vmatrix} \mathbf{i} & \mathbf{j} & \mathbf{k} \\ A_x & A_y & A_z \\ B_x & B_y & B_z \end{vmatrix}.$$
AI.6-4b

The cartesian form of the scalar triple product is

$$(\mathbf{A} \times \mathbf{B}) \cdot \mathbf{C} = \begin{vmatrix} \mathbf{i} & \mathbf{j} & \mathbf{k} \\ A_x & A_y & A_z \\ B_x & B_y & B_z \end{vmatrix} \cdot (C_x \mathbf{i} + C_y \mathbf{j} + C_z \mathbf{k})$$

$$= \begin{vmatrix} A_x & A_y & A_z \\ B_x & B_y & B_z \\ C_x & C_y & C_z \end{vmatrix}.$$
AI.6-5

The second kind of triple product, which may be formed from the vector $\mathbf{A} \times \mathbf{B}$, is of the type $(\mathbf{A} \times \mathbf{B}) \times \mathbf{C}$. This is a vector, and it is designated the vector triple product. In this symbol, both the position of the parentheses and the order of the terms must be maintained unaltered. If we write

$$\mathbf{V} = (\mathbf{A} \times \mathbf{B}) \times \mathbf{C},$$
AI.6-6

it may be observed that $\mathbf{V}$ will lie in the plane of $\mathbf{A}$ and $\mathbf{B}$. This follows from the fact that $(\mathbf{A} \times \mathbf{B})$ is perpendicular to that plane. The cross product with $\mathbf{C}$ then provides another ninety-degree rotation, putting the final vector, $\mathbf{V}$, back in the plane of $\mathbf{A}$ and $\mathbf{B}$. It follows from this observation that it should be possible to express $\mathbf{V}$ as the sum of vectors proportional to $\mathbf{A}$ and $\mathbf{B}$. To do this take x, y-axes in the plane of $\mathbf{A}$ and $\mathbf{B}$, with the x-axis in the direction of $\mathbf{A}$ (z, of course, is at right angles to the plane of $\mathbf{A}$ and $\mathbf{B}$). Then

$$\mathbf{A} = A\mathbf{i}, \qquad \mathbf{B} = B_x \mathbf{i} + B_y \mathbf{j}, \qquad \mathbf{C} = C_x \mathbf{i} + C_y \mathbf{j} + C_z \mathbf{k},$$

$$\mathbf{A} \cdot \mathbf{C} = A C_x, \qquad \mathbf{B} \cdot \mathbf{C} = B_x C_x + B_y C_y, \qquad \mathbf{A} \times \mathbf{B} = A B_y \mathbf{k}.$$

It follows from the last of these expressions that

$$(\mathbf{A} \times \mathbf{B}) \times \mathbf{C} = A B_y (C_x \mathbf{j} - C_y \mathbf{i})$$

$$= A C_x (B_x \mathbf{i} + B_y \mathbf{j}) - A\mathbf{i}(B_x C_x + B_y C_y)$$

$$= (\mathbf{A} \cdot \mathbf{C})\mathbf{B} - (\mathbf{B} \cdot \mathbf{C})\mathbf{A}.$$
AI.6-7

Similarly,

$$\mathbf{A} \times (\mathbf{B} \times \mathbf{C}) = (\mathbf{A} \cdot \mathbf{C})\mathbf{B} - (\mathbf{A} \cdot \mathbf{B})\mathbf{C}. \qquad \textbf{AI.6-8}$$

The last two expressions prove quite useful (e.g., Section 6.5). An alternative proof, free of the extrinsic element associated with the use of cartesian components, appears in Section 1.3. It will be noticed that the term *outside* the parentheses in the vector triple product appears *inside* the parentheses in both terms of the expansion, and that the positive term of the expansion contains the scalar product of the extreme vectors appearing in the triple product.

Properties of the Inertia Matrix

AII.1 The Definition of the Inertia Matrix

In this appendix, the inertia matrix is defined and its behavior under translation and rotation of axes is explained. The reader presumably knows, from his study of the integral calculus, how to evaluate the integrals representing the moments and products of inertia of a body in a given configuration with respect to a coordinate system. We shall therefore not consider that problem but rather the one mentioned in the first sentence—how may these quantities be computed with respect to other coordinate systems if they are known with respect to one system, without again evaluating the defining integrals directly?

After the transfer-of-axes theorems are developed, some general comments on their use and on other properties of the inertia matrix will be made, in Section AII.4 of this appendix. Section AII.5 summarizes the fundamental equations developed in the appendix. Section AII.6 is a table of the inertial properties of some simple uniform bodies. We begin with the definition of the inertia matrix at a point.

(a) *The particle:* For a single particle of mass m, the *moment of inertia*, I, with respect to any line in space is defined to be

$$I = md^2 \qquad \textbf{AII.1-1}$$

where d is the perpendicular distance from the position of the particle to the line (Fig. AII.1-1a). The moment of inertia is always non-negative, and vanishes only if the line passes through the position of the particle.

The *product of inertia*, P, of the particle with respect to any two perpendicular planes is defined to be

$$P = md_1 d_2,$$ **AII.1-2**

where d_1 and d_2 are the signed distances from the two planes to the particle's position. By signed distances, we mean that a positive sense is assigned normal to each plane; then, if the particle is on the positive side of the plane, its distance from the plane is taken as positive and, if on the other side, its distance is counted as negative (Fig. AII.1-1b). Thus the product of inertia may be positive, negative, or zero.

From these two basic definitions, we derive the more sophisticated notion of the inertia matrix at a point. For a particle, this is not a particularly useful notion. The importance of it arises in the study of systems, both because of the appearance of the elements of the matrix in the angular momentum vector and because of the transformation properties of

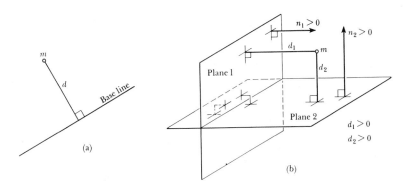

Fig. AII.1-1

the matrix, which are typical of many quantities of physical and geometrical interest.

For a particle, we define the inertia matrix at point P, denoted $\tilde{I}_P$, in the following way. With point P as origin, select a rectangular Cartesian coordinate system (x, y, z), and compute the three moments of inertia of the particle about the coordinate axes and the three products of inertia with respect to the coordinate planes (taken two at a time). Denote the moments of inertia by

$$I_{xx}^P, \quad I_{yy}^P, \quad I_{zz}^P$$ **AII.1-3a**

(with respect to the x-, y-, and z-axes at P respectively) and the products of inertia by

$$I_{xy}^P, \quad I_{xz}^P, \quad I_{yz}^P$$ **AII.1-3b**

(with respect to the xz- and yz-planes, the xy- and yz-planes, and the

xy- and xz-planes at P respectively). These six numbers are the basis of all further computations. We now do two things that appear completely artificial, and will remain so until we have examined the transformation property of the inertia matrix under rotation of axes. We introduce three more product-of-inertia symbols:

$$I^P_{yx}, \qquad I^P_{zx}, \qquad I^P_{zy}, \qquad\qquad \textbf{AII.1-3c}$$

defined to be equal to the products of inertia of AII.1-3b having the same subscripts. The nine quantities AII.1-3 now may be arranged as a symmetrical 3-by-3 square matrix array:

$$\begin{pmatrix} I^P_{xx} & I^P_{xy} & I^P_{xz} \\ I^P_{yx} & I^P_{yy} & I^P_{yz} \\ I^P_{zx} & I^P_{zy} & I^P_{zz} \end{pmatrix}.$$

The moment-of-inertia terms fall along the main diagonal of the matrix; the products of inertia occur in equal pairs in positions reflected in the main diagonal, this being the reason why the array is called symmetrical. One more step is taken: we enter the negatives of the products of inertia in the matrix, and call the result the *inertia matrix* at P of the particle:

$$\tilde{I}_P = \begin{pmatrix} I^P_{xx} & -I^P_{xy} & -I^P_{xz} \\ -I^P_{yx} & I^P_{yy} & -I^P_{yz} \\ -I^P_{zx} & -I^P_{zy} & I^P_{zz} \end{pmatrix}. \qquad \textbf{AII.1-4}$$

At this stage, we should really call this the inertia matrix at P with respect to the (x, y, z) axes, but we shall show that this is just a particular representation in a particular coordinate system of a basic entity—just as we speak of a vector $\mathbf{r}$, and then give different coordinate representations $x\mathbf{i}+y\mathbf{j}+z\mathbf{k}$ or $r\mathbf{e}_r+z\mathbf{k}$ of it.

We close our discussion of the inertia matrix for a particle by noting the following. First, if the base point for the computation is clear, we need not use the superscript P on the individual elements of the matrix; if we are comparing the values of these for two different origins, then it is wise to keep the full notation. Second, there are alternative notations used in the literature, some of which are

$$I_{xx} = I_x = A, \qquad I_{yy} = I_y = B, \qquad I_{zz} = I_z = C,$$
$$I_{xy} = P_{xy} = F, \qquad I_{xz} = P_{xz} = G, \qquad I_{yz} = P_{yz} = H.$$

Third, the explicit definitions of each of the inertia elements for the particle located at $\mathbf{r} = x\mathbf{i}+y\mathbf{j}+z\mathbf{k}$ from P are (Fig. AII.1-2):

$$I^P_{xx} = md^2_x = m(y^2+z^2), \qquad I^P_{yy} = md^2_y = m(x^2+z^2),$$
$$I^P_{zz} = md^2_z = m(x^2+y^2),$$
$$\textbf{AII.1-5}$$
$$I^P_{xy} = I^P_{yx} = mxy = myx, \qquad I^P_{xz} = I^P_{zx} = mxz = mzx,$$
$$I^P_{yz} = I^P_{zy} = myz = mzy.$$

(b) *System of discrete particles:* Suppose, for each of a system of N particles, we know the mass m_i, $i = 1, 2, 3, \ldots N$, and the position $\mathbf{r}_i = x_i \mathbf{i} + y_i \mathbf{j} + z_i \mathbf{k}$ with respect to point P; the inertia matrix at P of the system is defined as for the single particle, each element of the matrix being the sum of the corresponding elements for each particle. Typically,

$$I_{xx}^P = \sum_{i=1}^{N} m_i(y_i^2 + z_i^2),$$

$$I_{xy}^P = I_{yx}^P = \sum_{i=1}^{N} m_i x_i y_i.$$

AII.1-6

(c) *Continuous distributions of mass:* For distributions of mass, we obtain the elements of the inertia matrix as integrals, these being limits of Riemann sums of the type of AII.1-6. Consider the body to be divided into N parts of masses Δm_i, $i = 1, 2, 3, \ldots N$, and let $\mathbf{r}_i$ be the position vector relative to P of any point in Δm_i. Form sums such as

$$\sum_{i=1}^{N} (y_i^2 + z_i^2)\, \Delta m_i, \qquad \sum_{i=1}^{N} x_i y_i\, \Delta m_i;$$

if the limits of these sums exist as $N \to \infty$, each $\Delta m_i \to 0$, independently of the mode of subdivision and of the choice of the $\mathbf{r}_i$, then the definite integrals exist and are typically of the form

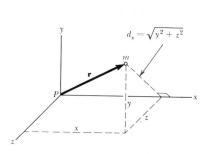

Fig. AII.1-2

$$I_{xx}^P = \int (y^2 + z^2)\, dm,$$

$$I_{xy}^P = I_{yx}^P = \int xy\, dm.$$

AII.1-7

If the mass distribution can be prescribed by a mass density function, then these integrals can be transformed into ordinary line, surface, or volume integrals. If the mass is distributed through a volume V of space, introduce the volume mass density (mass per unit volume) $\rho(x, y, z)$ so that $dm = \rho\, dV$; then $I_{xx} = \int_V \rho(y^2 + z^2)\, dV$. If the mass is distributed over a surface A, introduce σ, the mass per unit area, so that $dm = \sigma\, dA$ and $I_{xx} = \int_A \sigma(y^2 + z^2)\, dA$. If the mass is distributed over a curve C in space, introduce λ, the mass per unit length of arc, so that $dm = \lambda\, ds$ and $I_{xx} = \int_C \lambda(y^2 + z^2)\, ds$.

AII.2 The Parallel-Axis Transfer Theorems

The problem we wish to consider is, as indicated above, not the one of evaluation of a typical inertia integral. Rather, we wish to compute the values of the inertia integrals, or elements of the inertia matrix, with respect to a given coordinate system at some point, knowing the matrix with respect to a different coordinate system based at some other point—without having to recompute the necessary sums or integrals directly. This can be done using simple algebra and analytic geometry.

The general computation can be split into two parts, paralleling the conception of the division of the motion of a rigid body into a translation and a rotation. In this section, we treat the computation of the new inertia matrix under translation of the coordinate axes. That is, suppose we know $\tilde{I}_P$ at some point P with respect to a given (x, y, z) coordinate system; what is $\tilde{I}_Q$ at point Q with respect to parallel axes with origin Q?

Suppose a particle of mass m has position $\mathbf{r}$ with respect to P and $\mathbf{R}$ with respect to Q, with the position of P relative to Q being $\mathbf{p}$ (Fig. AII.2-1). Suppose further that $\mathbf{r} = x\mathbf{i} + y\mathbf{j} + z\mathbf{k}$, $\mathbf{R} = X\mathbf{i} + Y\mathbf{j} + Z\mathbf{k}$, and $\mathbf{p} = \xi\mathbf{i} + \eta\mathbf{j} + \zeta\mathbf{k}$. Then the relative position equation $\mathbf{R} = \mathbf{r} + \mathbf{p}$ gives us the scalar relations

$$X = x + \xi, \qquad Y = y + \eta, \qquad Z = z + \zeta.$$

The fundamental definition of moment of inertia gives

$$I_{xx}^Q = m(Y^2 + Z^2) = m[(y+\eta)^2 + (z+\zeta)^2]$$
$$= m(y^2 + z^2) + 2m(y\eta + z\zeta) + m(\eta^2 + \zeta^2);$$

therefore,

$$I_{xx}^Q = I_{xx}^P + m(\eta^2 + \zeta^2) + 2m(y\eta + z\zeta). \qquad \textbf{AII.2-1a}$$

Similarly, a typical product-of-inertia computation results in

$$I_{xy}^Q = mXY = m(x+\xi)(y+\eta) = mxy + m\xi\eta + m(x\eta + y\xi),$$

or

$$I_{xy}^Q = I_{xy}^P + m\xi\eta + m(x\eta + y\xi). \qquad \textbf{AII.2-1b}$$

These, together with the appropriate expressions for the rest of the moments and products of inertia, give the parallel-axis transfer theorems for a particle. Again, these are not particularly useful, except as an indication of the pattern to be expected for systems. As a check on the expressions, let us identify P with the position of the particle; then Eqs. AII.2-1 should reduce to the fundamental definitions for I_{xx}^Q and I_{xy}^Q. In this case, $\mathbf{r} = x\mathbf{i} + y\mathbf{j} + z\mathbf{k} = \mathbf{0}$, so that $\mathbf{p} = \mathbf{R}$; then AII.2-1 become

$$I_{xx}^Q = m(\eta^2 + \zeta^2) = m(Y^2 + Z^2),$$
$$I_{xy}^Q = m\xi\eta = mXY, \qquad \textbf{AII.2-2}$$

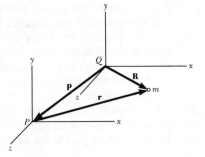

Fig. AII.2-1

as they should.

For continuous systems, the parallel-axis transfer theorems take the form—as should be clear from the definitions AII.1-7 and the particle equations AII.2-1—

$$I_{xx}^Q = I_{xx}^P + \int (\eta^2 + \zeta^2)\, dm + 2 \int (y\eta + z\zeta)\, dm,$$

$$I_{xy}^Q = I_{xy}^P + \int \xi\eta\, dm + \int (x\eta + y\xi)\, dm.$$

Since (ξ, η, ζ) are the coordinates of a fixed point Q relative to P, they are constants in the computation and may be factored out of the integrands and placed before the integral sign. Introducing the total mass $m = \int dm = \int \rho\, dV$ and the position coordinates of the mass center relative to P by the relations

$$mx^* = \int x\, dm, \qquad my^* = \int y\, dm, \qquad mz^* = \int z\, dm,$$

we may rewrite the transfer formulas in the form

$$I_{xx}^Q = I_{xx}^P + m(\eta^2 + \zeta^2) + 2m(y^*\eta + z^*\zeta),$$

$$I_{xy}^Q = I_{xy}^P + m\xi\eta + m(x^*\eta + y^*\xi). \qquad \textbf{AII.2-3}$$

These typical formulas hold for a system of discrete particles as well as a continuous system, of course, and are the system analogues to AII.2-1. The useful forms for computation result by forming analogues to AII.2-2 by identifying P with the mass center of the system, so that $x^* = y^* = z^* = 0$:

$$I_{xx}^Q = I_{xx}^* + m(Y^2 + Z^2),$$

$$I_{xy}^Q = I_{xy}^* + mXY. \qquad \textbf{AII.2-4}$$

In words, these basic results may be stated as:

(i) The moment of inertia of a system with respect to any axis is equal to the moment of inertia of the system about a parallel axis through the mass center of the system plus the product of the mass of the system and the square of the distance between the axes.

(ii) The product of inertia with respect to two orthogonal planes is equal to the product of inertia with respect to parallel planes, similarly oriented, through the mass center plus the product of the mass of the system and the signed distances from the planes at the mass center to the given planes.

From the transfer theorem for moments of inertia, one can prove the important result that, of all moments of inertia with respect to parallel axes, the moment with respect to the axis through the mass center is a minimum.

AII.3 The Rotation-of-Axes Transfer Theorems

Consider now the problem of computing the elements of the inertia matrix with respect to a set of axes having the same origin P as a given set of (x, y, z) axes, but rotated through a given angle about a given axis from them. (By Euler's theorem, we know that such a single rotation is all we need to obtain a final position of a coordinate frame from an initial one, treating the frame as a rigid body with a fixed point.) Here we are considering only proper rotations that transform right-handed coordinates into right-handed coordinates; no reflections are permitted.

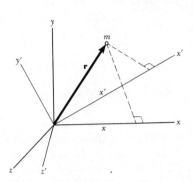

Fig. AII.3-1

Let $Pxyz$ be the original set of axes, and $\tilde{I}_P$ the inertia matrix relative to these axes; let $Px'y'z'$ be the new axes, and $\tilde{I}'_P$ the representation of the inertia matrix relative to the new coordinates. Our problem is: find $\tilde{I}'_P$, knowing $\tilde{I}_P$ and the location of (x', y', z') with respect to (x, y, z).

Start with the single particle of mass m again. Suppose that its position vector $\mathbf{r}$ is given by $x\mathbf{i} + y\mathbf{j} + z\mathbf{k}$ and by $x'\mathbf{i}' + y'\mathbf{j}' + z'\mathbf{k}'$ in the two coordinate systems respectively (Fig. AII.3-1). Knowing the transformation of coordinates, i.e., knowing x' as a function of (x, y, z), etc., we may formally compute the elements of $\tilde{I}'_P$, and we shall do this. The formal computation tends to obscure the significance of the result, however, and so we shall present the result from a geometric point of view first.

The central important fact is that, if we know $\tilde{I}_P$ with respect to one coordinate system, we can find the moment of inertia of the mass distribution about any axis through P.

Consider a single particle located at $\mathbf{r} = x\mathbf{i} + y\mathbf{j} + z\mathbf{k}$ with respect to P; we wish to compute its moment of inertia I about a line PR (Fig. AII.3-2). From the definition, $I = md^2$, where d is the perpendicular distance from the particle to PR. How do we find d? From Fig. AII.3-2, we see that $d = r \sin \theta$, where $r = |\mathbf{r}|$ and θ is the angle between $\mathbf{r}$ and PR. Introducing the unit vector $\mathbf{e}$ along PR, we see that d is given by the magnitude of the cross product of $\mathbf{r}$ and $\mathbf{e}$:

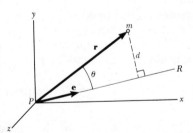

Fig. AII.3-2

$$d = |\mathbf{r} \times \mathbf{e}| = |\mathbf{r}|\,|\mathbf{e}| \sin \theta$$
$$= r \sin \theta. \qquad \textbf{AII.3-1}$$

Let $\mathbf{e}$ have cartesian representation $e_x\mathbf{i} + e_y\mathbf{j} + e_z\mathbf{k}$; then

$$\mathbf{r} \times \mathbf{e} = (ye_z - ze_y)\mathbf{i} + (ze_x - xe_z)\mathbf{j} + (xe_y - ye_x)\mathbf{k},$$

and

$$d^2 = |\mathbf{r} \times \mathbf{e}|^2 = (ye_z - ze_y)^2 + (ze_x - xe_z)^2 + (xe_y - ye_x)^2$$

$$= (y^2 + z^2)e_x^2 + (x^2 + z^2)e_y^2 + (x^2 + y^2)e_z^2$$

$$- 2xye_xe_y - 2xze_xe_z - 2yze_ye_z.$$

Therefore,

$$I = md^2 = I_{xx}e_x^2 + I_{yy}e_y^2 + I_{zz}e_z^2 - 2I_{xy}e_xe_y - 2I_{xz}e_xe_z - 2I_{yz}e_ye_z. \qquad \textbf{AII.3-2}$$

It is easy to see that AII.3-2 holds for a system, discrete or continuous, as well as for a single particle.

The last relation tells us that any moment of inertia about an axis through P may be computed, provided all of the six independent elements of $\tilde{I}_P$ are known with respect to one set of coordinates. We can give a geometric interpretation to this relation. Divide both sides of Eq. AII.3-2 by I ($I \neq 0$; i.e., the mass of the system is not all on the axis PR), and replace (e_x, e_y, e_z)—the direction cosines of PR with respect to (x, y, z)—by the direction numbers

$$\xi_x = \frac{e_x}{\sqrt{I}}, \qquad \xi_y = \frac{e_y}{\sqrt{I}}, \qquad \xi_z = \frac{e_z}{\sqrt{I}}; \qquad \textbf{AII.3-3}$$

then AII.3-2 becomes

$$I_{xx}\xi_x^2 + I_{yy}\xi_y^2 + I_{zz}\xi_z^2 - 2I_{xy}\xi_x\xi_y - 2I_{xz}\xi_x\xi_z - 2I_{yz}\xi_y\xi_z = 1. \qquad \textbf{AII.3-4}$$

Now with the point P in ordinary space let us associate an abstract direction number space with origin O and coordinates (ξ_x, ξ_y, ξ_z), and consider the surface in the new space given by Eq. AII.3-4. Since I_{xx}, I_{yy}, and I_{zz} are all non-negative, this surface will be (in general) an ellipsoid, called the *momental ellipsoid* of the system associated with point P (Fig. AII.3-3); the center of the ellipsoid is at O, of course.

Now consider the position vector ρ drawn from O to any point on the ellipsoid; the magnitude of ρ is

$$\rho = [\xi_x^2 + \xi_y^2 + \xi_z^2]^{1/2} = \frac{1}{\sqrt{I}}[e_x^2 + e_y^2 + e_z^2]^{1/2} = \frac{1}{\sqrt{I}}.$$

The momental ellipsoid thus provides two basic items of information. First, the ratios $\xi_x : \xi_y : \xi_z$ of the coordinates of any point on the ellipsoid are the ratios of the direction numbers of an axis in the real (x, y, z) space; second, the length of the line from the origin to the point (ξ_x, ξ_y, ξ_z) on the ellipsoid is the reciprocal of the square root of the moment of inertia about the axis in the (x, y, z) space.

Observe what has been done here. We have taken a particular computation for I, involving particular numbers e_x, e_y, e_z and a particular axis PR—Eq. AII.3-2—and, by elimination of the reference to a particular

I, have obtained a means of talking about any axis through P in the physical space in terms of a surface in the direction number space associated with P.

We emphasize that there is a momental ellipsoid—a different ellipsoid in general—associated with every point in space. There is no such thing as the momental ellipsoid for the whole body. Further, the particular orientation of the momental ellipsoid with respect to (ξ_x, ξ_y, ξ_z) will depend on what (x, y, z) axes have been chosen at P; but, as we shall see, the size of the ellipsoid does not. The momental ellipsoid concept is important, among other reasons, because it enables us to visualize the behavior of the moments of inertia in terms of a relatively simple surface—however complex and unsymmetrical the actual physical body may be.

From the geometrical properties of the ellipsoid, a number of results may be deduced—most important of which is the concept of the *principal axes of inertia* at P. As we know from analytic geometry, one can always choose three orthogonal axes (ξ'_x, ξ'_y, ξ'_z) emanating from the center O of the ellipsoid such that, referred to these axes, the equation of the ellipsoid takes on the standard form

$$\left(\frac{\xi'_x}{a}\right)^2 + \left(\frac{\xi'_y}{b}\right)^2 + \left(\frac{\xi'_z}{c}\right)^2 = A\xi'^2_x + B\xi'^2_y + C\xi'^2_z = 1. \qquad \textbf{AII.3-5}$$

These three axes in the direction number space correspond to three perpendicular axes (x', y', z') at P in ordinary space. Choose (x', y', z') as the basic coordinates at P, and compute the moment of inertia about any axis with direction numbers (ξ'_x, ξ'_y, ξ'_z) relative to (x', y', z'); the same computation that led to AII.3-4 will now lead to the momental ellipsoid for P in the form AII.3-5. Comparing AII.3-5 with AII.3-4, we see that we have

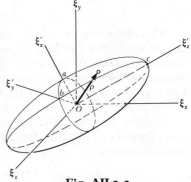

$$I'_{xx} = A, \qquad I'_{yy} = B, \qquad I'_{zz} = C,$$

and all products of inertia relative to (x', y', z') vanish.

This, then, is the fundamental result: at every point P, there exists

Fig. AII.3-3

at least one set of mutually orthogonal axes, called the *principal axes of inertia* at P, such that the products of inertia at P with respect to these axes vanish. The moments of inertia about the principal axes are called *principal moments of inertia*. From the geometry of the ellipsoid, we see that the principal moments of inertia include the maximum and minimum moments about any axis through the base point. The shortest principal axis of the ellipsoid corresponds to the maximum moment of inertia, and the longest axis to the minimum moment: this is the case, since the length of the radius line to the ellipsoid is the inverse square root of the moment of inertia. If, in particular, $A > B > C (a < b < c)$, the momental ellipsoid appears as in Fig. AII.3-3.

A number of special cases of the momental ellipsoid can be treated easily. If two principal moments are equal, then the ellipsoid is an ellipsoid of revolution; any two axes perpendicular to the axis of revolution are principal axes for the ellipsoid, and hence any two corresponding axes in ordinary space are proper principal axes of inertia. This is true for the gyroscope discussed in Section 7.5. If all three principal moments are equal, then the ellipsoid becomes a sphere, and any axis through P is a principal axis of inertia. If the moment of inertia about any axis vanishes, then all the mass must lie on that axis. By the reciprocal relation between moment and distance to the ellipsoid, the distance to the ellipsoid in the direction of the axis becomes infinite; i.e., the ellipsoid becomes a circular cylinder with generators parallel to the line in direction number space corresponding to the line of mass distribution. Finally, if the moments about two lines through P both vanish, then the system must be a single particle at P, for which the inertia matrix is identically zero for all coordinate systems.

Note that the inertia matrix, referred to principal axes of inertia, takes on the simple form

$$\tilde{I}_P = \begin{pmatrix} A & 0 & 0 \\ 0 & B & 0 \\ 0 & 0 & C \end{pmatrix}. \qquad \textbf{AII.3-6}$$

This discussion has told us what to expect in our study of the properties of the inertia matrix; it has not told us exactly how to compute the principal moments, for instance. Equation AII.3-2 (or AII.3-4) computes a moment of inertia only; we have not yet seen how to compute the products of inertia. Let us compute I'_{xx}, I'_{xy}, etc., from the coordinate transformation (x, y, z) into (x', y', z').

Suppose that the direction cosines of the x'-axis with respect to (x, y, z) are (e_x, e_y, e_z); then Eq. AII.3-2 computes the moment of inertia about x' directly:

$$I'_{xx} = I_{xx}e_x^2 + I_{yy}e_y^2 + I_{zz}e_z^2$$
$$- 2I_{xy}e_xe_y - 2I_{xz}e_xe_z - 2I_{yz}e_ye_z. \qquad \textbf{AII.3-7}$$

If the direction cosines of the y'-axis are (f_x, f_y, f_z), then I'_{yy} is given by an expression of the form AII.3-7 with the f's replacing the e's; and if the direction cosines of the z' axis are (g_x, g_y, g_z), then I'_{zz} may also be computed. Remember that the direction cosines must satisfy the relations

$$e_x^2 + e_y^2 + e_z^2 = f_x^2 + f_y^2 + f_z^2 = g_x^2 + g_y^2 + g_z^2 = 1, \qquad \textbf{AII.3-8a}$$
$$e_xf_x + e_yf_y + e_zf_z = e_xg_x + e_yg_y + e_zg_z = f_xg_x + f_yg_y + f_zg_z = 0. $$
$$\textbf{AII.3-8b}$$

Also, to preserve the right-handed nature of the coordinate system, we must have

$$g_x = e_y f_z - e_z f_y,$$
$$g_y = e_z f_x - e_x f_z, \qquad \textbf{AII.3-9}$$
$$g_z = e_x f_y - e_y f_x,$$

these being the scalar forms of the relation $\mathbf{i}' \times \mathbf{j}' = \mathbf{k}'$.

We must still compute the products of inertia. Start again with the particle at position $\mathbf{r} = x\mathbf{i} + y\mathbf{j} + z\mathbf{k} = x'\mathbf{i}' + y'\mathbf{j}' + z'\mathbf{k}'$. We have the basic coordinate transformations

$$x' = \mathbf{r} \cdot \mathbf{i}' = x(\mathbf{i} \cdot \mathbf{i}') + y(\mathbf{j} \cdot \mathbf{i}') + z(\mathbf{k} \cdot \mathbf{i}')$$
$$= xe_x + ye_y + ze_z,$$
$$y' = \mathbf{r} \cdot \mathbf{j}' = xf_x + yf_y + zf_z, \qquad \textbf{AII.3-10}$$
$$z' = \mathbf{r} \cdot \mathbf{k}' = xg_x + yg_y + zg_z;$$

therefore,

$$I'_{xy} = mx'y' = m(xe_x + ye_y + ze_z)(xf_x + yf_y + zf_z)$$
$$= mx^2 e_x f_x + my^2 e_y f_y + mz^2 e_z f_z$$
$$+ mxy(e_x f_y + e_y f_x) + mxz(e_x f_z + e_z f_x) + myz(e_y f_z + e_z f_y).$$

In this expression, the products of inertia (I_{xy}, I_{xz}, I_{yz}) are easily recognized, but the moments of inertia are not. Solve the first of the orthogonality relations AII.3-8b for $e_x f_x$, $e_y f_y$, and $e_z f_z$ in turn in terms of the other two products; i.e., $e_y f_y = -e_x f_x - e_z f_z$. Substitute these into the expression for I'_{xy}; we find

$$I'_{xy} = -mx^2(e_y f_y + e_z f_z) - my^2(e_x f_x + e_z f_z) - mz^2(e_x f_x + e_y f_y)$$
$$+ mxy(e_x f_y + e_y f_x) + mxz(e_x f_z + e_z f_x) + myz(e_y f_z + e_z f_y)$$
$$= -m(y^2 + z^2)e_x f_x - m(x^2 + z^2)e_y f_y - m(x^2 + y^2)e_z f_z$$
$$+ mxy(e_x f_y + e_y f_x) + mxz(e_x f_z + e_z f_x) + myz(e_y f_z + e_z f_y).$$

The basic transformation equation for products of inertia, which clearly holds for systems as well as for the single particle, is therefore

$$I'_{xy} = -I_{xx}e_x f_x - I_{yy}e_y f_y - I_{zz}e_z f_z$$
$$+ I_{xy}(e_x f_y + e_y f_x) + I_{xz}(e_x f_z + e_z f_x) + I_{yz}(e_y f_z + e_z f_y). \qquad \textbf{AII.3-11}$$

The other products of inertia I'_{xz} and I'_{yz} in the (x', y', z') system can be computed by appropriate changes in subscripts and direction cosines.

Equations AII.3-7 and AII.3-11 are typical of the full three-dimensional transformations for moments and products of inertia under rotation of axes. In this form, they are almost impossible to remember or to use easily. A change in notation will lead us to more readily usable forms and will show why we introduce all nine elements of the inertia matrix. Moreover, we shall also see why the minus sign is attached to the products of inertia.

Introduce a single symbol for direction cosines, say m, and distinguish between the different cosines by attaching two literal subscripts to m. The first subscript will refer to an axis of the (x, y, z) system; the second, to an axis of the (x', y', z') system. That is, m_{xz} will be the direction cosine of the z'-axis with respect to the x-axis, or the cosine of the angle between the lines Px and Pz'. The fundamental coordinate transformation is

$$x' = m_{xx}x + m_{yx}y + m_{zx}z,$$

$$y' = m_{xy}x + m_{yy}y + m_{zy}z, \qquad \textbf{AII.3-12}$$

$$z' = m_{xz}x + m_{yz}y + m_{zz}z.$$

Now we may rewrite AII.3-7 and AII.3-11 in a quite suggestive form. In AII.3-7, replace (e_x, e_y, e_z) by (m_{xx}, m_{yx}, m_{zx}) respectively; also, make use of the fact that $I_{xy} = I_{yx}$, etc. Equation AII.3-7 becomes

$$I'_{xx} = m_{xx}m_{xx}I_{xx} - m_{xx}m_{yx}I_{xy} - m_{xx}m_{zx}I_{xz}$$

$$- m_{yx}m_{xx}I_{yx} + m_{yx}m_{yx}I_{yy} - m_{yx}m_{zx}I_{yz}$$

$$- m_{zx}m_{xx}I_{zx} - m_{zx}m_{yx}I_{zy} + m_{zx}m_{zx}I_{zz}. \qquad \textbf{AII.3-13}$$

Similarly, replacing (f_x, f_y, f_z) by (m_{xy}, m_{yy}, m_{zy}), AII.3-11 becomes

$$I'_{xy} = -m_{xx}m_{xy}I_{xx} + m_{xx}m_{yy}I_{xy} + m_{xx}m_{zy}I_{xz}$$

$$+ m_{yx}m_{xy}I_{yx} - m_{yx}m_{yy}I_{yy} + m_{yx}m_{zy}I_{yz}$$

$$+ m_{zx}m_{xy}I_{zx} + m_{zx}m_{yy}I_{zy} - m_{zx}m_{zy}I_{zz}. \qquad \textbf{AII.3-14}$$

The pattern of computation begins to be clear now. Examine any term on the right of either of these expressions. The term consists of the product of two direction cosines and an element of the inertia matrix relative to (x, y, z). Each of the direction cosines has, as its second subscript, one of the subscripts of the inertia quantity we are computing. The direction cosines are arranged so that their product produces the same order in their second subscripts that the subscripts of the I'-term have. Then the first subscripts of the direction cosines, taken in order, show which element of the inertia matrix relative to (x, y, z) is multiplied by the direction cosines. This is the reason for including all nine elements of the matrix, rather than the six independent ones; I_{yx} occurs naturally in the computational scheme. Finally, we must decide whether to place a plus or minus sign before our typical term. In the moment of inertia transformation expression, all terms involving moments of inertia have a plus sign; all terms involving products of inertia, a minus. The same rule can be applied to the product of inertia expression if we multiply it by

(-1) or, equivalently, write the transformation rule for $(-I_{xy})$ rather than I_{xy} itself. And now we see that the minus sign may be eliminated entirely from the transformations.

Quantities such as the inertia matrix, the components of which transform by the rule AII.3-13 or AII.3-14, are of great importance in mechanics (and in physics in general). Such quantities are called tensors; specifically, the inertia matrix as we have defined it is a cartesian tensor of order two. The tensor concept is a generalization of the vector concept; the vectors we treat are cartesian tensors of order one. Generalizations to curvilinear coordinates and to higher orders are possible and useful. Among other tensorial quantities of importance in applied mechanics are the stress and strain tensors at a point in a three-dimensional deformable body.

One final problem remains: the computation of the principal moments of inertia and corresponding principal axis directions. One way of proceeding would be the formal way. That is, we know that the products of inertia must vanish relative to the principal axes. Set $I'_{xy}=0$ in AII.3-14, and I'_{xz} and $I'_{yz}=0$ in the two similar relations. These three equations, together with the six relations that hold among the direction cosines $(m_{xx}^2+m_{yx}^2+m_{zx}^2=1,$ etc.$)$, are nine equations for the nine unknown direction cosines. Solve for the direction cosines of the principal axes of inertia. Substitute in AII.3-13, and the two similar relations for I'_{yy} and I'_{zz}, and compute the principal moments. This procedure, though straightforward enough to state, is obviously most difficult to carry out. Let us look at an alternative procedure, more sophisticated mathematically, but one that leads to a type of determinant equation of great importance not only here but also in the analysis of stress and strain, the determination of vibration frequencies, and in other branches of mechanics.

Examine the momental ellipsoid again, Eq. AII.3-4 and Fig. AII.3-3. Our problem is equivalent to finding the principal diameters and their directions for the ellipsoid. This can be stated as an extremal value problem. The value of the distance to the ellipsoid at the end of the third axis is, though neither the maximum or minimum distance, an extremal value for points in its immediate neighborhood in the sense of a saddle point: going away from ξ'_y toward ξ'_x, distances from O decrease as fast as possible, whereas going away from ξ'_y toward ξ'_z they increase as fast as possible. Our problem may then be stated: for what values of (ξ_x, ξ_y, ξ_z) satisfying Eq. AII.3-4 does the square of the distance (and hence the distance itself) from the origin attain stationary values? Here, as in any maximum-minimum problem of the calculus, we wish to take derivatives and set them equal to zero; the difficulty arises in taking into account properly the *constraint condition* AII.3-4. Without proof, we show what to do, referring the reader to an advanced calculus text* for a discussion of the *Lagrange multiplier* method.

---

* E.g., A. E. Taylor, *Advanced Calculus* (Boston: Ginn & Co., 1955), p. 198.

Introduce a parameter λ—the Lagrange multiplier—and consider the function ($\lambda \neq 0, \infty$)

$$\Phi(\xi_x, \xi_y, \xi_z, \lambda) = (\xi_x^2 + \xi_y^2 + \xi_z^2) - \lambda^{-1}[I_{xx}\xi_x^2 + I_{yy}\xi_y^2$$

$$+ I_{zz}\xi_z^2 - 2I_{xy}\xi_x\xi_y - 2I_{xz}\xi_x\xi_z - 2I_{yz}\xi_y\xi_z - 1]. \qquad \textbf{AII.3-15}$$

This function of four variables attains its extremal values when the four partial derivatives vanish:

$$\frac{\partial \Phi}{\partial \xi_x} = \frac{\partial \Phi}{\partial \xi_y} = \frac{\partial \Phi}{\partial \xi_z} = \frac{\partial \Phi}{\partial \lambda} = 0.$$

In particular, $\partial\Phi/\partial\lambda = 0$ if, and only if, ($\lambda \neq \infty$) (ξ_x, ξ_y, ξ_z) satisfy the equation of the ellipsoid. Thus the extreme values of Φ occur only at points of the ellipsoid, where, since the bracketed quantity in AII.3-15 vanishes, Φ is the same as the distance function $\xi_x^2 + \xi_y^2 + \xi_z^2$; thus the extreme values of Φ are the same as those of the square of the distance to the ellipsoid.

The other three derivative equations lead to three equations in the four unknowns ξ_x, ξ_y, ξ_z, and λ. Performing the indicated differentiations, multiplying the results by ($-\lambda/2$), and rearranging using $I_{xy} = I_{yx}$, etc., these become

$$(I_{xx} - \lambda)\xi_x - I_{xy}\xi_y - I_{xz}\xi_z = 0,$$

$$-I_{yx}\xi_x + (I_{yy} - \lambda)\xi_y - I_{yz}\xi_z = 0, \qquad \textbf{AII.3-16}$$

$$-I_{zx}\xi_x - I_{zy}\xi_y + (I_{zz} - \lambda)\xi_z = 0.$$

Since these are linear homogeneous algebraic equations in (ξ_x, ξ_y, ξ_z), they will not have solutions different from zero for all values of λ, but only for those values of λ for which the determinant of the coefficients of the equations vanish:

$$\begin{vmatrix} I_{xx} - \lambda & -I_{xy} & -I_{xz} \\ -I_{yx} & I_{yy} - \lambda & -I_{yz} \\ -I_{zx} & -I_{zy} & I_{zz} - \lambda \end{vmatrix} = 0. \qquad \textbf{AII.3-17a}$$

This determinantal equation in λ is called the characteristic equation of the inertia matrix. Expansion of this 3-by-3 determinant leads to an equivalent form of the characteristic equation which is obviously a cubic in λ:

$$-\lambda^3 + I_1\lambda^2 + I_2\lambda + I_3 = 0. \qquad \textbf{AII.3-17b}$$

We state without proof the following conclusions that can be drawn from the study of the characteristic equation for the inertia matrix (these results do not all necessarily hold for the characteristic equations of other matrices):

(i) The three roots of AII.3-17 are all real and non-negative;

(ii) The three roots are the principal moments of inertia;

(iii) When each of the three roots is substituted into Eqs. AII.3-16, they may be solved for nontrivial ratios $\xi_x : \xi_y : \xi_z$; each of the three sets of ratios are direction number ratios of a principal axis of inertia (special cases may arise when two or more of the principal moments are equal, but we shall not detail these);

(iv) The numbers I_1, I_2, I_3 in AII.3-17b are scalar invariants of the inertia matrix at P; that is, since the principal moments of inertia are the same whatever representation of I_P we start with, the computation of the principal moments must be the same whether we start from I_{xx}, I_{xy}, etc. or I'_{xx}, I'_{xy}, etc. Thus, the coefficients of the cubic have the same values whatever coordinates are used, and, in particular, $I_1 = I_{xx} + I_{yy} + I_{zz} = I'_{xx} + I'_{yy} + I'_{zz} = A + B + C.$

Finally, we may note that a different geometrical representation of the transformation under rotation of axes is possible. Those familiar with the Mohr's circle representation of stress and strain in deformable body mechanics should see that the inertia matrix elements may be represented in the same way. The interested reader may pursue this subject for himself.

AII.4 Further Comments on the Determination of the Inertia Matrix

(a) *The uniform body:* A body with constant mass density is called uniform, all others nonuniform or of variable density. For uniform bodies, the determination of the mass center is the same as the determination of the centroid of the volume occupied by the mass; determination of the inertia matrix, the same as determination of the second moments of volume. For uniform bodies that are geometrically regular, there are often relatively simple formulas for $\tilde{I}^*$ in terms of the total mass and the dimensions of the body. Some of these are listed in Section AII.6.

(b) *Radii of gyration:* For nonuniform bodies, or uniform bodies that are geometrically complex, no simple formulas for the values of the inertia integrals can be given usually. The requisite inertia information is then prescribed by listing the values of the *radii of gyration* (k_x, k_y, k_z) with respect to principal axes of inertia at some point P:

$$I^P_{xx} = A^P = mk_x^2, \qquad I^P_{yy} = B^P = mk_y^2, \qquad I^P_{zz} = C^P = mk_z^2.$$

Usually, the point P is taken to be the mass center.

The student should check that numbers given or computed for a radius of gyration are reasonable. For instance, a sphere of radius three feet could not have a centroidal radius of gyration of four feet: if all the mass of the sphere were concentrated at one point on the surface, I about any axis through the centroid could not be bigger than $m(3)^2 = 9m$. In general, we can say that the radius of gyration about any axis cannot be bigger than the perpendicular distance from the axis to the farthest point in the body.

(c) *Bodies with a plane of symmetry of mass:* For bodies with a plane of symmetry of mass distribution (which a plane of geometrical symmetry will not necessarily be unless the body is uniform), finding principal axes of inertia is greatly simplified. Symmetry of mass distribution with respect to a plane means, of course, that the mass density is the same at points that are mirror images in the plane. The product of inertia with respect to the plane of symmetry and any plane perpendicular to it must vanish, since, to each element of mass at positive distance d from the symmetry plane, there is an equal mass at negative distance $-d$. We can conclude that, for bodies with a plane of mass symmetry, the axis perpendicular to that plane is a principal axis of inertia at every point of the plane.

(d) *Bodies with multiple mass symmetries:* If a body has two planes of symmetry of mass, then, at any point of their line of intersection, the normals to the two planes must be principal axes of inertia. Since the line of intersection is perpendicular to two principal axes, that line must itself be a principal axis of inertia at every point on it. If the two intersecting planes are orthogonal, then we have a set of three mutually orthogonal principal axes at every point of the line of intersection. If the two planes are not orthogonal, their normals are not orthogonal. Yet these normals must be principal axes. This can be so only if every axis perpendicular to the line of intersection is a principal axis; that is, for two nonorthogonal planes of symmetry, the momental ellipsoid for every point on the line of intersection is an ellipsoid of revolution.

If there are three or more planes of symmetry with a common line of intersection, then the situation is the same as that just described. If three planes of symmetry intersect at a point, then the normals to these planes must be principal axes of inertia at that point. If the three planes are orthogonal, this is all we can say. If one plane intersects the other two obliquely, then the momental ellipsoid for the point must be an ellipsoid of revolution about two of its axes and hence must be a sphere—that is, all axes through the point are principal axes, and all moments of inertia are equal. For more than three planes of symmetry at a point, the momental ellipsoid must necessarily be a sphere. The student should have no trouble in establishing by symmetry arguments that a uniform cube, for instance, has the same moment of inertia about any axis through its center.

A final word on symmetrical distributions: since the mass center must necessarily be in a plane of mass symmetry, the point of intersection of three or more planes of symmetry must be the mass center—precisely the point at which we wish to know the principal axes of inertia for simplest use of the parallel-axis theorems and in the computation of $\mathbf{H}^*$.

(e) *Method of decomposition:* Remember that moments and products of inertia are additive. Therefore, the computation for a complex, or composite, body may be effected by splitting the body into smaller components and adding the results for the separate parts. Uniform bodies with holes or hollows may be treated in this fashion by adding the result for a body in the shape of the hole with a negative mass to that for the solid body without the hole.

AII.5 **Summary**

In this section we summarize the procedures of the previous sections for easy reference.

Suppose that $\tilde{I}_P$ is known with respect to (x, y, z) axes with origin P, and that we wish to find $\tilde{I}_Q$ with respect to (x', y', z') axes with origin Q.

(a) Find $\tilde{I}^*$ with respect to (x, y, z) axes with origin at the mass center from $\tilde{I}_P$ by the parallel-axis theorems.

(b) Find $\tilde{I}_Q$ with respect to (x, y, z) axes at Q from $\tilde{I}^*$ by the parallel-axis theorems.

(c) Find $\tilde{I}_Q$ with respect to the (x', y', z') axes from $\tilde{I}_Q$ with respect to (x, y, z) by the rotation-of-axes theorems.

The parallel-axis theorems are typified by the following moment and product of inertia transforms:

$$I_{xx}^P = I_{xx}^* + m(Y^2 + Z^2),$$

$$I_{xy}^P = I_{xy}^* + mXY, \qquad \textbf{AII.5-1}$$

where $\mathbf{R} = X\mathbf{i} + Y\mathbf{j} + Z\mathbf{k}$ is the position vector of P relative to the mass center.

The rotation-of-axes theorems are typified by the following moment and product of inertia transforms:

$$I'_{xx} = m_{xx}m_{xx}I_{xx} + m_{xx}m_{yx}(-I_{xy}) + m_{xx}m_{zx}(-I_{xz})$$

$$+ m_{yx}m_{xx}(-I_{yx}) + m_{yx}m_{yx}I_{yy} + m_{yx}m_{zx}(-I_{yz})$$

$$+ m_{zx}m_{xx}(-I_{zx}) + m_{zx}m_{yx}(-I_{zy}) + m_{zx}m_{zx}I_{zz}; \qquad \textbf{AII.5-2a}$$

$$(-I'_{xy}) = m_{xx}m_{xy}I_{xx} + m_{xx}m_{yy}(-I_{xy}) + m_{xx}m_{zy}(-I_{xz})$$

$$+ m_{yx}m_{xy}(-I_{yx}) + m_{yx}m_{yy}I_{yy} + m_{yx}m_{zy}(-I_{yz})$$

$$+ m_{zx}m_{xy}(-I_{zx}) + m_{zx}m_{yy}(-I_{zy}) + m_{zx}m_{zy}I_{zz}. \qquad \textbf{AII.5-2b}$$

Here the m's are the direction cosines of the (x', y', z') axes with respect to the (x, y, z) axes, as given by the transformation equations

$$x' = m_{xx}x + m_{yx}y + m_{zx}z,$$

$$y' = m_{xy}x + m_{yy}y + m_{zy}z, \qquad \textbf{AII.5-3}$$

$$z' = m_{xz}x + m_{yz}y + m_{zz}z.$$

To form any other I', the second subscripts on the direction cosines in AII.5-2 are changed to agree, in order, with those of the I'-term we wish to find.

To compute the principal moments of inertia at P, knowing some representation of the inertia matrix at P, find the three roots λ of the characteristic determinantal equation

$$
\begin{vmatrix}
I_{xx} - \lambda & -I_{xy} & -I_{xz} \\
-I_{yx} & I_{yy} - \lambda & -I_{yz} \\
-I_{zx} & -I_{zy} & I_{zz} - \lambda
\end{vmatrix} = 0.
\qquad \textbf{AII.5-4}
$$

The student should note that, if (x, y, z) are principal axes of inertia at P, then parallel axes at Q are not necessarily principal axes at Q.

AII.6 Inertia Properties of Uniform Bodies

The table contains the following information for uniform mass distributions:

(1) Name of body, picture relative to a coordinate system $Oxyz$. The coordinate system is parallel to the principal axes of inertia at the mass center C; these are not necessarily principal axes at the given origin O.

(2) Basic geometric information, especially the length (L), area (A), and volume (V) of one-, two-, and three-dimensional mass distributions respectively; also, the location $\mathbf{r}^* = x^*\mathbf{i} + y^*\mathbf{j} + z^*\mathbf{k}$ of the mass center C with respect to the given origin O.

(3) Principal moments of inertia at the mass center: I_{xx}^*, I_{yy}^*, and I_{zz}^*.

(4) Other moments and products of inertia of importance.

In all cases, the total mass is denoted by m and equals the product of the appropriate constant density of the uniform body and the length, area, or volume occupied by the distribution.

Inertia Properties of
Uniform Bodies

Body	Axis System	$L - A - V$ $\mathbf{r}^*$	$\tilde{I}^*$	Other $\tilde{I}_P$
Thin Rod, Straight	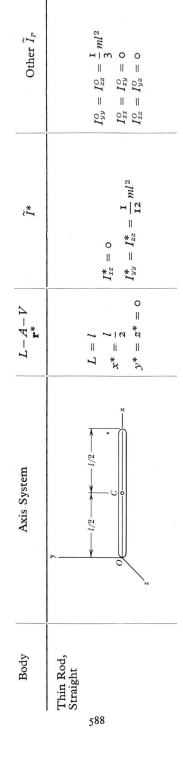	$L = l$ $x^* = \dfrac{l}{2}$ $y^* = z^* = 0$	$I_{xx}^* = 0$ $I_{yy}^* = I_{zz}^* = \dfrac{1}{12} m l^2$	$I_{yy}^O = I_{zz}^O = \dfrac{1}{3} m l^2$ $I_{xx}^O = I_{xy}^O = 0$ $I_{xz}^O = I_{yz}^O = 0$

Thin Rod,
Circular
Arc

$$L = 2r\theta$$

$$x^* = \frac{r\sin\theta}{\theta}$$

$$y^* = z^* = 0$$

$$I_{xx}^* = \frac{mr^2}{2}\left[1 - \frac{\sin 2\theta}{2\theta}\right]$$

$$I_{yy}^* = \frac{mr^2}{2}\left[1 + \frac{\sin 2\theta}{2\theta}\right] - \frac{mr^2\sin^2 2\theta}{\theta^2}$$

$$I_{zz}^* = mr^2\left[1 - \frac{\sin^2\theta}{\theta^2}\right]$$

$$I_{xx}^O = I_{xx}^*$$

$$I_{yy}^O = \frac{mr^2}{2}\left[1 + \frac{\sin 2\theta}{2\theta}\right]$$

$$I_{zz}^O = mr^2$$

$$I_{xy}^O = I_{xz}^O = I_{yz}^O = 0$$

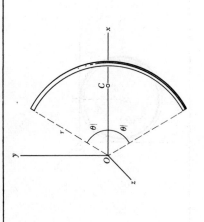

589

Body	Axis System	$L - A - V$ $\mathbf{r}^*$	$\tilde{I}^*$	Other $\tilde{I}_P$
Thin Rod, Circular Hoop	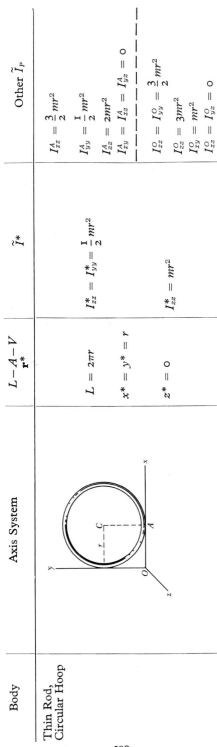	$L = 2\pi r$ $x^* = y^* = r$ $z^* = 0$	$I_{xx}^* = I_{yy}^* = \frac{1}{2} mr^2$ $I_{zz}^* = mr^2$	$I_{xx}^A = \frac{3}{2} mr^2$ $I_{yy}^A = \frac{1}{2} mr^2$ $I_{zz}^A = 2mr^2$ $I_{xy}^A = I_{xz}^A = I_{yz}^A = 0$ $I_{xx}^O = I_{yy}^O = \frac{3}{2} mr^2$ $I_{zz}^O = 3mr^2$ $I_{xy}^O = mr^2$ $I_{xz}^O = I_{yz}^O = 0$

590

Isosceles Triangular Plate

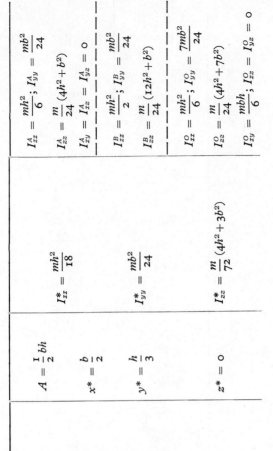

$$A = \frac{1}{2}bh$$

$$x^* = \frac{b}{2}$$

$$y^* = \frac{h}{3}$$

$$z^* = 0$$

$$I^*_{xx} = \frac{mh^2}{18}$$

$$I^*_{yy} = \frac{mb^2}{24}$$

$$I^*_{zz} = \frac{m}{72}(4h^2+3b^2)$$

$$I^A_{xx} = \frac{mh^2}{6}; \; I^A_{yy} = \frac{mb^2}{24}$$

$$I^A_{zz} = \frac{m}{24}(4h^2+b^2)$$

$$I^A_{xy} = I^A_{xz} = I^A_{yz} = 0$$

$$I^B_{xx} = \frac{mh^2}{2}; \; I^B_{yy} = \frac{mb^2}{24}$$

$$I^B_{zz} = \frac{m}{24}(12h^2+b^2)$$

$$I^O_{xx} = \frac{mh^2}{6}; \; I^O_{yy} = \frac{7mb^2}{24}$$

$$I^O_{zz} = \frac{m}{24}(4h^2+7b^2)$$

$$I^O_{xy} = \frac{mbh}{6}; \; I^O_{xz} = I^O_{yz} = 0$$

Body	Axis System	$L-A-V$ $\mathbf{r}^*$	$\tilde{I}^*$	Other $\tilde{I}_P$
Square Plate	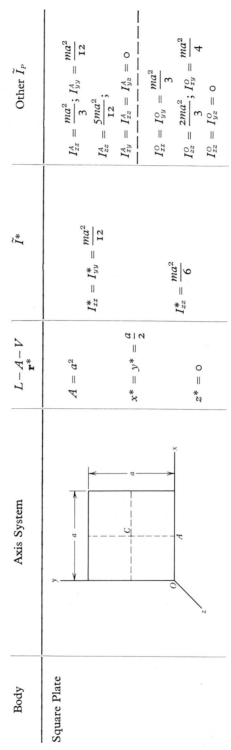	$A = a^2$ $x^* = y^* = \dfrac{a}{2}$ $z^* = 0$	$I^*_{xx} = I^*_{yy} = \dfrac{ma^2}{12}$ $I^*_{zz} = \dfrac{ma^2}{6}$	$I^A_{xx} = \dfrac{ma^2}{3}; I^A_{yy} = \dfrac{ma^2}{12}$ $I^A_{zz} = \dfrac{5ma^2}{12};$ $I^A_{xy} = I^A_{xz} = I^A_{yz} = 0$ --- $I^O_{xx} = I^O_{yy} = \dfrac{ma^2}{3}$ $I^O_{zz} = \dfrac{2ma^2}{3}; I^O_{xy} = \dfrac{ma^2}{4}$ $I^O_{xz} = I^O_{yz} = 0$

Rectangular Plate

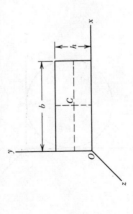

$A = bh$

$x^* = \dfrac{b}{2}$

$y^* = \dfrac{h}{2}$

$z^* = 0$

$I_{xx}^* = \dfrac{1}{12}\, mh^2$

$I_{yy}^* = \dfrac{1}{12}\, mb^2$

$I_{zz}^* = \dfrac{1}{12}\, m(b^2 + h^2)$

$I_{xx}^O = \dfrac{mh^2}{3}$

$I_{yy}^O = \dfrac{mb^2}{3}$

$I_{zz}^O = \dfrac{m(b^2 + h^2)}{3}$

$I_{xy}^O = \dfrac{mbh}{4};\ I_{xz}^O = I_{yz}^O = 0$

Body	Axis System	$L-A-V$ $\mathbf{r}^*$	$\tilde{I}^*$	Other $\tilde{I}_P$
Circular Disk	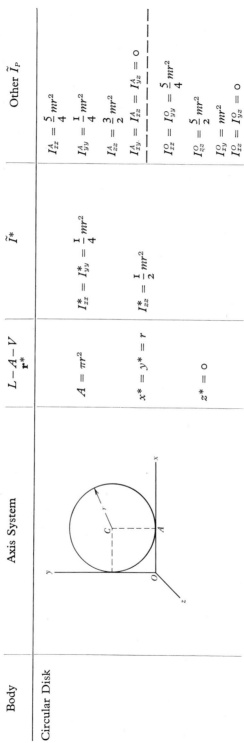	$A = \pi r^2$ $x^* = y^* = r$ $z^* = 0$	$I^*_{xx} = I^*_{yy} = \dfrac{1}{4} mr^2$ $I^*_{zz} = \dfrac{1}{2} mr^2$	$I^A_{xx} = \dfrac{5}{4} mr^2$ $I^A_{yy} = \dfrac{1}{4} mr^2$ $I^A_{zz} = \dfrac{3}{2} mr^2$ $I^A_{xy} = I^A_{xz} = I^A_{yz} = 0$ $I^O_{xx} = I^O_{yy} = \dfrac{5}{4} mr^2$ $I^O_{zz} = \dfrac{5}{2} mr^2$ $I^O_{xy} = mr^2$ $I^O_{xz} = I^O_{yz} = 0$

Circular Ring (Annulus)

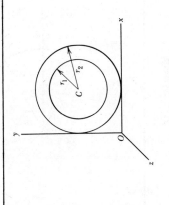

$$A = \pi(r_2^2 - r_1^2)$$

$$x^* = y^* = r_2$$

$$z^* = 0$$

$$I_{xx}^* = I_{yy}^* = \frac{m(r_2^2 + r_1^2)}{4}$$

$$I_{zz}^* = \frac{m(r_2^2 + r_1^2)}{2}$$

$$I_{xx}^O = I_{yy}^O = \frac{m(5r_2^2 + r_1^2)}{4}$$

$$I_{zz}^O = \frac{m(5r_2^2 + r_1^2)}{2}$$

$$I_{xy}^O = mr_2^2$$

$$I_{xz}^O = I_{yz}^O = 0$$

Body	Axis System	$L-A-V$ $\mathbf{r}^*$	$\tilde{I}^*$	Other $\tilde{I}_P$
Circular Sector	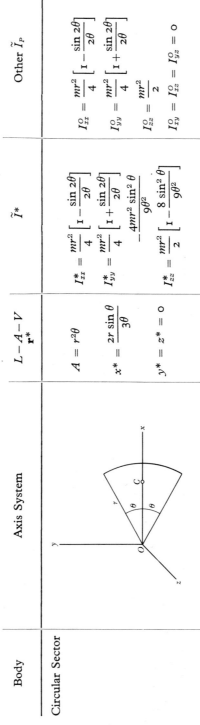	$A = r^2\theta$ $x^* = \dfrac{2r\sin\theta}{3\theta}$ $y^* = z^* = 0$	$I_{xx}^* = \dfrac{mr^2}{4}\left[\mathrm{I} - \dfrac{\sin 2\theta}{2\theta}\right]$ $I_{yy}^* = \dfrac{mr^2}{4}\left[\mathrm{I} + \dfrac{\sin 2\theta}{2\theta}\right]$ $- \dfrac{4mr^2\sin^2\theta}{9\theta^2}$ $I_{zz}^* = \dfrac{mr^2}{2}\left[\mathrm{I} - \dfrac{8\sin^2\theta}{9\theta^2}\right]$	$I_{xx}^O = \dfrac{mr^2}{4}\left[\mathrm{I} - \dfrac{\sin 2\theta}{2\theta}\right]$ $I_{yy}^O = \dfrac{mr^2}{4}\left[\mathrm{I} + \dfrac{\sin 2\theta}{2\theta}\right]$ $I_{zz}^O = \dfrac{mr^2}{2}$ $I_{xy}^O = I_{xz}^O = I_{yz}^O = 0$

Elliptical Disk

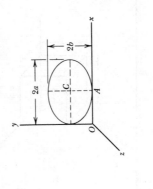

$A = \pi ab$

$x^* = a$

$y^* = b$

$z^* = 0$

$$I_{xx}^* = \frac{mb^2}{4}$$

$$I_{yy}^* = \frac{ma^2}{4}$$

$$I_{zz}^* = \frac{m(a^2 + b^2)}{4}$$

$I_{xx}^A = \dfrac{5mb^2}{4}$; $I_{yy}^A = \dfrac{ma^2}{4}$

$I_{zz}^A = \dfrac{m}{4}(5b^2 + a^2)$

$I_{xy}^A = I_{zz}^A = I_{yz}^A = 0$

$I_{xx}^O = \dfrac{5mb^2}{4}$; $I_{yy}^O = \dfrac{5ma^2}{4}$

$I_{zz}^O = \dfrac{5m}{4}(a^2 + b^2)$

$I_{xy}^O = mab$; $I_{xz}^O = I_{yz}^O = 0$

Body	Axis System	$L - A - V$ $\mathbf{r^*}$	$\tilde{I}^*$	Other $\tilde{I}_P$
Cube	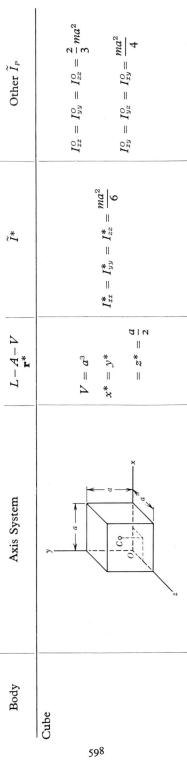	$V = a^3$ $x^* = y^*$ $= z^* = \dfrac{a}{2}$	$I_{xx}^* = I_{yy}^* = I_{zz}^* = \dfrac{ma^2}{6}$	$I_{xx}^O = I_{yy}^O = I_{zz}^O = \dfrac{2}{3}\,ma^2$ $I_{xy}^O = I_{yz}^O = I_{xy}^O = \dfrac{ma^2}{4}$

Rectangular Parallelepiped

$$V = abc$$

$$x^* = \frac{a}{2}$$

$$y^* = \frac{b}{2}$$

$$z^* = \frac{c}{2}$$

$$I^*_{xx} = \frac{1}{12}m(b^2+c^2)$$

$$I^*_{yy} = \frac{1}{12}m(a^2+c^2)$$

$$I^*_{zz} = \frac{1}{12}m(a^2+b^2)$$

$$I^O_{xx} = \frac{m}{3}(b^2+c^2)$$

$$I^O_{yy} = \frac{m}{3}(a^2+c^2)$$

$$I^O_{zz} = \frac{m}{3}(a^2+b^2)$$

$$I^O_{xy} = \frac{mab}{4}; I^O_{xz} = \frac{mac}{4}$$

$$I^O_{yz} = \frac{mbc}{4}$$

Body	Axis System	$L - A - V$ $\mathbf{r}^*$	$\tilde{I}^*$	Other $\tilde{I}_P$
Right Circular Cone		$V = \frac{1}{3}\pi r^2 h$ $x^* = z^* = 0$ $y^* = \frac{h}{4}$	$I_{xx}^* = I_{zz}^* = \frac{3m}{80}(4r^2 + h^2)$ $I_{yy}^* = \frac{3}{10}mr^2$	$I_{xx}^O = I_{zz}^O = \frac{m}{20}(3r^2 + 2h^2)$ $I_{yy}^O = \frac{3}{10}mr^2$ $I_{xy}^O = I_{xz}^O = I_{yz}^O = 0$ $I_{xx}^A = I_{zz}^A = \frac{3m}{20}(r^2 + 4h^2)$ $I_{yy}^A = \frac{3}{10}mr^2$ $I_{xy}^A = I_{xz}^A = I_{yz}^A = 0$

Right Circular Cylinder, Solid

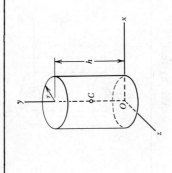

$$V = \pi r^2 h$$

$$x^* = z^* = 0$$

$$y^* = \frac{h}{2}$$

$$I_{xx}^* = I_{zz}^* = \frac{m}{12}(3r^2 + h^2)$$

$$I_{yy}^* = \frac{1}{2}mr^2$$

$$I_{xx}^O = I_{zz}^O = \frac{m}{12}(3r^2 + 4h^2)$$

$$I_{yy}^O = \frac{1}{2}mr^2$$

$$I_{xy}^O = I_{xz}^O = I_{yz}^O = 0$$

Body	Axis System	$L-A-V$ $\mathbf{r}^*$	$\tilde{I}^*$	Other $\tilde{I}_P$
Right Circular Cylinder, Hollow		$V = \pi h(r_2^2 - r_1^2)$ $x^* = z^* = 0$ $y^* = \dfrac{h}{2}$	$I_{xx}^* = I_{zz}^*$ $= \dfrac{m}{12}(3r_1^2 + 3r_2^2 + h^2)$ $I_{yy}^* = \dfrac{m}{2}(r_1^2 + r_2^2)$	$I_{xx}^O = I_{zz}^O$ $= \dfrac{m}{12}(3r_1^2 + 3r_2^2 + 4h^2)$ $I_{yy}^O = \dfrac{m}{2}(r_1^2 + r_2^2)$ $I_{xy}^O = I_{xz}^O = I_{yz}^O = 0$

Sphere, Solid

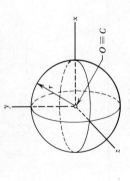

$$V = \frac{4}{3} \pi r^3$$

$$x^* = y^* = z^* = 0$$

$$I_{xx}^* = I_{yy}^* = I_{zz}^* = \frac{2}{5} mr^2$$

Body	Axis System	$L - A - V$ $\mathbf{r}^*$	$\tilde{I}^*$	Other $\tilde{I}_P$
Sphere, Hollow		$V = \dfrac{4}{3}\pi(r_2^3 - r_1^3)$ $x^* = y^* = z^*$ $= 0$	$I_{xx}^* = I_{yy}^* = I_{zz}^*$ $= \dfrac{2}{5}m\dfrac{(r_2^5 - r_1^5)}{(r_2^3 - r_1^3)}$	

Hemisphere,
Solid

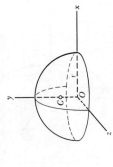

$V = \dfrac{2}{3} \pi r^3$

$x^* = z^* = 0$

$y^* = \dfrac{3r}{8}$

$I_{xx}^* = I_{zz}^* = \dfrac{83}{320} mr^2$

$I_{yy}^* = \dfrac{2}{5} mr^2$

$I_{xx}^O = I_{yy}^O = I_{zz}^O = \dfrac{2}{5} mr^2$

$I_{xy}^O = I_{xz}^O = I_{yz}^O = 0$

Ellipsoid

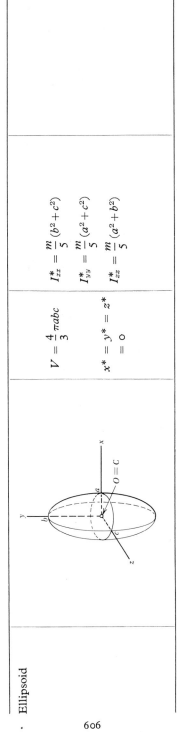

$$V = \frac{4}{3}\pi abc$$

$$x^* = y^* = z^*$$
$$= 0$$

$$I_{xx}^* = \frac{m}{5}(b^2 + c^2)$$

$$I_{yy}^* = \frac{m}{5}(a^2 + c^2)$$

$$I_{zz}^* = \frac{m}{5}(a^2 + b^2)$$

INDEX

INDEX